D1109728

THE PAPER DRAGON

THE PAPER

DELACORTE PRESS / NEW YORK

DRAGON

a novel by **EVAN HUNTER**

LIBRARY OF CONGRESS CATALOG CARD NUMBER: 66-12333
MANUFACTURED IN THE UNITED STATES OF AMERICA

TO

ANITA

MONDAY

1

HE FELT GIDDY and foolish and awkward, and he also felt like a thief. He was fearful and elated and apprehensive and uncertain, but beneath it all he felt like a thief and this was confusing because it was he who had been wronged. And yet, he felt much the same as he had that day when he was eight years old and stole a box of crayons from the school supply closet.

Just that way, with the same sort of trembling nervousness, the same heady swiftness of triumph—he had stolen the crayons, he had got away without anyone having seen him, he had tucked them under his sweater with no one the wiser—coupled with guilt, the overriding shamefaced embarrassment sitting just behind his eyes, the sickly somewhat pale smile on his mouth, he could not understand this feeling of guilt. It was almost as if he were identifying fully with the real thief, experiencing the thief's own reaction to capture and exposure, that's the goddamn trouble with me, he thought, I empathize too easily.

He was a man of medium build, with black hair and brows, brown eyes darting nervously as he climbed the courthouse steps. There was an awesome scale to the architecture of the building, ten monstrous, white, Corinthian columns rising to support a windowed entablature, wide white steps flowing in a long horizontal swell toward brass revolving entrance doors, more windows ornately decorated with curvilinear bars. The solemn majesty of the law's trappings added to his nervousness, and yet he wanted to yell aloud as he entered the building, wanted to shatter the serenity of these hallowed marbled halls, but the nervousness persisted, the feeling that *he,* and not James Driscoll, was the thief.

He walked into one of the waiting elevators, and then stood in the far corner of the car, worrying his lower lip, staring at the floor indicator as the car climbed, come on, come on. It was December, and the car was briskly cool, but he could feel the sweat trickling from under his arms in a slow, sliding descent over his ribs. The car doors opened at last. He stepped uncertainly into the seventh-floor corridor. A bank of gray elevator doors, six in all, were ranged on either side of the windowless corridor, interspersed with wooden doors along its length and on either end. The corridor was rather like a badly designed room, too long for its width, dimly lighted, divided at its halfway point by the double doors to 705 and 706, which were the courtrooms. The doors were constructed of what seemed like heavy oak, panels repeating the low paneled ceiling, bronze studs shaped like daisies punctuating the wood, a brass knob set on each right-hand door. He saw the numerals 705 in bronze on the door opposite him, and was walking across the corridor toward it when Sidney Brackman looked up from the water fountain. He was forty-eight years old, a short undistinguished-looking person wearing a brown suit and shoes, a striped brown tie on his white shirt. His hair was prematurely gray, as was his closely cropped mustache. He turned as Arthur approached, and then extended his hand quickly and said, "Good morning, Arthur, how do you feel?"

"I'm worried," Arthur said.

"You have nothing to worry about. You'll make a good witness. Do you remember all the points we covered?"

"Yes, I remember."

"Good. We'll go over those points in court, you'll tell everything in your own words. It's the truth that will win this case for us."

"I hope so."

"I *know* so. I have no doubt. It's been a long road, Arthur, but the end is in sight, and the end will be victorious."

"How long will the trial last?"

"I imagine it will be over by Wednesday. Thursday at the very latest."

"That's what I thought. It seems like such a short time."

"A short time? For what?"

"To present everything. I mean, so the judge'll understand."

"McIntyre's a smart judge, Arthur. *And* a fair one. I know him from when he was first out of law school. He was a brilliant lawyer even then. Brilliant. He'll give you a fair hearing, and he'll make a fair decision."

"I hope so."

"Try to appear a little more confident on the stand, eh?" Brackman said, and smiled.

"I'll try," Arthur said. "But I'd be much happier with a jury."

"Juries are unpredictable. Besides, you'll remember that I *did* ask for a jury. But Willow made a motion to strike the demand because we were asking for an accounting of every dollar. Willow's point was that historically . . ."

"You know all this law talk goes completely over my head."

"Yes, I know that, but I wouldn't want you to think I'd made a mistake. I haven't made any mistakes so far, Arthur, not that I know of. We *did* ask for a jury. But it was ruled that an equity action, such as this is, has always been tried in a chancery court rather than a law court. The historical precedent goes all the way back to England."

"I don't know anything about historical precedent," Arthur said. "It just seems to me that our chances would have been better with a jury."

"Our chances are excellent just the way they are, Arthur. Now please don't start getting despondent. I know you get into these despondent moods every now and then that are difficult to—"

"I'm not despondent."

"Good. Leave everything to me. Please. Just answer the questions I put to you as truthfully as you can, and everything will be all right."

"Is that a guarantee?"

Brackman smiled again. "No, Arthur. Nothing in the law is a guarantee, justice is not infallible. That's what makes practicing law so interesting. Let's go inside, shall we?"

The courtroom seemed too large for the scant handful of people it contained. Wood-paneled walls endlessly echoed themselves, like flecked mirrors repeating the same dull theme, a pattern broken only by the windowed wall facing the entrance. The windows were open just a crack to the winter street below. The sounds of traffic rose indolently, entering the courtroom in muted tones. A fierce December wind eddied in the right angle of wall-against-wall just outside the windows, and then fanned over the sills to riffle the papers on the long leather-topped tables. Jonah Willow and his assistant were at one of those tables, talking in normal speaking voices that somehow seemed like whispers. At the other end of the same table, Samuel Genitori, the attorney for API, leaned over to say something to his associate. As Arthur followed Brackman to the plaintiff's table, he heard Willow's assistant burst into laughter, and the sound infuriated him.

Seated in the otherwise empty jury box to the right of the judge's bench were James Driscoll and his wife. Arthur studiously avoided looking at either of them. The lone spectator, on one of the six benches at the rear of the room, was a thin boy carrying a spiral notebook imprinted with Columbia University's seal. There was an air of quiet displacement in the room, as though everyone were waiting for an event that would most certainly be canceled. When Judge McIntyre entered from his chambers at ten o'clock sharp, and the clerk called "All rise!" Arthur felt a new rush of panic, an urgent need to bolt from this arena with its alien trappings and its professional cold-eyed combatants. Quickly, he glanced toward Brackman to see if his fear had communicated itself, and then immediately dried the palms of his hands on his trouser legs.

"The United States District Court, Southern District of New York, is now in session," the clerk intoned, "the Honorable Frank H. McIntyre presiding. Take your seats, please. Arthur Nelson Constantine versus James Driscoll et al. Are all sides ready?"

Almost in a chorus, Brackman and the defense attorneys said, "Ready, your Honor."

"All ready, your Honor," the clerk repeated.

"Are you representing the plaintiff, Mr. Brackman?" McIntyre asked.

"Yes, your Honor."

"Are you ready to proceed?"

"Yes, your Honor."

"Then let's proceed."

"I would like Mr. Constantine to take the stand, please," Brackman said.

Arthur rose and walked toward the witness chair. He was having difficulty breathing, and he was certain he would stumble and fall before he reached the front of the courtroom. The clerk held out the Bible. Arthur put his left hand on it, and then raised his right hand.

"Arthur Nelson Constantine, you do solemnly swear that the testimony you shall give to the Court in this issue shall be the truth, the whole truth, and nothing but the truth, so help you God?"

"I do," Arthur said.

The clerk nodded briefly and then moved to a small table adjacent to and below the judge's bench. He put the Bible on one corner of the table and then moved his stenotab into place, fingers poised over the keys. Arthur climbed the two steps to the witness chair, glanced up briefly at the judge, whose swivel chair was parallel to his and a step higher, and then looked away. Sidney Brackman walked slowly toward Arthur, smiled encouragingly, and then said, "Mr. Constantine, what do you do for a living?"

"I'm a writer," Arthur answered. His voice was too low, he

knew he could not be heard. "A writer," he repeated more loudly.

"Do you write under your own name?"

"Yes, sir. Yes."

"How long have you been employed as a writer?"

"Since 1946."

"Can you tell us what works you've written, Mr. Constantine?"

"Since 1946?"

"Yes, since 1946," Brackman said.

"Yes, well . . ." He hesitated. For a moment, he had forgotten the question. He looked hopefully at Brackman who seemed completely unaware of his discomfort. They had been talking about 1946, hadn't they? Should he ask what the question was, something about, oh yes, "Yes," he said, "the first thing I wrote after my release from the United States Army was a play called *Catchpole.*"

"Mr. Constantine, are you familiar with this manuscript?"

"Yes, I'm familiar with it," he said, scarcely looking at it.

"Is this your name on the title page of the manuscript?"

"It is."

"Are you the sole author of this manuscript?"

"I am."

"Is this the play titled *Catchpole* which you wrote after your release from the United States Army in 1946?"

"Yes," he said, and wondered if he were supposed to say anything more about it at this point.

"I offer the manuscript in evidence," Brackman said, and handed it to the clerk.

"No objection," Willow said.

"No objection," Genitori repeated.

"I also offer in evidence the copyright registration certificate of the play."

Willow rose from his chair behind the defense table. "Your Honor," he said, "before trial, we conceded that the play was registered with the Copyright Office and a certificate granted in August of 1947. In fact, we conceded that it wouldn't be necessary to do anything more than offer the manuscript in evidence."

"Mr. Genitori, do you so concede for API?" McIntyre asked.

"I do."

Brackman nodded and approached the witness chair again. "Mr. Constantine," he said, "you have testified that you've been a writer since 1946. What else have you written besides this play?"

"Well," Arthur said, "I've been involved mostly with motion pictures and television."

"What films or television plays have you written?"

"Do you want me to go all the way back?"

"Please."

"Well, in 1948 I worked for Columbia under contract—Columbia Pictures. I wrote two films for them. Do you want the titles?"

"Please."

He was beginning to feel a bit more at ease. This wasn't going too badly after all. They were simply restating for the judge all the points they had gone over time and again in Brackman's office. He found himself relaxing. He crossed his legs and glanced at the judge, and then turned to Brackman and said, "The first was an adaptation of a *Collier's* story, a Western. I don't remember the title of the original story, but the movie was called *Brother to the Sun,* and was a very successful film. I then worked on an adaptation—or really a translation, I suppose you might say—of *King Lear*. I worked for several months with another writer on this, trying to get it into suitable form for the screen, and then the project was abandoned." He felt more and more relaxed. He looked at the judge once again, tempted to smile but restraining the urge, and then said, conversationally, "Olivier had already done *Hamlet,* you see, and I think Orson Welles was getting ready to release his *Macbeth,* and the feeling was that the trend had already peaked. Besides, it was proving very difficult to get a good screenplay from something as complex as *Lear.*"

"Now this film *Brother to the Sun* for which you wrote the screenplay . . ."

"Yes," he said.

". . . you mentioned that it was a very successful film. Just what does that mean?"

"It grossed nine million dollars."

"I see. Go on, Mr. Constantine. What did you do after you worked on *King Lear?*"

"I left Columbia early in 1949, and did several films for Metro-Goldwyn-Mayer. The first of these was—"

"Excuse me," Willow said, rising. "Your Honor, I hesitate to interrupt the witness's testimony, but it seems to me that his career subsequent to the writing of *Catchpole* is not relevant at this point."

"I'd like to see where counsel is heading," McIntyre answered. "I hope this won't go on forever, though, Mr. Brackman."

"No, your Honor, it won't. As a matter of fact, Mr. Constantine, in order to save time, perhaps you could simply tell us how long you were employed by Metro as a writer?"

"From March of 1949 to February of 1952."

"For three years, is that correct?"

"Yes, almost three years to the day."

"And how many films did you write for them during that period of employment?"

"Eight films. A total of eight films."

"And you left Metro in February of 1952, is that correct?"

"Yes, sir."

"What did you do then?"

"In March of 1952, I was employed by API under contract to write and direct four films for them."

"By API, are you referring to one of the defendants in this action, Artists-Producers-International, also referred to as Kessler, Inc.?"

"I am."

"And you have testified that in 1952 you were hired to write and direct four motion pictures for API, otherwise known as Kessler, Inc.?"

"I was. I did so testify."

Genitori rose suddenly and said, "Your Honor, may the record show that the title of the defendant, Kessler, Inc., was changed by court order to Artists-Producers-International in January of this year?"

"Let the record show it."

Brackman seemed annoyed by the interruption. He looked at Arthur sympathetically, cleared his throat, and asked, "*Did* you, in fact, write and direct those four films for API?"

"I worked on one of them which was later produced and directed by someone else," Arthur said.

"What was the title of that film?"

"*Area Seven.*"

"And you say it was produced?"

"Yes, sir."

"When was it shown?"

"Released, do you mean?"

"Yes, released."

"In May of 1953. It was nominated for an Academy Award that year."

"Did it receive the Academy Award?"

"No, sir. *From Here to Eternity* did."

"Your Honor," Willow said, "I must repeat my objection to the plaintiff's going into what happened after the writing of *Catchpole.*"

"If your Honor please," Brackman answered, "I think this is relevant in two respects: one, principally, is to indicate that Mr. Constantine was actively employed by API from March of 1952 until April of—"

"Your Honor, witness has not yet testified as to the length of his employment."

"Nevertheless, Mr. Willow," McIntyre said, "the witness's employment by API would certainly seem to be relevant."

"And also, your Honor," Brackman said, "defendants might wish to create the impression that *Catchpole,* which was admittedly a failure, was Mr. Constantine's one and only creative endeavor. I want to indicate that Mr. Constantine is a man of recognized talents. I will certainly afford Mr.

Willow the same opportunity to enumerate James Driscoll's writing credits when—"

"Objection overruled, Mr. Willow."

Brackman smiled thinly. "Mr. Constantine," he said, "can you tell me when your employment at API terminated?"

"I was there for more than two years. I left in April of 1954."

"After having worked on the screenplay for *Area Seven* which—"

"Yes, that's right."

"—was later nominated for an Academy Award."

"Correct."

"Why did you leave API?"

"There was a difference of opinion about the movies I was being asked to write and direct."

"To make this brief then, Mr. Constantine, would it be accurate to say that from 1946 to 1954 your sole employment was as a writer and/or director?"

"That is entirely accurate."

"And without going into laborious detail, would it be equally accurate to state that since you left API in April of 1954, you have continued to work as a writer and/or director of screenplays and television plays, sometimes under contract and sometimes on a freelance basis?"

"That is equally true, yes."

"Are you actively engaged on a project now, Mr. Constantine?"

"Yes, I am."

"Could you tell us—"

"Your Honor, haven't we already indicated that Mr. Constantine is a man of recognized talents?" Willow asked.

"Let's try to make this brief, Mr. Brackman," McIntyre said.

Brackman nodded. To Arthur he said, "Can you tell us what that project is?"

"We are currently casting my new play for Broadway production," Arthur answered.

"Who is producing the play?"

"Stuart Selig and Oscar Stern."

"And are you the sole author of the play?"

"I am."

"Mr. Constantine, I would now like to take you back to your other play, the play called *Catchpole,* which you testified you wrote in 1946."

"That's correct," Arthur said.

"Was this play *Catchpole* ever produced?"

"Yes, sir, it was."

"Where was it produced?"

"It opened at the Fulton Theatre here in New York and it ran for twelve days."

"When was that?"

"In October of 1947. October 14th, I believe the date was. And it ran until the 25th, through the 25th."

"Had it been seen anywhere else prior to its Broadway opening?"

"Yes, sir. There were a series of previews held while we were still rehearsing the play in a loft on Second Avenue."

"Previews? For whom?"

"For college students."

"Of which colleges?"

"C.C.N.Y., Hunter, Brooklyn College, L.I.U., Pratt Institute, and several others."

"Was there a charge for these performances?"

"No, sir. We were still in rehearsal and we wanted the reaction of college students, since this was a play about young men in a time of intense personal strife."

Brackman paused, moved away from the witness stand, glanced at Willow, and then slowly walked back to confront Arthur again. His voice lowering to a solemn pitch, he asked, "Have you read the novel *The Paper Dragon?*"

"Yes, sir."

"Have you seen the movie *The Paper Dragon?*"

"Yes, sir."

"Can you tell us when you read the book?"

"I saw the movie in September of 1964, and I read the book shortly after that. A week or so afterwards."

"What course of action did you pursue after seeing the movie?"

"Well, I had been out of town working on a television pilot for MCA, Music Corporation of America. The pilot dealt with a team of construction workers who move around from one part of the country to the other—"

"Your Honor," Willow said, "the answer is not responsive."

"Please answer the question," McIntyre said.

"What was the question?"

The clerk consulted his notes. "What course of action did you pursue after seeing the movie?" he repeated.

Arthur nodded. "I was trying to explain that I had been out of town for several months because we were visiting the site of a dam in construction . . ."

"Yes, what did you do when you came back?" Brackman prodded.

". . . which is why I missed the opening of the movie, and all the hullabaloo around New York at that time. In any case, when I got back to the city, I went out with a young lady one night, and she said, 'Have you seen *The Paper Dragon?*' I didn't know what *The Paper Dragon* was, and I said so. She then told me that it was a direct steal from my play, and that I had better make sure I saw it."

"And did you then go to see it?"

"Yes, I did."

"And after seeing it, did you take the matter to an attorney?"

"Yes, I did."

Brackman nodded, walked back to the plaintiff's table, and returned with his hands full. "I would like to offer in evidence," he said, "this book which is the hard-cover edition of *The Paper Dragon,* as written by James Driscoll and published by Mitchell-Campbell Books, Inc."

"Any objection?"

"No."

"Mr. Genitori, any objection?"

"None."

"I also offer in evidence the reprint edition of *The Paper*

Dragon, published by Camelot Books, Inc., New York, a subsidiary of Mitchell-Campbell, Inc."

"No objection."

"No objection."

"I offer in evidence the shooting script of the film *The Paper Dragon,* as written by Ralph Knowles, and produced by Kessler, Inc."

"Is this being offered as against the defendant API only?" Willow asked. "Or is it offered as against the defendant Mitchell-Campbell?"

"It is being offered against API."

"No objection."

"No objection."

"Your Honor, the defendants have previously conceded publication of *The Paper Dragon,"* Brackman said, "and also of the motion picture."

"Conceded."

"Conceded."

Brackman returned to the witness stand. "Mr. Constantine," he said, "you have stated that between March of 1952 and April of 1954 you were employed by API as a writer-director, and that you worked on one film while you were so employed, a motion picture titled *Area Seven,* which was later nominated for an Academy Award."

"Yes, sir."

"Did you at any time during your period of employment at API have opportunity to submit . . . I'll rephrase that, your Honor. Did you ever submit the manuscript of *Catchpole* to anyone at API while you were employed there?"

"I did."

"To whom did you submit the manuscript? Can you remember the names?"

"I can."

"Would you tell us, please?"

"I first showed the manuscript to a man named Matthew Jackson, with whom I was working on *Area Seven."*

"What were Mr. Jackson's duties?"

"He was under contract as a writer at API, and was sort of

overseeing the *Area Seven* project, since I was a new writer there and had never directed anything before. He was working very closely with me on the screenplay. We got to know each other rather well, and I thought I would show him a copy of *Catchpole* in the hope he could see movie possibilities in it."

"Did he indeed see movie possibilities in it?"

"No."

"Did you not, in fact, later have a conversation with Mr. Jackson wherein he definitely stated that Kessler's did not wish . . ."

"That's right."

". . . to buy the motion picture rights to *Catchpole?*"

"We had a conversation about it, yes."

"Your Honor, that was a leading question," Willow said.

"I am refreshing his memory on a point that is already in the record," Brackman replied.

"You were leading the witness, Mr. Brackman," McIntyre said, and Brackman shrugged in resignation.

"Did you have a conversation with Mr. Jackson?" he asked.

"I did," Arthur answered.

"Would you repeat the content of that conversation?"

"Jackson said, 'This is tremendous, but you know as well as I that this company is still back in the thirties with its musicals and silly romances. I think they'd be leery of an Army theme that tries to show the stupidity and foolish waste of war, especially since we've had this Korean thing since World War II. But I'd like to hold onto it, because I really like it immensely and if I can do anything for it, I will.' "

"Did Mr. Jackson ever return the manuscript to you?"

"No."

"To whom else at API did you show the manuscript?"

"Well, there was Joe Edelson, who was at that time head of API's story department. And Rudy Herdt, who was a producer, and Iris Blake, who was also in the story department."

"Were there any others?"

"Yes, I also showed it to Betty Alweiss, who was Mr. Kessler's personal secretary."

"What were the reactions of these various people to whom you showed the manuscript?"

"Their reactions—their collective reaction, I should say—was basically the same. They all liked the play, they thought it had some important things to say about a situation that needed comment. But they felt API wasn't ready to do anything as strong as this was, not right then, anyway. The collective reaction, I would say, was that the play was too outspoken, that the United States wasn't ready to take criticism of its armed forces, not when we had just come through a major conflict and also a minor one in Korea, which happens to be the setting of *The Paper Dragon*. To my mind, there was no question that everyone who read the script thought—"

"Your Honor, I regret having to interrupt the witness again," Willow said, "but he has just now made a statement as to the operation of his mind, and I think you'll agree that is clearly inadmissible."

"Sustained."

"Mr. Constantine," Brackman said, with a sigh directed at Willow, "would you please tell us what was said about the script, and not what you surmised or thought?"

"That's all that was said about it. They all liked the script, but they felt it was too strong for API to do."

"Were any of these scripts ever returned to you?"

"No."

"As I understand it then, Mr. Constantine—and please correct me if I'm wrong—during the period of time between March 1952 and April 1954, you showed a copy of your previously produced play *Catchpole* to five people at API?"

"Five people, that's correct."

"Were these five people all executives?"

"Not all of them. But they all had the power to recommend a story for purchase."

"And your story was not recommended."

"My play."

"Your play."

"No, it was not recommended for purchase."

"Nor were any of the copies returned."

"No, they were not returned."

"Mr. Constantine, have you examined your work *Catchpole* and also the book and movie versions of *The Paper Dragon?*"

"I have."

"What did your examination reveal?"

"That there are close similarities between *Catchpole* and *The Paper Dragon*."

"Similarities to both the book *and* the film?"

"Both the book and the film, yes."

The courtroom was silent. Brackman took a deep breath. "What similarities did your examination reveal?" he asked.

"Your Honor, if I may . . ."

"Yes, Mr. Willow?"

"I think we might be able to save a little time here, if the plantiff is willing."

"How might we do that, Mr. Willow?"

"The plaintiff and his attorneys were good enough to prepare—for the pretrial examinations—several charts containing the alleged similarities between the works in question. These are rather detailed as to specific language, plot structure, and character. I would have no objection to the offer of these charts at this point."

Brackman shook his head. "I wish the witness to testify to the similarities in his own words."

"His own words are already on the record," Willow said.

"Your Honor," Genitori said, rising, "we have reams and reams of charts prepared by the witness and his attorneys. The entire matter is before us ad infinitum."

"If his Honor will allow," Brackman answered, "I would like to bring the matter before us once again—*from* the witness, *in* person, *before* this Court."

"I will allow it. Let him proceed."

Arthur looked at the judge, and then at Brackman. Brackman nodded.

"I would like to start with the thematic similarity of my play and the other works," Arthur said.

"Go ahead, Mr. Constantine."

As Arthur began speaking, he could feel the alert presence of James Driscoll sitting in the jury box on his left, patiently watching with the cold blue guileless eyes of a thief. He could feel the judge erect and attentive beside him at the raised bench on his right, someone only vaguely defined, someone who had the power to rule on what could and could not be said, someone who would in the final analysis make the sole decision as to whether he, Arthur Constantine, had been wronged. He could feel, too, and it added to his sense of security, the enormous paneled dignity of the courtroom, a federal court, copyright offenses were tried in federal courts, the American flag to the right of the bench, the wan December sunlight outside. He was completely at ease now, confident that the truth would be heard and justice would be done. His earlier panic, in fact, now seemed inexplicable, like the terror of a very young child waking in the dark.

"In my play," he said, "I was attempting to illustrate—"

"Your Honor," Willow said at once, "I move to strike that from the record. Whatever Mr. Constantine *attempted* to illustrate is not relevant to the issue before this Court."

"He is trying to be responsive," McIntyre said. "I will allow it."

"I maintain, your Honor, that any similarities must be solely between the works in question."

"I would agree to that."

"And that therefore the author's intent is irrelevant."

"I believe I will allow him to tell it in his own words, Mr. Willow. I think this will take us where we want to go."

"Does your Honor mean the end of the trial?"

"No, I'm referring to the testimony relating to similarities. The end of the trial, however, is another consummation devoutly to be wished. Please go on, Mr. Constantine."

"Thematically, my play deals with the lunacy of war," Arthur said. "My hero is a new lieutenant who feels that human life is more important than the quarrels of nations, and this theme is stated in Act I, Scene 4, pages 21 and 22 of *Catchpole*. This is also the theme of *The Paper Dragon*, where the hero is the same new lieutenant who feels exactly the same way, and who voices his feelings on pages 121, 122, 123, and 124 of the book."

"Do you consider this theme unique?" Brackman asked.

"I do not, sir."

"Do you consider it original?"

"I do not, sir."

"Do you consider it your exclusive property?"

"No, sir. But this suit is not based on a similarity of theme alone. In fact, if my play had developed its theme along certain lines and the novel had developed the very *same* theme along different lines, I would never have brought suit at all."

"How *are* these themes developed?"

"They are developed along *identical* lines," Arthur said. "To begin with, the hero of my play is shipped to the Pacific to wage war against the Japanese on Eniwetok. The hero of *The Paper Dragon* is also shipped to the Pacific to wage war, this time against the enemy forces in Korea. Now the men in the platoon to which the lieutenant is assigned, and specifically the men who are in one squad of that platoon—"

"Excuse me," Brackman said, "but are we discussing plot or character?"

"This is plot," Arthur said.

"Very well, go on."

"The men in the squad are described in Act I, Scene 1, page 3 of my play as 'battle-weary and battle-hardened.' In the book, the men in the squad are described with the words—may I have a copy of the book, please?"

"Certainly," Brackman said. The clerk handed him the exhibit copy, which he in turn handed to Arthur. Arthur quickly found the page.

"These are the words Driscoll uses to describe *his* squad. This is on page 42. 'Weary-eyed and cynical, they studied their new lieutenant in his college boy crewcut and freshly issued fatigues, and wondered how he could possibly lead them into hell.' In short, the men in both combat squads are hardened veterans in juxtaposition to inexperienced commanding officers—and the word 'weary' is used to describe them in both works."

"Go on, please."

"The first time Lieutenant Mason—who is the hero of my play—leads his platoon into battle, this particular squad is ambushed and a young private is killed by a sniper. In the book, this basic situation has been altered only slightly. The lieutenant's name has been changed, of course—to Cooper—and the incident of the sniper takes place *before* his arrival in Korea. It is a major this time who is killed by a sniper who has infiltrated the lines. That's on page 18. But the plot development is essentially the same, and it continues along parallel lines.

"In my play, for example, the men come to resent Mason enormously because they hold him responsible for the private's death. This is stated in Act I, Scene 3, pages 14 and 15. And whereas Mason tries to reach them in various ways, they remain resentful. In the book, the men resent Cooper because he is taking the dead major's place. That's page 51. The same attempts to reach the men are present, and the same continuing resentment is there. Moreover, the biggest troublemaker in Cooper's platoon is a man named Private Colman, and it is implied on page 56 that he has had homosexual relations with the dead major."

"You mean when he was alive, of course," Brackman said, and McIntyre burst into laughter. "I was trying to clarify," Brackman said quickly, "the relationship between—"

"Yes, of course," McIntyre said, still laughing. "Go ahead, Mr. Constantine."

"I mention this homosexual attachment," Arthur said, "only because in my play, a senior officer is also suspected of homosexuality and is sent back from the front to a hospital unit. This is in Act II, Scene 2, pages 6 and 7. It is there that he becomes the patient of an Army nurse who later falls in love with my hero. I think it is significant that an Army nurse appears in *The Paper Dragon* on page 124, and that a love affair between her and Lieutenant Cooper develops along lines parallel to my play."

"Your Honor," Willow said, rising, "I wonder if I might interrupt to ask Mr. Brackman how long this will take. I think we all agree that the final test in a case of this sort is a comparison of the works themselves. Mr. Constantine's opinion as to similarities is not in my judgment competent testimony. Couldn't we shorten this by putting in a paper calling your Honor's attention to the alleged similarities? I would certainly have no objection to that. But if Mr. Constantine intends to go on interminably, I must raise an objection."

"Mr. Brackman?" McIntyre asked. "What do you say to that?"

"I quite agree with Mr. Willow that a comparison of the works themselves is the heart of the issue involved here. But that is exactly what we *are* doing, your Honor, comparing the works themselves. As for the second objection, Mr. Constantine's testimony is *definitely* competent, and I believe precedent will so indicate."

"How much longer do you suppose he will be testifying, Mr. Brackman? Concerning these similarities?"

"The similarities of plot, do you mean?"

"I mean *all* the similarities."

"There are several more similarities of plot, your Honor, and then we had hoped to go into character and specific language."

"Won't there be an overlap between plot and character?"

"Only to a limited extent."

"How long will it take to outline the plot similarities?"

"Mr. Constantine?"

"Only five or ten minutes, your Honor," Arthur answered.

"And the others?"

"At least forty-five minutes, your Honor," Brackman said. "Perhaps longer."

"Well, I notice that Mr. Constantine has been making frequent reference to the prepared charts. Couldn't we simply submit those, as Mr. Willow suggested? I know you want the Court to form an impression of your witness, but I feel we've already done that sufficiently. I do think any means of saving time would be appreciated."

"Your Honor, I would prefer to do it this way," Brackman said. "If it will help, perhaps the witness can leave out the specific page references wherever possible."

"I stand on my objection," Willow said. "I do not see why Mr. Constantine cannot testify that he prepared these charts, and then offer them in evidence as an aid to the Court. *Solely* as an aid to the Court, your Honor, and *not* as expert testimony. To that, I would have no objection."

"Mr. Willow, I don't like to limit an attorney's latitude," McIntyre said. "If Mr. Brackman wishes to present his case in this manner, I think it only fair to allow him to proceed. But if he can think of another way to shorten the testimony, in addition to eliminating page numbers, I think we would all be enormously grateful."

"If he's going to eliminate page references," Willow said, "can he supply a list of them so—"

"I assumed . . ."

"Yes, of course."

". . . that he planned to do that, Mr. Willow."

"So that we may have them for reference during the cross, your Honor."

"Certainly. Please proceed, Mr. Constantine."

"In order to save time," Arthur said, "it might be possible to combine plot *and* character in explaining these three soldiers. Would you want me to do that?"

"Which three soldiers?" McIntyre asked.

"Private Colman in the novel, and Corporal Janus and Colonel Peterson in my play."

"Yes, please do," McIntyre said. "We would appreciate any means of saving time."

"Just so we can keep this straight," Arthur said, "let me again say that Private Colman is the prime troublemaker in the novel, and is also suspected of having had homosexual relations with the major. In fact, there is a stream-of-consciousness passage beginning on page 212—"

"We want to leave out the page references," Brackman reminded.

"Yes, I'm sorry. I was going to say that this interior monologue clearly indicates, *beyond* mere suspicion, that Private Colman *did* have homosexual relations with the major. In my play, the prime troublemaker is a man named Corporal Janus, but in addition there is the homosexual colonel who is sent up for observation—he later goes psycho, but that's beside the point. The point is the *two* characters in my play, Corporal Janus and Colonel Peterson, are *combined* in Driscoll's book to form the single character named Private Colman. In other words, Driscoll has taken a troublemaker and a homosexual and put them together to form a homosexual troublemaker."

"Did you find any other evidence of this merger?"

"Yes. The private's first name in Driscoll's book is Peter. His full name is Peter Colman. If we put this alongside the name of the character in my play, Colonel Peterson, we see that one name is an anagram of the other."

"Your Honor," Willow said, rising, "an anagram transposes the exact letters of a word or sentence to form a *new* word or sentence. There is no such transposition here, and I object to the misleading use of the word."

"May I amend that?" Arthur asked.

"Please do," McIntyre said.

"May I simply say that the names, when reversed, are very similar?"

"Shall I strike the anagram reference?" the clerk asked.

"Strike it," McIntyre replied.

"Please go on," Brackman said.

"Where was I?" Arthur asked.

"You were explaining . . ."

"Oh, yes, the combining of two characters to form a single character. The final evidence of this is what happened in the film based on the novel. For some unexplainable reason, the character named Peter Colman in the book has once more become two *separate* characters in the film. One of them is still Colman the troublemaker, but he is no longer homosexual. The other is a corporal who does not appear in the book, and who is very *definitely* homosexual. In other words, the screenwriter reversed Driscoll's copying process, and went back to the original play to recreate a character who was in the play but not in the book."

"Are these characters important to the play?"

"They are important to the play, the book, *and* the movie. Without them, the plot would stand still. In fact, it is Janus in my play and Colman in the book who suggest that the lieutenant be murdered."

"How do they plan to murder him?"

"In my play, a Sergeant D'Agostino volunteers to shoot the lieutenant from ambush. In the book, the men plan to lead the lieutenant into a Chinese stronghold where he will be killed. The motive is identical in both works, only the means differ slightly."

"Does the lieutenant actually get killed?" Brackman asked.

"Again, there is only a very slight difference in story line," Arthur said. "In my play, the psychopathic colonel steals a bayonet and escapes his guard on the night of the planned murder. He accidentally stumbles on Sergeant D'Agostino where he is waiting to ambush Lieutenant Mason. There is a struggle during which D'Agostino is stabbed and killed by the ranting colonel. And there is speculation later as to whether D'Agostino actually sacrificed himself in order to avoid having to murder the lieutenant."

"And how has this been changed in the book?"

"Your Honor," Willow said, "I have let one such allegation pass, but I must object to . . ."

"Sustained. Please rephrase the question, Mr. Brackman."

"Can you tell us the plot sequence in the book?" Brackman said.

"In the book, Lieutenant Cooper realizes at the last moment that the men are leading him into a death trap. But he also recognizes that his scout, Sergeant Morley, is in danger of losing *his* life as well. He takes the point from Morley, and sacrifices himself to the Chinese guns."

"How does your play end, Mr. Constantine?"

"It ends when the men in the squad, shaken by the turn of events, come to realize the idiocy of war, and gain a new respect for their lieutenant. The troublemaker, Corporal Janus, is exposed and court-martialed."

"And how does the book end?"

"The book ends when the men in the squad, touched by the lieutenant's sacrifice, come to realize the idiocy of war, and gain a new respect for him. The troublemaker, Private Colman, is exposed and court-martialed."

The courtroom was silent. Brackman looked up at the judge, and then turned away from him, nodding his head as though in silent agreement with an evident truth.

"Does that conclude your testimony concerning similarities of plot?" he asked Arthur.

"Yes, sir, it does."

"Would you tell us now—"

"Forgive me for interrupting, Mr. Brackman," McIntyre said, "but as I indicated earlier in chambers, I have an appointment this afternoon which necessitates my leaving at two-thirty. I was hoping we could take a very short recess now—aren't you tired, Mr. Constantine?"

"Thank you, your Honor, I'm fine," Arthur said.

"Well, I thought we might take a ten-minute recess now, and then perhaps continue without a lunch recess, adjourning at two, or a little after if we have to. Would anyone have any objection to that?"

"We would have no objection," Willow said. "But Mr. Constantine and his attorney may be exceedingly hungry."

"We would have no objection to continuing through the lunch recess," Brackman said dryly. "And we will try to conclude the direct by two o'clock, your Honor."

"I have no objection," Genitori said.

2

HE HAD RECEIVED what he supposed were stock words of encouragement from Brackman—You're doing fine, Arthur, you're coming across very well, I think the judge is considerably impressed—and then had left him in the courtroom with his partner. Now, standing near a door marked STAIRWAY at one end of the gray corridor, he lighted a second cigarette and glanced briefly at the closed courtroom doors. He honestly did not know how he was coming across, he had never been very sure of himself as a speaker. He felt that Willow was objecting too much and too energetically, and he suspected that Brackman was losing more points than he was winning, but he was completely ignorant of his own performance, grateful only that his earlier nervousness had miraculously dissipated.

Willow and his assistant came out of the courtroom and walked toward Arthur, heading for the men's room, he supposed. Willow was a tall ungainly man, and he moved with the uncertain awkwardness of a large water bird, neck craned forward, head bobbing, hair uncombed and hanging on his forehead, black-rimmed spectacles reflecting the pale light of the ceiling fixtures. Arthur supposed he was in his late thirties, but there was about him a boyish vitality that made him seem even younger. Neither he nor his assistant, a squat, very dark Negro wearing a gray tweed suit, even glanced at

Arthur in passing. They were in animated discussion as they walked by, but all Arthur could hear was a reference to "the evidentiary question." He watched as they pushed open the door to the men's room, and then he looked at his watch.

It was twenty minutes past twelve.

He felt alone, utterly and completely alone, he had never felt so isolated in his entire life. He thought it odd that he should have come through thirty-nine years of family togetherness, surrounded by aunts and uncles and cousins and *compares* to find himself here and now, at what was possibly the most important juncture of his life, entirely alone. How do you come through it all, he wondered, and suddenly find yourself standing on the edge of the universe waiting for the waves to crash in, maybe to get washed out to sea, without Aunt Louise telling you every other week that you were "her baby," meaning she had served as midwife when you were delivered to your mother in a coldwater flat on East 118th Street? I could use Aunt Louise now, he thought, silly Aunt Louise who accompanied Italian immigrants when they went for their first papers, who was an active member of the Republican Club, who wrote songs in her spare time and claimed that they were all later stolen by the big band leaders—a family trait?—and who sent Queen Elizabeth a hand-tatted bonnet for young Prince Charles when he was born. "Look, Sonny," she had said, "I got a thank-you note from the Queen's secretary, a *personal* thank-you note," and Arthur had thought to himself it was probably a mimeographed note sent to all the Aunt Louises of the world who tatted bonnets for infant princes. And yet he could use Aunt Louise now, he could use her quiet strength and penetrating eye, God but that woman was a dynamo of energy, what the hell was it she concocted—Aunt Louise's Ointment, did she call it? And wasn't it really and truly sold in drugstores all over Harlem, the indefatigable Louise running around selling her product the way she plugged her terrible songs, she'd have made a great rumrunner, or in recent times an excellent dope pusher.

They called him Sonny when he lived in Harlem. I grew

up in Harlem, he always told people, and they looked at him as if wondering whether or not he had traces of Negro blood flowing in his veins, whereupon he always felt compelled to explain that there were *three* Harlems. You see, there is Negro Harlem and there is Italian Harlem and there is Puerto Rican Harlem. They are all very different and they are all identical, they are all bug-ridden and rat-infested, those are the three Harlems. But that of course was a mature judgment, a qualified appraisal by a man who was now thirty-nine years old, and not the way he had seen it as a boy. There were no rats in Harlem for Sonny Constantine—he still did not know why they had called him Sonny, he supposed there was a Sonny in every Italian-American family that ever existed. Or perhaps Al Jolson was hot at the time of his boyhood, perhaps any kid became a Sonny Boy and then a Sonny all because of Al Jolson singing through his goddamn nose like a Harvard man, perhaps that was it. But there were no rats in Harlem—well, once a mouse was in the toilet bowl, but only a mouse. It scared hell out of his mother, she came running out of the bathroom with her dress raised and her bloomers down, her behind showing, he wanted to look, but didn't dare, yelling to his father that there was a mouse in the bowl. So his father just flushed the toilet, naturally, goodbye mouse, out to sea where all good mice eventually go. His sister was terrified. He had called her a baby and a dope and a silly jerk, and then had listened to her crying in her room, really in his parents' bedroom because that was where she slept on a little cot against the wall near the window that looked down on 118th Street four stories below.

There were no rats in Harlem for him, there were no street gangs, there were no rumbles, there was only a placid ghetto —terrible word—a *neighborhood,* a haven surrounded by relatives, you could not throw a stone without hitting a relative. If your mother wasn't home, you dropped in on Aunt Tessie, and she gave you cookies and milk, or you went around to see Grandpa in the grocery store where he worked for a man he had known in Naples, or maybe you ran into Uncle Mike driving his truck for the furniture company. It was said that Uncle Mike knew gangsters, and that the time the social club was held up and they stole Uncle Danny's ring and Uncle Sal's watch, it was Mike who got on his Neapolitan high horse and went off some place into the mysterious underworld where they talked of Petie Red Shirt and Legs Diamond and got the goddamn jewelry back the very next morning; he was a tough guy Uncle Mike, he could break your head with a glance. His sister loved Uncle Mike, she would almost wet her pants every time he stopped by. There was an argument once, Arthur couldn't even remember what it was all about, Mike taking out some girl from the bakery, and Tessie getting all upset and coming to see her sister, Arthur's mother, and her having a big argument with Mike and calling him everything under the sun while his father stood by and listened patiently and Arthur remembered how simply he had flushed the mouse down the toilet, so very simply, pull, flush, and out to sea without a whimper.

Christmases, they all got together, Christmases *then,* but not anymore, blame it on urban renewal, blame it on the decentralization of the family, the speedier means of communication and transportation, there were no more Christmases once his grandparents died. The family died when they died, it shriveled outward from the center, everybody just disappeared, where the hell were they all now? Dead or living in California, which is the same as being dead. He had dropped in to see Aunt Tessie and Uncle Mike when he was out in Hollywood, and Mike who had known gangsters, Mike who had threatened to break heads unless his brothers'-in-law jewelry was returned at once, immediately if not sooner, Mike was a tired old man, bald, his muscles turned to flab, this was the man who used to move furniture and mountains and fearsome gangs. They sat in the living room of the Tarzana development house and had nothing much to say to each other, how is your mother, tell her to write, did you go to Aunt Louise's funeral, and Arthur had wanted to say, "Don't you remember Christmas at Grandpa's house, don't you remember?" But Uncle Mike was an old man, you see, and Aunt Tessie limped, and there was nothing to say to either of them, there was only strong Italian coffee to sip and Italian pastry to nibble, he had not remembered it as being so sweet. Boy, what his grandfather used to buy for Christmas, boy the way that house sang, that crumby apartment on First Avenue, it *must* have been a crumby apartment and there probably *were* rats in the walls. He certainly could remember cockroaches in his own house whenever they turned on the kitchen light, an army in hurried retreat. "Step on them, Sonny," his mother would yell, "get them, get them!" a game each night, the scurrying mob, and then they would all disappear into cracks and crannies, gone like the mouse flushed out to sea, except they would return again. "Where do they go?" he once asked his father, and his father replied, "Home."

Home.

There was everybody there on Christmas and his grandfather welcomed one and all, not only the family but also everybody he knew from the grocery store, the nice old man who wore thick glasses, Alonzo, Alfonso, something like that, who had the idiot son who would come in alongside his father like a ghost and sit there quietly and perhaps sip a little red wine his grandfather poured. And the men would talk about the old country and about Mussolini and about how beautiful Rome was at Christmastime, and Arthur would listen, standing between his grandfather's knees, with his grandfather's strong hands on his shoulders, and the women would be bustling about in the kitchen, Grandma fretting and fussing, and the girls—her two daughters and later Danny's wife, and then Sal's wife—all would be busy with the preparations in the kitchen, and the Christmas gifts would be piled to the ceiling under the Christmas tree, and Grandpa would keep pouring wine for all the relatives and friends who kept dropping in from all over Harlem, all over the world it seemed, *Buon Natale, Buon Natale,* the wine being poured and the smell of tomato sauce in the kitchen. God, there were things to eat, things Grandpa used to get in the grocery store, all imported, great provolone and salami, and fresh macaroni and bread, and Aunt Louise would make the pimientos, she would roast the peppers over the gas jet until they turned black, he always thought she was burning them, but no then she would scrap off all the black part and reveal the sweet orange-red meat, and then she fixed them with oil and garlic, oh God. She sent him pimientos in a jar every month, once a month like clockwork, the last day of the month, until she finally died, always the pimientos in a jar because once he helped her with the grammar in one of her song lyrics, just helped her put it in order, that was all, pimientos for life, a great title.

The meal went on for hours, they would sit at the table and dip cling peaches in wine, allowing the thick golden fruit to soak there for a bit, and then bringing it dripping red to the mouth on a toothpick. His grandfather would say "Sonny, here, have some," and hold out the red-stained toothpick with the rich juicy slice of fruit on its end, tart, strong, sweet, everything. The kids would run through the length of the railroad flat, chasing each other, and his grandmother would yell for them to stop before the people downstairs banged on the ceiling with a broom handle, and they would stop for a little while, collapsing on the big bed in the front room, his head close to his sister's, all of them sweating, all the kids in the family, more kids all the time, all of them giggling and sweating on the bed with the picture of Jesus Christ over it holding his hand above his exposed heart and sunshine spikes radiating from his head. "That's God," his cousin Joey once said. "The Jews killed him." He asked his grandmother about it one time, and she said, "That's right, Sonny, the Jews killed him," and then she told a story about a Jew who went to church one day and received holy communion and then ran out of the church and took the wafer out of his mouth immediately and went home and nailed it to the wall. "And do you know what happened to that holy bread, Sonny? It began to bleed. And it never stopped bleeding. It just kept bleeding all over that Jew's floor."

"What did he do?" Arthur asked.

"What did *who* do?" his grandmother said.

"The Jew. What did he do about all that blood?"

His grandmother had shrugged and gone back to cooking something on the big wood stove in the kitchen, black and monstrous, always pouring heat and steam. "Wiped it up, I guess," she said. "How do *I* know what he did?"

But every time he looked at that picture of Jesus with the heart stuck on his chest as if he had just had surgery and they were showing how easy it was to expose a human heart these days, the drops of blood dripping down from it, and Jesus' hand just a little above it, and his head tilted back with his eyes sort of rolled up in his head like a character in an Eisenstein movie, he always thought of the Jew who nailed the communion wafer to the wall, and he always wondered first why the Jew would want to nail the thing to the wall to begin with, and second what he had done about all the blood. In high school, after he had moved to the Bronx and met Rubin, he realized his grandmother was full of shit, and he never trusted her very much after that, her and her communion nailed to the wall.

His sister Julia broke his head one time, this was about the time he fell in love with Virginia Kelly. Irish girls after that were all premised on Virginia, the sixth grade Virginia with long black hair and green eyes fringed with black lashes and budding little breasts—he hadn't been too aware of those at the time—and a way of tilting her head back to laugh, at *him* most of the time, which was the unfortunate part of it all. But oh how he loved that girl! He would watch her and watch her and notice everything she did or said, and then come home and tell his sister about it, which is why she broke his head one day. She broke his head with a stupid little kid's pocketbook by swinging it at him on its chain and clobbering him with the clasp, and all because he told her she would never be as beautiful as Virginia Kelly, no one in the world would ever be as beautiful as Virginia Kelly, she had clobbered him, wham! Even then she had a lot of spunk, you had to have spunk to live in the same house with a man like his father, boy, what a battle *that* had turned out to be years later. Where the hell are you now, Julie, living with your engineer husband and your two Norwegian kids in where the hell, Minnesota? There's no such place as Minnesota, don't kid me, sis. Do you remember breaking my head, and then crying when Mama took me to the druggist, and he examined it—who went to doctors in those days?—and wiped the blood away and said, "You've broken his head, young lady," and then put a strip of plaster on it? It was okay in a week or so, but boy did you cry, I really loved you Julie. You were a really nice sister to have, I hope your Norwegian loves you half as much as I did.

He met Virginia Kelly in the hall one day, he was coming back from the boys' room and he had the wooden pass in his hand, and Virginia stopped him. He was nine years old, and she was ten and big for her age, and she stopped him and said, "Don't look at me anymore, Stupid."

"Who's looking at you?" he said, but his heart was pounding, and he wanted to kiss her, wanted to kiss this quintessence of everything alien to him, the sparkling green eyes and the wild Irish way of tossing her head, all, everything. Years later, when he read *Ulysses,* he knew every barmaid in the book because they were all Virginia Kelly who told him once to stop looking at her, Stupid, and whom he never looked at again from that day forward though it broke his heart.

When he moved to the Bronx, the only person he thought he missed was Virginia Kelly. He would lie awake in bed at night and think of Virginia, and when he learned how to masturbate, he would conjure visions of this laughing Irish girl and ravage her repeatedly until one morning Julie said to him, "Hey, *I* have to make the beds around here, you know," and he pretended he didn't know what she meant, but after that he masturbated secretly in the bathroom and carefully wiped up after him with toilet paper. Somewhere along the line, he switched from raping Virginia Kelly to raping Hedy Lamarr, and he never thought of her again except once or twice when he remembered that there were people in this world who drove in red convertibles with their long black hair blowing in the wind, laughing, wearing silk stockings and loafers, the idealization of everything that seemed to him American, everything that seemed to him non-

Harlem and non-Italian. Once, in high school, Rubin said to him in the boys' room, jokingly, "Where else but in America could an Italian and a Jew piss side by side in the same bowl?" and he had laughed because he laughed at everything Rubin said, Rubin was so much smarter and better informed than he, but he didn't really get the joke. He did not by that time see anything funny about being Italian, nor could he understand what Rubin thought was so funny about being Jewish. It never once occurred to him, not then, and not later when he was hobnobbing it around Hollywood with stars and starlets and all that crap, nor even when he laid a famous movie queen who kept calling him Artie, for which he almost busted her in the mouth, except she really was as passionate as she came over on the screen, not in all those years, not ever in his life until perhaps this moment when he felt so terribly alone enmeshed in a law system created by Englishmen, not once did he ever realize how dearly he had loved Harlem, or how much it had meant to him to be Italian.

There was in his world a cluttered brimming external existence, and an interior solitude that balanced each other perfectly and resulted in, he realized, a serene childhood, *even* in the midst of a depression, even though his father was a mysterious government employee known as "a substitute" instead of "a regular," which he gathered was highly more desirable. There was an immutable pattern in his household, the same foods were eaten on the identical night each week, Monday was soup which his mother made herself, he hated soup meat, it was stringy and tasteless. Tuesday night was spaghetti with either meatballs or *braciòla,* Wednesday night was breaded veal cutlets with spinach and mashed potatoes, his mother once dumped a whole bowl of mashed potatoes on his head because he was trying to catch a fly as a specimen for the microscope he had got for Christmas. He threw a dissecting needle at the fly on the wall and, uncanny luck, pierced the fly, even Errol Flynn couldn't have done better. ("You *got* 'im, Sonny!" Julie shrieked in delight.) But a lot of gooey white glop came out of the fly and he refused to eat his mashed potatoes after that. So his mother, naturally, having inherited a few Neapolitan traits from Grandpa, even though she herself had been born and raised in the garden spot called Harlem, picked up the bowl of potatoes and dumped the whole thing on his head. His father laughed. He hated his father for two months after that. Couldn't he have at least said it wasn't nice to dump a bowl of mashed potatoes all over a kid who was maybe a budding scientist and certainly the best dissecting needle thrower in the United States?

Thursday night was some kind of macaroni, either *rigatoni* or *mostaccioli* or *fusilli,* again with meatballs, or maybe sausage, and Friday night was fish, of course. Oh, how he hated fish. There were three kinds of fish his mother made, and he hated each and every one of them. The first was breaded filet of flounder, dry and white and tasteless. The second was breaded shrimp, she sure had a mania for breading stuff, equally as tasteless, except they seemed to come in bite size. The third was a white halibut which she made with a tomato sauce, fresh tomatoes he remembered because the sauce was always pulpy and sometimes had seeds. This was the best of the lot because it was a little juicier than the two breaded concoctions, but he hated each with a passion and deplored the approach of Friday each week. He did not learn how to eat lobster until he went to Maine with a girl from Barnard one weekend, and had not discovered until just recently that his mother hated fish as much as he did and had only made it every Friday because she was a sort of half-ass Catholic who never went to church or confession, but who nonetheless made fish every Friday night. Breaded.

Saturday was either lambchops or steak. Sunday was Grandpa's house, the biggest feast of the week, the family represented in smaller groups except on the holidays, antipasto, spaghetti, meatballs, roast beef or chicken or turkey, fruit, nuts, pastry—his grandfather always went out to buy *cannoli* and *cassatini, sfogliatelli* and *baba* on his name day, a sort of pilgrimage every year. He would come back flushed with the cold (his name day was in November) carrying two white cartons of Italian pastry, tied with white string, "Did you get them, Papa?" his mother would ask. And Grandpa would nod and smile and then grab Arthur playfully and say, "Sonny, help me cut the string, the string is too strong for me."

Structured, everything structured and ordered, the activity in the streets as patterned as the regularity of meals and holidays, each season bringing its own pursuit, its own hysterical joy to the slum. (Slum? What's that? What's a slum?) Roller skates, and stickball, and pea shooters, and pushos, and hi-li paddles, and baseball cards, and roasting mickeys, and black leather aviator hats with goggles, and rubberband guns, one kid had six of them mounted in tandem like a machine gun, and pigeons on the roof, and stoopball, and boxball, and Skullies (I love you, Virginia Kelly) and Statues, and Johnny-on-a-Pony and Ring-a-Leavio, and little girls skipping rope, or playing that game where they lift their leg over a bouncing ball, skirts flying, "One-two-three-a-nation, I received my confirmation," Virginia Kelly had a plaid skirt, blue plaid, she wore white socks, she once beat up Concetta Esposito for calling her a lousy Irish mick, which after all she was. Patterned, structured, safe, secure, there were no rats in Harlem, there was only a street that was a city, a dozen playmates who populated the world, a million relatives who hugged and kissed and teased and loved him and called him Sonny, a busy universe for a small boy.

And juxtaposed to this, the inner reality of Arthur Constantine, the quiet, thoughtful, solitary child who played with his soldiers on the dining room floor, the big oaken table serving as suicide cliff or soaring skyscraper, the intricacy of its hidden structure becoming a bridge to be blown or a gangplank to be walked, each separate lead soldier—the heads were always breaking off, when that happened, you fixed them with a matchstick, but they never lasted long—each separate soldier or cowboy or Indian assuming an identity of its own. Shorty was the one with the bow legs, he had a lariat in his hand when Arthur bought him for a nickel at the Woolworth's on Third Avenue, but later the lariat got lost. Magua was the Indian, he was made of cast iron rather than lead, and he never broke, he outlasted all the others. Naked to the waist, wearing a breechclout, he was Arthur's favorite, and Arthur always put words of wisdom into his mouth, carefully thought-out Indian sayings that helped the white man in his plight. Magua never turned on anybody, Magua was a good Indian. Red Dance was the bad Indian, he had a bonnet full of feathers. When his head finally broke off because Arthur caused Magua to give him a good punch one day, Arthur never bothered to repair him. Instead, he bought an identical piece and named him Blue Dance, who he supposed was Son of Red Dance, and when Magua knocked *his* head off, too, Arthur switched to a villain named El Mustachio who was a soldier carrying a pack, and who didn't have a mustache at all. He would talk aloud to himself while he played with the tiny metal men, he would construct elaborate conflicts and then put everything to rights with either a wise word from Magua or a sweep of his hand, scattering the pieces all over the floor. If his sister ever tried to enter one of these games, he shrieked at her in fury, and once he shoved her against the wall and made her cry and then went to her afterwards and hugged her and kissed her and said he was very sorry, but he still would not let her into any of the solitary games he played with the metal men. He wondered once, alone in his bed and listening to the sounds of sleep in the room next door, whether he would even have allowed Virginia Kelly to play soldiers with him—and he decided not.

Where do they go, he wondered, all those black-haired girls with the green eyes and the wonderful laugh, when the hell have I ever loved anyone as deeply or as hopelessly as I loved Virginia Kelly? Where does it all go, and how does it happen that I'm alone on this day, with Christmas coming and no Grandpa to ask me to help him break the string on the white carton of pastries, this day, when God knows I could at least use Aunt Louise to tell me she has a friend who knows a magistrate, "Don't worry, Sonny, I'll speak to them at the Club," the Republican Club would set it all straight, or if not, then certainly a dab of Aunt Louise's Ointment would. Where? he thought. Where? I've been invited to orgies in Hollywood (and refused)—"The ideah is to have a few drinks ontil ever'one get on-in-hib-ited, you know whut I mean?"—I've seen my name on motion picture screens and television screens and once on a theater program, Arthur Nelson Constantine, the "Nelson" added by yours truly as a bow to our cousins across the big water, an acknowledgment of my veddy British heritage, Arthur *Nelson* Constantine ("What?" Aunt Louise would have said. "Don't worry, I know somebody in the Republican Club.") I have gone to bed with young girls, and some not so young, and once I went to bed with *two* girls, and another time I went to bed with a girl and another guy and I think we sent that poor little girl straight from there to an insane asylum, but that was in Malibu where such things happen often, I am told. I have sat at the same table with John Wayne, who offered to buy me a drink and then told a story about shooting *The Quiet Man* in Ireland, and I have been blasted across the sky at five hundred miles an hour while drinking martinis and watching a movie written and directed by a man I knew. And it seems to me now, it seems to me alone in this cold corridor that the most important thing I've ever done in my life was skewer a fly with a dissecting needle from a distance of five feet, shooting from the hip, did I ever tell you *that* story, Duke? And my mother rewarded me by dumping a bowl of lukewarm mashed potatoes on my head. And my father laughed. And the fly dripped its white glop all over the wall.

Where else but in America could a little Italian boy from the slums of Harlem (Well, you see, there are *three* Harlems) sit at the same table with John Wayne and listen to a very inside story about the shooting of *The Quiet Man* in Ireland? Where else, I ask you, indeed. Oh man, I played the Slum Kid bit to the hilt, everybody likes to hear how you can make it in the face of adversity. The mouse that almost bit my mother became over the years a foraging bloodthirsty sea monster with matted hair dripping seaweed and coming up out of the water with its jaws wide ready to swallow her bottom and everything else besides. That apartment on 118th Street became the Black Hole of Calcutta, it's a wonder the swarms of flies did not eat the eyes out of my head as I lay helpless and squirming in the squalor of my pitiful crib, it's a wonder the rats did not tear the flesh from my bones and leave me whimpering helplessly for an undernourished mother to hobble into the room and flail at them ineffectually. I was born and raised in Harlem, you hear that, Duke? Not only was I born and raised in Harlem, but I managed to get out of Harlem, which is no small feat in itself. Moreover, I was educated at Columbia University, which is a pretty snazzy school you will admit, and I managed to become an officer in the Army, came out as a captain don't forget, and then went on to become a very highly paid screen and television writer who this very minute is negotiating, or at least *hoping* to negotiate, with one Hester Miers, you've *got* it, mister, the very same, for the starring role in my new play which will be coming to Broadway shortly. (I'll stand in that lobby on opening night, Virginia Kelly, and when you walk in and recognize me and come over to wish me luck, I'll tell you to go bounce a ball on the sidewalk, one-two-three-a-nation. I'll tell you I've got an apartment of my own now in a very fancy building on East 54th Street, with a doorman *and* an elevator operator, and I'll tell you I date the prettiest girls in New York almost every night of the week and I've been sucked off by more black-haired Irish girls than there are in your entire family or perhaps in the entire city of Dublin. And then I'll ask the usher or perhaps the porter to please show you out of the goddamn theater as you are disturbing my equilibrium.) I was born and raised in Harlem, so look at me. Something, huh? You don't have to be colored to be underprivileged, you know. Look at me, and have pity on the poor skinny slum kid, man, did I play that into the ground.

So here stands the poor skinny slum kid (not so poor, not so skinny, never having come from a slum anyway because it sure as hell wasn't a slum to me, it was the happiest place I've ever known in my life) standing alone in an Anglo-Saxon world being represented by a Jew (Where else but in America can a wop, etc.) and going up against a man named Jonah Willow, who sounds like a Eurasian philosopher, and

I'm scared. I'm scared not because there were rats in Harlem, I'm scared not because there were pushers lurking on every street corner, I'm scared not because teenage hoods came at me with tire chains and switch blades, I'm scared because I'm alone.

I'm scared because I've been making it alone ever since I was eighteen and got drafted into the United States Army, I'm scared and I'm tired, and I would like to rest.

He took a last drag on his cigarette, searched for an ash tray in the corridor, and found four of them fastened to the wall. He glanced over his shoulder to see if Willow and his assistant were coming back—the *hell* with them, let them be late—and then walked swiftly toward the courtroom. He pulled open one of the bronze-flowered doors and immediately saw Brackman and his partner at one of the long tables, Genitori and his assistant at the other. He saw Driscoll and his wife sitting in the empty jury box, just as before. He saw the court clerk hovering near the door to the judge's chamber, waiting to call, "All rise!" No one seemed to realize that beyond that paneled door the judge might be reading his newspaper or blowing his nose or laughing on the telephone or tying his shoelaces—or perhaps pondering the decision that would mean the difference between a sweet, staggering success and . . . what?

What you have now, Arthur thought.

Exactly what you have now.

Unnoticed, he took his seat at the plaintiff's table, and waited for the trial to resume.

"Mr. Constantine, would you please continue where you left off before the recess?" Brackman said.

"I was just about to begin with specific character similarities," Arthur said. "I was going to start with the character of Lieutenant Roger Mason in my play *Catchpole* and the character called Alex Cooper in *The Paper Dragon*. There are similarities there that go beyond the realm of coincidence, and I'd like to enumerate them."

"Please do."

"To begin with, the hero of my play is twenty-one years old, and fresh out of college. He goes into the Army as a private, is sent to O.C.S., and is shipped to the Pacific to fight the enemy. The man who played him on the New York stage was at least six feet tall, and he had dark hair and blue eyes—did I say he was a second lieutenant?"

"Your Honor, could the clerk—"

"Yes, certainly."

"Witness has referred to him only as 'a new lieutenant,'" the clerk said.

"Would you like to amend that in some way?" McIntyre asked.

"Yes, your Honor, if I may. I'd like to say that he was a *second* lieutenant. That's very important. Especially since the hero of *The Paper Dragon* is a second lieutenant, too. He is described in the book, in fact, as being twenty-one years old, fresh out of Pratt Institute, and drafted into the Army. He goes to O.C.S. and then is shipped off to the Pacific to fight the enemy. The enemy is a different one this time, admittedly, and the setting is Korea, not Eniwetok—but the similarity stands. In addition, the hero of the book is described as being six feet tall, and having dark hair and blue eyes. Physically, these two different men in two so-called separate works look exactly alike. You could almost say they were twins.

"Now the second similarity of character is the fact that there is a nurse in my play, and also a nurse in the book. In my play she is called Diane Foster, and in the book she is called Jan Reardon. Both girls are blond, both are young, both are from New York City. In fairness, I must say that the girl in the book is *not* a native New Yorker, whereas the girl in my play is. But in both the play and the book, there's a romantic attachment formed between the hero and the nurse."

"You're getting into plot again, aren't you?" Brackman asked.

"Only as it illuminates character."

"Go on, please."

"There is in my play a sergeant who is a member of a minority group, his name is Sergeant D'Agostino and he is an Italian. In the book there is also a sergeant who is a member of a minority group. His name is Sergeant Morley, and he is a Negro. Both these men play important parts in plot development, as I explained earlier."

"Yes, let's just stick to character similarities right now."

"There is a man killed in my play, right at the outset. His name is Private Hapsberg. There is also a man killed in *The Paper Dragon,* even before the hero arrives on the scene. *His* name is Major Randolph. I don't think the rank makes much difference, it's the idea of a sniper killing each of these men that—"

"Your Honor," Willow said, "it would appear to me that we are simply going over ground already covered. Unless this testimony regarding character similarities can demonstrably add to what we earlier heard, I must object to the witness continuing along these lines."

"It would seem, Mr. Brackman," McIntyre said, "that there *is* an overlap here."

"May I explain, your Honor?" Arthur asked.

"Yes, please."

"In developing a work of fiction," Arthur said, "the interplay between plot and character—"

"Your Honor," Willow said, "I do not believe this Court is interested in fiction techniques. We are here to determine whether or not an act of plagiarism took place. It is hardly to the point—"

"Please let him finish, Mr. Willow," McIntyre said.

"I was going to say," Arthur said, with a sharp glance at Willow, "that character and plot are inseparable in a good work of fiction. Character determines plot, and in turn plot shapes character. In other words, it would be practically impossible to discuss either without referring to the other."

"Yes, I understand that," McIntyre said. "But it *would*

seem that the character similarities you are now listing were adequately covered when you testified about plot. In that respect, I would agree with Mr. Willow."

"This is merely an amplification, your Honor," Brackman said.

"Well, I will allow the witness to continue," McIntyre said, "but I think we would all appreciate the elimination of material already covered."

"This is simply backing and filling, your Honor," Willow said.

"Whatever it may be, Mr. Willow, the witness may continue—with the reservation I have already mentioned."

"Well," Arthur said, and hesitated. "I'm not sure I understand, but . . ."

"We would like you to continue with character similarities," McIntyre said, "but we ask you to limit—"

"I understand *that,*" Arthur said, "but it seems to me . . ."

"Yes?"

"I don't know if I'm allowed to say this," Arthur said, and looked at Brackman.

"Allowed to say what, Mr. Constantine?" McIntyre asked.

"Well, it seems to me that the only opportunity I'll get to present my case . . ."

"The Court has asked you to continue with your testimony," Brackman said, a note of warning in his voice. "If you have a question concerning—"

"I will hear the witness," McIntyre said.

"No, nothing," Arthur said, and shook his head.

"We're not trying to give you a fast shuffle here, if that's what you think," McIntyre said, and Arthur turned to look at him, and saw him as a person for the first time. He was close to fifty years of age, Arthur supposed, partially bald, with mild blue eyes and a pink face. He was frowning now, and his hands, delicate and small, were folded on the bench before him as he looked down at Arthur and waited for an answer.

"I didn't mean to imply that, your Honor," Arthur said.

"We have, I believe, allowed you every opportunity thus

far to present your case fairly and adequately. I assure you that we have already studied the play and the novel and that we saw a screening of the film on Friday. We have read the pretrial examination transcripts, and we have carefully studied the charts prepared by you and your counsel. You will remember that we yielded to your counsel's request to have you elaborate on these similarities in your own words, despite defendants' objection. We are now asking, in the hope of saving time, only that you limit your testimony to similarities not already covered by your previous testimony. We believe this is a reasonable request, Mr. Constantine."

"Yes, it's reasonable," Arthur said.

"Very well, then."

"But . . ."

"Mr. Constantine," Brackman said sharply, "are you ready to continue?"

"Is something still troubling you?" McIntyre asked.

"Yes, your Honor."

"Then please say what's on your mind."

"Your Honor, this case is very important to me."

"I realize that. I'm sure it's equally important to Mr. Driscoll."

"I'm sure it is, sir, but . . . well, Mr. Driscoll doesn't happen to be on the stand right now, and I am."

"Your Honor," Willow said, "I must object to the witness engaging this Court in argument. We are trying—"

"I will hear the witness," McIntyre said flatly. "Go on, Mr. Constantine."

"Your Honor, tomorrow morning Mr. Willow will begin his cross-examination and *that,* I'm afraid, is *that*. If there's anything I left out or forgot today, it'll be just too bad. I know the charts are a help, but . . ."

"*That,* I'm afraid, is *not* that," McIntyre said, "nor will it be just too bad, either. Your attorney will have ample opportunity to conduct a redirect. I'm sorry, Mr. Constantine, but I must now agree with Mr. Willow. This is a court of law and not a first semester course on evidence or tactics. You will please continue with your testimony, and you will limit it to similarities not previously covered."

"I apologize for the witness, your Honor," Brackman said. "Please continue, Mr. Constantine."

"Yes, sir," Arthur said, and swallowed. He was embarrassed and angry. Alone on the witness chair, feeling abandoned even by his own lawyer, he searched in his mind for character similarities, every eye in the room upon him, foolish and stupid, struck dumb by the judge's reprimand, his anger building, eyes smarting, hands trembling in his lap.

"If the witness could care to examine the charts to refresh his memory . . ." Willow said.

"I don't need the charts, thank you," Arthur snapped, and looked at Willow in anger, and then at Brackman in anger, and then glanced up at the judge in anger, the son of a bitch, shutting him up that way, humiliating him, Brackman allowing the humiliation and adding to the indignity by apologizing. The anger and embarrassment were identical to what he had felt the night the critics killed his play, those rotten egotistical bastards sitting in exalted judgment on something about which they possessed no real knowledge. How could McIntyre or Willow or even Brackman hope to understand the intricacies of a work of fiction? Oh yes, they would nod their heads in accord as they had this morning, Willow and McIntyre, two legal masterminds agreeing that an author's intent had no place in a court of law, no place in the judgment of a plagiarism suit, casually eliminating the inexplicable beginning of creation, snuffing out the spark of *idea,* eliminating conscious direction from the work—"I maintain, your Honor, that any similarities must be solely between the works in question."

"I would agree to that."

"And that therefore the author's *intent* is irrelevant."

Oh yes, irrelevant, and why hadn't Brackman objected, or had he secretly agreed with his colleagues? Perhaps he had only wanted to apologize at that point, perhaps that was it, apologize for Arthur ever having conceived and written *Catchpole* at all. How could one possibly hope to explain anything to them if they had already ruled out intent, already decided that only words were on trial here, words and nothing more? Never mind the act itself, the intent or its realization, hadn't he been a little bit insane when he created the psychopathic colonel, hadn't he hated with Janus and suffered with the lieutenant, loved the nurse and died with D'Agostino, never mind, never mind, it is all cut and dried. There are only one hundred and twenty mimeographed pages of a play called *Catchpole,* there are only four hundred and twelve pages of a pirated novel called *The Paper Dragon,* there is only an hour and fifty minutes of a film supposedly based on the novel, that is our concern here, the comparison of the works. The author's intent is irrelevant, the author is irrelevant, the *self* is irrelevant, the *man* is irrelevant. That almighty God son of a bitch McIntyre will sit there with his watery blue eyes and his pink puffed face and humiliate him the way the critics had humiliated him in October of 1947, the shame and embarrassment of meeting people you knew, the goddamn solicitous smiles as though a stranger had passed away, but not a stranger, something very real and intimate called *Catchpole* which had taken four months to write and five months to sell, and two months to rehearse, not a stranger at all. The guarded knives, the secret delight behind the words of condolence. You have dared, my friend, you have dared to expose yourself, and they have killed you, and I am glad, I am secretly and enormously delighted, how sorry to hear that your play closed last night, but after all what do the critics know? Yes, after all, what do the critics know, or the lawyers or the judges, Arthur thought. He had tried to explain how important this trial was to him, and McIntyre had countered by saying it was important to Driscoll as well, yes. Yes, assuredly, oh certainly but not in the same way. There was more on trial here than words, more than the comparison of two similar works of fiction, more even than the enormous amount of money that would go to the victor. There was an identity on trial, there was this very self McIntyre refused to allow, there was a *man.* And if Arthur allowed Driscoll to steal the work of fiction, then he also allowed him to steal the intent and the realization, the self and the person, the man. And then there would be nothing left, nothing at all.

"We are waiting," Brackman said.

"I'm thinking," Arthur answered.

"Take your time," McIntyre said.

"Thank you," Arthur answered, and he hoped the sarcasm was evident in his voice. "There are," he said, "in addition to those character similarities already mentioned, just a few others. In both my play and in the book, for example, there is a soldier who comes from Brooklyn, a soldier who comes from the South, and a soldier who is Jewish. They are all in the squad that becomes the focus of both the play and the book, the one the lieutenant has all the trouble with in the platoon he commands. Also, in the play and in the book, there is an elderly nurse who is a sort of friend and mother-confessor to the heroine. In the play, she has recently lost her husband—which is why she joins the Medical Corps. In the book, she has also lost her husband and become a nurse." Arthur paused. "I think those are the rest of the specific character similarities, those not already mentioned."

"Your Honor," Brackman said, "should any others occur to the witness . . ."

"Yes, of course, you may bring them out in the redirect."

"Thank you, your Honor. Would you now tell us please what specific similarities of language you found in the play and the novel, Mr. Constantine?"

"Yes, certainly," Arthur said. He turned to McIntyre. "I thought I might quote from the respective works, if that wouldn't take up too much time, your Honor."

"We have time," McIntyre said. "If you don't finish before two o'clock, there's always tomorrow."

"I'd like to quote then."

"Go right ahead, please."

"In my play, when Lieutenant Mason first arrives on Eniwetok, I have Corporal Janus, the troublemaker, say, 'Another ninety-day wonder. *I* wonder how long he'll last.' In *The Paper Dragon,* Private Colman looks at the lieutenant right after he first addresses the men, watches him as he's walking away and says, 'Straight out of college. They sent him here for his master's degree,' and Sergeant Morley says, 'Cheer up, Pete, maybe he'll flunk out.' That's his first name, Pete. Peter Colman."

"Mr. Constantine, we're all interested in saving time, but it's not necessary to speak this rapidly," Brackman said.

"I didn't realize I was."

"Just take as much time as you need."

"All right. I guess we are all familiar by now with what has been called the 'female rifle' scene in *The Paper Dragon,* where the men are disassembling their rifles. The lieutenant is going through the authorized method, straight from the book, and every time he comes to a word like 'rod' or 'butt' or 'trigger,' it breaks the men up. They're handling pieces, you see, which is Army terminology for a gun, and they keep making sexual allusions, and getting hysterical when the lieutenant says things like 'now twist the rod toward your body with your right hand and then exert a slight pull to the right,' I'm not quoting exactly, but the scene is intended sexually, and the men are doing all this to infuriate the lieutenant, who is running the session according to the book and trying to get a little order into what is a pretty bedraggled band of fighting men."

"This is in *The Paper Dragon?*"

"Yes, but its counterpart is in *Catchpole*. In my play I have the men discussing, within earshot of the lieutenant, the attempt of one of the men to capture a wild pig. Their references to the pig are purely sexual, and they are engaging in this kind of talk because the lieutenant had warned them he was going to try to 'clean up' the outfit before the final assault on Parry Island, those are his exact words. The pig is referred to as 'a juicy morsel,' and 'something to sink your teeth into,' and also at one point one of the men says, 'We almost *had* that sweet little piece of meat.' A piece of meat, of course, is a girl. I see there's a lady in the courtroom, and I hate to talk this way, but I'm referring to actual words in the works that are being questioned."

"You may say what you want to say, Mr. Constantine."

"In the motion picture, of course, this entire so-called 'female rifle' scene was eliminated. Now, in *Catchpole,* there are a great many references to Glenn Miller who was, as you know, a well-known bandleader during the thirties and forties and who was reported missing at about the time of the Eniwetok campaign, and I have the men speculating on what might have happened to him. In *The Paper Dragon,* which takes place in Korea in 1950, the Army men begin discussing Glenn Miller and how he could play trombone, whereas this is a new generation of men who actually would have very little knowledge of Glenn Miller or how he played trombone. The same references apply to the movie, and are mostly given to Sergeant Morley, the Negro."

"The same references to Glenn Miller, do you mean?"

"Yes. Now regarding the love story, the nurse in my play is a first lieutenant and of course the hero is a second lieutenant. There is a great deal of playful love-making where she constantly kids him about rank, and about reporting him to the company commander if he doesn't kiss her right that minute, all jokingly of course, but very important to the development of their affair. In the book, there is an extremely erotic sex scene where the couple are alone together for the first time, and she suddenly says, 'You'd better kiss me now,' and he says, 'Do you think it's safe?' and she replies, 'Do as I say, Coop. I outrank you.' The identical line is used in the motion picture. I'd like to say something here about the names of these characters, by the way."

"Go right ahead."

"This has to do again with specific language. My lieutenant's name is Roger Mason, and he is familiarly called 'Mase' by the nurse and by his fellow officers. The lieutenant's name in *The Paper Dragon* is Alex Cooper, and he is called 'Coop' by the nurse and by his friends. Which leads me to another startling similarity between—"

"Your Honor," Jonah said, "might we not do without the editorializing adjectives?"

"If you will simply state the similarities, Mr. Constantine," McIntyre said, "that will be sufficient."

"Yes, sir, I was only going to say that in my play the men keep calling the lieutenant 'Loot,' that's all. At one point in my play, the lieutenant says, 'How about lengthening that to Lieutenant Mason?' and Janus replies, 'Isn't that what I said, *Loot?*' stressing the word. Well, in *The Paper Dragon,* there's a scene where the lieutenant says to the men, 'A *lieutenant* is an officer in the United States Army. A *lute* is a Chinese stringed instrument.' And Colman, the troublemaker, answers, 'Maybe those Mongolian bastards would prefer lutes to bugles, Loot.' This same line is used in the motion picture, though of course the word 'bastards' is deleted. But the reference is the same in all three versions of my play."

"Objection, your Honor," Willow said. "There is only *one* version of the play, as I understand it."

"Sustained. Strike that."

"From where, your Honor?" the clerk asked.

"The reference to all three versions. There has been, as Mr. Willow pointed out, only one version of *Catchpole* submitted to this Court."

Brackman glanced at Willow ruefully, and then turned again to Arthur. "Would you tell us what other specific similarities of language you found?" he said.

Arthur cleared his throat. "In the stage play," he said, "we obviously could not use profanity in the New York theater, or at least the kind of profanity a combat squad would be apt to use in the midst of one of the bitterest campaigns in the Pacific war. But I had one man in the squad addicted to the use of a word which was easily understood by the audience as a substitute—an acceptable substitute, I should say—for a more obscene word. I had this one character, one of the minor characters in the squad constantly using variations of the word 'bug,' so that he would be saying 'This bugging Army food,' or 'This bugging war,' or 'Bug off, Mac,' expressions like that, which made it absolutely clear which word I really meant. In *The Paper Dragon,* because such language is allowed in novels, one of the characters in the squad is addicted to the use of the actual word, I think we all know the word I mean, in all of its various forms, the same way my character uses the word 'bug.' I don't remember this character's name. I think—"

"Is it Kenworthy?"

"That's right, his name in the book is Kenworthy. And every other word out of his mouth is an obscenity, identical to the character in my play."

"Go on, Mr. Constantine."

Arthur paused. Brackman studied him for a moment and then said, "Yes?"

"I beg your pardon?"

"You seemed to be hesitating."

"Oh. I was only trying to remember if I'd left anything out, before I come to the most amazing similarity of all."

"Your Honor . . ." Willow started, rising.

"I do think we might get along better without the descriptive adjectives, Mr. Constantine," McIntyre said.

"I'm sorry, your Honor. To my mind, this next similarity *is* amazing, and—"

"Objection, your Honor."

"Please, Mr. Constantine."

"I'm sorry. May I tell this last specific similarity of language?"

"Yes, certainly," McIntyre said.

"Well, in the actual campaign for Eniwetok, the 106th was the United States Infantry Regiment that made the assault, and the other forces involved were the 22nd Marine Regimental Combat Team, and a temporary command echelon called Tactical Group One—this was all in February of 1944 when I was there on the island. I was attached to C Company, and I guess you know that Army companies are broken down into platoons and then squads, as was the Army company in my play. A squad consists of twelve men, and that's the number of soldiers I focus attention on in my play—this was done because of technical reasons, I wanted to get a microcosm of the Army into this relatively small group of men. When I started writing the play, however, I thought it would be best to use a *fictitious* infantry division, so I—"

"Why did you want to do that, Mr. Constantine?"

"I didn't want to run into any possible trouble with the Army, or with the inadvertent use of names that might possibly belong to real men who had been in the 106th Regiment during the Eniwetok campaign."

"You were afraid of possible lawsuits, is that it?"

"Yes, I didn't want to libel anyone who might be an actual living person. So I invented a division, and I called it the 105th, the digits one-oh-five, and I almost changed the name of the atoll to a fictitious one. That is, I almost changed it from Eniwetok, but I decided that would be taking too much historic license. So I didn't, after all. But I would like to say that there were only sixty-seven infantry divisions in the United States Army at that time, and that there was not then during 1944, nor was there during the Korean conflict, nor is there today at present an Army infantry division called the 105th. That's important when we come to compare this with *The Paper Dragon.*"

"Would you explain that, please?"

"Well, the actual Army divisions involved in the battle for Korea when the Chinese began their Ch'ongch'on River offensive were the 2nd, the 24th, and the 25th. There was no 105th Division involved because there is no such division in the United States Army. The novel *The Paper Dragon* is set in Korea during October and November of 1950, prior to and during the Chinese offensive across the Ch'ongch'on. It is significant to me that James Driscoll chose to call *his* division in *his* novel the 105th, the identical number I chose for the division in my play. I think it's safe to say that the possibility of coincidence involving those three digits, one-oh-five—the odds against hitting on those same three digits accidentally and in sequence would be staggering. Yet those same three digits are used to label a division in my play and in the novel." Arthur paused, and then looked up at the judge. "That's all I have to say about the similarities between the two works, the three works when we include the movie."

"Your Honor, may I now offer copies of the various charts?" Brackman asked.

"Does anyone object?"

"No objection," Willow said, "if Mr. Brackman will tell us which chart is which."

"I offer this chart titled Plot Similarities."

"Do we understand that these charts represent Mr. Constantine's *complete* list of similarities?" Willow asked.

"These four charts include each and every similarity Mr. Constantine found between the works in question. We have one additional chart listing the similarities between the play and the movie, and I would like to offer that as well."

"I would like to have it understood that these charts were prepared by Mr. Constantine, and are being offered to show James Driscoll's access to the play *The Catchpole,*" Willow said.

"It's *Catchpole,*" Arthur said.

"What?"

"It's *Catchpole*. There's no article. It's not *'The' Catchpole.*"

"Oh. I'm sorry," Willow said. "But are we clear as to their offer?"

"We are clear, Mr. Willow," McIntyre said.

"The second chart is labeled Character Similarities."

"Mr. Brackman, we did not get the number designation of the first chart."

"Plot Similarities is—do you have the number?"

The clerk consulted his notes. "Plaintiff's Exhibit 5 is Plot Similarities," he said. "Character Similarities is Plaintiff's Exhibit 6."

"Then this chart," Brackman said, "Language Similarities, would be number 7. The last chart, Play and Movie Similarities, is number 8."

"That's correct."

"No objection."

"No objection."

"Does that conclude the direct, Mr. Brackman?" McIntyre asked.

"It does. Defendants may examine."

"In that case, I would like to recess until ten A.M. tomorrow morning, at which time you may begin the cross-examination, Mr. Willow."

"This court is recessed until ten tomorrow morning," the clerk said.

"I don't know why you let him do that to me," Arthur said outside the courthouse. He was watching the oncoming traffic for a taxicab, his eyes squinted against the strong wind, his back to Brackman, who stood with his gloved hands in his coat pockets, homburg tilted down, muffler tight about his throat, heavy briefcase resting beside him on the sidewalk.

"You let him do it," Brackman said. "You walked right into it."

"You should have stopped him. You're my attorney."

"You were your *own* attorney at that point."

"I was getting angry."

"Yes. So you attempted to argue your own case. That was a brilliant move, Arthur, absolutely brilliant."

"Someone had to argue it. *You* certainly weren't."

"Thank you, Arthur."

"Don't get petulant, Sidney. Petulance is unbecoming on a middle-aged man."

"Yes, and ingratitude is unbecoming on a man of any age."

"If we win this case . . ."

"If we win this case, I'll be amply rewarded, yes. *If* we win it. In the meantime, it's cost me a considerable amount of time and money, and I would appreciate your letting *me* handle it from now on."

"I didn't think McIntyre was being fair. He can't—"

"He can do whatever he wants in his own courtroom."

"But he has to be fair."

"No, he only has to be judicious."

"I still think he was rushing us," Arthur said, and raised his hand to signal an empty cab.

"Let it go by," Brackman said. "I want to talk to you."

"I have to get to the theater."

"The theater can wait. Let it go by."

Arthur waved the taxi away and turned wearily to Brackman. "What is it?" he asked.

"Arthur, do you want to lose this case?"

"You know I don't."

"You can lose it if you're not careful."

"I thought you said . . ."

"Yes, that we had an airtight case. But believe me, Arthur, you can lose it. And one sure way of losing it is to antagonize the man who'll be making the decision. That's one sure way of slitting your own throat."

"I'm sorry."

"Tomorrow's going to be a rough day, Arthur. Willow—"

"I said I was sorry."

"Willow is *not* on our side, you know, and he'll do everything he can to rattle you and confuse you and make you lose your temper. I want your promise that under no circumstances will you again address the judge personally, not to ask him any questions, not to offer any explanations, not for any conceivable reason. I don't even want you to *look* at him, Arthur, I want your promise on that."

"I promise," Arthur said. "I have to get to the theater."

"Can you be here at nine-thirty tomorrow?"

"I guess so. Why?"

"There are a few matters I want to discuss when you're not in such a hurry."

"All right, I'll be here."

"Nine-thirty," Brackman said. "There's another empty one, grab him."

"Can I drop you off?"

"No, I'm going east."

The taxicab pulled to the curb. Arthur opened the door, and then said, "Judicious *is* fair."

"Look it up," Brackman said, and Arthur climbed in and closed the door behind him. "The Helen Hayes Theatre," he said to the cabbie, "Forty-sixth and Broadway."

It had turned into a bleak, forbidding day, the sun all but gone, dank heavy clouds hanging low in the sky and threatening snow. Through the taxi windows, he could see pedestrians rushing past on the sidewalks, hurrying to cross the streets, their heads ducked, their hands clutching coat collars. Behind them and beyond them, the store windows beckoned warmly with holiday tinsel and mistletoe, colored lights and ornaments, wreaths and sprigs of holly. This was only the twelfth of December, with Christmas still almost two weeks away, but the stores had begun preparing for the season long before Thanksgiving, and the city wore a festive look that unified it now as it did each year. He could remember the long walks to the library from his home on 217th Street, the store windows decorated as they were here but with a shabby Bronx look. They had moved to the Bronx when he was twelve years old, the decentralization was beginning, the second generation was starting its exodus to what then passed for the suburbs. The trip to Grandpa's house each Sunday would be longer and more difficult to make, discouraging frequency, trickling away at last to family gatherings only on holidays or occasional Sundays, disappearing entirely when his grandfather died. The street they moved into was another ghetto, smaller, cleaner, with a rustic country look (or so it seemed after Harlem) trees planted in small rectangular plots of earth dug out of the sidewalk, mostly two-family brick houses, Olinville Junior High School across the street, its fence stretching halfway up the block from Barnes Avenue, they used to play handball in the schoolyard. He tried out for the handball team when he entered high school, but did not make it. He was a good student, though, his marks always up in the eighties and nineties, and an omnivorous reader. He would go to the library on 229th Street and Lowerre Place maybe two or three times a week, even before it got to be a gathering place for the high school crowd.

There was a feeling of prosperity to the new apartment (he recognized now that it was hardly less shabby than the four rooms they'd had in Harlem) with its new furniture and its new linoleum, the three-piece maple set his mother bought for him, with the dresser that had a hidden dropleaf desk full of cubbyholes, and the pink curtains in Julie's room. She was nine at the time, and had already begun to hang all kinds of crazy signs on her door, GENIUS AT WORK and BEWARE VICIOUS DOG, he got such a kick out of her, she was really a great kid. His father had become a "regular" by then, and was working out of the Williamsbridge Post Office on Gun Hill Road. He would set the alarm for four-thirty every morning, waking up the whole damn house, and clamoring for his breakfast, a real ginzo with ginzo ideas about the woman's place and so on. He could have let Mama sleep, instead of making such a big deal about breakfast, racing around the apartment in his long johns. "There he goes," Julie would yell, "they're off and running at Jamaica," and Arthur would lie in his bed under the quilt Aunt Louise had made for him, and quietly snicker, he sure was a nut, that old man of his.

There was, too, the same feeling of belonging in this new ghetto, though now there weren't aunts and uncles to meet on the street or to drop in on during the afternoon. But there were Italians all up and down the block, half of them barely able to speak English, and there was a funny kind of intimacy, a feeling of safety, an instant understanding that was not present out there in the White Protestant world, though at the time he was not aware such a world even existed. He knew only that he felt comfortable on his own block, with people who were easily recognizable, like the business with all the women named Anna, for example. His mother's name was Anna, but there were also four other women named Anna on the block. So instead of using their last names, which is what any decent New Canaan lady would have done, instead of referring to them as Anna Constantine or Anna Ruggiero or Anna Di Nobili, the women had a shorthand all their own, Naples-inspired he was sure, instant ginzo communication. His mother was Anna the Postman, and the other women were respectively Anna the Plumber, and Anna the Butcher, and Anna the Bricklayer and also Anna From Wall Street, he smiled even now, thinking of it. But he was comfortable then, comfortable in his growing body, and comfortable in his new home, where in the silence of his bedroom (unless Julie was practicing her flute in her own room next door) he would take the little maple lamp from the dresser top, the lamp shaped like a candlestick with a little shade on it, and he would put the lamp on the floor and play with his soldiers in the circle of light it cast. The dining room table had been sold before they left Harlem, they now had a three-piece living room suite and a big floor radio that looked like a juke box, but there were worlds to discover on his bedroom floor and he searched them out with his faithful Magua and his intrepid Shorty, his imagination looser now, fed by the books he withdrew from the library each week.

Every now and then he would take Julie to the library with him, leaving her in the children's section while he roamed in his mature twelve-year-old masculinity through the adult section, taking a book from a shelf, scanning it, deciding whether or not he wanted to read it. He never bought any books then, and he did not know there was such a thing as the bestseller list of the *New York Times Book Review*. He had not ever, in fact, even *read* the *New York Times*, although kids used to come around to the classrooms selling the *Times* and also the *Trib*. He grew up with the *News* and the *Mirror* and the *Journal-American* (he later felt betrayed when even these friendly and well-known newspapers killed his play). He wondered now when he had last gone to see a play that had not received rave notices, when he had last read a book that was not on the bestseller list. It had been much simpler then, the long walk to the library along White Plains Avenue, the library snug and warm, the aroma of books, the feel of them in his hands. And at Christmas, the tree opposite the main desk, decorated with popcorn, the Dickens novels bound in burnished red leather, tooled in gold, spread on the floor beneath the tree, more appropriate at Christmas than at any other time. The librarian was a nice German lady named Miss Goldschmidt. "Merry Christmas, Arthur," she would say. "What are you reading *this* week?"—the cherished copy of *The Talisman* with the jacket picture of the knight on horseback, he slid the book across the desk and Miss Goldschmidt beamed approval.

"You sure that's on Forty-sixth?" the cabbie asked.

"I'm sure," Arthur said. There were not too many things he was sure of, but he was dead certain that the Helen Hayes was on Forty-sixth Street because *Catchpole* had opened at that identical theater when it was still known as the Fulton in 1947, to be mercilessly clobbered by all ten gentlemen of the press the next day—back then, *PM*, the *Mirror*, the *Sun*, and the *Brooklyn Eagle* also had a say about what would be permitted to survive. He thought it supremely ironic that his new play was holding readings at the same theater, but he fervently wished it would open someplace else, *anyplace* else, where he would be safe from the evil eye. Evil eye, my ass, he thought, but hadn't his grandfather come to America from an impoverished mountain village called Ruvo del Monte, and wasn't there still enough of this heritage in Arthur to cause suspicion and doubt? In fact, hadn't his Aunt Filomena been hit by the iceman's runaway horse on First Avenue the very night after his mother had dreamt it? Any place but the Fulton, he thought. You can change the name, but the jinx remains. And yet he knew his fears were idiotic, God, look at what the wind was doing out there, papers blowing in the gutter, hats skimming off heads, look at that woman trying to control her skirts, God this was a city, what a city this was.

He wanted to own this city.

But more than that, or perhaps a part of it, an extension of it, he wanted to know that this was where he belonged, this city into which he had been born, this city whose streets and gutters he knew from the time he had felt for immies in deep puddles along the curb, this city whose rooftops held secret fluttering pigeons to watch, hot, sticky tar to mold into huge, strange shapes, chimney pots behind which you could pee, this city that had grown to include the Bronx and a two-family house opposite the junior high school, hide and seek behind hydrangea bushes, fig trees wrapped in tarpaper against the winter's cold, a two-cent Hooton with nuts every afternoon on the walk home from Evander, Bronx Park and the winding river path, Laura in the woods behind the

Botanical Gardens, they'd been eaten alive by mosquitoes, this city, this.

He wanted to claim it, but more than that he wished to be claimed by it.

Those solitary walks to the library alone, when alone his thoughts would spiral and somersault, when alone he would build magic castles bright with minarets and floating golden banners, when alone he was master of a world in which he walked proud and unafraid and people knew his name and dreaded it, hands thrust deep into the pockets of his mackinaw, the library books dangling at the end of a long leather strap except when it was raining and his mother made him put them in a shopping bag from the A&P, those solitary walks when he knew without question who he was and what he would become.

He wanted the city to tell him who he was again.

He paid the driver and got out of the taxi, walking directly to the stage entrance and opening the door onto the long alley that led to the rear of the theater. Selig and Stern were standing at the end of the alley, in whispered consultation just outside the metal stage door. Selig was wearing a black overcoat with black velveteen collar and cuffs, puffing on a cigar and standing alongside the iron steps that ran to the upper stories of the theater. The alleyway was gray, capped by an ominous piece of gray sky that hung high above it like a canopy. Selig stood in black against the rusting iron steps, surrounded by gray walls and gray smoke. His face appeared gray, too, as though someone very close had passed away during the night.

Stern was wearing a blue plaid sports jacket with a navy blue sweater under it. He was rubbing his big hands together as though chiding himself for having anticipated spring in December, his shoulders hunched, shivering with each swirling gust of alley wind. He looked up in surprise as Arthur approached, and then said, "Is the trial finished already?"

"No, we broke early," Arthur replied. "Is Kent here?"

"Not yet," Selig said.

Kent Mercer was their director, a faggot whose nocturnal revels ("I'm a *night* person," he would protest, "that's why I'm *in* the theater, really") often terminated along about dawn when less talented citizens were rising and banging on the radiators for heat. No one expected him to be on time because he never was, and no one ever mentioned his tardy appearances—except Selig, who would invariably remark, each time Mercer arrived late and pantingly out of breath, "Have a good night's sleep, Kent?"

"Where is it?" Stern asked, shivering. "The trial, I mean."

"All the way downtown. Foley Square."

"Is that near the traffic court down there?" Stern asked.

"I think so."

"I was down there once on a speeding ticket," Stern said.

"Mmm," Arthur said, and wondered how Stern could possibly equate a traffic ticket with something as important as a plagiarism suit. Of the two men, he liked Stern least, which in itself was no recommendation for Selig. "Have you heard from Mitzi?" he asked.

"Not yet," Selig said.

"Well, what's happening with Hester's contract?"

"You know as much about it as we do," Selig said mildly, and then puffed on his cigar and looked at the wet end as though suddenly displeased with its taste.

"Last Wednesday—"

"That's right," Stern said. Stern had an annoying habit of agreeing with a statement before it was finished. Arthur was tempted to say, "Last Wednesday someone told me you were a son of a bitch." Instead, he glanced at Stern in brief anger, and then said, "Last Wednesday you told me Hester liked the play."

"That's right," Stern said.

"That's what her agent told us," Selig agreed.

"Aren't you fellows cold out here?" Stern asked.

"No," Arthur said. "And on Friday, you told me she wanted to do it, and it was now a matter of negotiation."

"That's right."

"This is Monday," Arthur said.

"You know Hester."

"No, I don't know Hester."

"She's not sure now."

"If she was sure Friday . . ."

"We don't even know if she was sure Friday. We only know what her agent told us."

"Her agent said she wanted to do the play, isn't that right?"

"That's right."

"And that she was ready to negotiate."

"That's right."

"Well, has an offer been made?"

"She's getting a thousand a week at Lincoln Center, that's whether she's in any of the plays or not. If we even *hope* to spring her, we've got to offer at least fifteen hundred."

"Well, how much *did* you offer?"

"It hasn't come to that yet."

"Look, would someone please talk straight?" Arthur said.

"We've always talked straight with you, Arthur," Selig answered.

"*Was* an offer made?"

"No."

"Why not?"

"Because she still has to talk to the people at Lincoln Center about getting sprung."

"Won't they let her go?"

"We think they will, but it's a matter of sitting down with these people and discussing it."

"Well, when is she going to do that?"

"As soon as she's sure she wants to do your play."

"That's right," Stern said.

"Let me try to get this straight," Arthur said. "*Does* she want to do my play?"

"It would seem so."

"When will we know?"

"I'll call her agent again, if you want me to," Selig said. "Is that what you'd like?"

"Yes."

"I don't think we should push this," Stern said.

"Why not?"

"Because if we can get Hester Miers to take this part, we'll raise all the money for the play immediately. That's why."

"I thought we *had* all the money already," Arthur said.

"This show will cost eighty thousand dollars," Stern said.

"Have we got all the money, or haven't we?"

"No, Arthur," Selig said. "We have *not* got all the money."

"You told me . . ."

"That's right," Stern said.

"You told me all the money was in. You said . . ."

"That's right, but a few of our people have dropped out."

"Well, even if a few of them have dropped out, that doesn't mean . . ."

"One of our people was a man who'd promised us a very large sum of money. He'd decided to put it into a musical instead."

"How much do we still need?"

"We still need sixty thousand dollars," Selig said flatly.

"That means we've hardly got *any* of it," Arthur said.

"If we sign Hester, we'll get all of it," Stern said.

"Then for God's sake sign her!"

"She's not sure she wants to do it."

"Call her agent. I want to know."

"Mitzi will say what she said over the weekend," Stern said. "Hester's not sure."

"If you want me to call her, I will," Selig said. "I'll do whatever you want me to do, Arthur. After all, this is *your* play."

"That's right," Stern said, "but calling Mitzi won't do a bit of good."

"If Arthur wants me to call her, I will."

"Is that what you want, Arthur?"

"I want this play to go on," Arthur said fiercely.

"We all do."

"That's right. But calling Mitzi isn't going to help. She'll say she hasn't been able to reach Hester."

"Look . . ."

"This is the theater, Arthur. These people are sensitive individuals who—"

"Sensitive, my ass!" Arthur said. "My play is in danger of collapsing, and you're telling me some twenty-two-year-old kid has the power . . ."

"She's twenty-five, and she's very talented, and your play is *not* in danger of collapsing."

"I won't let this happen," Arthur said, and there was such an ominous note in his voice that the alley went immediately still. "Call Mitzi. Tell her we have to know, and we have to know right away."

"Don't push this," Stern warned.

"Oscar, if *I* don't push this, perhaps you'd like to tell me just who will."

"We all want the play to go on. We love this play."

"You've loved it for eleven months now, your option expires in January."

"That's right."

"Yes, that's right, and January is next month."

"We can always talk about an extension," Stern said. *"If* we get Hester."

"If we get Hester," Arthur repeated.

"That's right, *if* we get Hester. If we get Hester, we get the money, it's as simple as that. Once we get the money, we can talk extension. If you're willing to grant it, we can go into rehearsal as soon as we finish casting these minor parts. Probably in time for a spring opening."

Arthur nodded. "And if we *don't* get Hester?"

"Let's see what she has to say, okay?"

"Okay, call Mitzi," Arthur said.

"It'll have to wait till tomorrow."

"Why?"

"Because she's in Philadelphia," Selig said. "One of her clients, Boris Whatsisname, opens in Philadelphia tonight. She's got to be there to hold his hand."

"Well, can't you call her there? Philadelphia's only—"

"I don't want to bother her with something like this when she's got an opening. Be sensible, Arthur. It's not going to pay to get impatient here."

"All right."

"All right, Arthur?"

"I said all right."

"I'll call her in the morning, first thing."

"All right."

"And then I'll get to you."

"I'll be in court. The cross starts tomorrow."

"You call me when you're free then, all right?"

"All right," Arthur said.

3

SIDNEY LOOKED AT HIS WATCH the moment he entered the vestibule of her building. It was a quarter to four, and she had promised to wait until at least five, but he was afraid now that she had grown impatient and left earlier. The nameplate over her bell was lettered in delicate black script, *Charlotte Brown,* and it annoyed him just as it always did. He knew her as Chickie Brown, and the formal black script—especially since it had been clipped from her business card—conjured an image of a person about whom he knew very little, Charlotte Brown, who was part owner of a travel agency on Madison Avenue, where she arranged vacations to Haiti or Istanbul for fat matrons. Scowling at the nameplate, he pressed the button below it, and hoped there would be an answering buzz. He gripped the knob on the inner vestibule door with his right hand, put his briefcase down on the floor, patted his hair into place with his free left hand, and waited. Sighing, he walked back to the row of mailboxes, rang the bell a second time, returned to grip the doorknob again, waited, went back to the bell a third time, waited again, and had to ring yet another time before she answered. Her buzz sparked an intense and immediate anger within him, how *dare* she keep him waiting so long? The anger mounted as he pushed open the frosted-glass door and stepped into the hallway. Did a man have to ring a bell four times before he was admitted to a building? An attorney? Angrily, he climbed the steps to her third-floor apartment. Angrily, he knocked on the door.

"Sidney?" she called.

"Yes," he said. "It's me." For a moment, he thought his anger had caused him to forget his briefcase in the vestibule below, and then he realized that he was holding it tightly in his sweating left hand. The door opened.

"Hello," he said brusquely.

"Hello, luv," she answered warmly.

She was wearing dark green slacks and a white silk blouse. A string of green beads circled her throat. Her long hair was piled carelessly on top of her head, held there haphazardly with a green ribbon, bright russet strands falling onto her cheek and forehead, trailing down the back of her neck.

"Come in," she said, "come in," and walked barefooted toward the plush-covered chair near the window, where her cat lay supine on the arm, his tail switching nervously. She passed her extended forefinger along the length of the cat's back, and then lowered the shade against the gathering dusk. The cat's name was Shah, and Sidney despised him.

Chickie turned from the window with a pleased smile on her face, as though she had been contemplating his arrival all day, and was now enormously satisfied by his presence. She touched the cat again in passing. He lifted his head to accept her hand, and then the tail switched again, and he turned to look at Sidney with a malevolent jungle stare.

One day, you little son of a bitch, Sidney thought, I will be in this apartment alone with you, and I will drown you in the tub.

"What kind of a cat is he?" he asked Chickie.

"A nice cat," she answered.

"I meant the breed."

"Persian."

"Is that why you call him Shah?"

"No."

"Then why?"

"Because he's a nice cat. Aren't you a nice cat, Shah

sweetie?" she asked, and she dropped to her knees before the chair and put her face close to the animal's. "Aren't you a lovey-cat, Shah honey?"

"Please, you'll make me vomit," Sidney said.

"I think Sidney has had a hard day in the mines," she said to the cat, and then rose and grinned and said, "Would you like a drink, Sidney? Would that help?"

"I had a very easy day," Sidney said, glaring at the cat. "I just don't happen to like your cat."

"Sidney!" she said. "I thought you *loved* Shah."

"No, I *don't* love Shah."

"I thought you did."

"No, I do not. Point of fact, I do not love *any* cat in the world, *least* of all Shah. Don't ever leave me alone in the apartment with him, or I'll drown him in the tub."

"Do you hear that, Shah?" she said playfully. "Watch out for Sidney because he'll drown you in the tub."

The cat made an ominous sound from somewhere back in his throat. "That's right, you heard her," Sidney said, and Shah made the same ominous sound again.

"He understands you," Chickie said.

"I hope he does. Why do you keep him around?"

"He was a gift."

"From whom?"

"A man."

"Who?"

"Before I knew you."

"I didn't ask you *when*, I asked you *who*."

"An Indian."

"From India?"

"Yes, of course. Did you think I meant a Mohican or something?"

"I never know what you mean, exactly," he said, and sighed.

"Don't you want to know *why* he gave me the cat?"

"No."

"All right, then I won't tell you."

"Why did he give you the cat?" Sidney asked.

"Why do you think he gave me the cat?"

"Because he knew you loved cats."

"No. That is, he knew I loved cats, yes, but that's not why he gave me a present. The cat was a present, Sidney."

"Why did he give you a present?" Sidney asked, and sighed again.

"You think it's because I went to bed with him, don't you?" Chickie said.

"Did you go to bed with him?" he asked wearily.

"Sidney, what a question to ask!"

"Well, then why *did* he give you the filthy little animal?"

"You're angry now."

"No, I'm not angry now. But sometimes I get awfully goddamn tired of these Burns and Allen routines."

"I didn't mean to make you angry," she said, "I'm sorry." She rose quickly, lowered her eyes, and padded to the bar. "I'll make you that drink," she said.

"Thank you."

The room was silent. It could have been a shuttered room in Panama, there was that kind of afternoon hush to it, the waning light against a drawn shade, the silk-tasseled lower edge, a contained lushness, the green plush chair with the gray cat purring on its arm, the moss green of the velvet curtains and the burnt sienna walls, the scent of snuffed-out candles and perfume.

He had felt in Panama a centuries-old decadence that clung to every archway and twisted street, a miasma of evil, a certain knowledge that anything ever devised by humans had been done in this city, and he had been excited by it. Now, watching Chickie as she moved barefooted over the rug, the drink in one hand, he felt the beginning of that same kind of excitement, a welcome loss of control that he experienced whenever he was near her, a heady confusion that threatened to submerge him.

She handed him the drink. "What is it?" she asked.

"I had to ring four times," he said.

"What?"

"Downstairs."

"Is that what's bothering you?"

"Yes," he said, and accepted the drink.

"I'm sorry, Sidney, but you'll remember—"

"It's all right."

"You'll remember that I advised you not to come in the first place. I have to leave in a very few minutes. . . ."

"Where are you going?"

"To the agency. I told you that on the phone, Sidney, and I told you I'd be very rushed."

"Why are you going to the agency?"

"I have work to do."

"I thought . . ."

"I have work to do, Sidney."

"All right, I'll pick you up later for dinner," he said.

"No, I can't have dinner with you tonight."

"Why not?"

"I'm having dinner with Ruth. We have a trip to work out. I told you all about it."

"No, you didn't."

"A very important trip that may materialize," she said, nodding.

"That *may* materialize?" he said. "I don't understand."

"Ruth and I have to work out this trip together," she explained very slowly, "that may be materializing."

"A trip to where?"

"Europe."

"For whom?"

"For a client, of course."

"But what do you mean it *may* be materializing?"

"Well, it isn't certain yet."

"When will it be certain?"

"Very soon, I would imagine. Your hair sticks up in the back, did you know that?"

"Yes. Can't Ruth handle it alone? There's something I wanted to—"

"No, she can't. Do you want a refill, Sidney?"

"No. Why can't she?"

"Because it would be a very long trip, Sidney. *If* it materializes. It would be for the entire winter, you see."

"I see."

"Until the fifteenth of June."

"I see."

"Which is why it's so terribly complicated. Are you sure you don't want a refill?"

"No, thanks. Maybe I can see you later then. There's something—"

"I'll be busy all night."

He stared at her for a moment, and then said, "Chickie, are you lying to me?"

"What?"

"Are you lying?"

"About what, for God's sake?"

"About this trip, about tonight, about . . ."

"Sidney, I'm a very bad liar. I wouldn't even attempt lying to you."

"I think you're lying to me right this minute," he said.

"Now stop it, Sidney," she warned. "You may have had a difficult day, but let's not start hurling silly accusations around, shall we not?"

"I'm sorry," he said. "I h-h-have had a d-d-difficult day, I'm sorry."

"That's all right, Sidney, and don't start stammering."

"I'm sorry."

"What you need is another drink," she said, and took his glass. "And then I've got to get dressed." She put two ice cubes into his glass and poured more bourbon over them. She handed the glass to Sidney and then said, "Shall I take Shah out of the room? Would you like me to do that?"

"Yes, I'd appreciate it."

"I will then. Come, Shah," she said, "come, pussycat. Sidney doesn't like you because of the Indian, isn't that true, Sidney? Come, Shah, sweetie."

She lifted the cat into her arms, cradling him against her breasts. "Drink," she said to Sidney, and then suddenly stopped alongside his chair. "Drink," she repeated in a whisper. A strange little smile twisted her mouth. She stared at him another moment, smiling, and then turned her back to him abruptly and went down the hall to her bedroom.

He sat alone in the darkening room, sipping his drink.

He supposed he would ask her when she returned, though he would have much preferred doing it over dinner. He did not relish the thought of postponing it again, however. He had been on the verge of asking her for the past week, and each time he had lost his courage, or become angry with her, and each time he had postponed it. He had the feeling he could put it off indefinitely if he allowed himself to, and he did not want that to happen. No, he would ask her when she returned, even though he was still a little angry with her.

He had to watch the anger, that was the important thing. Oh yes, there were other things as well—he talked with his hands a lot, he had got that from his father; and the stammering, of course, but that was only when he got excited; and his inability to extricate himself sometimes from a very complicated sentence, three years of Latin at Harvard, a lot of good it had done him. But the anger was the most important thing, that was the thing he had to control most of all because he knew that if he ever really let loose the way his mother . . . well.

Well, she was dead, poor soul, nor had it been very pleasant the way she went, lingering, lingering, he had gone to that hospital room every day of the week for six months, at a time when he had just begun the partnership with Carl and really should have been devoting all of his energies to building the practice. Well, what are you supposed to do when your mother is dying of cancer, not visit her? leave her to the vultures? God forbid. And the anger, her immense and enormous anger persisting to the very end, the imperious gestures to the special nurses day and night, oh the drain on his father, the shouted epithets, thank God most of them were in Yiddish and the nurses didn't understand them, except that one Miss Leventhal who said to him in all seriousness and with an injured look on her very Jewish face,

"Your mother is a nasty old lady, Mr. Brackman"—with the poor woman ready to die any minute, ahhh.

The anger.

He had never understood the anger. He only knew that it terrified him whenever it exploded, and he suspected it terrified his father as well, who always seemed equally as helpless to cope with it. His mother had been a tall slender woman with a straight back and wide shoulders, dark green eyes, masses of brown hair piled onto the top of her head, a pretty woman he supposed in retrospect, though he had never considered her such as a child. They lived on East Houston Street, and his father sold shoes for a living, shoes that were either factory seconds or returns to retail stores. He did a lot of business with Bowery bums when they were sober enough to worry about winter coming and bare feet instead of their next drink of smoke. He had always admired the way his father handled the bums, with a sort of gentleness that did not deny their humanity, the one and only thing left to them. Except once when a drunken wino came into the store and insulted Sidney's mother, and his father took the man out onto the sidewalk and punched him twice in the face, very quickly, sock, sock, and the man fell down bleeding from his nose, Sidney remembered how strong his father had been that day. The wino came back with a breadknife later, God knows where he had got it, probably from the soup kitchen near Delancey, and his father met him in the doorway of the store, holding a length of lead pipe in his right hand and saying, "All right, so come on, brave one, use your knife." His mother called the police, and it all ended pretty routinely, except for his mother's later anger.

The anger exploded suddenly, the way it always did, they were sitting in the kitchen upstairs, the second floor over the store, and his mother began berating Sidney's father for what Sidney thought had been his really courageous behavior and suddenly she went off, click, it was always like that, click, as though a switch were thrown somewhere inside her head, short-circuiting all the machinery, click, and the anger exploded. She got very red in the face, she looked Irish when she did, and her green eyes got darker, and she would bunch her slender hands into tight compact fists and stalk the kitchen, back and forth, the torrent of words spilling from her mouth in steady fury, not even making sense sometimes, repeating over and over again events long past, building a paranoid case, well, no not paranoid, building a case against the world, reliving each injustice she had ever suffered at the hands of the goyim, at the hands of childhood friends, at the hands of his father's family, at the hands of her ungrateful whelp of a son, nothing whatever to do with the drunken wino (or whoever or whatever it happened to be), the supposed original cause of her anger. "No justice," she would scream, "there's no justice," and the flow of words would continue as she paced the kitchen before the old washtub, and Sidney's father would go to her and try to console her, "Come, Sarah, come, darling," and she would throw off his imploring hands while Sidney sat at the oilcloth-covered table in terror, thinking his mother was crazy or worse, well not crazy, "She's excited," his father would say, "she's just excited."

Those were not happy times. The war had ended long ago, but the Depression was on its way, and there would come a day when even Bowery bums no longer cared whether or not they were wearing almost-new shoes, or *any* shoes for that matter, when the best defense against a nation sliding steadily downhill was indeed a bottle of hair tonic in a dim hallway stinking of piss. He came to look upon those Bowery ghosts as a symbol of what America had become, and he dreaded growing up, becoming a man in a world where there were no jobs, and no justice, especially for Jews. He was very conscious of his Jewishness, not because anyone called him Jewboy—hardly anyone ever did since he hung around mostly with other Jewish kids, and since all of his relatives were Jews, and every function he attended was either a Jewish wedding or a bar mitzvah or a funeral, well, yes, there was that one incident, but even that was not so terribly bad, his mother's anger afterwards had been worse than the actual attack—he was conscious of his Jewishness mostly in a religious way, strange for a young boy, almost a holy way, everybody in the family said that Sidney would grow up to be a rabbi. In fact, his Uncle Heshie from Red Bank used to jokingly call him Reb Shiloach, and this always pleased him enormously because he thought of the town rabbi, the old rabbi in the Polish town from which his mother and father had come, as a very learned man who dispensed justice, who read from the Holy Book and dispensed justice to Jews, the one thing that had somehow been denied his mother only because she *was* Jewish. He sometimes visualized himself in the role of the Talmudic scholar, searching for the holy word that would put an end to his mother's anger, "Look, Mama," he would say, "it is written here thus and so, so do not be angry." And all the while, he feared the anger was buried deep within himself as well. He had seen murder in his mother's eyes, he had heard hatred in her voice, had the seed really fallen too terribly far from the tree? Was it not possible that he too could explode, click, the switch would be thrown in his head, click, and being a man he would kill someone? Later, when it happened with the Irish kids, when they surrounded him that day and pulled down his pants and beat him with Hallowe'en sticks and he did not fight back, he wondered whether he was really a person in whom there lay this secret terrible wrath, or whether he was simply a coward. He only knew for certain there had been no justice for him that day, that he had done nothing to warrant such terrible punishment, such embarrassment, the girls standing around and looking at his naked smarting behind, and later crossing their fingers as he walked home, "Shame, shame, we saw Sidney's *tushe,* shame, shame," chanting it all the way home like a litany, there was no justice that day, but neither had they called him Jewboy. Maybe they just wanted to take down my pants, Sidney reasoned later, who the hell knows?

The wrath exploded that night, he was certain it would, and it did. He did not at the time connect any of his mother's explosions with sex—if you had asked anyone on the Lower East Side who Sigmund Freud was, they'd have recalled the man who peddled used china from a pushcart on Hester

Street and whose name was Siggie Freid—but in later years it seemed to him that the justice she so avidly sought was somehow connected with events that invariably concerned sex, and he began wondering what could possibly have happened to his mother back in Europe. But no, he never really consciously thought that, no one ever consciously thinks that about his own mother, it only came to him on the gray folds of semirecognition—the wino had said, "You've got some tits there, lady," the Irish boys had taken down Sidney's pants, the sewing machine salesman had asked if he could step into the parlor for a moment, the argument with Hannah Berkowitz had involved the use of too much rouge, the girl his mother found him with on the roof was Adele Rosenberg who was sixteen years old and wore no bloomers in the summer, but *everybody* knew that, not only Sidney, and besides they weren't even *doing* anything. All these events returned to him grayly, darkly, as though on a swelling ocean crest that dissipated and dissolved before it quite reached the shore, leaving behind only vanishing bubbles of foam absorbed by the sand. The black and towering fact remained his mother's anger, which was to him inexplicable at the time. It was simply *there*. Uncontrollable, raging, murderous. He would dream of bureau drawers full of women's hair, brown and tangled. He would dream of hags sitting next to him in movie theaters, opening their mouths to expose rotten teeth and foul breath. He would dream of running through castles where dead bodies were stacked end upon end, decomposing as he raced through them, filling his nostrils with suffocating dust.

He feared his mother, and he pitied his mother, and he despised his mother. And he loved her as well.

Because of her, he never lied about being a Jew. A lot of the kids in the neighborhood and on the block were lying in order to get jobs, this was 1934, 1935, the NRA had already come in, the blue eagles clutching lightning were showing in all the shop windows all over the city, things were a little better, but it was still difficult to get a job, especially a part-time job, and especially if you were a Jew. He never lied about being a Jew, and he never told himself later that the reason he didn't get the job was because he was Jewish. He blamed his inability to find work on a lot of things—his looks, his height, the stammer he had somehow developed and which always seemed to crop up when he was being interviewed for a position, the somewhat high whininess of his adolescent voice, all of these things—but never his Jewishness. His Jewishness was something separate and apart, something of which he could be uncommonly proud, the old rabbi quietly studying the Holy Book in the sunset of his mother's town, the townspeople standing apart and waiting for him to dispense justice.

He was able to enter Harvard only because Uncle Heshie from Red Bank died and left his favorite nephew a small sum of money, sizable enough in those days, certainly enough to pay for Sidney's undergraduate education. He left for Boston in the fall of 1936. He was eighteen years old, and five feet eight inches tall (he assumed he had grown to his full height, and he was correct). He had black hair parted close to the middle and combed into a flamboyant pompadour that scarcely compensated for the cowlick at the back of his head. He came directly from Townsend Harris High School, where his grades had averaged 91 per cent, and from which he had graduated with honors.

At Harvard, in his freshman year, they called him Lard Ass, and he once drank fourteen bottles of beer and passed out cold. At Harvard, in his sophomore year, he joined the Dramatic Club and became reasonably famous for his clubhouse imitation of Eddie Cantor singing "If You Knew Susie." At Harvard, in September of 1939, when the Germans were overrunning the Polish town where his mother had been born and perhaps putting to death forever the image of the village rabbi studying the Holy Book by the light of the setting sun, Sidney met a student nurse named Rebecca Strauss—"Watch out for those nurses, Sid," his roommate told him. "They can give it a flick with their finger, and whap! it'll go right down, quick as that"—and began dating her regularly. Rebecca lived in West Newton and worked at Massachusetts General where her father was a resident surgeon. She had dark green eyes and masses of brown hair, and she was the most beautiful girl Sidney had ever met in his life, prettier even than Adele Rosenberg who wore no bloomers in the summer. He grew a mustache for Rebecca because he always felt he looked silly and immature beside her, even though he was two months her senior. She said she loved the mustache and that it didn't tickle at all when they kissed. When he finally told her in confidence about his mother's raging fits—he had by that time begun to think of them as "fits," similar to epileptic seizures or paranoid delusions—she said they did seem very much like hysterical symptoms, collaborating his own feelings that something dreadful had happened to his mother when she was still a girl in Poland.

"She may have been raped or something," Rebecca said.

"Do you think so?"

They were lying in the grass bordering the Charles, she was in his arms. It was the spring of 1940, he could hear crickets chirping in the night, and the gentle flow of the river, and in the distance the highway traffic.

"Yes," Rebecca said. "Sometimes a man can't control himself, you know. And he'll do things. To a girl."

"Maybe," Sidney said, thinking of the time with the sewing machine salesman, had the man been unable to control himself?

"And sometimes a girl can even *want* a man to. Do things, you know."

"I g-g-guess you're right," Sidney said. Had his mother *wanted* the salesman to do things?

"Do you ever feel . . ." Rebecca moved closer in his arms. He could smell her hair, the crickets seemed suddenly louder.

"What?" he said.

"That you can't control yourself?"

"I'm always afraid of that," he said.

"Of not being able to control yourself?"

"Of losing my temper. Of g-g-getting angry the way my m-m-mother does."

"I meant . . ."

She was silent again. Her hand was resting on the side of his face, she was curled in his arms, he could feel the swell of her breasts against him, the crisp starched white of her nurse's uniform.

"What I meant," Rebecca said, and again fell silent.

"I know, you mean people sometimes . . ."

"Yes," she said, nodding.

"Sure, which is . . ."

"That it's understandable," she said, nodding. "If a man and a woman."

"Yes, it's possible," nodding.

"Yes."

"If they're close to each other."

"Yes."

She moved. Her starched skirt edged back over one knee and she took her hand from his face to lower the skirt again, long legs sheathed in white stockings, she moved closer.

"I myself, I know," Rebecca said.

"Sure," Sidney said.

"Get hot sometimes," she said, and quickly added, "I've never told this to anyone in my life."

"Reb-b-becca . . ."

"So hot I can't stand it," Rebecca said. "I've never talked this way to anyone in my life."

"You . . . you ought to be careful," he said, "t-t-talking that way."

"I know, I know," she said, moaning the words. In the silence, she moved again. The starched uniform made tiny crisp sounds as she adjusted her body to the length of his, moving minutely in against him, her arms tight around his neck, trembling.

"Do *you* get hot?" she whispered.

"Yes."

"So hot you can't *stand* it?"

"Yes."

"Are you now?" Her voice so small.

"Yes."

"I can feel you." A whisper.

"Are . . . *you?*" he asked.

"Yes, oh yes."

It all happened, it was too, he didn't plan, hands under starched, and her white thighs, she turned, white stockings, and it happened and he, she moved beneath him, silk, all opening, the slip and, in a tangle of, and white garters, hands under, wet, and she said, oh she said, oh she said, wide, and was all, he didn't, held and clawed and, legs spread, and he was, she moaned, wet and garters, wet and, oh she said, oh love she moaned, oh, her head was, she was, he could feel, tossing, it happened, it was happening, he was, baby, he was, honey, lips and wet and hard and hard, I love you, I love you, I love you.

Ahhh me, he thought back with a sigh, it has never been like that again, not the way it was with Rebecca in Boston, two dumb young kids discovering what humping was all about, and going at it with a secret eagerness that, God we couldn't wait to see each other each time. Three, four times a week, sometimes more, going at it with a secret soaring joy that shouted to the world, *we* knew what it was all about, *we* had discovered it, *we* had patented it, we were the only two people humping in Boston—by the river, and in the back seat of the '36 Plymouth I bought, and in a Providence hotel one weekend, and once in Dr. Strauss's Oldsmobile parked behind the hospital, and then day and night in the apartment I took on Massachusetts Avenue in Cambridge, when I entered law school. Day and night, it's a wonder I learned any law at all, the only law I knew was whatever sweetly called to me from between Rebecca's legs. And then, I don't know, I don't know what happens, war happens, I guess. You get put into 1-A when you're in your second year of law school, and I guess you figure you'd better get into the Navy where the beds are always clean, so the legend goes, and there're always three square meals a day, so the legend goes, before they draft you into the infantry and you get your ass blown off invading the fortress of Europe. And besides, by that time Rebecca had met a young captain who was stationed at the Air Corps base on Jeffries Point. It was wartime—I saw him once, he was very tall and blond, he had blue eyes, he looked a little like Terry in *Terry and the Pirates* which Papa brought home every Sunday when he bought bagels on Rivington Street—it was wartime, so who could blame anyone? Who could blame the captain for succumbing to Rebecca's Law, and who could blame Rebecca, blossoming wild and willful Rebecca, young, sweet Rebecca, for wanting to go to bed with Terry, or even Pat Ryan, for that matter? I'd certainly have done it with the Dragon Lady if she had come along. Or Burma.

My ship was commissioned in Boston, I guess it was 1943, and I called Rebecca Strauss, or at least I called her number in West Newton, and her father got on the phone, Dr. Strauss, and he said, "Hello, there, Sidney, how have you been, fellow?" sounding like a goy, I could visualize him in Bermuda shorts, holding a five iron. I told him I'd been down to fire control school in Fort Lauderdale—"Oh, learning how to put out fires, huh, Sidney?"—(I didn't bother to correct him)—and that I'd been assigned to a destroyer and we were here in Boston before heading down to Gitmo (I used the Navy slang for Guantanamo just to show him how salty I was, and also to imply to him somehow that I had been humping his daughter for three years, put *that* in your scalpel case, Dr. Strauss) on shakedown cruise and I was wondering if I could talk to Rebecca, say hello and all that. Well, gee, Sidney, Dr. Strauss said, sounding more and more like the president of the local Grange, I'd be very happy to let you talk to Rebecca, but she doesn't live here anymore. You see, Sidney, she was married in October, perhaps you know the fellow (*fellow* again), perhaps you know him, a very nice fellow from Detroit, Michigan, his name is Lonnie Scott, S-C-O-T-T. No, I said, I'm sorry, Dr. Strauss, I don't think I ever met any friend of Rebecca's named Lonnie Scott, S-C-O-T-T. Oh, he's a *very* nice fellow, Dr. Strauss said, very very nice, they're living in California now, he's stationed out there, he's a major in the Air Corps, a very *nice* fellow, Sidney. Well, Dr. Strauss, I said, if you should have the opportunity to write to Becks (I used this pet name in an attempt once more to inform Dr. Strauss that his daughter *Becks* and I had been intimate for three years, get it, Dr. Strauss? Intimate. I-N-T-I-M-A-T-E) if you should happen to write to old Becks, why you just tell her Sidney called on his way through Boston to say hello and remind her of old times (in your Oldsmobile behind the hospital, for instance, Dr. Strauss, which I thought but didn't say). Why, sure, Sidney, Dr. Strauss said, sounding more and more like an Ohio preacher every minute, sure, fellow, I'll tell her you called—and say, good luck with that fire fighting, it's a dangerous business especially aboard ship. It sure is, I told him (do you get hot, Sidney, so hot you can't stand it?). Goodbye, Dr. Strauss.

Goodbye, fellow.

The war meant nothing to Sidney. He never saw any action, and the only danger to which he was exposed was that of tedium, even though he was aboard a destroyer. (Once they shot at a floating Japanese mine, and exploded it. Everyone cheered.) He was honorably discharged in September of 1946, and spent the summer with his parents who had moved from Houston Street to Walton Avenue near Yankee Stadium. His mother had one of her "fits" in August, shortly before he left for school again, it had to do with the doctor she had begun visiting, something about his nurse, Sidney couldn't follow it, nor did he try. He simply sat in terrified patience while the raving and ranting ran its course, his father fluttering about her like a broken butterfly, trying to calm her, Sarah's green eyes flashing, brown hair streaked with gray now, back straight and stiff, pacing, pacing (he remembered the soft embraces of Rebecca Strauss, they *do* sound to me like hysterical symptoms, she may have been raped or something, Rebecca's Law. Only once did they ever exchange harsh words, the time she was ten days late and they were frantic, no, twice actually, because she was also late after that long weekend in Providence, she almost climbed the ceiling that time, Rebecca, Becks, my love).

His mother died in 1953, after he had been practicing law for five years and had already started the partnership with

Carl. He was so enormously relieved by her passing that for several weeks afterward he walked around in a gloomy cloud of guilt, questioning his love for her, had he wanted her dead? blaming himself for not having insisted on chest X-rays earlier, and yet delighted, but had it been his fault? had he wished it once too often? and yet deliriously happy that she was dead and finally in the ground where nothing but the worms could tremble if she took a supernatural fit. He began to question, too, his own monumental anger, was it really such? Or had he simply built an elaborate defense against his own fear, constructing an image of a violently dangerous human being (inside every skinny Jew there is a fat Nazi) whom you had better not fool around with, Mama, because he is as equally capable of murderous rage as you are. He didn't know. Even now, he still thought of himself as a person with a low boiling point, a violent man who easily lost his temper—and yet he knew he hardly ever raised his voice to anyone.

Well, Chickie made him angry, yes, but that was different because with her it was a teasing sort of thing, and more like, well—when he was with her, and she began to tease him that way, began to coax him into anger almost, he would feel an odd quaking inside him, something like what he had known on Houston Street, sitting at the oilcloth-covered kitchen table, which was odd because he certainly wasn't *afraid* of Chickie. And yet, the way she came at him, the way she approached everything they did together, the sex so different from what it had been with Rebecca, she created a, a turmoil in him, yes, that was both exciting and confusing and, he supposed, well, yes, he supposed so, yes, frightening sometimes. He could never understand, for example, why she constantly made oblique references, and sometimes not such oblique ones, to the men she had known. Surely she knew the habit infuriated him—or was that why she persisted? He could not understand. Point of fact, there were a great *many* things that baffled him about Chickie Brown, nor was his confusion something recent. It had been present six months ago when she first walked into his Wall Street office, and if anything it had assumed greater dimensions since.

"Mr. Brackman," she had said, "I'm Charlotte Brown," and he took her extended hand. He had known a great many women since Rebecca Strauss, both casually and intimately, but he had never felt for any of them an iota of what he had felt in Boston. And now, shaking hands with this tall and magnificently proportioned young lady, his heart began to pound foolishly and he found himself staring into her eyes, offering her a seat, barely knowing what he was saying to her. There was a fullness to her palm, a moistness to her flesh that he found intensely exciting, as though her handshake had inadvertently revealed a guarded secret and become a shared intimacy.

She sat opposite his desk, and he found he could not take his eyes from her, found that he was openly coveting her, and wondered that she was not embarrassed by his lavish attention. There was about her, he supposed, a look of easy availability that brought her youthful beauty dangerously close to the edge of cheapness, a look he found wildly stimulating. Her hands were in constant motion, now moving to touch her throat, now absently toying with a button on her blouse, now drifting toward her thigh to rest there a moment, now brushing at her cheek or her eye. She crossed and uncrossed her legs constantly and a shade too carelessly, but completely without guile. She kept jiggling her foot, and she had a habit of giggling unexpectedly. As she related her legal problems to him—she was part owner of a travel agency, and they were having trouble collecting from a client the monies advanced for airline tickets, hotel deposits, and so on—he barely heard a word of what she said, so intense were the lewd fantasies he built around this innocent young girl. It was not until toward the end of their interview, after he had agreed to take her case, that he began to suspect she was enjoying his insistent scrutiny, if not actively encouraging it. Surprising himself, he asked if she would like to discuss the case more extensively over a drink, and she surprised him even further by accepting his invitation.

He had not understood her then, six months ago, and he did not understand her now. He was proud of her beauty, flattered by her youth, but embarrassed by the tawdry look she narrowly escaped. He was wildly excited by her readiness and her intense passion, but frightened sometimes by her sexual knowledge. He was amazed by her shrewdness and appalled by her stupidity. She could doggedly argue a subject until he flew into a rage, and then instantly calm him with a subjugating kiss. She could bring him to the very edge of climax and then infuriatingly declare she was not in the mood for sex. She could cause him to roar with laughter, or weep in supplication. The first time they had gone to bed together, she had whispered, "Come, Sidney, I am going to take you where you've never been," and she had kept her promise.

He heard the bedroom door closing. To the closed door, she said, "Now you be a good pussycat, you be a good little Shah, do you hear me?" Her heels clattered along the corridor. She came into the living room buttoning her suit jacket. She smoothed her skirt over her hips, turned a small pirouette, and asked, "Do I look all right? I feel as though I dressed in a hurricane. I *hate* to rush."

"You look beautiful," he said.

"You dear man," she answered, "how can you even *see* without the light on?" She turned on a table lamp, and then stooped to kiss him on the cheek. "I really have to run, Sidney. You can sit here and finish your drink, if you like. Just pull the door shut behind you when you leave, it'll lock automatically."

"When will you be back?" he asked.

"Not until late."

"Maybe I'll stay here and wait for you."

"No, I'd rather you didn't."

"Why not?"

"Because I'll be exhausted, Sidney dear."

"All right." He paused. "Have you got at least a minute?"

"Yes, but barely."

"There's something I want to ask you."

"Not about the Indian."

"No, not about the Indian."

"Good." She smiled and sat on the arm of his chair. "What is it?"

"I don't know if I've ever explained my situation to you."

"What situation?"

"With the firm."

"No, I don't think you have. But Sidney . . ."

"It's not a very big firm, Chickie, not a very big firm at all. There's myself and my partner, and we each earn somewhere between ten and fifteen thousand dollars a year, I want you to know that."

"Sidney, I never asked you what—"

"I know, and I appreciate it, but I want you to understand the full picture. I'm not what you would call a very successful lawyer."

"Sidney, you're a very *good* lawyer."

"Well, I hope so, but I'm not a very successful one. There are lawyers in this city who can count on a hundred thousand dollars even in a bad year. I'm not one of them, Chickie."

"Why are you telling me this?"

"Because I want you to know."

She looked at him curiously, and then frowned. "You're not going to cry or anything, are you, Sidney?"

"No."

"Because I really haven't got time for that."

"No, I'm not going to cry," he said.

"Good. What is it then?"

"If I win this case, Chickie, I will be a very big lawyer."

"Will you?"

"We're suing for an accounting of profits, Chickie. It's our estimate that the movie earned in the vicinity of ten million dollars. We can't tell for certain because API isn't required to produce its books unless we win, or unless they're necessary to show we *are* entitled to an accounting. But ten million dollars is our guess."

"Sidney . . ." she started, and frowned, and glanced at her watch.

"I'll tell you the truth, neither Carl nor I wanted to take it on at first, my partner. We weren't sure there was a case, we knew very little about plagiarism. But you'd be surprised, Chickie, you'd really be surprised at how many plagiarism cases have been won on evidence that seems silly at first, similarities that seem ridiculous. The ones Constantine pointed out seemed just that way to us in the beginning, until we had a chance to examine them in the light of other cases. There *was* copying, Chickie, I sincerely believe that now. Driscoll was clever, yes, he altered, yes, disguised, yes, but he copied. I believe that, Chickie, I'd *better* believe it—the case has already cost the firm close to ten thousand dollars, not to mention time, but it'll be worth it if we win." Sidney paused. "The fee we agreed to is forty per cent of whatever we recover. Do you understand me, Chickie?"

"I think so," she said. She was still frowning, but she was listening intently now.

"Forty per cent of ten million dollars is four million dollars, Chickie. If we win this case, my partner will get two million dollars and *I* will get two million dollars. I will be a very r-r-rich man, Chickie, and v-v-very well-known." Sidney paused. "I will be a successful lawyer, Chickie."

"You're a successful lawyer now," she said.

"Not like J-J-Jonah Willow."

"You're every bit as smart as Willow," she said. "Don't stammer."

"Yes, but not as successful." He paused. "Maybe not as s-s-smart, either, I don't know."

"You're just as smart, Sidney."

"Maybe," he said. He paused again. "Chickie, as you know, I have a widower father to support, he has a garden apartment in Queens, he's a very old man, and no trouble at all. I pay the rent each month, and I give him money to live on, that's about the extent of it."

"Yes, Sidney."

"Chickie, I've been wanting to ask you this for a long time now, but I never felt I had the right. I'm forty-eight years old, going on forty-nine, and I know you're only twenty-seven and, to be quite truthful, I've never been able to understand what you see in me."

"Let *me* worry about that," she said, and began stroking the back of his neck.

"B-b-but, I feel certain I'm going to win this case and that would ch-change things considerably. That's why I f-f-feel I now have the right."

"What right, Sidney?"

"I guess you know I l-l-love you, Chickie. I suppose that's been made abundantly apparent to you over the past several months. I am very much in love with you, Chickie, and I would consider it an honor if you were to accept my p-p-proposal of matrimony."

Chickie was silent.

"Will you marry me, Chickie?"

"This is pretty unexpected," she said. Her voice was very low. He could barely hear her.

"I figured it would come as a surprise to you."

"I'll have to think about it, Sidney. This isn't something a girl can rush into."

"I realize that."

"I'll have to think about it."

"I'll be a very rich man when I win this c-c-case," Sidney said.

"You dear man, do you think that matters to me?" Chickie asked.

He lay full length on the bed opposite the window, his hands behind his head, staring up at the ceiling. He had been lying that way for close to an hour now, ever since their return to the hotel room. He had not closed his eyes in all that time, nor could Ebie fool herself into believing he was actually resting. There was a tautness in his very posture, an unseen nervous vibration that she could feel across the length of the room. His silence was magnified by the rush-hour babble from below. In the echoing midst of headlong life, he lay as still as a dead man and stared sightlessly at the ceiling.

"Are you all right?" she asked.

"I'm fine," he said.

"Dris?"

"Yes?"

"I'm afraid."

"Don't be afraid, Edna Belle."

"Can't we talk?" she asked.

"What would you like to talk about?"

"Can't . . . can't you reassure me? Can't you tell me we're not going to lose?"

"I'm not sure of that, Edna Belle."

"Please don't call me Edna Belle."

"That's your name, isn't it?"

"My name's been Ebie for the past God knows how long, please don't call me Edna Belle. I hate the name Edna Belle. You know I hate the name."

"Ebie is an affectation," he said.

"It's not an affectation, it's my *name*. It's an important part of me."

"Yes, I'm sure it is."

"Yes, it is."

"I said yes."

"Then please don't call me Edna Belle."

"I won't."

"And if you feel like getting angry, please . . ."

"I'm not getting angry."

". . . don't get angry with me. You have no reason to get angry with me."

"That's true. No reason at all."

"Get angry with Constantine, if you want to get angry. Or his lawyer. *They're* the ones who are trying to ruin us."

"If you ask me," he said, *"you're* the one who's getting angry, not me."

"Because you're not giving me the assurance I need."

"False assurance is a beggar's—"

"Don't try to get literary," Ebie said.

"Was I getting literary?"

"You were trying to, there's a difference. I can't stand it when you try to sound like a goddamn novelist."

"Have no fear. I am not a goddamn novelist."

"What are you then?"

"A Vermont farmer."

"You were a novelist before you were a farmer."

"I have never been a novelist," he said.

"No? What do you call *The Paper Dragon?*"

"Luck," he said, and closed his eyes.

The room was silent. From the street below, she could hear someone shouting directions to a truck driver at the *Times* depot. In the distance, Sardi's neon sign stained the dusk a luminous green, and the surrounding gray and shadowy buildings began to show lights in isolated window slits. She stared at him without speaking, and then pressed her face to the glass and watched the truck as it backed into the depot. How simple it is, she thought. How simple they make everything. When she turned to him again, her voice was very low. "They can take it all away from us," she said. "We can lose everything, Dris."

"We lost everything a long time ago," he answered. His eyes were still closed.

"No."

"Ebie. We lost everything."

"Thank you," she said, and sighed. "That's the reassurance I wanted, thank you." She glanced through the window. "That's the encouraging word I wanted, all right," she said, and pressed her forehead to the glass.

At home they called her Edna Belle, and they called her brother George Benjamin, always using their full Christian names. In the center of the town, there was an enormous statue of Andrew Jackson, said to have been razed by the Yankees during the War between the States and left there as a grim reminder to the people of the South, never repaired or rebuilt, standing in ruinous splendor. She and George Benjamin would go down to the monument and play at its base with the other children. Once she cut herself falling on a piece of broken glass there; she still had a crescent-shaped scar on her thigh as a reminder of the accident. Sometimes she would wander down to the center of town alone, and she would sit and sketch the monument in charcoal, the way the general's broken sword ended abruptly against the sky, with the bell tower of the church beyond, and down the street the white clapboard courthouse. She loved to work in charcoal, smearing the black onto the page with her index and middle fingers, rubbing it, shading it, smoothing it into the paper. It was very hard to draw niggers, even in charcoal.

She found the bird one day at the base of the monument, a sparrow who had broken his leg, probably by flying into the general's broad bronzed back or the shell-torn rim of his campaign hat. The bird lay on his back with his beak open, his throat pulsing, no sound coming from him, but his tongue or whatever it was leaping into his throat, beating there, as though he were mutely begging for assistance. She reached down for the bird, and he tried to regain his feet, the broken leg hanging crookedly and, still dazed, flopped over onto his side. No eyes were showing, his eyes were rolled back into his head, only an opaque white showed. She cradled him in her hands, and then couldn't pick up her sketching pad or her box of charcoals, so she left them at the base of the monument and walked slowly home holding the bird gently in her hands, his throat working. She was terrified lest he try again to fly away and fall from her hands to the pavement—she knew that would kill him. They all said the bird would die, anyway, even George Benjamin said so. But she took care of him until he got better, just as she knew he would, and one day he flew off before she had a chance to take him back to the monument where she had found him. She used to look for him at the monument after that, thinking he would maybe come back, like in picture books, but he never did.

Her father owned the dairy in town, the name of it was Clover Crest Farms, which she had helped him pick. He had wanted to call it *Dearborn* Farms, but even George Benjamin thought *that* was pretty corny, and a bit egotistical, naming the thing after yourself. Her father was a very tall man, with blond hair like her own. Her mother had blond hair, too, well everybody in the family did, except George Benjamin. His was a sort of reddish color, like Aunt Serena's and Grandmother Winkler's. Edna Belle looked a lot like her mother, leastwise that's what everybody was always telling her, and she was proud to believe it because her mother was a very beautiful and elegant woman. They had two niggers working for them, Lucy who was the kitchen help, and Aurora who did the cleaning, and who was always pregnant. They both adored Mother, you could just see they thought she was beautiful and very elegant, which she was. But it was surprising the two niggers thought so, there never was no love lost in that town.

Edna Belle especially loved the way her mother talked, she could sit and listen to her talk all day. She had a voice, well, there was just nothing like it, that was all, deep and warm, and breaking into a marvelous laugh when you least expected it. She always made Edna Belle feel very grown up, because she talked to her about real things and not the usual dopey stuff grownups say to children. Whenever they talked together, Edna Belle felt as though she were talking to an older and much smarter friend who was beautiful and wise and very elegant besides; well, she was a wonderful person, the niggers were right. And her father, he was simply the happiest person she knew, always joking, always making mother and everybody laugh. One time he filled the refrigerator with milk for her, just filled it from top to bottom with milk, and when Mother came home from marketing that afternoon and opened the refrigerator door, why there they were! maybe thirty or forty bottles of *milk!* "Oh, that nut!" she said, laughing, she used to laugh a lot, Mother.

George Benjamin was the least talented person she had ever met in her life, he couldn't even draw a straight line. He would always come up to her and say, "Edna Belle, show me how to draw a damn horse," or "Edna Belle, how do you make it look like it's getting smaller in the distance?" but he was just hopeless, no talent at all, she sometimes used to feel sorry for him. He had a chemistry set, and once he burned his hand, and she took care of him the way she had the bird. Well, not *exactly* the same because it was Aurora who changed his bandages and all, but she made sure there were always fresh-picked flowers in his room, and she would leave little drawings on his pillow for him to find when he woke up in the morning. The hand business only lasted maybe two weeks, but she took very good care of him in those weeks, she really loved him a lot, even though he begrudged Daddy a few laughs at his jokes. He kept one of her pictures, the one she made of the pond on the old Barrow place near the mill. He said he liked that one best because it reminded him of fishing there. She knew, of course, that he fished there when she'd *made* the drawing, of course, that's why she'd made it in the *first* place.

Her best friend was a girl named Cissie Butterfoster, whose name broke her up, but who was a nice girl, anyway. Cissie wore pigtails, and Daddy used to kid with her, saying, "Why do you wear your hair like the niggers, Cissie?" and Cissie always would blush. Until much later, when she was in high school, and then one day she just said to Daddy, almost making *him* blush, "You sure do take a deep concern over my hair, Mr. Dearborn," which was sort of snippy even though she *had* developed a very good pair of boobs by then, but to imply Daddy was flirting with her or something! But when they were small together, they did have some very good times together, Edna Belle and Cissie, even when they teased about her last name, Butterfoster, what a last name. Edna Belle once said to her father that they ought to start a division of the dairy called Butterfoster Farms, and that broke him up, with George Benjamin sitting there smiling and watching Daddy, and Cissie laughing, too—she was a pretty good sport. She was the first girl in the crowd to start menstruating, and she always bled a fearful lot, and had the most dire cramps. She made Edna Belle cry in pity one day, writhing the way she was on her bed and saying, "Oh, Edna Belle, you don't know how lucky you are! You don't know what it *is* to be a grown woman," which Edna Belle learned soon enough, and without half as much hysterics. But still and all she *had* felt genuine pity for Cissie that day, and she had no doubt the cramps were real. Cissie told her Tampax could break your cherry, what a lie. She also said horseback riding could break it, and doing pushups could break it. According to Cissie anything could break it, a girl had to be careful just getting out of *bed* in the morning, otherwise Goodbye, Charlie. She stopped hanging around with Cissie in their sophomore year at high school because everybody was saying things about her by then, and besides Daddy warned Edna Belle about her reputation in a small town, and about chumming with Cissie who had taken to wearing such tight sweaters. Edna Belle figured if Cissie *had* them, why not? though she never said this to anyone, least of all Daddy, and anyway her own were so small, like Mother's.

Besides, she was very much interested in art by this time, and was being encouraged to undertake all sorts of school art projects by Miss Benson, who was her teacher. It was Miss Benson who helped her to overcome her fear of working in pen and ink, which she had always had trouble with before, being left-handed and smearing the ink every time her hand moved across the page. Miss Benson also taught her there was a freedom to art, that once you knew what you were about, why then you were entitled to this freedom, but that first you had to earn the right to it by learning what you were about. That until you knew how to draw something in its right proportions, why then you had to draw it correctly and properly each and every time, and then, only then could you afford to go off and make an arm longer or a leg shorter or give a face three eyes or whatever. Well, she had Picasso in mind, you see, or someone like that, though Edna Belle never thought of herself as having *that* kind of talent, still Miss Benson was terribly encouraging.

There was no question that most of the two hundred students who attended the high school liked to hear Miss Benson's stories about Rembrandt (Charles Laughton) and Gauguin (George Sanders). Miss Benson made these men come to life somehow, as though she were adding personal information even Hollywood had missed. Besides, for students like George Benjamin *anything* was better than having to draw. True, it got to be something of a drag when Miss Benson went on and on about sculpture in Mesopotamia during the fourth and third millennia before the Christian era (like, man, who *gave* a damn?) or when she showed slides of all those broken Greek statues, but for the most part, the kids thought she was less painful than many of the biddies around. None of them, however, thought quite as highly of her as did Edna Belle.

She was, Clotilde Benson, a fluttery old woman who indeed spoke of Van Gogh as if she had personally been the recipient of his severed ear, an uncompromising, old-fashioned instructor who insisted on certain artistic verities and some artistic conceits, an unkempt and sometimes slovenly person who habitually wore a loose paint-smeared smock and who stuck colored pencils haphazardly into her gray and frizzled hair, a vain and foolish woman whose students laughed behind her back each time she sneaked a look at herself in the reflecting windows of the supply cabinet, an inadequately trained art teacher working in a scholastically poor high school in a town that had gone dead a hundred years ago. It was rumored, too, and this only by Cissie Butterfoster who was given to lurid sexual fantasies, that Clotilde Benson had once conducted a scandalous love affair with a nigger lawyer in Atlanta. The romance had supposedly begun when she was twenty years old and going to art school there, and it had ended when six righteous Georgians rode the attorney off the highway one night and proceeded to educate him (they were all carrying knives) as to why it was highly improper for a colored man to pluck a Southern flower, you dig, boy? They then casually dropped in on Clotilde that same night at about three A.M., and while she stood shivering in a flannel robe over girlish cotton pajamas with delicate primrose pattern, told her she had better get the hell out of Atlanta before somebody cut her similar to how they had cut that nigger lawyer, or hadn't she heard about that yet? Clotilde admitted as to how she hadn't heard a word, trembling in the night and holding her flannel robe closed at the neck over her primrose-patterned girlish cotton pajamas. The six gentlemen all took off their hats and murmured good night to her in the dark, and she heard one of them laugh softly as they went out of the driveway and into the waiting car and—according to Cissie—that very same morning Miss Benson caught an early train out of Atlanta and back home, apparently having decided she'd had enough of all this Gauguin-type reveling, and convinced that such living only led to shame and degradation. That was Cissie's story, and it sounded good, and there were plenty of kids who were willing to believe it, although none of them ever had the courage to repeat it. The only one who neither repeated it nor believed it was Edna Belle. Oh yes, she believed that *maybe* Miss Benson might have *possibly* been in love with a nigger (although the idea was pretty repulsive) but she would never in a million years believe Miss Benson had turned tail and run like that, even if the man *had've* been a nigger like Cissie said, though Cissie was a big liar, anyway.

One afternoon—autumn came late to Edna Belle's town that year, the leaves were just beginning to fall, they trickled past the long high school windows in the waning afternoon light—Edna Belle stayed behind to work with Miss Benson on the layout for the school magazine, which was called *Whispers,* and which Edna Belle hoped to serve as art editor next term. The art editor this term was a senior named Phillip Armstrong Tillis, who was very talented and who had drawn both the cover of the magazine as well as the end papers, and who Edna Belle had dated once or twice and who, frankly, she was really crazy about. He was not a very good-looking boy, his nose was too large for his face, and he wore eyeglasses, but he had a wonderful sense of humor and a crazy way of looking at things, very offbeat and cool ("I used to have this little turned-up button nose," he once said, "but I had an operation done to make it long and ugly") and she loved being with him because he was always thinking up nutty things to do, like pulling into Mr. Overmeyer's driveway to neck one night, instead of going over to the hill near the old burned Baptist church that had been struck by lightning. When Mr. Overmeyer came out to see what was going on, Phillip Armstrong got out of the car and bowed from the waist and said, "Good evening, sir, we were wondering if we might park here for a few moments to discuss a matter that's of great importance."

"With *me,* do you mean?" Mr. Overmeyer asked.

"No, sir, the young lady and I wished to discuss it privately."

Mr. Overmeyer looked so relieved that (*A*) it wasn't some hoods from Connors who were looking for trouble, that (*B*) it wasn't some crippled war veterans selling magazine subscriptions, and that (*C*) he *personally* would not have to get involved in this discussion, whatever it was, that he mumbled, "Sure, certainly, go right ahead," and then went back into the house and drew the blinds to assure Phillip Armstrong of the privacy he wanted. They had necked up a storm that night, and she had let Phillip Armstrong touch her breast right there in the driveway, but only twice.

The reason Phillip Armstrong wasn't there that November afternoon to help with the layout was that he had come down with the mumps, of all things ("You know what *that* does to a grown boy, I suppose," Cissie said) and was home in bed. It was just as well because if Phillip Armstrong *had've* been there, then Edna Belle and Miss Benson wouldn't have talked, and Edna Belle's whole life wouldn't have changed. In looking back on the conversation, Edna Belle couldn't remember exactly what they'd said that was so terribly important, what they had discussed in such personal terms, this woman and her sixteen-year-old student there in the gathering gloom of a high school classroom, the light fading against the long windows, the empty desks stretching behind them, and the smell of paste on their fingers, and snippets of shining proofs clinging to their hands, the drawn pencil lines on the blank pulp pages, the long galleys from the editorial staff, and the careful selection of a rooster drawn by Annabelle Currier Farr and something called Monsoon by a freshman named Hiram Horn, the proofs spread out on Miss Benson's desk top, "There, Edna Belle," and "There," and "How's that?" completely absorbed in the work they were doing, Miss Benson finally snapping on the desk lamp, and the warm circle of light flooding the dummy as the magazine began to take shape and form, the colored pencils sticking out of Miss Benson's hair and reflecting light. Whispers, they whispered now, the school was empty, but what did they say, after all, that had not been said a thousand times before? What was there in Miss Benson's impromptu and heartfelt talk that was not clichéd and hackneyed and shopworn and, yes, even trivial? It had all been said before, there was the tinny ring of half-truth to it, and whatever importance it seemed to possess at the time surely came only from the dramatic setting, the classroom succumbing to dusk, the desk lamp being turned on, the young girl listening while the older woman earnestly and sympathetically talked to her about life and living, about pity and understanding, about art, and about love. All of it said before. And better, surely, so very much better than old Miss Benson could ever have said it even if she were skilled with words, which she was not, even if she were half the gifted artist Edna Belle supposed she was, which she was not. All of it said before.

But never before to Edna Belle.

And so she listened, nodding her head as they worked at the desk, fingers thick with paste, and she smiled, and once she giggled and covered her mouth, and tilted her head again in fascination, and brushed a golden spray of hair from her cheek and said, "Yes, oh yes, I know, I *know*."

They walked as far as the monument together. Edna Belle watched Miss Benson as she turned left at the corner near the courthouse, walking with the peculiar waddle that made the other kids laugh, but walking with her head very high, and she suddenly knew it had been true about the nigger.

She sat at the base of the monument.

She could remember only snatches of what Miss Benson had said, something about honesty, about always being true to whatever it was she believed, and of not being afraid, something about talent and its use, and something about a larger talent which she called, Edna Belle was not sure, a *capacity* for giving, yes, for loving, "Yes, oh yes," Edna Belle had said, thinking of Phillip Armstrong. And then Miss Benson said how it was important to get out of this town, go to New York or Chicago, study there, or Rhode Island, there was a fine art school in Rhode Island, but get out of this town, Edna Belle, get out of the South before they cut a piece out of your life and leave you to shrivel and die. It is not shameful to love, she said earnestly, it is never shameful to love, almost on the edge of tears.

The leaves swirled about Edna Belle's feet, the lights were on in the square, a sharp wind swept from the north around the corner of the church. She nodded quietly and to herself because she had made up her mind that she was a woman now, and then she rose and walked home, occasionally nodding, and then tilting her head in wonder because everything seemed so suddenly clear. And yet she knew Miss Benson had not told her anything she did not already know.

In September of 1946, when she was eighteen years old, she followed Miss Benson's advice and left for Pratt Institute in New York City. She rarely thought of the old woman anymore, except to wonder if she was still alive, still living in the South. But whenever she remembered her, as she was remembering her now in a seventh-floor room at the Hotel Astor, staring through a window at the traffic below, the lingering image was always of Miss Benson turning the corner near the courthouse, her head held high.

Without moving from the window, Ebie said to her husband, "In Alabama, when I was a little girl . . ."

"Spare us the magnolia blossoms and white linen suits," he said.

". . . before I even knew there were such things as witty novelists who . . ."

"I'm not a novelist."

". . . who could make clever remarks about magnolia blossoms and linen suits, when I was still a little girl in Alabama . . ."

Her voice trailed. She kept staring through the window.

"They loved me," she said at last.

4

THE CAR PULLED IN AHEAD UNEXPECTEDLY, entering the highway after barely braking at the full stop sign on the approach ramp. Sally Kirsch had opened her eyes not a moment before, seeing the other car, hearing the squeal of tires as Jonah applied his brakes, and bracing herself for what she knew would be an accident. Across the river on the New Jersey shore, she could see the Spry sign blinking idiotically as the automobile swerved, parkway lights ahead in a winding curve downtown, the glare of northbound traffic on the left, and then a splash of sudden brighter yellow as Jonah's headlights illuminated the other car.

"You dumb bastard!" Jonah shouted, and these seemed to Sally the first human words he had uttered all day long. He yanked sharply on the wheel, trying to avoid the crash, braking desperately, tires whining. The other car was a yellow Buick, vintage 1953, and the man driving it glanced to his left an instant before the cars collided, noticing Jonah's car for the first time, it seemed, and opening his eyes wide and then wrenching the wheel over to the right too late. Left fender hit right fender with terrible crunching impact. The cars ricocheted one from the other like billiard balls veering in opposite directions. Sally felt herself being hurled forward, perversely grateful for the break in the monotony, pushed her hands out in front of her, and then pulled them back instantly when she remembered she could fracture both wrists that way. Her head collided with the padded dash, there was the further squeal of tires behind them, and then silence. She shook her head. She could taste blood in her mouth. One of her teeth felt loose.

"Are you all right?" Jonah asked, and she nodded, and he got out of the car. She heard other car doors slamming, and she sat up tentatively, surprised that nothing was broken. "Didn't you see that stop sign?" Jonah was yelling.

She glanced through the windshield which was miraculously intact, she was certain everything would have been shattered by the collision, including herself. The man getting out of the other car was a short dark man in a short green coat and baggy slacks, a black fedora pushed onto the back of his head. He had apparently cut himself when the cars collided, and a thin line of blood was trickling down the right side of his face. Jonah was holding his left hand in his right and Sally wondered whether he had broken any bones. Dazed, she watched the two men as they approached each other.

"Are you talking to me?" the little man said. "To me, are you calling a bastard?"

"What's your name?" Jonah said. "Damn you, I'm going to . . ."

"To me, are you asking the name?" the little man said. "I will throw you in the river, you stringbean! I will pick you up and throw you in the river."

"I'd like to see you try that," Jonah said, and took off his glasses and moved closer to the little man, as though he would step on him and squash him flat into the pavement.

"You hit me, and I die," the little man warned. "I bleed from the head now, you murderer. Hit me, and I die. Get away from me!"

"You're a maniac," Jonah said. "How dare you drive a car without looking where—"

"To me, are you calling a maniac? A *fink* is what you are, to call a decent man a maniac. Get away, get away, do you see him?" he asked the gathering crowd. "He is making obscene and threatening gestures!"

"Let me see your license," Jonah said.

"Let me see *your* license, fink!" the little man answered. "Do you hear?" he said to the crowd. "Do you hear his threatening?"

"There's the police," someone said, and Sally heard the sound of a siren and turned her head to see a police car approaching in the distance, its red dome light revolving and blinking.

"Good," the little man said. "The police, you hear, fink? Now we'll see who threatens, fink."

"Did anyone here see this accident?" Jonah asked.

"I, the maniac," the little man said. "I, the maniac saw it! I saw *all* of it, a hundred miles an hour this fink comes swooping down a public highway!"

"You're a lying little bastard," Jonah said, "and you're making me very angry."

"You, I am making angry, you?" the little man asked incredulously. "I am here bleeding in a hundred places, and *you* are standing angry? Where are the police, those finks? Where are they, I ask!"

"All right, what's the trouble here?" the patrolman said, coming out of the squad car. His partner stepped into the highway and began waving traffic around the wrecked autos.

Sally, dazed and certain she was in shock, began giggling. She had not, until the moment the two cars struck, enjoyed either the drive to Poughkeepsie, their brief stay at the college, or any part of their return trip. Jonah had left her to wander the campus that afternoon while he chatted with his world history professor, and she had been unexpectedly depressed by the sight of all those young girls in candy-striped stockings and short suede skirts, God, had it really all been *that* long ago? Nor could she honestly say that Jonah Willow was exactly an exciting conversationalist. There was a tenseness about him that made her want to scream aloud, a social unease that seemed to translate itself into a physical deformity as he drove the convertible, knuckles white, body hunched, long legs cramped. All the way up to the college, his conversation had consisted of a series of ominous grunts designed to stifle discussion. Not once did he mention the trial, and this puzzled her. She was a lawyer, certainly not as experienced or as well known as he, but a lawyer nonetheless; she had thought he would welcome her opinions, or at least her thoughts. But even on the return trip, when she tentatively asked whether his meeting with the professor had been profitable, he replied only, "Not very," and once again fell silent. Weary and discouraged, she retreated to her corner of the car, closing her eyes and listening to the lulling hum of the tires against the road.

"Are you asleep?" he asked at last.

"What?" she said, startled.

"Are you asleep?"

"No. Where are we?"

"On the West Side Highway. We just went through the Spuyten Duyvil toll booths."

"No, I'm not asleep," she said, suspecting she had been. "I just have to close my eyes every now and then. Otherwise, I read everything."

"Oh," he said, and she looked at him a moment, expecting more, and then closed her eyes again when she realized nothing was forthcoming. He did not speak again until shortly before the accident. She must have dozed off a second time because she sat up in alarm when she heard his voice.

"What do you mean?" he asked.

"What?"

"About reading everything."

"I'm a compulsive reader," she said.

"Oh," he answered.

End of conversation, Sally thought.

"Yes," she said, persisting in spite of better judgment, "I can reel off word for word every sign and billboard we passed on the road today. My mind's like a hall closet."

She waited for him to make some comment, hardly expecting that he would. When he did not, she sighed, and closed her eyes again. The accident occurred not two minutes later. Now, watching the police officer as he examined both men's licenses, watching him turn solicitous and then obsequious as Jonah casually mentioned the name of a circuit judge, watching the little man go pale and almost faint when he realized he had rammed into someone with high legal connections, Sally still felt giddy and numb, and her front tooth hurt like hell, what a damn silly thing to get involved in, an accident when she was so close to home.

Still, Jonah's profanity had exploded into that dreary automobile ride like a mortar shell, and she was grateful for the careless little man who was now explaining to Jonah and the policeman and anyone who would listen that he was a poor but honest bricklayer coming home late from a job in Harlem, anxious to be reunited once more with his wife and six kids—she was sure he had said *five* kids the first time around—and therefore perhaps a bit unheedful of traffic signs, but he *had* stopped at the sign, he had come to a full if brief stop. What *was* he, did the attorney think, some kind of maniac who would endanger the life and limb of innocent people on a public highway? Did the attorney, did these honorable law enforcement officers, did these good citizens believe for a moment that he would do a fink thing like that, crashing into innocent people—arguing his case right there on the highway without benefit of counsel while Jonah kept holding his left hand in his right, and Sally could see now that he was wincing in pain.

She got out of the car suddenly and walked to where the small man was still pleading his case, turning to a fat smiling bleached blonde now, and advising her that he had been a citizen for fifteen years, having come from Cairo, and that he had never been in any kind of trouble with the law before this, nor ever in an automobile accident though he had been driving since 1956, did he look like a fink, he asked the bleached blonde. The blonde smiled and then clucked her tongue sympathetically, but remained noncommittal as to whether he was or was not a fink.

"I think he's hurt his hand," Sally said to the nearest

patrolman. "Are we going to be much longer here, or can we get him to a hospital?"

"You're bleeding, miss," the patrolman said.

"I'm all right," Sally said.

"Can you drive?" the patrolman asked Jonah.

"Yes, I can."

"Maybe we'd better do as the young lady suggests. We can run you right over to Harlem Hospital, right on Lenox."

"No, it's nothing," Jonah said. "I just wrenched it when we collided, that's all."

"Something might be broken in there," the patrolman said.

"Why is nobody here to worry about *my* head?" the man from Cairo asked. "I'm sorry, your worship, but my head is bleeding, too, don't forget."

"You'd better get him to the hospital," Jonah said.

"You come along, too, Mr. Willow. No offense meant, but I think we'd better take a look at that hand."

"It's beginning to swell," Sally said.

"Miss, do you know your lip is cut?"

"What?"

"Your lip, miss. It's bleeding pretty bad."

"I think we'd *all* better take a little ride over to the hospital," the other patrolman said.

"I don't see any need for that," Jonah said.

"Begging your pardon, Mr. Willow," the patrolman said, "but I don't think Judge Santesson would like it if we let a friend of his go home with a broken hand or something."

"All right," Jonah said, "let's get it over with."

They did not get it over with until eleven o'clock that night. By that time Jonah was in a surly, cantankerous mood. He told the frightened little man from Cairo that he was going to do his damndest to have his driver's license revoked, and then got into an argument with the policemen about the advisability of doing any further driving that night.

"Let's take a taxi," Sally said.

"How can I lay bricks without the license to drive?" the Egyptian said.

"Why don't you take a taxi, Mr. Willow?" the cops said.

Jonah took Sally's arm and led her out of the hospital and then got into a further argument the moment they entered the automobile, simply because Sally suggested that *she* ought to do the driving, a swollen lip seeming to her less restricting than a sprained and taped wrist. Jonah testily informed her that he was in perfect physical condition, and then proceeded to prove his point by racing down to the Village (*your* license ought to be revoked, she thought, but did not say), scaring her half to death, and parking the car in a clearly marked No Parking zone in front of her building.

The hallway was silent. They climbed the steps to her fourth-floor apartment, Sally leading, Jonah following. He did not say a word to her as they walked up, radiating only what seemed to be sullen anger. Outside her apartment, she opened her bag and searched for her key in silence.

"I'm sorry about the accident," he said abruptly.

"It wasn't your fault."

"Your eyes were closed, I thought perhaps . . ."

"No, I saw what happened."

"In any case, I'm sorry." His manner was still brusque and scarcely civil. She found her key and inserted it in the lock. "And I'm also sorry you had such a terrible time," he said, "but you see . . ."

"I didn't, don't be silly."

". . . I'm not very good at small talk."

The hallway was silent again.

"I have a great many things on my mind," Jonah said. "I'm sorry."

"That's all right," Sally said. She twisted the key. The tumblers fell with a small oiled click.

"I'm sorry about the profanity, too," he said.

"That's all right," she said again. She listened as he continued to apologize for his swearing in the car and on the highway, his voice lowering, listened as he told her how sorry he was for having argued with the policemen and for having threatened the little Egyptian, "I know this is the first time we've been alone together, without a lot of people chattering away, and I wish I could have been more entertaining. But you see . . ."

"That's all right, Jonah," she said.

". . . I had hoped this friend of mine could help me, he's an expert on military engagements, that's his forte, Sally. He's written several really good books, and I thought he could help me. I thought he could come up with something more than he did."

"I know it was a disappointing day for you."

"Yes, it was."

"But I *did* enjoy the accident. The accident was fun," she said, and smiled.

"May I see you again?"

"Yes," she said.

"I'll call. The trial should be over by the end of the week, perhaps we can get together Friday or Saturday."

"Well, call," she said.

"I'd give anything to possess your trick," Jonah said suddenly.

"What trick?"

"Of closing your eyes to shut out the print, to shut out the noise of the world."

"I do it in defense," she said, watching his face.

"That's just it," he answered. "I *have* no defense."

"What do you mean?"

"Nothing," he said, and smiled. "Good night, Sally. I'll call you soon."

"Good night, Jonah," she said, and went into the apartment.

He went down the steps rapidly, keeping his left hand off the banister because the wrist was throbbing and each time he tried to flex his fingers a sharp pain shot up the length of his arm, damn stupid little man. It was bitter cold in the street outside; he feared they would have sleet or hail rather than snow—nor gloom of night can stay these couriers from the swift completion, would they tear down the post office now that they had demolished Penn Station? There was nothing permanent in this city, it was a city determined to obliterate its past. If there is one thing all Americans share in common, he thought, it's this lack of an historical sense, a tendency to want to change the recent past as well as the nation's ancient heritage. Oh certainly, destroy the jail where they kept the accused in the Salem witchcraft trials, cover the shame of hysteria, but Penn Station? That noble structure razed to the ground to make way for a sports arena? Heinous crime, I sound like my father, he thought.

He walked quickly to the car, his ears tingling, and then fumbled with the key in the lock, it's foolish to lock a convertible, he thought, they only slit the canvas top. He closed the door behind him rapidly, started the car, and then sat in silence for several moments while the engine warmed and the heater began to operate. He took a pair of fur-lined gloves from his coat pocket, put them on, pulled the tails of his coat out from under him, twisted himself into a comfortable position, turned on the radio, and then eased the car away from the curb. There was an order to everything he did, he was certain he performed the same operations in sequence each time he entered his automobile. He was equally certain that his father, Zachary Willow, drove in an identical manner, and that his grandfather and *his* father before him had undoubtedly performed similarly in a horse and buggy on the cobbled streets of Danvers, Massachusetts. He had gone back there once to trace the heritage, a tribute to Zachary, who insisted that a man should know his roots, though Jonah had been born in Stamford, Connecticut, and could not have been less interested in a pilgrimage to the home of his forebears. But he had found there in the library records the history of a family, the cursive script difficult to read, embellished with curlicues and substituting *f*'s for *s*'s, words capitalized for no apparent reason, the ink brown and fading on yellowed brittle pages—Benjamin Willow married to Margaret, and before him Nathan married to Elizabeth Anne, and somewhere back in the almost illegible record, a Jonah Willow, apprentice seaman on a whaling ship out of New Bedford. He had made the drive back along the turnpike, the road markers showing peaked Pilgrim hats and witches on broomsticks, possessed if not with a sense of self, then at least with a better understanding of his father.

Zachary Willow was a lawyer, and his father and grandfather had been lawyers before him. There was in him a sense of order that was firmly rooted in a judicial system evolved from the English, and based in part on the Roman Corpus Juris Civilis, derived in turn from such early systems as the Code of Hammurabi and the Laws of Manu. In the law, there was stability and certainty, precedent and continuity. Zachary ran his Stamford house as though it were a courtroom, meting out justice to Jonah and his brother Lucas as though they were prisoners before the bar, firmly imbuing in them the knowledge that there was right and there was wrong and there was nothing in between. The law, to Zachary Willow, was inflexible and clearly defined: it prescribed social behavior as surely as the Bible prescribed moral behavior. The law was the law, and you did not fiddle around with it, and you did not try for fancy interpretations because it had not been designed for that. It was simply and indestructibly created by men, to instruct them in, and to enforce for them, the rules of civilized behavior. "Where law ends there tyranny begins," read one of the inscriptions chiseled in marble on the Criminal Courts Building, and Zachary Willow might have chiseled it there himself.

That the behavior in the old Stamford house was sometimes less than civilized could not be blamed on Zachary. His eldest son, Lucas, must have been a trial to him from the very beginning, although Jonah only became aware of the conflict much later, when his brother entered high school and began playing football. Until that time, frightened of his father and simultaneously respecting him, almost venerating him, Jonah did not once suspect that his brother's opinion of the old man could be any different than his own. Surely there was serenity in the Shippan house, its green shutters facing Long Island Sound, the lawn sloping down to a seawall from which you could see sailing ships and pleasure boats, a view that never tired Jonah; there was, perhaps, still a trace of the original Jonah Willow in him, the man who'd sailed for whale out of

New Bedford. "Call me Ishmael," he had once dreamily said to his brother while they sat side by side on white wooden lawn chairs on the green grass sloping to the Sound, and watched a double-masted sailboat cleaving the water. Lucas had replied, "Call *me* Shlemiel," but this, of course, was after he had joined the football team and was playing offensive back and feeling his oats. "I like physical contact," Lucas always said, "I like knocking guys around."

Jonah's mother was a slender woman with a flawless English complexion and magnificent brown eyes. Her family had come to Massachusetts in 1734, from a town in Wales—she always pronounced it quickly and melodically for him, slurring her *l*'s and *m*'s, but he could never pronounce it himself and had only seen it written out once. Watching her as she stepped surely and lightly over the sparkling grass to the seawall, he often visualized her ancestors walking in just such a manner, the hands delicately clasped, the head expectantly tilted as though listening for a hidden sound, before the splendid ruins of a castle overlooking the valley. She was soft-spoken and spoke rarely, but her silence could fall upon a room like a thunderclap in recrimination never voiced against one or another of his father's stern pronouncements. Her smile was sometimes like a knife; he had often seen his father's bluster grow larger and therefore less meaningful as he rushed suicidally against that naked blade of a smile, her brown eyes solemn and unamused above it. His mother was not an affectionate woman, or at least not a demonstrative one. He could only remember her truly embracing him once, holding him close to her breast and frantically stroking his face, and that was the time Lucas pushed him off the seawall and he cut his hand on a sharp rock.

There was never any doubt that Jonah would one day become a lawyer like his father, nor ever any doubt that he would eventually marry Christine Dunseath. Looking back, he supposed now that the divorce was also inevitable. But he never had an inkling of *that* until it was fully upon him, and he certainly didn't anticipate it when he was courting her as a boy or when they were newly married and trying to make their way in New York. His courtship (the word was his father's and not his) was a natural development encouraged by proximity; the Dunseath family lived next door to them on Shippan Point. Albert Dunseath was Stamford's water commissioner, a ruddy-faced man with a hearty laugh, sparse blond hair covering his tanned pate, combed sideways to disguise the encroaching baldness. His wife was a dark-haired beauty from whom, fortunately, Christie had inherited her looks. She was an avid horsewoman, and was always stamping in and out of her house in jodhpurs and riding boots, flicking a riding crop against her legs, Lady Fitz-Ashton returning from an outing on the moors, Some tea, Lady Fitz? She scared hell out of Jonah with her imperious air and her startling beauty, the black hair cut in severe bangs across her forehead, the proud nose and generous mouth, blue eyes flashing, the riding crop flicking against her thigh, terrifying. Christie was hardly less terrifying as a child, a hellcat who gave Lucas a bloody nose once when he tried to take off her pants behind the tool shed near the big dying maple. Lucas was eleven at the time, and Jonah was ten, and Christie was perhaps eight, yes just eight. Lucas had got her pants halfway down over her knees when she suddenly decided she didn't like the game they were playing. She twisted away from him, her small white bottom flashing in the dappled shade, and hit him with her bunched fist. Jonah was terrified that she would tell her mother what had happened and cause her to descend upon their household like the mounted fury she most certainly was. But Christie was as frightened as he, and never said a word about it. She studiously avoided Lucas from that day on, though, and maintained a cool and barely polite attitude toward him to the end.

Jonah began seriously dating her when they were still in high school—boat rides up the Connecticut River, and long drives to New Haven where they went to see out-of-town tryouts of incoming Broadway plays, and into New York to see the stage shows at Radio City and the Roxy, or the big-name bands at the Paramount and Strand. He once waited in line with her for three hours outside the Paramount on a freezing day in February, to see Frank Sinatra, whom he hated the moment Christie began shrieking; he thought she would faint dead away right there in the balcony, many of the girls actually did. Or just being together, walking home together from school on a bright spring day, or sitting on the lawn at night, fingers barely touching, a farewell kiss behind the shed where Lucas had tried to take off her pants, the sight of her as she walked between the forsythia bushes that separated the two properties, a curious walk, so unlike her mother's, almost as though she were gliding, a model's walk, with pelvis thrust forward and head erect.

She wore a blue gown to his high school prom, she had taken to wearing her hair like her mother's by then, sharp bangs across the forehead, blue eyes twinkling beneath them in secret amusement (secret *contempt,* he later came to realize), the pale blue of the gown emphasizing her eyes and clinging to her childish body. She was almost seventeen, but her figure seemed to resist all womanly transformation. Narrow-hipped and small-breasted, slender and slouched, she achieved a look that only years later would become fashionably chic. Her face was undeniably beautiful, though, her eyes sometimes flashed at older men who stopped dead in their tracks and then quickly surveyed the slender body and shook their heads in wonder, dazed by their obvious mistake. When he danced with her, he could feel every inch of her body pressed against him, the small budding breasts that would never really develop into an abundant bosom, the protruding bones of her hips, the mound of her pubis, the curve of her back where his hand rested, his fingers sometimes spread to touch the tight firm buttocks, he had seen her almost naked once, white and dappled with maple-shadow as she twisted away from his brother's hands, the blue eyes angry and not at all amused that day.

He asked her to marry him on that graduation night, resplendent in his white dinner jacket, holding her cool and slender in his arms. The senior class had rented the country club and hired the best young band in the area, a fourteen-piece orchestra with monogramed stands and identical blue jackets, white shirts, blue bow ties. The trumpet section rose to take their chorus of "Summertime," straight mutes protruding from the golden glowing bells of their horns, ceiling lights glistening with blues and reds and greens that shimmered in brass-bound reflection, he danced with Christine Dunseath and asked her to be his wife. He was eighteen years old, and a languid June breeze blew in fresh over the dew-misted golf course and through the open French doors of the ballroom. She nodded when he asked her, and he said, "You will?" in surprise, and when she answered, "Of course," he whispered a kiss into her hair.

He had thought at the time, being eighteen, the United States involved in another great war for democracy, that he would naturally be called into the Army, that he would naturally serve his country, become a hero perhaps, though not a dead one. When he registered for the draft, however, he was afraid he might be rejected because of his eyesight, and even debated memorizing an eyechart before going down for his physical. But he decided against it, sweated through the examination instead, and immediately afterwards asked the doctor how he had done. The doctor told him his eyes were okay as far as the Army was concerned, proving once again the old military adage about healthy seeing-eye dogs. The military, however, did not yet possess either an adage or a deterrent for poison gas seeping into a man's system through a hole in his eardrum. Jonah was surprised to discover that he possessed just such a punctured eardrum and that the Army did not want him, better luck next war, Mac. Poison gas at the time was the ultimate weapon, the dread weapon each nation hoped would never be used again. In later years, Jonah would come to appreciate the irony of having been rejected because of the fear of poison gas, only to have the war finally decided by the use of a weapon a million times more heinous. He would also come to appreciate (and this only very much later) the supreme irony of fighting wars under the guise of preventing them, and would come to the conclusion (never admitted to a soul) that all men, *including* Americans, were warlike and that the invention and use of "The Bomb" was restraining them from doing what they really loved doing most: killing each other. ("I like physical contact," Lucas had said, "I like knocking guys around.") Lucas himself had enlisted in the Marine Corps when he was just eighteen, against Zachary's wishes, but what could the old man do? He was a hero, his captain later wrote, who managed to kill sixteen Japanese soldiers before being killed himself by a mortar explosion. "I am sending you a small carton of his effects, please know that we respected your son highly and share your loss deeply," kind captain sitting out there in the Pacific with jungle rot on his balls and dead youngsters on his hands. The small carton of effects included the maroon-and-white letter Lucas had received in high school for being the team's star halfback, a hero even then. Jonah's keenest memories of his brother would always be of those crisp October days, the sky above the high school field, the handoff to Lucas and the plunge, God, how he could run! Even at Yale years later, even as a law student there (his father and grandfather had of course studied law at Yale) he would experience a strange, odd sensation whenever the team came out onto the field, a shudder would run up his spine, and he would once again see Lucas charging into the opposing line, would remember once when Lucas got up and limped away from a pile-on and then waved to Jonah where he was sitting in the stands, his grin cracking white and sharp across his mud-stained face. *I like physical contact, I like knocking guys around.* He had knocked around sixteen of them before they'd brought him down, you do not get up and wipe mud from your jersey after a mortar explosion, you do not smile into the stands at your kid brother.

He married Christine Dunseath in the First Presbyterian Church on Stamford's Bedford Street in the summer of 1952, after he received his law degree from Yale. The reception was held at her parents' home on Shippan Point, outdoors in the garden. The forsythias were still in bloom, spilling their petals onto the ground, he remembered fleetingly the image of a younger Christie threading her way through those bushes on too many nights too long ago. She had not changed that much perhaps, there was still the look of a very young and vulnerable creature about her, except for the snapping eyes that flicked as surely as a riding crop against a jodhpured thigh. At twenty-four, she was still wearing her hair in bangs, continued to wear it that way even to the time of the divorce when she was thirty-four and a mother, and when her eyes betrayed the fact that she was no longer a high school girl. Across the lawn, moving from guest to guest, her champagne glass in one delicately poised hand, while Jonah's mother sat unsmiling with a fan spread on her lap, dark eyes solemn as she watched her son's bride—did she ever think of Lucas in his jungle grave, or had there even been a grave? Christie Dunseath, radiant in white, black shoulder-length hair, swooping black brows over blue eyes, laughing. And water commissioner Dunseath, almost entirely bald now, ruddy-faced and a trifle drunk, embracing her as she came across the lawn, Mrs. Dunseath uncomfortable in a yellow diaphanous gown, no riding crop in her hand, no horse between her legs, older now, but her face still clinging to its girlish mold, the way Christie's would for years to come, except for the eyes.

Their first apartment was a three-room flat in a tenement on East 73rd Street, a street teeming with children during the summer, swarming with traffic that headed west from the East River Drive exit, noisy and smelly and wretchedly hot. Christie had never been able to stand heat, she ran from the sun the way albinos do, always seeking the comforting shade of an umbrella or a tree, her white skin turning lobster red if she were exposed for as long as five minutes. The apartment was an inferno, and the secondhand fan he bought on Canal Street did little to dispel the fetid air. He would come home from work each day to find her limp and haggard on the bed, her eyes silently accusing, and he would remember his mother's mute disapproval of Zachary, the cutting edge of her smile. He later wondered if their marriage did not really suffocate forever in those first terrible months in that grubby apartment. But at the time, he was too involved in coping with the profession he had chosen, hurling himself against an indifferent city swarming with talented young lawyers like himself, expecting Christie to cheer his efforts, applaud his small triumphs, urge him on to greater heights. She did this unfailingly until, almost a year to the day after her marriage, she became pregnant. Then, frightened by the changes in her body and the impending responsibility of motherhood, wishing for the Shippan house and the easy life she once had known, she turned to Jonah—childishly perhaps, unrealistically perhaps—wanting him to take care of her, wanting him to tell her that everything would be all right, that there was nothing to worry about, that this was all a part of it, all a vital part of it. And he might have provided her with the assurance she desperately needed and sought, had not a very important change taken place in his own life at exactly the same time.

Raymond Gauthier was a bald-headed New Yorker of French descent who had lost his right eye in Italy, and who wore a black patch over the empty socket. He resembled a motion picture pirate, with powerful shoulders and chest, pepper-and-salt hair curling over the open collar of his shirt, the dangling arms of a gorilla, thick thighs and enormous hands. Jonah always visualized him with a belaying pin in his fist, following Burt Lancaster over the side of a burning Spanish vessel. His wife was a Brooklyn girl named Helen, whom he openly and frankly described as an ex-junkie who had married and later divorced a saxophone player. Jonah surmised that Raymond was kidding about this, at least about the junkie part, but he nonetheless watched Helen very carefully, and every time the poor girl scratched at an itch, he assumed she was overdue for her next fix. Helen had dark black curly hair which she wore cut very close to her head. She had slightly bucked teeth, and her eyes were green and faintly Oriental; sometimes when Jonah looked straight into them, he could believe she had once been an addict. He was tempted on several occasions to ask her about it directly, but then of course he knew it was just another of Raymond's jokes.

Raymond had been practicing law in New York since 1951, and felt it was time he took a partner, an idea Jonah clutched at immediately; Raymond had a going practice, Jonah was still chasing ambulances. Neither of them knew that the treason case would come their way so soon, or that it would catapult their newly formed partnership into that rarefied upper atmosphere of the legal profession, where clients were abundant and fees were outrageous, and fame was suddenly upon them like a sunburst. They knew only that they liked each other, and respected each other, and could possibly put their separate talents to fruitful use in a partnership. The treason case was still six months away. The plot itself was at that very moment, in fact, taking definite shape and form in a Jersey City basement, the plans being drawn, the bombs manufactured; the execution and subsequent capture were still in the offing. But the formation of the partnership meant that he and Christie could move instantly from their shabby East 73rd Street townhouse (Mr. and Mrs. Jonah Willow of New York and Shippan Point) into a better apartment on Central Park West, large and airy, and not terribly expensive because the neighborhood was supposedly succumbing to the Puerto Rican influx.

The new apartment did little to lift Christie's spirits. She had begun to show in her second month, and she now tried to conceal the pregnancy as though she were the victim of a back-alley rape. She incessantly blamed Jonah for what she called his "animal impetuosity," and one night delivered a five-minute kitchen diatribe on "the primitive and unreliable birth control methods available to American women." She then developed a theory relating her pregnancy to Jonah's work, claiming he was always too busy to do anything but make love, and further claiming they had used sex that summer as a substitute for other forms of entertainment ("*What!*" Jonah said) which would not have been necessary if he'd taken her to dinner or the theater every now and then ("*What!*" he said again). Besides, she said, this new partnership of his was all craparoo, and he knew it, the same as everything else in this stupid world, "craparoo" being one of Mrs. Dunseath's more choice expressions, passed on to her daughter the way some families pass on the Limoges or the

Sheffield plate, an expression Jonah hated, and one which Christie used with increasing frequency to describe almost anything.

Stalin's succession by Malenkov that year was craparoo, as was Salk's development of a trial polio vaccine. Hillary's and Tenzing's conquest of Everest was likewise craparoo, and even the first test explosion of a hydrogen bomb by the Soviet Union was so classified by Christie. The exchange of ideas in those last few months of 1953 became virtually impossible. Coupled with Christie's craparoo concept was an almost biblical attitude that found voice in her second most favored expression, undoubtedly inherited from the water commissioner himself: *This too shall pass.* Why bother wondering whether Dag Hammarskjöld would make a good secretary general of the UN? His term would only last five years anyway. Why concern oneself with Senator McCarthy's belief that a Communist Party cell was in operation at the Lynn, Massachusetts, plant of General Electric? Wouldn't this eventually blow over? The theory applied to everything, all human endeavor fell before it and was trampled: the latest world event, the newest novel, the most recent motion picture, the goddamn Pillsbury bakeoff. All was either trivial at worst or transient at best, and who really gave a damn?

I really give a damn, Jonah thought, and began wondering whether or not anything at *all* mattered to Christie. Well, she's pregnant, he thought, she's going through a difficult time, she's only twenty-five years old, been married a year and a little more, this is difficult for her. She's really a very sensitive and vulnerable person, it's easy to see how things in this neurotic world of ours can confuse her and force her to build defenses against involvement, she's only exhibiting the symptoms of our times, she's a sweet confused kid, and I've got to help her. But where do you start when someone doesn't even realize that "craparoo" is as phony as whatever it purports to define? Crap is crap, and shit is shit, and craparoo is neither, no matter what Mrs. Albert Dunseath astride her Arabian stallion may believe or have caused her daughter to believe. So where do you begin, and what do you say?

He said nothing, he did not begin. Instead, the marriage began to die in that second year while Amy grew inside her belly and Jonah fell into Christie's own trap: it was all trivial and inconsequential, the normal difficult adjustment newlyweds have to make, it would pass, it would pass. It did not pass, and eight years later he would wonder whether he could have said or done anything to change the situation, whether there was still time then before the treason trial began, before everything else became terribly more urgent and important than the woman who was his wife.

The treason case broke in July of 1954, two months after Amy was born. His daughter weighed nine pounds two ounces, huge for a girl, causing Christie to go into shock shortly after the delivery, throwing up all over the floor of her room while the night nurse ran to fetch a mop instead of a doctor. He cornered the nurse in the hospital corridor, a big red-faced mean bitch with gray hair and a nose like a cleaver, and he told her she had better get the doctor immediately before he strangled her. Her red face went very white, two glacial spots showing one on each cheek and then spreading to the rest of her features as she struggled with indignation and anger, and then swallowed both and went trotting off down the corridor, white skirts flying, crepe soles padding, you're goddamn *right,* Jonah thought. His daughter had the Dunseath look, passed directly from Lady Fitz to Christie, each lineal reproduction slightly less perfect, as though the mold were losing its firmness: Mrs. Dunseath had been breathtakingly lovely; Christie was merely beautiful; and Amy, his daughter, was only pretty. But oh what a true loveliness about her, something Mrs. Dunseath could not have acquired in a thousand years of breeding, the black hair and the light eyes, yes, the finely turned profile and the generous mouth, yes, all these though less classically stated, but her manner as well. Ahh, her gentle, shy, and inquiring manner, the delicate grace of her, *this* was the Willow legacy. *This* was his mother gently walking toward the seawall, her head tilted in anticipation, his Amy, his darling girl.

In July of 1954, a young man named Kaneji Yoro, accompanied by another young man named Peter Koenig, set a series of homemade bombs against the walls of Gracie Mansion, detonated them, and began running downtown in the direction of Wall Street, hoping to lose themselves in the lunch hour crowds. They were picked up before they had traveled three blocks, and were immediately charged with attempted murder, the mayor and the governor having been in executive conference within when the bombs went off. The charges were later expanded in the indictment to include arson (because the building caught fire), anarchy (because they found in a Jersey City basement several documents in the defendants' handwriting which outlined an escalating scheme of methodical destruction that would eventually lead to chaos and insurrection), conspiracy (because the two men had been out of state when they conspired to commit their act against the peace of New York), and, finally, treason. Treason, of course, was the most serious of all the charges and was a crime punishable by death. Since Article 212 of the New York State Penal Law defined treason as consisting of "a combination of two or more persons by force to usurp the government of the state, or to overturn the same, shown by a forcible attempt made within the state, to accomplish that purpose," Jonah could not see how the district attorney hoped to prove there had been an attempt at overthrowing the government, notwithstanding the timely presence in Gracie Mansion of the state's highest executive. The documents in the Jersey City basement indeed supported a charge of anarchy, bolstered as they were by copies of books by Engels and Marx, issues of the *Daily Worker,* and even one or two party directives. Attempted murder was also well within the bounds of realistic possibility, and a conviction on that charge alone would have netted the perpetrators twenty-five years each in prison, a long enough span for any young bomber. The enormity of the crime, however, this attempt on the lives of two important officials (by Communist anarchists, no less) undoubtedly called for more severe punishment than the law allowed, so the district attorney had gratuitously tacked to his indictment the charges of arson, conspiracy, and treason. The arson charge amused Johah. The conspiracy and treason charges incensed him. He could not believe that Yoro's and Koenig's respective Japanese and German ancestry had anything whatever to do with the indictment ("Of course not," Christie said. "The war's already forgotten. It's all craparoo") but he nonetheless detected in the public reaction an attitude of outraged piety and righteousness. Hadn't we been reconstructing and regenerating those dirty Nazi bastards and sneaky Jap finks ever since the war ended, a war *we* had won, mind you? So now two snotnosed red Communist Fascist punks try to blow up Gracie Mansion with our beloved mayor and governor inside, dirty red subversive Jap rat bastard Nazis—notwithstanding the fact that Yoro was born and raised in San Francisco or that Koenig's father was a respected employee of the *Reader's Digest* in Chappaqua, where he had been born and where he had sired his anarchist son.

Jonah wanted to take the case because he felt the treason charge was unjustified and unjustifiable. Raymond wanted to take the case because he was shrewd enough in his ancestral French way to realize that whoever defended these two young Communists would become famous overnight. Their initial separate motives were later ironically reversed: it was Raymond who wrote a paper explaining the principles involved in the case, which he read at the annual meeting of the American Bar Association; it was Jonah who conducted the court trial, Jonah whose name and picture appeared in all the newspapers, Jonah who came out of the proceedings a well-known legal figure and a champion of the rights of the individual in a free society.

The district attorney eventually dropped the absurd arson charge, but Jonah permitted his clients to plead guilty only to attempted murder and anarchy, fighting the treason charge as well as the linked charge of conspiracy (if there had been no treason, how could anyone have conspired to commit an act against the peace?) on the grounds that whatever eventual overthrow may have been contemplated by the pair, its execution had certainly not begun with the bombing of the mayor's residence. Youthful ego and exuberance aside, even these misguided twenty-year-old boys could not possibly have intended their deed (he almost said "childish prank") as the beginning of a bona fide uprising. The jury was out for six hours. It convicted Yoro and Koenig of the first two crimes, and the judge sentenced them to consecutive prison terms of twenty-five years for attempted murder and ten years for anarchy. The case was won, and a style was set. The style was not immediately manifest, though. Like the dissolution of Jonah's marriage, it resisted definition until it was fully recognizable. By the time the tone of the partnership was realized, the tone of the marriage was also realized, and it was curious that both marriage and partnership dissolved in the same year, only several months apart, though neither had anything to do with the other. Or was that true?

He pulled the car to the curb outside his building. The doorman standing just inside the glass entrance doors immediately put on his gloves and came out to greet him.

"Put her away for the night, Mr. Willow?" he asked.

"Please, Dave."

"What happened to your fender here, Mr. Willow?"

"I had a little accident."

"Really got mangled, didn't it?"

"Mmm."

"There's a good body man over at the garage, if you want to . . ."

"I'll talk to him about it in the morning, Dave."

"Will you be using her tomorrow, or . . ."

"No, I'll need a taxi."

"Right, Mr. Willow. G'night now."

"Good night, Dave."

He walked quickly into the lobby, stopping at the long table with the mirror over it, picking up his mail. There was nothing from Amy. He scanned the envelopes rapidly, and then walked back to the elevator bank.

"Good evening, Fred," he said.

"Evening, Mr. Willow." The elevator doors closed. "Getting pretty cold out there, isn't it?"

"Bitter," Jonah said.

He got off on the sixth floor, and walked to his apartment at the end of the hall. Bessie had left a light burning for him in the entry alcove; the apartment was otherwise dark. He went into the kitchen, turning on lights ahead of him, and found a note from Bessie scotch-taped to the refrigerator door. *Your daughter called,* she had written in pencil, *says you should called her back at school tonight or Wesday noon.* He nodded briefly, took off his coat, and then went through the apartment to the master bedroom overlooking Park Avenue. He was about to place his call to Pennsylvania when he realized it was past midnight. He would have to call on Wednesday.

His wrist hurt like hell. He undressed slowly and carefully, cursing the Egyptian under his breath—that was another call he'd have to make, to Judge Santesson, see what he could do about that crazy son of a bitch.

The cross begins tomorrow, he thought.

Wearily, he pulled back the covers, the blue and violet flower-patterned sheets Christie had brought home from Lord & Taylor, traces of her lingering in the bedroom even though the divorce had become final in August of 1962, the painting they had bought in Rome, St. Peter's in sunlight, the crayoned drawing Amy had given them as a Christmas gift when she was only four, traces, traces.

The cross begins tomorrow, he thought.

In a little while, he fell asleep.

TUESDAY

5

It began snowing early in the morning, but by nine-thirty there was scarcely any cover at all on the sidewalk outside the courthouse. The snow was fine, a sharp powder that sifted from the sky only to be blown off the streets and sidewalks, patches of gathered white suddenly in motion, rearranging to reveal black asphalt and gray concrete, moving again like mist on a bog, to form yet another pattern directed by the wind. Arthur stood with Brackman just inside one of the barred windows fronting the street, looking past the thick white columns to the shifting snow beyond. He had not been able to sleep last night, and his eyes felt heavy and puffed.

"I want to give you some tips about Jonah Willow," Brackman said.

"I feel like hell," Arthur said.

"You'll wash your face before we go in. That'll make you feel better."

"That'll make me feel worse."

"Arthur, do you want me to tell you about Willow, or do you want to make wisecracks? If you want to make wisecracks . . ."

"You have no sense of humor, Sidney," Arthur said.

"That's right. Not when ten million dollars is at stake."

"All right, tell me about Willow. What should I know about him?"

"He's very smart," Brackman said. "That's the first thing you should know."

"I'm smart, too," Arthur said.

"Yes, but you're not a lawyer. Willow is smart, and he knows the law, and you can bet he's researched this case from top to bottom and can quote you precedent in Sanskrit. Don't underestimate him at any time during the cross. That's my first word of advice."

"All right, I won't underestimate him."

"Especially if he seems to be fumbling for words. That's an old trick of Jonah's, he does it to give the witness a false sense of confidence. Then he springs like an animal."

"I'll watch for it."

"He has a habit, too, of shooting questions at you from every corner of the universe, seemingly without logical order. *He* knows where he's going, but very often the witness can't connect the line of progression because the questions aren't in sequence. Watch out for that, Arthur. He can have you admitting your mother is a whore, and then ten minutes later contradicting it."

"You *do* have a sense of humor," Arthur said.

"So watch for that," Brackman said, ignoring him, "questions out of sequence. I'll help you all I can from the table, but there'll be times when I can't object, and I won't. You're up there alone, and you've got to watch yourself."

"I'll be very careful."

"Take your time with him. If he asks a question that sounds at all tricky, hesitate before you answer. If he pushes for an answer, ask him to repeat the question, even though you heard it the first time around."

"That'll fool him, I'll bet."

"It won't fool him for a minute, but it'll gain time for you while you think. And if you need more time, even *after* the question has been repeated, simply say you did not understand the question. While he explains it to you, you keep thinking. And then you answer it."

"Okay," Arthur said.

"If he asks a question that requires a 'yes' or 'no' answer, and you feel that such an answer will hurt you, I want you to say—and please memorize this, Arthur—I want you to say, 'I can answer that with a yes or no, but the answer will be misleading.' Have you got that?"

"I can answer it with a yes or no, but the answer will be misleading, right, I've got it."

"Good. Don't lose your temper."

"I won't."

"Don't raise your voice to Willow."

"I won't."

"Don't argue with him. Just answer . . ."

"I won't."

". . . the questions."

"Okay."

"And don't let him trick you into saying anything you don't want to say."

"I doubt if he can do that."

"I'm telling you he can."

"Words are my business, Sidney."

"They're Willow's, too, and you're playing in his ball park."

"I'll remember."

"Be especially careful of the negative question—where if you answer yes, you're really saying no."

"I'll be careful."

"This is the cross-examination, Arthur, and during the cross he's going to try to get you to contradict everything you said in the direct. Failing that, he'll try to make you appear foolish or ridiculous. He can be a ruthless man when he wants to, I've seen him in action, and he can make you feel like a child or a stuttering moron. If that happens, just take your time, regain your composure, and continue answering the questions truthfully. Don't lie, Arthur. Not about anything. I can guarantee that if you lie, Willow will pick up the lie later, and then your credibility will be questioned and that could very well lose the case for us. Am I making you nervous?"

"Yes, you damn well are."

"Good. I want you to be nervous because that'll make you careful. Don't forget, Arthur, this is where they got Jesus."

"What?"

"By the cross," Brackman said, and grinned.

"Mr. Constantine, had you ever met James Driscoll before the publication of *The Paper Dragon?*" Willow asked. "Just a moment, and I'll set a date for that."

"October of 1963," Brackman said.

"Thank you, Mr. Brackman," Willow replied. "Yes, Plaintiff's Exhibit 2 does indeed show that the copyright was in 1963. Thank you very much." He turned again to the witness chair. Arthur studied Willow's face and wished he could see through the reflecting lenses of his glasses.

"Had you met Mr. Driscoll at any time before October of 1963?"

"No, I had not," Arthur replied.

"Had you in fact ever set eyes on him before the beginning of this trial yesterday morning?"

"No, I had not."

"Is it correct to say that you never gave a copy of your play to Mr. Driscoll?"

"That is correct. I did not."

"Did you ever submit copies of your play to Mitchell-Campbell Books?"

"I don't think so."

"Well, surely you must *know,* Mr. Constantine."

"I have an agent, Mr. Willow, and he takes care of such matters for me. If you want to know whether I myself ever sent a copy to Mitchell-Campbell, no, sir, I did not. Nor to Camelot Books, nor to Mr. Driscoll, either."

"Did you ever ask your agent to send copies of your play to *any* publishing house?"

"I did not."

"Before this action began, Mr. Constantine, had you ever met Mr. Chester Danton of Mitchell-Campbell Books?"

"I had not."

"Had you ever met any other person employed by Mitchell-Campbell Books?"

"No, sir."

"Had you possessed any personal knowledge of James Driscoll's writing habits or procedure?"

"No personal knowledge, no."

"Had you possessed any personal knowledge of the editorial work done on *The Paper Dragon?*"

"No."

"Had you possessed any knowledge whatever of the author-editor relationship between James Driscoll and Chester Danton?"

"No knowledge whatever."

"Are you aware of the complaint in this action?"

"I am," Arthur said, and glanced quickly at Brackman.

"Is it based upon information you supplied to your attorneys?"

"Yes."

"Did you read the complaint after it was drawn?"

"I did."

"Did you swear to its truth?"

"I did."

Willow walked to the defense table. His assistant handed him a document, and he carried it back with him to the witness chair. "This is from paragraph 12 of your complaint, Mr. Constantine." He adjusted the glasses on the bridge of his nose, flipped through the document—which Arthur now recognized—and began reading: " 'On information and belief, James Driscoll and Mitchell-Campbell Books conspired to deprive plaintiff of his rights in the copyrighted composition.' " Willow looked up from the document. "Did you swear to that statement, Mr. Constantine?"

"I did."

"Did you then possess any knowledge or information concerning a conspiracy to plagiarize your work?"

"Oh, I see," Arthur said.

"Yes, what do you see?"

"Mr. Willow, I can only repeat what I said at the pretrial examination. I do *not* know how the plagiarism was effected, I do *not* know of any confidential meetings, or secret correspondence, I did *not* wiretap anyone's telephone. But I do know that there are similarities between my play and *The Paper Dragon* that far exceed the possibility of . . ."

"Please answer the question," Willow said. "Did you in fact possess any knowledge or information of such a conspiracy?"

"I had no such knowledge or information, no, sir."

"You have testified that you swore to the truth of your complaint."

"Yes."

"Did you swear to the truth of a similar complaint against API?"

"Yes, but . . ."

"Even though you then possessed no knowledge or . . ."

". . . these complaints are only legal terminology for . . ."

". . . information as to its truth. Thank you. Mr. Constantine, can you tell me if any other play of yours was ever produced? In addition to *The Catchpole,* I mean."

"It's *Catchpole,* not *'The' Catchpole.* I think I pointed that out to you before."

"Yes, *Catchpole,* forgive me."

"The code name for the invasion of Eniwetok Atoll was 'Operation Catchpole.' That's where I got the title."

"Isn't there another meaning of the word 'catchpole'?" Willow asked conversationally.

"Not that I know of. I believe it was coined for military purposes, a coined word."

"I think there's another meaning, Mr. Constantine."

"I wouldn't know it."

"It's archaic, of course," Willow said, "but a catchpole was a petty officer of justice, especially a man who made arrests for debt."

"Is that so?"

"Yes."

"I didn't know that."

"You were not aware of this other meaning when you wrote your play?"

"No."

"In any case, I will try to remember the correct title from now on. *Catchpole.*"

"I'd appreciate it."

"*Have* you had any other plays produced?"

"I have a play in production now," Arthur said.

"Do you mean you have a play in rehearsal?"

"No, we're not in rehearsal yet. We're still casting it."

"When do you plan to open?"

"We haven't set a date as yet."

"In what theater will you open, Mr. Constantine?"

"That hasn't been decided yet."

"Has the play been fully capitalized?"

Arthur hesitated.

"Mr. Constantine? Has the play . . . ?"

"Not yet."

"Then this 'play in production,' as you refer to it, is really in a very *early* stage of production, isn't that so?"

"That's so, yes."

"In fact, we might say that until it is capitalized . . ."

"The play is under option," Arthur said. "It's our intention to produce it as soon as possible."

"Your *intention*, yes."

"Yes."

"But in fact, you have not had a play actually produced, actually presented since *The Catchpole,* forgive me, *Catchpole.* I'll try to remember."

"I've had movies and television plays produced."

"Yes, but not a stage play."

"No. Not until this play, which is in production now."

"Which is 'under option' now, isn't that what you mean?"

"No, I mean 'in production' now. We are actively casting it."

"But we may say, may we not, that since October of 1947, which is when *Catchpole* was produced—a period of more than nineteen years—you have not had a play produced on Broadway or off-Broadway or, in fact, anywhere in the world. Isn't that true?"

"That's true."

"Thank you. Mr. Constantine, you testified that you were sent to the Pacific as a new lieutenant, a *second* lieutenant I believe you said, after a short period of training as an officer."

"I did not say that."

"I beg your pardon?"

"I said that Roger Mason, my character in *Catchpole,* was sent overseas after a short period of training."

"Would you say that your character bears any resemblance to you?"

"Some."

"Were *you* also sent overseas after a short period of training?"

"I was."

"Do you feel this experience was unique?"

"Unique?"

"Yes, sir, unique. You know the meaning of the word 'unique.' "

"Yes, but I don't understand the question."

"I am asking you, Mr. Constantine, if during World War II, during the period of time before and during the Eniwetok landings, I am asking if it was unique to send an officer overseas after only a short period of training?"

"I don't know if it was unique or not."

"Have you ever heard the expression 'ninety-day wonder,' Mr. Constantine?"

"I have."

"It was a common expression, was it not?"

"It was a derogatory expression."

"But common. You did, in fact, use this very expression in your play. One of the enlisted men refers to Lieutenant Mason as a ninety-day wonder, doesn't he?"

"Yes, I suppose so. I don't recall exactly."

"Let me refresh your memory then," Willow said, and turned again toward the defense table.

"I'll take your word . . ."

"Here we are," Willow said, leafing through the manuscript. "Act I, Scene 1, page 4. This is Corporal Janus speaking. He says, 'Another ninety-day wonder. *I* wonder how long he'll last.' Do you recall the speech now?"

"If it's there, I recall it."

"It is here, Mr. Constantine. As a matter of fact, you cited it only yesterday in referring to one of your specific character similarities."

"Yes, I remember now."

"When you wrote your play, you were undoubtedly fully aware of what the Army called 'ninety-day wonders,' weren't you?"

"I suppose I was."

"And therefore you must have also been aware that so-called ninety-day wonders were not unique, Mr. Constantine."

"Yes."

"You know they were not unique?"

"I know that."

"Do you think they were unique at the time of the Korean conflict?"

"I have no knowledge of the Korean conflict."

"Then you are possibly not aware that the average training time for an officer in October and November of 1950—which is the time span covered by the novel *The Paper Dragon*—the average training period for an officer was ninety days. Did you know that, Mr. Constantine?"

"I did not know that."

"Will you accept my word for it? Or need I produce a letter received from the Office of the Chief of Information, United States Army, stating it as a fact?"

"I will accept your word for it."

"And will you further agree that ninety-day wonders were not unique during World War II, nor were they unique during the Korean conflict?"

"I would agree to that."

"That Roger Mason being a ninety-day wonder was not unique?"

"Yes."

"And that Alex Cooper, the lieutenant in *The Paper Dragon* was not unique, either."

"Yes."

"That both characters in fact are commonplace characters who might be found in any war at any time in the world's history?"

"I don't know about that."

"But you *do* agree, Mr. Constantine, that wherever there are wars, there are also officers hastily trained to fight them?"

"Yes, I would agree to that."

"Thank you. You are a writer, Mr. Constantine . . ."

"Yes, I am."

". . . so surely you must know that the basis of all drama is conflict."

"Yes, I know that."

"If a man were writing about an Army combat squad, wouldn't it be natural to have the conflict take place between an officer and his men?"

"No, it would not."

"It would *not* be natural?"

"I can imagine any number of conflicts taking place in a combat squad, and they need not all be between an officer and his men."

"The question was whether this would be a natural development."

"And the answer is that this would be only *one* of the possible developments."

"Would you say that one of the developments in *The Naked and the Dead* is a conflict between a man or men in command, and those who are not?"

"I have not made a study of *The Naked and the Dead.*"

"Would you say that one of the developments in *From Here to Eternity* is a conflict between a man or men in command, and those who are not?"

"I haven't studied that one, either."

"You testified that the film based on that book won the Academy Award in 1953."

"Yes."

"Did you see the film?"

"No."

"Did you read the book?"

"No."

"Did you read *The Caine Mutiny?*"

"Yes."

"Do you agree that one of the developments in *The Caine Mutiny* is a conflict between a man in command and men who are not?"

"*All* the men in *The Caine Mutiny* are in command."

"You mean that the leading characters are officers, don't you?"

"Yes."

"But Captain Queeg is in command."

"Yes."

"And Maryk and Keefer and the others are all subordinate officers."

"Yes."

"And the conflict is between them."

"Yes."

"The conflict is between the man in command and those below him in rank."

"If you wish to put it that way, yes."

"Is there another way to put it, Mr. Constantine?"

"I am merely saying that this is only *one* of the paths a war story can take."

"But this is a very natural development that has been utilized time and again by a great many writers producing works about men in war."

"Yes, I would say so."

"Would you also say that another possible development would be a conflict between an officer and a *specific* enlisted man?"

"That's one of the possible developments, yes."

"Such as the conflict between Roger Mason and Corporal Janus in your play, and the conflict between Alex Cooper and Private Colman in *The Paper Dragon*."

"Is that a question?"

"The question is would you consider this conflict a natural development in a work dealing with an Army combat squad?"

"I don't know if it is a natural development or not. It was a development of *mine* when I was writing the play."

"Do you claim it as a *unique* development?"

"I claim it as an integral part of my play. In that respect—"

"But not unique."

"Not unique, but—"

"Thank you, Mr. Constantine. Would you also—"

"I would like to finish what I—"

"You have sufficiently answered the question."

"I'd like to hear what he has to say, Mr. Willow," McIntyre said. "Go on, please."

"I was going to say that simply because a line of development is a natural one doesn't mean that two separate writers would automatically choose it as their approach. If we pick apart the play and the novel, piece by piece . . ."

"I am prepared to do *exactly* that," Willow said.

". . . the isolated pieces and fragments would *seem* to be coincidental, I mean the similarities between them would seem coincidental. But when we put them all together, we're presented with overwhelming evidence of . . ." Arthur hesitated.

"Yes, Mr. Constantine?"

"Of copying," Arthur said.

"You seemed reluctant to use the word."

"I don't like to call a man a thief."

"But that's exactly what you've done in your complaint," Willow said and paused. *"Do* you or do you *not* believe Mr. Driscoll copied your play?"

"Actually sat down and copied it, I don't know. I mean, I don't know if he actually had a copy of my play on his desk while he was writing his novel."

"You are aware, are you not, Mr. Constantine, that access must be proved in a plagiarism case?"

"I have been so informed by my attorneys."

"But you don't know whether or not James Driscoll actually *possessed* a copy of your play when he was writing his novel?"

"I was not there when he was writing his novel."

"Please answer the question, Mr. Constantine."

"No, I don't know if he had a copy." Arthur paused. "But if he didn't have one, then he must have seen the play."

"When it was performed in New York, do you mean?"

"I don't know when. The similarities are too astonishing for someone who did not have prior knowledge—"

"We are here to decide whether there *are* similarities, Mr. Constantine, astonishing or otherwise. In the meantime, do you believe that James Driscoll saw your play during its brief twelve-day run at the Fulton Theatre in October of 1947?"

"I don't know."

"But you testified that he must have seen it."

"Yes."

"Well, *when* do you think he saw it?"

Arthur glanced at Brackman, and Brackman nodded. "There was also a series of previews," Arthur said.

"Are these the previews you testified to during the direct examination yesterday?"

"Yes."

"Did you personally distribute the tickets to those previews?"

"I did not."

"Who was responsible for the distribution?"

"Our press agent."

"How do you know they were distributed?"

"I was told."

"Then all you know about the distribution is what you were told."

"Well, we were concerned with getting a representative college audience."

"Yes, but all you actually *know* about the distribution is what you were told, is that true?"

"Yes. But I know the tickets were sent out to various colleges and universities."

"Do you know *which* colleges and universities?"

"Yes."

"Of your *own* knowledge?"

"No. The names of the schools were given to me."

"By whom?"

"We had a meeting and decided we wanted this play to be seen by representative college kids, and we decided to distribute a limited amount of free tickets."

"*Who* gave you the names of the colleges to which the tickets were actually sent, Mr. Constantine?"

"I don't remember exactly who. It could have been anybody involved with the show, though it was most likely the man who was handling our press for us, I'm not sure."

"All you know is that somebody said something about having sent these tickets out."

"That's right."

"Which schools, to your recollection, were these mysterious tickets sent to?"

"Objection," Brackman said.

"Sustained."

"Which schools received these tickets, Mr. Constantine? Would you name them, please?"

"I named them yesterday."

"Please do it again, would you?"

"They were sent to City College, Hunter, Brooklyn College, L.I.U., Pratt Institute, and Fordham, I believe."

"You *believe?*"

"I believe they were sent to Fordham. I'm not sure about Fordham."

"But you *are* sure about Pratt Institute?"

"Yes, I am."

"Are you aware, Mr. Constantine, that in 1947 Pratt Institute was a highly specialized school teaching art, engineering, library, and home economics?"

"Architecture, I thought," Arthur said.

"Yes, as part of its art program. Were you aware of that?"

"I thought it was primarily an architectural school."

"In any case, more than half the students there at the time were taking courses like Industrial Design, or Illustration, or Food and Clothing. Would you agree that it was a highly specialized school?"

"Yes."

"And yet, in your search for 'a representative college audience'—I believe that was your exact language—you included Pratt among these other schools?"

"Yes."

"Did you know that James Driscoll was a student at Pratt Institute in 1947?"

"I didn't know that."

"You've never heard that before, Mr. Constantine?"

"I knew he was a student at Pratt Institute, but not that he was there in 1947."

"In other words, when you testified that free tickets were sent to Pratt Institute in 1947—a highly specialized school, even though you were looking for a representative college audience—when you so testified, you were not aware that James Driscoll had been a student there at the time?"

"I was aware that Mr. Driscoll went to Pratt Institute, but I had no knowledge as to the date, I just told you that. If you want to know whether I think Mr. Driscoll could have seen my play in performance, *yes,* I think he could have seen it."

"That was not my question."

"It seemed to be your question."

"It was *not.* I'll rephrase it so that it will be perfectly clear to you. Do you not feel, Mr. Constantine, that your having sent free tickets to Pratt Institute at the very time James Driscoll was a student there is a remarkable coincidence?"

"I do not. To the best of my knowledge, we sent the tickets to Pratt. If Driscoll happened to be a student there at the time, that's a plain fact, and there's nothing coincidental about it."

"Thank you." Willow sighed and walked toward the defense table. He leafed through a batch of papers his assistant handed to him, his back to Arthur all the while. Apprehensively, Arthur waited for Willow to turn toward him again. Brackman caught his eye and nodded encouragingly.

"Mr. Constantine," Willow said, walking slowly toward him, "you have testified that you served in the United States Army during World War II."

"I did."

"Were you an officer?"

"I was a second lieutenant."

"Like the character in your play?"

"In that he was a second lieutenant also, yes."

"Were you in command of a platoon?"

"I was."

"How many men were in the platoon?"

"Forty-one."

"As in your play?"

"As in *any* Army platoon during World War II."

"What was the composition of this platoon?"

"What do you mean?"

"What sort of men were in it?"

"I still don't understand you."

"Where were they from, what was their education, their racial or religious background, and so on?"

"I don't remember. There were all types of men in the platoon. And there were replacements from time to time. I can't remember all the background details of each man."

"Was there a man from New York City in your platoon? Besides yourself, I mean."

"I think so."

"Was there a Southerner?"

"There might have been."

"And possibly someone from the Middle West? Or California?"

"Possibly."

"Men of high school or college education perhaps?"

"Perhaps."

"Was there a Catholic?"

"Yes."

"And a Protestant, and a Jew?"

"There could have been. I don't remember."

"Was there a Negro?"

"No."

"The Army was not integrated at that time, was it?"

"No."

"Was there an Italian in your platoon?"

"Yes."

"Was this the only platoon you ever commanded, Mr. Constantine?"

"I commanded several other platoons later on. And when I made captain, I was given command of a company. This was shortly before I was discharged."

"Would you say that the composition of these other platoons you commanded was roughly the same as that of the first one? In terms of background?"

"Roughly, yes."

"There were New Yorkers possibly, or Southerners, or men from California or the Middle West. There were Catholics and Protestants and Jews. There were men of Irish descent or Italian descent. There was, if you will, a cross-section of America."

"I would say so."

"Do you suppose this was true of *any* platoon in the United States Army during World War II?"

"I would suppose so."

"Do you suppose it was also true of any platoon in the United States Army during the *Korean* conflict?"

"Possibly. But that doesn't necessarily . . ."

"If a man sat down to write a play or a novel about the Army, would he not be likely to include men of various backgrounds, such as those who might be found in a *real* platoon?"

"Yes, but . . ."

"Would he not be likely to include a member of a minority group?"

Arthur hesitated, and then looked out at Brackman.

"Mr. Constantine," Willow said, "would you answer the question, please?"

"I could answer that with a yes or no," Arthur said, "but the answer would be misleading."

Willow looked up in what seemed like genuine surprise. He stared at Arthur for a moment, and then said, "Please answer it any way you wish."

"A writer would include a member of a minority group only if it served a purpose," Arthur said.

"What purpose does Sergeant D'Agostino serve in your play?"

"He is a catalyst."

"For what?"

"For everything that happens on the island. He's the man who sacrifices himself for the lieutenant. He's the man who—"

"What does this have to do with his being Italian?"

"It adds to the conflict. Corporal Janus harps on this. It causes further conflict between the lieutenant and the squad."

"The fact that D'Agostino is Italian?"

"Yes. Driscoll does the same thing in his novel. Only the character is Negro."

"You mean that Mr. Driscoll uses a Negro character to further the conflict between the lieutenant and the squad, is that true?"

"That's it, yes."

"By having a scene in which the lieutenant is suspected of bigotry, is that what you're referring to? Where Sergeant Morley believes the lieutenant is a bigot?"

"Yes, that's the scene."

"And you had earlier used this same device in *Catchpole,* is that right? This is why you chose to put an Italian in your fictitious squad. To point up a conflict with the lieutenant along lines of possible prejudice."

"Yes."

Willow walked to the defense table. "Here's a copy of your play," he said. "Would you kindly show me the scene or scenes wherein Lieutenant Mason and Sergeant D'Agostino confront each other in such a manner?"

"What manner do you mean?"

"Show me a scene where the lieutenant is suspected of prejudice."

"It isn't a scene, there are only references."

"Show me the references."

"I'll have to look for them."

"Please take all the time you need."

Arthur accepted the manuscript. He began leafing through it. He could feel sweat running down the sides of his chest. He wiped a hand across his lip. "I don't know if this is what you're looking for . . ."

"I'm looking for any lines in your play that would indicate Sergeant D'Agostino suspects the lieutenant of being prejudiced against Italians. Or rather, Mr. Constantine, *you* are looking for them."

"May I read this?"

"Certainly."

"This is in Act II, it's Corporal Janus speaking to Sergeant D'Agostino. He says, 'I understand you, Mike. You're a Wop and I'm a Pole, and we just don't fit.' "

"And this—"

"There's more."

"Please read it."

"He answers—"

"D'Agostino answers?"

"Yes. He answers, 'We're just poor little orphans, huh, Danny?' and Janus says, 'We're misfits. They'll never understand us as long as we live.' That's the reference."

"The reference to what?"

"Prejudice."

"As I understand it, Mr. Constantine, this series of speeches you have just read to us constitute the sole reference to prejudice . . ."

"There are others."

"Find them, please."

"Perhaps more specific," Arthur said.

"Yes, please find them."

He wiped his lip again. He knew *exactly* why he had made

D'Agostino Italian. He had done it to point up the conflict, the very conflict Willow was harping on, and which Driscoll had stolen and amplified in his book, making the character a Negro to cash in on the burgeoning civil rights movement, where *were* those other scenes? "Well, here," he said, "on page 2–16, there's another short encounter between Janus and D'Agostino that I think points up this business of racial prejudice between the lieutenant—"

"*Racial* prejudice?"

"No, I mean his prejudice against Italians."

"Please read it, Mr. Constantine."

"D'Agostino is talking about the feast of La Madonna di Carmela which they have every year on 115th Street in Harlem. I don't know whether or not you're familiar with it."

"No, I'm not."

"Well, he's talking about the feast—he refers to it as 'the *festa,*' that's the Italian word for it—and he says, 'Whenever I went to the *festa,* Danny, I felt as if I was stepping into a world I knew inside out and backwards, you know what I mean? All the sounds and all the smells and all the people. It was where I belonged.' And Janus replies, 'Yeah, not on a goddamn island in the middle of the Pacific with a lieutenant trying to get us all killed.' "

"This is the specific reference?" Willow said.

"Yes, it links D'Agostino's Italian background with the lieutenant."

"In what way?"

"D'Agostino is talking about where he belongs, and Janus subtly implies that he does not belong here with the lieutenant."

"Are there any other references, Mr. Constantine?"

"There are several more, I'm sure. This was a thread I put into the play, a constant nagging by Janus, a constant reminder that the lieutenant is aware of D'Agostino as an Italian."

"If you can find any more references, we would be grateful," Willow said.

"Well, if you'll give me a few moments . . ."

"Certainly."

"Oh, yes," Arthur said, "that's right. The scene with the Jap, when they capture the Jap. Just a second now." He began turning pages. "Yes," he said, "no, wait a minute, yes, here it is, the end of Act II, just before the end of the act. They've captured a Japanese soldier, and they're trying to interrogate him, but they can't find anyone who speaks Japanese. So Meredith, he's one of the men in the squad, says, 'Do you think the Loot speaks Japanese?' and Janus says, 'Don't be silly, the Loot speaks white American Protestant.' Then he turns to D'Agostino and says, 'How about you, Mike? Japanese is just like Italian, ain't it?' That's the thread being picked up again, of course, the constant juxtaposition of D'Agostino being Italian and the lieutenant being aware of it, that's the reference here."

"I see," Willow said. "Are there any others?"

"I'm sure there must be, but those are all that I can think of at the moment." He leaned forward to hand the manuscript back to Willow.

"No, please hold on to it," Willow said. "There are several other things I'd like you to find."

"If I knew you were going to ask me for specific references . . ."

"That's what we're dealing with here, Mr. Constantine. Specifics."

"I thought we were dealing with plagiarism."

"That is *your* allegation."

"Wouldn't it be more to the point to compare the two works instead of—?"

"Mr. Constantine, it would be more to the point to allow me to conduct my own cross-examination, if that's all right with you."

"Certainly."

"Thank you. You said yesterday in testifying about thematic similarities that your hero, and I am reading from the record now, 'is a new lieutenant who feels that human life is more important than the quarrels of nations, and this theme is stated in Act I, Scene 4, pages 21 and 22 of *Catchpole.*' Would you please turn to those pages now?"

"Pages 21 and 22?"

"That's right."

"I have them."

"Would you read to me the line or lines that indicate the lieutenant felt human life was more important than the quarrels of nations?"

"May I look this over?" Arthur asked.

"Certainly."

Arthur slowly and carefully read the two pages, and then read them again. "I believe this is the reference," he said.

"Yes, which?"

"Lieutenant Mason is talking to the men, it's this one speech beginning on the bottom of page 21, and carrying over onto page 22. 'I know you men are wondering what we're doing on this godforsaken island,' he says, 'I know that's foremost in your minds especially when intelligence tells us there are thirty-five hundred Japs dug in on this atoll. You're all experienced soldiers and you know that even if we blast them out of their holes here, we've got the next island to take and the next one after that, so what's the use, what are we doing here? I know you're thinking that some of us may die, *all* of us may die, and for what? For a barren stretch of Japanese real estate in the middle of the Pacific? No. We're here because there's a job to do. It's as simple as that.'" Arthur looked up. "I believe that's the reference," he said.

"To human life being more important than the quarrels of nations?"

"Not in that specific language. I never claimed that identical language was used in the statement of this particular theme. But there are the springboard references here, the touchstones Driscoll used in shaping his theme, the references to death and dying, the references to empires and their holdings, the references to the grim realities of war, the thirty-five hundred Japs holed up on the atoll, and having to be blasted out. All of these add up to a specific similarity of theme, though not of language."

"Thank you. You also testified yesterday, and this too relates to the theme of your play, you testified that Mr. Matthew Jackson at API, in expressing his reaction to *Catchpole,* said—and again I quote from the record—'I think they'd be leery of an Army theme that tries to show the stupidity and foolish waste of war.' Mr. Constantine, do you agree with Mr. Jackson's statement? Would you say that your play tries to show the stupidity and foolish waste of war?"

"Yes, it does."

"Would you say that this is also the theme of Mr. Driscoll's novel?"

"It is very definitely his theme. The themes are identical."

"Now would you mind showing me where in your play, which scene or which speech or even which line illustrates this theme, the stupidity and foolish waste of war?"

"The entire play illustrates the theme."

"In what way?"

"The antagonism of the men is stupid, the plot to kill Mason is stupid, the accidental killing of D'Agostino by the psychopathic colonel is stupid, everything that happens from the moment the lieutenant *arrives* is stupid. And the men finally realize this at the end."

"Where do they realize it?"

"At the very end of the play."

"Find the place for me."

"Certainly. They realize just what we've been talking about, that war is stupid and a foolish waste."

"Please show me where this realization takes place."

"It's here at the end of the play," Arthur said. "Here, it's on page 3–4–36, shortly after D'Agostino is killed and Janus is exposed. The speech is given to one of the minor characters, his name is Franklin. This is what he says: 'Lieutenant, we didn't know what we were doing. You get out here in the middle of nowhere, and you forget what reality is. You're surrounded by so much bugging killing, so much bugging blood, that you forget what's right or wrong. Now Mike is dead, and for what? The *real* enemy is still out there. We were wrong, lieutenant. We apologize.' This was a very moving scene, as it was done, and it clearly stated the theme of the play."

"Which was what?"

"That war is idiotic."

"Where does it say that?"

"A writer doesn't state his theme that obviously, Mr. Willow. If he did, it would become tract writing, it would become transparent and condescending. I tried to state the theme in human terms, one human expressing himself to another, one human apologizing to another. The man who apologizes for the rest of the squad is a grizzled combat veteran who kills Japanese soldiers the way you or I would brush our teeth in the morning. He comes to the lieutenant and he says in effect that war changes men, makes them lose their sense of reality, wastes their minds and their bodies. He says this in very human and believable terms, but he is nonetheless stating the theme of the play."

"You also testified that the collective reaction of those who had read the play at API was, and I quote, 'that the play was too outspoken, that the United States wasn't ready to take criticism of its armed forces, not when we had just come through a major conflict and also a minor one in Korea.' Do you feel this was a legitimate reason for the rejection of the play?"

"I don't know if it was legitimate or not. I *do* know that's why the play was rejected."

"Because—and again I quote—'it was too strong for API to do.' Is that correct?"

"That's what I was told."

"This was when, Mr. Constantine?"

"What do you mean?"

"When were these reactions to the play given to you?"

"In 1952 sometime."

"Mr. Constantine, would you say that *From Here to Eternity,* which won the Academy Award in 1953, was a strong movie that dealt harshly with the United States Army?"

"I couldn't say. I neither saw the picture nor read the book."

"From what you know of it, Mr. Constantine, would you—?"

"Objection," Brackman said, rising. "Witness has already stated he has no personal knowledge of either the film or the book in question."

"Sustained."

"If I told you that the book and the film were both highly uncomplimentary to the United States Army, would you accept my word for it?" Willow asked.

"Yes, I would."

"Thank you. Why then do you suppose these people at API said the United States wasn't ready to take criticism of its armed forces?"

"I cannot account for the actions of API."

"Is it true, Mr. Constantine, that your play was submitted to API in September of 1947, a month before it was produced on Broadway?"

"That's true."

"Why was it submitted?"

"To try for a preproduction deal."

"Was it rejected at that time?"

"Yes."

"Is it also true that the head of API's story department in New York was invited to the opening night performance of *Catchpole* on October 14, 1947?"

"I think so, yes."

"Why was he invited?"

"*All* the movie people were invited. We were trying for a movie sale, of course. That's standard procedure."

"Was an offer made after opening night?"

"No."

"Did you see the reviews of your play *Catchpole* after it opened?"

"I did."

"I ask you to look at this review from the *New York Times* of October 15, 1947, and tell me whether it is the one that appeared after the opening of your play." Willow turned to McIntyre. "Your Honor, Mr. Brackman has already agreed that we would not have to prove publication, which would be a simple matter."

"Do you concede publication, Mr. Brackman?" McIntyre asked.

"Yes, of any material that appeared in a magazine or newspaper."

"Please answer the question then, Mr. Constantine."

"Yes, that's the *New York Times* review of my play," Arthur said.

"I would like to offer it in evidence," Willow said.

"I object to it as irrelevant, your Honor. Whether it praises or faults Mr. Constantine's play, it hardly pertains to the matter of plagiarism."

"Why are you offering it, Mr. Willow?"

"Your Honor, the critical appraisal of *Catchpole* is of enormous relevance to this case. Mr. Driscoll is said to have plagiarized the play, but the only support for this allegation is a purported similarity between the two works. I ask now why anyone would *wish* to steal a play that had already been rejected by each and every major motion picture studio, that had been greeted with universally bad notices, and that ran for only twelve days on Broadway."

"Your Honor," Brackman said, "the law books already show that it is the relatively unknown work which most often becomes the target of the plagiarist."

"We could argue that all day, your Honor . . ."

"Yes, I'm sure we could," McIntyre said.

". . . and still not come to an agreement," Willow continued. *"Abie's Irish Rose* was certainly highly successful, and I'm sure my opponent recognizes it as one of the most prominent plagiarism cases. And whereas there are examples of plagiarism from more obscure properties, I still feel that critical and popular acceptance of a work is relevant to the issue here."

"Mr. Constantine has already testified that the play ran only twelve days," McIntyre said. "This does not indicate, to me at any rate, that it was a hit. Why you would wish to offer additional evidence to that point is beyond me, Mr. Willow. I will not admit it."

"Will you allow it to be marked for identification, your Honor?"

"I will."

"Mark it 'Defendants' Exhibit A for identification,'" the clerk said.

"May we also mark for identification the review that appeared in the New York *Herald Tribune* on October 15, 1947?"

"Is this another review of *Catchpole?*"

"Yes, your Honor. Your objection is only to relevance, is it not?"

"It is not admissible."

"I made the offer first in evidence, so that the record will be clear."

"The record will note your exception."

"Mark it 'Defendants' Exhibit B for identification,'" the clerk said.

"Thank you," Willow said. "Mr. Constantine, when did you begin work on your play *Catchpole?*"

"When I got out of the Army. That was July of 1946."

"And when was the play completed?"

"About three or four months later. Toward the end of the year."

"November or December, would you say?"

"Yes. November, I think it was."

"When did you begin attempting to find a producer for it?"

"In January of 1947. There was no sense trying to do anything during the holidays. I had the play mimeographed shortly before Christmas, and I began sending it around after New Year's."

"Is this customary procedure?"

"Sending the play to producers, do you mean?"

"No. Having copies mimeographed."

"Some authors do, others don't. It depends on how many

people you want to reach. And also whether you can afford to have the work done."

"How many people did you want to reach, Mr. Constantine?"

"As many as possible. I wanted my play to be produced."

"How many copies were mimeographed?"

"A hundred, a hundred and fifty, I don't remember the exact amount."

"And I take it the result of all this was that you succeeded in getting a producer?"

"That's right."

"So it would seem to have been a good procedure," Willow said.

"It worked for me."

"To get back, you say you began work on *Catchpole* shortly after you were discharged from the United States Army. Would you say that your Army experience was still fresh in your mind when you began writing?"

"I would say so, yes."

"Army routine, Army terminology, Army regulations?"

"Yes, all of it."

"As well as the language used by soldiers, of course."

"Of course."

"In your military experience, Mr. Constantine, did you meet many men who used obscene language?"

"I met some."

"Who used obscene language such as Mr. Driscoll uses in his novel, and such as you more discreetly use in your play?"

"Yes, I met some. Mostly uneducated men."

"There *were* some of these in the Army."

"Is that a question?"

"Yes, it's a question."

"Yes, there were uneducated men who used obscene language."

"Do you think they were rarities?"

"No."

"They were commonplace?"

"They were to be found everywhere in the Army."

"During World War II?"

"Yes, and during the Korean War also, I would imagine. That's where you're leading, isn't it?"

"Do you feel, Mr. Constantine, that the character named Franklin in your play—the man who is addicted to the use of obscene language—do you feel he is a unique creation?"

"I do."

"You feel that a soldier addicted to the use of obscene language is unique?"

"Franklin swears in a specific manner. He uses a specific word as verb, noun, adjective, adverb. I think we know the word I mean."

"Yes, I'm sure we do."

"I changed it to the word *bug* in my play."

"And you feel that a character who uses this word as verb, noun, adjective, and so on is a unique creation of your own, is that correct?"

"That's correct."

"And not simply a valid fictional representation of a commonplace individual who is to be found wherever there are armies or Army posts or barracks?"

"I consider him unique."

"Would it surprise you, Mr. Constantine, to learn that in a play titled *The Eve of St. Mark* . . . do you know the play?"

"Yes, I know it."

"It's by Maxwell Anderson, he's won several awards for playwriting, including the Drama Critics Circle Award and the Pulitzer Prize. I think you may know of him."

"Yes, I know of Maxwell Anderson."

"In his play *The Eve of St. Mark* there is a sergeant named Ruby, who is addicted to the use of the word *ruttin'* . . ."

"Rotten?"

"No, *ruttin'*. R-U-T-T-I-N-apostrophe, very similar to your use of the words *bug* or *bugging*. Does that surprise you, Mr. Constantine?"

"I'm not that familiar with the play."

"It opened at the Cort Theater in New York on October 7, 1942, five years before *Catchpole*. It ran until June 26th of the following year, and was later made into a motion picture. Do you still maintain that your character Franklin is a unique creation?"

"I do. He is unique in my play."

"But not in someone else's play? He is unique only in *your* play?"

"I had not seen Mr. Anderson's play, nor was I aware of the sergeant in it. Besides, the word *bugging* is not the word *ruttin'*."

"Nor are either of them the actual word Mr. Driscoll uses, isn't that so?"

"It's so, but the intent is the same."

"The same as what?"

"The same as using the word *bug,* which I had to use for the stage."

"But not the same as the word *ruttin',* which Mr. Anderson had to use for the stage?"

"I merely said the words *bugging* and *ruttin'* were not identical."

"But they are similar?"

"Yes, they are similar."

"In intent?"

"Yes, in intent, too, I suppose. But . . ."

"Yet you still maintain that your character's use of obscenity is unique?"

"It is unique, yes."

"Thank you. Mr. Constantine, what procedure did you follow in submitting your play for production?"

"I usually mailed it out."

"To whom?"

"To anyone I thought might be interested. This was my first play, and I was new at this sort of thing. I didn't have an agent at the time. I sent it to anyone I thought might help me in getting it produced."

"And that included?"

"What?"

"To whom exactly did you send it, Mr. Constantine?"

"Producers, agents, investors, anyone interested in the theater . . ." Arthur's voice trailed. It had occurred to him that this was the second time Willow had brought up the matter of submission, and he wondered now where he was leading. He sensed a trap. Every intuitive power he possessed told him that Willow had picked up the scent of something the first time around, and was now tracking it down. But Arthur did not know what. He found himself suddenly alert, staring intently at Willow, leaning forward in the witness chair, waiting for the trap to make itself more evident so that he could avoid it.

"Did you send a copy to Mr. Hollis Marks?"

"I don't know any Hollis Marks."

"He is an agent. Did you send the play to him?"

"No. Oh, is he Driscoll's agent?" Arthur asked suddenly.

"Yes, that's right."

"No. I did not send a copy of the play to Driscoll's agent. But there were enough copies around the city. Driscoll could have easily seen one."

"Yes, you testified that there had been a hundred or a hundred and fifty copies mimeographed, didn't you?"

"That's right."

"Who mimeographed these copies, Mr. Constantine?"

"York Duplicating."

"Here in Manhattan?"

"Yes."

"Was the number a hundred? Or a hundred and fifty? Which?"

"A hundred and fifty, I believe."

"And you began mailing these out in January of 1947?"

"Yes."

"To producers, agents, investors, and anyone interested in the theater?"

"Yes."

"Did you deliver any of these manuscripts personally?"

"Some of them. Most of them were sent through the mail."

"With covering letters?"

"Yes, of course."

"Did you ask for their return?"

"I don't remember."

"Did you enclose a stamped, self-addressed envelope for their return?"

"No."

"Do you know of anyone at Mitchell-Campbell who saw a copy of the play at the time you were distributing it?"

"No, I do not."

"But there were hundreds of copies distributed, weren't there?"

"A hundred and fifty."

"*All* of the mimeographed copies were distributed?"

"I don't know. I assume most of them were. Let's say somewhere over a hundred copies were being sent around to various people."

"And yet you have no knowledge that either James Driscoll or anyone at Mitchell-Campbell saw a copy of your play at that time."

"No direct knowledge, no."

"Your entire allegation is based on the fact that you believe the works are similar?"

"They're virtually parallel."

"Since you have the script in your hand, Mr. Constantine, I wonder if you would mind pointing out to me the line or lines that label the Army division as the 105th."

"It was not labeled in a line."

"Then how exactly was it labeled?"

"In a stage direction."

"Would you point this out to me, please?"

"Certainly." Arthur began leafing through the manuscript. He was beginning to think he had been wrong, that no trap had been conceived or intended.

"Here it is," he said. "The top of the second act, page 2–1–1. It describes the command post, and it says, 'A battered jeep is parked just outside the headquarters shack. The division insignia hangs over the door to the shack, the number 105 in yellow on a black field.' That's the reference."

"Thank you. Did you see this play in performance, Mr. Constantine?"

"I did."

"Did you see every performance?"

"Every performance."

"Was the insignia a part of the scenery for the play?"

"It was part of the set dressing."

"By which you mean it was affixed to the wall of the headquarters shack."

"The *outside* wall of the shack, yes."

"The number 105 in yellow on a black field."

"Yes."

"Was this your own description of the set?"

"It was."

"Did this description appear in the mimeographed version of the play? The one you sent around for people to read?"

"It did."

"It was not later added? I mean, Mr. Constantine, was the description of the set and its dressing added *after* the play was actually produced?"

"No, it was in the original copies I distributed."

"And the insignia *did* actually appear in the play as it was produced on the New York stage?"

"Yes, it did. If you want to call our set designer as a witness . . ."

"I don't think that will be necessary. When you held your preview performances in the Second Avenue loft, Mr. Constantine, the ones to which the college audiences were invited—was the play performed with scenery?"

Arthur hesitated.

"Mr. Constantine, would you answer the question?"

"No. The play was not performed with scenery."

"Is it my understanding, then, that the division insignia was *not* hanging on the wall of the headquarters shack during the preview performances in the Second Avenue loft?"

"It was not."

"Was there indeed a headquarters shack at *all* in the Second Avenue loft?"

"There was not."

"The play was presented on a bare stage?"

"With furniture."

"Then anyone who had been present at those preview performances could not possibly have seen the number 105 in yellow on a black field."

"That's right," Arthur said.

"In other words, in order for Mr. Driscoll to have seen the number 105, he either had to be present at one of the Broadway performances, or else he had to have a copy of your manuscript. Those are the only two ways in which he could conceivably have known about the number, is that right?"

"Unless someone told him about it."

"Someone who had seen the play on Broadway or read the manuscript?"

"Yes."

"But you have testified that you did not send a copy of the manuscript to Mitchell-Campbell Books?"

"That's right."

"It would have been someone else then, is that it? Someone *not* connected with Mr. Driscoll's publishers?"

"I don't know who it might have been. Copies of the manuscript were floating all over the city. It could have been anyone who read the play, or anyone who saw it. It ran for twelve days. There were matinee performances on some of those days, so we can add . . ."

"Whoever saw or read the play undoubtedly attached great significance to the number 105."

"I did not say that."

"Do *you* attach great significance to that number, Mr. Constantine?"

"I do."

"Do you feel it is an integral part of your play?"

"I do."

"Even though it appears only briefly in one scene of the play, and then only as part of a background insignia hung to the wall of a shack?"

"It was clearly visible to the audience. Yellow on black is a particularly vibrant color combination."

"But do you feel the number added to the value of your play?"

"It was a part of the play."

"Was it of value?"

"To me it was."

"In what way?"

"It designated the division."

"Was this designation significant?"

"To me it was."

"Would it be significant to anyone else?"

"Apparently it was also significant to Mr. Driscoll."

"Was the number of any significance to the audience?"

"It told the audience what division was involved in the invasion."

"Was this of great importance?"

"I think so."

"How?"

"It was a part of *my* play. It came from *my* mind. It was a numerical designation for a division *I* invented. *That* is its significance and its importance and its value. It is *mine,* and not another man's."

"You began working on this play of yours in July of 1946 . . ."

"Possibly August."

". . . and completed it in November sometime, is that what you said?"

"Yes."

"You then had a hundred and fifty copies mimeographed, and in January of 1947 you began distributing those copies."

"That's right."

"And you distributed well over a hundred of them?"

"A hundred and ten, a hundred and twenty, something like that."

"Mimeographed copies?"

"Yes." Willow had returned again to the mimeographed copies, and now Arthur was certain a trap was being baited. He wondered why Brackman did not object, wondered why

Brackman did not rise to give him some clue as to the nature of the trap. He looked at Brackman hopefully, but the man seemed completely unaware that Willow had again returned to the same topic. Couldn't he see that this was a persistent and recurring thread, similar to the thread in *Catchpole,* where Janus is constantly badgering D'Agostino about . . .

". . . to different people?" Willow said.

"I beg your pardon?"

"The question was, Mr. Constantine: Were these hundred and twenty mimeographed copies distributed to different people?"

"Yes, they were."

"Beginning in January of 1947?"

"Yes."

"And ending when?"

"When I found a producer."

"Which was when?"

"May of 1947. May 11th, to be exact, I won't forget that date. That's when the play was optioned by Mr. Frederick Gerard, who eventually produced it later that year."

"You personally arranged for or actually made delivery of one hundred and twenty mimeographed copies of your play between January and May of 1947?"

"Yes, I did."

"Do you believe Mr. Driscoll somehow came across one of these copies at that time?"

"You'll have to ask *him* about that."

"I am asking *you.*"

"How would I know whether or not he saw a copy at that time?"

"Mr. Constantine, instead of engaging me in argument, would you please answer my question: Do you believe that Mr. Driscoll saw a copy of your play at that time?"

"He could have, yes."

"Do you think he *did?*"

"It's possible that he did."

"In addition to having seen a performance of your play?"

"Yes, in addition."

"Do you feel he could have successfully plagiarized your work after having seen only one performance of the play?"

"Yes."

"That would have been sufficient?"

"Yes. Besides, it ran for twelve days. He could have seen it any number of times."

"He could have been so impressed by it the first time that he ran back to see it again and again, is that it?"

"Ignoring the sarcasm, that is *not* it. I don't know what goes on in Mr. Driscoll's head, either now or in 1947."

"Do you know how old Mr. Driscoll was in 1947?"

"No, I do not."

"He was eighteen."

"I was eighteen when I got drafted into the Army to fight a war," Arthur said.

"Which is commendable, but hardly to the point. Did you go into the Army as an officer, Mr. Constantine?"

"No. I was sent to O.C.S. after my basic training."

"And emerged as a second lieutenant."

"Yes."

"And you were sent to the Pacific in time for the Marshall Islands landings."

"Yes."

"Did your men ever call you 'Loot'?"

"Yes, they did."

"The way they call Mason 'Loot' in your play?"

"No. In my play, they use the word in a derogatory manner. If we're going to get into this again . . ."

"Into *what* again?"

"Into hastily trained officers, and platoons composed of cross-sections of America, and the prevalence of minority group members, and ninety-day wonders and soldiers who use obscenity, all in an attempt to show that Mr. Driscoll was only following his natural bent, he was only creating a wholly original work of fiction out of common everyday experience, I'm sorry, Mr. Willow, but I don't agree with you, and I see exactly what you're trying to do."

"I am *trying* to ask some questions," Willow said, "if I may be permitted, your Honor."

"Please go on, Mr. Willow. I find nothing objectionable in your line of questioning."

"Your Honor," Brackman said, rising, "Mr. Constantine is not an attorney, though perhaps he did feel Mr. Willow was badgering him."

"I am not aware of any badgering," McIntyre said. "Please go on, Mr. Willow."

"Would you not agree, Mr. Constantine, that the word 'Loot' is a common expression in the United States Army, whether it be used affectionately *or* derogatively?"

"I would agree," Arthur said tightly.

"Your claim, however, is that both in your play and in *The Paper Dragon,* the men use this expression in order to annoy the lieutenant. They use it derogatively. In fact, you pointed out an example of its use in your play, and an example of its use in the novel. Your claim is that they constitute *specific* similarity of language, isn't that so?"

"That's right. And they do."

"The language you referred to in your play was, and I quote, 'How about lengthening that to Lieutenant Mason?' to which Corporal Janus replies, 'Isn't that what I said, *Loot?*' You indicated in your testimony yesterday that the word 'Loot' was stressed, isn't that so?"

"That's absolutely correct."

"Now would you please show me the page in your play where those lines appear."

"They're in the second act," Arthur said.

"Please find the page."

Arthur was angry, and worried, and not a little confused, and very disappointed in Brackman who, he felt, had apologized again rather than objecting, and who had completely missed the point of what was happening, missed the trap that Arthur was sure Willow had baited and somehow sprung, though he still did not know what the trap was. That was supposed to be *Brackman's* job, goddamnit, to see a closing trap and to prevent its jaws from clamping down, what the hell kind of a lawyer *was* he? Angrily, he flipped through the pages, and then suddenly stopped.

"Have you found it?" Willow asked.

"It wouldn't be in this version," Arthur said.

"I beg your pardon?"

"Those two lines were not in the original mimeographed version of the play."

"Am I to understand that there is yet *another* version of *Catchpole?*"

"Not another *version,* actually. But certain line changes were made in rehearsal and appeared in the play as it was produced. These would not be in any of the original mimeographed copies."

"In what copy *can* these line changes be found?"

"I imagine in the actors' scripts, or the stage manager's. The ones that were used during the actual rehearsal of the play."

"Do you *have* any of these copies, Mr. Constantine?"

"No, I haven't."

"Does *anyone?*"

"Not to my knowledge. The members of the company may have retained them, I wouldn't know about that. This was almost twenty years ago."

"In other words, these two lines to which you refer are not to be found in the copy of the play now before this Court."

"That's correct. But the lines *were* spoken on the stage."

"And you heard them spoken?"

"I did. At every performance."

"Am I to understand, then, Mr. Constantine, that with respect to these two lines—which you claim have their counterpart in the book titled *The Paper Dragon* and also the film of the same name—with respect to these particular lines, unless James Driscoll actually saw a *rehearsal* script of the play, he could not possibly possess any knowledge of these lines, is that correct?"

"No. He could have seen the play in performance."

"We have got down to the point, have we not, where in order to show access, we must also show that Mr. Driscoll saw the play during its twelve-day Broadway run. Otherwise he would not have known of these lines inserted during rehearsal, nor would he have known of the division insignia bearing the number 105. Isn't that correct?"

"Your Honor," Brackman said, "I would like to remind Mr. Willow that it is not our burden to prove that James Driscoll actually *attended* a performance of the play, no more than it is the burden of a plaintiff to prove, for example, that a defendant actually *read* a novel he is said to have plagiarized. It is sufficient to show that the opportunity for copying existed. The play *Catchpole* was there to be seen in New York City, and I think we are very very safe in assuming James Driscoll was *also* here in New York City at the time and perfectly capable of visiting the Fulton Theatre to take a look at the play. I would not like Mr. Willow to lead us into believing it is our burden to supply witnesses who actually *saw* James Driscoll entering the theater and taking notes on the play."

"I believe Mr. Willow is sufficiently aware of the meaning of access," McIntyre said. "Please go on, Mr. Willow."

"I have no further questions," Willow said.

"Thank you," McIntyre said. "Mr. Genitori, I know you would like to begin your cross, but I see it's ten minutes to twelve, and I think we had better take a recess for lunch."

"Certainly," Genitori said.

"This Court is recessed until two P.M.," the clerk said.

6

THE SNOW ON THE GROUND before the federal courthouse seemed an extension of the white steps themselves, blanketing sidewalk and street, blurring the defining lines of the five concrete islands that formed Foley Square. The largest of these islands was directly opposite the courthouse, across a narrow stretch of pavement that seemed more like an expanded footpath. Duane Street on the left of the courthouse, and Pearl Street on its right bracketed the building and pierced the square which was not a square, Duane continuing west toward Broadway, Pearl abruptly ending against a long green fence behind which construction was in progress, the fence surrounding a barren lot where pile drivers, tractors, and trucks were inactive during the lunch hour. The benches on the island opposite the courthouse were lightly dusted with snow, as were the green shrubs backing them. The steps leading down to the BMT subway were similarly covered with snow, and a man coming up from underground looked skyward as though surprised to find it was still snowing, and then hesitated at the top of the steps to adjust his muffler and to put on his gloves. The area from Reade Street north was dismally gray except for the bright orange sign of the Nedick's on the corner of Duane. There was another touch of color looking south, where a tall building on Centre Street rose out of the swirling snow, its red brick and green trim lending a festive holiday look to the area.

There were two good restaurants on Duane near Broadway, both of which were habitually frequented by the men whose business was the law—Gasner's, and slightly further west, Calate's. In addition, there were dozens of small coffee shops and cafeterias, delicatessens and hamburger joints, a Schrafft's on Park Place, and a Longchamps on Murray Street across from the statue of Nathan Hale. The restaurant Sidney chose was on Reade Street, closer to the courthouse but not as popular as Gasner's. Mother Sauce's featured an authentic Jewish cuisine and a proprietress named Martha Schwartz, who had earned her nickname, or so the legend went, the afternoon she drank three off-duty detectives from the D.A.'s office clear under the table and almost through the floor. Sidney could not vouch for the authenticity of the legend but he recounted it nonetheless to Arthur as they entered the place and waited for Mother Sauce to seat them.

She was a woman in her late sixties, silver-haired and sharp-eyed, wearing a white apron over a severe black dress, and moving around her small crowded restaurant with uncanny speed. The place had been designed with total architectural disregard, its low ceiling supported by a myriad of wood-paneled columns and partitions, tables and booths shoved into niches and nooks or built around posts and into crannies and cul-de-sacs, jutting from behind paneled walls, angled against sealed doors, nestled against windows. In the midst of this monumental disorder, Mother Sauce moved swiftly from table to table, around column and post, into paneled alley and byway, along a labyrinthine route to the kitchen, haranguing and harassing her waiters, circuitously back to the cash register, carrying a menu to a hidden booth, rushing toward the paneled bar, coming again to the door, where she greeted Sidney by name, beaming a smile, and then leading them to a booth at the rear of the restaurant, partitioned on each side to conceal the booths flanking it. Sidney excused himself at once—"A courtroom is bad on a man's kidneys," he explained—and left Arthur alone at the table. A waiter appeared immediately and took his order for a Dewar's on the rocks. Mother Sauce handed him a menu and then hurried away. The booth was small and cozy, upholstered in rich green leather like the tabletops in the courtroom. A pair of small shaded lamps hung on the wall over the booth. The tablecloth was spotlessly white, and the drink when it came was more than generous. Arthur felt himself relaxing for the first time that day. Grateful for Sidney's absence, he studied the menu in silence and with increasing appetite, only vaguely aware at first of the voices coming from behind the paneled partition on his left.

". . . in command of the situation, I would say," a man's voice said.

"Are we?" a woman asked.

"Yes, I would say so."

Arthur glanced at the partition, and then studied the menu again. He was ravenously hungry, and everything looked good, the consommé with noodles and matzoh balls, the borscht . . .

"I don't think we have anything to worry about," another man's voice said. "We're not going to let them get away with anything."

"Except maybe Dris's reputation," the woman said.

"No, not that either," the first man answered, and Arthur suddenly recognized the voice as belonging to Jonah Willow.

"We won't let them get his reputation, either, don't worry," the other man said. "Only a miracle could convince McIntyre there was any plagiarism here."

"That's right," Willow agreed. "In fact, this case should never have come to trial."

"Then why did it?" the woman asked. She had been speaking with a Southern inflection that suddenly disappeared, leaving behind a voice honed razor-sharp.

"An offer to settle would have been an admission of guilt," Willow said.

"Even a token settlement?" the woman asked.

"*Any* settlement. Besides, these people aren't looking for tokens. They've asked for damages and an accounting of profits."

"Will they get it?"

"I've never met a Harvard lawyer I couldn't beat," Willow said.

"I'm a Harvard lawyer," the other man said.

"Yes, but unfortunately you're on my side."

Arthur started to rise. He knew for certain now that one of the men in the adjacent booth was Jonah Willow, and he was fairly confident that the other man was his assistant. In which case, the woman was undoubtedly Mrs. James Driscoll, and Arthur had no right sitting there listening to them talk about the trial. As he rose he wondered whether Driscoll himself was at the table, maintaining a discreet silence, and he suddenly wanted to hear whatever Driscoll might say. Abruptly, he sat, telling himself again that he really should leave, he really should move out of the booth and away from this conversation, but remaining where he was, fascinated, compelled to listen, and actively hoping they would reveal a piece of information that would prove helpful to his case.

"What if they win?" the woman asked. She had to be Driscoll's wife, she couldn't be anyone else. Her Southern inflection had returned, her tone was again calm and reasonable, her voice softly resonant.

"They won't," Willow said.

"But if they do."

"We appeal."

"And if we lose the appeal?"

"We pay the two dollars."

"Yes, and then API and Mitchell-Campbell will turn right around and sue my husband for their losses. Isn't that so, Mr. Willow?"

"Your husband made certain warranties and indemnities in the contracts he signed, Mrs. Driscoll. One of those was that the work was entirely original with him and did not infringe on the rights of any other individual. If we lose this case, yes, API and Mitchell-Campbell would have the right to counterclaim over and to recover against him, yes."

"Whom would you represent in such a case, Mr. Willow?"

"I'm not sure I understand you."

"My husband? Or Mitchell-Campbell Books?"

"Such a case is an impossibility," the other man said. "We're going to win this suit, Mrs. Driscoll."

"I'm only asking Mr. Willow *suppose.* Whom would you represent, Mr. Willow?"

"I would have to represent Mitchell-Campbell," Willow said. "My firm works for them on a retainer basis."

"And would you then claim, for Mitchell-Campbell, that my husband did indeed steal Mr. Constantine's play?"

"If this court decides . . ."

"Would you?"

"Mrs. Driscoll, if this court decides against us, we would most certainly appeal to a higher court."

"You're evading my question, Mr. Willow."

"I think I've got *another* Harvard lawyer on my hands," Willow said, and laughed.

"What I want to know, Mr. Willow, is whether you really believe my husband is an honest man."

There was a slight hesitation.

"Yes," Willow said. "I do."

"You don't think he stole that play?"

"I do not," Willow said. "Do *you?*"

"What?"

"Do *you* think he stole it?"

There was another hesitation. Then Mrs. Driscoll said, "Of course he didn't steal it."

"Then we have no problem," Willow said.

Arthur rose suddenly and left the booth, his back to the partitioning wall, his heart pounding. He should not have eavesdropped, he should have warned them, he should have said Stop, I don't want to hear this, his father and mother in the room next to his, the wind outside and the sound of an occasional automobile in the street below, his father whispering in Italian, whispering, don't let me hear, he thought, don't you know Julie's in the room with you? I do not want to hear. Blankly, he moved away from the booth and into the restaurant, circling the columns, moving between the tables, trapped in a forest of furniture and glistening white tablecloths, the hum of conversation, the brittle sound of laughter and the clink of silverware, where should he go, should he find Mother Sauce and ask her to change their table, where was Sidney, where the hell was the men's room, where behind these columns and walls had Mother Sauce hidden the men's room? He saw the telephone booth and hurried toward it, entering it and swiftly closing the door behind him, hiding, I should not have listened. He dried the palms of his hands on his trousers. His face was flushed and he felt feverish and weak. He sat silently expectant, certain that the phone would ring and expose his hiding place. He caught his breath and looked at the dial. Selig, he thought. He dried his palms again, and searched for a dime, and then he dialed Selig's office number slowly and carefully. Selig answered on the fourth ring.

"Did you reach Mitzi?" Arthur asked. His heart was still pounding. He looked through the glass door of the booth furtively, fearful he would be discovered by Willow, exposed by Willow who would reconstruct the eavesdropping and berate him for it, scold him the way McIntyre had yesterday, make him feel foolish and guilty and afraid.

"Not only did I reach Mitzi," Selig said, "but I also asked her to ask Hester to call me at the office, which Hester did not ten minutes ago. I've been on the phone with her all this time."

"What did she say?"

"She likes the play."

"Good, will she—"

"But she has some questions about it."

"About the play?"

"Well, about the character."

"About Carol?"

"Yes, that's the part we want her to play, isn't it?"

"Yes, of course."

"Well, that's the part she's got questions about."

"What kind of questions?"

"I don't know, she wants to talk to you," Selig said. "She won't talk to anyone but you."

"When?"

"Tonight?"

"Where?"

"It'll have to be late, Arthur. She has a perform . . ."

"I don't care how late . . ."

". . . ance at Lincoln Center, you know. She probably won't be free until eleven-thirty or thereabouts."

"Fine. What shall I do, pick her up at the theater?"

"No, she said she'd rather meet . . ."

"Where?"

"The Brasserie. She doesn't eat until after performance, so she can grab a bite there, if that's all right with you."

"That's fine."

"Eleven-thirty at the Brasserie."

"Right," Arthur said.

"You know what she looks like, don't you?"

"Yes." Arthur paused. "She didn't tell you what's bothering her, huh?"

"She didn't say anything was bothering her, Arthur. She said it was a charming play, and she loved the character, she loved the girl Carol, but before she did anything or said anything or instructed her agent to do anything, there were some things in the character she wanted to clarify, so that she would understand the character more fully and be able to approach it more intelligently."

"Did she say that? That she wanted to approach it more intelligently?"

"I'm repeating word for word what she told me, Arthur."

"Well, that sounds pretty encouraging, doesn't it to you?"

"Actresses are strange people," Selig said.

"Granted, but—"

"She may simply want to have an intelligent approach for the next time she *reads* it, Arthur. It could mean nothing more than that."

"Still, she wouldn't—"

"She's a very talented and high-strung girl who is afraid of her own shadow because she's so lovely, and talented, and insecure," Selig said. "She likes the play, she likes the part, but she's afraid to make a move from Lincoln Center where she's got only a little role in a Restoration comedy, but at least she's got respect and she's working steady and she doesn't have to rely on her own judgment, God forbid your play should be a flop. So she says she wants to talk to you about the character. What she really wants, Arthur, is for you to convince her she'll be doing the right thing by kissing off Lincoln Center and taking a chance on an unknown quantity. That's what this is all about."

"Okay," Arthur said.

"So explain the character to her."

"I will."

"You're a good talker."

"I'm not so sure about that."

"How's the trial going?"

"Okay."

"Call me tonight no matter how late it is," Selig said. "I want to know what she says."

"All right, I will. The Brasserie at eleven-thirty, right?"

"Right. Good luck, Arthur."

"Thank you," Arthur said, and hung up.

He sat in the booth for several moments, silent. Then he opened the door and looked for Mother Sauce. When he found her, he said, "I wonder if you could change our table."

"Something's wrong?" she asked.

"No, but I think Mr. Brackman and I would prefer another table."

"You're in litigation?"

"Yes."

"I understand," she said knowingly, and led him swiftly to the other side of the room.

European posters covered the walls of the small travel agency, brightly printed in yellows and whites and tans and greens, blatantly selling sunshine and sand while outside the plate-glass window the snow continued to fall. From where Chickie sat behind one of the two desks in the office, she could look out at street level onto Madison Avenue where lunch-hour pedestrians were battling the strong wind and wildly swirling flakes. She shivered involuntarily and looked up at the wall clock. It was ten minutes to one, and Ruth was not due back until the hour, but Chickie was very hungry and hoped the snow would drive her back sooner. She sat with her legs crossed, her skirt above the knee, amused whenever a male passerby stopped to peer through the front window of the agency, and then embarrassed and flushed if the scrutiny persisted, wanting to giggle.

The poster to the left of her desk, cluttered with travel folders and carbon copies of letters to hotels and auto-rental establishments, advertised Positano, the white and pastel houses climbing the hillside, the beach below, the rowboats hovering on the water. She glanced at it idly and then reread a letter from the Dorchester in London, confirming a room for Mr. and Mrs. Bernard Jannings, beginning January 10th. She wondered why anyone would want to go to England in January, and then immediately thought of Italy and Greece, and then of course remembered Sidney's proposal.

As she saw it, life was merely a matter of making the right decision at the right time; she should have known that long ago, when she was seventeen, but she hadn't. Well, she knew it now. Sidney had asked her to marry him, this is so unexpected, she had said, I'll have to think it over, meanwhile thinking that two million dollars was a lot of money, if he won his case he would get two million dollars. *If* he won, but how could he *possibly* win, a jerk like Sidney? Still, the possibility had to be considered. She could manage to live with *anyone* for two million dollars, and besides, Sidney wasn't all that bad, even though she didn't love him. There was a lot to be said for Sidney, but at the moment she couldn't think of a thing.

The decision, anyway, had nothing to do with Sidney. It had only to do with two million dollars, which he might or might not get, that was the trouble, too uncertain. Decisions were never easy for a girl to make even if she knew all the facts, but sometimes the damn facts came in too late or not at all, that was it. How could she possibly second-guess this idiotic trial? No jury, isn't that what he'd said? Two million dollars riding on an Irishman's heartburn. Or lack of it. How could you decide? Better to take the bird in the hand. Still, two million dollars.

(*Take it, no, take it, no, no,* and then his hand under her skirt, and she slapped him without wanting to, without thinking, forgetting for the moment, completely forgetting he was from the college. "Go out with the college boys, Duck," her mother advised. "Get yourself a rich boy from New York who'll be a doctor or a lawyer one day.")

Well, here he was, a rich (if he won the case) New York boy (forty-eight years old) who was a lawyer (but not a very good one) and he had made an honest old-fashioned proposal: I am forty-eight years old, harumph, harumph, and I know that you are only twenty-seven, but I think you know I love you, I think you truly know that. Yes, I *know* you love me, baby, I can wrap you around my finger, I can make you jump through hoops, I can get you to run naked in the snow on Madison Avenue, you little *shmuck,* of course I know you love me. Come sing for me, baby, sing your little heart out and then come on down on Northeast Airlines, brother *do* I know you love me!

But what to do?

Use your instinct, sweetie, use that famous woman's intuition they're always talking about, where was it in the winter of 1957? Or maybe it was operating full blast, maybe I knew *exactly* what would happen if I slapped him, who knows? And maybe the flushed, no, the, the almost I don't know, that tight hot embarrassed feeling (I always see myself as a frightened young girl standing alone on a station platform, a suitcase in my hand) that feeling of, heavy eyes, and almost smarting, tears about to come if something doesn't happen, frightened for two weeks after that night in his car when I slapped him, was it really fear? Or was I waiting for what was about to come, not knowing what, the way I feel embarrassed and hot and try not to giggle when a man stops at the front window to look at my legs, and want to touch myself, who the hell knows?

So he asks last night, naturally. Knows me six months but asks last night when I'm on my way to Ruth's apartment to meet Jerry Courtlandt and his brother there, to go over the European trip with them. I should have said no immediately (*Take it, no, I don't want to!*) I should have said Look Sidney, this is a lot of fun and all, you know, I mean I kind of enjoy having you around, you dear man, to play with, you know, you're a very nice playmate to kick around the block, but marry you? Now, really, Sidney, let's not get ridiculous. I'm twenty-seven years old, I am a *beautiful* young girl! Please don't make me laugh, Sidney.

Touching, though.

Really touching that he should ask.

Really.

And two million dollars, *if* he gets it, well, with two million dollars, who knows, Sidney? Maybe I could learn to love you, who knows, baby? Italy and Greece. Hot sand under me. Stretch, mmmm, relax.

Come on, Chickie, just relax, will you? No, I want to go home.

Home was a two-family clapboard house in a town called Ramsey, four miles from the university. The houses were semidetached, each with a small backyard and a peaked attic, identical except for the paint jobs. Their own house was further distinguished by the aspidistra her mother kept in the window, even the college boys had to ask what aspidistra meant. Her grandmother had kept one in the window of their tenement flat in London, when Agnes Brown nee Mercer was a child. And so now Agnes kept one in the window of the small house in Ramsey, Pennsylvania; it was important to maintain one's heritage, keep the bloody aspidistra flying, the man had written. Pennsylvania was Fourth Street in Ramsey, and an occasional trip into Philadelphia, and it was also the high school on Buchanan Street, and later on—even before it happened—trips to the college, the road straight as an arrow along the railroad tracks and past the power plant and then out into the beautiful rolling Pennsylvania countryside.

Her father owned the drugstore in Ramsey, an aging pharmacist who had also come from London in his youth (the sign outside his shop read "Chemist"). His name was Edwin Brown, but Mother called him Luv or Duck and Chickie called him Dads, and all of his customers called him Mr. Brown. She doubted if he even *knew* his first name, for all the use it got. For that matter, she herself had been called Chickie ever since a cousin from Philadelphia spent the summer with them (coming out of the slums on the city's south side to breathe a little country air) and had trouble pronouncing the name Charlotte, being only three years old and barely able to pronounce her own name, which was Mary. She liked the name Chickie because her mother made it sound like a synonym for Duck, which was her favorite term of affection, and also because when she got to be thirteen and developed a good bosom, the name seemed to apply somehow, seemed to impart a mysterious sort of womanly glamor to her, or so she thought. Chickie Brown, Chickie Brown, Chickie Brown, she would practice writing it in a broad developing hand, using a thick pen point, heavily capitalizing the C and the B.

She was kissed for the first time at her sixteenth birthday party by a boy named Frank Simms, whose father worked out at the gun factory. She blushed furiously, and then quickly raised her eyes to where her father stood in the doorway gently smiling, and hastily lowered them again. The university boys discovered her when she was seventeen, as inevitably they had to, but her mother approved of her dating, and in fact encouraged it. She knew that Chickie was a good clean girl who would probably marry young and raise a houseful of kids, so why not someone with a college education? Chickie, in her seventeenth year, was proud of her appearance, not a little annoyed whenever she asked her father how old she looked, and he smilingly replied, "Why, seventeen, luv," when she knew damn well she looked much older. She was taller than most of the girls at school, with very good breasts she had had from thirteen, and wide hips that everyone said were excellent for the bearing of children, and a narrow waist, and shapely legs—you were supposed to have good legs if the ankles were slender, which hers were. Agnes had taught her to carry herself as tall as she was, and not to slouch the way some big girls do, so she wore high heels with authority even when dating shorter boys. Her walk was rapid and direct; she never pranced or paraded the way a lot of the other kids did, as if they practiced wiggling their behinds when they were home in their own rooms. Chickie thought of herself almost as her mother did; she was good and clean and wholesome, and she was sure her innocence accounted for her fresh good looks, the shining green eyes and fine complexion, the full mouth touched with just a bit of lipstick, the red-gold hair trailing halfway down her back because it had never been cut, or sometimes swinging across her mounded sweater front in twin braids, tiny green bows picking up the color of her eyes. She thought of herself as an English girl or something. A healthy English country girl. She did not know she was just a townie.

They taught her that in the first six months of 1957, after she had dated the president of one of the most powerful fraternities on campus, or so she had been told. In fact, one of the reasons she began dating Buddy was because she *knew* he was the president of a big fraternity, and *knew* it was powerful. She could not imagine what *kind* of power a fraternity could wield, but the notion was intriguing nonetheless, and a little frightening. Perhaps nothing would have happened were she not both frightened and intrigued, perhaps that was all a part of it. Even now, when she thought back upon it, she could feel a tremor of fear, and she quickly pulled her skirt down over her knees, very flustered all at once—the image of a frightened girl on a station platform, that girl on the empty platform.

They had parked after the movie, and Buddy was kissing her—she let most of the boys kiss her, but never on the first date—when he gently tugged her hand toward him, and she realized he had opened his zipper, and he said, "Take it, go ahead." She said no, she didn't want to, but he kept insisting and pulling her hand toward him while she kept saying No,

No, and suddenly he let her go and thrust his own hand up under her skirt, and she slapped him. The automobile was very still for perhaps a minute, it seemed like a year, and then Buddy said, very softly, "You shouldn't have done that, miss," and started the car and took her home.

She did not know why she was so frightened in the two weeks that followed, unless it was remembering the tone of his voice and the word "miss," which seemed to be promising something terrible. She had no idea that they were carefully mapping out their campaign in those two weeks, or that she would assume the importance of a military target in the patient months that followed. She did not know that men could be that way, or would want to be that way. She only knew that she was frightened. And yet, oddly, she kept waiting for the phone to ring, waiting for Buddy to call.

The campaign started on a Saturday afternoon two weeks after she had slapped Buddy. It started in her father's drugstore, and it started with an apology from Buddy, who was all smiles and embarrassment and who told her he had behaved very badly and wished she would forgive him. He was with another boy, a good-looking blond boy named Paul, whom Buddy introduced as a brother and one of his closest friends. Paul nodded shyly, and they all chatted for a few more minutes, and then left Chickie. She felt very happy about the chance encounter with Buddy, and not a little relieved that she had misread the tone of his voice that night two weeks ago. The next morning her telephone rang, and she was surprised when her caller identified himself as Paul, "You know, we met yesterday in the drugstore."

"Oh, sure, Paul," she said. "Hi."

"Hi. Listen, I hope this isn't out of line."

"What do you mean?" she said.

"Well, Buddy is a fraternity brother, you know, and . . ."

"Yes, I know that."

"I didn't want to ask *him* whether you were, you know, whether you had any kind of an understanding or not. But if you *have* . . ."

"No, we haven't," Chickie said.

"Well, in that case," Paul said, and he sighed in relief, "I was wondering if you'd like to go see a movie tonight. I know this is sort of short notice, and tomorrow's school and all, but I promise I'll get you home early, that is if you'd like to."

"Well, it *is* short notice," Chickie said.

"Yeah, I know that."

"And I'd have to ask my mother."

"Well, would you *want* to?"

"Well, if she says it's all right, I guess I would."

"Well, fine." He paused. "Would you ask her?"

"Sure, can you hang on?"

She asked her mother, who said it was all right, as long as they didn't get home too late. Paul picked her up at seven that night, and they went to a movie in town and then stopped for hamburgers, where they met a few other fellows from the frat, all of whom were formally introduced by Paul, who seemed very proud of her, and who watched with a sort of quiet glow while they offered their hands and very gentlemenly said, "Pleased to meet you, Chickie." He took her home early, as he had promised, and did not even try to kiss her good night. She learned later, only much later when they told her all about it, that the meeting in the drugstore had been no accident, that Paul had made his first call from the frat house, with the other fellows standing around him, and that the subsequent introduction to the boys in the hamburger joint had all been carefully planned and synchronized because they were out to get her. But she did not know it at the time, and she felt only flattered and not at all suspicious when Paul called again on Monday to ask if she'd like to have a soda or something Wednesday night, and she said Yes, she'd love to. He took her home at ten-thirty, and again did not try to kiss her good night. She wondered about that a little, somewhat puzzled, but figured he was just a shy boy. On Thursday, a boy named John called to say he had met her Sunday in the hamburger joint, "Remember me, I'm one of Paul's brothers, I've got straight brown hair?"

"Oh sure," she said.

"I know this might seem a little forward," he said, "calling when we hardly know each other, but there's going to be a party at the house tomorrow night and look, I'll be honest with you. A girl who was supposed to be coming down from Bryn Mawr for the weekend got a bad cold and she can't make it, and I'm really up the creek. I thought maybe, well . . . I know I'm not putting this right, and I wouldn't blame you for saying no. But it's just that I really *am* hung up, and I honestly would like to take you to the party. If you think you'd like to come with me. Though I know this is all very sudden."

Chickie agreed that it was very sudden, but she saw nothing wrong in helping out a fellow whose girl had come down with a cold, especially since he was one of Paul's brothers. The party that Friday night was a nice gathering with some girls from town and some girls from colleges in Pennsylvania and here and there. Everyone was very nice to her, even Buddy and Paul who were with other girls but who each danced with her once and told her what a really nice person she was. John, the fellow who was her date, was a very good-looking boy who resembled Tony Perkins and who had cultivated the same sort of shy smile. He drove her home to Ramsey at two o'clock in the morning in a red MG convertible, and thanked her profusely at the door, telling her she had saved his life and wondering if he could see her again maybe next weekend. She said she would love to, and they made a date for the coming Saturday. But before then, she received calls from two other frat boys she had danced with, and before she knew it the weekend was booked solid. Then Paul called and asked if she'd like to hack around with him again this Wednesday the way they had last, have a soda or something, and she said yes, she'd love to. Buddy called that same day to tell her they were showing some old monster movies over at the school gym on Tuesday, and would she like to go with him?

The scheme had been devised in the reading room at the frat house, Buddy telling the others what had happened and then enlisting their aid in teaching this kid a lesson she would never forget, that you don't go around slapping the president of their frat, or *anybody* in their frat for that matter. The boys all agreed that this was a horrible offense and if permitted to gain circulation, if permitted to spread to all the other townies, could lessen their stature and their ability to get into townie pants every now and then.

These were all nice boys, Chickie was later made to understand, who really had nothing against her and who perhaps, for all any of them knew, simply wanted an activity to carry them through the long winter months and into the spring. Chickie was unfortunate to have been chosen as their extracurricular project for that semester, but then she shouldn't have slapped old Buddy, nor should she have been so obviously intrigued nor so obviously frightened. The boys knew she was frightened, and they also knew she was intrigued. In addition, they were all much older than she, being nineteen or twenty or thereabouts, worldly-wise in the ways of townie maids, and bolstered by the solidarity of brotherhood and the knowledge that they would not have to score *this* one alone. *This* one was to be a joint effort without a chance of failure, a little cooperative project which, if they played their cards right, could provide something steady for the rest of their college days.

The plan was rather clever, if they said so themselves, and once it proved effective against Chickie, they tried it often and with varying results against several other girls—until a supposed virgin named Violet Plimpton discouraged any further joint efforts by causing twelve boys in the frat to come down with cases of the clap. Chickie, though, was a clean girl, and a nice girl, and in fact a very sweet girl against whom they harbored no ill feelings, if only she hadn't slapped a fraternity brother. They modestly admitted that not a single one of them working unassisted would have had a prayer of getting her, but neither were they about to attempt an assault without first manipulating the odds and insuring the outcome. Permutations and combinations, said Richard Longstreet, who was a very bright and ugly boy from Palm Beach, Florida, the frat genius, peering through his black-rimmed spectacles and grinning at his brothers who listened attentively as he outlined his plan.

The assault, as Longstreet explained it, had to be slow and patient because first of all she wouldn't be eighteen until May and they didn't want to take any chances with jail bait (hear, hear, the brothers chanted) and secondly because it just wouldn't work unless they played it cool and easy. She had to believe that each of the seven hand-picked frat brothers were independently competing for her favors, and she had to believe that they did not exchange notes and, as a point of honor, never *never* discussed a girl they were simultaneously dating. (They established this without question in the third week of the campaign, when four of the frat boys separately called to ask for a Saturday night date, seemingly ignorant of the fact that she had already made a date with another of their brothers.) To further allay any of her suspicions, Longstreet said, they would evolve a system of staggered advances that could not possibly seem like the result of collusion, but would seem instead random and erratic. Paul would be the first to touch her breast, for example, but Mitch would only *later* soul-kiss her, a seeming regression, and David would then try to get his hand under her skirt. We will even, Longstreet said, make provision for a villain in the group of seven, an expendable man who will try to go too far with her, unclasping her bra and going for her naked breasts, *knowing* the move is premature and hoping Chickie will stop dating him. He will subsequently be replaced by a more civilized fellow, selected right now, who will participate up to the time of the final assault. Paul, until then, and as part of the overall scheme, will never try to get further with her than his first grab.

Longstreet admitted that this would all be very unfair to poor Chickie because what they were going to do was drive her out of her mind (hear, hear, the brothers chanted) without her ever once realizing she was being led down the garden. What we're going to do, Longstreet said, is manipulate and control her psychological and emotional responses so that by a process of gradual conditioning she will be ready for whatever we choose to put before her next. Her responses will all be calculated beforehand, *we* will decide when to give her a surfeit of affection and understanding, *we* will decide when to deprive her or when to resume the attack. In short, we will destroy her defenses one by one, creating a permissive climate that will make it simpler for the next man to take her yet a step further in persuasion, until she is conditioned to *expect* a certain amount of stimulation, until she is indeed looking *forward* to it. And by the time we have brought her to the point of highest expectation, why then we'll see who's gonna pluck her. After that, Longstreet said, it's anybody's.

The plan in practice worked almost the way Longstreet outlined it, not because it was foolproof, but only because Chickie contributed a certain amount of confused eagerness to its execution. Whatever she told herself later, whatever eventual surprise she professed to the boys when they explained to her in a very friendly and open manner how the plan had worked, she *really* suspected something from the very beginning, and her suspicions were all but confirmed by the end of the second month. To begin with, she knew without doubt that all girls exchanged notes, and it must have entered her mind almost at once (whatever protestations they made to the contrary) that seven boys from the same frat might just conceivably say a word or two about her in passing. So she never really bought the "independent dating" routine or the "point of honor" nonsense, nor did she believe it accidental that she was being rushed by the seven best-looking and most popular boys in the frat. She was somewhat thrown off stride when Freddie Holtz took off her bra and began fumbling around with her breasts, big clumsy football player, especially when all the others were so tiptoey apologetic if they for God's sake accidentally brushed against her or anything. But even then she had the feeling she was *supposed* to stop dating him, which was exactly what she did. And, of course, he was immediately replaced by another of the frat boys, so that there were always seven of them (in the final week they were dating her every night, dating her in sequence and getting her so completely confused and excited that she was ready for anything) but hadn't she been aware from the very beginning? Frightened, yes, when Mitch thrust his tongue into her mouth and tightened his arms around her; surprised, yes, when she found her own tongue eagerly searching the soft inner lining of his mouth; surprised, too, when she felt so suddenly wet, and idiotically thought her period had come, and then pulled away from him breathlessly, terrified, yes, but aware, aware. And later when David provisionally touched her leg, and immediately pulled back his hand, she knew without question that one or another of them would go further the next time, and was not at all surprised when Mark worked his hand up under her bra and onto her naked breast the following Saturday. She had begun to detect a pattern by then, however erratic and hidden it was, and she was aware of a steady progression, a series of escalating liberties that were infallibly calculated to lead to greater liberties. She knew. But she permitted it.

She permitted it with a feeling of rising suspense, curious to discover what they had planned for her next, gradually more and more anxious to participate. She did not think beyond the ultimate and inevitable act, knowing only that by the time it finally happened, two weeks after her eighteenth birthday, she was eagerly seeking the relief it brought. Beyond it, she vaguely visualized a continuing though certainly unpromiscuous sort of girlish sexual activity. She did not know that nothing but complete and utter subjugation would satisfy her captors.

She was finally made to understand this on the weekend the frat boys rented a Philadelphia hotel room and repeatedly used her, all twenty-six of them, one after the other throughout the night and the next long day. They had prepared for the event by purchasing condoms at the drugstore owned by Chickie's father (a brilliant touch thought up by Richard Longstreet) and then had come to Chickie with a ready-made alibi. She was to say a girl from Penn had invited her up for the weekend. They even supplied her with the girl's name, Alice Malloy. Chickie had no doubt she was a real girl the boys knew. She was too frightened to refuse the invitation, and besides she didn't know what was in store for her, or perhaps she did, it was all very confusing. All through the night, they kept saying, "You love it, don't you, Chickie?" to which she kept answering, "No, I don't, no," the next boy asking the same question, "You love it, don't you, Chickie?" and always she answered no, and thought of escape, and was terrified, and finally on the afternoon of the second day, she shrieked, "Yes, I love it, I love it, I *love* it!" and began giggling uncontrollably, and knew at last she was only what they said she was, a townie piece of twat.

In later years, when these nice fraternity boys got married to girls from Radcliffe and Smith and Sarah Lawrence and Vassar, and settled down to raise families, and went to work in business suits, they separately felt a pang of guilt when they recalled what they had done to Chickie in the winter and spring of 1957. But their guilt was dissipated by memory of the strange excitement they had known at the time, the knowledge that they (or rather Richard Longstreet, the frat genius) had inadvertently stumbled upon the key to Chickie Brown: she was a terrified little girl waiting to be victimized. This was exactly what they did to her, repeatedly, until finally their own lust seemed inspired by Chickie's appetite, and they could absolve themselves of any blame they may have felt at the time; they were obviously in the company of an insatiable nymphomaniac with masochistic tendencies, or so she was described by Richard Longstreet, who was a genius.

And in later years, when Chickie thought back upon that winter and spring, as she was doing now in her office while the snow swirled against the plate-glass window, she felt again the same surge of excitement, the same flushed embarrassment, the same tremor of fear she had known then and ever since with a variety of men including the Indian who had beat her until she ached and had given her a Persian cat in remorse. So Sidney Brackman, the dear silly man, wanted to marry her. She thought again of Italy and Greece, and the warm sand beneath her. She would be wearing a bikini, they would stare at her breasts and her legs, she would experience that familiar feeling of terrified lust engorging her, rising into her throat and her head until she wanted to scream aloud, or giggle, or die.

Will you win your stupid case, Sidney Brackman? she wondered.

If I were only sure you would.

Samuel Genitori, the chief counsel for API, was a rotund little man with a balding head and mild blue eyes. He was wearing a blue pinstripe suit with a light blue shirt and a dark blue tie. He carried a pair of eyeglasses in his hand as he approached the stand, but he did not put them on. To the court clerk, he said, "Plaintiff's Exhibit Number 8, please," and when he received the chart he put on the glasses briefly, studied the chart for a moment, took the glasses off again, and looked up at Arthur.

"Mr. Constantine," he said, "yesterday afternoon a chart was submitted to this court, and marked Plaintiff's Exhibit Number 8. It listed the alleged similarities between the movie *The Paper Dragon* and your play *Catchpole.* I show this to you now, and ask if this list was prepared by you."

"By me and my attorneys, yes."

"And it purports to show, does it not, the alleged similarities that were not present in Mr. Driscoll's book?"

"Yes, it does."

"It contains *only* those that appear in the play and in the film, is that correct?"

"That is correct."

"In your examination before trial, Mr. Constantine, you testified to some other alleged similarities between the play and the film, did you not?"

"That was a long time ago," Arthur said.

"Please answer the question."

"I don't remember whether I did or not."

"Perhaps I can refresh your memory."

"Please do," Arthur said.

"Did you not testify that there is a scene in the movie where a man is shown with his foot wrapped in bandages?

Did you not claim that this man with his foot wrapped in bandages was stolen directly from your play?"

"I don't remember making that claim."

"Then let's try to be a bit more precise, shall we? This is the transcript of your pretrial examination, and I'm going to read now from page 198, this is you talking, Mr. Constantine: 'In the motion picture, there's a scene between the lieutenant and his commanding officer, and in the background we can see a line of men returning from the front. One of these men has his foot wrapped in bandages. This man was not described anywhere in the novel, but there's a scene in my play where a group of men are waiting for a stretcher, and one of the men has his foot wrapped in bandages.' Did you say that, Mr. Constantine?"

"If it's there, I said it."

"Then I take it you also said, because it's here on page 199, you also said, 'This man is a minor character, and his appearance in the movie can only be explained as an unconscious copying from the play.' Did you say that?"

"I did."

"Do you still feel this similarity indicates copying?"

"It's a minor point," Arthur said, "and I believe it was later withdrawn. That's why it doesn't appear on the chart."

"You no longer claim the man with his foot in bandages as a similarity?"

"That's right."

"Did you also testify during your pretrial examination that marksmanship was discussed in both your play and in the movie?"

"Possibly."

"Well, let's—"

"Probably, as a matter of fact."

"As a matter of fact, Mr. Constantine, I would like to read now from page 211 of the transcript, so that we can see whether it was *possibly* or *probably* or just *what* it was, shall we do that?"

"I'm willing to concede that . . ."

"On page 211, and I'm quoting from the transcript now, we have the following exchange:

Question: Please explain the 'marksmanship' references.
Answer: In the movie, the sergeant says, 'You're a regular Annie Oakley.'
Question: And what is the reference in your play?
Answer: In my play, there's a dialogue between the psychopathic colonel and the nurse. I'd like to read it if I may.

COLONEL PETERSON

Because I'm an old man, sister, a very old man, practically decrepit.

DIANE

Your records show you're only fifty-two, sir.

COLONEL PETERSON

That's old, sister. I'm shot. I'm as shot as some of those poor bastards out there. Listen to those guns, sister, listen to those guns.

Question: Do the words 'You're a regular Annie Oakley' appear in your play?
Answer: Not specifically.

"That's the end of the testimony, Mr. Constantine. Do you remember it now?"

"I remember it."

"Do you still feel a similarity exists here?"

"No, I do not, and again I must say that this claim has already been withdrawn, which is why it does not appear on the chart. If the evidence were all as flimsy as these two examples, the entire case would be absurd. You've picked on two points which have already—"

"These two points are flimsy and absurd?"

"That's why they were withdrawn."

"Mr. Constantine, didn't you also say that another similarity between the play and the movie was the fact that both Private Colman and Corporal Janus wear eyeglasses?"

"I did."

"And that this is another malevolent example of—"

"Did I say malevolent?"

"No, that's my word, Mr. Constantine. But you *do* feel this similarity indicates copying by Ralph Knowles, who wrote the screenplay based on the novel."

"My character Corporal Janus wears eyeglasses. Driscoll's character Private Colman does not wear eyeglasses. Yet in the movie, we have Private Colman wearing eyeglasses. Now if that doesn't indicate . . ."

"Do you still claim . . ."

"The similarity exists."

"It's not one of the flimsy and absurd ones?"

"It is an indication of either deliberate or unconscious copying. Alone, it might not be significant. But when we look at the other similarities, the fact that both men are troublemakers, and the homosexual references, and when we add the eyeglasses to that . . ."

"You're not suggesting that Private Colman is homosexual."

"In the book he is."

"But not in the film?"

"The film has taken my homosexual colonel and used him instead. I believe I've already explained the blending of two characters to form one in the book, and the subsequent separation in the film."

"And you still wish to claim this matter of the eyeglasses as a similarity?"

"I wish it to remain, yes."

"Remain *where,* Mr. Constantine? It does *not* appear on your chart, which you said earlier was a complete list. Do you now wish to add it to that list?"

"Yes."

"Very well. Would you like to add any others, Mr. Constantine. We'd like to be perfectly clear as to what you've alleged."

"No, that's all."

"You do not wish to add any other similarities to this list?"

"I do not."

"I wonder if I might now ask you, Mr. Constantine, why you chose to include in your list several similarities which you regarded as flimsy and absurd?"

"I don't know why. The examination had been going on for a long time. I was tired and . . ."

"Mr. Constantine, do you remember asking for time to go over your charts and lists in an attempt to determine whether or not you had covered everything?"

"When do you mean?"

"During the pretrial examination."

"I don't remember."

"And after you had studied your charts and lists—I believe you were gone for close to an hour, Mr. Constantine—you came back and said, and these are your exact words which I'm reading from the transcript, 'There are several other similarities I'd like to mention.' One of those similarities was the man in bandages, isn't that so?"

"Perhaps. You and Mr. Willow seemed determined at that point to get me to say this was a complete list, so I . . ."

"Yes, you said you wanted a chance to study it. Which you did, Mr. Constantine. For close to an hour, isn't that correct?"

"I suppose so, but . . ."

"Without any pressure from Mr. Willow, or me, or anyone. Isn't that so?"

"It was a very hot day, and everyone seemed to be—"

"Please, Mr. Constantine, I will have my question answered. Were you under any pressure when you reviewed your charts and came back to add the man in the bandages?"

"I've already answered the question."

"You've answered it by saying it was hot and you were tired and Mr. Willow and I were pressuring you."

"I said you seemed determined to have me say it was a complete list. I did not mention anything about being pressured."

"*Were* you being pressured?"

"I was being interrogated."

"Mr. Constantine, I am suggesting that you were *not* being

interrogated when you left the room and spent an hour alone with your charts."

"That was merely an extension of the interrogation. I knew the interrogation would be waiting for me when I returned, and you and Mr. Willow had made it clear that if I didn't list each and every similarity at that time, the opportunity—"

"Can you tell me, Mr. Constantine, who decided to withdraw these similarities which you now consider flimsy and absurd?"

"Your Honor," Brackman said, rising, "I fail to see the purpose of this line of questioning. These similarities have been withdrawn. Does Mr. Genitori wish them to be claimed again? The witness has testified that he no longer considers them valid. Why, then, does Mr. Genitori—"

"He is examining as to the witness's credibility," McIntyre said. "I will allow it."

"If your Honor please," Genitori said. "Mr. Constantine, I repeat my question. Who decided to withdraw these similarities which you now consider flimsy and absurd?"

"Your Honor," Brackman said, "those were not the witness's words. He said something about . . ."

"I said if all the evidence were as flimsy as those two examples—"

"Yes, you did say the examples were flimsy," Genitori interrupted, "*and* absurd."

"I said the *case* would be absurd, the *case*."

"*If* all the examples were as flimsy as these two which have now been withdrawn," Brackman said. "*That* is what the witness said."

"The record will show exactly what he said, Mr. Brackman."

"In any case," Arthur said, "Mr. Brackman and I decided after deliberation to withdraw these specific claims. I think that answers your question."

"Yes, it does," Genitori said. "Now, if I understand this correctly, Mr. Constantine, there are five alleged similarities on Plaintiff's Exhibit Number 8, to which you now wish to add Private Colman and his eyeglasses, which makes a total of six alleged similarities between your play and the movie."

"Yes. Plus those that appear in the book as well, of course."

"We are talking now only of those that were *not* in the book, but which you claim are only in the movie and the play."

"That's right, there are six."

"And do you base your claim upon these six similarities alone?"

"I don't think I understand your question."

"It's perfectly clear, Mr. Constantine. Do you base your claim upon these six similarities alone?"

"No, sir."

"You do not?"

"My claim is based on all the similarities that appear in the play, the book, *and* the film."

"It is our contention, your Honor," Brackman said, "that both James Driscoll *and* API copied freely from the plaintiff's play. Mr. Genitori's concern at the moment would seem to be API's right to counterclaim should—"

"Mr. Brackman," McIntyre said, "I do not see where API's right to counterclaim is a matter for discussion right now."

"The plaintiff is suing for an accounting. API's right to counterclaim later is most certainly before your Honor, if we are to be realistic."

"Your Honor," Genitori said, "my question does not go to the matter of counterclaim, though I would agree this is a consideration. It deals instead with the specific allegations against API."

"You will answer the question, Mr. Constantine."

"What is the question?"

"Do you base your claim against API on these six similarities alone?" Genitori said.

"I base it on *all* the similarities," Arthur answered.

"That concludes my cross-examination, your Honor."

"I have no redirect," Brackman said.

"Very well. Thank you, Mr. Constantine, you may—"

"Your Honor, I have one further question."

"Forgive me, Mr. Willow."

Willow walked to the witness chair and, without looking at Arthur, said, "Mr. Constantine, you said yesterday morning that you worked on a film titled *Area Seven*, is that correct?"

"That's correct."

"In what capacity did you work on that film?"

"I worked on the screenplay."

"You wrote the screenplay?"

"I worked on it together with Matthew Jackson."

Willow suddenly looked up. "Mr. Constantine," he said, "did you receive screen credit for *Area Seven?*"

"I did."

"As co-author of the screenplay?"

"We worked on it together."

"Did the screen credit state 'Screenplay by Matthew Jackson and Arthur Nelson Constantine'?"

"Screen credits are determined by the Writers Guild. They very often—"

"Please answer the question."

"No, that's not what the credit stated."

"Did it not, in fact, state 'Adaptation by Arthur Nelson Constantine, Screenplay by Matthew Jackson'?"

"Yes, that's what it stated. But 'adaptation' is a word—"

"Thank you, Mr. Constantine."

"Mr. Brackman?" McIntyre asked.

"That is the plaintiff's case, if your Honor please."

"You may step down, Mr. Constantine."

"Thank you," Arthur said. Bewildered for a moment, he began walking toward the jury box on the left of the courtroom, saw James Driscoll and his wife sitting there, started for the benches at the rear, and then responded to Brackman's signal to join him at the plaintiff's table.

Willow was still standing before the bench.

He took off his glasses, pressed his fingers into his eyes, head bent for a moment, and then put the glasses on again, and looked up at the judge.

"May I at this time," he said, "move to dismiss the action

on the ground that this court has no jurisdiction with respect to the play *Catchpole*."

He delivered the words calmly and emotionlessly, startling even Genitori, who looked up in surprise. Arthur immediately turned to Brackman, puzzled, but Brackman rested a reassuring hand on his arm, leaned forward, his attention focused on Willow, and then patted Arthur's arm twice in further reassurance. Arthur did not know why Willow was suggesting that a federal court had no jurisdiction in a copyright case. He sensed intuitively, though, that the motion had been conceived as a result of the trap Willow had set and sprung in his earlier circuitous questioning. Apprehensively, he leaned forward and waited for Willow to continue. The courtroom was silent.

"Section 13 of the Copyright Law," Willow said, "clearly states that no action for infringement may be maintained if copies of the work in question have not been deposited with the Library of Congress."

Brackman was on his feet instantly. "Mr. Willow knows very well that the play *Catchpole* was copyrighted in August of 1947," he said. "Point of fact, he conceded before trial that it would not be necessary to produce a certificate of copyright, and that . . ."

"That's on the record, Mr. Willow," McIntyre said. "I'm not sure I understand your motion."

"Your Honor," Willow said, "I believe it was proved today that this work was published a full seven months *before* any copyright protection was sought."

"May I ask . . ." Brackman started.

"Publication, your Honor," Willow interrupted, "may be defined as the earliest date of unrestricted sale or distribution of copies. In this case, the first authorized edition of *Catchpole* was the play Arthur Constantine had mimeographed in December of 1946."

"Your Honor . . ."

"He distributed copies of that play starting in January of 1947, and continuing through May of that year, when the play was optioned. This mimeographed version was *not* copyrighted, nor was the play registered with the Copyright Office until August of 1947, seven months *after* the general distribution."

"Your Honor," Brackman said, "we are engaged in a matter of semantics here. The distribution made by Mr. Constantine was not a *general* distribution, as my learned friend claims, but rather a *limited* one to theatrical producers and investors, for the sole purpose of securing production of the play."

"The fact remains, your Honor, that one hundred and twenty copies were, in the witness's own words, 'floating all over the city,' distributed without copyright notice, placing them in the public domain. I cite Section 10 of the Code, which specifies that publication or distribution without the statutory copyright notice constitutes dedication to the public."

"This was neither a publication *nor* a general distribution," Brackman said. "Under Section 12 of the Code, the common-law protection of a work is perpetual so long as the work remains unpublished. *Catchpole,* which was a dramatic composition, was 'published,' if you will, on the night the play opened in New York City to paid performances. Until that time . . ."

"A hundred and twenty copies were printed, your Honor."

"Were *mimeographed,*" Brackman said.

"And generally distributed."

"It was a *limited* distribution."

"We can argue this forever," McIntyre said. "I will reserve judgment on the motion, Mr. Willow."

"May I then, your Honor, for the defendants Mitchell-Campbell Books and Camelot Books move for dismissal of the complaint under Rule 41, on the ground that on the facts and on the law the plaintiff has not made out a cause for action."

"I will deny that motion," McIntyre said.

"If your Honor please," Willow said, "I have no desire to waste the Court's time, but may I point out that our grounds are set forth in our main brief and in our reply brief?"

"I know that."

"Thank you, your Honor," Willow said.

Genitori rose from behind the API table and walked toward the bench. "May it please your Honor," he said, "Mr. Willow has made a motion to dismiss under Rule 41, and I would now like to join that motion as it refers to the first claim against API. But in addition, I would like to make another motion directed to the second cause of action, which charges independent infringement by API.

"For the purpose of this motion, your Honor, I must assume *arguendo* that Ralph Knowles, the man who wrote the screenplay and directed the film, had access to the play *Catchpole,* and that the five similarities listed in Plaintiff's Exhibit Number 8, together with the 'eyeglasses' incident which was added today—these six items were copied by Mr. Knowles directly from the play. I submit to your Honor that even *assuming* access and copying—and access alone means nothing, as your Honor well knows—even assuming *both,* these six incidents alone do not form the basis for copyright infringement.

"Let us examine them for a moment, if we may, your Honor. They are all as flimsy and as absurd as the man with his foot in bandages, or the far-fetched allusion to marksmanship, both of which claims have already been withdrawn. They are as meaningless, your Honor, as the incident of the eyeglasses, which was added to the list in this courtroom today.

"We are asked to accept as a unique idea, for example, the use of a bayonet as a weapon, your Honor—the use of a *bayonet* as a *weapon*—merely because the plaintiff's psychopathic colonel uses one. Never mind the fact that bayonet charges were prevalent during the Korean conflict, and that whereas none were mentioned in the novel, Mr. Knowles made pictorial use of them in the film. Or for example, your Honor, the plaintiff insists that because some soldiers are drinking coffee at one point in his play, and some soldiers in the film *also* drink coffee, this is another indication of access and direct copying from the play. I don't think I need bring up the other three points which are just as meaningless, and upon which the plaintiff bases his charge of independent infringement by API.

"I submit that the plaintiff's case is lacking in *any* evidence of infringement of copyrightable material. I call your attention to one of the more prominent plagiarism cases—*Morris versus Wilson,* cited on page 24 of our brief—in which Judge Weinfeld said, 'In order to suppose that these authors should have found in the plaintiff's play cues for the farfetched similarities which she discovers, one must be obsessed—as apparently unsuccessful playwrights are commonly obsessed—with the inalterable conviction that no situation, no character, no detail of construction in their own plays can find even a remote analogue except as the result of piracy.' The judge later quoted, poetically, 'Trifles light as air are to the jealous confirmations strong as proof of holy writ.'

"Your Honor, that's exactly what these six isolated incidents are, trifles light as air. Let us examine the rest of them a moment, if your Honor will allow. There is an enemy soldier being shot at and falling out of a tree, a supposedly *unique* event in time of war. There is an American soldier bursting into tears when his buddy is killed. And finally, there is a nurse putting on lipstick and using the back of a mess kit for a mirror. Your Honor, I submit that the first two of these alleged similarities are stock incidents to be found in *any* war film ever made, and that the incident with the nurse and her lipstick is noncopyrightable.

"If you will refer to page 31 of our brief—the case of *Rush versus Oursler*—Judge Thacher of this court observed, 'When two authors portray the same occurrence in the same setting; presupposing the presence of the same people in the same environment; similarities of incident unaccompanied by similarities in *plot* are not persuasive evidence of copying. The authors having worked with the same material to construct the environment or setting in which the action is laid, such similarities are inevitable; and the products of such labor are comparable to the paintings of the same scene made by different artists.'

"And a little later on, your Honor, he remarked, 'It may usually be said that such material is so unimportant and so trivial that its appropriation by copying, even if shown, would not be a substantial taking of copyrighted material.' Your Honor, the six incidents upon which plaintiff bases his second cause of action—the enemy shot from a tree, the eyeglasses, and so forth—are likewise not susceptible of copyright.

"I now respectfully submit that there is no evidence at all to support this second claim against API, and I beg your Honor to dismiss it from the case."

"Mr. Brackman?"

"I did not realize, your Honor, that Mr. Genitori was going to read us his entire brief," Brackman said dryly. He rose and walked slowly toward the bench. "Needless to say, I do not agree with him concerning the basis of our complaint, which he seems to have completely misunderstood. We are *not* claiming that these six incidents alone constitute our claim of infringement. Our complaint is quite clear on that. Our action against API is based on these six incidents *plus* all of the other similarities of theme, plot, and character which Mr. Constantine enumerated yesterday. It is a simple matter, of course, to label these similarities 'flimsy and absurd,' as Mr. Genitori has done, it is certainly much simpler than trying to explain them. But, your Honor, I feel defendant *should* and *must* explain them, especially when we consider Mr. Constantine's testimony, which indicates that in 1952 he worked with a man named Matthew Jackson, to whom he submitted a copy of his play *Catchpole*. This man Jackson . . ."

"Your Honor," Genitori said, "I only assumed access for the purpose of my motion."

"Yes, we understand that."

"API *had* access," Brackman said firmly. "There is no question about that. The play was submitted to five people at the studio in 1952, *including* Mr. Matthew Jackson, who later worked with Ralph Knowles on *The Paper Dragon*. Carl, may I see that brief a moment, please?" he said, turning to his partner. Arthur, watching him, saw that he was getting angry, and he immediately thought, Good, it's about time. Give it to the bastards.

"I don't like to waste this Court's time reading from cases. There are hundreds and hundreds of cases, as your Honor well knows, and it seems we have already heard a goodly percentage of them from my learned friend." Arthur saw Genitori smile, in spite of the withering glance Brackman directed at him. "But our brief is not exactly destitute of examples, your Honor, and if I may I would like to quote from it at this time."

"Please," McIntyre said.

"I thank your Honor for his indulgence," Brackman said. "In the case of *West Publishing Company versus Edward Thompson Company,* it was pointed out, and I quote, 'To constitute an invasion of copyright it is not necessary that the whole of a work should be copied, nor even a large portion of it in form or substance, but that, if so much is taken that the value of the original is sensibly diminished, or the labors of the original author are substantially, to an injurious extent, appropriated by another, that is sufficient to constitute an infringement.'

"So you see, your Honor, it does not matter whether we are dealing here with six incidents, or ten incidents, or twelve, or *twenty*—so long as these similarities have indeed sensibly diminished the value of the original. I'm sure your Honor is familiar with the now famous *Teton versus Caddo* case, this circuit, Judge Madison presiding, wherein it was claimed—as both Mr. Willow and Mr. Genitori are claiming—that the similarities were insignificant, even though there were a great many of them, a substantial number of seemingly unimportant similarities. There was, however, in the midst of these so-called insignificant similarities, one that was *indeed* significant, your Honor. I refer, and I'm sure you're ahead of me, to the misspelling of a place name in the original work, and the identical misspelling of that place name in the alleged piracy. This was, your Honor, the misspelling of a town in Michigan, Chippewa, which was spelled with an H at the end of it in both books, C-H-I-P-P-E-W-A-H, Chippewah—the identical error in both books, your Honor. The thief had left behind his fingerprints."

Brackman turned to look at the empty jury box where Driscoll and his wife sat, and then turned to the judge again.

"Your Honor, the thief has left behind his fingerprints in this case as well. I refer now to the numerical designation of the 105th Division, which is identical in both the play *Catchpole* and the novel *The Paper Dragon,* and which has been carried over to the film produced by—"

"Your Honor, this does not pertain to my motion," Genitori said. "I made no reference to the 105th Division."

"I appreciate that, Mr. Genitori," McIntyre said, "but if I understand Mr. Brackman correctly, he's saying there *is* a cause of action and that it goes beyond the six incidents and includes *all* of the other similarities as well."

"That's *exactly* what I'm saying."

"I'll continue to hear argument on the point."

"I was saying, your Honor, that the thief's fingerprints are clearly visible without the need of a magnifying glass, they are able to be seen with the naked eye, the 105th Division. If I may, your Honor, I would like to point out once again that there were only sixty-seven actual infantry divisions in existence during the time of the Eniwetok campaign, and that when we come to the divisions beyond the designation '100' we have the 101st, 102nd, 103rd, 104th, and *106th*. There is no 105th division. Nor was there a 105th division in 1950. There were only seven actual infantry divisions at that time, the 1st, 2nd, 3rd, 7th, 24th, 25th, and the 1st Cavalry. Today, there are twelve infantry divisions and, needless to say, none of *them* is the 105th, either.

"Perhaps Mr. Driscoll can adequately explain to this Court how he happened to hit upon those three digits in sequence. Until he can do that, I will continue to be amazed by the remarkable use of this designation, appearing again and again and again, first in the play, then in the novel, and again in the motion picture. Out of all the possible numbers Mr. Driscoll could have used to label his infantry division, he chose the identical number that appears in Mr. Constantine's work. This is an amazing coincidence, your Honor, it is almost an impossible coincidence.

"Now, your Honor, in much the same way that there are laws governing our society, there are also laws governing chance, and these are called the laws of probability, and it is against these that we must examine this use of an identical division number. If we were to take all the digits from zero to nine and try to figure out all the possible different combinations for any *three* of those digits, we would have to raise ten to the third power, which means we would have to multiply ten times ten times ten, and that would give us an answer of one thousand possible combinations. In other words, the odds would be a thousand to one that any man would choose a specific combination over any other possible combination. A thousand to one, your Honor. And those odds, as impressive as they may sound, are only the odds for a *single* event. When we come to two mutually independent events, the odds are overwhelming.

"What exactly is the probability that both these men, given the same ten digits, would then arrange three of them in identical order? I will tell you, your Honor. The laws of probability state that in the case of two mutually independent events, we must multiply the odds against Event One happening by the odds against Event Two happening. In other words, we must multiply a thousand-to-one by a thousand-to-one, and we then discover that the odds against Driscoll hitting on this same combination were a *million* to one. He had one chance in a million, your Honor, a deplorable cliché to use in a case dealing with literary matters, but those are the true odds nonetheless, a *million* to one, the figures do not lie. And even if we wish to give both men the benefit of the doubt, and say that neither of them would have designated an Army division with the number zero-zero-zero—although stranger things *have* happened in fiction, as we well know—even if we were to exclude this possibility, the odds for both men would be 999 to one, and when we multiply that by itself, the odds against Driscoll hitting on the same combination would be 998,001 to one. A million-to-one is a neater figure, your Honor, and will serve our purposes here, I believe.

"And I believe, too, that with odds such as these, we are justified in demanding an explanation, beyond the labeling of such similarities as flimsy and absurd. Thank you, your Honor."

"Do you now wish to reply, Mr. Genitori?"

"Only to say, your Honor, that my motion did not concern the 105th Division or any other similarities common to both the novel and the film."

"Yes, I understand that. Well, I want to reserve decision on your motion, and on Mr. Willow's as well."

"Your Honor?"

"Yes, Mr. Willow?"

"I understood you earlier to say you were *denying* my motion."

"If that's what I indicated . . . no, Mr. Willow, I meant that I'm reserving judgment on it."

"Thank you, your Honor."

McIntyre looked up at the wall clock. "It seems to be the end of another day," he said. "So unless there's anything further, we'll recess until tomorrow morning at ten o'clock."

7

THICK WHITE SNOWFLAKES were swirling in the air when Sam Genitori and his assistant came out of the courtroom. A cover of white clung to rooftop and pavement, hushing the city, and snow shovels scraped on courthouse steps and sidewalk, a rasping steady counterpoint to the metallic jingle of skid chains on distant streets. Genitori put on his hat, ducked his head against the fierce wind, and stepped into the vortex of flying flakes. Beside him, Michael Kahn sucked in a draught of cold air and shouted over the wind, "I love snow, I *love* snow." Sam lost his footing on the slippery steps at that moment and would have gone tumbling to the sidewalk below were it not for Kahn's suddenly supporting arm. The assistance annoyed Sam more than Kahn's redundant confession had—"I love snow, I *love* snow"—an emotional involvement Sam could neither share nor understand. Sam detested snow. It was cold and wet and damned uncomfortable, and besides it caused accidents and traffic jams. Leo Kessler was waiting for him uptown, and he didn't need a snowstorm to delay his arrival. He looked up, squinting into the wind, and saw the chauffeured limousine across the street, on Duane. "There it is," he said to Kahn, and walked swiftly toward the big car, its roof and hood covered with snow, its sides a wet shining black. The chauffeur was reading a copy of *Mad Magazine;* he barely looked up when Sam opened the back door. Kahn climbed in, and the chauffeur reluctantly put aside the magazine. Then, with the unerring instinct of all servants everywhere, he lunged straight for the jugular.

"This snow'll make us late," he said.

"Just get there as fast as you can."

"580 Fifth?" the chauffeur asked.

"No, Malibu Beach," Sam said dryly.

"By way of Santa Monica or the freeway?" the chauffeur asked, deadpan.

"580 Fifth," Sam answered, demolished by superior wit. He stretched his legs, took off his hat, patted his thinning hair into place, and then tilted his head back against the cushioned seat.

"Were you impressed?" Kahn asked.

"By whom?"

"The witness."

The car was in motion. Sam always felt a bit queasy in a moving vehicle, a reaction he attributed to his ulcer, or perhaps only to his proximity to Kahn, who seemed to be occupying a great many moving vehicles with him of late. He was constantly amazed by the fact that Kahn was not related to someone in the company. He could not imagine how anyone as imbecilic as this young man had ever managed to get through law school, no less become an employee of the firm, all without being someone's nephew. "The witness left me cold," he said, and belched.

"Excuse *me,*" Kahn supplied.

"Do me a favor," Sam said. "When we get to Leo's office, shut up."

"What do you mean?"

"I mean shut up. Don't talk about the witness, don't talk about the case, just shut up and listen. You'll learn a great deal about law and high finance and tits."

"I know all about those already," Kahn said, offended.

"You can *never* know all about tits," Sam answered. "There's always something new to learn. The subject is inexhaustible.

"And I don't happen to like that expression," Kahn said. "I *don't* happen to like that expression," he repeated.

"Tits?"

"Yes, that."

"Did the witness impress *you?*" Sam asked, shrugging.

"Yes."

"In what manner?"

"I think he was telling the truth," Kahn said. "I think Driscoll *did* steal the play. Why else would Willow have moved for dismissal on a jurisdictional technicality? I'll tell you why. He knows his man stole the play, and he's afraid to put him on the stand."

"That's ridiculous," Sam said. "Willow was only trying to save time, energy, and money. If he could have got the case kicked out of court today, that would have been the end of it forever."

"I still think Driscoll's guilty. And I wouldn't be surprised if Ralph Knowles dipped into the company files, too, when he was writing the movie."

"My young friend," Sam said, "have you ever been thrown out of a seventh-floor window?"

"What?"

"All you have to do in the presence of Leo Kessler is suggest—*suggest,* mind you—that API was in any way a party to this plagiarism, and I can guarantee he will hurl you seven stories to the street below, where you will be crushed by oncoming traffic."

"Then you do think it was plagiarism?"

"Who said so?"

"You just called it plagiarism, didn't you?"

"I should have said *alleged* plagiarism," Sam amended, and then shrugged again.

"Well, what *is* your position?" Kahn asked.

"My position is the position Artists-Producers-International pays me to maintain. There was no plagiarism involved here, neither on the part of James Driscoll nor on the part of any person or persons employed by API. That is my position."

"That's your *official* position."

"That's my *only* position."

"But how do you feel personally?"

"I feel fine, thanks, except for my ulcer."

"You know what I mean."

"Sure, I know what you mean."

"Well?"

"There was no plagiarism," Sam said flatly.

They had come uptown past Canal Street, where the big black limousine had nosed its way silently through the truck traffic heading for the bridge, making a sharp left turn onto Third Avenue. The Chinese banks and groceries had given way to the wholesale clothing and lighting fixture stores, the fleabag hotels and flophouses only sparsely represented until just now, when they suddenly appeared like dim gray specters in the blinding snow. Derelicts shuffled along the sidewalks here and lay in gutters and doorways, making Sam sick just to look at them. His most vicious nightmare was one in which he suddenly woke up divested of his law degree and his position with API, his house in Massapequa gone, his boat scuttled, everything he had fought for in the past twenty years vanished with the night to leave only a trembling immigrant Italian struggling with the language, selling chestnuts on a Bronx street corner for five cents a bag. He awoke from this dream each time in a cold sweat, the smell of roasting chestnuts in his nostrils, and each time he held his hands out in front of his face, peering at them in the dark, certain that the fingers would be stained brown from the juice of the nuts. His wife would say, "Go to sleep, Sam, you had a bad dream," but he would lie awake trembling in the dark, terrified by his near miss—they had almost taken it all away from him, they had almost closed the jaws of the trap before he'd had a chance to scurry out of it. He could not account for the basis of this dream, since he had never in his life sold chestnuts in the Bronx. Nor, for that matter, had he ever even *lived* in the Bronx. Moreover, neither of his parents were immigrants, and they had never been really poor. The dream-trap was more like a race memory that could be traced back to a grandfather he had never known—and yet his grandfather hadn't sold chestnuts, either, so what the hell could it be? His grandfather had come to this country when he was twenty-one years old, after studying economics at the university in Milan. When he arrived here, he had been given a job immediately in a bank on the Bowery, where he dealt mostly with Italian-speaking immigrants. The job paid a good salary each week, and he had managed to save enough for the purchase of the house in Massapequa, which had since been passed down to Sam's father and recently to Sam himself. So what was this business with the chestnuts? And why did the sight of all these ragged bums all over the sidewalk trouble Sam so badly?

He was grateful when Cooper Union appeared on the left of the limousine. In the small park outside the school, a coed in a black hooded parka, her legs crossed, leaned forward eagerly to divulge some secret of the universe to a budding young artist or engineer, and another girl, wearing a paint-smeared smock and lighting a cigarette, came through the glass-paneled doors of the building, looked up at the sky, and sniffed the snow, ahh, to be young again.

Sam took in a deep breath. The Bowery and its dregs were falling behind the car, the hock shops appeared now like glittering toadstools. Beside him, he could smell the always-present slightly sour smell of Michael Kahn, as though someone had recently burped him but neglected to wipe his lips afterwards. Sam closed his eyes, and remained silent for the rest of the trip uptown.

There were wags in the industry, as there will be wags in any industry, who were of the opinion that the initials API did not really stand for Artists-Producers-International but stood instead for Asses, Pricks, and Imbeciles. If such was truly the case, the façade of the organization revealed neither ineptitude nor villainy, but seemed instead to echo a benign and somewhat informal attitude toward crass commercialism. The New York API offices covered the entire sixth, seventh, and eighth floors of the Longines-Wittnauer Building at 580 Fifth Avenue, just next door to Brentano's. The decorating scheme of the offices had been carefully calculated to disarm by none other than Mrs. Leo Kessler herself, better known in the industry as Katie Kessler, whose credit card—SET DRESSER: KATRINA L. KESSLER—had flashed from a hundred or more silver screens in the past two decades. To her further credit, the offices seemed to relax all visitors immediately, setting the tone for businesslike discussions in an atmosphere as informal as the living room of a Bel Air ranch. There were some who preferred the mid-Victorian decor of MCA's offices, with its old English prints in the elevators, and its green leather furniture, but Sam Genitori never failed to experience a slight lessening of tension the moment he stepped off the elevators here, and he silently thanked Katie each time.

"He's waiting for you," the seventh-floor receptionist said.

"What time is it?" Sam asked.

"Almost five. He said to send you right in."

"Is he alone?"

"Myrna's taking dictation."

"You'd better buzz him," Sam said.

The receptionist made no comment. She lifted the phone at her elbow, dialed a number, and waited. "Mr. Genitori is here," she said, and paused. "Yes, sir, right away." She hung up, nodded, and said, "You can go right in."

"Thank you."

"How's the trial going?" she asked.

"Nicely," Kahn replied.

"Mr. Genitori?" she asked, ignoring Kahn.

"Nicely," Genitori said, and walked immediately down the long corridor, followed by Kahn, who was beginning to sulk. Halfway down the hall, they passed a harried-looking brunette with a steno pad.

"He's waiting for you," she said.

"We know, Myrna."

"How's the trial going?"

"Nicely," Sam said, and glanced at Kahn, who said nothing. Kessler's office was at the end of the hall. Sam knocked on the door before opening it, and waited for Leo to shout his customary "Enter!" to which he customarily replied, "All ye who abandon hope here," and which customarily went clear over Leo's head, as it did now.

"What the hell does *that* mean?" Kessler asked.

"It's an old Milanese adage," Sam said, and started to close the door behind him.

"Michael, get lost someplace, will you?" Kessler said.

"Me?"

"Yes, I have something to discuss with Sam personally, okay? That's a good boy."

"If this relates to the trial," Kahn said, "I think . . ."

"Go get a cup of coffee, huh?" Kessler said, and waved him out impatiently. The sulking look on Kahn's face gave way to one of crumbling petulance. Sam was certain he would begin crying before he reached the corridor. He ushered Kahn out and closed the door behind him.

"Lock it," Kessler said.

Sam locked it. "Mr. President," he said, "I wish to report that the Russians have just bombed San Francisco."

"Very funny," Kessler said. "Someday you'll learn that the motion picture business is not funny."

"What *is* the motion picture business, Leo, if not funny?"

"The motion picture business is a vast fantasy surrounded by twat," Kessler said, "but not funny, not funny at all. How's the trial going?"

"All right."

"Will we win it?"

"I hope so."

Kessler rose from his desk suddenly. He was sixty-two years old, a tall slim man who wore a black suit each and every day of the week, augmented by black shoes and socks, black tie, white shirt, and generally a vest of either red or yellow corduroy with brass buttons. He was partially bald, and his nose was either naturally hooked or had once been badly broken, so that his profile had the curvilinear beauty of a modern piece of sculpture, rounded flesh sweeping into the arc of nose and jutting jaw, fierce eyes glinting from beneath black bushy eyebrows. He paced the office with his hands tucked into his jacket pockets, the thumbs overhanging, his shoulders hunched as though he were balancing an invisible load, his step springy and disjointed. He neither looked at Sam nor acknowledged his presence, speaking as though dictating a memo to a recording machine or explaining a particularly difficult dream to an unresponsive analyst.

"Scimitar," he said, "I wish I'd never heard of it. Thirty million dollars to make, plus all the trouble later with that bastard Nasser and his filthy Arabs, they should all drop dead from constipation. Thirty million dollars, and it's playing hard-ticket in twelve American cities, and with the business we're doing we won't get back that thirty million for the next thirty years, is it any wonder the stockholders are a little nervous? A *little* nervous, who's kidding who? There's a stockholders' meeting next month, January the 18th, to be exact, and I know just what's going to be proposed at that meeting because it was proposed at last year's meeting while we were still pouring money into that lousy *Scimitar,* even before Mr. Nasser started up with us, that bastard should rot in his grave. It was proposed at last year's meeting, January the 12th, to be exact, that Leo Kessler, whose father happened to found Kessler's, Inc.—before we got so cockamamie fancy with all the tax dodges and the Artists-Producers-International—it was proposed at last year's meeting that Leo Kessler step down as head of studio operations, mind you this was *before* the movie opened, *before* it started losing money even in Los Angeles, where they'll go see *anything.*

"So this year, on January the 18th, the stockholders of this fine company are going to sit back and look at the figures and they're going to learn that *Scimitar* has earned back only ten million dollars in a six-month showing, and that's a far cry from the thirty million dollars it cost to make, and an even farther cry from the two and a half times we have to earn back because that rotten director talked me into doing it in color, seventy-five million dollars before we're even off the hook. The stockholders are going to jump on that the way Moses jumped on the water, seventy-five *million* dollars. Will anyone remind them that I've earned *ten* times seventy-five million dollars for this company since my father died, God rest his soul? Will anyone remind them of *Dust,* which earned twelve million at a time when twelve million was equal to thirty-five million today? Will anyone remind them of *The Peddlers* at ten-and-a-half million profit, or *Marcia Steele* at six million profit, or *The Paper Dragon* at fourteen million, which book we bought for thirty-five thousand dollars, and which entire picture cost us only eight-fifty to make, will anyone remind them of what Leo Kessler has *done,* or only of what Leo Kessler has failed to do?

"Oh, let me tell you they are going to remind us of *The Paper Dragon* if we lose this trial. They are going to remind us that in the past three years we have had only one film that really made any kind of money, and that film was *The Paper Dragon,* which only enabled us to get rolling on *Scimitar.* Without Driscoll's book, we'd never have got involved in that lousy desert out there with that Swedish bitch screwing everything in sight, including the Moslem camel boys, and maybe the camels, too, what a production, I wish I'd never heard of it! They are going to remind us that here was a winner, *The Paper Dragon,* a profit of fourteen million dollars, and due to Mr. Leo Kessler's expert handling of the company, it turns out that this winner, ha! was plagiarized from something that was offered to API back in 1947 and again in 1952, something that is right there in our studio files for Ralph Knowles to look at while he's doing his screenplay. And when we add that to *Scimitar* and the money that's going down the drain with *that* one, you can rest assured that Mr. Leo Kessler will be out on the street selling pencils, look what happened to Griffith."

"What happened to Griffith?" Sam asked.

"*Birth of a Nation,* the biggest movie ever to be made in the history of the business, he dies a pauper in a Hollywood fleabag. Who'll remember *Dust* when Mr. Leo Kessler is kicked out on his ass?"

"Nobody," Sam said.

"You said it."

"We'll win the case," Sam said. "Don't worry."

"That's good," Kessler said, "but that's not why I sent

young snotnose Kahn out to ogle the office girls, and it's not why I asked you to lock the door, either. If we win the case, we don't need locked doors. We'll have the stockholders down on us *anyway,* but at least I can then say 'What the hell are you yelling about? Who was it who *made* the money for us to later invest in *Scimitar,* Sam Goldwyn maybe? It was *me,* it was *me* who saw possibilities in *The Paper Dragon,* it was *me* who brought it to the screen, it was *me* who made fourteen million dollars with it, so who has a better right to be daring with a picture that could still maybe earn out the cost once we're through with two-a-days and can go into general release, the Swedish bitch is big box office, and don't forget it.' That's what I can say." He paused. *"If* we win the case."

"We'll win it," Sam said. "Willow's a good lawyer."

"Is he Jewish?"

"I don't know."

"Brackman *is,"* Kessler said. "Never sell a Jew short."

"With all due respect, Leo, he's made a few mistakes already."

"Good, he should only make a *hundred* of them. I'm not worried about what happens if we *win* this case. I'm worried about what happens if it looks like we're *losing* it."

"I don't get you," Sam said.

"You don't get me?" Kessler paused. *"Did* he steal that play or not, Sam?"

"I don't think so."

"But will the *judge* think so?"

Sam shrugged. "That's why we're having a trial, Leo."

"What do *you* think the judge will think?"

"I think the judge will decide against Constantine."

"You think we'll win?"

"Yes. I think we'll win."

"But when will we know?"

"When the judge gives his opinion."

"Which will be when?"

"He can give it immediately after our summation, or it can take as long as two months. Who knows?"

"Two months after the trial *ends,* do you mean?"

"That's right, it could take that long."

Kessler nodded. He walked to the leather chair behind his desk, slumped into it, and laced his thin fingers across his chest. "You know, of course, that Ralph Knowles is flying in from the Coast, don't you? To testify."

"Yes, I know that."

"I want protection," Kessler said.

"Against what?"

"Against being kicked out of this company, what the hell do you think I've been talking about here for the past ten minutes?"

"How can I give you that?"

"By making sure Ralph Knowles is very carefully prepared before he goes on that witness stand."

"All witnesses are prepared, Leo. Knowles will—"

"We had nothing to do with this," Kessler said.

"What do you mean?"

"Neither API nor Mr. Leo Kessler had anything to do with this."

"With *what?"*

"I bought a book. I paid thirty-five thousand dollars for it in good honest American money. I bought it from galleys even before it became a bestseller. It was a good book, I thought it would make a great movie. I had no way of knowing it was stolen from a play written back in 1946."

"Who says it was stolen?"

"If we lose," Kessler said.

"I'm having trouble following you," Sam answered.

"If we lose—and don't tell me this can't happen, Sam, don't tell me innocent men haven't been sent to the electric chair or the gas chamber for crimes they never committed—*if* we lose this case, I want it to be clear in the record that James Driscoll was the crook. *We* had nothing to do with it, Sam, we had no way of knowing."

"Granted. But, Leo, I think he's innocent. I think he really did write the damn book all by himself, without ever having heard of Arthur Constantine *or* his play."

"Sam," Kessler said, "I respect your opinion highly, but I must tell you that your opinion isn't worth two cents. It's the *judge's* opinion that matters. And if the judge says James Driscoll stole that play, then James Driscoll *did* steal that play, and that's all there is to it."

"Well, that's not quite *all* there is to it. We can still appeal."

"Fine, we'll appeal. And by the time we appeal, I'll be out on my ass in the street selling pencils."

"Or chestnuts," Sam said.

"Everything is funny to you," Kessler replied. *"I'm* a man gasping for breath, and *you* make jokes. When I want comedians, I'll hire Charles DeGaulle."

"Okay, what do you want?"

"Ralph Knowles is the biggest horse's ass I know, and there are some very big horse's asses in this industry. I want you to make sure he understands *exactly* what he's going to say before he testifies, and that he doesn't say a word that would lead anyone to think he even *suspected* there was a copy of *Catchpole* in our files out there on the Coast."

"Did he know there was a copy of the play in our files?"

"I don't know what he knew or didn't know. Directors are to me traffic cops, and worse than actors. The only good director I ever met was the one who dropped dead on the sound stage of a picture we were making, causing us to abandon it. He saved us a half-million dollars."

"All right, I'll see that Knowles is carefully prepared."

"See that he's more than carefully prepared. Put the words in his mouth, let him memorize them. He wrote his screenplay from Driscoll's book, he consulted only Driscoll's book, he followed Driscoll's book to the letter, making only those changes necessary to adapt it to the screen. Like everyone else at API, he had no idea Driscoll was a crook."

"Leo," Sam said, "do you want to *win* this case, or simply lose it with honor?"

"I want to keep my job," Kessler said.

"Un-huh."

"Win it, lose it, I don't give a damn—so long as API comes

out clean. And if that means throwing Driscoll to the wolves or the lions or whoever, then throw him and good riddance. I'm not married to him."

"Well," Sam said, and paused. "If it's any consolation, I think we'll win it, anyway. In fact, I don't see how we can lose."

"So win it. Am I telling you to lose the damn thing? What do you think this is, a club fight in New Jersey? I saw that picture, thank you. It was with Robert Ryan."

"Julie Garfield."

"That was another one."

The office went silent. Sam looked at his watch. "What time does Knowles get in?" he asked.

"Late tonight. He'll be ready for you tomorrow morning."

"We'll be starting with Chester Danton tomorrow morning."

"Well, when will Knowles go on the stand?"

"In the afternoon, most likely. That's up to Willow. He's running the case, we agreed to that."

"Then you've got plenty of time to talk to him."

"Yes."

"What's the matter?" Kessler asked.

"Nothing."

"What's the look on your face?"

"I was thinking of Driscoll."

"What about him?"

"All the poor bastard did was write a book."

By six-thirty that evening, the three men had each consumed four martinis, and the atmosphere at their table was convivial and relaxed, to say the least. Even James Driscoll, whom Jonah usually found rather reserved, seemed cheerful and optimistic, and it was he who suggested they have another drink before parting. Jonah was not ready to part just yet, not until he had fully discussed what was on his mind. He readily agreed to the fifth drink, and Norman Sheppard raised his arm to signal the waiter.

"What we're asking you to do," Jonah said, "is to reconstruct the events that led to your calling your division the 105th. That's all we're really trying to do."

"The hell with it," Driscoll said.

"No, we can't say the hell with it," Jonah said.

"We're having a good time here," Driscoll said. "The hell with it."

"We won't have such a good time if we lose this case," Norman said. "That's why we're asking you to try to remember, Jimmy. Try to remember how you hit upon those three digits."

"I just did," Driscoll said.

"But how?"

"I don't remember."

"Well, think about it."

"I *am* thinking about it."

"Maybe you've got some notes on it," Norman said. "You've supplied us with a lot of other material, so perhaps . . ."

"No, I wouldn't have kept notes on anything like that."

"All we're trying to do is trace the origin, that's all."

"It's a coincidence, plain and simple," Driscoll said.

"I think I'm getting drunk," Jonah said suddenly.

"I *know* I'm getting drunk," Driscoll said, and laughed. "That's good. Relax from the trial."

"We can't relax," Norman said.

"*I* can relax," Driscoll answered.

"I wish *I* could relax," Jonah said, and removed his glasses and wiped his eyes. His eyes were a pale blue. He pressed them with thumb and forefinger and then replaced his glasses.

"Brackman is going to harp on that 105th Division," Norman said, "and unless you can come up with a reasonable explanation, I feel we're going to be in trouble. I think those are Jonah's feelings as well, aren't they, Jonah?"

"Let me say that the coincidence unless explained will seem extraordinary."

"Well, it *is* extraordinary," Driscoll said. "I think a great *many* of the similarities between my book and the play are extraordinary."

"On Monday afternoon, I drove up to Vassar," Jonah said. "To see a friend of mine who teaches World History there. Now, I know your novel takes place during October and November of 1950, and that the action you describe was against the Chinese—but is it possible you also ran into some North Korean troops?"

"No."

"You did not?"

"I did not."

"Is it possible you overheard talk about engagements with North Korean troops?"

"It's possible, I suppose. Most of the talk was about Chinese intervention, though. We kept wondering when it would happen—even after it *did* happen."

"Would you recall anyone mentioning the North Korean 105th?"

"No. Should I?"

"Well," Jonah said, and shrugged. "You never heard it mentioned, huh?"

"Not to my knowledge. Was it an infantry division?"

"No, it was an armored brigade."

"Then that lets it out, doesn't it?"

"Not necessarily," Norman said. "If we could show it was involved in—"

"It wasn't," Driscoll said. "The major battle in the book is against Chinese troops. And even the patrol is into territory held by the Chinese."

"Well, that's the end of *that* possibility," Norman said.

"That's what I thought on Monday," Jonah answered. "But I was hoping Jimmy would say, 'Why, yes, of course! I had a long discussion with some veterans of the June-July fighting, and they told me all about the 105th Armored Brigade and their Russian-built T-34 tanks."

"Why, yes, of course!" Driscoll said, grinning. "I *did* have a long discussion with some veterans of the June-July fighting, and they told me all about the 105th Armored Brigade and their Russian-built T-34 tanks."

"Chicane," Jonah said, "for which I could be disbarred." He shook his head. "You'll just have to remember where the 105th *really* came from."

"How can I? I don't *know* where it came from."

"Did you steal that play?" Jonah asked suddenly.

"I never stole anything in my life," Driscoll answered.

"Good," Jonah said.

"Do you believe me?"

"Yes."

"That's nice, because I don't give a damn whether you do or not," Driscoll said, and burst out laughing. "Here're our drinks. Let's forget the trial for a minute, can't we?"

"Brackman has already brought up this matter of the thief leaving his fingerprints," Norman said, "and I can assure you . . ."

"I'm not a thief," Driscoll said.

"Nobody said you were."

"Brackman said I was. And Constantine said I was. I didn't steal his play."

"Well, we know you didn't steal it," Norman said.

"How does it feel to be colored?" Driscoll asked.

"Fine," Norman said. "How does it feel to be white?"

"I only ask because Sergeant Morley in my book is colored, and I often wondered while I was writing it how it feels to be colored, how it *really* feels to be colored."

"Listen, Jimmy," Jonah said suddenly, "you'd better start thinking about this because I'll tell you the truth I'm very concerned about it, very very concerned."

"So am I," Norman said.

"So am I," Driscoll said.

"So start thinking about it," Jonah said.

"About what?"

"The 105th."

"Oh."

"Yes."

"I *have* been thinking about it."

"What was your serial number?"

"What?"

"Your Army serial number."

"714-5632."

"Where did you live before you went into the Army?"

"On Myrtle Avenue in Brooklyn."

"The address?"

"61 Myrtle."

"What was your telephone number?"

"Main 2-9970."

"Were you married at the time?"

"I got married two months before I was drafted."

"What was your wife's address?"

"Well, the apartment on Myrtle was hers, you see. I moved in with her after we got married."

"Where were you living before then?"

"With my parents."

"Where?"

"West End Avenue. 2426 West End."

"What floor, what apartment?"

"Apartment 12C."

"And on Myrtle Avenue?"

"Apartment 37."

"Your life seems singularly devoid of the number 105," Jonah said sourly, and lifted his drink.

"Did you have a car?" Norman asked.

"Yes."

"What was your license plate number?"

"Who the hell remembers?"

"Have you ever been to 105th Street?" Jonah asked.

"No."

"What high school did you go to?" Norman asked.

"Music and Art."

"Did you have a locker?"

"What?"

"A locker. For the gym."

"Oh. Yes, I had a locker."

"With a combination lock?"

"Yes."

"What was the combination?"

"24 right, 17 left, 14 right."

"How can you possibly remember that, but not your license plate number?"

"I didn't have to open my license plate every day of the week," Driscoll said.

"You will have to think harder," Jonah said.

"I don't have to think harder if I don't want to," Driscoll answered. "I don't have to think at *all,* if I don't want to." He picked up his glass and drank from it, and then put the glass down and stared into it, aware of the sudden silence at the table. Well, the hell with you, he thought. You sit here and throw questions at me, don't you think any of this *means* anything to me, Ebie's apartment on Myrtle Avenue, and the telephone number I called maybe ten thousand times, or the old Buick I used to drive when I first started at Pratt, and my locker at Music and Art, or the apartment on West End Avenue?

I can remember every inch of that apartment the way it used to look when Pop was still alive and before my mother sold all the furniture and brought in that Danish modern crap which my father would have thrown out of the house in a minute. But her new husband Mr. Gerald Furst is in the furniture business, so what else do you do but throw out all the old mahogany stuff and bring in a sleek new line to go with your sleek new husband? The piano, too, getting rid of that. Well, nobody played it but Pop, and he's been dead for five years, so I suppose she was right in giving it away. Christ, the way he used to sit at the piano with a tumbler of whiskey resting on the arm, banging out those Irish songs while Uncle Benny stood there singing at the top of his lungs. Pink shirts. Uncle Benny always used to wear pink shirts. And Pop would offer me a sip of booze, and I'd turn my head away, pulling a face, things sure change. Here I am getting squiffed in a bar, thirty-seven years old, things sure change. Everything changes. Even Uncle Benny finally got married and moved off to Fort Lauderdale.

He could draw like an angel, that man. I would have given my *soul* to be able to draw like him when I was a kid, or even, for that matter, after I'd had more training than he'd ever had in his life. You stuck a pencil in Uncle Benny's hand, and he would conjure a world for you, name it and Uncle Benny would draw it. It was he who first got me hooked, the sweet old pusher whispering to the innocent kid, Hey, Jimbo, want to try this? Guiding my hand along the page at first, showing me how to copy things from the newspaper comic strips, easy stuff at first like Mickey Mouse and Donald Duck, all clear sharp heavy lines, and then into the more complicated stuff from *Abby an' Slats,* or *Prince Valiant.* I did a marvelous copy of the Viking with the red beard who used to be in *Prince Valiant,* what was his name? I colored his beard the same color it was in the paper, and I also did one of Val himself swinging that mighty singing sword of his against a man with a helmet that looked something like an upended garbage pail. Uncle Benny said the perspective was off, but he praised the drawing anyway. I used to have a terrible handwriting in those days, so I would ask Uncle Benny to sign all my work for me, J. R. Driscoll, which was James Randolph Driscoll, the Randolph being in honor of my grandfather, who died when I was only four months old. Uncle Benny would sign each of my drawings in the lower right-hand corner, J. R. Driscoll, and then outline the signature with a narrow box that had a very heavy line on the bottom and on the right-hand side, so that it looked as if it were throwing a shadow on the page. I colored that guy's beard with crayon, what the hell was his name?

Pop wasn't much help in the art department, except in terms of criticism, *You made his nose too long,* or *Whoever saw a dog with a tail like that?* But he was very proud of the work I did, and always asked me to bring it out whenever any of his cronies from Gimbel's stopped by. He was an upholsterer, my father, and he used to work for Gimbel's, an uneducated man who nonetheless taught himself to play the piano and who studied the dictionary night after night, taking it a page at a time and learning new words which he would spring on all of us while we sat at dinner in the big dining room overlooking the Hudson. "Do you know what a dimissory letter is?" or "What is the meaning of equitation?" or "What is the difference between geminate and germinate?" I remember one night especially because he gave us a word which became the basis for a game we later played. He said, "Use the word caruncle in a sentence," and I said, "Caruncle Benny have some more mashed potatoes?" and Pop almost died laughing, though my mother didn't think it was funny at all. In fact, I doubt if she even got it. But Pop invented the game called Caruncle, and we used to play it two or three nights a week, the three of us sitting on the brown sofa near the old Chickering, while my mother sat in the wing chair tatting; she used to make these antimacassars which she gave to everyone at Christmas, and which always looked faded and dirty when you put them on the furniture. The game Caruncle had no real rules and we played it by ear each time, the way my father played the piano. The idea was to give a word which the next person would then define incorrectly. For example, if my father used the word "disseminate," my uncle might have defined it by saying, "When you disseminate, it means you make a distinction," and then I would say, "No, that's discriminate," and my father would say, "No, discriminate is when you burn your garbage," and Uncle Benny would say, "No, that's incinerate," and I would say, "No, incinerate is when you hint at something," and Pop would say, "No, that's insinuate," and Uncle Benny would say, "No, insinuate is meat on Friday," and we would always end up laughing. Another word game we played was called Progression and was a variation of Ghost, except that the idea here was to make a new word on each turn by adding a letter to the word we already had. Pop might start with the word "man," and Uncle Benny would add a letter and change it to "mane," and then I would make it "mange," and Pop would make it "manger" and Uncle Benny would make it "manager," and so on. Or I might start with "rid" and Pop would make it "dire," and Uncle Benny would make it "rived" and I would make it "divers" and Pop would make it "diverse," the idea being to reach ten letters which was the highest score and which hardly anyone ever got. My mother never played any of these word games with us. She had an Irish brogue and was ashamed of it.

When I was about twelve years old, I made up the comic strip called *The Cat.* It was a direct steal from *Batman.* My character was a very wealthy socialite named Jim Dirkson, which name I arrived at by transposing the letters of my own name and substituting a letter here and there. The Cat was dedicated to fighting crime and evil. He wore a black costume just like Batman's, except that his face mask had whiskers on it. Uncle Benny helped me lay out the panels, and he also did all the lettering in the balloons. It was in full color, though I used Mongol pencils instead of ink. I did forty-eight panels, which I figured was enough for about twelve days, and I asked Pop if he thought I should try sending it around to the newspapers. He said, "Sure, why not? It's an excellent comic," but I never did submit it because I didn't think it was good enough. Besides, I felt funny about Uncle Benny having done all the lettering. I didn't know at the time that a lot of comic strip artists hire people just to do their lettering for them. After I saw *Pinocchio,* I decided I would make an animated movie, even though I didn't have either a camera or the faintest understanding of single-frame photography. I created all these characters freely stolen from the film, including one called Swat Fly, who was based on Jiminy Cricket and who even carried an umbrella the way he did. But I also had a two-headed giant named Galoppo, whom Walt Disney had never even dreamt of. The two heads were constantly arguing with each other. I borrowed Pop's old Remington and began typing up the outline of the movie, starting in this tiny star-washed village (like the village in *Pinocchio*) and showing Swat Fly walking down the cobblestoned street and searching for the shop of a poor-but-honest butcher named Ham. Well. I got through six pages of it, single-spaced, but nothing seemed to be happening, so I gave it up. Uncle Benny liked the sketches I'd made of the characters, however, and only casually hinted that they were somewhat derivative. "That's when you make fun of something," I said, and Pop immediately said, "No, that's derisive," and Uncle Benny said, "No, derisive are on either side of Manhattan Island."

Uncle Benny drank a lot. My mother used to call him "a disgosting drunk." He was Pop's brother, and he slept in the end bedroom, next to my room. He worked in a pool parlor, and once he took me there and ran off a whole rack for me, and then taught me how to hold the cue and how to put English on a ball, and he taught me a trick shot with which I later won a lot of money, making bets in the Army; I never forgot that shot he taught me. He also taught me geometry when I was flunking it at Music and Art. Numbers always threw me, I never was good at arithmetic. When I started geometry, there was suddenly more than numbers to cope with; there were angles and curves and Given this, Prove that, and I got hopelessly lost in the first three weeks. Uncle Benny stepped in, telling me he had once won a medal in math, and then proceeding to drill me every night, going over each formula again and again, "There, now wasn't that easy, Jimbo?" painstakingly working through every problem until he was certain I understood completely. I used to wake up in the middle of the night sometimes and see triangles and circles floating in the air, equilateral has three sixty-degree angles and three equal sides, isosceles has two equal sides, circumference equals π r^2. I ended up with a 90 on the Regents exam, thanks to Uncle Benny's persistence. He gave me a Bulova watch when I graduated from Music and Art. Engraved on the case was the inscription "To a geometrid genus," which was an inside joke based on Caruncle, "from your loving Uncle Benny."

My best friend at Music and Art was a colored fellow named Andrew Christopher, who was an art major like myself but who also played trombone in the school band. Andy lived on Lenox Avenue and 123rd Street, and I would meet him each morning on the 125th Street platform of the Broadway-7th Avenue Line, which I took up from 96th Street, and which we rode together to 137th Street. We would walk up past City College and then to the school, talking about everything under the sun, but mostly about his girl friend whose name was Eunice and who went to Washington Irving High School where she was studying fashion design. Eunice was a light-skinned girl and her parents objected to Andy simply because he was darker than she. He told me this very openly, and neither of us felt any embarrassment talking about it. It was just one of the facts of life. I never went to Andy's house, though, and he never came to mine. My mother used to call Negroes "boogies."

Andy and I both won scholarships to the Art Students League in January of 1957, after we got out of Music and Art. We had submitted samples of our work in a city-wide competition, and I think only Andy and me, and a girl from Evander Childs and another girl from a school in Brooklyn were chosen, though I still can't figure why. We really weren't that good. The first day we went to the school, they showed us around the various classes so that we could decide which courses we wanted to take—we were allowed to take two courses—and at the front of one of the classrooms there was what we thought was a white plaster statue of a naked woman until she moved. We both signed up for that course, which was Life Drawing, and we also signed up for Oil Painting. I was lousy with oils. The thing I hated most about them was cleaning up afterwards. The girl from Brooklyn had red hair, and we called her Flatbush. She was always speculating about why a girl would take off her clothes and pose naked. Both Andy and I got the impression that Flatbush would have very much enjoyed taking off her clothes and posing naked. The scholarship ended in June, by which time Andy and I were both jaded by the sight of all those naked women draped on the posing stand, and by which time I had taken the entrance exam for Pratt Institute. I was notified in July that I had been accepted. And in that same month, when Andy insisted that I pay him the dime I'd bet him on the Yankee-White Sox game, I said, "Come on, don't be so niggardly," and he got upset and refused to believe there was such a word and that it meant stingy or cheap or miserly or parsimonious. He said to me, "I knew it would come sooner or later, Jimmy, and you're a son of a bitch." Andy said that to me. Maybe I did mean niggardly, maybe I *really* meant niggardly. Or maybe, accustomed to playing word games almost every night of the week, twisting meanings and spellings and generally slaughtering the language, maybe I was making another pun, and maybe Andy was right to get sore, I don't know.

He went to Cooper Union in September, to study art there, and I never saw him again.

"I think I smell wood burning," Jonah said.

"Yes, indeed," Norman said. "He is thinking very hard, Jonah."

"My brother always used to say he smelled wood burning," Jonah said.

"Can you remember where that 105th came from?" Norman asked.

"No," Driscoll said.

"You've *got* to remember," Jonah said.

"Why? I'm not even being sued. I think I ought to remind you gentlemen of that fact."

"Not serving you was a little gambit Mr. Brackman will come to regret," Jonah said.

"Why wasn't I served?"

"I asked that very same question in a Georgia restaurant once," Norman said, and laughed.

"What did they say?" Driscoll asked.

"They said the cook had gone home."

"*Had* he gone home?"

"Certainly not. The cook was my cousin," Norman said, and laughed again.

"My wife is a Southerner, you know," Driscoll said.

"Yes, I know."

"I don't think she's consciously prejudiced, however," he said, and finished his drink. "Would anyone care for another martini?"

"Only unconsciously?" Norman asked.

"What do you mean?"

"Prejudiced?"

"No, I don't think so. She's a very nice girl, Ebie. Yes. Do you know how she got to be named Ebie?"

"No, how?"

"Edna Belle," Driscoll said.

"Huh?"

"Edna."

"Yes?"

"Belle."

"Yes."

"E and B."

"I don't get it."

"E. B. Ebie."

"That's very clever," Norman said. "Let's have another drink."

"I think we ought to work out this 105th Division," Jonah said.

"The hell with the 105th Division," Driscoll said. "Let Brackman work it out. Why *didn't* he serve me?"

"He was hoping you'd wash your hands of the whole thing."

"I almost did."

"What made you change your mind?"

"I knew Mitchell-Campbell would have brought me in, anyway."

"It's best you joined the action voluntarily," Jonah said.

"Best for whom?"

"For all of us."

"If we win this case, you know . . ." Driscoll started, and then shook his head.

"Yes."

"No, never mind."

"What were you about to say?"

"Nothing. Let's have another drink."

"That's a good idea," Norman said.

"Don't you have to get home?" Jonah asked.

"What's the hurry? You think the rats'll get lonely?"

"Have you got rats?" Driscoll asked.

"Very *large* rats."

"What are their names?" Driscoll asked, and Norman burst out laughing.

"Have you really got rats?" Jonah asked.

"Absolutely."

"You ought to get out of Harlem."

"I can't."

"Why not? You make enough money."

"My mother likes it there."

"My mother likes it on West End Avenue," Driscoll said.

"West End Avenue ain't Lenox Avenue," Norman said.

"That's for sure. Hey, waiter, we want another round."

"Listen, we've got to get back to this," Jonah said. "The 105th Division appears in *The Catchpole,* and it also . . ."

"Catchpole," Norman corrected. "There is no article. You have been told that several times already, Mr. Willow, and I'll thank you to refer to the play by its proper name."

"Yes, but nonetheless," Jonah said, laughing, "if we can discover how you hit upon that number when you were contemplating your novel, we could—"

"When I was contemplating my *navel,* you mean," Driscoll said.

"That's very clever," Norman said, laughing. "Have you ever tried writing?"

"Too serious a business," Driscoll said.

"Law is a very serious business, too," Norman said. "Let's open a whore house."

"I wish you gentlemen would try to be properly serious," Jonah said. "There's a great deal of stakes here. *At* stakes. *Stake."*

"Jonah is drunk," Norman said.

"I will concede that, your Honor," Jonah said.

"Thank you," Driscoll said to the waiter, and then lifted his glass. "Gentlemen, I give you the play named *Maypole* and the novel named *The Paper Asshole,* and I defy you—I defy you, gentlemen—to find any real difference between these two *oeuvres,* which is French for eggs. In the play we have a degenerate leper who writes to Dr. Schweitzer, asking how he can cure his vile leching after twelve-year-olds. This same pervert is present in the novel, only this time he writes to Graham Greene for advice, and Greene being an expert only on leprosy advises him to write to Vladimir Nabokov, who is an expert on lechery. The similarity stands. In the novel, on page seventy-four, the girl enters, and she has two breasts—*two* breasts, gentlemen—exactly as in the play. I submit that a girl with two breasts is a unique invention, and I defy you to explain this remarkable coincidence, these footprints left in the sand by the thief. Now, I am not an expert on such matters, but I am willing to bet that the possibility of finding *two* young girls in the same room, both of whom have *two* breasts—gentlemen, this staggers the imagination. That is the plaintiff's case, your Honor, and I drink to it."

"All right, what about this 105th Precinct?" Jonah asked briskly.

"Division."

"Yes, what about it?"

"It's there," Driscoll said.

"Where?"

"In my book."

"It's also in the play," Jonah said. "So how about it?"

"How about it? *It's* there, and *we're* here, so the hell with it."

"I wish you could explain it," Jonah said. "I seriously wish you could explain it."

"I won't."

"What?"

"I said I can't."

"You said you won't."

"I meant I can't."

"Jimmy," Norman said, "do you *know* why you labeled your division the 105th?"

Driscoll looked across the table and said, "No, I do not. And that's the God's honest truth."

As the big jet orbited Kennedy in a holding pattern, Ralph Knowles wondered if the field were still open, and once again conjured an image of the giant airliner skidding around on the runway as it braked to a stop. The forecasters early that afternoon had reported heavy snowstorms all along the Eastern seaboard, and he had called Kessler collect from the Coast to ask whether it was still imperative that he come east today.

"Can't it wait till tomorrow?" he had asked. "I don't want to die in a goddamn airplane skidding around in the snow."

"That's not funny, God forbid," Kessler said, even though Knowles hadn't been trying to make a joke. "You will probably be called to testify tomorrow afternoon, so you get on that plane and come east like a good boy, and stop worrying about a little snow."

"It's a *lot* of snow, from what I hear," Ralph said.

"They always exaggerate out there," Kessler answered. "It's to make you appreciate California."

"But is it still snowing?"

"Just a little."

"Well then maybe . . ."

"Ralph, this trial is important," Kessler said. "Now you just get on that plane—what plane are you getting on?"

"The four-thirty flight."

"You just get on it, and let me worry about the snow."

"I knew you could move mountains," Ralph said, "but I didn't know you could also stop snow."

"That's not funny, either," Kessler had said. "Do me a favor, and don't ever direct a comedy for us."

He could see lights below. It was never like Los Angeles, where the approach to the city was beautiful, truly beautiful, reds and greens and whites spilled across the landscape, he sometimes felt like weeping as the plane banked in over the airport, not the same here at all. He had never liked New York City, too damn big and dirty, noisy people rushing around all the time, business deals over breakfast and lunch and cocktails and dinner, no nice backyard barbecues, never any sunshine, rotten place New York, he hated it.

He shouldn't be coming here now, either, should be going in the opposite direction to meet Matt Jackson in Japan where they'd be shooting the new picture, not coming east to testify at a stupid trial, as if the trial meant anything anyway. Specious case according to what he'd heard at the studio, absolutely groundless, should have kicked it out of court, bring a man all the way east for something as dumb as this, waste of time. Only reason he was bothering was because Kessler seemed to be making an important thing of it, couldn't antagonize Kessler, not now, not when the Samurai picture was going to cost so much. Had to hold hands with the old man, six million dollars wasn't cornflakes.

The stewardess was walking up the aisle checking seatbelts, nice knockers on her, Ralph thought, how would you like me to film those beauties, honey, in wide-screen Technicolor, she doesn't even know who I am. It disturbed him that nobody ever knew who the hell he was. He always got the choice seat on a plane only because API's transportation department made sure of it, but every time he boarded the plane he could see the disappointed look on the face of the stewardess. Since API had reserved the seat, the airlines people always expected a movie star or a director they could recognize, like Hitchcock or Huston or Preminger. He knew he was a better director than any of them, but who ever recognized his face, nobody. Or, for that matter, did anyone outside the industry even recognize his *name,* seventeen movies to his credit, all of them hits, well, most of them. Anyway, ten of them. Ten resounding box-office successes, shattering spectacle *Variety* had called one of them, and this Samurai thing would undoubtedly be another big blockbuster, provided Kessler didn't balk at the six million price tag, well why should he? He wanted a hit, didn't he? Everybody in America, everybody in the world wanted a hit, I know how to deliver hits, Ralph thought, ten of them in a row, twelve if you count the critical but not box-office bonanzas, you have to spend money to make money, Kessler knows that, he'll be very sweet about the whole thing, he's a sweet old Jew bastard. God, this trial is a pain in the ass, should be heading for Tokyo, wonder if Matt has set everything up, those Japanese do good work, even Kurosawa has his face in the magazines more than I do. Open any magazine, there's *Huston* grinning up at you, it makes me want to puke. Hitchcock? don't even mention him. Supposed to begin shooting next week, can't be wasting all this time in New York, still I'll talk to Kessler about the money, getting the money is important.

"Why aren't we landing?" he asked the stewardess. "Is there snow on the field?"

"No, sir."

"There's snow on the field, isn't there?" he whispered. "You can tell me."

"No, sir, there are just several airplanes ahead of us, that's all."

"That's all, huh?"

"Yes, sir."

"How old are you?"

"Twenty-two, sir."

"That's a good age."

"For what?"

"For anything."

"Are you going to put me in pictures?" she asked, and then smiled and went up the aisle to talk to the other stewardess.

Bet she knows who I am, Ralph thought. What the hell, I'm not *that* anonymous. Maybe she saw the article they did on me in the *Saturday Evening Post,* the one that had that good shot of me when we were on location down there near Juarez, man it gets hot as hell down there in Mexico, those mules, what a stink. Must have seen that piece on me, the shot wearing the white ducks, bare-chested, all brown, the gray hair, that was a good picture of me. Have to ask her what her name is, look her up maybe, show her a good time. Must know who I am, otherwise why the crack about putting her in pictures, I'll put you someplace all right, baby.

They were coming down.

Ralph caught his breath, certain the field would be

covered with snow, no matter what anybody said. The descent seemed very rapid, they never did it this way in Los Angeles. The stewardess was hurrying down the aisle again, he wondered what her name was, too fast, this damn plane was coming down too fast.

"Miss?" he said.

"I'm sorry, sir, I have to take a seat now," the stewardess answered.

"Aren't we coming down too fast?"

"No, sir."

"What's your name?"

"I have to take a seat now."

"I'll talk to you when we land."

"All right."

"You've got great knockers," he whispered.

"I know," she whispered back, and then walked forward to take a seat in the lounge.

This was the worst part of any flight, it scared him senseless. Closer and closer to the ground, he could see buildings capped with thick snow now, were they sure none of it was on the field, everything blurring as the plane leveled, the bump of the wheels, and then the noise of the jets as the engines were reversed, the sudden lurch of the plane slowing, "We have landed at Kennedy International Airport," the stewardess said, "please remain seated until we have taxied to the terminal building and all engines are stopped. The temperature in New York is thirty-seven degrees, and the local time is twelve-seventeen A.M. Thank you for flying with us. We hope to serve you again in the future."

I hope to serve *you* in the *very* near future, Ralph thought, and kept watching her as the plane taxied. Before he left the aircraft, he asked her what her name was and where she stayed in New York. She told him her name was Sylvia Mott, and she was engaged to a boy in Pasadena, and she never dated anyone else, but it had been a pleasure flying with him, nonetheless, and she really hoped she *could* serve him again in the future.

"Thanks a lot," Ralph said, and went down the steps and walked to the baggage pickup area.

Sam Genitori was waiting there for him, small consolation.

By one o'clock that morning, the snow had stopped completely, and Hester Miers took off her shoes and went walking barefoot in the plaza outside the Seagram Building, parading past the pools and the small lighted Christmas trees. Arthur was not terribly surprised.

He was not surprised because she had been exhibiting all through supper this same phony *joie de vivre,* the single identifying characteristic of any actress he had ever met. The quality was deceptive at first. He had recognized it only belatedly in Eileen Curtis, the young lady who had played Lieutenant Diane Foster in *Catchpole.* There had been a curiosity about Eileen, a vitality, an intense concern that was contagious and inspiring. He could never be in her presence without feeling a pang of envy—God, if only *he* could be as concerned with life and living, if only *he* could bring such minute scrutiny to matters large and small, finding everyone interesting and alive, glowing with excitement at each suggested idea or phrase or isolated word, taking up the banner for any worthy cause, burning with energy, searching and working and learning and living, secure in the knowledge that this was the chosen profession, humbly grateful for the opportunity to be allowed to carry on this illuminating, sacrificing, enriching, and dedicated work.

He learned later on the Coast—where he was surrounded day and night by an intolerable army of actors and actresses—that Eileen Curtis's seeming love affair with life had merely been a love affair with herself. The same enormous ego and delicately executed phoniness were evident in Hester Miers, who squealed in delight over the crispness of the seeded rolls and smacked her lips over the "summer sweetness" of the butter, and then secretly asked him to observe the magnificent topaz brooch on the old lady at the next table, and then flirted with the waitress (the *waitress!*), using her humble and ingratiating Famous Actress smile, and then cooed over the marvelous glowing green of the Heineken bottle, and then asked Arthur if he believed in astrology, and then put five lumps of sugar in her coffee ("I *adore* it sweet, but I never stir it") and then asked the doorman outside whether it was still snowing, and to his respectful, "It stopped a half-hour ago, miss," replied in mystic meaningfulness, "Good, because it's only fair, you know," and then of course took off her shoes and hiked up her skirts and went running barefoot in the snow, "Oh, Arthur, it's deliciously cold."

This is the girl, he thought, who is supposed to play Carol, the simple daughter of an honest Bronx mailman. This is the girl.

He would have said good night to her then and there—oh, perhaps he would have helped her dry her feet, he was after all a gentleman—were it not for the fact that the presence of Hester Miers in his play would insure the capitalization. Had not Oscar Stern himself, cigar compressed between his lips, shivering in the alley of the Helen Hayes, replied only yesterday in answer to a foolish question, "Because if we can get Hester Miers to take this part, we'll raise all the money for the play immediately," had not the unquestionable Oscar said those very words only yesterday?

Yesterday was yesterday, of course, dead and gone. Yesterday the trial had begun, and by Thursday or Friday it would be concluded—but who knew when the judge would give his decision? If the judge said, "Why, yes, my son, you have been wronged, good Arthur Constantine," then he could tell Selig and Stern and even Hester Miers—who was romping in the snow now with her skirts up, fully aware that her legs were long and excellently shaped but trying to give the impression nonetheless of a six-year-old abandoning herself to her first wintry experience—he could tell all of them to go straight to hell because he would be in actual possession of, or at least in loan-acquiring promise of, ten million dollars or more. His hands began trembling.

Don't think about it, he told himself. You may *lose* this damn trial, stranger things have happened, don't even think about it. If you get Hester Miers, you get the money for the play, the play goes on, that's all you have to know. Don't think about the other, there's no fairness in this world, you learned that the night the critics killed *Catchpole* and Freddie Gerard began crying like a baby, "Why can't I bring in a winner, Arthur, why can't I ever bring in a winner?" Don't think about winning the trial, think only about getting Hester for the part. Think only about getting Hester.

She had admitted to being twenty-five years old, but Arthur suspected she was something closer to thirty. She was a tall, slender girl (she claimed she ate only one meal a day) with blond hair cut very close to her head in a haphazard coiffure, deliberately unkempt, and lending a look of overall unpredictability to her face. She was not a beautiful girl, nor could he even find anything terribly attractive about her, except perhaps her coltish legs. Her face was an elongated oval, her eyes brown and highlighted with black liner, her lipstick a pale orange on a mouth too generous for the rest of her features. A nose job had apparently been performed on her some time ago, but it was beginning to fall out of shape, and it gave her face a faintly lopsided look. She was definitely not pretty, and he was disappointed by her looks, but he kept reminding himself that she possessed a vibrant, almost luminous quality on stage, even though she looked like some kind of a jackass now, galloping around in the snow that way.

When she finally came over to him again, out of breath and flushed, he said, "What seems to be troubling you about the part?"

"Oh, I don't know."

"Well, *something* is."

"Oh, sure, something is."

"Well, what?"

"I don't know." Hester sat on the edge of the pool. The lighted Christmas trees behind her put a high gloss on her blond hair. She took a small lace-edged handkerchief from her bag, crossed her legs, and ineffectually began drying them.

"I think it's a perfect part for you," Arthur said.

"You do?"

"Certainly."

"I don't know."

"Really, Hester."

"Well, I don't know. You still haven't explained it to me. I wish you'd explain it to me," she said, and in the same breath added, "How tall are you?"

"Five-ten," Arthur said. "Seriously, Hester, I don't think Lincoln Center would object to your leaving. Not for a part like this one."

"I'm not sure about that," she answered. "Do you have a handkerchief?"

"Yes." He took a handkerchief from his breast pocket, unfolded it, and handed it to her.

"Thank you," she said. "I don't think Kazan liked me very much, but things are different now. I'm not sure they'd let me go just like that."

"It's a matter of how much you want the part, I guess," Arthur ventured.

"Yes, of course."

"So if there are any problems about it, I wish you'd tell me what they are."

"Oh, I don't know," Hester said, and rose suddenly, picking up her shoes in one hand, returning Arthur's handkerchief with the other, and then walking down the steps and onto Park Avenue barefooted, the shoes swinging at the end of her arm. Arthur took a deep breath, hesitated alongside the pool for a moment, and then followed her.

"This is the greatest street in the world," Hester said. "Tell me about Carol."

"Where do you want me to begin?"

"Where is she from?"

"The Bronx. That's pretty clear in the—"

"Do you know where I'm from?"

"No."

"Originally?"

"No, where?"

"You won't believe it."

"Try me," he said.

"Seattle, Washington. How about that?"

"Really?"

"Yes. My father was a lumberjack. Do you know you can get mugged on this street at this hour of the night, and your body dumped in the river?"

"No, I didn't know that. Carol . . ."

"A boy I know got mugged on Fifth Avenue, would you believe it?"

". . . is a girl who feels—"

"He was one of the gypsies in *Hello, Dolly.* This was after the show broke. He lived, I don't know, on 48th Street, I guess, and he was walking down Fifth Avenue, and these hoods jumped him. This city . . ."

"The Bronx is different, you know. Carol grew up in a neighborhood . . ."

"It's not *too* different really. You read about Bronx muggings all the time, don't you just love these reminders, 'Just a Drop in the Basket,' they really gas me."

The hell with it, Arthur thought, the goddamn rotten hell with it.

"You know what?" he said.

"What?"

"Actresses give me a severe pain in the ass," he said.

"Oh, really?" Hester said, and shrugged, and ran up the street to the corner, her arms raised winglike, the shoes dangling from one hand. "Oh, it's *marrr*-velous!" she shrieked. "Snow is *marrrrvelous!*"

Arthur walked slowly to the corner. There were lighted Christmas trees on the islands dividing the avenue, lighted trees perched on the marquee of the Sheraton-East, enormous wreaths hanging from the buildings, blues and greens reflecting on the snow. There was no wind, and the city was hushed. He felt like weeping.

"Would you like to know why actresses give me a severe pain?" he said angrily.

"In the ass," Hester amended. "You forgot in the ass."

"A severe pain in the ass, thank you. Would you like to know why?"

"No," Hester said. "I'll bet you always got the prettiest girl in the class, didn't you?"

"What?"

"You. Did you always get the prettiest girl?"

"What the hell are you talking about?"

"In your class."

"No, I always got the ugliest one," Arthur said.

"Do you think *I'm* pretty?"

"Not particularly."

"I have beautiful legs."

"Hester, do you want this goddamn part or not?"

"I *know* I have beautiful legs."

"Who *cares* about your legs?"

"You're not telling me anything I don't already know. In fact, you're boring me. Do you want to discuss your play, or do you want to go home?"

"I want to go home," Arthur said.

"Good night," she answered, and turned left on 52nd Street.

"No, wait a minute," he said.

"No, go home," she said. "Really, I'm bored to death. I was offered a part in a play by William Inge, did you know that? Just two weeks ago."

"No, I didn't know that."

"I could have had *After the Fall,* too, in spite of Kazan. I just didn't think it was right for me. But I could have had it."

"You'd have been terrible," Arthur said.

"That's beside the point. I could have had it if I wanted it. They think very highly of me at the Rep."

"I think very highly of you right here."

"Cut it out," she said.

"Cut *what* out?"

"When I was a struggling young actress, longer ago than I care to remember, a wise old lady said to me, 'Hester baby, don't ever ball a writer, a director, or a producer. It won't get you the part.' I followed her advice, and now I don't *have* to ball writers, directors, or producers."

"Who do you have to ball *now?*" Arthur asked.

"Don't get smart."

"I'm sorry, but I think I'm missing your point."

"My point is don't come on with me."

"I didn't know I was."

"You were," Hester said, "and the answer is no. Give me your arm, I want to put on my shoes." She caught his arm at the elbow and, leaning against him, put on first one shoe and then the other. "What are you smiling about?" she asked.

"Nothing."

"I don't like people who get dumb smiles on their face. How tall did you say you were?"

"Five-ten."

"That's short."

"It's not so short."

"It's short. I'm five-eight."

"Where do you live, Hester?"

"Over there someplace," she said, and gestured vaguely uptown. "In my stocking feet. I'm a very tall girl."

"I live on Fifty-fourth and Third," Arthur said.

"So?"

"Why don't we go there?"

"What for?"

"I'm cold."

"I'm not."

"We can discuss the play there."

"We can discuss it right here."

"Anyway, I'd like a drink."

"I know what you'd like."

"What would I like?"

"You'd like to jump right into bed with me."

"No, I only . . ."

"Forget it."

". . . want to discuss the play someplace where it's warm."

"If you want to discuss it, discuss it here."

"Okay."

"And stop smiling like that."

"Okay."

"Do you want me to play the part?"

"Yes."

"I don't believe you. I don't believe your character, and I don't believe you, either."

"Okay."

"Stop smiling. I don't even know if it's such a good play."

"It's a good play, believe me."

"Sure, you wrote it."

"It's still a good play, no matter who wrote it."

"I think it's a confusing play."

"It's real."

"My part is confusing."

"Your part?"

"The girl. Carol."

"She's honest."

"That's what's confusing."

"That's what's real."

"I don't know anybody like her."

"I do."

"She's impossible to play. I don't even *understand* her."

"I understand everything about her."

"Then *you* play her."

"No, you play her, Hester."

"I wouldn't know where to begin. Besides, why should I? Your last play was a flop."

"So was yours."

"That was before Lincoln Center."

"It was still a flop."

"I got rave notices."

"The critics hated the play."

"That doesn't mean it was bad."

"It closed, didn't it?"

"That wasn't my fault."

"Of course not, Hester. In New York, it's never the actor's fault."

"You're talking like a writer."

"What *should* I talk like?"

"You're being defensive and hostile . . ."

"But honest."

"Besides, the critics loved me."

"The hell with the critics."

"Oh, sure, the hell with them, I agree. But they loved me. Did you see the play?"

"Yes."

"Didn't *you* love me?"

"I loved you."

"You're lying."

"No, I'm being honest."

"Whenever I meet anybody who claims he's honest, I run and hide the family jewels. You just want me in your play, that's all."

"Is that all?"

"What else?"

"You're right, Hester."

"What?"

"About what else I want."

"I'm always right about what men want."

"I'd like to . . ."

"Stop working so hard," she said. She looked at him steadily. "You turned me on at least ten minutes ago."

. . . knew then I wanted to be an actress, and that nothing else would ever satisfy me, no wait here, I want to check. I have a woman sleeping in, you know, I think it's all right, yes, her door is closed. I put a television set in her room, one of those little GE's, do you know them? If she's awake I can hear the set going. I'll put the light on when we get upstairs, watch the flowerpot on the bottom step. Do you really like my legs, you never *did* say you liked them, you know. My bedroom is at the other end of the hall, there's a little wrought iron balcony that overlooks the backyard, there are dozens of daffodils in bloom in the spring, I go out every morning to say hello to them. I put them in myself last year, the bulbs. A boy dying of leukemia sent them to me, he wrote the nicest letter. His parents had taken him to see me downtown, knowing he was going to die and all, they own a seed order business upstate. He sent me the daffodil bulbs later, with this marvelous letter telling me what a dazzling actress he thought I was, and how beautiful, do you think I'm beautiful? I planted them myself last fall. I bought one of those tools, it's a hollow circle you press into the earth, it makes the hole just the right depth, and I planted them all one afternoon, there were four dozen of them. They came in a specially protected bag, you should see them now, they're gorgeous. I go out to look at them each morning in the spring, and I feel the world is coming alive, even though that poor lovely little boy is probably dead by now, leukemia, what a terrible thing. I wrote him a nice thank-you note, I hope he died happy, give me your hand, it's this way.

I don't want to put the light on, do you mind? Let's just sit here by the window. I bought this loveseat in London at the Portobello market, do you like it, it's red velvet, you can't see the color in the dark, I know, but it's the most brilliant red, and really in excellent condition. It's a genuine antique, you know, the man gave me papers for it and everything, sit here, are you comfortable? I sometimes sit here by the window and look out at the city and try to superimpose London on it, those marvelous little slate roofs, and the chimney pots, and the London sounds. I try to transport them here. I knew a very wonderful man in London, he was a correspondent for the B.B.C., they came to interview the cast one day. This was two summers ago, the weather was so marvelously sunny and bright, so rare for London, so rare. I was there with *The Alchemist,* which was like carrying coals to Newcastle, I suppose, but they seemed to love it. The critics said I was radiant, I adore the English, don't you adore the English? He had a mustache, this man in London, a big bristling cavalry mustache, and very blue English eyes, and that florid complexion all Englishmen seem to have, that fine aquiline nose, very much like your nose, Arthur, you're not English, are you? We had tea at the Stafford, and I told him all about myself, I am Hester Miers, I said, I've been acting since the time I was sixteen and won a high school contest sponsored by KJR in Seattle, well not quite *all* about myself, I've never told anyone everything about myself, do you mind the dark? I love to make the room dark. When the drapes are closed, the blackness, try to see my eyes in the dark, Arthur. Put your face very close to mine, can you see my eyes? Kiss me.

In Clovelly, you can walk miles down to the sea, a cobbled path goes down the side of the cliff, it's teeming with Englishmen on holiday.

He took me there one weekend and bought me a dish of ice cream from an old man in one of the shops, Bed and Breakfast the signs all say. He got stung by a bee while we lay in the grass on the side of the hill, the weather still so beautifully mild and bright, we lay in the high grass, and the bee flew into his open collar and stung him on the back of his neck. Oh, you should have seen him fuss, the big baby, ranting and shouting, you'd think he was about to die, I couldn't stop laughing, Arthur, it was *so* funny. On the way to Dorset, we drove up Porlock Hill, do you know what heather looks like? The hill was covered with heather, and sheep grazing, and we got out of the car and looked out over the sea, with the wind howling, I hugged my sweater around me. I was wearing a blue cashmere I'd bought in Birmingham in the Ring, have you ever been there, it's a science-fiction city, you must touch me, Arthur. George Bernard Shaw had one of his plays done there for the first time, at the Birmingham Rep, that was before the bombings, touch me everywhere.

Is it really a good part, Arthur? I read a play nowadays, and I can't tell anymore, it used to be so easy. When I was hungry, *every* part was a good part, and I wanted them all, I wanted to play every woman ever invented. And now I can't tell anymore, do you know how old I am? I'm twenty-five years old, did I tell you that? How old is Carol supposed to be, she's younger than that, isn't she? Are you really sure you want me to take the part? Arthur, I hope you don't think, Oh God, you're so warm, I hope you don't think there's a connection, I hope you haven't got it in your mind that this has anything to do with whether I play the part or not, because it doesn't. It wouldn't matter, it *doesn't* matter, oooh, what are you doing, I *love* it, there's no connection between this and the play, don't you see, this is something *else*. She's so young, how could I play a girl so young, is she supposed to be a virgin? He said I had no breasts, in Ohio this was, do you like my breasts? I was playing summer stock there, I was only seventeen. The moment he said it my nipples began to show through my sweater, and he knew, oh *boy* did he know, he was a very wise old bastard, he knew from the first day the summer began. He made love to me on the floor of the theater, upstairs where we used to paint the flats, we could hear them rehearsing down below, they were doing *Winterset,* the girl playing Mariamne was having trouble with her lines, she kept repeating them over and over again while he made love to me, oh God I was *so* excited, I was only a *girl,* Arthur, I was only seventeen. I really *don't* know about this play of yours or the confused girl in it, it's driving me crazy, I *mean* it, she is *really* a very confused person. Oh, I admit it would be a challenge, don't misunderstand me, the smell of the paint and Mariamne's lines, *And I came back because I must see you again. And we danced together and my heart hurt me,* I learned the part that afternoon, what a *long* afternoon, but I can't remember his name, isn't that funny? I'd just hate to accept your play and then disappoint you, I couldn't bear that, Arthur, disappointing anyone. I can't bear failing anyone. If I thought my note to that poor lovely boy, do I excite you, that poor lovely boy with leukemia, do I excite you very much, had failed him, well I just couldn't bear the thought, give me your cock. You have a big beautiful cock.

WEDNESDAY

It was a cast-iron day, bitter and brooding, with fierce winds lashing the streets, and dark clouds menacing the city. Sometime during the night the temperature had plummeted to six above zero, and the freshly fallen snow had hardened to form a thick, impenetrable crust. By morning, the situation had scarcely improved, the temperature hovering in the teens, the wind keening over ice-covered streets, solemn clouds above threatening further snow.

The courtroom was sunless and dim. Gusts of wind shuddered along the length of each long high window, rattling the panes. A cold hard light streamed through the windows, draining the wood-paneled walls of their luster, tinting the room and its occupants a solemn gray. Even Chester Danton, pink-faced and pink-pated, seemed to lose some of his high flushed color as his name was called and he walked from the jury box to the witness chair. Jonah watched him as he moved into the aura of harsh light spilling through the windows. He was a rotund little man with fierce black eyebrows and a hooked nose. He wore a brown suit, and he walked with a rolling gait, pausing and then pulling up his trouser leg to preserve the crease as he climbed onto the stand and turned to face the clerk. Jonah's wrist was hurting him. Tiny darts of pain radiated from the bones into his arm, triggering memories of the accident, and then of Sally, and then of the little Egyptian and his flaring anger against the man, his murderous anger. In the jury box, James Driscoll sat with his wife, both of them intently watching Danton as he raised his hand preparatory to taking the oath.

". . . whole truth and nothing but the truth, so help you God?"

"I do," Danton said.

Jonah massaged his right wrist, and then rose from behind the defense table to walk toward Danton, who sat expectantly, his bushy brows lowered, his dark eyes glowering beneath them.

"What do you do for a living, Mr. Danton?" he asked.

"I work for Mitchell-Campbell Books."

"What do you do there?"

"I'm an editor."

"And your title?"

"Executive vice-president."

"Did you work for Mitchell-Campbell in July of 1962?"

"I did."

"In the same capacity?"

"Yes, sir."

"Had you ever heard of James Driscoll before July of 1962?"

"No, sir."

"Or seen any of his work?"

"No, sir."

"When was the first time you saw anything written by James Driscoll?"

"In July of 1962."

"What was this writing?"

"A hundred pages of a novel in progress, together with an outline of the remainder of the novel."

"And the title?"

"The Enemy."

Jonah nodded and walked back to the defense table. Norman handed him a sheet of paper which he carried back to the witness chair with him. "Mr. Danton, would you look at this, please?" he said, and offered the sheet to Danton, who glanced at it summarily, and then looked up at Jonah again.

"Would you please tell the Court what this is," Jonah said.

"It's an editorial report form used by Mitchell-Campbell Books."

"Was it in use in 1962?"

"Yes, and still is."

"In this identical style and shape?"

"Yes, identical."

"What is its purpose?"

"There are a great many people at Mitchell-Campbell who read manuscripts. Each person so doing is required to record his or her reaction to the manuscript on a form such as this one."

"Does this particular form refer to a specific manuscript?"

"Yes, it refers to James Driscoll's partial novel *The Enemy,* and it is dated July 12, 1962. The novel came in over the transom and was sent directly to me, and this is my first report on it."

"By 'over the transom' you mean . . ."

"I mean it was simply mailed to Mitchell-Campbell Books, without being addressed to any specific person in the company."

"Is it usual for a manuscript to come immediately to the attention of an executive vice-president?"

"No, the first readings are usually made by others in the company. But I had edited several war novels for the firm, and it was assumed I would have special interest in a novel of this sort. I imagine that's why it was directed to me."

"You said a hundred pages . . ."

"I see the number of pages is listed in the report. It was ninety-eight pages."

"Of a novel titled *The Enemy.*"

"Yes."

"Did this later become *The Paper Dragon?*"

"Yes, sir."

"I would like to offer this in evidence," Jonah said, and handed a copy of the report to Brackman.

Brackman glanced at it, and then said, "I do not see its relevance, your Honor."

"If your Honor please—"

"We already know that it's a report on Mr. Driscoll's novel. I don't see—"

"The plaintiff has claimed, your Honor, that *The Paper Dragon* was pirated from the play *Catchpole*. By tracing the development of the book, I intend to show that there was independent creation."

"Is this offer being made . . ." McIntyre began.

"This offer, your Honor, is being made to show that there were no special or mysterious circumstances surrounding the submission, the editing, or the subsequent development of the novel written by James Driscoll. We have already heard that the book came in 'over the transom,' addressed to no specific person in the company, and that it was treated as any other submission might have been, in accordance with the normal business procedure at Mitchell-Campbell Books."

"Mr. Brackman may wish you to explore this 'normal business procedure,' " McIntyre said.

"No, that won't be necessary," Brackman said. "I am ready to concede that editorial reports are the normal business of a publishing firm."

"Very well," McIntyre said.

"I am not objecting to whether or not this was normal procedure."

"What is your objection, Mr. Brackman?"

"Only that it is irrelevant, your Honor."

"Well, I will admit the report," McIntyre said. "Is it dated, Mr. Willow?"

"It is, your Honor. The date on it is July 12, 1962, but the content of the report states that the manuscript was received on July ninth."

"Mark it 'Defendants' Exhibit C,' " the clerk said.

"You have stated that you wrote this report," Jonah said.

"Yes," Danton replied.

"What did you do with the manuscript after you wrote this report?"

"I sent it to Miss Anita Lang."

"Who is Miss Lang?"

"She's an editor at Mitchell-Campbell Books."

"You sent it to her for her opinion?"

"Yes, and for subsequent transmittal to Mr. Campbell for a final decision."

"What was your own opinion?"

"I felt we should publish the book."

"Did Miss Lang make a report on the book?"

"She did."

"I ask you to look at this, Mr. Danton, and tell me what it is."

Danton took the extended sheet of paper, glanced at it, and said, "This is Miss Lang's report on the book, and I see that Mr. Campbell has indicated on it that he is to see the manuscript at once. The report is dated July 16th."

"You are familiar with Mr. Campbell's handwriting?"

"I am. That's his handwriting."

"And is this paper the actual editorial report made by Miss Lang?"

"It is."

"A report which, similar to yours, was part of the normal business procedure at Mitchell-Campbell Books."

"Yes, sir. We regularly get several opinions on any book thought to be a publishing possibility."

"I offer it in evidence," Jonah said.

"I object as before," Brackman said.

"Overruled," McIntyre answered.

"Mark it 'Defendants' Exhibit D in evidence' " the clerk said.

"Was the manuscript eventually sent on to Mr. Campbell, together with the reports by yourself and Miss Lang?"

"That's right."

"Did Mr. Campbell subsequently comment on the novel?"

"He did."

"Incidentally, is this 'Mr. Campbell' the president of Mitchell-Campbell Books—Leonard Campbell?"

"Yes."

"I ask you to look at this, Mr. Danton, and tell me what it is."

"It's the memorandum Mr. Campbell sent to me after he read the Driscoll novel."

"I offer it in evidence."

"Objection."

"Overruled."

"Mark it 'Defendants' Exhibit E in evidence.' "

"Now, Mr. Danton, I would like you to refer to Miss Lang's report on the novel. There's a paragraph in it that's marked with a pencil and then with the words 'Good suggestion.' Do you see that paragraph?"

"Just a moment," Danton said. He reached into his jacket pocket, took out a pair of eyeglasses, and settled them on the bridge of his nose. Then he studied the report and said, "Yes, I have it now."

"Can you identify the handwriting in the margin?"

"I can. It's my handwriting."

"Would you read that paragraph to the court, and explain what you meant by your penciled comment?"

Danton cleared his throat and then began reading. " 'However, one thing that does not seem well-motivated (in this initial segment, at least) is Colman's instantaneous dislike of the hero, which triggers the squad's subsequent resistance to his attempts at reaching them. Since the novel gathers its impetus from the Colman-Cooper conflict, I found it implausible that these men would be so immediately antagonistic to each other. Can't there be a stronger motivation for their hatred? It seems to me this certainly requires deeper thought from Driscoll.' " Danton looked up. "That's the second paragraph of her report," he said. "And in the margin, as you pointed out, I scribbled the words 'Good suggestion,' and of course initialed it 'CD' for Chester Danton."

"You agreed with Miss Lang that there was not sufficient motivation for hating the lieutenant?"

"Yes, I agreed with her, as I indicated in my marginal note."

"The novel did *not* contain this motivation?"

"Not when we first received it."

"Does it now?"

"Yes, it does."

"Was it Miss Lang's suggestion that this motivation be added?"

"Yes."

"And was it added?"

"Yes."

"In what way?"

"I suggested to Mr. Driscoll that perhaps the squad's attachment to their previous commanding officer made them unable to accept his replacement."

"When did you make this suggestion?"

"I don't remember the exact date. It was certainly during our first meeting about the book."

"*Whose* first meeting?"

"The first editorial meeting I had with Mr. Driscoll."

"Did you enlarge upon the suggestion in any way?"

"Yes. I proposed the idea that the former commanding officer be a major who'd been killed by a sniper."

"This was your suggestion?"

"Yes."

"Did this major exist in the novel when it was first delivered to you?"

"No, sir, he was not in the novel."

"He was added after you met Mr. Driscoll?"

"Yes, sir."

"Are you aware that the plaintiff claims as a specific similarity the fact that a man is killed by a sniper in his play, and a man is killed by a sniper in Mr. Driscoll's novel?"

"Yes, I am aware of that."

"But you have just testified that the man being killed by a sniper was your idea and not Mrs. Driscoll's."

"That is correct."

"Did you ever see the play *Catchpole* when it was produced in New York?"

"I did not."

"It was produced in October of 1947, opening on the 14th,

and closing on the 25th. Can you tell us where you were at that time?"

"Yes, sir. I was in England."

"Doing what?"

"I was handling subsidiary rights for Mitchell-Campbell at that time, and part of my duties involved arranging for the foreign publication of titles on our list. I went to England at the beginning of October that year, and I did not return until November 28th."

"You were out of the United States from October 1st to November 28th, is that correct?"

"October 3rd, I believe it was."

"And did not see the production of Mr. Constantine's play?"

"I did not see Mr. Constantine's play."

"Prior to the beginning of this action, had you ever read *Catchpole?*"

"No, sir."

"Had you ever met or heard of the plaintiff, Arthur Constantine?"

"No, sir."

"Did anyone other than yourself have anything to do with the editing of James Driscoll's book?"

"Outside of these several memorandums from Miss Lang and Mr. Campbell, the editor-author relationship was solely between Mr. Driscoll and me."

"And so it was you alone who suggested that the major be killed by a sniper, and that the squad's attachment to him form the basis of their subsequent hatred of Lieutenant Alex Cooper."

"Yes, sir, the suggestion was mine alone."

"Did you have any other editorial suggestions to make?"

"Well, the remarkable thing about the book was that it was so good and so fully realized that there were very few suggestions an editor *could* make."

"Your Honor," Brackman said, "the answer is unresponsive."

"Mr. Danton . . ."

"I made very few editorial comments, except for suggesting a new title."

"What was the title on the manuscript as it was submitted?"

"*The Enemy.*"

"Were any other titles subsequently considered?"

"Yes. One suggestion was *The Other Enemy,* but this was discarded."

"Who suggested that the title be changed to *The Paper Dragon?*"

"I did."

"You made this suggestion directly to Mr. Driscoll?"

"I did."

"When was that?"

"I don't recall the exact date. We'd been trying for a new title all along, and I believe the idea for this one came to me while Jimmy was still working on the book. I called him, and we discussed it on the telephone."

"What was the nature of the discussion?"

"The discussion concerned the theme of the book. It has since been universally accepted as an indictment of the United States Army, a bitter treatise against war. It seemed to me, however, that this was not Mr. Driscoll's intention. I thought he was attempting to show that—"

"Your Honor, Mr. Willow earlier objected to the relevancy of what a writer was *attempting* to show as opposed to what he actually *did* show. I make the same objection now."

"Mr. Danton is repeating a discussion he had with Mr. Driscoll. I believe the title of the book pertains to the theme, your Honor, and as such is relevant."

"Overruled. Proceed, Mr. Willow."

"You were saying, Mr. Danton?"

"That Jimmy . . . Mr. Driscoll did not perhaps realize what the *real* theme of his book was. This very often happens with writers. It seemed to me, though, that this was a book about, well, I deplore clichés, but it was certainly a book about man's inhumanity to man. When I suggested this to Jimmy, he seemed surprised. But it was then that I suggested

The Other Enemy, meaning not the *enemy* enemy, but the enemy that is in all men, do you see?"

"How did the idea for the present title come to you?"

"The Paper Dragon?"

"Yes."

"The term 'paper dragon' is familiar to most writers and editors. It's used to denote a story problem that is really nonexistent."

"Would you explain further?"

"Well, let's assume a man comes home reeking of perfume. His wife immediately suspects that he has been seeing another woman, and this creates the conflict, which in turn provokes a series of plot complications, and at last a resolution. The explanation, of course, is that the man had been buying perfume for his wife, and the salesgirl sprayed a little on him—in short, a paper dragon, a nonexistent problem. If the wife had come right out and asked her husband about it, and if he had explained, there would be no conflict, and of course no story."

"A paper dragon is, then, a nonexistent problem or conflict."

"Yes. But this doesn't prevent a lot of people from becoming energetically involved in the series of events it triggers. It's a specious literary device."

"Why did you suggest this title for Mr. Driscoll's novel?"

"I suggested it on various levels. To begin with, his novel deals with that period of time when the Chinese were coming into Korea in force, and I thought the title would indicate that the book was, after all, about war with the Chinese. Secondly, using it in an allusive sense, I thought it would indicate that the Chinese army was only a paper dragon, whereas the *real* enemy, the *real* dragon was man's innate cruelty. And lastly, I thought it would clearly label Colman's fake and private war against our hero, the conflict he constructs out of whole cloth, the way he turns the other men against Cooper, the whole chain of events based on a problem that need not have existed in the first place, a paper dragon."

"And what happened when you suggested this title to Mr. Driscoll?"

"He liked it."

"And it was decided that this title would be used on the published novel?"

"Yes."

"To get back for a moment, after your first talk with Mr. Driscoll—you said it was in July of 1962—did you then offer him a contract for the publication of his novel?"

"Yes."

"Is this the contract you sent to him?"

"It is."

"I offer the contract in evidence, your Honor."

"For what purpose, Mr. Willow?"

"To show that the book was only partially completed when submitted to Mitchell-Campbell. The contract clearly states that the company is in receipt of only ninety-eight pages and an outline, and it further specifies that the completed novel is to be delivered by January 1, 1963, and will consist of some eighty-thousand words."

"Mr. Brackman?"

"No objection."

"Received."

"Defendants' Exhibit F received in evidence," the clerk said.

"Mr. Danton, did you in November of 1962 send Mr. Driscoll a company questionnaire?"

"I did."

"Did he return the questionnaire to you, and is this the questionnaire?"

"Yes, this is what he filled out in November of '62."

"Is it signed by him?"

"No, we don't require a signature on these questionnaires. They're used only to get information which we'll need later for promotion and publicity. Most books, as you know, carry biographical information about the author, either on the jacket flap or on the last page of the book, or both. These questionnaires are helpful to the person preparing the copy.

And, too, we need information for newspaper publicity, anecdotes about the writer, his educational background, honors he may have received, and so forth."

"Are these questionnaires sent to every author on Mitchell-Campbell's list?"

"They are."

"As a part of the normal business procedure?"

"As a part of the normal business procedure."

"I offer it in evidence, your Honor."

"No objection."

"Mark it 'Defendants' Exhibit G in evidence.' "

"Mr. Danton, I ask you to recall now any further editorial suggestions you may have made concerning Mr. Driscoll's novel. Did you, for example, make any suggestion about the use of profanity?"

"Yes, I did. There was a scene in which Lieutenant Cooper met his fellow officers, and it seemed to me the profanity in that scene was excessive."

"I show you a second editorial memorandum with the initials 'CD' and I ask you now to describe it to the Court."

"Well, this is my comment . . . the report I wrote after the completed novel was delivered to me. It's dated February 4, 1963, and it mentions the fact that my earlier editorial suggestions had been successfully incorporated into the novel."

"Does it make any comments about further changes?"

"Yes, it does."

"Would you tell us what those comments are?"

"I'll simply read the last two paragraphs of the report, which are the only parts pertaining to your question. 'If anything, Driscoll has delivered a better novel than the portion and outline promised. His enlargement upon the slain major, for example, with the subsequent homosexual development of Private Colman is inventive and fresh, and completely satisfies our request for stronger motivation. I am, to be truthful, overwhelmed by the depth and scope of this novel, and it's only because the book is so good, in fact, that I bring up what might seem a carping point. I refer to the profanity.

This is a realistic war novel, of course, and the combat setting and soldier-characters make the inevitable Anglo-Saxonisms essential to the tone and the very structure. But it seems to me they can be softened somewhat in the scenes where they are used arbitrarily—as in the officers' mess scene—if only to mollify some of the more militant censors. Elsewhere, I'm afraid we can't do very much about the language because excising the four-letter words would damage the authentic sound of the entire work. One excellent scene, for example, where the men are ostensibly involved in the field-stripping of a rifle, would lose all of its sexual connotations if the language were even slightly changed.' And here, penciled in the margin alongside that paragraph, is a note dated February fifteenth, and stating that these points had been taken care of. Do you want me to go on with the next paragraph of the report?"

"Please."

"Again, I'm quoting: 'In my opinion, the last chapter is anticlimactic especially when placed in juxtaposition to the enormously effective penultimate chapter. The book needs a coda more than it does anything else, perhaps a short scene between Colman and the nurse. I have no doubt that Driscoll can come up with something to fill the bill. He has up to now delivered beyond our highest expectations. We have a fine novel here, and it's by a writer who is only thirty-three years old and who will, I am certain, go on writing many more excellent books. I feel we've made a true discovery.' That's the end of the report."

"Was the final chapter changed after you wrote your report?"

"Yes."

"And were there also subsequent changes?"

"I would guess so. Every book we publish goes through a subtle process of evolution during the copy editing and styling. Small changes are inevitable."

"I offer this report in evidence, your Honor."

"Is it dated?"

"It is dated February 4, 1963, and a note at the bottom of

the report states, 'All revisions completed March 6, 1963.' "

"My objection as before, your Honor," Brackman said.

"Overruled."

"Mark it 'Defendants' Exhibit H in evidence,' " the clerk said.

"Now Mr. Danton, you had by March 6, 1963, a completed manuscript of James Driscoll's book, had you not?"

"Yes, I had a finished manuscript by that date."

"Did you show it to anyone else working for Mitchell-Campbell?"

"I passed it on to Anita Lang."

"Did she subsequently make a report on it?"

"Yes."

"Is this the report?"

Danton took the extended sheet of paper, glanced at it, and said, "This is Anita's report."

"I offer in evidence Miss Lang's second report."

"Objection as before."

"Overruled."

"Mark it 'Defendants' Exhibit I in evidence.' "

"Would you please look at the next to last paragraph of the report where Miss Lang writes, 'It seems to me that the two flashbacks revealing segments of Private Colman's civilian life are extraneous. They advance neither theme nor plot and seem particularly obvious since we do not have similar civilian flashbacks for any of the other soldiers.' When *The Paper Dragon* was published, were these two flashbacks still in the book?"

"No, sir, they were not."

"They were deleted after Miss Lang made her report?"

"Yes, sir, they were."

"Who transmitted the request to Mr. Driscoll?"

"I did."

"In the last paragraph of her report, Miss Lang writes, 'Don't you feel we need another scene between Coop and the nurse to show how the squad's pressure on him is beginning to affect his behavior elsewhere?' In the margin, we have the penciled words, 'Fine, will do,' and the initials 'CD.' Did you write that in the margin?"

"I did."

"Was another scene between Coop and the nurse added to the book?"

"I don't remember, but I would imagine so. If Miss Lang made the suggestion, and I indicated it would be taken care of, then I'm sure I passed the request on to Jimmy. He was very receptive to most editorial suggestions, so I would say it was likely he added this scene as well."

"Before the book was finally published—what was its publication date, by the way, Mr. Danton?"

"October of 1963."

"When would you estimate you had a manuscript ready to go to the printers?"

"I would imagine some six months before then. That would be . . ."

"That would be . . ."

"In May, I would . . ."

"April, wouldn't it?"

"April or May, yes. We like at least six months' time for our salesmen to get on the road with a book."

"When did API see the book, would you know that?"

"Well, Mr. Driscoll took on an agent shortly after we contracted for the book, and I think his agent began showing it to the motion picture companies when it was still in galleys."

"Did API buy it from the galley proofs?"

"Yes."

"Would you know how much they paid for the motion picture rights?"

"Thirty-five thousand dollars."

"How much of that went to Mr. Driscoll's agent?"

"Ten per cent. Thirty-five hundred dollars."

"And how much went to Mitchell-Campbell Books?"

"Our contract called for twenty-five per cent of all subsidiary rights."

"You received twenty-five per cent of what was left after Mr. Driscoll's agent took his commission?"

"No. Our twenty-five per cent came off the top."

"In other words, you received a quarter of thirty-five thousand dollars?"

"That's right."

"You received eight thousand, seven hundred and fifty dollars?"

"That's correct."

"And Mr. Driscoll's agent received thirty-five hundred dollars, which means that Mr. Driscoll was left with twenty-two thousand, seven hundred and fifty dollars."

"If your addition is correct."

"I think it is."

"I'll accept it."

"That was his share of the sale of motion picture rights to his novel."

"Yes."

"The novel that later earned millions of dollars for API."

"Objection, your Honor. I do not see . . ."

"Sustained. Where are you going, Mr. Willow?"

"I am merely trying to show, your Honor, that Mr. Driscoll's alleged 'theft' hardly seemed to be worth all the trouble. The only ones who made any real money out of this supposed plagiarism were the people who made the movie."

"Your Honor," Brackman said, "I think a sum in excess of twenty-two thousand dollars can be considered 'real money.' Men have robbed banks for less."

"I quite agree, Mr. Brackman," McIntyre said. "I think we've had enough of this, Mr. Willow, and I see no point in pursuing it further."

"Getting back then," Jonah said with a sigh, "before publication, did you talk to Mr. Driscoll about anything in the book that might later prove troublesome?"

"Yes, we always do, as a matter of routine."

"Can you explain what you mean?"

"We're always concerned about the possibility of lawsuits. Invasion of privacy, usually. Or libel. In any work of fiction, there's the danger that someone will identify with a fictitious character and bring suit. We try to make sure that the names of the characters, for example, are not the names of any real people."

"What about telephone numbers?"

"We check those out to make sure they do not correspond to any real numbers in service."

"Did you take such care with Mr. Driscoll's book?"

"Well, there were no telephone numbers involved since the book is set in Korea, as you know. But we did ask Jimmy whether any of the names he used were the actual names of men he may have known during his Army service. He assured us they were not."

"Were any other precautions taken?"

"Yes. At one point in the book, Jimmy mentioned the lieutenant's serial number. The actual numeral appeared in the book, you see."

"Yes?"

"So we wrote to the Army and had them give us a non-existent serial number we could use."

"I seem to recall a case involving another publisher in which a telephone number in a novel—the number for a house of prostitution—turned out to be a real number for a respectable woman living in New York."

"Yes, that's a well-known story in the trade. We try to be careful of such occurrences."

"So the serial number finally used was nonexistent?"

"Yes. A dummy number supplied by the Army."

"Did you have any similar qualms regarding the use of the digits one-oh-five to label Mr. Driscoll's division?"

"No."

"Why not?"

"We had no reason to believe the 105th was anything but an actual Army division."

"You thought the 105th was a *real* division?"

"We did."

"Didn't this trouble you?"

"It did not. An Army division consists roughly of eighteen

thousand men. Worrying about the designation of such a large unit would be similar to worrying about the designation of a city the size of Scarsdale."

"Then you never brought up the division number in any of your discussions with Mr. Driscoll?"

"Never. We thought it was one of the real divisions involved in the Ch'ongch'on River fighting, and it never occurred to us that we should try to change history."

"Did Mr. *Driscoll* ever say it was a real division?"

"He never mentioned it at all."

"Not at any time during any of your discussions?"

"Never."

"Thank you. Mr. Danton, how long have you been an editor?"

"I've been with Mitchell-Campbell Books since my discharge from the Navy in 1946. I was hired to handle subsidiary rights for the firm, but I began doing editorial work in, oh, it must have been '48 or '49. I've been an editor since that time."

"As part of your job, are you called upon to pass literary judgment on manuscripts submitted to the company?"

"I am."

"Mr. Danton, have you in this past week read the play *Catchpole?*"

"I have read it, yes."

"Mr. Willow," Brackman said, "I haven't objected until now to these leading questions—but I can't remain silent when you first supply your witness with a date, and only afterwards ask him if he read the play."

"Forgive me," Jonah said. "*Have* you read the play *Catchpole,* Mr. Danton?"

"I have."

"When did you first read it?"

"I read it last week. Last Tuesday night."

"Where did you obtain a copy of the play?"

"You gave it to me."

"Did I ask you to read it?"

"You did."

"Do you have any editorial opinion on it?"

"Objection. Mr. Danton's opinion of the play is immaterial."

"Your Honor," Jonah said, "the testimony of an expert on such matters, a man who has been an editor for more than twenty years, would certainly seem relevant to me. As with my earlier offer, I am merely attempting to ascertain whether or not anyone would *want* to steal this play."

"Your Honor . . ."

"Please," McIntyre said. "What earlier offer do you mean, Mr. Willow? The newspaper reviews of *Catchpole?*"

"If your Honor please."

"Mr. Brackman?"

"The quality of this play does not go to the question of plagiarism, your Honor. On Monday, Mr. Willow remarked that many well-known works have been plagiarized in the past, and he cited *Abie's Irish Rose* as a prime example. I'm sure his reversal of the facts was inadvertent, but nevertheless the plagiarism was charged *against Abie's Irish Rose,* which was purported to have been stolen from an unknown property. Point of fact, I think we all must realize that no one in his right mind would try to steal from a *famous* book or play—unless he was intent on being exposed and brought to justice. Moreover, with all due respect to Mr. Danton's abilities, I hardly think he is the man to pass judgment on Mr. Constantine's play."

"If he has a qualified editorial opinion . . ."

"I do not see where his opinion, qualified or otherwise—"

"I will exclude it, Mr. Willow," McIntyre said.

"In that case, your Honor, I have no further questions."

"Very well."

Brackman rose from behind his table, consulted a list of notes he had made, put the notes on the table again, and walked slowly toward the witness chair.

"We know each other, don't we, Mr. Danton?" he asked conversationally.

"We met at the pretrial examination, yes."

"How are you?"

"I'm fine, thank you."

Brackman nodded, and smiled. "Mr. Danton," he said, "I'd like to go over these editorial changes you just told us about. Would that be all right with you?"

"Yes, certainly."

"To begin with, you suggested the title *The Paper Dragon,* is that right?"

"Not to *begin* with. That came much later."

"I didn't mean chronologically, Mr. Danton."

"What did you mean?"

"Was it or was it not one of your editorial suggestions?"

"It was."

"And another of your suggestions was that the squad be provided with a stronger motivation for its dislike of Lieutenant Cooper?"

"I suggested that a major—"

"Please answer the question."

"Yes, that was another of my suggestions."

"And yet another concerned the use of profanity in the officers' mess scene?"

"Correct."

"And the deletion of flashbacks showing the civilian background of Private Colman?"

"Yes."

"You also suggested that a final chapter be written . . ."

"Yes."

". . . between Lieutenant Cooper and the nurse Jan Reardon."

"No. Not between—"

"I quote from your own Exhibit I, where Miss Lang said, 'Don't you feel we need another scene between Coop and the nurse . . .' "

"Yes, but—"

" '. . . to show how the squad's pressure on him is beginning—' "

"Yes, but that was not a suggestion for the final chapter. That was earlier on in the book, a scene set in the hospital."

"But you agreed with her comment?"

"Yes, I did."

"And suggested the change to Mr. Driscoll?"

"Yes. As well as suggesting a better last chapter."

"These were two *separate* changes, is that it?"

"Yes, I thought I'd made that clear."

"It's clear now, thank you. Do you consider these changes important?"

"Which changes?"

"All of them."

"They were important to the full realization of Mr. Driscoll's book, yes."

"What do you mean by that?"

"The book was potentially excellent. I believe the changes helped Mr. Driscoll to realize that potential. Yes, the changes were important."

"During your pretrial examination, Mr. Danton, you mentioned only *two* editorial suggestions which you considered important: the change of title and the profanity. You weren't trying to mislead me, were you?"

"I certainly was not!"

"You just didn't remember these three or four other suggestions, is that it?"

"Yes, of course that's . . ."

"Which you now consider as important as the others? Important to the *full* realization of Mr. Driscoll's book?"

"I've had a chance to reread *The Paper Dragon* since then, and to remember . . ."

"Yes, but at the pretrial, you did not recall these other suggestions when we asked you about them, did you?"

"No, not at the time."

"Your Honor," Jonah said, rising, "I do not see . . ."

"He is examining the witness as to credibility, Mr. Willow, and I will allow it," McIntyre said.

"I call your attention now to the following question in your pretrial examination: 'Mr. Danton, would you say that the editing—' "

"Excuse me, Mr. Brackman," Jonah said.

"This is page 21," Brackman said over his shoulder.

"Thank you."

"And the question was, 'Mr. Danton, would you say that the editing of a book is a process of offering the suggestions and opinions of others to an author for possible assimilation into the work?' and your answer was, 'Basically, yes.' And further down on that same page, Mr. Danton, you were asked, 'Did suggestions concerning *The Paper Dragon* originate entirely with you?' and your answer was, 'No, some of the suggestions originated elsewhere in the company.' I ask you now, Mr. Danton, where else in the company these suggestions originated?"

"They came from Miss Anita Lang, as I testified earlier."

"You also testified earlier, Mr. Danton, that—and I quote—'the editor-author relationship was solely between Mr. Driscoll and me.' Do you recall that?"

"I said it was between Jimmy and me except for the memorandums . . ."

"Solely between Mr. Driscoll and yourself."

"I also mentioned the memorandums," Danton said.

"Your Honor," Jonah said, rising, "I believe Mr. Brackman is attempting to fuse two separate answers . . ."

"I repeat his answer," Brackman said. " 'The editor-author relationship was solely between—' "

"Yes, the personal relationship," Jonah said.

"Was it or was it not an exclusive relationship?"

"Should I answer that?" Danton asked.

"Please," McIntyre said.

"It was the only personal relationship."

"What do you mean by that?"

"I mean that I was the only editor at Mitchell-Campbell who transmitted suggestions for change to Mr. Driscoll."

"Including suggestions for change that might have originated elsewhere?"

"Yes."

"Do you know for a fact, Mr. Danton, that no one at Mitchell-Campbell Books saw or read the play *Catchpole* before the publication of *The Paper Dragon?*"

Danton hesitated.

"Mr. Danton?"

"No, I do not know that for a fact."

"Do you know for a fact that Miss Anita Lang did *not* see or read the play?"

"No, I do not know that for a fact, either. But Miss Lang is only—"

"You have answered the question."

"I would like to explain . . ."

"Your Honor . . ."

"I will hear the witness," McIntyre said.

"I would like to explain that Anita Lang is a very young woman. In fact, she couldn't have been more than twenty-two or three when *The Paper Dragon* first came to us. She must have been seven or eight years old when *Catchpole* was produced in New York, so I hardly think she could have seen the play, unless her mother took her to it in a baby carriage."

"Do you know for a fact that she did not *read* the play?"

"No, I don't."

"Mr. Danton, I call your attention to a report of your own, Defendants' Exhibit H, in which you said, and I quote: 'We have a fine novel here, and it's by a writer who is only thirty-three years old and who will, I am certain, go on writing many more excellent books. I feel we've made a true discovery.' This was dated February 4th, and the notation that all the points were cleared up is dated March 6, 1963. I ask you now, Mr. Danton, whether James Driscoll has delivered any other manuscript to you since that time?"

"He has not."

"To your knowledge, Mr. Danton, is he presently at work on another book?"

"Not to my knowledge."

"To your knowledge, Mr. Danton, had he ever written anything prior to the novel called *The Paper Dragon*?"

"I believe it was his first novel."

"Was it in fact his first published work of fiction?"

"I don't know."

"I call your attention to Defendants' Exhibit G, the questionnaire sent by Mitchell-Campbell Books to James Driscoll, and I refer you to the section asking the author to list his previous works. Would you please read Mr. Driscoll's answer to the Court?"

"He says, 'I have never had anything published before.' "

"Do you accept the statement in this questionnaire?"

"I do."

"He would have had no reason to falsify an answer to that question?"

"Mr. Driscoll is not a man who falsifies anything."

"Then Mitchell-Campbell Books accepted his statement that *The Paper Dragon* was the first work of fiction he had ever had published."

"Yes, Mitchell-Campbell Books accepted the statement."

"In other words, Mr. Danton, *The Paper Dragon* in addition to being the *first* thing Mr. Driscoll ever had published, is also the *only* thing he has ever had published."

"That's correct."

"Thank you, Mr. Danton."

"Is that all?"

"That's all, thank you."

"Are you through, Mr. Brackman?"

"Yes, your Honor."

"Mr. Genitori? Any further questions?"

"No, sir."

"Thank you, Mr. Danton. I'd like to recess for lunch now."

"This Court will reconvene at two P.M.," the clerk said.

"Mom?"

"Yes?"

"This is Arthur."

"Oh, hello, son, where are you?"

"Downtown, in the courthouse. I'm in the hall here. In a phone booth."

"What is it?"

"What do you mean?"

"Did you lose?"

"It's not over yet, Mom."

"When *will* it be over?"

"Tomorrow, I guess. Or Friday."

"So soon?"

"Yes. Well, you know, it's a pretty simple case."

"Did you tell them?"

"Oh, sure."

"That he stole from you?"

"Sure."

"What did they say?"

"Well, they don't say anything, Mom. I mean, there's only the judge and the people who're involved, you know. So we present our side, and then they present theirs, and that's it."

"Did they ask you questions?"

"Oh, sure."

"And it was all right?"

"Yes, it was fine."

"How's the play?"

"Well, we're still casting it."

"When will it be?"

"When will it go *on,* do you mean?"

"Yes."

"I don't know."

"Because I want to tell my sister."

"Oh, sure. I'll let you know in plenty of time."

"Good."

"How's Papa?"

"He's in the sun porch, working on his clocks. Shall I call him?"

"No, that's okay."

"You don't want to talk to him?"

"Well, I want to get some lunch, Mom . . ."

"Anyway, he's busy. You know how he gets when he's taking one of those things apart."

"Sure. Well, give him my love, anyway."

"I will."

"Have you heard from Julie, Mom?"

"Last week. I told you. I got a letter last week."

"I meant *since.*"

"No."

"I'll have to write to her. I owe her a letter."

"Do you know who died?"

"Who?"

"Do you remember Mr. Danucci, he was a housepainter? He always used to chase you kids off the stoop?"

"Sure, I remember him."

"He died Monday."

"What of?"

"In his bed."

"Oh."

"Well, he was an old man. You remember him, don't you?"

"Sure, I remember him."

"Well, he died."

"That's too bad. Well, listen, Mom, I'd better go get some lunch."

"Yes, call me when the trial is over."

"I will."

"Good."

"Give my love to Papa."

"Yes. Goodbye, son."

"Goodbye, Mom."

"Goodbye."

"Hello, Amy?"

"Daddy? Is that you?"

"Yes, sweetheart, how are you?"

"Fine. Why didn't you call Monday night?"

"I got in too late."

"The reason I didn't say to call Tuesday was because we were going on a trip to Philadelphia, to see all that independence craparoo, and I didn't know what time we'd be getting back. So I figured Wednesday would be safe around noon when we have our lunch period."

"Why'd you call, Amy?"

"Did you see the paper?"

"No. Which paper? What do you mean?"

"About Mother."

"No."

"It said she caused another disturbance in a night club."

"Oh?"

"Daddy?"

"Yes?"

"It didn't come right out and say she was drunk, but it made it pretty clear."

"Where'd you get a New York paper?"

"A girl in tenth showed it to me. A friend of mine."

"Some friend."

"She didn't mean any harm."

"Well."

"Daddy?"

"Yes?"

"Will you call her?"

"Why should I?"

"If she's going around getting drunk . . ."

"No, Amy."

"Please? For me?"

"I'm sorry."

"Daddy, I'll be home Friday, the Christmas vacation starts Friday, that's the sixteenth, and I don't even know if she's picking me up. She hasn't written in weeks. Could you call and ask her?"

"Ask her what?"

"If she'll be at the station. She *is* my mother, you know."

"I know that, Amy."

"And I'm worried."

"About what? She's perfectly capable—"

"About her falling down drunk in some damn night club, if you want to know. *Can't* you call her, Daddy?"

"I'm sorry, Amy."

"I tried to reach her three times last week, but I couldn't get an answer. Nobody even *answers*. Daddy, *please* call, won't you?"

"Amy . . ."

"Please."

"Amy?"

"What?"

"Amy . . . don't cry."

"I'm not crying."

"Please, honey."

"I'm . . . not, Daddy."

"I'll call her. Only please don't . . ."

"Daddy, you don't have to. I know you really . . ."

"Now stop crying, Amy. Please."

"I'm sorry, Daddy."

"Amy?"

"Yes. Yes, I'm fine."

"I'll call her."

"Thank you."

"How's . . . how's everything there at the school?"

"Fine."

"Everything okay?"

"Yes. I got an eight on a Latin test—that's eighty, you know. And we . . ."

"Yes, I know."

". . . won a soccer game against St. Agnes."

"Honey, what time will you be coming in? On Friday, I mean."

"Well, we usually get to Penn Station at about six."

"Would you like me to meet you?"

"Oh, *could* you, Daddy? I'd love it. Hey, I bought something very nice for you in New Hope."

"I'll be there. Six o'clock Friday, Penn Station."

"Daddy, if the train's late . . ."

"I'll wait, don't worry. I miss you, Amy."

"Yes."

"Well . . ."

"You'll call Mother, too, won't you?"

"Sure, honey."

"Thank you."

"I'd better say goodbye now. I've got some people waiting."

"Daddy?"

"Yes?"

"I love you."

"Who's this?"

"Sidney."

"Who?"

"Sidney. Your son."

"Oh, Sidney, *Sidney!* I thought you said *Shirley."*

"No, I said Sidney."

"I was wondering how a Shirley could have such a deep voice."

"Yes, well, it's me, Pop."

"What's the matter? You're not coming?"

"No, I'll be there."

"Good. I found some nice things for you, Sidney."

"Oh. Fine."

"I'll show you tomorrow, when I see you."

"Okay. Fine."

"You're coming, aren't you?"

"Yes, certainly. I said I was. Have I ever missed a Thursday?"

"Well, I know you have a trial."

"No, I'll be there, don't worry."

"Six o'clock?"

"Six o'clock."

"Some nice things, Sidney."

"What is it? I have a headache."

"I just talked to Amy, and—"

"What does she want this time?"

"Apparently she saw an item about you in—"

"That's true, I was drunk."

"Christie . . .

"Anything else?"

"Nothing except she was concerned enough to call you three times last week . . ."

"I haven't been home."

". . . and then finally call me in desperation. Now look, Christie, your life is your life . . ."

"Here it comes."

". . . and I don't give a damn *what* you do with it . . ."

"But *our* daughter is *our* daughter."

"Yes."

"I am fully aware of my responsibility to Amy."

"Then why haven't you written to her?"

"I wrote to her last Tuesday."

"She said she hasn't heard from you in weeks."

"She's lying."

"Amy doesn't lie."

"That's true, I forgot that Amy is a paragon who doesn't lie, cheat, steal, swear, smoke, screw, or—"

"Christie . . ."

"Christie . . ."

"Christie, you've . . ."

"Christie, you've . . ."

"Christie, you've got a twelve-year-old . . ."

". . . twelve-year-old . . ."

". . . daughter two hundred miles away from home . . ."

". . . away from . . ."

"Damn you, Christie, *cut it out!*"

"Jonah?"

"What?"

"Go to hell, Jonah."

"Did you know she'll be coming home Friday?"

"Yes, I knew."

"I told her I'd pick her up at the station. Is that all right?"

"That's fine."

"In the meantime, you might call to let her know you're alive."

"All right, I will. Is that all?"

"That's all."

"Goodbye."

Dris is right, Ebie thought. Nothing in that courtroom is real, it can't be. All of them have their own ideas, the truth is only what they *want* to believe. Even the judge, even *he* doesn't know what's real, and he's the one who's supposed to decide. How can he? Does *he* know what the book is about? None of them do. So how can any of it be real, the courtroom, the conversation here at this table, how can any of it be the slightest bit real?

"I don't think I get you," Jonah said.

"There's no reality in that courtroom," Driscoll answered. "There can't be."

"It seems real enough to me each day," Jonah said. "What do you think, Mrs. Driscoll?"

"I think it's real enough," Ebie answered.

"Anyway, the reality is that you didn't steal his play," Jonah said. "And the further reality is that it's a bad play, and no one would have *wanted* to steal it."

"Who says it's bad?"

"Jimmy, there's no question about it."

"You mean the critics said it was bad, and the movie companies, and the editorial expert, Chester Danton, right?"

"That's right."

"So that makes it a bad play."

"I would say so."

"Constantine doesn't think so."

"Constantine is mistaken."

"Yes, and the man who produced it was mistaken, too, because *he* obviously thought it was a good play. And the actors who agreed to play it, *they* were mistaken as well because *they* thought it was good. Everyone involved in it was apparently mistaken because the critics came to see it and said it was bad. Tell me something, Jonah. If the Honorable Frank H. McIntyre decides I stole Constantine's play, will that suddenly make it *good?*"

"You didn't steal it."

"You didn't answer my question."

"Constantine is a bad writer who wrote a bad play. Whatever McIntyre decides, it will still be a bad play. There's your reality, Jimmy."

Reality, she thought.

My first year in New York was real, the school and the small apartment I took on Myrtle Avenue, the elevated trains roaring past the window. And after that, and before I knew James Driscoll existed, reality was a boy named Donald Forbes, who limped. I'm a cripple, he said, okay? You're not a cripple, I insisted. No? Then what? I drag my leg, I limp, I'm a cripple, don't lie to me, Ebie, I'm a goddamn cripple. Holding him in my arms while he wept. He was not a good-looking boy, he reminded me of Phillip Armstrong whose nose had been too long ("I used to have this little turned-up button nose, but I had an operation done to make it long and ugly") and who was always coming down with a cold or something. Donald was that way, thin and looking like one of the hundred neediest, with large pleading Keane eyes. He took to carrying a cane in January because there was such a heavy snow that year, he said. That was just before I began sleeping with him.

". . . real or otherwise, that's my point."

"You may be giving him more credit than he's due. I'm still not sure he really thinks you stole it."

"Then why did he bring suit?"

"There's a lot of money involved here, Jimmy."

"There's more than just money involved here. Constantine thinks I stole something that is very valuable to him, no matter *what* anyone else says about it. He wants credit for his work."

"No. He wants credit for *your* work."

"What makes *my* work any better than his?"

"Jimmy, this is a foolish argument. You know *The Paper Dragon* is far superior to *Catchpole*. Now why . . . ?"

"We're not in that courtroom to judge the value of the two works, are we?" Driscoll said. "That's why I don't approve of what you were trying to do."

"What was I trying to do?"

"Make him ashamed."

"No," Jonah said.

She had never been ashamed of what she'd done, though of course she lied in her letters home, even in her letters to Miss

Benson. And yet she always felt a pang of regret at not having told her the truth, because she was certain Miss Benson would have been the only one to understand. Wasn't this what she and Miss Benson had *really* discussed on that waning afternoon, wasn't this what Miss Benson had meant by a capacity for giving? In February, when Donald stopped using the cane, she thought she must have known how that Negro lawyer in Atlanta felt when he began sleeping with Miss Benson. If a nigger in the South (and she stopped calling them niggers the moment she realized Donald disapproved of the expression) if a *Negro* in the South could just once in his life stand up and be counted as a man, be accepted as a man by a woman like Miss Benson, why then maybe he could think of himself as a man from that day forward. And maybe, if they had let him alone, if they had allowed him to give this woman love and to accept it from her in return, if they had not been so desperately threatened by the notion, then maybe he'd have walked proud the rest of his life, without dragging his leg, without limping. But of course they couldn't allow that to happen. No, you see, we can't allow that to happen, Missie, standing in the driveway and talking in low voices to the schoolgirl in her cotton pajamas and robe, we cannot allow it, Missie, you had better get the hell out of Atlanta. Maybe that's what Donald was all about, because she knew without question that she did not love him, and yet she gave him love. And in February he threw away the cane, said the streets weren't as slippery, but she knew. She would watch him combing his hair in the morning, whistling as he studied his own face in the mirror over the sink, and she knew. And she would nod silently, a small smile on her mouth, and think of Miss Benson, and think she should write to her and tell her, thank her, say something to her. But she never did. It would have been too difficult to explain, the way it was impossible to explain later on. Oh not *Donald,* you could always explain the lovers of your past, especially if they were not really lovers. Though even then, there'd been a scene, my young James Driscoll laying down the law, you will not do this, you will not do that, yes my darling, yes my darling, yes, I love you.

". . . that the work is *unworthy* of piracy, that's all."

"How do you know it is?"

"What are you talking about, Jimmy?"

"Let's suppose for the moment that I did steal his play, okay?"

"I would rather not suppose that."

"It's entirely possible."

"It is not possible," Jonah said firmly.

"I could have seen it in 1947 when they gave out those free tickets to Pratt . . ."

"I don't believe they gave any free tickets to Pratt."

"Constantine testified to it under oath."

"Better men than Constantine have lied under oath."

He's lying now, Ebie thought. He doesn't believe a word of this, he's teasing you, Jonah, playing a game and enjoying every minute of it, the way he enjoyed that first afternoon in Bertie's on DeKalb Avenue, teasing the little Southern girl who had just cut her hair, the way he teased the world with his book, *I* know what that book is about, James Driscoll.

"Even if I didn't see it at any of those preview performances, why couldn't I have caught it on Broadway? I was eighteen years old in '47, why couldn't I have seen the play? I started going to the theater when I was twelve, you know, used to go every Saturday with my father. Isn't it plausible that a play about the Army might have appealed to me?"

"Not a flop play."

"Maybe I've got a mind of my own, Jonah."

"I'm sure you have."

"Maybe I wanted to form my own opinion, despite what the critics had to say."

"That isn't the way it works, and you know it."

"Or maybe I read the reviews and decided there was the kernel of something good there. Maybe I went to the theater with a notebook, intent on stealing whatever—"

"And then waited fifteen years to write your book, is that

it? You're really an arch-criminal who entered Pratt Institute under the guise of studying art, though really wanting to be a writer all along. You searched the daily reviews to see what you could steal, and your imagination was captured by what you read about *Catchpole*. So you went there to copy it, realizing you would have to wait fifteen years before you could use the material. Is that it?"

"It's a possibility."

"Dris," Ebie said, "I wish you wouldn't talk this way. Even in jest."

"Ebie thinks I *did* steal it, you see," Driscoll said, and grinned.

"I think nothing of the sort."

"It's what she thinks, Jonah."

"Not at all."

"Tell the truth, Ebie. You think I stole that play, don't you?"

"You know I don't."

"Come on, Edna Belle, 'fess up."

"Stop it, Dris."

My name is Jimmy Driscoll, he had said. The tables in Bertie's were long and scarred, and she could remember looking away from him, down at the table top, initials in hearts, a group of engineering students singing at the other end of the room, November light filtering through the stained glass behind the tables, the room smelling of beer and steam heat, wet garments hanging on wooden pegs, his eyes were blue, she dared to look up into them. He teased her about her short hair and about her age. He imitated her Southern drawl, and then bought her a second glass of beer, the last of the big spenders, he said, and asked her out for Saturday night. She promptly refused.

You'll be sorry, he said. I'm going to be a famous artist.

Yes, I'm sure.

Come out with me.

No.

"There are good things in that play," Driscoll said. "It's

not a good play—but there are things worth stealing in it."

"I wouldn't advise you to say that on the witness stand," Jonah said.

"Why not? I'll be swearing to tell the truth, won't I?'

"Yes, but . . ."

"You wouldn't want me to lie under oath, would you? Even though better men than Constantine have lied under oath?"

"I'm not enjoying this, Jimmy," Jonah said.

"That's too bad," Driscoll answered. "What am I supposed to do, pretend Constantine is an ogre? Well, I can't. I feel closer to him than I do to you or anyone else in that courtroom. He made something with his hands, he pulled it out of his head and his heart, that play of his, that terrible play, oh yes, unanimously panned and reviled—well, that play is Arthur Constantine, and not just words for lawyers to argue over and judges to decide about. He thinks he was wronged, Jonah, first by all the critics who sat in exalted superiority the way McIntyre is sitting, completely on the outside, the external critics who could find nothing good to say about his ugly little child. And next by me, who took his miserable bastard and combed its hair and shined its shoes and made a million dollars on it. That's what he thinks and believes, Jonah, and I can understand him better than I can this cold contest between professional assassins, or this almighty judge who may murder him yet another time. I weep for him, Jonah. Don't try to shame him again."

"Do you want to lose this case?" Jonah asked flatly.

"It might matter more to Constantine than to me," Driscoll said.

"Why?"

"Because I'll never write another book as long as I live."

"That's nonsense, Dris," Ebie said.

"And don't repeat it on the witness stand," Jonah warned.

"Why not?"

"Because this case can go either way, and I don't need any more headaches—not if we're to win."

"Is that so important to you? Winning?"

"Yes," Jonah answered.

It's important to Dris, too, Ebie thought, don't think it isn't. He may *say* it's unimportant, Mr. Willow, he may *say* he'll never write another book as long as he lives, but I know him better than that, I know him better than any human being on earth. He knows he'll lose, you see. He knows that, and he's hoping against hope that he'll come out of it with honor somehow, without having to speak; that somehow a miracle will come to pass, he'll win without having to say what he tried to say in his novel and only failed to say. He'd give his *life* to be free of that Vermont rock garden where he pretends to grow his meager crops, living on royalties that still come in from the foreign editions and the paperback, constantly dwindling. He'd give his *soul* to be able to come back to New York, which is his home, his *only* home, come back and look this city in the eye again, be able to feel like a man in this city that's his, maybe not even to write again, though I know that's what he wants, I know, I know. I know this man so well, I know this fierce proud stupid stubborn man, I love this man so much.

He could do it. He could do it all, he could be free at last, if only . . . we could win this case so easily, we could do it so simply, if only he would . . .

We'll lose, Ebie thought.

He'll never tell them.

9

Gray hair rising in waves from a high forehead, combed straight back without a part so that it seemed to extend the flowing line of his profile, gray eyes intelligently alert beneath black beetling brows, Ralph Knowles took the oath, and then sat, crossed his long legs, and waited for Genitori to begin.

The lawyers had decided between them that Genitori, as chief counsel for API, would conduct the direct examination. Their decision puzzled Ralph, who had never found Genitori impressive either in looks or in bearing, and who wondered now what empathy this dumpy little man could possibly evoke from the judge. He watched critically as Genitori walked slowly and ponderously toward the witness stand, and his feelings were somewhat like those of a star in the hands of a bad director. Genitori cleared his throat, sniffed, looked once at the gray sky beyond the courtroom windows, nodded to the judge, smiled, and then turned again to Ralph.

"Mr. Knowles," he said, "what do you do for a living?"

"I'm a motion picture writer and director," Ralph said.

"Have you always been a motion picture writer and director?"

"No, sir."

"What did you do before you began working in motion pictures?"

"I was a freelance writer of magazine pieces, and after that I did a great deal of dramatic work for radio. This was before the war, during the late thirties and early forties. Before television."

"What radio programs did you write for?"

"Lux Radio Theater, Suspense, Mister District Attorney, The Green Hornet, The Shadow . . . most of the shows that were around, I would say. One of my radio plays for *Suspense* was later made into a movie called *Armitus.* That was when I first became involved with motion pictures. I went to the Coast for story conferences on it, you see, and while I was there someone asked me if I would like to do a screenplay for him—not on my own property—and I said yes. I began doing screenplays after that, and a while later I began directing."

"How many motion pictures have you written, Mr. Knowles?"

"Since 1954, I've written seventeen screenplays, and directed nine of them myself."

"Did you write and direct *The Paper Dragon?"*

"Yes, sir."

"Alone?"

"Sir?"

"Were you the only writer of the screenplay for the motion picture titled *The Paper Dragon?"*

"I was."

"In what year was that screenplay written?"

"1963, I think it was. Yes, it must have been the latter part of '63."

"Until that time, had you ever heard of the plaintiff, Arthur Constantine?"

"No, sir."

"Or the play *Catchpole?"*

"No."

"Had you ever seen a synopsis of *Catchpole?"*

"I had not. I try to avoid synopses whenever possible. It seems unnatural, to me, for anyone to condense a five-hundred-page novel into a fifty-page report on it. If you did that with *Hamlet,* you'd end up with what sounded like a ghost story. I can remember the synopsis I read on my own radio play, the one they were filming, and I was appalled by what they'd done, eliminating all the nuances, all the depth, all the range of character, leaving only the bare bones—terrible. I made up my mind right then and there that I'd have nothing to do with synopses ever again. I've pretty much hewed to that line since."

"You did *not,* then, read a synopsis of *Catchpole?*"

"No, sir."

"Did you ever see it performed?"

"Performed?"

"Yes. At the Fulton Theatre in New York?"

"No."

"Or anyplace else?"

"No, sir."

"Have you ever served with the United States armed forces?"

"I have."

"When?"

"May I ask where this is going, your Honor?" Brackman said.

"You'll see in a minute, Mr. Brackman," Genitori replied. "When were you in the armed forces, Mr. Knowles?"

"From July of 1943 to January of 1948."

"In what branch did you serve?"

"I was a fighter pilot in the Army Air Corps."

"Did you ever serve overseas?"

"Yes, sir. I left the United States in January of 1945, and was assigned to the Pacific Theater of Operations, where I remained until the time of my discharge."

"Where were you stationed in October of 1947, when Mr. Constantine's play was showing in New York?"

"I was stationed in Tokyo. Japan."

"When did you begin working for API?"

"In August of 1954."

"As what?"

"A writer at first. And later on, a director."

"During your initial period of employment there, was material ever submitted to you for consideration?"

"Material?"

"Plays, novels, television scripts?"

"Do you mean as possibilities for motion pictures?"

"Yes."

"Well, no. No one ever asked my opinion on whether or not a story should be purchased, if that's what you mean. In the beginning, I was simply handed a novel or a play, or whatever, and told it was my next assignment."

"To write a screenplay on it?"

"Yes. And when I first began directing, it worked much the same way. I would be assigned to direct a film, and I would direct it. Later on, of course, I was *asked* to direct, a producer would *come* to me with the material and ask if I would like to direct it or not."

"Material that had already been purchased?"

"Yes. And now, of course, *I* can ask the studio to buy a property that I think is interesting, and if they agree it'll make a good movie, they'll usually go along with me and buy the property for me to make."

"Did you see synopses of any material you did not later translate to the screen?"

"No, sir. I told you, I avoid synopses like the plague."

"Now, you said earlier that you wrote the screenplay for *The Paper Dragon . . .*"

"Yes, sir, and directed it as well."

"How did you go about writing this screenplay?"

"I don't think I understand you."

"What did you use as source material?"

"Oh. Well, the *book,* of course. It had been submitted to the studio in galleys, and a producer there liked it—Jules Fairchild—and asked me to take a look at it, and I thought it was something I'd like to do. I think I saw the magazine serialization, too, which was pretty close to the book, *McCall's* published it, I think, or *Redbook,* I'm not sure which, a two-part serial."

"The book was your basic source, would you say?"

"Yes. Although I did do additional research on my own. A book, you understand—even a fine book like *The Paper Dragon,* for which I have only the greatest respect—it's still only a book, you see, and there's a great deal involved in turning it into a motion picture . . . well, I don't know if I should go into all of this."

"Please do," McIntyre said.

"I was introduced to Mr. Driscoll for the first time this morning," Ralph said, "but I suppose he must have been a little puzzled by the changes made in bringing his book to the screen—so perhaps this will be instructive to him as well." Ralph turned and smiled at Driscoll, who was watching and listening attentively from the jury box. "There are some people who feel that the novel and the motion picture are similar in technique and in scope, but I disagree with them. They argue that a novelist can immediately turn from a minute examination of a woman's mouth, let us say, to a battlefield with hundreds of men in an infantry charge, that sort of thing—in other words, from a closeup to a full shot, and all without any transition, in much the same way that a camera would handle it. But we must remember that the novelist is dealing with the written word, and he must describe that woman's mouth in words, he must describe that infantry charge in words, which means that those words must first be registered on the reader's eye, and then carried to the reader's brain where, depending on how good or bad the writer is, there will be an intellectual response that will hopefully trigger an emotional response.

"Well, we have a situation completely diametrical to this in the motion picture, because we go directly for the emotional response; there is no need for a middleman, there is no need for a brain that will translate words into images that may or may not stimulate the tears or laughter we are going for. We *start* with the images, you see. That is our job, putting images on the screen in sequence, arranging and editing and putting in order these images that are designed to evoke a *direct* emotional response. I can tell you that if I come at that screen with a blood-stained knife, you are going to rear back in fright and I don't need any words to accompany it, that knife is its own motivation and its own explanation. Or if I fill that screen with a beautiful woman's face, and I show her eyes lidded and her lips parting, I don't have to accompany it with any interior monologues, I don't *need* poetry to describe her, we *know* she wants to be kissed, and we *want* to kiss her because the appeal is direct and emotional, the response is immediate.

"So, in beginning my work on a screenplay, I look upon the novel or the stage play or whatever it is I'm translating only as an outline of something that will become larger and grander than the printed word allowed. Even an excellent book like *The Paper Dragon,* for which I have nothing but the deepest veneration, becomes a detailed study for what will be my film. I sift through it and sort through it, trying to cut through the maze of words, trying to get through to the emotion hidden there, distilling what the author meant, translating his *words* directly into *images* so that the audience reaction will be immediate and overwhelming. In short, I eliminate the intellectual response in favor of the emotional. *Then,* if we're lucky, when these images have registered, when they have evoked the proper *emotional* response, why then the audience, if we are lucky, will experience an *intellectual* response as well. That's the difference between a novel and a motion picture, and it is this very difference that makes the film a much more difficult form in which to work and, in my estimation, a much higher art form."

"I see," Genitori said.

"Yes," Ralph said, and glanced toward the jury box to smile at Driscoll.

"You said you did some additional research . . ."

"Yes."

". . . before you began work on your screenplay?"

"Yes."

"Can you tell us what this research was?"

"Yes, certainly. As I indicated earlier, I spent a great deal of time in the Pacific during and after World War II, and I think it was the setting of Mr. Driscoll's fine novel that first attracted me to it—the possibility of shooting in Korea, a beautiful country, we got some really excellent footage of the countryside, you know. But in addition to that, I was interested in the book as a study of war, as an extension really of my own attempts to understand war in my early radio plays and also in one or two other films I had made before *The Paper Dragon.* War and its impact on man, what it does to men, what it causes them to become, this was what interested me. I discovered that a lot of material had been written on the subject, not only fiction, and not only the elongated minute-by-minute battle breakdowns, but serious studies that appeared in a great many of the magazines—*Life, Look,* the *Saturday Evening Post, The New York Times Magazine*—learned and informative articles about the behavior of our soldiers during the Korean conflict, the Korean *war,* I should say.

"These articles, and books as well, were written by military analysts, and psychiatrists, and historians, all of whom were probing the behavior of our men during that small war—I thought at one point of changing the title of the picture to *The Small War,* by the way, which I thought would be more emotionally effective than *The Paper Dragon,* but the studio objected because they didn't like the use of the word 'small' in any title. Where was I?"

"Books and magazine articles . . ."

"Yes, about the behavior of our men in Korea, the betrayal of comrades, the informing, the brainwashing, all of it. I studied these books and articles very carefully, using Mr. Driscoll's novel, of course, as my primary source because it was an excellent book and, let's face it, the only one we owned the rights to. We didn't own any of these other books or articles I studied for background material, you see, and besides Mr. Driscoll's novel was very exciting in itself and a firm basis upon which to build a movie. But before I began translating it into images, I also went to several Army bases to get a feeling of what the situation was like *today* as opposed to what I experienced during World War II. I visited Fort Bragg in North Carolina, and Fort Dix in New

Jersey, and also the infantry school at Fort Benning. That was the extent of the research I did before I began writing my screenplay."

"Would it then be fair to say that a screenwriter must perforce make certain changes in translating a novel into a film?"

"Absolutely."

"I ask this because I would like to explore some of the *specific* changes you made, Mr. Knowles, and perhaps find an explanation for them. For example, in Mr. Driscoll's novel, the character named Private Colman does *not* wear eyeglasses. Yet when you brought this character to the screen, you chose to show him *wearing* eyeglasses. Now why did you do that?"

"For the actor," Ralph said.

"What do you mean?"

"Not entirely, but at least that was a major consideration. The actor who portrayed Private Colman was a man named Olin Quincy, and he wears eyeglasses. I mean, off the screen, as a part of his normal life. There was a part of the screenplay that called for him to read from a map, and he asked me if it would be all right for him to wear his glasses throughout, so that he could actually do the reading as called for. I said it would be all right. So that was one consideration. But also, if you remember, there's another soldier in the book who wears eyeglasses—Kenworthy, the fellow who swears a lot—and in one scene there's a mortar attack and his glasses are lifted from his face by the concussion. It seemed to me that if he were the only one in the movie wearing eyeglasses, it would look like a put-up job, as if we had him wearing glasses only so they could be later knocked off, do you understand? So to take the curse off this, I decided to put glasses on another soldier as well, and the logical choice was Private Colman."

"Why was he the logical choice?"

"I like to avoid the obvious in my films. It would have been obvious to present Colman as a sneering sort of person, the way he is in the book—though you can get away with that in a book because there are also interior monologues and thought passages revealing various aspects of a character; however, you can't do that in a film. And rather than present Colman as a stereotyped villain, I thought it would add to his menace if he seemed to have a scholarly look about him, a rather meek look. In other words, if he wore eyeglasses. Which is not unusual, anyway. Many men in the Army, even in combat, wear eyeglasses."

"Now do you remember a scene in your film where you have a group of soldiers drinking coffee together?"

"Yes, sir, I do."

"This scene is not in the novel, is it?"

"No, sir, I don't believe it is."

"Why did you put it in your film?"

"For a very good reason. It is in this scene that I have Private Colman suggest they murder the lieutenant. Now, if you'll remember this same sequence in the novel—and this is what I was trying to illustrate earlier about intellectual as opposed to emotional response—Colman's decision to murder the lieutenant takes place entirely in his mind. Mr. Driscoll handled this static scene very well, to be sure, but the appeal was intellectual, and I was searching for an emotional approach to put across this very important plot point. All right, I decided to have these men doing something very commonplace, something almost homey, very cozy, you know. All of them sipping steaming coffee—the way we shot it, you could see the vapor rising from the cups—a break in the battle and these grizzled combat veterans have their hands wrapped around these steaming coffee cups, not even discussing the lieutenant, just enjoying the coffee, and bam! out of the blue, Private Colman says, 'Let's kill him.' Now that's an emotional shock, for the audience to hear those words, and the shock is heightened by the very mundane act in which the men are engaged, the drinking of coffee. That's why I put that scene in my film. I took something that was introspective and static, with all due respect to the excellent writing in that particular passage, and created instead an image that would shock and startle."

"You also put a bayonet charge in your movie, and this was not in the novel either."

"Correct."

"Can you explain why you did this?"

"Yes. To foreshadow the death of Lieutenant Cooper."

"But he isn't killed by bayonet, is he?"

"Correct."

"He is not?"

"No, sir, he is not. The lieutenant is killed by Chinese guns. I chose to foreshadow this by showing a vicious, almost bestial bayonet charge by our own soldiers, Americans. Also, I use the bayonet charge as a visual symbol. These men have been knifing the lieutenant in the back all through the movie, and now we see a visual representation of how cruel men can be to each other, bayonets being plunged, men dying just as the lieutenant later dies when he sacrifices himself to save Morley."

"Now, there's also in the movie you made a scene depicting an enemy soldier being shot at and falling out of a tree. Can you tell us the origin of this?"

"I don't know the origin."

"It was not in the book, was it?"

"Not to my recollection."

"Do you remember how you came to put it into your screenplay?"

"It was a vignette, part of a montage of scenes showing the horrors of war. Certainly a man being shot at and falling from a high place is almost a cinema cliché. I have seen it before in many movies, both war pictures and Westerns, too. I don't claim to have originated that particular image, though I must say we used an extraordinary camera angle on it, pointing directly up at the tree, and when the soldier is shot, he falls directly toward the camera, getting bigger and bigger until he fills the entire screen. That was a really fine piece of camera work, and I credit my cameraman Andy Burstadter for it."

"In this same montage of scenes, you show an American

soldier bursting into tears when his buddy is killed. This, too, is not in the novel, and I wonder if you can tell me where it originated."

"Your Honor," Brackman said, "in a case without a jury, I would as a matter of course refrain from objecting to a question containing a description, such as the one Mr. Genitori just put to the witness. But I think you will agree that the witness was being led, and that this was a blatant violation of the rules of evidence."

"Sustained. Please rephrase it, Mr. Genitori."

"Is there a scene in your film where an American soldier bursts into tears?"

"There is."

"What was the basis of this scene? Where did it originate, can you tell us?"

"Yes, I can. It originated, the idea for it came from a book of photographs called *The Family of Man*. Since motion pictures are really a series of still photographs arranged in sequence, I will very often leaf through books of photographs, and this happened to be an extremely fine collection. I believe the actual photos had hung in exhibit at the Museum of Modern Art here in New York, and this was an artful presentation of most, if not all, of them. The idea for that particular scene came to me in one of the photographs. I don't remember who the photographer was, a war photographer for *Life,* I believe, and it showed two soldiers, and one of them is comforting his buddy who is crying. That's the origin of that particular vignette."

"What about the nurse putting on her lipstick?"

"What do you mean?"

"You have a scene, not part of this montage, but an actual scene in the film, where the nurse is putting on lipstick and she uses the back of a mess kit as a mirror. This was not in the novel, but there is a similar scene, or at least a stage direction to that effect, in Mr. Constantine's play. Now where did you get the idea for this scene?"

"It happened during the shooting."

"Of the film?"

"Yes. The screenplay called for the girl to put on her lipstick, and when she began to do so—with the camera rolling—she discovered that the prop man hadn't put a mirror in her bag. So she picked up a mess kit that was on the table, and she turned it over and discovered it was shiny, and she used that. She was a very inventive actress, Miss Shirley Tucker, and she sensed the scene was going very well, this was the first take, and rather than risking another take where we might not get the same dramatic qualities, she ad-libbed with the mess kit, and we left it in."

"You left it in the completed film?"

"Yes, sir."

"But it was *not* in the screenplay?"

"No, sir."

"Thank you, Mr. Knowles."

"Is that it?" Brackman asked, surprised.

"I'm finished, Mr. Brackman," Genitori answered.

Brackman nodded, consulted his notes, and then walked toward the witness chair. Ralph watched him as he approached. If anything, he was even less impressive than Genitori, a short, unattractive man whose clothes looked rumpled, whose hair stood up ridiculously at the back of his head, whose tie was the wrong color for his suit.

"Mr. Knowles," Brackman said suddenly, "would you say that a screenplay is similar to a stage play?"

"No, sir."

"They both deal with the spoken word, do they not?"

"Yes, sir."

"And with a visual arrangement of scenes?"

"Yes, sir."

"With actors portraying parts created for them?"

"Yes, sir."

"Then you would agree that there is at least *some* similarity between a screenplay and a stage play? At least the similarities we have just enumerated?"

"Yes, but they are really very different. I've adapted several Broadway plays to the screen, and it's an enormously difficult job. If they were as similar as you seem to think they are, the job wouldn't have been nearly so difficult."

"You have adapted plays to the screen?"

"Yes."

"Stage plays?"

"Yes."

"In addition to adapting novels?"

"Yes. I've also adapted short stories and television plays. If the material is good, it doesn't matter what form it's originally written in. It must all be translated to the screen, anyway."

"So I understand. But before you begin these screen translations, do you always engage in additional research?"

"I do."

"As you did with *The Paper Dragon?*"

"As I do with every project."

"We're concerned here with *The Paper Dragon.*"

"My career did not suddenly begin with *The Paper Dragon,* you know. I had written and directed a great many successful movies before that one."

"And for each of these you engaged in thorough research?"

"Correct."

"Such as visiting Army bases?"

"For *The Paper Dragon,* yes."

"You said you went to Fort Bragg, and Fort Benning, and Fort Dix."

"Yes."

"Did you visit any Army bases in Korea?"

"No, sir."

"Even though the novel was set in Korea?"

"Correct."

"Why did you go to these bases in the United States?"

"To catch up on the language of the men, the slang, their conversation, little things they might be doing, little things that caught my eye and remained in my memory during the shooting of the film."

"At any of these Army bases, Mr. Knowles, did you witness a man being shot out of a tree?"

"No, sir."

"Did you witness an American soldier crying because his buddy had been killed?"

"No, sir."

"Did you see a nurse using a mess kit as a mirror?"

"No, sir."

"You certainly didn't see a bayonet charge?"

"No, sir."

"Or a man killed by a bayonet?"

"No, sir."

"Mr. Knowles, you said you were a fighter pilot during World War II."

"Yes, sir."

"What kind of plane did you fly?"

"I flew most of the aircraft in use during World War II, sir. Fighter planes, that is."

"Like what?"

"I flew the P-51 Mustang, and the P-38 Lightning and P-39 Airacobra. On one occasion, I even flew a Navy fighter plane, the Hellcat, sir, the F6F."

"You had very little opportunity then, while you were flying, I mean, to witness ground troops in action."

"I witnessed them from the air."

"But never on the ground. You were never on the ground during combat?"

"I flew forty-three combat missions, sir."

"On any of these combat missions, did you ever witness a man being shot out of a tree?"

"No, sir."

"Did you ever witness a bayonet charge?"

"No, sir."

"Then these 'little things that caught your eye and remained in your memory'—I think I'm quoting accurately—were things you saw neither during your time in the Air Corps nor during your subsequent visits to Army bases in the United States. They must have come from somewhere else, isn't that so, Mr. Knowles?"

"I've already told the Court where they came from."

"What does a story editor do, Mr. Knowles?"

"At a motion picture studio, do you mean?"

"Yes."

"I'm not sure I know."

"Well, there must be story editors at API."

"Yes."

"Do you know what they do?"

"I think they look over material that's published or produced and then make recommendations to the front office."

"What sort of recommendations?"

"As to whether the material should be considered for purchase."

"Do you think *The Paper Dragon* was seen by story editors?"

"The novel? I would guess so."

"Story editors employed by API, I mean."

"I'm not too sure of their function, so I can't say whether this would be a routine thing or not. I simply can't answer that question."

"Do you know a man named Joseph Edelson?"

"He's dead."

"Did you know him when he was alive?"

"Yes, I did. He was the head of API's story department."

"Did he work in any capacity on *The Paper Dragon?*"

"No, he did not. I wrote the screenplay without any assistance, and I directed—"

"I want to know if he worked in *any* capacity on the film."

"Not to my knowledge."

"Do you know Miss Iris Blake?"

"Not personally."

"Have you ever heard of her?"

"Yes. She's in API's story department too."

"Did she work in any capacity on *The Paper Dragon?*"

"No, sir."

"You said you began working at API in—when was it?"

"In August of 1954."

"Were Joseph Edelson and Iris Blake working there at the time?"

"Joe was because that's when I met him. I don't know Miss Blake, so I couldn't tell you about her."

"Had you ever been to the studio before August of 1954?"

"Yes, I had been there for consultations on a property of mine—the radio play—which they were turning into a movie."

"Were you ever at the studio before April of 1954?"

"Yes, I believe so."

"Did you ever meet Mr. Constantine on any of your visits to the studio?"

"Never."

"He was working for API until April of 1954. Is it conceivable that you may have met him and perhaps forgotten . . ."

"I remember everyone I've ever met in my life," Ralph said flatly.

"But you *did* know two of the people to whom Mr. Constantine showed his play in the time he was working for the studio."

"Which two people would they be?" Ralph asked.

"Mr. Edelson and Miss Blake."

"I knew Mr. Edelson. I have never met Miss Blake, though I understand she is a charming and a beautiful woman."

"And you insist they had nothing to do with the filming of *The Paper Dragon?*"

"That's correct."

"Do you know Mr. Andrew B. Langford?"

"I do not."

"He is the secretary of Artists-Producers-International."

"I can't be expected to know every secretary at—"

"You misunderstand me, Mr. Knowles. He is *the* secretary of API."

"Whatever he is, I don't know him."

"You've never met?"

"Never."

"We asked Mr. Langford, on May 16th, to supply us with a list of anyone who had worked on *The Paper Dragon* either before or during its production. As Script Writer and Director he listed 'Ralph Knowles, under employment to the studio.' You are that same Ralph Knowles, are you not?"

"I am."

"As Story Editors he listed 'Joseph Edelson and Iris Blake, under employment to the studio.' Mr. Langford swore to the truth of his responses, so we have good reason to believe they were accurate. Yet you seem to disagree with him."

"In what way?"

"You have told this Court that neither Mr. Edelson nor Miss Blake had anything to do with your production of *The Paper Dragon.*"

"Correct."

"Yet Mr. Langford swears they were employed by the studio . . ."

"That may be so, but—"

". . . as story editors on *The Paper Dragon.*"

"I'm telling you they had nothing to do with my film."

"Were they or were they not story editors?"

"I don't know what they were. This is the first time I'm hearing of this credit. Was it in the titles?"

"What?"

"Of the film. Did this credit show in the titles? I never heard of it before today."

"Mr. Langford swears . . ."

"Well, he ought to know who was hired or who was not hired by the studio. But even if they *were* story editors, would you mind telling me what that has to do with my movie?"

"That's what I'd like *you* to tell *me,* Mr. Knowles."

"I've already told you. Neither of them had anything to do with *The Paper Dragon.*"

"Yet you knew Mr. Edelson personally?"

"Yes, I did."

"If I told you that Mr. Constantine knew both Mr. Edelson and Miss Blake, would you take my word for it?"

"Why not?"

"But you yourself never heard of Mr. Constantine before this action began?"

"The only Constantine I'd ever heard of was the Roman emperor," Ralph said, and smiled.

"But not Arthur Constantine?"

"No. *Not* Arthur Constantine."

"Are you familiar with a film called *Area Seven?*"

"I am."

"In what way?"

"I saw the film, and I know the man who wrote the screenplay."

"Which man are you referring to?"

"Matthew Jackson."

"Was it a good film?"

"It was nominated for an Academy Award. Whether that makes it a good film or not is open to debate."

"Has Mr. Jackson ever mentioned Arthur Constantine to you?"

"Never."

"Were you aware of the fact that Arthur Constantine worked on that film?"

"I was not."

"Yes. He adapted it."

"I didn't know that."

"Will you take my word for it?"

"Certainly."

"Do you know a man named Rudy Herdt?"

"No, sir."

"A woman named Betty Alweiss?"

"No, sir."

"They are both presently employed by API, and have been working there since 1949. Are you sure you do not know them?"

"I am positive."

"You don't seem to know too many people at the studio, do you, Mr. Knowles?"

"I'm not gregarious," Ralph answered.

"How about Mr. Silverberg?"

"Who?"

"Mr. A. Silverberg. Or it may be *Miss* A. Silverberg, I can't tell from this. Mr. Genitori, would you know . . .?"

"It's *Mr.* Silverberg," Genitori said. "Abraham Silverberg."

"I don't know him," Ralph said.

"Have you ever read any synopses prepared by Mr. Silverberg?"

"I do not read synopses."

"And therefore you have not read the synopsis Mr. Silverberg prepared on *Catchpole?*"

"No, I have not."

"Have you ever read *any* synopsis of the play *Catchpole?*"

"Never."

"But you *have* read the play itself."

"No, I have not."

"No one at API gave you a copy of the play to read?"

"That's correct."

"I am referring now to the period of time since this action began."

"I have never read *Catchpole,* nor do I intend ever to read it."

"Didn't your attorneys suggest that you read it before coming here to testify?"

"They did."

"But you chose not to read it?"

"I am too busy to read anything that does not personally interest me."

"And I take it that *Catchpole* does not personally interest you?"

"Correct."

"How can you tell this without reading it?"

"I've read transcripts, or depositions, or whatever they were, and I knew from those that the play would not interest me."

"Do you mean transcripts of the pretrial examinations?"

"Correct."

"And I take it you were not overly impressed with Mr. Constantine's work?"

"I was not."

"Are you ever impressed with anyone's work other than your own?"

"Objection, your Honor."

"Sustained. Let's leave off with this, shall we, Mr. Brackman?"

"Mr. Knowles, did Matthew Jackson work with you on the filming of the motion picture *The Paper Dragon?"*

"He did."

"In what capacity?"

"As assistant director."

"What does an assistant director do, can you tell us?"

"Certainly. It's his job to see that everything is functioning properly, actors have their scripts and know their lines, props are ready, extras are in place, quiet and order are maintained on the set. An A.D. is an invaluable person on a film, and Matthew Jackson is a good one."

"Does an assistant director ever *direct?"*

"Sometimes."

"Did Matthew Jackson direct any of the scenes in *The Paper Dragon?"*

"He may have."

"Which scenes?"

"Second-unit stuff, I would imagine."

"Was the bayonet charge second-unit stuff?"

"It may have been."

"Who directed the bayonet charge?"

"I'm sure I directed the sequences involving the principals."

"And the other sequences?"

"Matt might have. Mr. Jackson."

"Was the montage second-unit stuff?"

"Which montage?"

"The one containing vignettes of the soldier being shot out of a tree, and the soldier crying . . ."

"I directed all of that."

"Mr. Jackson did not help with it?"

"Only as A.D. on the sound stage, that's all, his normal function."

"Let's talk about Private Colman for a moment, shall we?"

"Certainly."

"You portrayed him as wearing eyeglasses . . ."

"Yes."

". . . and you testified that you did this because the actor playing the part, Mr. Olin Quincy, wore glasses in real life?"

"Correct."

"And would not be able to *see* unless—"

"No, I didn't say that. He's as blind as a bat, that's true, but I wouldn't have given him glasses if the part didn't call for him to *read* something. There was a very complicated scene in the film where the positions on a map are being traced, just preparatory to heading into enemy territory, the same as in the book, and Olin thought it would be a good idea if he could *see* all these Oriental place names and actually *read* them from the map, rather than trying to memorize them."

"Do you remember the character of Colman well?"

"Yes, sir."

"As presented in the book?"

"Yes, sir, I do."

"Was he wearing eyeglasses in the book?"

"No, sir."

"Was there a character named Corporal Finlay in the book?"

"No, sir."

"Was there a Corporal Finlay in the movie?"

"Yes, sir."

"Would you say that he possessed some of Private Colman's characteristics?"

"What do you mean?"

"Colman's characteristics from the book."

"Yes, sir, I would say so."

"Would you say that Private Colman and Corporal Finlay in the movie were *both* derived from the single character of Private Colman in the book?"

"I would say so, yes."

"You would say that both these characters were derived from the single character of Colman?"

"Well," Ralph said, and hesitated. "Finlay was a composite."

"Of whom?"

"Of Colman and several other characters in the book."

"Which other characters?"

"Characters who were dropped from the film."

"Which?"

"Well, I would have to think for a moment."

"Yes, please do."

"There were a lot of soldiers in the platoon . . ."

"Yes . . ."

". . . and we obviously couldn't use all of them in the film, or we'd have had a picture that ran for six hours."

"Yes, I understand that."

"But many of these were minor characters, and I sort of bunched them together to create the single character called Corporal Finlay."

"Yes, but from which characters *besides* Colman was this character derived?"

"I don't recall their names offhand."

"Can you remember their characteristics?"

"Not offhand."

"Would you say that Corporal Finlay was derived primarily from Colman as he appeared in the novel?"

"Yes, primarily, I suppose."

"In that Colman in the novel became *two* characters in the film: Colman and Finlay."

"Correct."

"Are you familiar with the character named Colonel Peterson in *Catchpole?*"

"No, sir."

"The character description of him states that he is a tall, slender, frail-looking man. Would you say that the man who played Corporal Finlay in your film—what was his name?"

"John Rafferty played the part."

"Would you say that he is a tall, slender, frail-looking man?"

"I don't know what you might consider tall," Ralph said.

"Well, *I'm* a short man, Mr. Knowles, and *you're* a tall man. Is John Rafferty more your size or more mine?"

"He's about as tall as I am, six feet give or take an inch."

"Is he slender?"

"I would say so."

"And he does, does he not, give an impression of frailty?"

"Well, I don't know about that."

"We have all seen the film, Mr. Knowles, and I think you will have to agree that John Rafferty gives an impression of frailty on the screen."

"All right, all right."

"In *Catchpole,* Peterson is a psychopath. Would you say that Corporal Finlay is a psychopath?"

"No, sir."

"Would you say he is a neurotic?"

"I don't know the distinction."

"Would you describe Finlay as being disturbed?"

"He is disturbed, yes. But you're forgetting that the character in the book was disturbed, too."

"Which character? Private Colman, do you mean?"

"Yes."

"Yes, and you've testified that Private Colman was divided to form two *separate* characters in the film."

"Correct."

"One who was still called Private Colman, and the other who became Corporal Finlay. I'm a little puzzled by this, Mr. Knowles, because it was my impression that in writing a screenplay the idea was to *eliminate* extraneous characters, tighten the action, generally bring a novel—which can be loose and sprawling—into sharper focus. Why then did you choose to make two characters out of what was a *single* character in Mr. Driscoll's novel?"

"I must have had reasons, though I'm not sure what they were right now. This may have been a suggestion from Olin, who played the part of the troublemaker, I'm not sure. Actors do have a say, you know."

"Yes, of course. Can you remember what it was he might have objected to in the character Colman as presented in the novel?"

"No."

"But whatever it was, it caused you to invent another character, the one you called Finlay."

"I would suppose so."

"Mr. Knowles, do you remember a scene in which you have Lieutenant Cooper requesting Corporal Finlay to assist him with some paperwork, and Finlay replies, 'I can't, sir. Paperwork is for sissies,' and the other soldiers burst out laughing, do you remember that scene?"

"Yes, I do."

"If you'll look at this . . ."

"What is that?"

". . . in reel 3, page 4 . . ."

"Oh, yes. What page was that?"

"Page 4."

"Thank you. Yes, I have it."

"Would you look at the dialogue there, please?"

"Yes?"

"Where, right after the speech I just quoted to you, Private Colman says, 'Why don't you give him a hand, sweetie?' And then Kenworthy says, 'You could work in his tent, honey,' and Colman shouts, 'You'll enjoy it!' Do you see those speeches?"

"I do."

"What do they mean?"

"They mean, Oh boy, here comes the lieutenant with some more paperwork, everything according to the book. These men are joking, they're trying to make a fool of the lieutenant."

"How about the words 'You could work in his tent, honey'? What do those words mean? These are *men* talking, you understand."

"Of course. That simply means they consider paperwork to be sissy work."

"Is Corporal Finlay a sissy?"

"No, but he feels the way the others do, that paperwork is sissy work. And the men pick this up and make a big thing out of it, the way they do with everything throughout the film, badgering the lieutenant and trying to make him feel ridiculous, the idea that paperwork could be even remotely enjoyable to this soldier . . ."

"Enjoyable?"

"Yes."

"In what way?"

"Just the suggestion that it could be enjoyable, the suggestion Colman makes, you'll enjoy it."

"Enjoy it?"

"All right, I see where you're going, why don't we put it right on the table?"

"Sir?"

"Homosexuality."

"Yes, what about it?"

"That's what you're driving at, isn't it? You're trying to say there was a homosexual implication in this scene."

"Was there?"

"Certainly not."

"The words 'sweetie' and 'honey' used between men do not suggest homosexuality to you?"

"No, sir, they do not. Lieutenant Cooper is not supposed to be a fairy."

"Is Corporal Finlay supposed to be a fairy?"

"No, sir."

"And yet, he is based on Private Colman in the book, isn't that what you said?"

"That's what I said."

"Isn't Private Colman a homosexual?"

"No, sir."

"Not in your movie, I realize that. But how about the book?"

"I don't know what he is in the book."

"Surely you read the book?"

"Yes, of course I read the book."

"Then surely you are aware of the stream of consciousness passage—it is seven pages long, Mr. Knowles—wherein Private Colman clearly remembers and alludes to a homosexual episode with the dead major. Surely you remember reading that?"

"If I read it, I automatically discarded it as possible movie material. There is no homosexuality in any of my films, or even suggestions of homosexuality."

"But we do have a disturbed corporal whom the men rib about doing sissy work."

"Yes."

"Calling him names like 'honey' and 'sweetie' . . ."

"Yes."

"And suggesting that going into the lieutenant's tent might prove enjoyable."

"I didn't say that. *Nobody* says that. They only say he might enjoy the *paperwork.*"

"Is that what they actually mean? Paperwork?"

"Yes. They're kidding the lieutenant about the paperwork, about how he thinks it's enjoyable, they're belittling his idea of enjoyment."

"I see. And you intended no homosexual reference, either concerning the lieutenant *or* the corporal."

"Absolutely not."

"Let's get to the girl in your movie, shall we, Mr. Knowles?"

"Fine."

"You said that she invented the business with the mess kit while you were shooting the film, that it did not appear in your screenplay. Miss Tucker ad-libbed it on the set because your property man had neglected to include a mirror in her handbag."

"That's right."

"When you noticed the missing mirror, why didn't you stop the shooting?"

"Because the scene was going very well."

"Yes, but it was only a first take, wasn't it?"

"Of a very difficult shot."

"Well, surely you could have stopped the camera, and then given Miss Tucker a mirror, and continued shooting. Movies are a matter of splicing together scenes, anyway, aren't they?"

"That would have been impossible with this particular shot. If I had stopped the action, we would have had to go again from the top. Besides, as I told you, I didn't *want* to stop the action. The scene was going very well, and when I saw what Shirley was up to, I just let her go right ahead."

"Why would it have been impossible to stop this particular scene without starting again from the beginning of it?"

"The camera was on a boom and a dolly both. There was continuous action, the dolly moving in . . ."

"The dolly?"

"It's a . . . well, I guess you can call it a cart or a wagon on tracks, and the camera is mounted on it. As the scene progressed, the dolly was coming in closer and closer to Miss Tucker, and then as she picked up the lipstick we began to move up on the boom . . ."

"I'm afraid you'll have to tell me what a boom is also."

"It's a mechanical—well . . . a *lift,* I guess would describe it—that moves the camera up and down, vertically. When we were in close on her, we went for the boom shot, all without breaking the action. In other words, I wanted this scene to have a complete flow, without any cutting, and it was necessary to shoot it from top to bottom without stopping. That's why I let her use the mess kit. As it turned out, we got the scene in one take and were delighted with it. It's one of the best scenes in the movie, in fact."

"An ad-libbed scene?"

"Well, the part with the mess kit was ad-libbed."

"It was not in your screenplay?"

"No, sir."

"Would you turn to reel 5, page 2 of this, Mr. Knowles?"

"What?"

"Please. Reel 5, page 2."

"Yes?"

"Do you see the numeral 176, right after the lieutenant says, 'Colman's the one who's responsible for their anger and their hatred.' Read on after that, would you, from DS—which I assume means 'downstage.' "

"No, it means 'dolly shot.' It says, 'DS—JAN—AND INTO BOOM SHOT: She takes lipstick from her purse and then, finding no mirror, picks up a mess kit from the table, discovers that its back is shiny, and uses it as she applies her lipstick.' "

"Now you testified that this scene was ad-libbed. Yet right here in your screenplay . . ."

"This is *not* my screenplay," Ralph said.

"It has your name on it."

"It's the cutting continuity of the film."

"Isn't that the same as . . . ?"

"No, sir. This is the *cutting* continuity, reel by reel. It's a record of all the action and dialogue in the film as it was shot. The cutter put this together."

"From the shooting script?"

"No, sir, from the completed *film.*"

"Exactly as it was shot?"

"Exactly. But this is not a screenplay. This was not in existence until the film was finally completed."

"It is nonetheless a script, no matter what you choose to call—"

"No, sir, it is the continuity of the actual *film.* It is not a script in any sense of the word."

"But it nonetheless shows exactly what happened on the screen?"

"Yes."

"And what happened on the screen was that the girl used a mess kit for a mirror."

"Yes."

"That's all, thank you."

"Have you concluded your cross, Mr. Brackman?"

"I have, your Honor."

"Any further questions?"

"None, your Honor," Genitori said.

"None," Willow said.

"Thank you, Mr. Knowles," McIntyre said.

"Thank *you,* sir," Ralph said.

"Your Honor, Mr. Knowles is on his way to the Orient where he is beginning a new film. Would it be possible to release him at this point?"

"Certainly."

"Thank you," Ralph said, and rose and began walking toward the jury box. Behind him, he could hear the judge telling everyone that it was now ten minutes to four, and then asking Willow whether he wanted to begin his direct examination of James Driscoll now or would he prefer waiting until morning. Willow replied that he would rather wait until morning, and McIntyre commented that this was probably best since he thought they were all a bit weary, and then the clerk said something about the court reconvening at ten in the morning, and Ralph kept walking toward the jury box and then realized that everyone was rising to leave the courtroom and turned instead to head for the bronze-studded doors. He was very pleased with himself, and he nodded and smiled at Driscoll, who was rising and moving out of the jury box, and then he glanced over his shoulder to see Genitori rising from behind the defense table and moving very quickly toward him, and he continued smiling as he opened the door because he knew without doubt that he had performed beautifully and perhaps saved this miserable little trial from total obscurity.

"You're a son of a bitch," Genitori said.

"What?" Ralph said. "What?"

"You heard me, you prick!"

"What? What?"

He had wedged Ralph into a corner of the corridor, and now he leaned toward him in fury, his fists bunched at his sides, his arms straight, his face turned up, eyes glaring, as though he were restraining himself only with the greatest of effort. He is very comical, Ralph thought, this little butterball of a man with his balding head and pale blue eyes, hurling epithets, I could flatten him with one punch— But he did not raise his hands because there was something terrifying about Genitori's anger, and Ralph knew without question that the lawyer could commit murder here in this sunless corridor, and he had no intention of provoking his own demise.

"What's the matter with you?" he said. "Now calm down, will you? What's the matter with you?"

"You son of a bitch," Genitori said.

"Look, now let's watch the language, do you mind? You're . . ."

"What do you think we're doing here? You think we're playing *games* here, you son of a bitch?"

"Now look . . ."

"Shut up!"

"Look, Sam . . ."

"Shut up, you egocentric asshole!"

The juxtaposition of adjective and noun amused Ralph, but he did not laugh. The anger emanating from Genitori was monumental, it was awesome, it was classic. He knew that a laugh, a smile, even a mere upturning of his lips might trigger mayhem, so he tried to ease his way out of the cul-de-sac into which Genitori had wedged him, but the walls on either side of him were immovable and Genitori blocked his path like a small raging bull about to lower his horns and charge.

"Now take it easy," Ralph said.

"What did we discuss last night, you miserable bastard?" Genitori said. "Why did I drive all the way to Idlewild . . ."

"Kennedy."

"You son of a bitch, don't correct me, you miserable jackass! All the way in from Massapequa, you think I *enjoy* midnight rides?"

"Now look, Sam . . ."

"Don't look *me,* you moron! There's a man's career at stake in that courtroom, we're not kidding around here! We lose this case, and James Driscoll goes down the drain!"

"What did I *do,* would you mind . . ."

"What *didn't* you do? You gave them everything they wanted!"

"How? All I . . ."

"*Is* there a homosexual colonel in that goddamn play?"

"What?"

"I said—"

"How do *I* know? I didn't say there was a—"

"Well, there *isn't.* But you were so busy denying even the *suggestion* of one in your movie . . ."

"How was I supposed to know . . ."

"Is even the *suggestion* threatening to you?"

"Now look here, Sam, nothing about homosexuality threatens *me,* so let's not . . ."

"Then why did you insist a clearly homosexual scene *wasn't* one?"

"I told the truth as I saw it!"

"Yes, and made it sound as if you were hiding a *theft.*"

"I didn't intend . . ."

"Were you also telling the truth about dividing Colman into two characters?"

"Of course. What's wrong with that? I was explaining . . ."

"It's exactly what they *claimed* was done."

"Huh?"

"Huh, huh? They said Driscoll changed it when he copied the play, and you changed it right back again. *Huh?*"

"I did?"

"That's what you *admitted* doing, isn't it, you stupid ass!"

"I was under oath. I had to explain how I wrote the screenplay. That's what he asked me, and that's what I had to tell him."

"Do you even *remember* how you wrote it?"

"Yes. Just the way I said I did."

"I don't believe you. I think if Brackman said you'd made *fifteen* characters out of Colman, you'd have agreed."

"Now why would I do anything like that, Sam?"

"To show that your movie was an original act of creation, something that just happened to pop into your head, the hell with Driscoll and his book, you practically ad-libbed the whole movie on the set!"

"I never said that! The only scene we ad-libbed was the one with the mess kit. How was I to know all this other stuff was so—"

"Why didn't you read the play, the way we asked you to?"

"I have better things to do with my time."

"Like what? Destroying the reputation of a better writer than you'll ever be?"

"Now that's enough, Sam. You can't—"

"Don't get me sore, you . . . you *porco fetente,*" Genitori said, apparently having run out of English expletives. "You've done more toward killing this case . . ."

"Look, Sam . . ."

". . . than any witness the *plaintiff* might have called!"

"Look, Sam, I don't have to listen to this," Ralph said, having already listened to it.

"No, you don't, that's true. All you have to listen to is that tiny little voice inside your head that keeps repeating, 'Ralph Knowles, you are wonderful, Ralph Knowles, you are marvelous.' That's all you have to listen to. Are you flying?"

"What? Yes."

"Good. I hope your goddamn plane crashes," Genitori said, and then turned on his heel and went raging down the corridor.

Boy, Ralph thought.

10

He saw her for the first time in Bertie's on DeKalb Avenue, a girl with short blond hair, wearing sweater and skirt, scuffed loafers, her elbow on the table, her wrist bent, a cigarette idly hanging in two curled fingers. Unaware of him, she laughed at something someone at her table said, and then dragged on the cigarette, and laughed again, and picked up her beer mug, still not looking at him while he continued to stare at her from the door. He took off his parka and hung it on a peg, and then went to join some of the art-student crowd jammed elbow to elbow at the bar. Some engineering students at the other end of the long, narrow room were beerily singing one of the popular sentimental ballads. He watched her for a moment longer, until he was sure she would not return his glance, and then wedged himself in against the bar with his back to her, and ordered a beer. The place smelled of youthful exuberant sweat, and sawdust, and soap, and booze, and of something he would have given his soul to capture on canvas in oil, a dank November scent that seemed to seep from the windswept Brooklyn street outside and into the bar.

He knew all at once that she had turned to look at him.

He could not have said how he knew, but he sensed without doubt that she had discovered him and was staring at him, and he suddenly felt more confident than he ever had in his life. Without hesitating to verify his certain knowledge, he turned from the bar with the beer mug in his hand and walked directly across the room toward her table—she was no longer looking at him—and pulled out the chair confidently without even glancing at any of the other boys or girls sitting there, nor caring whether they thought he was nuts or whatever, but simply sat and put down his beer mug, and then looked directly at her as she turned to face him.

"My name is Jimmy Driscoll," he said.

"Hello, Jimmy Driscoll," she answered.

"What's *your* name?"

"Goodbye, Jimmy Driscoll," one of the boys at the table said.

"Ebie Dearborn," she said.

"Hello, Ebie. You're from Virginia, right?"

"Wrong."

"Georgia?"

"Nope."

"Where?"

"Alabama."

"It figures."

"What do you mean?"

"Honey chile, that's *some* accent you-all got there."

"Don't make fun of it," she said, and then turned toward her friends as laughter erupted from the other end of the table. "What was it?" she asked them, smiling in anticipation. "I *missed* it, what was it?"

"Ah-ha, you just try and find out," one of the boys said, and they all burst out laughing again.

"Would you like a beer?" he asked.

"All right," she said.

"Waiter, two beers," he said over his shoulder.

"Who'd you just order from?" she asked, and laughed.

"I don't know. Isn't there a waiter back there someplace? Two beers!" he yelled again, without looking behind him.

"Come and get them!" the bartender yelled back.

"You think you'll miss me?"

"Huh?"

"When I go for the beers."

"I doubt it. There's lots of company here."

"You may be surprised."

"I may be," she said.

He went to the bar and returned with two mugs of beer. She was in conversation with her friends when he approached, but she immediately turned away from them and pulled out a chair for him.

"How'd it work out?" he asked.

"I missed you, sure enough."

"I knew you would."

"Here's to your modest ways," she said, and raised her glass.

"Here's to your cornflower eyes."

"Mmm."

"How's the beer?"

"Fine."

"Would you like another one?"

"I've just barely sipped on this one."

"So what? Let me get another one for you."

"Not yet."

"Do you always wear your hair so short?"

"I cut it yesterday. Why? What's the matter with it?"

"You look shaggy."

"Say, thanks."

"I meant that as a compliment. I should have . . ."

"What *else* don't you like about me?"

". . . said windblown."

"What?"

"Your hair. Windblown."

"Oh," she said, and brushed a strand of it away from her cheek.

"That's nice."

"What is?"

"What you just did. How old are you?"

"Nineteen."

"That's good."

"Why?"

"Older women appeal to me."

"What do you mean? How old are *you?*"

"Eighteen."

"Oh? Really?"

"I'm a first-year student."

"Oh?"

"But very advanced for my age."

"Yes, I can see that."

"You think this'll work out?"

"What do you mean?"

"I don't know, the age difference, the language barrier . . ." He smiled hopefully, and let the sentence trail.

"Frankly, I don't think it has a chance," she said, and did not return his smile.

"Let me get you another beer."

"I'm not ready for one yet."

"I'll get one, anyway."

"I'm really not that thirsty."

"It doesn't matter. I'm the last of the big spenders," he said, and smiled again, but she only glanced toward her friends, who had begun a lively discussion about Mies. "Well, I'll get one for you."

"Suit yourself," she said, and shrugged.

He rose and went for the beer, half afraid she would leave the table while he was gone, aware that he was losing her, desperately searching in his mind for something to say that would salvage the situation, wondering where he had made his mistake, should he not have told her he was eighteen? or kidded her about the accent? if only he could think of a joke or an anecdote, something that would make her laugh. "One beer," the bartender said, and he picked it up and walked back to the table with it.

"Drink it quick before the foam disappears," he said, but she did not pick up the mug, and they sat in silence as the bubbles of foam rapidly dissipated, leaving a flat smooth amber surface an inch below the rim of the mug.

"Tell me about yourself," he said.

"My hair is shaggy," she said, "and I have a thick Southern accent, and . . ."

"Well, I know all that," he said, and realized at once he was pursuing the same stupid line, the wrong line, and yet seemed unable to stop himself. "Isn't there anything *interesting* you can add?"

"Oh, shut up," she said.

"What?"

"Just shut up."

"Okay," he said, but he could not remain silent for long. "We're having our first argument," he said, and smiled.

"Yes, and our last," she answered, and began to turn away from him. He caught her hand immediately.

"Come out with me this Saturday night," he said.

"I'm busy."

"Next Saturday."

"I'm busy then, too."

"The Saturday after . . ."

"I'm busy every Saturday until the Fourth of July. Let go of my hand, please."

"You'll be sorry," he said. "I'm going to be a famous artist."

"I'm sure."

"Come out with me."

"No."

"Okay," he said, and released her hand, and rose, and walked back to the bar.

He knew then perhaps, or should have known then, that it was finished, that there was no sense in a pursuit that would only lead to the identical conclusion, postponed. But he found himself searching for her on the small windswept campus, Ryerson and Emerson, the malls and the parking lots, Steuben Walk in front of the Engineering Building, and then in the halls and classrooms themselves, and even on the Clinton-Washington subway station. In his notebook, he wrote:

She never happened. I am sure she never did. In Bertie's yesterday where I went to look for her, a girl walked over to me -- blue smock, brown eyes, black hair hanging loose over one eye, that type -- and said, "Who broke your nose?" And when I said, "No one," she answered, "You're a liar," and walked away laughing. I don't know who she was or is, had never seen her before that minute, and haven't seen her on campus since. Was she real? Or did she exist only in my imagination, like Ebie Dearborn?

I sometimes think I'm crazy.

The notebook, which he had begun in October, and which he would continue to keep through the next several years, was a curious combination of haphazard scholarship, personal jottings, disjointed ideas and notions, doodlings, line drawings, and secret messages written in a code he thought only he could decipher. He had learned from his uncle a drawing technique that served him well all through high school, though it was later challenged by his instructor at the League. Revitalized provisionally at Pratt, it was an instant form of representation that sometimes veered dangerously close to cartoon exposition. But it nonetheless enabled him to record quickly and without hesitation anything that came into his line of vision. The technique, however, candid and loose, did not work too well without a model, and as his memory of the girl he'd met only once began to fade, he found himself relying more and more upon language to describe her and his feelings about her. A struggle for expression seemed to leap from the pages of the notebook, paragraphs of art history trailing into a personal monologue, or a memorandum, or a query, and then a sketch, and now a poem or an unabashed cartoon, and then again into desperate prose, until the pages at last were overwhelmed with words:

as those artists who populated the 15th century Burgundian court of the Duc de Berry.

Pol De Limbourg (Tres Riches Heures du Duc de Berry)

1- Prayers, calendar, psalms, lessons for layman's devotions.
2- Vivid, realistic landscapes.
3- Free from ecclesiastical.
4- Wealth of detail, no crowding or confusion.
5- Tremendous influence on Hubert and Jan Van Eyck.

Jan Van Eyck (Adam and Eve, Ghent Altarpiece, St Bavon Ghent)

1- Designed to fit specific space (as opposed to later Arnolfini and Wife, where space becomes ELEMENT OF DESIGN).
2- Harsh, almost photograph (as opposed to A & W's humanity).
3- Ecclesiastical symbol.

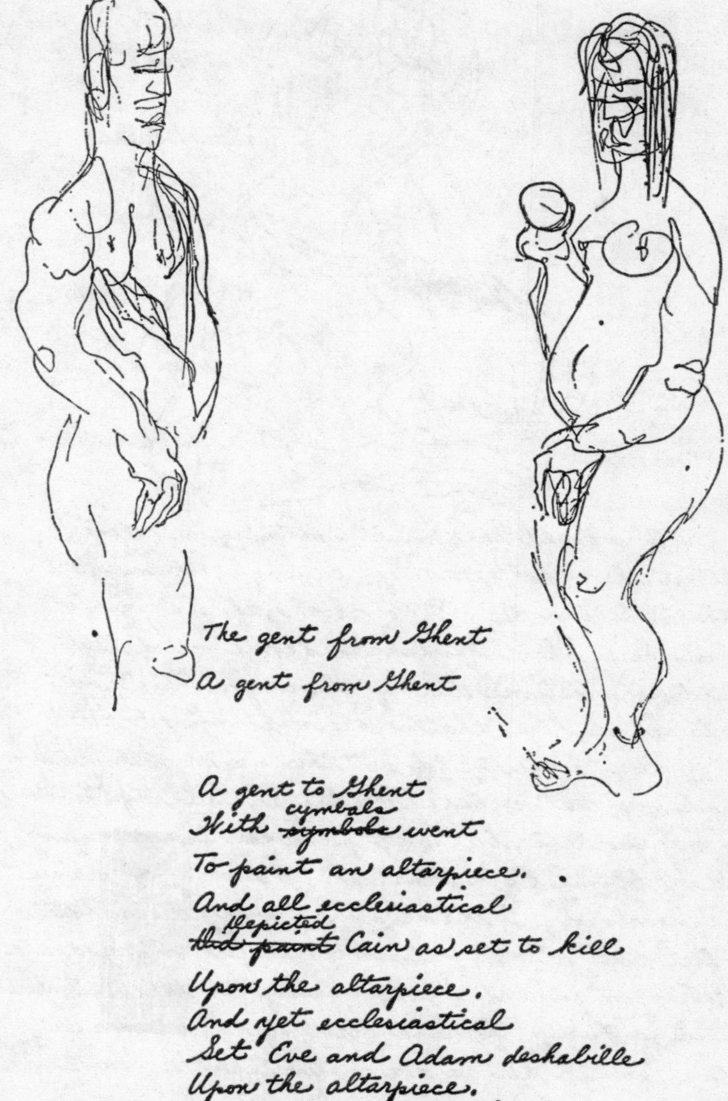

The gent from Ghent

A gent from Ghent

A gent to Ghent
With ~~symbols~~ cymbals went
To paint an altarpiece.
And all ecclesiastical
~~they paint~~ depicted Cain as set to kill
Upon the altarpiece.
And yet ecclesiastical
Set Eve and Adam deshabille
Upon the altarpiece.
If Evie's ass elastic'll
Entice our Adam, jump he will
Upon the altar piece.

How could she possibly not appear when I sat out there half the day, cutting 2-D and 3-D both, watching Main? Now look, if she goes to school here, she'd have had to come out of that building sometime during the day. She doesn't go to school here, that's all. I imagined her.

Boy, was it cold out there, I'm still numb. I had my coat collar pulled up, and my hands in my pockets, but my feet were freeeeeezing, and I blame Ebie Hearborn (I love your name Ebie Hearborn). I blame <u>you</u> for my discomfort of feet and also my discomfort of heart. You are breaking my heart by appearing as the Mysterious Vanishing Lady, for the First Time in America, Folks, watch her as she captivates the hearts and feet of helpless young men, subjugates them with a cornflower glance, enslaves them forever, now listen, Ebie, where the hell are you?

There was once today when I thought I saw her, and I got up off the bench, feet freezing, slapping my hands against my sides, and ran after this blonde girl in a peacoat, guess what, it wasn't Ebie; surprise!

Listen, Ebie Dearborn, we are standing here on the threshold of what may turn out to be the Romance of the Century, you hear me? So stop this idiotic game of hide and seek and come rush into my loving arms because there are a multitude of things I desire to say to you, and I can't say them alone on a bench in the goddamn cold November, shaking. You hear?

help!

My Ebie's hair is like a golden helmet
Poured molten, sitting on her head.

My Ebie's hair is like a golden helmet
Poured molten, shaped to fit her head
Haphazardly.

My Ebie's head

My Ebie's hair is like a golden helmet
Poured molten, shaped to fit
Haphazardly.
And yet despite

Due Tuesday 11/8
Finish Chapter XXI - Painting of late
Middle Ages
Answer all questions at end chapter,
pp 511-512

<u>Jerome Bosch</u> (1450–1516)

1– Recorder of horror, reflection of terror of Middle Ages.

2– Illustrated man's depravity with creatures, monsters, psychos, etc.

3– Master of graphic invention.

4– Keen observer of human behavior.

5– <u>Christ Before Pilate</u> (Museum of Historic Art, Princeton)

A– Painted 1502.

B– Christ subordinate figure to soldiers, Pharisees, and Pilate.

C– Modern day lynch mob (similar)

D– Helpless man in grip of unreasoning mob — hatred dominates picture.

E– Sacrifice for man's inhumanity.

Nineteen years old would mean she was born in 1928, a good year for the Chateau Mouton Rothschild, monsieur. Thank you very much, this wine tastes of cork. Nineteen, which means she's been at the school a year, and is practically halfway toward graduation. Why would she want to waste time with me, the lowest of the low, the bottom of the social order? Balls.

McCarthy had a party

The thing to do is to find out specifically whether or not she goes to Pratt, and the only way to do that is to track down some of those people who were in Bertie's with her. Only thing is I can't remember what any of them look like. Great.

I'm beginning to forget what _she_ looks like.

umber and ochre,
palette knife

Eyes cobalt,
touch of white

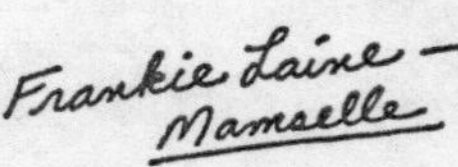

Ebie Dearborn
Or does she spell it Ebey
Or Ebee?
Ebee Dearborn

Ebie Dearborn

Mrs. Ebie Driscoll
Mrs. James Randolph Driscoll
Mr. and Mrs. James Randolph Driscoll

Mr. and Mrs. Blank Dearborn
of Blank, Alabama
announce the imminent eminent marriage
of their daughter
Ebie Ebey Ebee Dearborn
to
James Randolph Jose Hans Fritz Henri
Sven Running Deer Driscoll
Come one Come All Come all o3 h2 2lly Yeah!

Due Monday 11/15
Chapter XXII, XXIII Greek Sculpture, Hellenistic Sculpture
Sketch: Three Fates, Lapis Battling a Centaur,
Victory of Samothrace, Laocoon and
his Sons.

On Friday, November 12th, he hit upon the idea (and dutifully recorded it verbatim in his notebook) of perhaps asking a second-year art student about Ebie. Outside an illustration class, he stopped a girl with her arm in a cast, her hair pulled back into a pony tail, and asked her if she knew Ebie Dearborn.

Who?
Ebie Dearborn.
The little Southern girl?
Well, she's not so little.
But the one from Alabama.
That's the one.
Sure, I know her.
Have you seen her around lately?
No.
Do you know where she is?
She's sick, I think.
With what?
I don't know.
Well, where does she live?
On Myrtle Avenue.
Where on Myrtle?
I don't know. Near the school.
But where?
Why don't you look it up in the phone book?

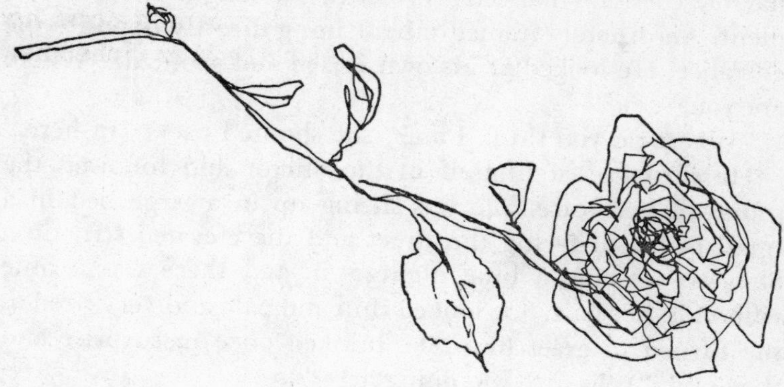

Late that afternoon, he spent the last of his week's allowance on a dozen red roses, and went up to her apartment without calling first. The building she lived in on Myrtle was a crumbling red brick structure with enormous bosses on either corner, a simulated keystone arch over the front doorway. The elevated trains roared past the building, but he scarcely heard them over the pounding of his heart, or so he wrote faithfully in his notebook that night:

> *She lives in the third floor front apartment. I framed the stairwell in wintry afternoon light, building my secret rectangle around the scene, choosing my pigments for the hand worn banister, and the chipped white tiles on the floor, and the smudged hallway window (a blue-gray light bathes the door.) the numerals 3 and 7, with the 7 hanging slightly crooked on one screw, the brass gleaming dully in the pale light, my heart beating wildly. I knocked on the door.*

"Come in," she said.

He tried the door, found it unlocked, and stepped into a narrow corridor that seemed to run the length of the apartment. An ornately framed mirror hung directly opposite the entrance. He looked at his own image and shouted, "Where are you?"

"Where do you think I am?" she shouted back. "In here."

He shrugged at himself in the mirror and followed the sound of her voice. She was sitting up in a large bed in a small bedroom facing the street and the elevated structure. She was wearing a blue nightgown, and there was a blue ribbon in her hair. She looked thin and pale and very tired as she turned to greet him. She blinked once in surprise and then said, "What are *you* doing here?"

"Who'd you think it was?" he asked.

"Peter."

"Who's Peter?"

"The boy who lives upstairs. He's been bringing me chicken soup and such." She paused. "How'd you know where I lived?"

"I've been searching for you."

"What are those?"

"Roses."

"For me?"

"Yes."

Ebie nodded, and then stared at him and continued nodding. At last she said, "I'm sick."

"Yes, I know."

"Who told you?"

"A girl with a broken arm."

"Cathy?"

"I don't know her name."

"With a pony tail?"

"Yes."

"That's Cathy Ascot. She's accident prone."

"She told me you were sick and that you lived on Myrtle Avenue. Why are you listed in the book as Dearborn, E.B.?"

"So everyone'll think it's a man living here and I won't get calls from all the nuts in Brooklyn."

"I know one nut who's going to be calling you a lot."

"Who? Oh. You mean you?"

"That's right."

"Well, I don't guess I can stop you from calling."

"No, I don't guess you can."

"Are you going to just stand there with those roses in your hand?"

"I should put them in something, huh?"

"I think there's a vase in the kitchen. The cabinet over the stove."

"You won't disappear, will you?"

"What?"

"When I go for the vase."

"I don't usually disappear," Ebie said. "I just happened to get sick the day after I met you, that's all."

"What've you got?"

"Oh, it's so clichéd it makes me want to puke."

"What is it?"

"Mononucleosis."

"I never heard of it."

"Peter didn't know what it was, either. Hey, can you see through this gown?" she asked suddenly, peering down at her breasts.

"No."

"I wasn't expecting anyone but him," she said, and shrugged.

"You mean Peter?"

"Yes. He usually stops by in the afternoon."

"I don't think I like Peter."

"He's very sweet."

"What's his last name?"

"Malcom. Peter Malcom. He's an actor."

"Mmm?"

"Yes. He works mostly in television. Usually, he plays heavies. He's blond and has sort of a curling lip. He can look very sinister when he wants to."

"I'll bet."

"But you didn't come up here to talk about Peter," she said, and looked down at the bed covers. "Did you?" she said.

"No."

"I didn't think so."

"I don't even know Peter, you see," he said. He was beginning to get very angry. He stood at the foot of the bed, foolishly holding the goddamn roses, and wishing he had not bought them, and wondering what mononucleosis was, and wondering if it was contagious; it sounded like something you sprinkled on meat to tenderize it. "Look, uh . . . where'd you say the vase was?"

"In the kitchen. Over the stove."

"I'll just put these in water for you, and then I'll take off."

"Why?"

"Well, you're expecting Peter, and I really . . ."

"Well, he may not come. He doesn't always come."

"I see."

"And . . ." She shook her head.

"And what?"

"Nothing."

"Okay." He walked out of the bedroom and down the corridor and into the kitchen where he found a cut glass vase in the cabinet over the stove. He filled the vase with water, put the roses into it, and carried them back to the bedroom.

"Where shall I put these?" he asked.

"On the dresser yonder, I guess."

"Yonder," he said.

"Yes. Please."

He put the roses down. When he glanced up into the mirror, he saw that she was staring at his back. His eyes met hers, and she quickly looked away. He turned and leaned against the dresser. Without looking at him, and in a very small voice, she said, "What *did* you come up here to talk about?"

"You," he said.

"What about me?"

"I came up here to tell you I love you."

"Oh."

"Yes."

"Oh, I see," she said.

"Yes." He shrugged. "And so, having said it, I will clear the premises so that Peter can come down with his chicken soup and such, and look through your nightgown."

"You *can* see through it, can't you?"

"No."

"Tell me the truth."

"That's the truth."

"Is it true what you said before?"

"What did I say before?"

"That you love me?"

"Yes, it's true."

"I think that's very sweet."

"Yes."

"Really," she said.

"Mmm."

"Gee," she said, and grinned, and heaved her shoulders in a massive sighing shrug. "I've never had anyone fall in love with me just like that. I really think it's so sweet I can't tell you."

"Well, I think it's pretty sweet too," he said.

"Oh, it is," she said, "it *is.*"

"Well."

"Mmm."

They stared at each other silently. He decided he would kiss her. He leaned against the dresser gathering courage, turning to touch one of the roses, plotting. He would cross the room swiftly, cup her face in his hands, taste her mouth, risk all, *now,* do it now, go ahead, go, man. The outer door to the apartment opened. It opened with the speed of familiarity, banging back against the doorstop, no knock, nothing, bang went the door, and heavy footsteps pounded surely through the apartment toward the bedroom. "Ebie!" a man's voice shouted, and he knew with certainty that this was Peter, enter Peter, would he be carrying chicken soup? and hated him at once and intensely, even before he laid eyes on him.

He was a tall blond man of about twenty-two, handsome, with the curling lip Ebie had described, blond eyebrows thick over pale gray eyes, a clean profile, even white teeth that looked as though they had been capped. He was smiling when he came into the bedroom, but he saw immediately that Ebie was not alone, and the smile dropped from his face.

"Oh, hi," he said. "I didn't know you had company."

"Peter, this is . . . what's your name again?"

"Jimmy Driscoll."

"This is Peter Malcom."

"Hi," Peter said.

"Hi."

They looked each other over. Unexpectedly, almost unconsciously, Peter reached into his jacket pocket and took out a pair of eyeglasses. Perching them on his nose, he turned to study Driscoll with deliberate scrutiny.

"You go to Pratt?" he asked.

"Yes."

"That where you know Ebie from?"

"Yes."

He nodded, took off the glasses, replaced them in his jacket pocket, and then turned toward the bed, completely dismissing Driscoll. "How do you feel?" he asked Ebie.

"Much better," she said.

"Good."

"She's got mononucleosis," Driscoll said.

"Yes, I know."

"It's what you put on meat to tenderize it," Driscoll ventured cautiously, and was immediately relieved when Ebie burst out laughing.

"That's very comical," Peter said dryly.

The room went silent.

"Well," Ebie said.

"Well, here we are alone at last," Driscoll said, and

grinned, and felt a new surge of confidence when Ebie laughed again.

"Listen, I sure as hell hope I'm not interrupting anything," Peter said, scowling.

"Well, yes, as a matter of fact you are," Driscoll said. "I came to bring her some notes."

"Notes? What do you mean?"

"For one of her courses."

"What course?" Peter asked.

"Sculpture," Ebie said.

"Really?" Peter said.

"Mmm."

"Well, in that case . . ."

"Maybe you can drop by later," Ebie said.

"Yes, well, it won't be till after dinner, Ebie. I've got to see my agent."

"That's all right," Ebie said. To Driscoll, she said, "He's an actor."

"Yes, I know. You told me."

"He's a very good actor."

"I'll bet you play a lot of heavies," Driscoll said.

"Yes, I do." Peter looked surprised. "How'd you know?"

Driscoll shrugged. "Intuition."

"Well," Peter said, "I'll see you later, Ebie." He glanced at Driscoll. "Nice meeting you."

"Pleasure," Driscoll said.

"So long now, Ebie."

" 'Bye, Peter."

"Yeah," he said, and scowled again at Driscoll, and then turned abruptly and went stamping through the apartment. The front door slammed shut behind him.

"He makes a lot of noise," Driscoll said.

"But he's very nice," Ebie said. "He really does bring me chicken soup."

"Mmm." He cleared his throat.

"Yes?"

"Nothing."

"I feel as if . . ."

"Yes?"

"Nothing."

"Listen, I . . ."

"Yes?"

"I think I'd better be going."

"You just got here."

"Well, still. He'll be back, and . . ."

"Not until after dinner."

"Still . . ."

"Well, if you have to go . . ."

"Yes, I think I'd better."

"All right."

"Fine," he said. He started for the door, turned, and said, "Well, I hope you get better."

"I feel better already," she said.

"Well, I'll see you around," he said.

"Listen . . ." she said.

"Yes?"

"Wouldn't you like to . . ."

"Yes?"

"Kiss me goodbye or something?"

"Well, yes, I would," he said.

"I would," she answered. "I would too."

"But what about . . ."

"Well, why don't you?" she said.

"What about Peter?"

"I mean, don't you want to?"

"Yes, but you've got mononucleosis, and . . ."

"Oh, boy," she said.

"It's just . . . who'll take care of you? If I get sick too."

"Peter can bring us *both* soup. Come on over here and kiss me."

"You really think I should?" he said, grinning.

"I really think so. As you yourself pointed out, I'm much older than you . . ."

"Hey, I'm sorry I said that. I didn't mean to . . ."

". . . and it's my mature opinion that you should come

here and kiss me because you can't just go saying sweet things like I love you and then not even kiss a girl goodbye."

"I do love you, Ebie," he whispered.

"Then kiss me."

"I love you."

"Kiss me."

"I love you."

"Kiss me, kiss me, kiss me."

Her mouth then in that small bedroom on Myrtle Avenue, the elevated train rushing past outside as he took her face in his hands and covered her lips with his own, the softness of her mouth. Her mouth now in the hotel room as he lay full length on the bed and looked across the room to where she sat before the dresser putting on lipstick, the same mouth, deeper lines radiating now from the flaps of her nose to the edges of her lips, but the same mouth, nothing could change her mouth, she could live to be a hundred and that perfectly formed mouth would sit upon her withered face like a rose blooming in the desert. The smell of roses wafting across the room from the dresser top, and her lips parting to accept his kiss while the train rushed past in a roaring clamor that rattled the windows of her bedroom. His hands touched her naked breasts beneath the blue nylon gown, he could feel her blossoming nipples and the warmth of her body, the low fever burning inside her. Everything seemed in that moment to take on a truer scent and color, a deeper intensity—the roses, the lowering dusk, the aroma of soap in her hair, the blue ribbon loosening and the golden strands falling free and whisper-light upon his cradling hands—as though her mouth demanded a fuller response, a keener awareness. He held her against him and felt rather than heard her murmur deeply, the sound moving into her lips to hum secretly against his own, trembling with vibration that deepened as she moaned against him, mouth locked to mouth. The sound of the elevated express engulfed the room, and suddenly there was only a whirling vortex the center of which was her mouth. He thought he would lose consciousness, struggled to catch his breath, felt certain he would come against the bedclothes covering her, her mouth persisted, there was nothing in the world but Ebie Dearborn's mouth.

They came up over the brow of the hill from beyond the river that cold November day, he could remember hearing only the bugles at first, could remember wiping his hand across his mouth, and thinking immediately of Ebie, and thinking he might never kiss her again, might never be able to kiss her again, and then he saw them in the distance. Stumbling out of the hole, he reached for his rifle and saw them silhouetted against the misty November sky, the bugles bleating, the terrifying shrill whistles, the shouts in Chinese. They were wearing strange fur hats that gave their faces a foxlike look, pointed, with sharp erect ears. The bugles kept sounding over and over again, like angry screams on the early morning air. There was rifle fire now as his men sleepily stumbled into the mist and tried to halt the charge. The letter, he thought, and touched the pocket of his combat jacket, and then began shooting angrily and randomly into the horde of advancing Chinese, shouting obscenities at them, firing with a wild glee.

"Dris?"

"Yes."

"Are you all right?" she asked.

"I'm fine, Ebie."

"Shouldn't you get ready for dinner? We ought to go down soon."

"I'll shave in a minute," he said.

"What were you thinking about?" she asked.

"I was thinking about November," he answered.

11

HESTER MIERS CAME INTO SARDI'S accompanied by fat Mitzi Starke who, despite her mink coat, looked as though the bitter cold outside had penetrated to her marrow and frozen her solid. Her face was red and her eyes were tearing, and she took off her gloves immediately and began kneading her hands as she scanned the tables just inside the entrance, her glasses fogging. Oscar Stern rose from the table where he was sitting alongside Arthur, and waved at the door, mouthing Mitzi's name. Mitzi did not see him because of the fogging glasses, but Hester took her elbow and began leading her toward where the three men were sitting. Mitzi took off her glasses as they walked, wiping the lenses on a tiny lace-edged handkerchief which she took from the pocket of the mink. She had replaced them on the bridge of her nose by the time they reached the table, and she smiled amiably in recognition, shaking hands all around, kissing Stuart Selig—whom she had known for many years—and telling Arthur she had heard a lot about him and thought he had written a wonderful play. Arthur thanked her, and then held out a chair for Hester, who sat directly alongside him, so that he was between Oscar and Hester, with Mitzi and Stuart on the other side of the table. Stuart asked if the ladies would care for a drink, We've had a head start already, and Mitzi said, Yes, she certainly would like a drink, it was too cold out there even for the brass monkeys. Hester pretended not to know which brass monkeys her agent was referring to. She pressed her knee against Arthur's under the table and said she would like a very dry martini.

"How did the opening in Philly go?" Oscar asked.

"Very well," Mitzi said. "Well, Boris is a marvelous actor, marvelous. He could read the telephone book and make it exciting, you know that."

"Certainly," Stuart said, and glanced at Arthur.

"But the play is a very good one, and that helps," Mitzi said, and smiled graciously at everyone, and then glanced over her shoulder to see what was keeping the drinks. When they came, she downed hers almost at once, and asked the waiter to bring another, a double this time. Hester sipped demurely at her martini, her knee pressed against Arthur's. The table was silent for several moments, and then Oscar said, "I can only remember once when it was this cold. That was four years ago, I'll never forget that winter."

"Yes, it's very cold," Mitzi said.

"I'm sure Arthur wants to hear about his play," Hester said.

"Well, that's why we're here," Stuart said, and smiled at her. "Mitzi tells me you'd like to do it, is that right?"

"Well, she has certain reservations," Mitzi said, and then said "Ahhhh" as the waiter brought her second drink. "Here's to your fine play, Mr. Constantine," she said, and Arthur nodded acknowledgment and raised his own glass.

"It *is* a lovely play, Arthur," Hester said.

"Thank you."

"Though, of course, it *does* need a few minor things done to it," Mitzi said.

"Well, any play needs changes," Stuart said. "A play isn't *written*, it's *rewritten.*"

"That's right."

"But nothing serious," Hester said. "Nothing basic to the structure."

"*Or* the theme, for that matter," Mitzi said.

"No, we wouldn't want to touch any of that. You can ruin a play by tampering too much with it," Stuart said.

"Oh, don't I know it," Mitzi said. "The changes we have in mind are really minor and transitional. If they were anything more than that, I assure you Hester wouldn't be interested in the part at all."

"Of course not," Stuart said.

"That's right," Oscar said.

"But Hester very definitely *is* interested in doing the play, and I'm fairly certain we can spring her from Lincoln Center. At least I'm hoping we can, I haven't discussed it with them yet. I wanted to get Mr. Constantine's reaction to the changes we had in mind before I contacted anyone."

"Arthur's been very reasonable about any suggestions thus far," Stuart said, "so I can't imagine . . ."

"That's right," Oscar said.

". . . him refusing to make a few minor changes now, when we're so close to getting the play on at last."

"That's right."

"We're dealing with a professional writer here," Stuart said, and smiled at Arthur.

"Well, thank you," Arthur said. He started to put his hand on Hester's knee, and then changed his mind. She looked very lovely, with her blond hair still arranged in its careless coiffure, and wearing a blue sheath scooped low in the front, a string of pearls around her throat. She smiled at Arthur assuringly, and he lifted his glass and sipped at it and began to feel a warmth spreading through him, a genuine feeling of fondness for all the people at the table, including fat Mitzi, who had put down her drink and was blowing her nose into a tiny handkerchief. She had still not removed the mink coat, and she still seemed to be suffering from exposure.

"Well now," she said, giving her nose a final wipe and putting the handkerchief back into her pocket, "I think we should start with the age of the girl, don't you think so, Hester?"

"Yes," Hester said, "I think that's important."

"Important, but minor. Hester's twenty-five, you know, and whereas she comes off a bit younger onstage, we think we'd be asking for trouble if she tried to pass for nineteen."

"Well . . ." Arthur said.

"That's right, we don't want the critics to start picking on stupid little things," Oscar said. "They'll find enough anyway, without any help from us."

"So we thought the girl's age might be raised to twenty-two or twenty-three," Mitzi said. "That would be more reasonable, in terms of Hester playing the part."

"Well, there's a lot of stuff in the play about her nineteenth birthday coming up," Arthur said. "I'd have to . . ."

"So it'll be her twenty-third birthday coming up," Oscar said. "That's no problem."

"No, but she's supposed to be leaving for college in the fall."

"Yes, we—"

"In fact, the conflict, you know, is between this girl who wants to go to college and . . ."

"Yes, that's a problem, admittedly."

". . . her uneducated father, a Bronx mailman who, you know, wants her to marry this guy and settle down. That's the conflict."

"Yes, we know."

"So she'd have to be a college girl, you see."

"Well, she can be a college girl at twenty-two," Stuart said.

"That's right."

"She can just be *graduating* college maybe," Stuart said, "and she wants to go to graduate school or something, and her father objects. That could be exactly the same."

"Well . . ." Arthur said.

"Of course, Hester played a college girl in the last thing she did at the Rep," Mitzi said.

"Mmm," Stuart said.

"If she keeps playing college girls . . ." Mitzi said, and shrugged.

"Well, Carol *is* a college girl," Arthur said. "That's the part. I mean, that's the part."

"The way it is now, yes," Mitzi said.

"But we'd have to make her older," Hester said. "Don't you think so, Arthur?"

"I don't know. I think you could pass for nineteen," he said, and decided to squeeze her knee after all, which he did.

"That's very sweet of you, Arthur," she said, and smiled, "but I think the girl *has* to be older."

"She's supposed to be a virgin," Arthur said. "Do you know any twenty-two-year-old virgins?"

"I don't even know any *seven*-year-old virgins," Oscar said, and laughed.

Mitzi laughed too, and then said, "Actually, she doesn't *have* to be a virgin, does she? That really doesn't add anything to the play."

"Well, there's an entire scene where . . ."

"Yes, with the boy . . ."

"Yes, the one her father wants her to marry . . ."

"That's right."

"And he tries to, well, to lay her, you know, and this is another thing that adds to the conflict of this girl trying to lead her own life without interference from her father or from the people her father has chosen for her."

"The boy, you mean?"

"Yes. So the scene has meaning only if she's a virgin, you know, and is, well, saving herself for . . . for the person *she* chooses."

"Well, do you think girls actually *save* themselves anymore, Arthur?" Mitzi asked, and smiled.

"I don't know, but Carol is supposed to be . . ."

"I mean, you said yourself not three minutes ago that you didn't know any twenty-two-year-old virgins."

"Carol's only eighteen, going on nineteen. I think . . ."

"There's a difference, certainly," Stuart said. "But, Arthur, is it really *that* important that she be a virgin?"

"Or even a college girl?" Hester asked.

"What?"

"Is it important that she plans to leave for college in the fall?"

"Sure it is."

"Why?"

"Because that's the conflict."

"Yes, but the conflict can be *any* conflict, isn't that true? So long as it's between the girl and her father."

"I think we all need another drink," Oscar said, and signaled to the waiter. "Mitzi? Hester?"

"Yes, I'm still cold," Mitzi said.

"I'd love another," Hester said, and smiled at Arthur.

"The same all around," Oscar said to the waiter.

"Double for the lady?"

"Yes, a double," Mitzi said.

"We ought to think about ordering," Stuart said.

"Oh, we've got plenty of time. Let's thrash this out, shall we?" Mitzi said. "I know Mr. Constantine is anxious to hear our views, and we're certainly anxious to know his reactions to them. I can't make a move with the Rep, you know, until . . ."

"Certainly," Stuart said. "What do you think, Arthur?"

"Well . . . about changing Carol's age, do you mean?"

"About having her a little more experienced," Stuart said.

"A nice girl," Mitzi said, "but a little more experienced."

"So she's been to bed with one or two guys already," Oscar said. "That doesn't make her a slut."

"A *dozen* guys wouldn't make her a slut," Stuart said.

"A dozen?" Arthur asked.

"Well, I don't think that's exactly the image we want for Hester," Mitzi said. "Arthur's right in that respect. We want Carol to be a sweet and confused young girl. If we have her sleeping around with half the men in the city . . ."

"I was only trying to indicate . . ."

"I think she may have had one affair," Hester said. "She *is* twenty-two, you know, going on twenty-three. It would seem implausible otherwise."

"One affair sounds reasonable," Stuart said. "What do you think, Arthur?"

"I'm trying to think of the whole," Arthur said. "We've got to think of what any revisions would do to the whole of the play. I really feel it's important that she be a virgin."

"Here're the drinks," Stuart said.

The waiter put their glasses on the table, and they all drank silently for a moment. Mitzi blew her nose again, and then said, "It's just that a girl like Carol who has, after all, been around a little . . ."

"But she hasn't," Arthur said. "Her father's kept her cooped up in—"

"Well, a social worker would get to meet a great many people," Mitzi said. "Isn't that so?"

"A great many people," Hester said.

"What do you mean?"

"A social worker."

"I still don't get you."

"If Carol were a social worker," Mitzi said.

"Instead of a college girl," Hester said. "Working for a state agency, you see. Or even a private agency."

"And her father objects to her wanting a life of her own, and insists that she marry this boy he has chosen for her. And the boy tries to lay her, just the way you've got it now, which only strengthens her resolve to lead her own life, choose her own friends, her own lovers, and this leads to the showdown in the third act, just the way you've got it now, between her and her father."

"A social worker," Arthur said blankly.

"Yes, instead of a college girl," Hester said.

"She played a college girl in that last thing at the Rep, you know," Mitzi said to Stuart.

"Yes, she was very good," Stuart said.

"Did you see it?" Hester asked.

"Yes, you were marvelous."

"But, of course, she's done the college girl bit," Mitzi said, "and there has to be a challenge, otherwise what's the sense?"

"That's right," Oscar said. "There has to be a challenge."

"I don't know anything about social work," Arthur said.

"What do you know about mailmen, for that matter?" Oscar said.

"My father was a mailman."

"Well . . ."

"Do you think the father in the play *ought* to be a mailman?" Mitzi asked.

"If his daughter is a social worker?" Hester said.

"Do you know anything about social work?" Arthur asked her.

"No, but we can find out anything we need to know. For any scenes showing the girl in her office."

"What office?"

"Where she works."

"Where she does her social work," Mitzi said.

"She could have a colored family she's working with," Hester said, "and maybe her father objects to that, too. Maybe he's a bigot."

"But he *isn't,*" Arthur said. "He's just narrow and . . . and oriented to . . . to . . . to the way things were in the old country. And in the old country, a girl didn't go running off to school, she . . . she got married and had children and . . ."

"Do you think that's a universal problem these days, Mr. Constantine?" Mitzi asked.

"What do you mean?"

"An immigrant father and a daughter who rebels . . ."

"I think the conflict between a father and a daughter *is* universal, yes. We're dealing with Electra here, what difference does it make whether the father is an immigrant or—"

"That's just my point. If we're dealing with something as universal as the Electra bit, why does the father have to be an immigrant mailman who can hardly speak English?"

"He speaks English fine," Arthur said.

"Well, you know what I mean."

"No, I don't. He's been in this country for thirty-five years. He's a man who's fifty-eight years of age, he speaks English fine. But he still clings to the old traditions, he's got a background of traditions . . ."

"That's *Fiddler,* isn't it?"

"What?"

"*Fiddler on the Roof*. That's Tevye's character, isn't it?"

"That's a different thing entirely," Arthur said. "I *lived* through this with my father and my sister, and I can tell you . . ."

"When was that, Arthur?"

"I don't know, she's married now and has three children, it must have been ten, twelve years ago. But I can tell you that the showdown between those two shook our house from the roof to the—"

"Very often, though," Oscar said, "something can seem very dramatic in life, but not when it's put on the stage."

"I think he's presented it *very* dramatically," Hester said, and smiled.

"Yes, no one has any objections to the dramatic structure," Mitzi said.

"It's just these few character changes."

"Why can't the father work in an office someplace? Or why can't he have his own business? If you insist on his being Italian, why can't he be a building contractor?"

"There are a great many Italian building contractors," Hester said.

"I don't see why he can't be a mailman," Arthur said. "The way I wrote it."

"We're trying to understand him in terms of the modern theatergoer."

"Besides, there was a mailman in the Schisgal play."

"Which Schisgal play?"

"*The Tiger.*"

"Write me a play like *Luv,*" Mitzi said, "and I wouldn't ask for a single change."

"Brilliant," Stuart said.

"Penetrating," Oscar said.

"Can't I be a social worker, Arthur?" Hester asked. "I'm *so* tired of playing college girls."

"If this man were educated . . ." Stuart said.

"Which man?"

"The father. If he were educated, we could offer the part to somebody like Fonda, you know."

"In fact, I hear Fredric March is looking for a play," Oscar said.

"They'd be great with Hester."

"I'd love to work with either one of them," Hester said.

"Don't think they wouldn't love to work with *you,* baby," Mitzi said, and finished her drink.

"You're a marvelous actress," Stuart said.

"Thank you. I see the social worker as a very dedicated person, don't you?" Hester said, turning to Arthur.

"I don't know anything about social workers," Arthur said. "My sister was a simple girl living in a house she wanted to get out of. That's what this play is about. The fight between her and my father. She wins the fight, Carol wins the fight and goes off to school. All this other stuff . . ."

"That's not your sister's real name, is it?" Mitzi asked.

"Carol? No."

"What's her name?" Oscar asked.

"Julie. Why?"

"I just wanted to know."

"I didn't know this play was based on an actual experience of yours, Arthur," Stuart said.

"Well, most fiction comes out of a man's life, doesn't it?" Mitzi said.

"I guess so."

"We're not asking you to change the *reality* of the situation," Hester said.

"We're just asking for a few revisions that would make the story more understandable to a modern audience."

"You talk as if I wrote it back in the Middle Ages," Arthur said, and Oscar immediately laughed. Everyone at the table laughed with him.

"Well, you understand what we mean," Mitzi said, drying her eyes.

"Yes."

"What do you say, Arthur?" Stuart said.

"I don't know. I'll have to think about it."

"Certainly," Mitzi said. "We don't expect a man to make a snap decision. Not when he's worked on something for such a long time."

"That's right," Oscar said.

"You think about it," Hester said.

"Can you let us know by Friday?" Mitzi asked.

"That's only the day after tomorrow," Arthur said.

"Yes."

"Well, I thought . . . I'm in the middle of a trial, you see, and . . . I thought I'd read the play over the weekend and see if your suggestions . . ."

"Well, the only reason I'm suggesting Friday," Mitzi said, "is because they're bringing the new Osborne play over from London, and they've asked Hester to play the part."

"Osborne," Arthur said.

"Yes."

"His new play."

"Yes. And I promised I'd give them an answer before the weekend. And then, of course, I'd still have to go to the people at the Rep and work all that out, so I think you can understand the reason for speed."

"Well, I . . ."

"The changes seem reasonable, Arthur."

"Well . . ."

"I think a social worker could be very exciting," Hester said.

"Fonda would be great for the father," Oscar said.

"Think it over, and let us know by Friday, will you?" Mitzi said.

"I'll think it over."

"He'll let you know by Friday," Stuart promised.

He had been watching the office from the drugstore counter across the street on Madison Avenue, drinking three cups of coffee, and then wandering over to browse the paperback racks near the plate glass window (*The Paper Dragon,* he noticed, was still in print) and then going back to the counter for a fourth, and finally nauseating, cup of coffee. He was heading for the paperback racks again when he saw the lights go off across the street. He quickly paid his check and went to stand just inside the entrance to the drugstore. Chickie came out onto the sidewalk first, wearing a black cloth coat with a black fox collar, and Ruth came out of the office immediately afterwards, pulling the door shut behind her, locking it, and then trying the knob once again before stepping out of the doorway. She looped her arm through Chickie's, and the two women started up Madison Avenue, their heads ducked against the wind. Sidney opened the door immediately and went outside. The sidewalks had been shoveled almost clear of snow, but the footing was treacherous, and the wind was brutally sharp. His eyes began to tear at once. He was wearing gloves, but he thrust his hands into his pockets nonetheless, looking up immediately to make sure the girls were still in sight, and then wondering again why he was behaving so foolishly, following them home from work this way, ridiculous, a man his age.

Ruth lived four blocks from the office, and he supposed they were heading there, though he didn't much care *where* they were heading so long as they *got* there quick. His feet were freezing, and his ears throbbed. He lowered his head as a fierce gust of wind knifed the avenue, took one hand from his pocket to clutch his homburg tightly onto his head, holding it there as the wind raged. His coat flapped wildly about his knees, his trousers were flattened against his legs, he coughed bitterly and hung on to his hat, pushing against the wind, trying to keep his footing on the slippery pavement. The wind died momentarily, and he took a deep breath and raised his head and then stopped dead in his tracks because the girls were directly ahead of him on the corner, not fifty feet away.

A tan Cadillac was parked at the curb, its engine running, white fumes billowing from its exhaust. The driver of the car had leaned over on the front seat toward the window closest to the curb, which was open. Both Ruth and Chickie, vapor pluming from their mouths, were slightly bent as they talked to the man in the car, snatches of sound rising, carrying unintelligibly on the wind to where Sidney stood rooted to the sidewalk. He watched a moment longer, and then realized how vulnerable his position was. Ducking into a doorway, he stared at the Cadillac from his new vantage point, watching as Ruth opened the front door and got onto the seat beside the man driving. She reached behind her almost immediately to unlock the back door, and Chickie opened the door and climbed in. Sidney blinked. The car idled at the curb a moment longer, and then gunned away in a burst of power, skid chains clanging.

Sidney emerged from the doorway and watched the car as it went up the avenue and out of sight.

In a moment, the wind rose again.

Leo Kessler was wearing an overlarge red robe, belted loosely at the waist. Beneath the robe, he wore a ribbed undershirt with shoulder straps, and red-and-white check undershorts with black piping on either leg. He had taken off his shoes and replaced them with fleece-lined slippers, but he was still wearing black socks supported by yellow and black garters. Every now and again, he dipped his nose into the brandy snifter in his hands, and then looked up at Sam Genitori, who was outlining what had happened that day in court. "Mmm-hmmm," Leo said, "mmm-hmmm," and then dipped his nose into the brandy snifter again, and looked up at Sam, and rose and walked to the windows and then walked back to his easy chair angled before the marble fireplace in his apartment on East 57th Street, and made himself comfortable, looking down at his long hairy legs and flashy garters, and nodding, and saying "Mmmm-mmm, mmm-hmmm," and then sipping a little brandy again.

"So I told him just where he could go," Sam said. "You got any more of that brandy?"

"Help yourself," Leo said.

"Damn egotistical jackass," Sam said, and poured some brandy into a shot glass.

"I think you were a little too rough with him," Leo said. "Don't you want a snifter for that?"

"I don't know where they are."

"Under the bar. Near the wine glasses."

"Too much trouble," Sam said. *"Salute,"* he said, raising the shot glass, and then downing the brandy in one swallow. "Ahhhhhhhh," he said. "What do you mean too rough on him?"

"He seems to think he did a good job today."

"Knowles, you mean?"

"Mmm-hmmm."

"How do you know?"

"He told me."

"You saw him today?"

"Yes."

"Where?"

"At the office."

"He came to the office?"

"Mmm-hmmm."

"Why?"

"To ask for six million dollars."

"Did you give it to him?"

"I gave it to him."

"You gave him six million dollars?"

"I authorized six million dollars for his new picture, yes."

"You gave that idiot six million dollars?"

"Someday, Sam, when I have a little time, I'll explain the motion picture business to you."

"Don't bother," Sam said. "All I know is that after his performance in court today, I wouldn't even trust him to walk my dog around the block. So you give him . . ."

"I don't have a dog," Leo said.

"Even if I *didn't* have a dog," Sam said, "I wouldn't trust Knowles to walk it around the block."

"He's a good director."

"He's a lousy witness."

"He makes good pictures."

"That's debatable."

"I'm not talking about *artistic* pictures, Sam. Artistic pictures can get you in the subway if you also happen to have a fifteen-cent token. Ralph Knowles is a good director because his pictures make money."

"Some of them."

"Most of them."

"He *still* almost wrecked our case today."

Leo shrugged. "I'm not so sure he did, Sam. I heard him telling it this afternoon, and I've just now heard you tell it again, and I'm not so sure he wrecked our case at all."

"Leo, take my word for it . . ."

"Driscoll, maybe. Maybe he wrecked *Driscoll.* But not the case, and not API."

"He told them—"

"He told them he used the book."

"Yes, but he also—"

"He also told them there are no fairies in his pictures. What's so bad about that?"

"Leo, the point—"

"You want a man to go around saying there are fairies in his pictures? Come on now, Sam."

"Leo, by saying what he said—"

"It made it seem like Driscoll wrote a dirty book."

"No! It made it seem—"

"Which Knowles made into a clean picture."

"Leo, I think you're missing something important."

"What's more important than making clean pictures the whole family can go see? Is Walt Disney doing so bad with it?"

"Leo . . ."

"He also said he made two characters out of one character, right?"

"Yeah, did he tell you about *that?*"

"He told me. But *they* claimed one of those characters was a fairy, and *that's* where he had them, Sam. Because it wasn't."

"What wasn't?"

"A fairy."

"Leo, he walked into a trap, don't you see that?"

"It would have been worse the other way."

"What other way?"

"If he denied something he actually did. If he told them he *didn't* make two characters out of one."

"Leo, the truth is he doesn't *remember* what he did."

"Oh, certainly he does. He wrote the picture, didn't he? He directed it, didn't he?"

"All right, suppose he *did* make two characters out of one?"

"That's exactly what he did."

"Then where did he get the idea?"

"What do you mean?" Leo asked.

"For the other character? The *second* character."

"Where?"

"From the play, Leo."

"What play?"

"Catchpole."

"What?"

"In our files, Leo."

"What?"

"At the studio, Leo."

"He never said that."

"He didn't have to say it."

"Why would anyone think . . ."

"Because first he said, Yes that's what I did, I made two characters out of one, but then he couldn't remember which characters he'd put together to form the second character, and then he said the villain in the book wasn't a queer, or even the guy in the picture, and Leo I am telling you he made a holy mess of the whole damn thing."

"Well, he may be a horse's ass," Leo said, "but he is a *bright* horse's ass. I cannot believe . . ."

"It's what he did, Leo."

"He's too smart for that."

"He's a jerk, Leo."

"A whole lot smarter than most directors around."

"A moron, Leo."

"And certainly smarter than a tinhorn shyster like Brackman."

"Leo, he may have wrecked our case beyond repair."

"The stupid bastard," Leo said.

If Christie were here, Jonah thought, she would pour some boric acid into hot water (it must be *scalding* hot, darling, she would say) and then insist that I soak my wrist in it, changing the water whenever it got lukewarm, that's what Christie Dunseath Willow would do. And I would allow her to do it while marveling at how adequately she ministered to my needs, and delighting in the sight of her, and simultaneously knowing that we did not have a marriage at all. Oh how surprised they all were, our friends, oh how shocked, stunned, disbelieving when they learned that Christie and I were going to part (but they're such a *darling* couple) that we were going to take up separate residence and live separate lives (so marvelously alert, so much *fun* to be with) that finally we were going to end this ridiculous, sham exercise, recognize it for what it really was, and chalk it off as a total failure (both so bright and talented, so very much alive).

Talented, yes, the very talented Jonah Willow who defended a pair of Communist adolescents trying to change the world by blowing up Gracie Mansion, and then found himself defending similar unpopular clients and causes in the years that followed. Talented, yes, and bright enough to recognize the public need for a champion, clever enough to set out to fill that need. A man loses his innocence once and for all time when he makes a calculation he knows is even slightly dishonest, makes it (he will tell himself) for the sake of Survival, or Ambition, or Health or Sanity, or for the sake of Honesty to Oneself (the most dishonest reason) but makes it coldly and shrewdly and with malice aforethought. Jonah was bright enough and clever enough to recognize that he had successfully defended two rather unsavory individuals (because their Rights Were Being Violated, he told himself, and perhaps was being Honest to Himself) and that his less than brilliant courtroom display had put his name before the public eye, where he intended to keep it. It was no accident that the firm of Gauthier and Willow defended in the next several years a succession of individuals accused of murder, rape, pornography, spying, draft evasion, government manipulation of contracts, obscenity, and other such exotic and lofty activities executed by believers, fanatics, followers and fools of every persuasion.

But if a man loses his innocence only once, a woman surely loses it twice, and neither time has anything to do with her defloration. Christie lost her innocence for the first time when she realized her father wasn't God, and she lost it for the second time when she realized Jonah wasn't God, either. She realized this in the early years of her marriage and was not bright enough to find any solace in historical precedent. She only knew that she had married someone who pretended to be what he was not. What she expected Jonah to be was never clearly defined to him, although she repeatedly told him he was a fraud and a fake, even *before* the succession of unpopular wrongdoers began parading to his office door. He quite naturally regarded this condemnation as unfair and a trifle hostile, even though he suspected it had nothing to do with professional ethics or personal ambitions, but only with Christie's image of him as a man, an image he was somehow destroying. He once asked her, "*Why* am I a fake and a fraud?" and she answered, "Because you *are,*" which was considerably enlightening and which helped to ease tensions between them that week, especially since she was in her sixth month of pregnancy by that time, and had begun denying him connubial rights in her fourth month. "You're insensitive," she told him. "You don't know what a woman feels."

Amy came on the seventh of May, 1954, and the birth was every bit as painful and as horrible as Christie knew it would be, an ordeal for which she never fully forgave Jonah. She made it clear the day she came home from the hospital that this was to be their one and only venture into parenthood, and that if he so much as looked at her before she was properly prepared for "having sex," she would strangle him without remorse. Her preparations for "having sex," as she invariably referred to it ("Do you want to have sex?" she would ask, not without a wicked glint in her eye) assumed ritual proportions in the months that followed. She would spend what seemed like hours in the bathroom before coming to him. Once he fell asleep waiting for her, and once he sent her a memo on a Tuesday, actually mailed it from his office to the house, reading: "Thursday night! Get ready!" But despite these rigorous preparations, they "had sex" often and with apparent satisfaction, and the only time he ever thought of getting himself another woman was in the year just before the divorce, by which time things had become really impossible.

Christie was a beautiful woman, and most beautiful women can say or do anything they wish, as long as they perform with a certain amount of style. She possessed style in abundance, from the tips of her Bendel shoes to the top of her Victor Vito coiffure. Her eyes snapped with whiplash certainty whenever she delivered another of her absurd banalities. She would stand with hands on narrow hips, flat-chested but sinuous and sexy as hell, splendid legs widespread as though she were trying to maintain balance on the deck of a lurching yawl, head tossed back, tiny beauty spot penciled near her lips, a spirited laugh (her mother's) erupting after each of her own half-witticisms. "Craparoo," of course, was her identifying theme, and was repeated with the regularity of the NBC chimes. But she knew other devastatingly funny catch phrases, too, and she used them with similar frequency, to the amusement of all their new friends.

Nor was her comic virtuosity limited to verbal thrusts alone. She began drinking too much, and told Jonah to go to hell whenever he brought this failing to her attention. He once found her in the bedroom with a young actor whose nose he punched, her skirt up over her knees, oblivious to what the son of a bitch was attempting. (On the night they decided to end it, she kept sipping a glass of sherry which she finally left on the dresser, and which the next morning had its surface covered with a scum of floating dead fruit flies.) Figuratively, Christie rode her mother's horse into every living room, theater, restaurant, concert hall, and night club in New York—and because she had a good seat and remarkable hands, everyone applauded her performance. Except Jonah. Jonah wondered what had happened to the little girl who used to pick her delicate way through the forsythia bushes.

Maybe she grew up too soon, or maybe she never grew up at all, or maybe they both grew up simultaneously but in opposite directions. This too shall pass, she assured him, but of course it did not. By the tenth year of their marriage he was ready to agree with her that it was all craparoo. The odd thing about it, he thought now as he struggled with his pajama top, his wrist throbbing, the odd thing about it was that he had loved her all that time, and probably had still loved her when they decided there was no use going any further with it. He could remember watching her undress one night, here in this bedroom, taking her time with her underthings, and then floating a nylon gown down over her slender body while he watched from the bed, delighting in her presence, could remember the sidelong glance she gave him as she turned out the light, could remember his intense excitement, and her cold "Put that away, buster. We're calling it quits, remember?" Yes, he could remember.

And remembering, could not understand. Or perhaps understood all.

He pulled back the covers and climbed into bed.

On impulse, he reached for the telephone, lifted the receiver, and began dialing Christie's number. No, he thought, and hung up. He sat staring at the phone for a moment. Then he lifted the receiver, waited for a dial tone, and called Sally Kirsch.

Her phone rang six times before it was answered. Sally's voice, edged with sleep, started to say "Hello," but the receiver must have slipped from her grasp. He heard a clatter as it tumbled onto a hard surface, and then heard her mutter, "Oh, god*damn,*" and then heard her recovering the receiver, and then her voice again, hardly more awake this time, "Hello?"

"Sally?"

"Who's this?" she said flatly, and suspiciously, and somewhat angrily.

"Jonah."

"Who?"

"Jonah." He paused. "Willow."

"Oh."

There was a silence.

"What time is it?" she asked, and yawned.

"Two o'clock, something like that."

"Mmm?"

"Were you asleep?" he asked.

"Mmm."

"Are you awake now?"

"Mmm."

"Would you like to have lunch with me tomorrow?"

"*What* time did you say it was?"

"Two o'clock."

"In the *morning,* do you mean?"

"That's right."

"Mmm," Sally said, and again was silent.

"How's your lip?" he said.

"Haven't you got court tomorrow?"

"Yes, I have."

"Don't you think you ought to go to bed or something?"

"I *am* in bed."

"To sleep, I mean."

"I wanted to ask you to lunch first."

"It's two o'clock in the morning," she said.

"I know. *Will* you have lunch with me?"

"Yes, I'll have lunch with you."

"Good. How about dinner?"

"When?"

"Tomorrow night."

"Tomorrow night," she repeated.

"Yes."

"What is all this, Jonah?"

"I want to have lunch with you tomorrow and dinner with you tomorrow night."

"All of a sudden."

"Yes. All of a sudden."

"All right," she said, and he was sure she shrugged.

"Can you meet me at Gasner's?"

"What time?"

"Twelve, twelve-thirty, give me a chance to get from the courthouse."

"Listen . . ." Sally said.

"Yes?"

"Aren't you married or something?"

"No."

"Somebody told me you were married."

"Who told you that?"

"A friend of mine. The night we met. At that party."

"Said I was married?"

"Yes."

"No, I *used* to be married," Jonah said. "That was a long time ago."

"*How* long ago?"

"Why?"

"Because I don't kid around," Sally said.

"I was divorced in 1962."

They were silent.

"You mean you thought I was married when you went up to Vassar with me?" Jonah asked.

"Yes."

"Do you usually go out with married men?"

"No. Well, once before I did."

They were silent again.

"Well," he said.

"Well," she said.

"They turn off the heat in this building at eleven o'clock," he said.

"Here, too."

"It's like an icebox."

"Yes, here too."

"Well," he said.

"Well," she said.

"Well, I'll see you tomorrow."

"I'm looking forward to it," she said.

"Good night," he said.

"Good night," she said.

Chickie did not come into the apartment until two-thirty A.M., using the key he had given her. He was asleep in an armchair near the bookcase, and he was startled into wakefulness by the sound of the key being turned in the lock, the tumblers falling. He opened his eyes and looked toward the door just as it opened. Chickie stood there for a moment, silhouetted by the light burning in the hallway. With one hand on the doorknob for support, she lifted first one foot and then the other to remove her shoes. Holding the shoes in one hand, she closed the door behind her and tiptoed into the room.

"Hello, Chickie," he said.

"Ooooo," she answered, "you scared me."

"Put on a light."

"I thought you were asleep."

"I was."

"Did I wake you?"

"Yes."

"You poor dear man."

"I thought you'd be here before midnight."

"What?"

"You said you'd be here before midnight."

"Oh, yes, I know, but we got all hung up. I'm terribly sorry, Sidney."

"I've got to get some sleep, you know," Sidney said. "Driscoll goes on the stand tomorrow morning."

"I know. Sidney, do you have any milk in the fridge? I'm dying for a glass of milk."

"I think so. What's today?"

"Wednesday."

"I think they deliver on Wednesday."

"Don't go away, you dear man," she said, and she padded out of the room and into the kitchen.

"What time did you leave the office?" he called.

"What, dear?"

"What time did you leave the office?"

"Oh, I don't know. It must have been six or six-thirty. Why?"

"I just wondered."

Chickie appeared in the doorway to the kitchen, holding a glass of milk in one hand and a cookie in the other. She took a bite of the cookie and then drained half the glass of milk. "Mmmm," she said, "that's good. Would you like some milk?"

"No, thanks. Where'd you go from the office?"

"We went out to eat."

"Where?"

"Oh my, listen to the lawyer," Chickie said. "How's the trial going?"

"Pretty well, I think. Where'd you eat?"

"Pavillon, where else?"

"Come on, Chickie."

"Chambord."

"Chickie . . ."

"The Four Seasons."

"I'm trying . . ."

"The Forum."

"I want to know where you and Ruth went."

"We went to eat at a restaurant on Madison, a few blocks from the office. I don't even know the name of it. It's a tiny little dump."

"And then where did you go?"

"Up to Ruth's, where we worked on the trip."

"What trip?"

"The trip I was telling you about."

"The one you said might materialize?"

"That's right. Only now it looks as if it might very *well* materialize. How's the trial going, Sidney?"

"I told you. Pretty well."

"Does that mean you'll win?"

"I don't know."

"Well, you must have some indication, Sidney."

"I think it's going our way. They put on a witness today who was a real *shmuck,* he did them a lot of harm."

"Who was that?"

"Ralph Knowles."

"I never heard of him."

"He's a movie director."

"What did he direct?"

"What difference does it make?"

"I'm only trying to understand what happened, Sidney. Do you mind if I take off my dress?"

"I've got to get some sleep," Sidney said.

"Are you afraid I won't let you sleep?" Chickie asked, and smiled.

"No, but . . ."

"I'm very tired myself, darling," she said. "Unzip me, will you?" She walked to where he was sitting, and then turned her back to him. He lowered the zipper. "Thank you," she said, and walked away from him into the bedroom. "It's very smoky in here," she said. "Were you smoking in here, Sidney?"

"What?"

"In the bedroom here."

"Yes, I had a cigar when I got home."

"What time did you get home?"

"About eight," he said. He paused. "I got a lift." He paused again. "In a Cadillac." He could hear her rustling around in the bedroom.

"I'm just exhausted," she said.

"Those Cadillacs are very nice."

"They're the only kind to have, Sidney," she said.

"What time is it?"

"It's a little past twelve. Come to bed, Sidney."

He rose and went into the bedroom. She had put on one of his robes, and was standing by the mirror brushing out her long red hair. "Have you ever been in a Cadillac?" he asked.

"Of course."

"Recently?"

"Sidney," she said, without turning from the mirror, "what is this?"

"What is what?"

"What is all this business about Cadillacs? Are you thinking of buying one, is that it?"

"Well, if I w-w-win this case . . ."

"Yes, you'll be very wealthy."

"I c-c-could . . ."

"You could buy three or four Cadillacs, Sidney, all in different colors."

"You don't believe me, d-do you?" Sidney said.

"Believe you about what, dear? That you're going to win your case?"

"I *am* going to win," he said.

"Well, don't get so fierce about it, Sidney. I believe you."

"I *am,*" he said.

"Mmm-huh."

"If you were to m-m-marry me . . ."

"Sidney, let's not go into that right now."

"I'm only saying."

"Yes, but not now." She put the brush down on the dresser top, and then turned and leaned against the dresser and folded her arms across her breasts and smiled thinly and said, "Would you like to do Eddie Cantor?"

"No," he said.

"I thought you might like to."

"No."

"The way you did at Harvard."

"No."

"What was it called, the group? Hasty Pudding?"

"No, it was just the Dramatic Club."

"Anyway, I thought you might like to."

"No."

"Well," she said, and shrugged. "I can't force you, I guess." She shrugged again and then took off the robe. Naked, she walked to the bed, pulled back the blanket, and propped herself against the pillows.

"Chickie," he said, "there's something we've got to talk about."

"It's a shame, though," she said, "because you know how much I love it."

"I get the feeling that something's going on and I don't know what."

"The way you roll your eyes, and wave your hands around, I just love that, Sidney."

"What's going on, Chickie?"

"What's going on where, baby?"

"With . . . with you and Ruth."

Chickie looked down at her breast, took it in one hand and idly examined the skin around the nipple. Without looking at him, she said, "Did you see us get into the Cadillac tonight, Sidney? Is that it?"

"Well . . . yes."

"Were you following us, Sidney?"

"Yes."

"What, Sidney?"

"Yes. I was."

"Following us?"

"Yes."

"To see where we were going, Sidney?"

"Yes."

"Because something's bothering you?"

"Yes."

"If I were to marry you, Sidney, would you still follow me around?"

"I . . . I don't know. I get the feeling . . ."

"Would you, Sidney?"

". . . that you're lying to me all the time, that something . . ." He shook his head. "I don't know wh-what, I j-j-just don't know."

"Don't stammer, Sidney," she said, and looked up at him.

"I j-j-just . . ."

"The man in the Cadillac was a man named Jerome Courtlandt . . ."

"I didn't ask you."

"Shut up, Sidney, and listen. He's the man we're arranging the European trip for, and he was heading for the office when he happened to spot us, and he asked Ruth if he could drop us off someplace, because it was so bitter cold, and she said, Yes certainly, and he drove us to the restaurant. Now that's what happened with Mr. Jerome Courtlandt."

"I didn't ask."

"No, you just sneaked around and followed me from work."

"Because . . ."

"Because you don't trust me."

"I t-trust you, Chickie. It's just . . ."

"Oh my," Chickie said, "how could I possibly marry a man who doesn't trust me?"

"I trust you, I do."

"Who doesn't care about me at all . . ."

"I care about you."

"Who follows me around . . ."

"I'm sorry, Chickie."

"Do Eddie Cantor," she said.

"No, I . . ."

"Do it."

"It's . . . undignified," he mumbled.

"Do it."

". . . and silly."

"Do it."

He hesitated. "If . . ." he started, and then stopped.

"That's it," she said.

"If you knew . . ."

"Go on, honey."

"If you knew Susie . . ."

"Go on, baby, go on."

"I can't. I feel . . ."

"Do it, Sidney."

"If you knew Susie," he sang, "like I know Suzie . . . oh, oh, oh, what a girl . . ."

"Roll your eyes. You're not rolling your eyes."

"There's none so classy," he sang, and then raised his hands, the elbows bent, and began hopping from one foot to the other in a sliding sideward motion, rolling his eyes, his voice suddenly going higher in imitation of Cantor, "as this fair lassie," rolling his eyes and hopping back and forth, mouth pouting, eyes rolling, "oh, oh, holy Moses, what a chassis . . ."

"That's it, baby," Chickie said, and began giggling.

"If you knew Susie," he sang, his voice stronger now, "like I . . ."

"Yes, yes," she said, giggling louder.

". . . know Susie . . ."

"You're marvelous," she said, "wonderful!"

". . . oh, oh, oh, what a girl!" he sang, and then abruptly turned toward the bed, and dropped to his knees and wrapped his arms around her waist and fiercely pressed his face to her naked belly.

"Yes," Chickie whispered. "Yes, baby, that's it."

THURSDAY

12

Every Thursday, Driscoll's mother would fuss and fret in the bedroom before coming out to breakfast. When she finally appeared, shawl draped over her shoulders even on the hottest summer days, she would complain bitterly about the simple fact of Thursday, letting everyone in the house know that she felt it was a mistake to get out of bed on Thursday, that the safest place to be on that hoodoo jinx of a day was under the covers with the blinds drawn and the windows closed and the doors locked. He wondered if she still complained about Thursdays to her new husband the Danish furniture man Mr. Gerald Furst. He could remember his mother making a joke only once in his life. His father had been playing the piano, and his mother was listening with her head cocked to one side, a slightly pained expression on her face. "In the old days," she said at last, "when your father played piano, the ladies used to stay home in droves." Uncle Benny immediately topped her by looking up from his drink and saying, "Even worse, Irene, the ladies often drove home in stays." He never learned why his mother so detested Thursdays. His father died on a Wednesday.

Now, as he stepped into the courtroom, he knew something of his mother's superstitious fear, and wished he were being called to testify on any day but this. He had hoped for sunshine, had listened to the forecast the night before with rising anticipation: warmer temperatures, they had said, the possibility of clear skies. The temperature had indeed climbed into the low forties during the night, and the thermometer reading had been forty-eight when he and Ebie left the Astor that morning. But the sky was heavily overcast, and he was afraid now that it would begin raining sometime during the day, turning the snow underfoot to slush, casting a pall over the city—Thursday, a hoodoo jinx of a day.

The courtroom was hardly less cheerless than the street outside. The same dull light streamed through the windows, giving the room a curiously one-dimensional appearance, negating perspective, dulling all reflecting surfaces. He led Ebie to the empty jury box, and then went to sit beside Willow at the defense table, shaking hands with him, and listening to his words of encouragement while his eyes roamed the courtroom. Brackman was in whispered consultation with his partner at the plaintiff's table. Constantine sat at the far end of the table, reading the paperback edition of *Lord of the Flies*. The court clerk was waiting near the door to the judge's chambers, watching the big wall clock over the bench. The spectators' benches were empty. Even the Columbia student had abandoned the proceedings.

At ten o'clock sharp, the clerk called "All rise!" and the judge entered and went directly to the bench and then gave a peremptory nod, the signal for everyone in the courtroom to sit again. Driscoll heard Willow call his name, and then rose with the dread of Thursday looming huge within him, and walked slowly and self-consciously toward the witness stand. He felt suddenly that he had dressed wrongly, that his dark blue suit looked too much like a confirmation garment, that his simple blue tie was not bright enough, that he gave an impression of someone drab and hardly inventive, barely intelligent, certainly uncreative, "truth and nothing but the truth, so help you God?" the clerk said.

"I do," he answered, and sat.

Willow rose from the defense table in sections, unfolding his length, walking loosely and easily toward the witness chair, and then smiling up briefly at Driscoll, and very quietly and calmly asking, "Are you the author of *The Paper Dragon?*" as if that were not the prime issue before this court.

"I am," Driscoll answered.

"Did you write it independently and of your own creation, without reference to any other work of fiction?"

"I did."

"What is the date of your birth?"

"March 12, 1929."

"How old were you in October of 1947, when the play *Catchpole* was produced?"

"Eighteen."

"Were you a theatergoer at that time?"

"Yes, sir. I began going regularly to the theater when I was twelve years old."

"Did you attend any performances of the play *Catchpole?*"

"No, sir."

"Had you, before this action began, ever read the play *Catchpole?*"

"Never."

"Or heard of the plaintiff, Arthur Constantine?"

"No."

"What high school did you attend?"

"The High School of Music and Art."

"Which is where?"

"It's on 135th Street and Convent Avenue."

"Where were you living at that time?"

"In Manhattan. On West End Avenue."

"Did you go to Music and Art for the full four years?"

"No, sir. I began as a sophomore, coming directly from a junior high school, and I remained until graduation. Three years."

"When was this?"

"From 1944 to 1947."

"Were you graduated from Music and Art in 1947?"

"Yes, sir. January of 1947."

"Did you then continue your schooling elsewhere?"

"I won an art scholarship to the Art Students League, and I went there for approximately six months, I forget the exact length of time, the duration of the scholarship."

"To study art?"

"Yes, sir. I was studying drawing and painting—oil painting."

"Were you an art major in high school?"

"Yes, sir."

"What happened after you left the Art Students League?"

"I began studying art at Pratt Institute in the fall of that year, 1947."

"For how long?"

"Until June of 1950."

"What happened then?"

"I graduated and was drafted into the Army."

"Until you were drafted into the Army, would it be correct to say that you were training to become an artist?"

"A painter, yes, sir."

"In 1947, did you receive complimentary tickets to a preview performance of the play *Catchpole?*"

"I did not."

"Do you remember a distribution of free tickets?"

"I do not."

"Were you advised of such a distribution?"

"I was not."

"Did you see the play in any preview performance?"

"I never saw the play in *any* performance."

"You were graduated from Pratt in June of 1950?"

"That's right."

"And went directly into the Army?"

"Yes, sir, almost immediately after graduation."

"Which would be?"

"I went into the Army on June 21, 1950."

"And when were you discharged?"

"August 11, 1953."

"Honorably?"

"What?"

"Were you honorably discharged?"

"Yes, sir."

"What did you do after your discharge?"

"In September of 1953 I began attending New York University."

"To study art?"

"No, sir. I was an English major."

"Why did you choose this major?"

"While I was in the Army, I decided that I would like to try writing."

"Did you receive a degree from N.Y.U.?"

"Yes, sir, I did. A Bachelor of Arts in June of 1957."

"And after you were graduated, did you begin writing?"

"No, sir."

"What *did* you do?"

"I held a series of jobs."

"Like what? Would you list them, please?"

"I worked for the telephone company, and I worked for an import-export firm, and an advertising agency for a little while. Things like that."

"Did any of these jobs entail writing?"

"No, sir."

"Art work?"

"No, sir. For the most part, they were stopgap jobs."

"When did you begin writing *The Paper Dragon?*"

"In 1961."

"Do you remember exactly when in 1961?"

"October."

"In other words, you began writing *The Paper Dragon* eleven years after the actual events it portrays."

"Yes, sir."

"The Chinese offensive across the Ch'ongch'on River was in November of 1950, isn't that correct?"

"That's correct."

"Why did you wait eleven years?"

"I wasn't sure I would write it at all."

"Why did you write it?"

"I had to."

"Why?"

"For my own peace of mind."

"You felt you had to put the events on paper for your own peace of mind?"

"Yes."

"Your Honor," Brackman said, "I do not see where these questions . . ."

"Yes, Mr. Willow, where are you heading?"

"Your Honor, I am attempting to trace the creative process."

"Very well, go ahead."

"Mr. Driscoll, how tall are you?"

"I'm six feet tall."

"What color are your eyes?"

"Blue."

"Would you say that your hair is light or dark?"

"Dark."

"How old were you in 1950 when you were drafted into the Army?"

"I was just twenty-one."

"And you went into the Army directly from Pratt Institute?"

"I did."

"Did you go into basic training?"

"Yes, sir, at Fort Dix."

"Did you then go to Officer Candidate School?"

"I did. At Fort Benning."

"And were you then sent to Korea?"

"I was."

"Would you consider this a fair description of Lieutenant Cooper in your novel: he is twenty-one years old, six feet tall, with blue eyes and dark hair. He is drafted into the Army from Pratt Institute, is sent to O.C.S. and then shipped to Korea?"

"I would consider that a fair description."

"Did you once live on West End Avenue?"

"I did."

"Did your fictitious character Lieutenant Cooper live on West End Avenue?"

"Yes."

"Did he attend Music and Art High School, as you did?"

"Yes, sir."

"Was he an art major, as you were?"

"Yes, sir."

"Did he later receive a scholarship to the Art Students League, as you did?"

"Yes, sir."

"And then went on to Pratt Institute, as you did?"

"Yes, sir."

"I probably need not even ask this question, Mr. Driscoll, but would you please tell the court upon whom you based the character Lieutenant Alex Cooper?"

"On myself, sir."

"Was he based on Lieutenant Roger Mason in *Catchpole?*"

"I had never heard of Lieutenant Roger Mason until last month when you showed me the play."

"Then your character was *not* based on him?"

"Definitely not."

"Mr. Driscoll, I show you these pages and ask you what they are."

Driscoll took the pages and studied them briefly. "They're a preliminary outline for the first several chapters of *The Paper Dragon.*"

"I offer the outline in evidence," Willow said, and handed the pages to Brackman.

"Any objection?" the clerk asked.

"None," Brackman said.

"Mr. Genitori?"

"No."

"Defendants' Exhibit J received in evidence," the clerk said.

"Please," Willow said to the clerk, "I'd like to refer to it." He took the extended outline, glanced at it, and then turned to Driscoll again. "Is this a detailed outline, Mr. Driscoll?"

"It is."

"Does that mean you followed it precisely when you were writing the first hundred pages of your book?"

"The first ninety-eight pages," Driscoll said. "But no, I didn't follow it precisely."

"You made changes as you worked?"

"Yes."

"As you went along?"

"Yes."

"Why?"

"Well, I didn't want to feel too tightly restricted by the outline. I wanted to leave some surprises for myself."

"Did you expand upon this outline at any time?"

"Yes. This covers only the first portion of the book. When I sent the completed portion to Mitchell-Campbell, it was accompanied by a longer outline, a less detailed outline, but one covering the remainder of the book, the full book as I hoped to complete it."

"And you sent your completed portion together with an expanded outline to Mitchell-Campbell?"

"Yes, sir."

"Did you know anyone working at Mitchell-Campbell?"

"No, sir."

"Why did you send the book to them, rather than to another publisher?"

"They seemed like good publishers."

"Upon what did you base this judgment?"

"They seemed to do a lot of advertising for the books on their list," Driscoll said, and McIntyre burst out laughing.

"I believe this is the standard writer's gauge, your Honor," Willow said, laughing with him. "Did you address the book to anyone's attention, Mr. Driscoll?"

"No, I simply sent it to the Editorial Department."

"With a return envelope?"

"Well, no, I sent the book in a box. But I accompanied it with a money order for the return postage. If it was rejected."

"Did you expect a rejection?"

"It was my first novel, I don't know what I expected."

"What happened next?"

"I received a letter from Mr. Danton, asking if I would come in to discuss the book."

"When was this?"

"I don't remember exactly. Either July or August."

"Of 1962?"

"Yes, sir."

"Did you in fact meet with Mr. Danton?"

"Yes, I went up to his office."

"Can you tell us what happened at this first meeting?"

"Chester wanted to know what my plans were for finishing the book, and I expanded verbally upon the outline I'd submitted. He then told me that the feelings of himself and another editor at Mitchell-Campbell were that the squad, and particularly Colman, should be given a stronger motivation for their hatred of Lieutenant Cooper. He suggested that I use the idea of a previous commanding officer being killed in action and my hero replacing him."

"Did he suggest how this officer might have been killed?"

"Yes, he suggested that a sniper kill him from ambush."

"Did he make any other suggestions?"

"Yes, I believe he was concerned about the book's profanity even then, and he suggested that it be toned down during the writing of the remainder. He also thought we should begin thinking about another title."

"Was that the substance of your conversation at this first meeting?"

"Yes, sir."

"What did you do then?"

"I went home to finish the book."

"What procedure did you follow?"

"Well, first I outlined the next four or five chapters in greater detail. And then I began writing them."

"Was this your standard working procedure?"

"Yes. I would outline several chapters at a time and then begin work on those chapters—the actual writing of them. When I'd finished those, or was close to finishing them, I would outline the next several chapters, and so on."

"Until you completed the novel?"

"Yes."

"You used your general outline as the basis . . ."

"Yes . . ."

". . . and then outlined in closer detail as you went along?"

"Yes, that's exactly what I did."

"Now here are some pages, Mr. Driscoll, with the words 'Chapter 7,' on the first page, and on the last page here, we have 'Chapter 15.' Are these pages part of your actual working outline?"

"Yes, sir, they are."

"The detailed outline?"

"Yes, sir."

"Now page 5 is torn, do you see that?"

"I see it."

"Only part of the page is here in the outline."

"That's right."

"Is this exactly how you found this page in your files?"

"It is."

"Do you know why a portion of the page is torn off?"

"I have no idea. The page following it is marked 5A so I imagine I didn't like what I had outlined and simply tore it off and put in another page called 5A. Yes, I probably tore off the bottom of this page, and then replaced it with a '5A.' "

"I offer the outline in evidence," Willow said.

"Have we seen this before, Mr. Willow?" Brackman asked.

"No, sir, you have not."

"I'm not objecting, but I would like to know why this was not previously shown to us."

"Because we only received it just before the trial began."

"Nevertheless, withholding it was in violation of the court order directing—"

"Your Honor, we have assiduously respected the court order, and have turned over to the plaintiff any papers received from Mr. Driscoll. He did not locate these until just before the trial began, and I did not have the opportunity to turn them over. May I say, however—"

"I think you might have *found* the opportunity, Mr. Willow," Brackman said.

"May I say that my friend has fallen prey to his own

gambit. Had he chosen to serve Mr. Driscoll as a party to this case, he could have examined him before trial. He chose not to, in the hope—"

"I don't think we need go into Mr. Brackman's tactics," McIntyre said. "Are you objecting to this going into evidence?"

"No, your Honor," Brackman said. "Nor did I dream of offending Mr. Willow."

"You haven't offended me," Willow said.

"This action has been going on for a long time now," Brackman said, "and I don't think we've once raised our voices to each other, either outside the courtroom or since this trial began. I only meant to say that I wish you'd have let me see these papers before now. Perhaps you'll allow me to study them at greater length later."

"Of course."

"Mark it 'Defendants' Exhibit K in evidence,' " the clerk said.

"Now, if you will look at this outline, Mr. Driscoll, you will see certain notations on it, such as '60,000 words, 10/12' and immediately following that, '58,500, 10/12.' On the second page here, in ink, '63,000 words, 10/19' and following it in pencil, '62,300 10/20' and it goes on in this manner throughout. Did you write these notations?"

"I did."

"What do they mean?"

"The numbers in ink, '60,000 words,' for example, '10/12' represent a goal and a target date. I hoped to have completed 60,000 words of the book by October 12th, that was probably a Friday. The penciled indication on the right shows the actual number of words I had written by that date—58,500 words."

"You fell short of the target that week."

"Yes. But that's what these notes indicate throughout."

"The number of words you hoped to have written by a certain date?"

"Yes, sir. There was a deadline, you see. The contract called for delivery of the book by January, I think it was, and

I tried to adhere to a schedule that would enable me to meet that deadline."

"And you felt it necessary to indicate what you *had* accomplished in addition to what you'd hoped to accomplish."

"Yes, as a guide to completion. I had to know that I would finish it one day, you see."

"What do you mean?"

"A book takes a long time to write."

"Yes?"

"Well, I can only speak for myself."

"Yes, go on."

"I'm not a professional, this was my only book. I can only tell you what I experienced when I was writing it."

"Which was what, Mr. Driscoll?"

"I thought it would never end."

"And is that why you kept your record?"

"Yes. I had started the book in October of 1961, and I . . . I wasn't even sure I'd *ever* start it, you see, but finally I did and it went very slowly. It took me eight months to finish those ninety-eight pages and the outline, and it was very difficult all the way, writing does not come easily to me. It began going a bit more smoothly after Mitchell-Campbell contracted for the book. I suppose Chester's enthusiasm for it, and his . . . his faith that I could complete it, this was an enormous shot in the arm. I found I was working much more quickly, that I could count on from three to five thousand words a week, that was a lot for me. But at the same time, I had to know that I wasn't writing into a void, that one day the thing would be *finished*. I could take the last page out of the typewriter and it would be done. That's why I kept a timetable. So that I'd know I was getting there."

"And, of course, eventually you *did* get there. You completed your book."

"Yes. Eventually."

"Before that time, before the book was actually finished, did you acquire an agent?"

"Yes, sir, Mr. Hollis Marks. He's still my agent."

"Here are some letters to Mr. Hollis, dated November 5th and November 9th . . ."

"Mr. *Marks.*"

"Mr. Marks, excuse me, and addressed 'Dear Hollis.' "

"Yes."

"November 15th, November 20th, November 23rd, December 3rd, December 7th, December 11th, December 12th, December 14th, December 20th, and December 28th. Did you send these letters to Mr. Marks?"

"I did."

"Reporting on your progress on *The Paper Dragon?*"

"That's right."

"If your Honor please, we can call Mr. Marks as a witness, but I know what he will tell the Court concerning these letters."

"What would that be, Mr. Willow?"

"That they were taken from his files and written by Mr. Driscoll on the dates indicated. I offer all of them in evidence as one exhibit."

"For what purpose are these being offered?" Brackman asked.

"Again, to show the creative process. Your Honor, if a book is being pirated, the thief would hardly send progress reports to his—"

"No objection," Brackman said.

"Defendants' Exhibit L received in evidence," the clerk said.

"Mr. Driscoll, when you were writing your book, did you contact anyone for information you needed?"

"Yes, sir."

"Whom did you contact?"

"Colonel Lewis Hamilton."

"He was your commanding officer . . ."

"The company commander, yes . . ."

". . . in Korea?"

"Yes, sir. He was a captain at the time."

"What was your initial contact with him?"

"I wrote a letter to him, explaining that I was working on

a book, and asking for his help. I suggested that we meet one afternoon for lunch or after working hours—he was working in this area at the time, at the Army Recruiting Office on Whitehall. He called me when he received my letter, and we met later that week, on a Friday I believe it was. At the beginning of November."

"Where is Colonel Hamilton today?"

"He was called back to active duty in Vietnam. I'm sorry to say he's dead."

"I show you this, and ask you to describe it to the Court."

"It's a carbon copy of the letter I wrote to Colonel Hamilton."

"I offer it in evidence."

"Your Honor," Brackman said, rising, "as I understand it, Colonel Hamilton is dead. Now Mr. Driscoll states that this is a copy of a letter he sent to the colonel, but I know of no way of ascertaining that. I cannot question a dead man."

"Your Honor . . ."

"I object to it as irrelevant, and I submit that it would be impossible for me to ascertain whether it is authentic."

"Is this letter necessary to your case?" McIntyre asked.

"To my mind, your Honor, anything that clearly shows the step-by-step development of Mr. Driscoll's novel is not only necessary but essential to the case. This letter shows beyond doubt that in addition to personal experience, Mr. Driscoll sought the advice of an expert on matters that were beyond his ken. If he were copying . . ."

"Yes, but won't Mr. Driscoll be testifying anyway about his meeting with the colonel?"

"Yes, your Honor, but his testimony will be more persuasive when supported by this letter."

"Is this letter being offered for the truth of what it contains, or simply to establish a working procedure for Mr. Driscoll?"

"I think it even goes beyond these matters, your Honor, to clearly indicate the kind of man Mr. Driscoll is. In his letter to the colonel, for example, he modestly, almost shyly, reintroduces himself . . ."

"Mr. Willow, it's my opinion that this letter is not the same as those from Mr. Driscoll to his agent, sent as part of a daily working routine. I will sustain your objection, Mr. Brackman. The letter will not be admitted."

"May I offer it for identification?" Willow asked.

"Of course."

"Mark it 'Defendants' Exhibit M for identification,'" the clerk said.

"You said earlier, Mr. Driscoll, that you met with Colonel Hamilton . . ."

"Yes."

". . . sometime after you wrote to him. Where did you meet?"

"In a restaurant down here someplace. I don't remember the name of it."

"Can you tell us what happened at this meeting?"

"I asked Colonel Hamilton a great many questions, and he answered them for me."

"I show you these four sheets of paper, and ask you if they are the notes you took at the meeting you just described."

"They are the notes I jotted down during the meeting."

"I offer the notes in evidence."

"Well, I must object to that, Mr. Willow," Brackman said, rising again. "You're showing here a collection of answers the witness supposedly got from a dead man. There is no possible way of questioning the dead man as to whether he really did give those answers."

"Is this being offered to show the truth of what it contains?" McIntyre asked.

"No, your Honor."

"I will admit it if its limited purpose is to show the witness's working procedure on his novel."

"To show the evolution of the book, your Honor."

"I will admit it."

"Mark it 'Defendants' Exhibit N in evidence.'"

"Mr. Driscoll, I show you another sheet of paper that lists the steps in the disassembly of an M-1. Did you use this information in your book?"

"Yes, sir. I had the lieutenant ask the men to strip their rifles, as an exercise."

"I am referring now to the so-called 'female rifle' scene."

"Yes, sir, I'm familiar with that scene."

"Was it based upon information you received from the colonel?"

"Well . . . yes and no. I did receive the information from the colonel, but what actually happened was that I told him what I needed when I spoke to him on the phone, and he brought a book called *Military Science and Tactics* with him, in which he had marked the section on stripping the M-1. I copied the information directly from the book."

"Onto this sheet of paper?"

"Yes, sir."

"I offer it in evidence."

"I object," Brackman said.

"On what grounds, Mr. Brackman?"

"The witness has testified that his scene was based on information in a book and not on what is now before this Court. I do not see the relevance."

"He has testified," Willow said, "that his notes were taken from a book given to him by the colonel . . ."

"I did not hear him say the colonel *gave* him the book."

"Mr. Driscoll, could you . . ."

"He didn't actually *give* me the book. He brought it with him to the meeting, and I copied these notes from it."

"We have only the witness's word, your Honor, that the colonel brought the book with him. The alleged exchange involves a dead man who purportedly—"

"Section 4519 does not apply here," Willow said. "In no way can this be considered a transaction with a deceased . . ."

"I understand that," Brackman said, "and this is not my objection."

"Now just a minute, just a minute," McIntyre said. "It seems to me that the offer is being made only to show that Mr. Driscoll had in his possession material which could have formed the basis of the scene in his novel. Isn't that so, Mr. Willow?"

"Yes, your Honor."

"I will admit it. I think your objection is unfounded, Mr. Brackman."

"Mark it 'Defendants' Exhibit O in evidence.' "

"Mr. Driscoll, when you were writing your book, did you prepare a map upon which were written certain numbers and notes?"

"Your Honor, it pains me to have to object so continuously, especially when I know how interested we all are in having this trial proceed smoothly and rapidly," Brackman said. "But during the pretrial examinations, I can clearly remember Mr. Willow objecting at one point because the witness was my own and I was leading him."

"I'm sure you can also clearly remember, Mr. Brackman, that at the time I also stated I was not objecting to ninety per cent of your questions because we had agreed to be informal about the entire matter."

"That was the pretrial, Mr. Willow, and this is the trial, and I must object now to these leading questions."

"Mr. Driscoll, I show you a drawing of a map, and on this drawing there are certain numbers and notes. Who prepared this map?"

"I did."

"You drew the map?"

"Yes, sir."

"Is this the original drawing?"

"Yes, sir."

"What is it a map of?"

"It's a map of Korea, an enlargement of the Ch'ongch'on River area."

"Do you recognize the handwriting on it?"

"Yes, sir. It is my own."

"What do these notes and numbers signify?"

"They purport to be a patrol route and a timetable."

"Was this map used in your novel?"

"Yes, sir. That's the map that was reproduced in the book.

It depicts the area between the Ch'ongch'on and the Yalu, and the map was put there for the reader's convenience so that he could follow what was happening, the trap being set for Lieutenant Cooper."

"The path of the patrol is indicated on this map, is it not?"

"It is."

"And the times at which the squad expects to reach certain marked areas on the map?"

"Yes, sir, the checkpoints."

"In other words, the notations on this map indicate goals and expected times of arrival, do they not?"

"They do."

"Similar to the goals and target dates you made for the writing of your book."

"Objection," Brackman said.

"Sustained. Really, Mr. Willow."

"Is this patrol an important incident in your book?"

"It is."

"A climactic incident?"

"It is."

"I offer the map in evidence."

"No objection."

"I'm grateful Mr. Brackman has no objection," McIntyre said, "but I must admit, Mr. Willow, that my own curiosity is somewhat piqued. For what purpose is this map being offered?"

"Again, your Honor, to show the evolutionary development of this novel. To show how it was written and rewritten, to show the research that went into each scene, to show the devotion to detail, the combination of personal knowledge and imagination that resulted in a unique creation which could not conceivably have been plagiarized from any existing work. This scene in particular, your Honor, this patrol, is one that plaintiff claims is based on the escape of his psychopathic officer and the subsequent accidental killing of a sergeant. When we see how carefully this patrol was conceived and detailed, when we recognize how everything in Mr. Driscoll's novel leads to this patrol and to the subsequent sacrifice his lieutenant makes, we can clearly see . . ."

"But doesn't this map appear in the novel?"

"A reproduction does, yes, your Honor."

"And has not the novel itself already been admitted in evidence?"

"It has, your Honor."

"Then why on earth do we need the original drawing?"

"Only to call attention to the fact that Mr. Driscoll thought the patrol important enough to make his own drawing illustrating it. That is all, your Honor."

"I do feel, Mr. Willow, that it might have been a simpler matter to have shown him the reproduction in an exhibit already admitted, and then asked whether or not he had drawn the original."

"If your Honor please," Brackman said, "I quite agree with you, even though I have been exceedingly reluctant to interrupt Mr. Willow. I remind him again that there was a court order we may be violating here, the one stating that all documents be delivered to us. I assume Mr. Willow is not deliberately sidestepping that order, and that several of these documents which I'm hearing of for the first time today were truly received just before the trial began. Nonetheless, the offer of so many of them is cluttering the record unnecessarily."

"How many more will there be, Mr. Willow?" McIntyre asked.

"I've tried to limit them, your Honor . . ."

"Yes, but how many more will there be?"

". . . to those concerning specific alleged similarities. But we will be brief."

"How many more?"

"Two or three, your Honor."

"I hope so, Mr. Willow. I will admit the map."

"Mark it 'Defendants' Exhibit P in evidence,' " the clerk said.

"Mr. Driscoll, when did you complete the first draft of your novel?"

"In January of 1963."

"Do you remember the exact date?"

"Yes, it was January 26, 1963."

"How do you happen to remember this date?"

"I remember it because I wrote a note to Hollis the next day, just before I delivered the book."

"I show you this and ask if it is the note to which you just now referred."

"It is," Driscoll said.

"I offer it in evidence, your Honor."

"No objection," Brackman said wearily.

"Mark it 'Defendants' Exhibit Q,' " the clerk said.

"What did you do with this note, Mr. Driscoll?"

"I put it in the box containing the completed manuscript, and I delivered the note and the manuscript to Hollis Marks."

"When?"

"That Monday. January 28th."

"May I ask how you happen to recall this date?"

"I marked it on my desk calendar."

"I show you this page torn from a desk calendar for January 1963, and ask if this is the notation to which you just now referred."

"It is."

"I offer the calendar page in evidence, your Honor."

"No objection," Brackman said.

"Mark it 'Defendants' Exhibit R in evidence.' "

"Mr. Driscoll, would you please read the notation to the Court?"

"It just says 'Deliver PD,' that's all. And the date is circled, January 28th."

"Is this your handwriting?"

"It is."

"And by PD, did you mean *The Paper Dragon?*"

"Yes, that's what it was called by that time. That was the new title."

"Mr. Driscoll, when did you receive galley proofs of your book?"

"At the end of May sometime."

"What did you do with them?"

"I corrected them and sent them back to Mitchell-Campbell."

"Did you request a set of corrected galleys from them?"

"I did."

"For what purpose?"

"I wanted my uncle to read the book before it was published."

"Did you subsequently send those corrected galleys to your uncle?"

"I did."

"I show you this and ask you to describe it," Willow said.

"It's the carbon copy of a letter I wrote to my uncle in June of 1963, telling him the galleys were on their way, and asking him for his opinion of the book."

"I offer it in evidence," Willow said.

"Your Honor, I cannot see its relevance."

"If a man has stolen another man's work, your Honor, he does not send galley proofs to his uncle for an opinion. I am merely trying to establish a logical order of events, culminating in the finished product which Mr. Driscoll showed to his uncle, a man he loved and respected, for his approval."

"I will admit the letter," McIntyre said.

"Mark it 'Defendants' Exhibit S in evidence.' "

"Your Honor," Brackman said, "we had Mr. Willow's promise to watch his P's and Q's, but we have come beyond those and now seem to be up to our S's in documents."

McIntyre burst out laughing. Brackman chuckled quietly, pleased by his own wit. Even Willow and his assistant began laughing. The laughter continued for perhaps a minute. Driscoll, observing the others, did not crack a smile. He noticed that Arthur Constantine, sitting at the plaintiff's table, was not smiling either.

At last Willow said, "There will be no further documents, your Honor."

"I guess that answers your doubts, Mr. Brackman," McIntyre said.

"Yes, and I'm greatly relieved, your Honor."

"Mr. Driscoll," Willow said, still smiling, "when your book was completed and delivered to Mitchell-Campbell, did your agent request a second copy of the manuscript?"

"He did."

"For what purpose?"

"For serial rights submission."

"Do you mean for submission to the magazines?"

"Yes."

"Did you sell first serial rights to the book?"

"Yes, sir."

"Which magazine bought the rights?"

"The *Saturday Evening Post*—and not *McCall's* or *Redbook,* as Mr. Knowles surmised yesterday."

"When did it appear in the *Post?*"

"In September of '63."

"And when was it published as a book?"

"In October of '63."

"Was the book successful?"

"I suppose so."

"Well, would you know how many copies it sold in its hardcover edition?"

"Chester Danton would be able to tell you that more accurately. I believe it was something like fifty or sixty."

"Fifty or sixty?" McIntyre asked.

"Thousand, I mean."

"Fifty or sixty thousand copies of a first novel, your Honor—and the figure may be a shade higher than that—is considered phenomenal. And this was exclusive of the book club edition, was it not, Mr. Driscoll?"

"Yes."

"It *was* a book club selection?"

"Your Honor, what is the purpose of all this?" Brackman asked.

"Mr. Willow?"

"If your Honor please, I wish to demonstrate for Mr.

Driscoll only what Mr. Brackman earlier attempted to demonstrate regarding the plaintiff: that he is a man of recognized talents."

"How would this be any more relevant than plaintiff's—"

"If your Honor please, the Court permitted Mr. Constantine to go on and on about his screenplays, most of which were obscure and frankly mediocre works. It would seem to me that Mr. Driscoll should in all fairness be permitted to enumerate the very real honors bestowed upon his novel."

"Your Honor, I don't see how playing the numbers game, telling us how many copies were sold and all that, is going to indicate anything about Mr. Driscoll's talents."

"We *did* permit Mr. Constantine, however, to list his credits. All right, I will allow it. Go ahead, Mr. Driscoll."

"May I answer the question?"

"Yes, go on."

"It was a book club section. Book-of-the-Month took it."

"Was a paperback edition sold?" Willow asked.

"Yes, to Camelot Books."

"Would you happen to know how many copies were sold in that edition?"

"We sold a quarter of a million copies in the first eight days of sale."

"And afterwards?"

"It went on to sell something more than two and a half million copies."

"May I say, your Honor, that this constitutes a wildly successful sale in paperback."

"What time is it?" McIntyre asked the clerk.

"Eleven-fifteen, your Honor."

"Let's take a ten-minute recess."

The little Egyptian had obviously dressed for the occasion, and looked considerably more formal than he had on the night of the accident. Uncomfortable and a trifle embarrassed, he informed Sally that his name was Ibrahim Hadad, and then took a cigarette tin from his pocket and nervously opened it. He was wearing a rumpled brown suit and white shirt, a striped brown and yellow tie hanging down the shirt front and tucked into the waistband of his trousers. He wore yellow socks and brown shoes, and his heavy brown overcoat and brown fedora rested on his lap as he fumbled inside the tin, spilling a half dozen cigarettes onto his lap, retrieving them with fingers caked with the grime of his trade, impregnated in every wrinkle and pore. He smiled up at her palely, white teeth appearing in a sickly grin below his long hooked nose, his face the color of dust, the thin smile doing little to add a semblance of cheer to the solemn purpose of his visit. He put one of the cigarettes between his lips and then belatedly offered the tin to Sally, who shook her head.

"Very good cigarettes," he said. "Turkish."

"Thank you, I don't smoke," she said.

Hadad shrugged, closed the tin with a suggestion of finality, adjusted his coat and hat on his lap, put a lighted match to the cigarette tip, shook out the match, exhaled a giant cloud of smoke, and then nervously smiled again at Sally, who tented her fingers and waited for him to resume.

"Criminal assault," he said. "That is what." He shrugged. He puffed again on the cigarette. "When was it, the accident? Monday night?"

"Yes."

"The hospital, everything, I go home to my wife and children, she almost breaks my head for me all over again." He smiled. Sally kept watching him. He had a fascinating way of holding his cigarette between thumb and forefinger, the wrist bent outwards, so that he seemed rather effete as he puffed on it, rather like Peter Lorre playing a spy on the Orient Express, completely unlike a bricklayer.

"Tuesday is okay," he said. "Yesterday all day is okay too," he said, "but last *night,* ah! Six o'clock, yes? I come home from work, and who is waiting there? A detective."

"A police detective?"

"Correct," he said, and gave a small nod of his bullet-shaped head, and then cupped the cigarette in his reversed manner, and took a long obviously satisfying drag on it, and again exhaled a cloud of sweet-smelling smoke. My mother should be here, Sally thought, she would die from the smell alone. What is he smoking, Sally darling—pot? Mother, I'm sure it's not pot, what do you know about pot? I read the *New York Post,* Gertie would reply.

"Is it bothering you, the cigarette?" Hadad asked.

"No," she lied. "What about this detective?"

"It comes around that your friend, the lawyer, he has called *his* friend, the judge. His name is Santesson, the circus judge."

"Circuit," Sally said.

"Correct," Hadad said, and puffed again on his cigarette. "This detective, he comes from the judge's suggestion, he is investigating the *big* accident!" Hadad waved the hand with the cigarette in a grand sweeping gesture, smoke trailing behind it. "Criminal assault, he says."

"Who?"

"Me, who else?"

"This detective was investigating a charge of criminal assault against you?"

"Correct."

"Yes, go on."

"A year in prison, he says. Is this true?"

"I'm not sure."

"Or pay five hundred dollars?" Hadad said, looking at her expectantly, as though hoping she would deny it.

"Perhaps," Sally said.

"I can't afford neither," Hadad said, and sighed deeply. He looked at the cigarette in his cupped palm, sighed again when he discovered it had almost burned down, and then took the tin from his inside jacket pocket again and began going through the same complicated and fumbling maneuver of extricating a fresh cigarette from the sliding, tumbling, willful cigarettes in the box, the task made more difficult because he was now holding a lighted cigarette in one trembling hand. Watching him, Sally felt a sudden empathy, as though this shoddy, nervous man in his Sunday clothes accurately reflected the shabbiness of her Fourteenth Street walkup legal firm, sidewalk law at discount prices. He sat before the huge plate-glass window overlooking the street, the goldleaf letters S. KIRSCH, ATTORNEY AT LAW inverted so that they read correctly from the street, and below that the word ABOGADO, and in the corner of the window, also backwards so that the street trade could read it and perhaps be tempted by it, NOTARY PUBLIC, and the red seal below that, and further down the word translated into Spanish for the benefit of the myriad Puerto Ricans in the city who were constantly being asked to have legal documents of all sorts notarized. She sat behind an old wooden desk which she had bought at one of the secondhand furniture places on 23rd Street, in a revolving chair her mother jokingly said had once belonged to Oliver Wendell Holmes or Sherlock Holmes, she forgot which one, and looked across as Hadad finally extricated a cigarette from the tin and then shakingly began plucking loose cigarettes from his lap as though they were scattered daisy petals, the dark green filing cabinets behind him, the ancient inoperative air conditioner built into one window panel, the sky beyond as gray as death. This is what I have, she thought. I'm thirty-three years old, and I was graduated from N.Y.U. Law in the summer of 1963 (a late bloomer, Gertie called me) and here I am in a shabby office on a shabby street, watching an Arab pluck cigarettes from his lap. Sally Kirsch, Attorney at Law.

Sally Kirsch, attorney at law, had moved out of her mother's apartment the week after she passed the bar exams. Her mother Gertrude, a stout blond lady of dubious German-Austrian-Serbian extraction, when informed that Sally's new apartment was in the Village, immediately asked, "What will you do now? Start sleeping with all those beatniks down there?" Sally informed her that she had not yet slept with anyone (a lie), beatnik or otherwise, although the opportunity had certainly presented itself on many an occasion even while living here in the sanctified atmosphere of this fine home on Third Avenue and 85th Street. She did not expect to begin now, she said (another lie necessitated by the first lie), unless she chose to, which is exactly what she would have done no matter where she lived. "A fine girl," Gertie said. "You wouldn't be so smart if your father was alive."

Unfortunately, her father was not alive, had in fact been dead since Sally was six, at which time he was struck down by a bus on Second Avenue while crossing the street from his dry goods store. Sally had always suspected he was drunk at the time. Her sharpest memory of her father was of a tall, thin man with her identical green eyes and sandy hair, stooping to kiss her on the cheek, his breath smelling of something she only later could identify as wine. She was *sure* he'd been drunk. A man didn't get hit by something as big as a bus unless he was too drunk to see the damn thing. Her mother (significantly, she felt) never drank. She sometimes wondered if her mother had ever made love, evidence of conception and birth to the contrary.

In some of her more lurid fantasies, Sally reconstructed an image of her own first bed partner, an N.Y.U. undergraduate, now married and teaching English somewhere in Schenectady, unable to forget that hot sophomore maniac who had almost eaten him alive. In soberer moments, she thought of herself as essentially healthy, but hardly very passionate, a girl who understood the biological needs of her body and periodically set out to gratify them. Her three affairs had been of short duration, the most recent having been with an internal revenue agent, of all things, and having ended in April when he asked her (after a particularly passionate session) whether she had remembered to file her W-2. He also happened to be married, which may have partially accounted for her sudden decision, although she did not normally consider this an excluding factor. She did not, in fact, know what specific rules governed her morality or lack of it, except a basic rule of survival which advised her never to get pregnant.

Getting pregnant, according to Gertie, was one of the most horrible misfortunes that could ever befall a woman. "You were such a cranky baby, Sally darling, kept me up half the night, my milk wouldn't flow, my breasts were always hurting, and besides your father wanted a boy"—which translated from the dubious German-Austrian-Serbian meant "I, *Gertie,* wanted a boy." In any case, the advice had stuck. It was bad to get pregnant under the best of circumstances, but tragic to get pregnant if you did not happen to have a husband. Since Sally did not happen to have a husband, nor particularly want one, she had immediately after her encounter with the budding Schenectady English teacher, and without any fuss or bother, rushed off to buy herself a diaphragm. (In later years, upon reading Mary McCarthy's precious "peccary" anecdote, she had said aloud, "Oh, how cutesy-cute!") Seven months ago, when she first took up with the internal revenue agent recently dispossessed, she abandoned the diaphragm in favor of birth control tablets, which she still religiously swallowed each morning. In one of her customary fishing expeditions, Gertie had asked what she thought of these new birth control pills, and Sally had replied, lying with a gracious blush, that she possessed no knowledge whatever of them. Her mother stuffed a dried apricot into her mouth, nodded her head sagely, and said, "They grow beards on women," and Sally almost brought her hand unconsciously to her chin.

She suddenly remembered, there was a time, she remembered, she could see, there was, it was the basement of a department store somewhere in Manhattan, a twelve-year-old girl trying on coats while her mother sat and watched, Gertrude Kirsch with her hands folded over her pocketbook, Sally trying on garment after garment for her approval. There was a time, it overlapped this silent shabby Fourteenth Street office, the pink coat suddenly and magically appearing on the rack, how had she missed it before? She touched the cloth, she lifted the coat from its hanger and held it tentatively for just a moment before putting it on. Gertrude Kirsch sat in silent expectation, her hands folded on her pocketbook. Sally came toward her hesitantly and executed a brief model's turn, elbows against her sides, arms up, fingers spread in delicate supplication. Quietly, she asked, "How do I look, Mama? Make believe I'm a person."

Hadad lighted the fresh cigarette from the butt of the old

one, and then looked for an ash tray. Sally pushed one across the desk.

"Why?" Hadad asked.

"Why what?" she said, but of course she knew what he meant and had wondered the same thing the moment he came into the office and began telling his tale.

"Why does he pick on me, your boy friend?"

"He's not my boy friend," Sally said, and then wondered about that, too.

"He is a big man."

"Yes."

"A big lawyer."

"Yes."

"Why me, a bricklayer? Was someone killed in this *big* accident, *no,*" he said, and again waved the skywriting cigarette. "Was someone serious injured, *no.* Is there enormous damage to the vehicles, *no.* Anyhow, I have insurance, the insurance will pay."

"Yes, Mr. Hadad, but . . ."

"Why does he make a stink?"

"I have no idea."

"Your own boy friend, you have no idea?"

"I only know Mr. Willow casually," Sally said, and felt immediately foolish. "I really don't know why he's . . . he's bringing this pressure to bear."

"Persecution," Hadad said. "Is he a Jew?"

"No," Sally answered.

Hadad shrugged. "You will help me?"

"How?"

"You will talk to him?"

"About what?"

"About he will leave me alone," Hadad said. "I do not wish to go to prison. I do not wish to pay five hundred dollars. I do not wish trouble of any kind. It was a dark night, it was anyone could have an accident, why does he pick on me? I am small beans. What does he want? My license, my living, my life? What does he *want* from me, this man?"

"I don't know," Sally said.

"Is there even a case?" Hadad asked. "Can there be criminal business here? Is it possible I can go to prison?"

"I don't know that, either. I'd have to read the law."

"I will pay you."

"For what?"

"For help, for advice, for salvation."

"I don't want your money, Mr. Hadad," Sally said.

"I am not a rich man, but I have some aside. I can pay."

"There's nothing to pay me for."

"You will talk to him?"

"I'll try."

"Ask him to stop," Hadad said, and then curiously added, "This is America."

They came back into the courtroom, both sides, plaintiff and defendants, considerably refreshed by their brief recess. They had exchanged words of reassurance, each to each, the plaintiff certain that Jonah Willow had extended himself beyond reasonable limits, introducing a plethora of documents that had only confused and bored the judge; the defendants convinced that Sidney Brackman had objected far too often and far too strenuously, irritating McIntyre and jeopardizing the case for the plaintiff. Brackman had told his client that he could read with fair accuracy the reactions of any judge, and he was certain McIntyre was beginning to lean more and more in their favor. Willow, on the other hand, assured his witness that he was coming over with dignity and calm, impressing the judge with his quiet integrity and his innate honesty.

So they all came back ready to engage each other in combat once again, seemingly forgetting that the real battle had been fought a long time ago, fought when Constantine committed his play to paper, fought when Driscoll later wrote his book. There was the scent of victory in the air, and both sides sniffed of it, and confidently surmised it was intended for their nostrils alone. Driscoll, after Jonah's peptalk in the corridor outside, felt certain that the trial was going their way, and that if no one involved in the defense brought up the matter of the 105th Division, why then no one on the plaintiff's side would mention it either. There was a curious holiday air in that courtroom when the trial resumed at 11:25 A.M. It belied the lowering clouds outside the long windows, it belied the fact that for every victor there is a loser, it belied the possibility that perhaps for every loser there is yet another loser or even a score of losers.

"Mr. Driscoll," Willow said, "before our recess, I was about to go into certain specific alleged similarities as listed on Plaintiff's Exhibit 6, which is titled Character Similarities. For the time being, I am going to bypass the character of Lieutenant Alex Cooper, who you have already testified is based on yourself. Instead, I am going to ask you about Private Colman, the troublemaker, who is certainly the second most important character in the novel, would you agree?"

"I would."

"Is Private Colman a homosexual?"

"He has had homosexual experiences."

"With whom?"

"With the major who had been commanding officer of the platoon."

"The plaintiff alleges, Mr. Driscoll, that your Private Colman is based on *two* characters in the play *Catchpole*. One of these characters is Corporal Janus, who is depicted as a troublemaker, and the other is Colonel Peterson, who is said to be a homosexual. Have you read Mr. Constantine's play?"

"I have."

"When did you read it?"

"Last month, when you gave it to me."

"Where was this, Mr. Driscoll?"

"You gave me the manuscript at your office in New York, and I took it home with me and read it there. In Vermont."

"Did you read it carefully?"

"I spent an entire weekend with it."

"Are you familiar with these two characters in the play? Corporal Janus and Colonel Peterson?"

"I am."

"Well now, wouldn't you consider it a remarkable coincidence that there are a troublemaker and a homosexual in Mr. Constantine's play, and there is a homosexual troublemaker in your book?"

"No, sir."

"Why not?"

"Because whereas Corporal Janus *is* a troublemaker, I could find no indication in the play that Colonel Peterson is a homosexual."

"He is *not,* in your estimation, a homosexual?"

"I do not think he could be considered homosexual in *anyone's* estimation."

"Has he not had homosexual experiences?"

"He has not."

"Does he not make homosexual references and allusions?"

"He does not."

"Does he not use endearing terms when talking to other men?"

"He does not."

"Did you find *any* character in the play who could be considered homosexual?"

"I did not."

"Your Honor," Brackman said, rising, "I am fully aware of Mr. Driscoll's reputation as a novelist, but I was *not* aware that he holds a degree in psychology. May I point out that what *he* considers homosexual or heterosexual may *not,* in the opinion of experts, actually be the case."

"If your Honor please," Willow said, "I believe Mr. Driscoll's testimony can be considered as competent as was Mr. Constantine's."

"Not when we are dealing with psychological matters, your Honor," Brackman insisted.

"Your Honor, we have allowed Mr. Constantine to testify that his colonel *was* a homosexual. I do not see the difference . . ."

"He *created* the character," Brackman said. "He ought to know whether or not he intended a homosexual."

"We have already agreed, Mr. Brackman, that *intent* is not on trial here," Willow said.

"I will allow the testimony," McIntyre said. "Mr. Driscoll is not offering a psychological analysis, nor does the Court consider it such. He is discussing a literary matter in literary terms. I believe even a layman can discern the difference between a homosexual and a heterosexual in a work of fiction, and I must certainly accept Mr. Driscoll as being someone considerably more advised than a layman. I will admit the testimony. Please go on."

"In other words, Mr. Driscoll, your character Colman could not have been based in part upon a homosexual colonel in *Catchpole* because no such homosexual colonel exists."

"That is correct."

"And the charge that Mr. Knowles later reverted to the original . . ."

"There was no original to which he could have reverted."

"While we are on Private Colman, we have had a great deal of testimony here about his wearing eyeglasses in the motion picture whereas he does not wear eyeglasses in your book. Corporal Janus in the play *does* wear glasses, of course, as I'm sure you noticed in your reading of *Catchpole*."

"Yes."

"How do you explain this appearance and disappearance of eyeglasses?"

"There's nothing to explain. Private Colman *does* wear glasses in my book."

"He does?" Willow asked, and turned to look at Brackman in mock surprise. "Where do you find any evidence of this, Mr. Driscoll?"

"There's a scene in which Lieutenant Cooper pulls up in a jeep, and just before he steps out, Colman takes a pair of glasses from the pocket of his blouse and puts them on to get a better look at him."

"What page does this occur on, Mr. Driscoll?"

"Page 37."

"May I add, your Honor, that there are eleven people in this courtroom at the moment, and five of us are wearing eyeglasses—almost half of the people present. In fact, Mr. Brackman's partner is one of those people."

"I wear glasses myself when I'm reading," McIntyre said, "so we can raise that number to six."

"Out of eleven, your Honor."

"I assume this is privileged, is it, Mr. Willow?" Brackman asked, and smiled.

"Merely an observation, Mr. Brackman, merely an observation."

"I do not see its relevancy."

"All right, all right, let's continue," McIntyre said.

"We have heard testimony here, Mr. Driscoll, to the effect that you named your private Peter Colman after Colonel Peterson in *Catchpole*. Is this in fact so?"

"It is not."

"How did you in fact come upon the name Peter Colman?"

"Peter is a phallic reference."

"Why would you use a phallic reference for a character who is clearly homosexual?"

"As a personal joke."

"And Colman? What is the significance of this surname?"

"It's a literary pun."

"In what way?"

"It refers to *The Iceman Cometh*."

"How?"

"The iceman in Mr. O'Neill's play means death. The character Colman in my book also means death—for the lieutenant."

"I still do not see either the connection or the pun."

"When I was a child, my mother used to tell me stories about buying ice for the icebox. She would take a wagon each morning and walk over to 96th Street, where there was a coal station. She used to buy the cake of ice there and then wheel it home. In my mind, 'iceman' and 'coal man' are identical and interchangeable. The name Colman is simply an elision of 'coal man,' which is in turn a pun on 'iceman.' "

"That's a rather complicated reference, isn't it?"

"All fictional references are complicated."

"Did you intend to—"

"Objection," Brackman said immediately.

"Sustained."

"Was this written for the reader to grasp?"

"No, sir. It was entirely personal. I did it for my own amusement."

"It was not, then, a reversal of Colonel Peterson's name."

"I had never heard of Colonel Peterson until last month when I read the play."

"You were present in this courtroom yesterday, were you not, when Chester Danton testified concerning several editorial reports made at Mitchell-Campbell?"

"I was."

"Do you recall the report made by Miss Anita Lang, the one containing suggestions about Private Colman's civilian life?"

"I do."

"And the flashbacks about his civilian life?"

"I do."

"She suggested, did she not, that there was too much emphasis on his civilian background?"

"Yes, she did."

"Did you change Colman's character in accordance with Miss Lang's suggestions?"

"I only met Miss Lang once before the book was published. I didn't know at the time that the suggestions were hers. I thought they came from Chester Danton, who was my editor at Mitchell-Campbell."

"But you did make the changes?"

"Yes, I deleted the flashbacks. There were two scenes showing his civilian life. I can recall them both very clearly, if you want me to take the Court's time to describe them."

"Very briefly, if you will."

"One of the scenes finally discarded from the novel described Colman's experience in a television studio during a rehearsal—all the hectic background, the setting of lights and cameras, the cueing-in of music, makeup men, costume people—Colman had been an actor in civilian life, you see, and this was supposed to be a rehearsal for a live drama series."

"Was this scene based on an actual experience of your own?"

"A friend of mine from Music and Art later became a set designer for television, and I once attended such a rehearsal with him, yes."

"And the other scene?"

"The second scene was between Colman and his mother, and tried to show the beginnings of his homosexuality. He's appearing in a high school play, and his mother is attending the performance, and after the play there is a short and very bitter . . . well . . . anti-mother scene, I guess you'd call it, while Colman is taking off his makeup in the dressing room. It was a good scene, and I'm sorry they asked me to cut it."

"But you did cut it."

"Yes, for the sake of the narrative flow."

"Were there any changes made in Colman's character aside from the deletion of these two scenes?"

"No. Once I hit upon the concept of him as a homosexual, the character remained more or less constant. And even after I cut those two flashbacks, his motivation was clearly understood by me, because the scenes were still there at the back of my mind."

"In other words, the flashbacks that were cut remained as a sort of underpainting?"

"Exactly."

"Referring again to Plaintiff's Exhibit 6, there is said to be a similarity between Sergeant Morley in your novel and Sergeant D'Agostino in *Catchpole*. Is Morley, in fact, based upon D'Agostino?"

"No, sir. Morley is an original creation."

"Is he based upon any real person?"

"Yes, he is based on a boy I knew at school."

"What was his name?"

"Andrew Christopher."

"Does this real name in any way account for the fictitious name you used?"

"Yes. Christopher Morley was a favorite author of mine.

The name Christopher automatically suggested Morley, and so I named the sergeant in my book Morley."

"Is Andrew Christopher still alive?"

"I don't know. I haven't seen him since we were in school together."

"Is Andrew Christopher a Negro?"

"Yes."

"Is the character Morley a Negro?"

"Yes."

"And a sergeant?"

"Yes."

"D'Agostino is also a sergeant, and a member of a minority group. How do you explain this similarity?"

"Sergeant D'Agostino is only *accidentally* a member of a minority group. Sergeant Morley is *deliberately* a Negro, for valid plot and character purposes."

"What are these valid plot and character purposes?"

"To further the conflict between the squad and the lieutenant."

"In what way?"

"By having Morley suspect the lieutenant of bigotry."

"Mr. Constantine has testified that there is a recurring thread of suspected prejudice in his play as well. Did you find this to be so?"

"No, sir."

"You did *not* find a recurring thread of suspected prejudice?"

"I did not."

"But there are references to D'Agostino being Italian, the lieutenant being white Protestant?"

"Yes, there are. But these are oblique and tangential and could not have been intended as development in a—"

"Objection, your Honor."

"Mr. Brackman?"

"We are getting into intent here, are we not?"

"Well, I won't know until I've heard the rest of his sentence," McIntyre said.

"If your Honor please, the witness has *already* used the word 'intended.'"

"Well, let's hear the rest of the sentence."

"I was only going to say that Mr. Constantine knows how to write a play, and there is ample evidence throughout that he knows how to sustain a thought and build it to a dramatic payoff. But he has not done this with D'Agostino's Italian background. The oblique references there seem intended only as incidental information."

"That's what I mean, your Honor," Brackman said. "I do not see how Mr. Driscoll can possibly know or even surmise what Mr. Constantine's intentions were."

"Yes," McIntyre said. "Well." He was silent for a moment. Then he said, "I think we will have to strike both the question and the answer, Mr. Willow."

Willow sighed and then said, "Mr. Driscoll, it has been alleged that the character called Kenworthy in your novel is based upon the character called Franklin in *Catchpole?* Is this in fact so?"

"No, sir."

"Both these men are addicted to the use of obscene language, are they not?"

"No. Again, we come to intent." Driscoll paused. "I really don't know how I can explain this without talking about *why* these characters are in the separate works."

"Your Honor?"

"Yes, Mr. Willow."

"May the witness proceed?"

"I have heard no objection."

"I most strenuously *will* object, your Honor, if he plans to analyze the thought processes of another man."

"He only plans to compare the characters, your Honor."

"That's not what he said."

"Mr. Driscoll?"

"I would have to go into intent."

"In that case, I would object," Brackman said.

"Well now," McIntyre said, and again was silent. "Will

this take the same form as the testimony you just gave concerning bigotry and so on?"

"I would imagine so."

"It does seem to me, Mr. Brackman, that we allowed your witness a similar latitude in his testimony."

"We did not permit him to testify as to intent, your Honor."

"Not in the strictest meaning of the word, perhaps. But was he not, for example, when discussing the reversal of Colonel Peterson's name to form Peter Colman's name, was he not then *really* analyzing Mr. Driscoll's intent?"

"He was basing his analysis on the actual works, your Honor, and not on what was intended."

"He may not have used the word 'intent,' but surely he was telling us that Mr. Driscoll *intended* an anagram."

"If your Honor please, I feel we are beginning to confuse execution with intent. We are here to compare the two works. In that manner alone can we determine whether or not an act of piracy was committed."

"But wouldn't it be helpful if we knew the intent as well?"

"Your Honor, it seems to me that a man can state in print that white is white, and then later claim he really intended to state that *black* is white, and the intent and the execution would be in direct contradiction."

"But isn't it important for us to know what both these men were *trying* to accomplish?"

"Not in a court of law, if your Honor please. We are not, after all, professional book or play reviewers."

"I think we *are* reviewing these works, nonetheless, Mr. Brackman."

"Only in an attempt to prove or disprove similarities. I know your Honor recognizes the gravity of this contest, and I'm certain the Court would not wish to compare these proceedings to something as trivial as the reviewing of books and plays."

"On the contrary, Mr. Brackman, we may be getting very close to the heart of the matter here."

"Which is what, if your Honor please?"

"What both these men were *trying* to do."

"It is our contention, your Honor, that James Driscoll was trying to do nothing more nor less than steal Mr. Constantine's play."

"And what was Mr. Constantine trying to do?"

"He was trying to write a wholly original work. Your Honor, in all frankness, I must say that anyone's comments—mine included—concerning this matter can only confuse the issue beyond understanding."

"You mean the matter of author's intent?"

"Yes, your Honor. It seems to me that it is the author's burden to make his intent clear in the execution."

"And it is the *judge's* burden to try for an understanding of both execution *and* intent."

"If that is your ruling . . ."

"That is my ruling."

"Will the record note my exception?"

"It will be noted. Proceed, Mr. Driscoll."

"I've forgotten the question," Driscoll said.

"Are both Franklin in the play and Kenworthy in your novel addicted to the use of obscene language?"

"No, sir, they are not."

"Do you accept the use of the word *bug* or its variations as a substitute for an obscenity?"

"I do."

"And you still maintain that Franklin in the play does not use obscenity?"

"He *does* use obscenity, but not excessively."

"On what do you base this?"

"On an actual count of the number of times the words *bug* or *bugging* are used in the play."

"How many times are they used?"

"The play runs one hundred and twenty pages, and is divided into three acts. Throughout the length of the play, Private Franklin uses this word a total of seven times. Compare this to *The Eve of Saint Mark,* where the word *ruttin'* is used a total of twenty-eight times during the course of the play . . ."

"Objection, your Honor," Brackman said. "We are not here to compare *Catchpole* with *The Eve of Saint Mark.*"

"Overruled, Mr. Brackman. The comparison is being made only to clarify this matter of excessive obscenity."

"How often does your character Kenworthy use obscene language in *The Paper Dragon?*"

"Every time he speaks."

"Did you count the times?"

"No."

"Moving to Plaintiff's Exhibit 5, Plot Similarities, it is alleged that in both your novel and the play the lieutenant falls in love with an Army nurse. Is this so?"

"Yes, it is."

"How do you explain the similarity?"

"I wanted to tell a love story. In order to tell a love story, I needed a woman. In a combat situation, the only possible female characters would be either a native woman or a woman connected with the services. I chose a nurse."

"Why couldn't you just as naturally have chosen a Korean girl?"

"Because this would have brought up the racial matter again, and I wanted to explore that in terms of Sergeant Morley."

"Does the nurse in *Catchpole* outrank the lieutenant?"

"Yes."

"Does the nurse in your book outrank Lieutenant Cooper?"

"Yes."

"How do you explain this?"

"The nurses in Korea were in a combat situation, and most of them were experienced officers."

"Did you meet any nurses in Korea who had been recently commissioned?"

"No."

"What was the lowest rank you came across?"

"A nurse's rank, do you mean? In Korea?"

"Yes."

"First lieutenant."

"What rank does Jan Reardon in your novel hold?"

"First lieutenant."

"Has she been in the service longer than Lieutenant Cooper?"

"Yes, a full year longer."

"And does this explain her higher rank?"

"Yes."

"It has been alleged in this same Exhibit 5 that the men in the respective squads hate their new commanding officer because someone they liked and respected had been killed by a sniper. Is this so?"

"Yes, but the sniper wasn't my idea. It was Chester Danton's."

"What was the plot development in your original version?"

"The struggle originated with Private Colman. It was strictly a personal struggle between Colman and the lieutenant. Only later did it assume larger proportions that led to the lieutenant's death."

"There had been no previous commanding officer killed by a sniper?"

"No. Besides, in the play the lieutenant is *really* responsible for the death of one of his men, and the squad's resentment is somewhat justified. In my novel, the major is killed a full month before Cooper even arrives in Korea. The resentment is solely Colman's, the struggle is strictly between the two."

"A struggle for what?"

"For . . ." Driscoll hesitated. "Survival," he said.

"Which the lieutenant loses?"

"Yes. The lieutenant is killed. What Colman finally does is to kill the lieutenant."

"Is this his plan?"

"Unconsciously, yes."

"Is this not also the plan of Corporal Janus in the play?"

"Yes."

"To murder the lieutenant?"

"Yes."

"How do they differ?"

"One is a melodrama."

"Which one?"

"The play. It is really a play about a murder conspiracy, and the events leading up to that murder and the eventual foiling of it through a series of further related events."

"Do you agree that the theme of *Catchpole* is 'The Idiocy and Foolish Waste of War'?"

"No, sir."

"What *is* the theme of *Catchpole?*"

" 'Crime Does Not Pay.' "

"And what is the theme of *The Paper Dragon?*"

"It would be difficult to express simply."

"How *would* you express it?"

"I suppose the theme is that people are capable of . . . of hurting each other beyond endurance by . . . by thoughtless and . . . ill-conceived actions."

"Like war, do you mean?"

"The war is inconsequential, it's only the background. I tried to . . . you see . . . the lieutenant knows a deep and very real love for this woman . . . the nurse . . . and this is wrecked . . . their love is destroyed by a single thoughtless act."

"But isn't it true that more than just their love is destroyed?"

"Yes, the . . . the future they might have had together."

"I'm referring, though, to the actual death of the lieutenant."

"Oh. Yes. But I saw that as symbolic."

"You did not see the nurse's deprivation as symbolic, did you?"

"No, that's real enough. She's lost him."

"Forever," Willow said.

"Yes." Driscoll paused. "Forever."

"But then, there *are* no winners in your novel, Mr. Driscoll, isn't that so?"

"Yes."

"The whole series of events, in fact, seem pointless by the end of the book."

"Yes."

"Everyone has been involved in a bitter struggle that solves nothing, a paper dragon. Moving on to Plaintiff's Exhibit 7, we are told that the 'female rifle' scene in your novel is based on the pig scene in Mr. Constantine's play. *Is* it?"

"No, it's not."

"It is alleged that these scenes are similar."

"I don't see how."

"They are both said to be sexual."

"Mr. Constantine's scene is about capturing a pig. My scene is about a woman."

"It's about stripping a rifle, isn't it?"

"No, it's about stripping a woman and taking her to bed."

"It purports to be about a rifle."

"The scene is transparently about a woman, whereas Mr. Constantine's pig scene is clearly a scene about *food*. There are no sexual allusions in it at all."

"Thank you, Mr. Driscoll," Willow said. "That is all for this witness, your Honor."

He nodded at Driscoll, smiled briefly, turned his back and walked to the defense table. Brackman took his time assembling his notes. Driscoll watched him warily. Constantine whispered something to him just before he rose from the table, and Brackman nodded and then walked toward the front of the courtroom. He pursed his lips, swallowed, looked up at Driscoll, and said, "Mr. Driscoll, if I understood your earlier testimony correctly, you said that you were an art major at the Art Students League and Pratt Institute. When did you enter Pratt?"

"In September of 1947."

"And you went into the Army in June of 1950?"

"Yes."

"Still intending to be an artist?"

"I'm sorry, what?"

"Did you plan on continuing with your art work when you got out of the service?"

"Yes."

"When did you change your mind?"

"I don't know when. I suppose it was a gradual process."

"Starting when?"

"Starting when I was at Pratt, I would imagine."

"And you entered Pratt in September of 1947?"

"Yes."

"A month before Mr. Constantine's play opened on Broadway."

"Yes."

"And that was when you began changing your mind about becoming an artist?"

"Not exactly then."

"Exactly *when?*"

"I said it was a gradual process."

"Starting in September of 1947?"

"It was a matter of beginning to gauge my own talents. There were a lot of talented people at Pratt. I began looking at my own work in terms of theirs."

"And decided to become a writer?"

"Not until much later."

"Not until *when?*"

"Sometime before I was discharged from the Army."

"So that when you returned to civilian life, you abandoned your study of art, and decided instead to take courses in writing?"

"Yes."

"You became an English major at N.Y.U.?"

"Yes."

"And I assume you took whatever creative writing courses the school had to offer."

"Yes."

"And that's where you learned to write."

"I don't know where a person learns to write."

"That is, nonetheless, where you had your formal training as a writer?"

"Yes."

"Did you begin writing for gain or profit immediately after you were graduated from N.Y.U.?"

"No."

"When did you begin writing?"

"Not until 1961."

"Four years after you were graduated."

"Yes."

"Even though you had been so splendidly prepared for a career in writing?"

"I don't know how splendidly I was prepared. I certainly didn't expect to step out of college and be acclaimed a new Hemingway."

"So you postponed writing your novel, is that correct?"

"Yes."

"Until you felt certain you *would* be acclaimed a Hemingway?"

"No, until I felt I could write the book I *wanted* to write. My *own* book. Not a Hemingway book, or anyone else's book."

"Had you written anything before you started your novel?"

"In college, yes."

"Was any work of yours published?"

"No."

"What sort of writing did you do in college?"

"Short stories mostly."

"Never a novel?"

"No."

"*The Paper Dragon* was your first novel."

"Yes."

"Your only novel."

"Yes."

"Did you submit any of your stories for publication while you were in college?"

"No."

"Why not?"

"They weren't good enough."

"Did you feel *The Paper Dragon* was good enough for publication?"

"Obviously, I did. I wouldn't have sent it out if I hadn't."

"Suddenly, out of the blue, you wrote a novel—never having written one before—and it was good enough for publication. In fact, according to Chester Danton's testimony yesterday, 'the remarkable thing about the book was that it was so good and so fully realized that there were very few suggestions an editor *could* make.' Do you agree with Mr. Danton?"

"In what way?"

"That the book was remarkable in its quality and in its realization."

"I would have no way of judging my own work."

"You seem perfectly capable of judging Mr. Constantine's work."

"But not my own."

"Do you think many first novels come to a publisher 'so good and so fully realized'?"

"I don't know."

"What would you guess?"

"Your Honor, the witness has already stated that he does not know."

"Sustained."

"Did you take any courses at N.Y.U. on the writing of a novel?"

"No."

"You just sat down to write one."

"Most novels are written by people who just sit down to write them."

"And they come out of the typewriter 'so good and so fully realized,' is that correct?"

"I don't know how anyone else's novel comes out of the typewriter."

"Were you satisfied with the way *yours* came out of the typewriter?"

"Not wholly. But it was the best I could do at the time."

"Can you do better now?"

"I don't know."

"The fact is, you haven't written anything since *The Paper Dragon,* have you?"

"No, I haven't."

"No other novels, no short stories?"

"Nothing," Driscoll said.

"Do you *plan* to write anything else?"

"No."

"But you're a writer, aren't you?"

"I'm a Vermont farmer."

"I thought you were a writer."

"You've been misinformed."

"Apparently," Brackman said, and smiled. "Mr. Driscoll, you have testified that Lieutenant Alex Driscoll . . ."

"Lieutenant Alex *Cooper.*"

"Yes, forgive me, Lieutenant *Cooper* is an idealized version of yourself, is that true?"

"Yes."

"He is not entirely yourself?"

"Not entirely."

"Because, for example, Lieutenant Cooper is killed in the next to last chapter of your novel, and you, sir, are obviously not dead."

"Obviously not."

"So he is only partially based on yourself?"

"Yes."

"Would it be fair to say that somewhere along the line he ceases to be you?"

"Yes, it would be fair to say that."

"Mr. Brackman, I'm sorry I must interrupt you at this point," McIntyre said, "but it's exactly noon, and I think we should recess for lunch."

13

THE TWO MEN had hot dogs and orange drinks at the Nedick's on Duane, and then walked up Centre Street, past the County Court House and the Criminal Courts Building, and then onto Baxter and Bayard and into Chinatown. The weather was not mild—there was in fact a strong wind blowing—but it seemed almost balmy in contrast to yesterday's bitter fierceness. As they turned into Mott Street, Arthur felt for the moment as though he were entering an actual Chinese street in a Chinese city—Shanghai or Tientsin, Canton or Soochow—the undecipherable Chinese calligraphs, the quiet watchful men in doorways, hands tucked into their armpits, exotic women rushing by in abbreviated coats and slit skirts, pushing shopping carts or carrying baskets, the snug, tight, intimate landscape of winter in a foreign place, where the language is strange and the faces are alien and the only link with past experience is the weather. The sudden appearance of a grinning cardboard Santa Claus in a window brimming with ivory and jade shattered the illusion, brought once more into focus the strictly Anglo-Saxon proceedings downtown and the presence of Kent Mercer at his side, walking briskly and prattling on about the horror of the ghetto and these poor underprivileged Orientals. Did Arthur know there was no juvenile delinquency among the Chinese? The women pushed their shopping carts. Somewhere, he could smell roasting pork. He thought suddenly of Lamb's *Dissertation,* and then heard Kent's voice again, the slightly lilting monotony of it, the strident note that told Arthur he was about to get to the point, at last.

". . . in the middle of a *trial* and everything, but I thought I *should* see you before this thing came to a head. That's why I called you this morning, Arthur."

"Um-huh," Arthur said.

"I understand they've made some suggestions concerning the play," Kent said.

"That's right."

"At least, that's what Oscar told me."

"Yes, they made some suggestions."

"What do you plan to do?" Kent asked.

"I don't know."

"Will you make the changes?"

"I don't know."

"Well, I don't like to *press* this, Arthur, nor do I wish to risk that *terrible* look you get in your eyes whenever . . ."

"I don't get a terrible look, Kent."

". . . whenever you're angry," Kent said, and smiled. "Oh, you *know* you do, Arthur. You're a completely menacing person when you're crossed."

"Well," Arthur said, and sighed.

"But I *would* like to know what your plans are because—I might as well be frank, Arthur—I've *got* to know where we're going with this play."

"Why?"

"I've got to know whether it's going to be done."

"It'll be done," Arthur said.

"Do you mean you've decided to make the changes?"

"Well, no, not yet."

"Did the changes sound reasonable to you?"

"No."

"Not at *all?*"

"Well, some of them maybe."

"Which ones?"

"I don't remember."

"Arthur, I'm going to be frank with you," Kent said, and stopped in front of a candy store, and turned to face Arthur, and put one hand on his arm. "I've always been frank with you, you've got to admit that."

"Yes, you have."

"Arthur, you *must* make those changes."

"Why?"

"Because Hester won't take the part unless you do. And if Hester doesn't take the part, the play will *not* be produced. I'm being frank with you."

"All right."

"All right what?"

"All right, you're being frank with me."

"*Will* you make the changes?"

"Was this Oscar's idea?" Arthur asked suddenly.

"What?"

"This. Your calling me, this little talk."

Inside the candy store, an old Chinese woman with her hair pulled back tightly into a knot, was handing a coin across the counter and smiling at the proprietor. Again, the feeling of strangeness came over Arthur; he had never seen a woman like this one before, her clothes had been stitched in Singapore, her hair had been greased with hummingbird fat by a hairdresser who traveled from province to province, he knew she had just consumed a rare exotic drink and was now paying for it in foreign coin. Probably an egg cream, he thought, and smiled, and saw that Kent thought the smile was directed at him and was offended by it.

"You needn't look so smugly superior," Kent said, "because this was definitely *not* Oscar's idea. This was my own idea. I've got to think of myself, too, Arthur, I can't *continually* think of everyone *else* involved in this project."

"I understand that."

"I've been offered certain other things and, I'm being frank, some of them look very attractive to me. I've got to give people a yes or no answer, Arthur, I'm sure you can understand that."

"Of course."

"And this has nothing to do with your play, believe me. I love your play, you know that. But I've got my own career to think of, you know how it is with these things. If you don't say yes or no, people think you're not interested and begin looking elsewhere. There are only so many jobs, Arthur, and I don't have to tell you how many directors."

"I see."

"So what do you plan to do?"

"I don't know."

"How well do you know Hester Miers?"

"Only casually," Arthur said.

"You mean she hasn't yet made a grab for your jewels?" Kent said, and laughed. "I'm surprised, really."

"What about her?" Arthur said.

"I'm told she's very good in bed," Kent went on, unmindful of Arthur's tone. "She gives magnificent head," he said, and laughed again.

Arthur stared at Kent for a moment, and then abruptly began walking away from him. Kent stood rooted to the sidewalk. The door behind him opened, and the Chinese woman came out, shuffling past Kent, who rolled his eyes heavenward in a gesture of despair that Arthur missed, and then quickened his pace to catch up with him.

"She's a very *good* actress, Arthur," he said solemnly.

"I know."

"And I think she could be right for Carol."

"Sure, if we make her twenty-three instead of nineteen, and change her to a social worker instead of a college girl, and make her father the head of General Motors, and . . ."

"Well, I think you're exaggerating . . ."

". . . make her a whore besides."

"What?"

"Instead of a virgin."

"No one suggested she be made a whore."

"No, not exactly."

"Not in *any* respect, Arthur."

"Okay, not in *any* respect."

"I love the faces on these Chinese children, don't you?"

"Yeah."

"*One* affair was what they suggested, actually," Kent said.

"I know."

"*Every*body's had at least one affair," Kent said, and shrugged.

"But not Carol."

"Art need not imitate life quite so closely, need it?" Kent asked.

"I see they told you she's based on my sister."

"Yes. There's nothing wrong with that."

"I should hope not."

"But at the same time . . ."

"At the same time, let's make all the changes."

"I'm being frank with you, Arthur."

"Sure you are. You want a job."

"Not *any* job, Arthur. I want *this* job. But I'll tell you frankly, if I thought *this* job was in danger of evaporating, I would most *certainly* take another one."

"If I win this case . . ."

"What?"

"Nothing."

"Let's not talk about personal matters right now, Arthur."

"My play *is* a personal matter. To me."

"I'm sure it is. And to *me,* too. Which is why I hate to see it scuttled."

"There are other actresses."

Kent sighed. The sigh encompassed a lifetime of talking to writers and producers and actors, the sigh was one of sorrow and wisdom, sorrow because he had to give this same speech again to a writer intent on suicide, wisdom because he knew without doubt that what he was going to say was incontrovertible and stark and absolutely valid. The sigh was a tired one; Arthur heard something in it that compelled him to listen to Kent for perhaps the first time during their walk.

"Arthur, I know a little more about this business than you do," Kent said. "I've been in it for close to forty years now, as actor and director both, and I can tell you frankly that there's a time to stop *thinking* about a project, and a time to begin *moving* on it. At this moment, your play and the people involved in it are ready to *move,* the whole project has a *feel* to it, a sense of growing *power,* a certainty that all the planets are finally in conjunction and that we are about to *move,* Arthur, we are about to get *moving.* All you have to do is make those changes, agree to make those changes, and the thing will start humming and ticking, they'll spring Hester out of that actor's graveyard, she'll sign a contract, the backers will be fighting to get a piece of the action, and your play will be *done.* That's the feeling I get, that's what forty years of theater experience is telling me right now. It's telling me to *move,* Arthur, to get this thing on its feet and *moving.* Because if we don't, Arthur, if we allow Hester to get away, your play will *not* be produced by Selig and Stern. They've exhausted their people, Arthur, they cannot raise the money, they will let the option expire."

"There are other producers."

"Arthur, I've been in this business too long, really. Oh, yes, there are the success stories about the plays that have made the rounds of four *hundred* producers, and lo and behold the four-hundred-and-*first* snaps it up and it becomes a smash hit and runs for fourteen years and makes everyone involved a millionaire. I have heard all those stories, Arthur, because I've been around a long long time, I was born in the proverbial trunk. But I can tell you that if you don't move when everything is right for moving, things may *never* be right again, things may *never* come to that exact spot in time and space again."

"Maybe I'm willing to take that chance."

"You'd be smarter to compromise a little, Arthur."

"I've been compromising a little all my life," Arthur said.

"Then do it one more time. Make the changes. There'll be God knows how many revisions during rehearsal, anyway. The thing may get changed right back to what it was originally."

"Come on, Kent."

"All right, it won't, but will that be such a great loss? No one's trying to *corrupt* your play, Arthur. They're only trying to *improve* it."

"They're trying to change it, Kent."

"But only to improve it."

"No, only to change it. Only to make it theirs and not mine. Goddamn it, Kent, this is *still my play.*"

"I've got news for you, Arthur. Without an actress, it isn't a play at all, yours or anybody's."

"No? Then what is it?"

"A manuscript."

"There are plenty of actresses around. We can always get—"

"No, Arthur."

They stopped on the sidewalk and silently turned to face each other. In the window behind Kent, a plaster statue of the Virgin Mary knelt beside a cradle bearing the infant Jesus. To the left of the manger, a large Chinese calendar hung, a slant-eyed girl in a bathing suit looking back over her left shoulder. To the right of the manger, alternating green and red cardboard letters spelled out the words MERRY XMAS, dangling from a string.

"This is the time," Kent said. *"Now!* Either *make* the changes, Arthur, or resign yourself to the fact that your play will never be *done."*

"I don't know," Arthur said.

"I'm being frank with you."

It's because I'm a Negro from Harlem, Norman Sheppard thought, and looked again at Ebie Driscoll and could not shake his feeling of discomfort. It's because I know the lady is from the Deep South, suh, and I am merely projecting her own discomfort onto myself. She is not used to dining with Nigras, suh, and this is why she constantly brushes that strand of blond hair away from her cheek, a gesture I have seen her perform a hundred times since this trial began, a nervous mannerism, that's all. And quite naturally, her nervousness has leaped across the table and I, being a sensitive person with a lot of natural rhythm, am reacting to it. I'll have to report this to Dr. Maloney on Monday, he'll find it very interesting. "What do you think about it, Mr. Sheppard?" he will ask, and I will then try to separate this extraordinary feeling of *déjà vu* from the very ordinary complicated feelings surrounding it, such as why I might feel uncomfortable in the presence of any beautiful, blond, white woman from Alabama even if I didn't think we'd met someplace before (a likely possibility, to be sure) even if I didn't think I knew her. Or, to be more exact, since Dr. Maloney insists on exactitude, not only do I feel I know Mrs. James Driscoll, but I further feel I know her exceptionally well. Or to be precise, Dr. Maloney, I feel the young lady and I have been intimate, yes, how about that for a clue to the Negro Revolution? I will bet you any amount of money, Dr. Maloney, that she has a small crescent-shaped scar on her thigh, and that she got it from a piece of broken glass at the base of a statue or something in her home town, what do you make of that, Dr. Maloney? "Well," he will reply, "what do *you* make of it, Mr. Sheppard?"

"You came over very well," he said to Driscoll. "I think McIntyre was impressed."

"I hope so," Driscoll answered.

Now how would I know about a crescent-shaped scar on the lady's thigh when I have never *seen* the lady's thigh? How did I know she was going to be left-handed even before I saw her pick up her utensils at lunch the other day, tell me that, Dr. Maloney. It *is* true, yes, Doctor, that I myself am left-handed and therefore am constantly on the alert for members of the race, human, who are similarly endowed, they being acknowledged leaders whatever their color or religion. Michelangelo was left-handed, did you know that? Kim Novak, as it happens, is left-handed. Mrs. James Driscoll is also left-handed, which fact I knew *before* I knew it, that's exactly what I mean about this *déjà vu* phenomenon, doctor. Am I making myself clear, or is it possible that all I want to do is lay Ebie Driscoll? "Well, let's examine that, Mr. Sheppard," he will say.

Ebie Driscoll brushed the same strand of hair away from her cheek. There it is again, Norman thought, and I knew she would do it even before she did it the first time we met, felt I had seen her do it a thousand times before that. Or the way she tilts her head, look, just before she's going to say something, look, telegraphing her words, here it comes, she is about to speak, "May I have the salt, please?" Ebie asked. Norman handed her the salt and pepper shakers together, and intuitively knew she would say exactly what she said next, "No, just the salt, please." He frowned and turned his attention back to Driscoll, convinced that he was possessed of extrasensory powers and determined to put them to better use, like perhaps opening his own numbers bank in Harlem and taking bets only on numbers he knew would lose, not a bad thought.

"I think Jonah's approach was the proper one," he said. "Tracing the creative process."

"Mmmm," Driscoll said.

"That's really his forte, you know, hitting on the right approach. That's not as easy as it may sound. A lot of lawyers commit themselves to the wrong strategy from the beginning. Jonah's never done that to my recollection, and he's certainly had some difficult cases over the years."

"Has he?"

"Oh, sure," Norman said. "I didn't join the firm until after the San Quentin case, of course, but even since . . ."

"What San Quentin case?"

"The one with the guard. Didn't you follow it?"

"No."

"It was in all the papers."

"I must have missed it somehow."

"Well," Norman said, plunging on despite a detected note of sarcasm in Driscoll's voice, "a prisoner there was serving a life term—an ax murderer no less, you can imagine the kind of sympathy he aroused—and one of the guards kept bothering him, so he picked up a fork in the dining room one day and stuck it in the guard's throat."

"He killed him?" Ebie asked.

"Yes."

"Illlffff," she said, and pulled a face, and the expression and the grimace were both familiar, he knew them from somewhere, but where? How come I pay you thirty dollars an hour, Dr. Maloney, and all you can tell me is that I must adjust as a Negro in a hostile society? Why can't you explain all these inscrutable things that keep happening to me?

"It was a mess," Norman said, "horrible case, but Jonah took it on. He's had a lot of tough ones. Listen, this one isn't such a cream puff, either." On impulse, he turned to Ebie and said, "Have you ever been up to Harlem, Mrs. Driscoll?"

"Never," she replied.

"Well," he said, and cocked his head to one side, and thought She's never been to Harlem, Dr. Maloney, so it isn't even possible we met in Small's Paradise or any of those other quaint places. "You ought to take her up to Harlem sometime, Jimmy," he said, and smiled.

"Invite us," Ebie said.

"I will."

"Do."

"If you mean it, I *will* invite you."

"I mean it," Ebie said.

"Ebie always means what she says, isn't that true?" Driscoll said.

His wife did not answer. She busied herself with her plate instead, cutting another piece of steak, and then meticulously and carefully placed her knife at the rear of the plate, as if this simple act required all her concentration.

"She's straightforward and honest," Driscoll said, staring at her with a cold, pained smile on his face. "It would hurt Ebie to lie, wouldn't it, Ebie?"

"Shut up, Dris," she said flatly, without looking at him, and the table went silent. Norman saw the anger that flared in Driscoll's eyes, and suddenly wondered whether he had misinterpreted the Harlem invitation. Here we are at the crux again, Dr. Maloney, here we are getting right down to the heart of the old matter, which is: Can a Negro Boy from Harlem Find Happiness with a White Woman in a Small Mining Town? And the answer is No, not if Whitey thinks you are eventually going to corral *all* of his women, leaving him nary a soul to set his table or warm his bed. Understand, Jimmy, understand Mr. Driscoll, suh, that I did not intend my invitation for your wife alone, I intended it to include yourself, suh. "Well, let us examine that," Dr. Maloney will say, "especially in the light of your feeling that you and this woman have been intimate. Tell me again about this small scar on her thigh, crescent-shaped, did you say?"

Casually, and without looking at either Driscoll or his wife, Norman said, "In any case, Jonah's approach is the right one, and it's plain to both of us that you're holding your own with Brackman."

"It didn't feel that way," Driscoll said. He addressed the words to Norman, but he was still staring at his wife.

"Don't let him scare you," Norman said. "All you have to remember is that McIntyre isn't an idiot. He'll see this as clearly as the rest of us do."

"Mmm," Driscoll said.

"I'll tell you how *I* know you didn't steal that play."

"How?"

"The patterns."

"Meaning?"

"The play and the book have entirely different patterns," Norman said, completely aware that neither of them were the least bit interested in what he was saying, but convinced he had to say *something,* anything, to avert a homicide right here at the table, and then perversely deciding he would ask Mrs. Driscoll whether she still had that cute little crescent-shaped scar on her thigh, and then deciding against it. I know, Dr. Maloney, I'm chicken, I'm afraid of the white man. Has it ever occured to you, Dr. Maloney, that *you* are a white man and that I am paying you for the privilege of informing you about how a Negro feels about white men like yourself? I know, I know, I'm paying you because I'm afraid of you too, man, you can't win. He sighed and said, "The patterns are obvious to anyone who's read both works carefully."

"Have *you* read them carefully, Mr. Sheppard?" Ebie asked.

"I read them both twice."

"And they're both about war, aren't they?" she asked, and looked up at her husband.

"Yes," Norman said, "but that's only the superficial pattern. I'm talking about something else. Look, there's a pattern to a bullfight, too. It never changes, it's always the same, it's timeless. But the *bulls* are different, and the *men* are different, and what happens each time is different from what happened the time before, even though the sequence of events may be identical. Or take a trial, for that matter, take any court case. Nothing changes there, does it? All rise, and the judge comes in, and the clerk tells us who the plaintiff is and who's defending, and the witnesses come up, and are sworn in and examined and cross-examined, all prescribed and tight, all according to strict rules and regulations—a pattern conceived and executed by men. It's my personal theory that *all* the civilized structures men create *have* to be patterned because life itself is so formless."

"I don't agree with that," Driscoll said.

"You don't think life is formless? Coincidental? Even inconclusive?"

"It's certainly not inconclusive. It ends."

"Who says an *end* is a *conclusion?*"

"Webster."

"What the hell did *he* know? All he did was give us a formal pattern for our language, which is exactly what I'm talking about. We *have* to have these patterns. Life would be unendurable otherwise. Look, the logical conclusion for life *is* death, isn't it—formless, mysterious, inexplicable? But do we accept it? No. We invent another pattern, an *after*life, a complex of heaven and hell, thereby extending life, and creating a concept we can hope to understand. We set up rules and regulations for everything, the same way *you* did when you were writing your novel, the same way Constantine did when he was writing his play. A pattern. A logical structure. You even went a step further by laying out a timetable for yourself, target dates and word goals, superimposing a *second* pattern upon the pattern already established for your novel. You had to know that at least the task would be conclusive."

"What do you mean?"

"The pattern you'd established for your book was inconclusive, Jimmy. You know that. The novel simply ends."

"It's conclusive, all right," Ebie said. "Perhaps you didn't understand it."

"I think I understood it."

"Perhaps not," she said. "In many respects, you see, *The Paper Dragon* is a mystery."

"What do you mean?"

"Just that it's a mystery," she said, and shrugged, and glanced at her husband.

"*Any* good novel is a mystery," Norman said.

"I don't mean a mystery *story,*" Ebie answered.

"What *do* you mean?" Driscoll asked sharply.

"A book with a key."

"Like a diary?" Norman asked, and smiled.

"Yes," Ebie answered unsmilingly. "Like a diary."

"I wish *my* diary could earn as much money for me," Norman said.

"I think my wife is trying to say that all fiction is personalized fantasy. In that respect . . ."

"No, that's *not* what I'm trying to say."

"But that's it precisely," Norman said, leaning forward. "That's why the two works are so very different, because one is exclusively *Constantine's* fantasy, and the other is exclusively *yours.* The patterns are as different as your fingerprints."

"What about the 105th?" Ebie asked, and the table went silent again.

"Patterns are created by humans," Norman said at last. "The 105th is a human coincidence, pure and simple."

Ebie's eyes met her husband's, but she said nothing.

Sidney Brackman ate quickly and alone, and then went out into the street to rehearse his plan, deciding again to go ahead with it, and then deciding almost immediately that he was behaving foolishly again and in a manner that could only incur Chickie's wrath. She had said it last night, of course, and she'd been absolutely right, was he going to distrust her even after they were married? What kind of foundation was that, how could two people live and grow together if they did not trust each other?

He supposed there was a Jerome Courtlandt, and he supposed the agency really was planning a trip for him, but it seemed very coincidental to him, well, what the hell, life was full of coincidences, still it seemed very coincidental to him that Jerome Courtlandt in his tan Cadillac just happened to be on the way to the agency at closing time, just happened to pick up the two girls and, according to Chickie's testimony, drop them off at a restaurant. Well, why not? It had been a bitter night, thank God the temperature was a little milder today, it looked like rain, and how was Courtlandt to know what time the agency closed? Still, it was rather late to be heading there, well no, not if he thought the agency was open. And she had, after all, *told* Sidney about this Courtlandt fellow, she wouldn't have mentioned his name if there were anything funny about it, would she? Of course not. So why had he conceived his ridiculous plan, and why was he intent now on putting it into action? He either believed the girl or he didn't, trusted her or didn't. And why would she jeopardize their very good relationship, a relationship that could only get better once he won the case, once he came into his share of what the Court awarded Arthur, once they were married, he would have to call.

No, don't, he thought. Don't ask for trouble. Leave well enough alone. You're going to marry this girl, leave well enough alone.

He found a telephone booth in the drugstore on the next corner. He lingered outside the booth while a woman chattered interminably with someone she kept calling *"Boon*dy," and then went to the Manhattan directory only after the woman had vacated the booth. He hesitated before opening the book, turned to the C's and hesitated again, closed the book and walked directly out of the drugstore and into the street, it still looked like rain.

I'm doing the best thing, he thought. Why would I want to check up on her, for God's sake, she told me what it was all about, didn't she, she even told me the man's name, Jerome Courtlandt, would she have given me his name if there'd been anything to hide? He spotted a bar in the middle of Murray Street, quickly turned right, and went into it. There were a lot of colored girls scattered at the tables, eating lunch and drinking beer, girls who worked in the various municipal offices in the area, he supposed—what would New York City do without its colored civil service employees, sink into the ocean, that's what. The juke box was playing a lovely melody, he could not place it, one of the new things. He had stopped remembering the tunes or words to songs when he was eighteen, and had always considered it a loss. The phone booth was at the end of the bar. A lighted sign above it advertised Miller's High Life. By the light of the sign, he searched the Manhattan directory and found a listing for Courtlandt, Jerome, on East 36th Street, well, he exists, he thought, and closed the book. He stood undecided for a moment. The bartender was watching him. He opened the book again, found the listing again, memorized the number, and went into the booth to dial it.

He dialed the first two numbers, and then hung up.

His dime clattered into the return chute.

He retrieved the coin, put it into his pocket, sat in the booth a moment longer, rose, opened the door, closed the door again, sat, took the dime from his pocket, lifted the receiver from its cradle, inserted the dime into the coin slot, heard the dial tone humming against his ear, and quickly dialed the number. He could hear the phone on the other end ringing once, twice, three times . . .

"Hello?" a man's voice said.

"May I speak to Mr. Courtlandt, please?" Sidney asked.

"This is he."

"Mr. Courtlandt, this is Mr. Simmons of Trans World Airlines."

"Yes?"

"About your European trip," Sidney said. His heart was pounding. He was certain his lie had already been detected, certain Courtlandt would instantly call his bluff.

"Yes?" Courtlandt said. There was a pause. "Trans *World* Airlines, did you say?"

"Yes."

"I don't understand. I thought we were flying Pan Am."

"Well, there seems to be some confusion about the booking," Sidney said.

"Why don't you call the agency?" Courtlandt suggested. "I'm sure they can straighten it out."

"What agency would that be?"

"Travel Time on Madison Avenue."

"Thank you, sir."

"I'm sure they said Pan Am. How'd this happen, anyway?"

"Probably a duplicate booking. We'll straighten it out, sir, don't worry about it."

"Okay."

"Thank you, sir."

"Thank you for calling," Courtlandt said, and hung up.

Sidney immediately replaced the receiver on its cradle and sat with his eyes squeezed shut, trying to catch his breath. All right, it was true. He was their client, he was taking a trip, it was true, it was true. He would call Chickie and apologize immediately, tell her he loved her, tell her he trusted her. Well, he couldn't apologize, he didn't want her to know he'd called Courtlandt. But he'd tell her he loved her and trusted her, that was what he'd do. He found another dime in his pocket, put it into the slot, and quickly dialed the agency. Ruth McCutcheon answered the phone.

"Travel Time," she said, "good afternoon."

"Good afternoon," he said, "may I speak to Miss Brown, please?"

"She's out to lunch right now," Ruth said. "May I help you?"

"Well, no, I don't think so," he said, and was about to hang up.

"Would you like to leave a message?" she asked. "May I say who called?"

"Yes, this is . . ." He hesitated. She had not recognized his voice; she did not know who he was. In the three seconds it took him to make up his mind, he did not even consider the fact that he was intuitively behaving like a lawyer, putting to practical use the years of experience he had had in courtrooms, covering ground already covered, stating and restating the same point, examining and re-examining, driving for the complete truth where only the partial truth was known. He knew only that he possessed information now, he had received information from Mr. Jerome Courtlandt, and that he could use this information to learn the whole truth, three seconds to make a decision, nothing but the truth, three seconds in which to conceive a strategy.

"This is Pan American Airlines," he said.

"Yes, well, this is Miss Brown's partner," Ruth said, accepting the lie.

"I see." He hesitated again. Let it go, he thought. Leave well enough alone. "I'm calling to verify a flight," he said.

"Yes?"

"For Mr. Jerome Courtlandt."

"That's been verified already," Ruth said.

"Not according to my information."

"I handled it myself," Ruth said.

"I'm sorry, but there's obviously been an error."

Ruth sighed. "I don't know why everything always has to be done six times," she said. "All right, let's get it over with."

"Which flight *is* that?" Sidney asked.

"Saturday morning. I haven't got the number right before me. Don't *you* have the number?"

"To London, is that?" Sidney said.

"No, to Rome. Oh, *boy,*" Ruth said. "It's four seats to Rome on Saturday morning, the nine forty-five flight. Just a minute, I'll get the flight number for you. Oh, boy."

He heard the clatter of the receiver on the desk, heard the clicking of high heels across a hard floor, heard another phone ringing somewhere in the distance, "Travel Time, good afternoon." He waited a moment longer. He could hear her indistinctly in the background. He did not know what further information he needed or required. Courtlandt was obviously leaving for Italy, they were obviously handling the trip for him, there was nothing more to know.

He hung up abruptly and came out of the booth, oddly unsatisfied.

They talked about Christmas gifts during lunch, exchanging ideas about the people on their lists, but she had the feeling Jonah's mind was elsewhere, and her own thoughts were about the little Egyptian who had come to her office that morning. They walked up Broadway afterwards, stopping now and then to inspect the wares displayed in each holiday window. There were decorated Christmas trees everywhere, and on each corner a Santa Claus despondently shook his bell at the passing crowd. On Park Place, a Salvation Army band was playing "Adeste Fidelis." The snow underfoot had turned to slush, and the weather was milder than it had been all week. It did not seem as though Christmas was only ten days away.

They walked back toward the courthouse slowly. It was only one-thirty and the trial would not resume until two. They discussed the change in the weather, and the possibility of more snow in time for Christmas—had she ever seen that movie with Bing Crosby and Fred Astaire, yes, *Holiday Inn,* wasn't it, yes, who was the girl in that film? They sat on a bench facing Centre Street on the smallest of the Foley Square islands. A sharp wind swept around the corner of Duane off the river beyond. Gray pigeons echoed the gray slush on the curb, nibbling for peanuts around the benches.

Jonah was quiet, hands thrust deep into his coat pockets, legs stretched, head bent, dark hair moving with each fresh gust of river wind. His glasses reflected the gray pavement and the parading pigeons, hiding his eyes from view. She wondered suddenly if anyone had ever looked directly into the eyes of Jonah Willow, and just as suddenly wondered what he looked like in bed, without his glasses. There were no more Christmas gifts to discuss, and all the talk about the weather had been exhausted. They had both seen *Holiday Inn* and could not remember the name of the girl in it, and now they sat in silence while he thought God knew what, and she thought of the Egyptian. She took a deep breath.

"Hadad came to see me this morning," she said.

"Who?"

"Ibrahim Hadad. The man we ran into Monday night."

"The man who ran into *us,*" Jonah corrected, and then suddenly sat erect and turned to face her. "What do you *mean* he came to see you? Hadad?"

"That's right."

"What'd he want?"

"He told me he'd been visited by a detective. He said you'd called Santesson of the Circuit Court . . ."

"Yes, so . . . ?"

". . . and that Santesson assigned a detective to investigate."

"Yes, that's what I asked him to do."

"Investigate what, Jonah?"

"Third-degree assault."

"You're kidding."

"No, I'm not."

"Are we talking about the same accident?"

"I think so."

"There was no assault, and you know it."

"Sally, with all due respect, I hardly think you're familiar enough with the penal law to give an opinion on . . ."

"I read Section 244 this morning, after Hadad left. How do you figure there was culpable negligence?"

"He went through a full-stop sign."

"He didn't."

"Sally, you were asleep. I saw him."

"I was *not* asleep. He stopped the car just before he came onto the highway."

"He may have hesitated, but he didn't come to a full stop."

"Jonah, the district attorney would still have to prove disregard of the consequences and an indifference to—"

"Please don't throw precedent at me. Hadad went through a stop sign on a very dark night, driving his vehicle in a culpably negligent manner, and causing bodily injury to two other people. That's third-degree assault."

In the silence, she heard the wind sweeping around the corner of the courthouse. Crossing over from Centre Street, two obvious prostitutes ducked their heads against the sudden gust, one taking the other's arm as they stepped gingerly over the slush against the curb and then ran across Duane, probably on their way to the Criminal Courts Building. Behind them, a sailor looked up as he lighted his cigarette, decided to follow them, then decided against it, and turned and headed downtown toward City Hall. Sally put her hands in her pockets and looked at the tips of her shoes.

"Jonah, I don't see why you're doing this," she said.

"He violated the law."

"He's a poor slob who was coming home late from a—"

"I don't care what he is. He could have killed us both on that goddamn highway."

"But he didn't."

"He could have. He's guilty, Sally."

"I thought people were innocent until . . ."

"Now cut it out, will you!"

"Jonah, there's something behind this."

"There's nothing . . ."

"There's more than just . . ."

"There's *nothing*, I said!"

They fell silent again. The pigeons cooed around the bench. In the distance, they could hear the sound of heavy trucks rumbling toward the Brooklyn Bridge.

"We don't know each other well enough for this," Jonah said.

"No, we don't."

He rose suddenly, startling the pigeons into frantic flapping flight. He stood before the bench for a moment, as though about to say something, staring down at her, his glasses reflecting the pavement—you can never see his eyes, she thought again—and then abruptly seemed to change his mind. He held out his hand. "Come," he said.

"Where?"

"I've got to get back."

They crossed over to the courthouse in silence.

"Will I still see you tonight?" he asked.

"Do you want to?"

"I want to."

"All right."

They stood on the courthouse steps without speaking. At last Jonah said, "He's guilty, Sally."

"The Egyptian?"

"No. James Driscoll."

He turned and walked up the steps.

"Mr. Driscoll," Brackman asked, "would it be fair to say that Lieutenant Alex Cooper is an idealistic officer?"

"It would be."

"Were *you* an idealistic officer?"

"No, I was not."

"So on that score at least, Alex Cooper is *not* James Driscoll."

"That's right."

"Alex Cooper is single, is he not?"

"Yes."

"Were you single when you went into the Army?"

"No, I was married."

"Mr. Driscoll, did you have a love affair with an Army nurse while you were in Korea?"

"No, sir, I did not."

"But Lieutenant Cooper did?"

"Yes."

"You're familiar with *Catchpole,* I know, and I'd like to ask you now if you recall that Lieutenant Mason in that play is an idealistic officer. Do you recall that?"

"Yes."

"That he is an idealist? The same as your Lieutenant Cooper."

"He is an idealist, yes. He is *not* the same as Cooper."

"In what respect do they differ?"

"In many respects."

"They physically resemble each other, do they not?"

"Yes."

"They're both single."

"Yes."

"They both have an affair with a nurse."

"Yes."

"And they are both targets in a murder plot."

"Yes."

"In those respects they are similar, are they not?"

"Yes."

"Point of fact, in those respects they are *identical.*"

"No. They are not identical. They are two separate men. I don't know who Constantine's hero is based on, but Lieutenant Cooper is based on *me.*"

"Even though you possess none of these characteristics which can be attributed to him?"

"I possess *most* of the characteristics that can be attributed to Lieutenant Cooper."

"Like his idealism?"

"No, not that."

"Or his single state?"

"No."

"Or his love affair with an Army nurse?"

"Those are three isolated aspects of his character. For the most part, Cooper's mental processes are identical to my own, and he behaves as I might have behaved in the circumstances."

"But you were in identical circumstances, were you not?"

"I was in Korea, if that's what you mean."

"In a combat situation."

"Yes."

"As the officer in charge of an infantry platoon."

"Yes."

"Just as Lieutenant Cooper is in your book."

"Yes."

"And as Lieutenant Mason is in the play *Catchpole*."

"Is that a question?"

"It is a question."

"Lieutenant Mason is an officer on Eniwetok during World War II."

"But similar in all other respects."

"If you mean that he's in command of a combat infantry platoon, yes."

"A great many things happen to Lieutenant Cooper in the course of your novel. Did all of these things happen to you while you were in Korea?"

"No."

"You invented some of them, is that it?"

"Yes."

"Which of the events *did* happen to you, Mr. Driscoll?"

"Many of them."

"Well, let's just go over them one at a time, shall we? Let's try to find out which were based on your own experience and which were invented. To begin with, you've testified that you did *not* have an affair with an Army nurse, so I think we can safely conclude you invented that particular character and that particular event. Did you invent Private Colman as well?"

"Partly."

"You mean there *was* someone like Colman in your platoon?"

"No. But I'd met people like him before I went into the Army."

"But not in Korea, not in a combat situation?"

"No."

"Was there a troublemaker in your platoon?"

"No."

"Was there a homosexual?"

"No."

"Yet Colman is a homosexual troublemaker."

"Yes."

"You testified earlier that Sergeant Morley was based on a Negro who did in fact exist."

"Yes."

"A boy you knew in school . . ."

"Yes."

". . . and whom you have not seen since."

"Yes."

"Did this real person ever fall under the influence of someone like Colman, as Morley does in your book?"

"No."

"Then this situation was invented?"

"Yes."

"Did this real man ever become instrumental in a murder scheme?"

"No."

"This, too, was invented?"

"Yes."

"Were you ever the target in a planned murder, Mr. Driscoll?"

"No."

"You *do* agree that the men in your novel actively plot the murder of Lieutenant Cooper?"

"His death."

"They plan to lead him into a trap, do they not?"

"They deliberately lead him into a concentration of Chinese troops."

"Which they know exists."

"Yes."

"This would be cold-blooded murder, wouldn't it?"

"Yes, I suppose so."

"But your men never planned such a murder, did they?"

"No."

"Nor did they ever lead *you* toward a strong concentration of Chinese soldiers . . ."

"No."

". . . as the men in the book do?"

"That's right."

"You invented this."

"Yes, I invented it."

"Did you similarly invent the 'female rifle' scene, as it has been called?"

"No, that actually happened to me."

"The men made sexual allusions to a rifle while they were disassembling it?"

"Yes, sir. I changed the emphasis in the book, though. This really happened at Fort Dix, and it was a very comical thing. In the book, I've made it a malicious episode inspired by Private Colman."

"Who is named after your mother's iceman, is that correct?"

"I never said that."

"Perhaps I misunderstood you."

"I'm sure you did."

"I thought you said your mother's iceman was named Colman."

"No, I didn't."

"Well, the record will show what you said."

"Yes, shall we go back over it right this minute?" Driscoll asked.

"I'm sure there's no need for that, Mr. Driscoll."

"Just to clarify exactly what I *did* say."

"It was a pun, isn't that what you said?"

"Yes. But I didn't say he was named after my mother's iceman."

"Forgive me. You mentioned *The Iceman Cometh,* though, didn't you?"

"Yes, I did."

"You said this was some form of literary joke, isn't that right?"

"Yes."

"Are you fond of puns and jokes?"

"Yes."

"And of course you're familiar with plays? You said you've been a theatergoer since you were twelve."

"That's right."

"Did you see *The Iceman Cometh?*"

"I did."

"And felt it was perfectly all right to make a literary allusion to it?"

"Yes."

"Saw nothing wrong with that?"

"*Is* there something wrong with it?"

"I'm asking *you,* Mr. Driscoll."

"No, there was nothing wrong with the allusion."

"Did you see the play *The Eve of Saint Mark?*"

"No."

"Did you see the movie?"

"Yes."

"And you read the play, of course."

"Yes."

"Before this trial began?"

"Yes, I read it many years ago, and again recently."

"Therefore, you were familiar with Sergeant Ruby long before you began writing your book."

"That's right."

"And before you created your character Kenworthy, the one who swears a lot."

"That's right."

"By the way, was *he* based on any actual person? Kenworthy?"

"He was a composite."

"An invention?"

"In that he was not any one person."

"Was his similarity to Sergeant Ruby another literary joke?"

"He is not similar to Sergeant Ruby."

"They both swear a lot, don't they? By actual count, the

word *ruttin'* is used a total of twenty-eight times in *The Eve of Saint Mark,* isn't that what you said?"

"That's right."

"Did you make the count recently?"

"Yes, last week."

"You didn't count all those *ruttin*'s before you began writing your book, did you?"

"No."

"And you see no similarity between Ruby and your character?"

"They both swear a lot. That's the only similarity."

"Yet you do not feel that Private Franklin in *Catchpole* swears a lot?"

"He does not."

"You have heard the old adage, have you not, to the effect that if a man takes one drink on the stage, he's a social drinker; two drinks, he's an imbiber; three drinks, he's an alcoholic."

"I've heard something similar to that."

"Expressive of the shorthand used in the theater."

"Yes."

"Do you think the same shorthand might apply to a character who swears?"

"It might."

"So that if Franklin swore once, he might be considered normally agitated, whereas twice would make him somewhat salty, and *seven* times would indicate he was addicted to the use of obscenity."

"Absolutely not."

"You do not feel this would apply to Franklin, who swears seven times during the course of *Catchpole?"*

"Certainly not. Especially when much stronger swear words are used by other characters in the play. Words like 'bastard' and 'whore' and—"

"I don't think we need catalogue them, Mr. Driscoll, though you do seem very familiar with the play."

"I am."

"You read it one weekend a month or so ago, is that right?"

"That's right."

"You must have read it very carefully."

"I did."

"Did you intend Colman to be a homosexual?"

"Obviously."

"This idea did not come from Chester Danton, did it?"

"No."

"The dead major came from him, however?"

"Yes."

"But not the idea of Colman as a homosexual. You invented that all by yourself."

"Yes."

"You testified earlier that you did not believe Colonel Peterson in the play *Catchpole* is a homosexual."

"That's right."

"Do you know a great many homosexuals, Mr. Driscoll?"

"I know some."

"Personally."

"Yes, personally."

"Would you say that homosexuals are as different one from the other as are heterosexuals?"

"I would say so."

"Would you also agree that it is sometimes difficult to tell whether or not a man is a homosexual?"

"Sometimes."

"Do you think it would be possible to know whether or not a man were a homosexual, for example, if he did not utter a word, if he never spoke?"

"It might be difficult."

"Might it be similarly difficult to determine homosexuality in a letter written from one person to another? The words themselves, the words in the letter, might seem absolutely noncommittal, might they not?"

"I'm not sure I know what you mean."

"I'm asking, Mr. Driscoll, whether words in a letter written from one person to another might not seem entirely heterosexual in character when unaccompanied by either mannerisms of gesture or voice. That is what I am asking."

"A letter from a homosexual, do you mean?"

"If you will."

"I suppose."

"Do you also agree that the words in a *play,* the words in a mimeographed copy of a play, such as the one you perused one weekend last month, could seem equally noncommittal?"

"If a writer intended a homosexual character . . ."

"Let us not for the moment go into Mr. Constantine's intent. He has already testified that he *did* intend a homosexual. I'm asking whether—"

"If that's what he intended, it did not come across in the play I read."

"Did it come across in the play you *saw?*"

"Objection!" Willow shouted.

"Sustained. I'll have no more of that, Mr. Brackman."

"Will you accept my word, Mr. Driscoll, if I tell you that Colonel Peterson as played on the New York stage *definitely* came across as a man with homosexual tendencies?"

"I found no evidence of that in the mimeographed play."

"If I tell you it was in the play as staged, will you accept it?"

"Not unless you also tell me the part was played by a homosexual actor."

"You would not accept it otherwise?"

"I would not."

"Because you found no lines or scenes in the play that indicated Peterson was homosexual."

"I found none."

"Would you take this please, Mr. Driscoll, and turn to page 2–6, the middle of the page, Colonel Peterson speaking. Do you have the place?"

"Yes."

"The colonel is in the field, he is standing in the midst of carnage left by a Japanese counterattack, and he is with Corporal Janus and Sergeant D'Agostino, two of our principal characters. Are we clear as to the background?"

"Yes."

"May I read this to the Court then? And would you please follow it in the copy I've given you."

Brackman cleared his throat. The courtroom was silent. From the corner of his eye, Driscoll could see his wife sitting erect and attentive in the otherwise empty jury box. At the defense table, Jonah Willow was idly toying with a pencil.

"This is the scene," Brackman said, and began reading:

PETERSON

Look at them.

D'AGOSTINO

Easy, sir.

JANUS

Try to get a hold of yourself, sir.

PETERSON

Who's this man?

(He kneels, rolls over one of the dead men.)

Sergeant, who is this man?

D'AGOSTINO

That's Kirby, sir. Sir . . .

PETERSON

(*Clasping his hands together*)

He has blood all over his hair, sergeant.

D'AGOSTINO

Sir, let's get out of here. Let's get back to . . .

PETERSON

All over his hair.

(*He touches Kirby's hair.*)

Kirby? Kirby, are you all right?

D'AGOSTINO

He's dead, sir.

PETERSON

Open your eyes, Kirby.

JANUS

Colonel, the man's . . .

PETERSON

(*Shrieking it*)

No!

(*He lifts the dead Kirby into his arms, slowly rocks him as he would a child.*)

"That's the end of the scene," Brackman said. "Were you able to follow it, Mr. Driscoll?"

"I was."

"Since you seem to be an expert on matters homosexual . . ."

"I never said I was an expert."

". . . perhaps you can tell me what this scene is all about, if not homosexuality?"

"This scene is all about a man on the edge of a mental breakdown."

"And nothing more?"

"On the next page, they take him to the field hospital, and he's raving about death and blood and—"

"We're concerned with *this* scene, Mr. Driscoll, and not with what follows it or precedes it."

"You're taking it out of context," Driscoll said flatly.

"I have read nothing in this particular scene out of context, and I would like to address my questions to *this* scene and to what is *in* this scene. Does the colonel touch the dead boy's hair in this scene?"

"He does."

"Do you consider that normal?"

"I've just told you that the colonel is about to crack up. Whatever he does—"

"Please answer the question."

"In the context of what is about to happen, this is a natural gesture."

"Do either of the other men touch the boy's hair?"

"No. But neither of them are about to suffer a mental breakdown."

"You find nothing homosexual about one man touching the hair of another man?"

"Not in this scene. The colonel is obviously losing control, he's just noticed blood in the dead man's hair . . ."

"Losing control in what way?"

"Losing control of his mental faculties."

"Not of his inhibitions?"

"Certainly not."

"Do you feel it is natural to touch hair that is covered with blood?"

"In this scene, in a combat situation, where a man suffering from battle fatigue . . ."

"Please answer the question."

"Yes, I think it's a natural gesture."

"What about rocking him in his arms?"

"I accept it in this scene."

"You do not feel there is anything homosexual about one man rocking another man in his arms?"

"The author did not indicate anything homosexual."

"He says in the stage direction that Peterson takes the dead boy in his arms and slowly rocks him."

"Read the rest of the sentence," Driscoll said.

"What?"

"Read the rest of the sentence. It says 'slowly rocks him as he would a child.' "

"Yes, well?"

"What's homosexual about that?"

"About a man rocking another man in his arms? That would seem clearly homosexual to me."

"It would seem only paternal to me, especially when the author indicates he's rocking him as he would a child. He does not say as he would a *woman,* or as he would a *lover,* he specifically says a *child.*"

"And you find nothing homosexual in that?"

"Nothing."

"I will accept your answer."

"What?"

"I said I will accept your answer. Do you recall the rank of your nurse, Jan Reardon, in *The Paper Dragon?*"

"She is a first lieutenant."

"Do you recall the rank of Mr. Constantine's nurse, Diane Foster, in *Catchpole?*"

"I think she's a first lieutenant."

"She is in fact so. How do you explain this similarity, Mr. Driscoll?"

"I've already said that the only nurses I met in Korea were–"

"Did you meet any nurses who were captains?"

"I did."

"Or majors?"

"Yes."

"Yet you chose to make your nurse a first lieutenant. Why?"

"A first lieutenant sounds more feminine somehow than either a captain or a major. Besides, she has only been in the service a year longer than Cooper, and a higher rank than first lieutanant would have sounded implausible."

"Mr. Driscoll, *you* wrote the book, did you not?"

"Yes."

"Therefore her length of time in the service was not proscribed. You *chose* the exact amount of time, you chose *one* year rather than two or three or four."

"Yes."

"And it was this length of time that determined her rank?"

"Yes."

"Are you sure it was not her *rank* that determined the length of her service? Which came first, Mr. Driscoll?"

"Her being a year . . . her being in the service a year longer."

"Are you certain?"

"I'm certain."

"And this is the only explanation you have of their identical ranks, the two nurses?"

"It's the only explanation."

"Or the identical line 'I outrank you'?"

"This line is not in Mr. Constantine's play."

"But his nurse *does* joke with the lieutenant about rank."

"Only superficially. A point is not made of it."

"I see. Mr. Driscoll, what do Alex Cooper's fellow officers call him?"

"Coop."

"What do Roger Mason's fellow officers call him?"

"Mase."

"You have stated that the character Alex Cooper is based upon yourself."

"Yes."

"What does Jonah Willow call you?"

"What do you mean?"

"Familiarly."

"He calls me Jimmy."

"What does Chester Danton call you?"

"Jimmy."

"What does your agent, Hollis Marks, call you?"

"Jimmy."

"Do any of your friends call you anything but Jimmy?"

"No."

"In *Catchpole,* Lieutenant Mason is called 'Mase,' and in *The Paper Dragon,* Lieutenant Cooper is called 'Coop.' Was your name ever shortened to 'Dris' while you were in the service?"

"No, it was not."

"Mr. Driscoll, in your novel there is a long discussion between the enlisted men about big-name bands, and especially about Glenn Miller. Do you recall the scene to which I'm referring?"

"Yes, but it was not especially about Glenn Miller."

"Glenn Miller is mentioned prominently in that scene, is he not?"

"Only in conjunction with the names of other band leaders. The men are playing a sort of guessing game, trying to remember the theme songs of the big-name bands."

"Yes, and isn't it true that an argument develops between two of the men as to whether Glenn Miller's theme song was 'Moonlight Serenade' or 'Sunrise Serenade,' and it is Sergeant Morley who correctly identifies the theme."

"That's true."

"A scene which was later carried over into the film. Your novel is set in Korea during the months of October and November in the year 1950, isn't that right?"

"Yes."

"The soldiers in this scene are all young men, aren't they?"

"Yes."

"Some in their late teens, some in their early twenties, is that right?"

"Yes, that's right."

"Do you know when Glenn Miller is presumed to have died?"

"Yes, I do."

"When was it?" Brackman asked.

"It was December of 1944."

"December 15th, to be exact," Brackman said. "Now, do you think it likely that people—especially very young people—would in 1950 still be discussing a band leader who reached the height of his popularity in the late thirties and early forties?"

"I grew up with the music of Glenn Miller and all the other big-name bands mentioned in that scene. When he was reported missing, I must have been fifteen years old, and I can remember being deeply affected."

"And you find nothing odd about men discussing him in the middle of Korea six years after his death?"

"I do not."

"Are you aware that in *Catchpole,* there is a scene where a group of men are discussing the death of Glenn Miller?"

"I am aware of that."

"How do you explain the similarity?"

"There is no similarity. The men in *Catchpole* are discussing Glenn Miller's death. The men in *The Paper Dragon* are discussing the theme songs of the big-name bands, and Glenn Miller's name is only incidentally mentioned."

"Is there not an argument about his theme song?"

"A difference of opinion, not an argument."

"And doesn't this difference of opinion, as you call it, focus attention on his name?"

"Momentarily."

"In much the same way that attention is focused on it in *Catchpole.*"

"We seem to be speaking two different languages," Driscoll said.

"I think we are speaking the same language, Mr. Driscoll, and I would like an answer to my question."

"I have already answered your question. I have already told you that the scenes are about two different things. One is about the death of Glenn Miller and the other is about the theme songs of the big-name bands. So when you ask me if attention is focused on the name in the same way, I can't add anything to what I've already said, which is that attention is focused in entirely *different* ways."

"And you find nothing unusual or odd about the similarity?"

"I've already testified that there *is* no similarity. But I did find something odd, yes."

"Are you now saying . . ."

"In *Catchpole.*"

"Yes, are you now reversing . . ."

"I found it odd that in February of 1944 those men were discussing the death of Glenn Miller, which did not take place until *December* of 1944. Don't *you* find that odd?"

"I'm not b-b-being examined, Mr. Driscoll."

"I just thought you might find it odd."

"I w-w-would imagine that was nothing more than d-d-dramatic license."

Hearing the stammer, seeing the sudden pink color rising in Brackman's cheeks, Driscoll realized with a feeling bordering on wild exultation that he had flustered him, and knew in the same instant that he was cleverer and brighter and infinitely more agile than the lawyer was. He glanced toward the defense table to see if Willow had noticed and appreciated his entangling maneuver, and saw only that Willow was frowning. Willow's displeasure, however, did nothing to quell the rising sense of triumph, the reckless knowledge that he could parry anything Brackman put to him, and then thrust with deadly accuracy to leave the inept little lawyer helpless and forlorn, bereft of any weapon. Come on, he thought. Let's go, Mr. Brackman. Come on.

"This m-m . . ." Brackman started, and then cleared his throat and consulted his notes, and Driscoll had all he could do to keep from laughing out loud. "This matter of the eyeglasses," Brackman finally managed to say. "When you say that Private Colman *does* wear glasses in your book, are you referring to this passage on page . . ." He turned to his partner. "What page is that, C-C-Carl?" he asked.

"37," his partner replied.

"Page 37," Brackman said. "Is this the p-p-p-passage you mean?"

"Which passage is that?" Driscoll asked, knowing full well which passage Brackman meant.

"I am about to read it to you," Brackman said.

"I'm waiting," Driscoll answered, and again glanced at Willow to find that he was still frowning. Imperceptibly, Willow shook his head. Brackman had already begun reading, but Driscoll missed the first few words of the paragraph, so startled was he by Willow's unmistakable warning.

" '. . . mud spattering from the wheels, as the jeep swerved into the compound and ground to a stop. Colman saw two officers on the front seat of the jeep, one of whom he recognized as Captain Benjamin. The other man was tall and lean, wearing his hair cropped close to his head in a boyish crewcut. Colman reached into his blouse and took out his glasses, which he perched on his nose. Peering through them owlishly, he studied the new officer with deliberate scrutiny.' And following that," Brackman said, "there's a detailed description of Lieutenant Cooper. Is that the passage?"

"That's the passage," Driscoll said.

"What sort of glasses does Colman take out of his pocket?"

"I don't think I understand you," Driscoll said.

"Are they the sort of glasses, for example, that Mr. Willow has been wearing in this courtroom every day this week?"

"No."

"Are they reading glasses?"

"I never specifically labeled them. If anything, they would be reading glasses, yes. Colman only wears them occasionally."

"Does he in fact wear them anywhere else in the book?"

"I don't think so."

"This is the only place in the book where you specifically describe Colman as wearing eyeglasses?"

"Yes."

"In just this one paragraph which is . . . . let me see . . . eight lines long. That's the only mention in the entire book."

"Yes."

"Mr. Driscoll, do you recall a character in your book called Major Catharine Astor?"

"I do."

"And who is also called Major Catastrophe by Lieutenant Cooper and Jan Reardon?"

"Yes."

"Is this another of your literary puns?"

"Yes, an affectionate one."

"How would you describe Major Astor, or Major Catastrophe as she is affectionately called?"

"She's a woman in her late fifties, and she's been a nurse for perhaps fifteen years or so. Irish background, rather tall and big-boned, ample-breasted, and . . . big feet, she has big feet. She's constantly predicting doom, which is how she earns her nickname. She carries a note from the lieutenant to Jan in one scene."

"I ask you now if you remember a character in *Catchpole* called Captain Sykes?"

"I do."

"Do you remember that she is an Army nurse?"

"Yes."

"Do you remember how old she is supposed to be?"

"No."

"Will you turn to the page immediately following the title page of Mr. Constantine's play, the page titled 'Cast in Order of Appearance,' and will you look down that page to the description of Captain Sykes? Have you got it?"

"Yes, I have."

"Do you see her age there?"

"I do."

"What is the age?"

"Fifty-two."

"Do you recall why Captain Sykes has joined the Medical Corps?"

"Yes."

"Would you tell us, please?"

"She enlists after the death of her husband."

"Let's get back to your character, shall we? Major Catastrophe. How does she happen to be in Korea?"

"She is sent there."

"Is it not true that she becomes a nurse after her husband dies?"

"Oh, boy," Driscoll said.

"I beg your pardon?"

"Are you going to claim . . ."

"Please answer the question, Mr. Driscoll."

"Yes, I'll be very happy to answer the question," Driscoll said angrily, "if I may be permitted briefly to go into the backgrounds of these two characters."

"Briefly, but not with as much volume, I hope," McIntyre said.

"I'm sorry."

"We're none of us deaf," McIntyre said. "Go on, go on."

"The senior nurse in my book, Major Astor, has been in the Army since 1935. She joins several years after her husband passes away, of natural causes, in his own bed. There is no indication that she enlists for patriotic reasons or for any reason other than to give herself a worthwhile occupation. The nurse in the play *Catchpole* is a woman who left nursing to get married. Her husband is a doctor who is killed in action in a bombing attack on a London airfield. To avenge his death, she joins the Medical Corps and is ironically sent to the Pacific where the enemy are the Japanese rather than the Germans. She is pictured as a rather bitter woman who strongly resents the developing love affair between Mr. Constantine's principal characters. I don't see any similarity between these two women, aside from the fact that they are both nurses in the same general age bracket."

"Is it not true," Brackman asked, "that Captain Sykes in *Catchpole* helps Diane Foster to arrange a rendezvous with Lieutenant Mason?"

"No, it is not true. She makes it extremely difficult for the pair to meet."

"Does she not deliberately leave them alone together one night?"

"She does not do it deliberately. One of Mason's friends gets her drunk and puts her to sleep in a weapons carrier. It's a comic scene in the play."

"Where is this scene, Mr. Driscoll?"

"In the second act someplace."

"Do you recall whether or not Captain Sykes has a nickname?"

"Yes, I think she does. They call her 'Big Red.' "

"Why do they call her that?"

"Because she has flaming-red hair."

"Is this fact ever mentioned?"

"Yes, when Mason's friend dumps her into the weapons carrier, he puts his Eisenhower jacket over her head because he's afraid someone will spot the red hair."

"What color hair does *your* nurse have?"

"Brown."

"You're talking about Major Astor now?"

"Yes."

"Does Major Astor deliver a note to Jan Reardon in your novel?"

"Yes, she does. Arranging a meeting with the lieutenant."

"Doesn't Captain Sykes in *Catchpole* also deliver a note to someone?"

"No."

"Isn't there a scene with the colonel where . . ."

"That isn't a note."

"What is it?"

"She shows him his medical record."

"Your Honor," Willow said, rising, "I do not see where this is going."

There was a peculiar note of warning in his voice, and whereas he had addressed the words to McIntyre, Driscoll had the certain feeling he was trying to communicate something, was objecting not to Brackman's questions but rather to his own answers. Confused, aware of the warning but unable to ascertain what he was doing wrong, he stared at Willow in puzzlement, and suddenly his hands began to shake.

"We are attempting to explore the similarities, your Honor," Brackman said. "That is all."

Brackman's explanation sounded reasonable enough, and yet Driscoll detected a note of confidence that had not been there several moments ago when he could barely stutter his way through a sentence. He tried to understand what had happened between then and now, but he could find no clue, and McIntyre's next words left him with a curiously unsettled feeling, as though he were on treacherous ground that was giving away beneath his feet, inch by crumbling inch.

"I find this all to the point," McIntyre said. "Proceed, Mr. Brackman."

"Mr. Driscoll, you have testified that you met with your erstwhile commanding officer, Colonel Hamilton, in order to get some information from him about specific scenes in your book."

"Yes."

"Some of this information was about disassembling a rifle, is that right?"

"Yes, I wanted the exact language describing the operation."

"You did not possess any books that might have given you this information?"

"No."

"Weren't you issued any such books when you were in the service?"

"Yes."

"Did you later discard them?"

"I must have."

"So you had to go to Colonel Hamilton for the information."

"I went to the library first, but I couldn't find it there. Nor could I find a breakdown of the Chinese troop concentrations, or some of the other information I needed."

"Like what?"

"Like some of the actual code names used in the Ch'ongch'on River operations."

"Which Colonel Hamilton supplied."

"Yes. This was no longer classified material."

"I understand that, nor am I intending to impugn a dead man's loyalty. In Officer Candidate School, Mr. Driscoll, you took a great many courses, did you not?"

"I did."

"And I assume you took notes in these courses."

"In most of them. In some courses, for security reasons, we were not permitted—"

"Yes, I understand that. But you *did* take notes in most of the courses?"

"Yes."

"Do you still have those notes?"

"No, of course not."

"When you were released from the Army, Mr. Driscoll, you attended N.Y.U., I believe you said, and you took some courses in creative writing."

"I took most of the writing courses the school had to offer."

"Did you take notes in those courses?"

"Yes."

"Do you still have those notes?"

"No."

"Your Honor," Willow said, "again I must ask . . ."

"It will become clear, Mr. Willow," Brackman answered.

"I hope so," McIntyre said.

"You have testified that you wrote several short stories while you were a student at N.Y.U. Did you make carbon copies of those stories?"

"Yes."

"Do you still have those carbons?"

"No."

"Do you generally save things?"

"Important things."

"You did not save any of your Army notes, or your college notes, or carbon copies of your short-story attempts."

"I did not think they were good enough."

"The stories?"

"Yes."

"So you discarded the carbons?"

"*And* the stories, too."

"So it would seem that there are some things you do *not* consider important enough to save."

"Yes."

"Yet you did feel it important to save every bit of material, every letter, every note you ever made concerning the novel *The Paper Dragon.*"

"Not *all* the material."

"The last document this court admitted was marked 'Exhibit S in evidence,' which means nineteen documents were submitted to this Court—letters to your agent, and letters to Mitchell-Campbell, and a letter to Colonel Hamilton, and notes you took at your meeting with him, and outlines, and the original drawing of your map, you saved all these things pertaining to *The Paper Dragon,* all of these things that purport to show the independent creation of the novel, isn't that so, Mr. Driscoll?"

"That was my working procedure."

"*What* was your working procedure?"

"I had a box full of typing paper. I took the cover off that box and put it on one side of my typewriter, and whenever I pulled a completed page out of the machine, I put it into the empty lid of the box."

"What does this have to do with your letters and notes?"

"When the book was completed, I put all the research material and information in the same box containing the carbon copy."

"Your letters as well?"

"No, I kept those in a separate file."

"Do you keep carbon copies of all your letters?"

"Yes. Would you like me to bring them in?"

"I don't think that will be necessary. Do you have a good memory, Mr. Driscoll?"

"I think so."

"Why did you meet with Colonel Hamilton?"

"To check certain factual aspects of the novel."

"Such as the disassembling of a rifle?"

"Yes."

"How many times, offhand, would you say you stripped a rifle while you were in the Army?"

"I don't recall."

"Did you perform the operation many times, or just a few times?"

"Many, I would say."

"Yet you could not remember the steps, and you had to—"

"I didn't say I couldn't remember them. I wanted the exact language because the success of the scene depended on the language in it."

"You would not trust your memory."

"That's right."

"So you went to Colonel Hamilton for the sake of authenticity."

"Yes."

"Even though you have a very good memory."

"I think I do. But I could not be expected to remember the technical language describing—"

"Yes, yes, I understand that. How many times would you say you stripped a rifle? Ten times perhaps?"

"Perhaps."

"Twenty?"

"Perhaps."

"More than twenty?"

"Yes, many times more."

"You stripped a rifle more than twenty times, *many* times more, but you could not remember the steps in detail when it came time to write about them."

"I could not remember the *language.*"

"Yet you read the play *Catchpole* only once last month, and you can remember in detail and with absolute accuracy some of the more obscure aspects of the play."

"I read the play more than once."

"How many times did you read it?"

"Five or six times."

"Not more than twenty times?"

"No."

"You could not remember an operation you performed more than twenty times, but you could remember details of a play you read only five or six times."

"I could not remember the *language.* How many times must I repeat that?"

"You thought this rifle scene was important enough to seek information about, didn't you?"

"Yes."

"And you thought it important enough to *keep* the notes you made on it."

"Yes. But only as part of all the other material I kept. Material pertaining to the book."

"Why did you keep this material?"

"I don't know. I save some things, and others I throw away."

"What else have you saved?"

"Scraps of everything."

"What kind of scraps?"

"Anything I think is important."

"Did you save your notebooks from your student days at Pratt Institute?"

"Some of them."

"Why? Were they important?"

"Yes. Some of them."

"And obviously the complicated process of writing your novel was also important, so important that we have a detailed step-by-step record of its creation. Do you have any notes concerning the 105th Division, Mr. Driscoll?"

"No."

"Did you ask Colonel Hamilton about the 105th Division?"

"No."

"You asked him about the *Chinese* divisions involved in the Ch'ongch'on River offensive, did you not?"

"Yes."

"Why?"

"For the sake of accuracy."

"You wanted the exact designations for those divisions?"

"Yes."

"Yet you designated your American division the 105th, and did not think of checking its authenticity with the colonel."

"There was no need to do that. I knew the division was fictitious."

"How did you know?"

"Because I knew which American divisions were involved in the battle."

"You trusted your memory concerning those divisions?"

"Yes."

"But you did not trust your memory concerning the stripping of a rifle."

"For the last time, the scene was built on a juxtaposition of sexual allusions to absolutely technical language. Its effectiveness was based on the accuracy of the technical detail. Which is why I consulted Colonel Hamilton."

"And the battle scenes? Was their effectiveness based on accuracy of detail?"

"Yes."

"So that it was essential to give the Chinese armies their proper designations?"

"And their strength. The climactic chapter in the book is the one in which the patrol moves up on an overwhelming force of Chinese."

"Did you use an actual division number for the Chinese force in that scene?"

"Yes, I did."

"And you checked this number with Colonel Hamilton?"

"He gave me the division designation, and also its estimated strength."

"Information from Army files?"

"Yes."

"You did not check the 105th Division with him?"

"No."

"Why not?"

"I told you. I knew it was fictitious. I knew I had invented it."

"*How* did you invent it?"

"I don't know."

"Well now, Mr. Driscoll, you seem to have a detailed record of every other piece of information that went into your novel, you have chapter-by-chapter breakdowns, and you have expanded outlines, and you have target dates and notes to yourself, and yet you can't remember how you happened to invent the 105th Division. Did it simply come to you out of the blue?"

"I don't know."

"Try to remember, Mr. Driscoll. Was the 105th a sudden inspiration?"

"Nothing about the book was a sudden inspiration."

"In that case, you must have pondered the designation for a long time before you decided on its use."

"No."

"Did you ponder it for a short time?"

"I didn't ponder it at all. I simply used it."

"But where did it come from?"

"It did *not* come from Mr. Constantine's play."

"I am not asking you where it did *not* come from. I am asking you exactly where it *did* come from, Mr. Driscoll, and I would like an answer."

"I don't know."

"Is that your answer?"

"That is my answer."

"I have no further questions, your Honor."

"Mr. Willow?"

"No questions."

"Thank you, Mr. Driscoll."

"Thank you," Driscoll said, and rose from the stand. He looked out over the courtroom for a moment, and then went to take a seat in the jury box alongside his wife.

"Is there any further evidence?" McIntyre asked.

"No, your Honor," Willow said. "That is all for the defendant Mitchell-Campbell."

"Your Honor," Genitori said, rising, "the contract between API and James Driscoll, dated August 16, 1963, contains the indemnity clause favoring API, and is annexed as Exhibit A to our answer and crossclaim. May it be deemed to have been submitted in evidence?"

"No objection," Willow said.

"Fine," McIntyre said. "Is there any further evidence to be offered by either side?"

"The plaintiff rests," Brackman said.

"Your Honor, may I at this time renew our motion to dismiss on the ground that no cause has been made?"

"I assume, Mr. Willow, that you will want to argue this motion as well as the merits of the alleged similarities, won't you?"

"Yes, your Honor."

"I hope, too, that both sides will be submitting proposed findings of fact and conclusions of law."

"Yes, sir."

"We will, sir."

"Well, it's almost four o'clock now, gentlemen, but perhaps we can be ready to do that tomorrow morning. In the meantime, I'll reserve any further comments and rulings until then."

"May we consider the case closed for all other purposes, your Honor?" Brackman asked.

"Yes," McIntyre said. "The case is closed for all purposes other than the submission of conclusions of law, findings of fact, and argument."

14

THEY TAKE YOU BACK, Driscoll thought, they force you to go back to a time and place forgotten or at least deliberately obscured. It is instant therapy, it is crash analysis, this confrontation with yourself, an odd meeting with a seeming stranger who moves steadily closer until you recognize him with a start—he is you, but he is no longer you. Comparisons are odious, the man said, I forget which man. But what were they doing to me today if not forcing me to resurrect my youth (upon whom was Sergeant Morley based?) and then moving by logical if tedious progression into my so-called maturity (when exactly did you begin writing your book, Mr. Driscoll?) until they had brought the biography to date, into my dotage, my slow if clinging expiration (you are a novelist, are you not, Mr. Driscoll? No, I am a Vermont farmer).

The farm in Vermont is the here and now, the present. It was purchased for eight thousand dollars, a portion of my share of the movie money on *The Paper Dragon.* The farmhouse is red, you approach it over a rutted, ice-covered road in the winter; in the spring, the road is running and wet, soggy and mired. There is a falling stone wall bordering the property, said to have been built by colonial settlers, which theory I personally buy since there are still enough boulders firmly embedded in the two acres of arable land to construct yet another wall from there to Boston and back. I pretend to grow forage crops there, alfalfa and hay and oats.

It is interesting, don't you think, that were I a novelist, were I truly a working novelist, my daily routine would be concerned primarily with seeking truth in terms of fabrication, the enlargement of fantasy, the exercise of imagination, a pretense hardly less energetic than that of being a Vermont farmer, which I am not, but which I purport to be.

I do not know what I am.

I have not known what or who I am for a very long time now, I thank *you* for that, darling.

We go to bed early in Vermont because a farmer, I am informed, must rise to take care of this and that, sowing, reaping, harvesting, breathing deep of clear Vermont air, ahhh, the outdoor life, rise and shine at five-thirty A.M., walk with springing step to the barn where Ebie begins her chores with the chickens. Yes, we have chickens, did I neglect to tell you that, Mr. Brackman? We have seventy-two chickens. We bought those with the movie money, too. So it is early to bed in Vermont, and since the bed part is never very good or very interesting anyway, it's really not too terribly difficult to throw back the covers before dawn and touch the cold wooden floor, scarcely colder than the bed in which Mr. and Mrs. James Driscoll lie, though we do sometimes make love. We lie in love, so to speak.

Stay, she used to say, why must you go home? But go I would. I still don't know why. Perhaps there was in me, at eighteen, more of my mother than I imagined there was, the humorless woman wearing her black shawl. How could I explain to her that I was deliriously in love with a girl in Brooklyn and that all I wanted to do was hold her and touch her and look at her and love her day and night? How could I explain with the sound of Holy Mary, Mother of God coming from her bedroom each night, as if she were doing penance for God knew what mortal sin, every night, Holy Mary, Mother of God. While I thought of Ebie lying alone in that large bed on Myrtle Avenue, waiting for the next afternoon when I would taste her once again—that is the distant past, that is the far distant past. The present is Vermont, and a love-making that is only necessary, a biological release for both of us. We have not spoken the words "I love you" in so long I think if I heard them said or uttered them myself, I would begin to weep. We perform mechanically, we lie in love, my Southern flower and myself, remembering a past when all was fire and death, "the little death" the ancients called it, was that Hemingway? Did you feel the earth move? Yes, *guapa*. Truly? Yes, truly. You old bewitcher, you seduced a generation.

The distant past. Long before the red Vermont farmhouse I insisted on buying, half hoping she would refuse to come with me, half hoping she would pull out at last, abandon the marriage, end the loveless grappling, but no. Not Ebie, not that determined Southern flower. She had made the vows, oh my yes, and she would honor them, come crumbling wall or overflowing spring, rutted roads or bone-chilling winter. And how are you today, Mrs. Driscoll? the Vermont ladies all say, and she answers with a pert nod of her head and tells them about the pies she has baked, or asks their opinion on how to rid the house of flies. There are a dreadful number of flies in the house all the time, she says to Mrs. Dimmity, who is our next-door neighbor in the gray farmhouse across the road. Mrs. Dimmity does part-time housework for the skiers who rent the old Kruger place. They are a noisy lot, college boys and girls who speed along the black road at midnight every winter Friday, racing over the dangerous ice. I visualize them booming mountains in the daytime, shagging themselves into exhaustion each night. They bring the past into our fake present. I saw one of them one cold forbidding morning, she was blond and tall, so young, she wore a black parka and black stretch pants, she raised her mittened hand to greet me in the frosty dawn as I came out of the barn. I returned the wave, my heart was pounding.

The exterminator has visited us some five times already, but he cannot rid the house of mice. I cannot bear the thought of them scurrying in the night, scarcely secret sharers of our roof. They are the final insult, the final invasion of a marriage that certainly needs no further intruders. I visualize them nibbling at the wallboard, or licking the wallpaper paste, undermining the rotting original timbers of the old house until one day it will fall down upon our ears and a great cloud of mouse dirt will rise on the air, and they will run, they will scatter away from the crumbling ruin, chattering and squeaking in triumph, having destroyed it at last, having destroyed even the meager shaky structure that has managed to survive until now.

It seemed so strong, it seemed so indestructible.

In the past, the distant past—and this goes back, my child, to a time when ships were made of wood and men were made of iron, all the way back at least to 1948, do you remember the blizzard that January? It was centuries ago. It was the time of the Great Brooklyn Renaissance, perhaps you may recall the legend of the Uncertain Knight who rode out of West End Avenue carrying a black tin watercolor box under his arm, coming into the Valley of Pratt where he met the Lady Edna Belle. My Ebie's hair is like a golden helmet/Poured molten, shaped to fit/Haphazardly/And yet despite—the ode ended there, because there were no words. Not then. Not as yet. No words to express what I felt for Ebie, the incredible awakening I knew in her arms and, yes, between her legs. Yes, that was a very real part of it, it *had* to be, I had known only one other girl before Ebie—Liz McPherson, known to every young and budding Studs Lonigan along 96th Street. She lived near Lexington Avenue, but the crosstown walk never fazed any of us, through the park's transverse path and over the hill to grandmother's house we went, grandmother being Liz who shared a room with her baby sister. The infant would lie asleep in her crib beside Liz's narrow bed where we made fitfully inexperienced love, with sometimes two or more other young bucks waiting outside the closed door in the tenement kitchen. Poor Liz, I wonder what ever became of her; Liz the Whore, we ungallantly called her.

When Ebie told me about the boy who limped, I was furious at first. I conjured the image of a Brooklyn Liz, far removed from 96th Street, but sisters under the skin, a long line of cock-in-hand suitors outside her apartment door. Donald was his name, *had* been his name; apparently the affair had run its course several months before we met in Bertie's, *l'affaire de sa jeunesse:* emblazon the motto on a field argent, two bronze balls pendant beneath a sinister hand couped at the wrist, holding erect a cane. I went to church the day she told me, I had not been inside a confessional since I was fifteen, and I was there to confess not my own sin, but the sin of a girl I deeply loved, or thought I loved, a girl who had become in six short months—this was May of 1948, I can still remember the day, bright with spring sunshine, a bird chirping incessantly in the budding tree just outside the stained glass window above the confession box, *Bless me, Father, for I have sinned*—a girl who had become in half a year my only reason for existence.

The priest spoke with a faint Italian accent, there was in his voice the echo of an ancient race, but in his words there was no wisdom. I left the church unsatisfied, the bird still chirping its inane song, the sun bright in an opaque sky, I could not understand why she had not waited for me to come along, why she had foolishly given herself to this boy who limped. I tried to tell Uncle Benny about it that night, the telephone beckoning, knowing that Ebie was waiting for my call in her Myrtle Avenue apartment, or at least *hoping* she was waiting. But I couldn't tell him. I sat there in the living room with him, we were both sitting on the piano bench, side by side, our hands separately clasped and hanging between our respective knees, like two old men in the park, staring solemnly at pigeons. But I could not tell him that the girl I loved had been living with some goddamn cripple for five months, how could I tell this to Uncle Benny or to *anyone,* for that matter? So we talked about my studies, Uncle Benny was always fascinated by the *theory* of art, and I told him I was having trouble with one of my instructors, I was sure the man disliked me, and Uncle Benny told me there would be instructors all through my life who took a dim view of me, or vice versa, and the thing to do with them was simply face the fact that it would be difficult, but to do my best, do my work the best way I knew how, and get through it somehow, that was the important thing. And we sat there on the piano bench with the question of Ebie hanging on the air, unresolved, unspoken. I nodded and said, Yeah, but Uncle Benny this guy is a real son of a bitch, and Uncle Benny said, That only means you've got to work harder, Jimbo, you've got to get what you can out of the course, *despite* the way he feels about you, you've got to rely on what's inside *yourself,* Jimbo, there's lots of good stuff inside you. Yeah, I said, and nodded. Sure, Uncle Benny said, and nodded. After a while, I got up and thanked him, and went into my room. I could hear my mother in her bedroom next door, already beginning the litany of Hello Mary, Mother of God. I threw myself down on the bed, and tried to figure out what I should do. I decided two things. First, I decided I could never let go of Ebie Dearborn because I loved her too much, and second, I decided I would extract from her a promise that Donald Who Limped was to be the last of her little adventures, that James Randolph Driscoll was now on the scene having ridden long and hard from West End Avenue, and he was on the scene to *stay,* and she had better get that through her golden-helmet head. I was still furious when I told it to her in the curtain-rustling stillness of her bedroom later that night. She sat in a straight-backed chair near the window, the curtains stirring behind her with each fresh spring breeze, unsmiling, sitting as straight-backed as the chair. When I was through, she started to say something but the goddamn elevated express roared by and we were caught in a moment of mechanical suspense, waiting for the train to pass, waiting for the room to be still again.

In a sense, that day in 1948 was the beginning. Oh yes, Norman Sheppard said only this afternoon that there are no endings in life, and perhaps he was right, perhaps there are no beginnings as well—but for me, it was a beginning, and I think it was for Ebie, too. For me, for us, it was the start of a gradual loss of identity. If the love we made was a little death, then the love we knew was a littler death still, this loss of self, this certain overlapping of person upon person, blending, merging, no longer Ebie and no longer me, a single unit responding and reacting in rare empathy, osmotically perhaps, or perhaps symbiotically because, yes, we surely fed upon each other and sustained each other and became each other, inseparable, indistinguishable, one.

Who can remember, can *I* remember, any of my own responses as apart from Ebie's? Reconstruct all of the events that led to our marriage in 1950, arrange them in sequence and what can I remember that does not include Ebie? Once I walked alone in the shadow of the Queensborough Bridge and wrote in my head a suspense story for Alfred Hitchcock, spies chasing counterspies over wet cobblestones and under dripping metal cross-supports, but the heroine of that movie (running through the rain, blond hair stringy and wet, head snapping back over her shoulder to steal a quick glance at God knew what awful pursuer) was Ebie Dearborn, all was Ebie Dearborn. And once I sat alone in the living room of the West End Avenue apartment, the winter afternoon waning, and tapped out a melody on the old Chickering, note by faltering note, using only one hand, but the symphony was Ebie Dearborn, all was Ebie Dearborn. You are wrong, Norman Sheppard; there are beginnings, and there are endings as well, and I have known them both. I can remember the day our Fainting in Coils instructor (Lewis Carroll's chapter was big with the students at Pratt, who quite rightfully thought of themselves as very *inside* concerning art and the art world and things artistic) took us to see the bona fide studio of a bona fide artist named Bernardo Casamorte, whose name we later learned meant "house of the dead," hilariously inappropriate after what we had seen. Casamorte lived on West 18th Street in a skylighted loft that had once been a hat factory. Hat molds, some of which he had decorated with grinning faces, most of which he had left unadorned, still rested on every flat surface in the place, cluttering the room. In order to stand or sit, the class—there were thirty of us—had to move molds, or easels, or finished and unfinished canvases, or palettes, or pots of paint and glue, or soiled clothing draped or tossed or hanging, or the remains of breakfast. There were seven cats in the place, and a large boxer who had dipped his snout in vermilion, and who gave the appearance of a comic strip drunk with illuminated nose. There was also a mistress-model who slunk around the loft in an electric-blue silk dressing gown while Casamorte gave us his lecture on what it was like to earn a living as a painter, a premise we seriously doubted on the evidence presented. We kept hoping the mistress-model would do a little posing for him while we were there; she was a dark brunette with enormous breasts swelling the gown; she held the gown closed with her folded arms, its sash having been misplaced in the general disorder of the joint. We decided afterwards, Ebie and I, that the loft was in reality a stage set designed and built by Pratt, and that Casamorte, his busty model-mistress, his seven cats, and his drunken boxer were all actors hired by the school for this special outing each year. This was the only class Ebie and I shared together, by dispensation, since she was a full year ahead of me. She was much better in oils than I was, I never could get the hang of oils. She had a fine sure touch with pigment, she really might have become a good artist if she'd stuck with it. In Vermont now, even in Vermont where she has all the time in the world, she never paints anymore. Never. It is as if everything in *her* has gone dead as well.

Casamorte was alive though, and real I suppose, certainly more genuine an artist than I was at the time. Oh, I loved the *role* of being an artist, I played the role a bit more amateurishly perhaps than Casamorte, but I played it nonetheless. I would sit on subway trains or buses, incessantly sketching, not because I really itched to draw—or perhaps I did, who the hell knows anymore?—but only because I wanted everyone sitting opposite me to see that I was an artist, to understand that I was an extremely talented and serious person who was sketching, sketching, sketching all the time, oh boy, was I serious! Sometimes I would walk into a luncheonette still wearing my paint-smeared workshirt, knowing that everyone at the counter would turn and stare at me and think again Oh lookie, there's an artist, especially if Ebie was with me in her dirty green smock, her cheek smeared with pigment, she was a good painter but a sloppy one. Or I would sometimes stop dead in the middle of the sidewalk, and raise both hands in front of my face, palms flat, thumbs touching, to form a fleshy picture frame around a tree or a bench or a building in the distance, once again courting appreciation from the people in the street, the onlookers, the outsiders, those poor, untalented, uncreative souls. I think I knew even then I would never become a painter. I have since seen music students practicing scales on subway trains, their fingers running over imaginary keyboards in their laps; I have watched architectural students describe with soaring hands the engineering feat of the Guggenheim; I have overheard playwrights discussing the interminable and incomplete second acts of their works in progress; and I have learned without question that those who *play* the part never *live* it. I was only playing at being an artist. *I* knew it, and *Ebie* knew it, but neither of us ever mentioned it.

And yet there were times when, visual evidence to the contrary, talented people surrounding me day and night, doing work I could see, work I could compare against my own, there were nonetheless times when I felt I really had it in me. Laboring late into the night in Ebie's apartment (stay, she would constantly plead, *must* you go?), I would feel a solitary isolation (never truly solitary because I knew she was there across the room) a total absorption with the drawing pad before me, the charcoal or pencil moving in my hand as though directed by someone, something, other than myself, the line clean and sure and unfaltering. That was real. *That,* at least, was real. That, and Ebie.

Ebie was everything; everything paled beside her.

I can recall the first time we saw El Greco's *Cardinal* at the Metropolitan, standing before the painting—silken scarlet robes stiffly parted over intricately detailed lace, beringed left hand tensely gripping the arm of the chair, eyes covertly regarding something beyond the frame—my own eyes were on Ebie alone, watching her reaction, thrilling to her response. She caught her breath in wonder, a radiant awestruck look crossed her face, and I watched her in soaring delight; El Greco, for all his magnificance, could have been for me that day a Greenwich Village hack exhibiting seascapes on a Sixth Avenue sidewalk.

I loved her so much.

So very much.

There were daffodils blooming in the courtyard of the church on the day we were married. A stone baptismal font, fallen into neglectful disrepair, stood lopsidedly in one corner of the garden against a stone wall covered with English ivy. Beyond the wall and behind it, the city's buildings rose against an April sky stretched in taut blue brilliance. We stopped in the garden after the ceremony. The wedding party was on the sidewalk in front of the church, the photographer wondering how he had managed to lose us in the blizzard of tossed confetti and rice, the rented limousines at the curb, relatives and friends shaking hands in greeting, exclaiming no doubt on the beauty of the bride and the nervousness of the groom, anxious to get on with the reception, all waiting for the newly married Mr. and Mrs. James Driscoll to join them. But we had seen the garden earlier, separately, and now we were drawn to it together, neither of us uttering a word, as we ran down the church steps through the flying rice and paper, Ebie's hand in mine, and then raced along the stone wall to the low iron entrance gate. The gate was painted green, chipped in spots to reveal the rusting iron beneath. I opened it, it squeaked into the silence. We went into the small cloistered garden, treading softly over the slate walk to where the daffodils ringed the fallen stone font.

The ceremony had already taken place, but it was there in the garden that we were really wed.

With her hand in mine and her eyes wet, Ebie looked up at me and said, "Forever."

And I whispered "Forever" to her.

Louis Brackman lived in a garden apartment in Queens, a complex of six buildings set around a grassy court in which there were concrete benches and a lily pond. In the summertime, the benches were invariably occupied by young housewives taking a late afternoon breather before the dinner hour, which was just about when Sidney arrived each time. In the winter, as now, the benches were empty, the lily pond was a dark amoeba reflecting the starless sky above. It was six o'clock. The lights in the buildings surrounding the court were aglow and cooking smells wafted on the evening air. Sidney quickened his step and moved along the shoveled concrete walk to his father's ground-floor apartment. Through the kitchen window, he could see Louis wrapping something at the table, why did he always *wrap* the stuff, Sidney wondered. Why not simply say "Here, Sidney, here's some worthless crap for you" instead of going through this idiotic ritual each time? Sidney sighed and rang the bell.

His father did not ask who it was because he knew this was Thursday, and he knew that Sidney arrived every Thursday at close to six o'clock. Sidney did not expect him to call out, nor did he expect anything less than a five-minute wait on the doorstep since that was usually how long it took his father to get from the kitchen to the front hallway, give or take a few thousand years. He did not ring the bell again, nor did he exhibit any signs of impatience. He leaned against the brick wall of the building instead and looked up at the sky, wishing there were stars, and smelling rain in the air, and beneath that the aroma of borscht, his father was cooking borscht again. When Louis finally opened the door, the two men embraced silently, and then walked slowly into the kitchen, where Sidney would spend most of the visit. Sidney supported his father as they walked, one arm around the old man's waist, deploring his smell and the smell of the beets boiling in the kitchen, permeating the entire apartment until Sidney thought he would suffocate.

Louis was eighty-two years old, and Sidney could not remember a time when the old man had not been a burden, even when his mother was still alive. Dimly, only dimly, he perceived in this shell of a man someone who had once punched a Bowery wino, who was strong, who had black hair and dark shining eyes. That person was a stranger to Sidney, as was the old man he helped down the hallway and into the kitchen.

"I'm making borscht," Louis said.

"That's good."

"You like borscht, don't you?"

"Mmm."

"Your mother, may she rest in peace, made the best borscht."

"Mmm."

"Look what's on the table, Sidney," he said.

"Sit down, Pop."

"I can stand, I'm not a cripple, thank God. Look what I found for you."

There were three packages on the kitchen table, each wrapped in brown paper and tied with white string. "Well, sit down, Pop," Sidney said, and looked wearily at the packages and thought, Here we go again. His father took a seat at the table, and then put his hands before him on the table top, palms down, and smiled and looked at the packages. Sidney nodded and looked at the packages too.

"Your cousin Marvin called this morning," Louis said. "Don't you want to open the packages, Sidney?"

"Sure, Pop. What'd he want?"

"Who? Oh, Marvin. Nothing, nothing, he was complaining about his wife again, who knows?" Louis waved the problem aside with his bony hand and again looked at the packages. Sidney lifted one of them, shook it, and said, "This isn't a time bomb, is it, Pop?"

"Sure, sure, a time bomb. Open it."

"It won't blow up the whole apartment, will it?"

"Sure, blow up the apartment," Louis said, watching as Sidney fumbled with the knots on the package. Sidney loosened the string, and then pulled back the folds of wrapping paper. He recognized the bank at once, a small wooden box made of bamboo, with sliding panels that were pushed back one at a time and in sequence to reveal the keyhole. His father had given it to him as a present when he was ten years old. He had never kept more than a few dollars in coins in it at any time, but the knowledge that he was the only one who knew the secret of the sliding panels was a source of comfort and security at a time when he needed assurance most.

"Do you remember it?" his father asked.

"Yes, I do. Where'd you find it?"

"Oh, with the stuff in the closet. There's lots of stuff in the closet."

"Mmm," Sidney said. Automatically, his fingers moved to the first sliding panel, and then the second. He could not remember the sequence after that. He put the bamboo box down on the table, a faint pained smile on his face.

"Will you take it with you?" his father asked.

"Sure." He would take it with him and then throw it in the garbage when he got home, the same as he did with almost everything his father gave him.

"Open the others," Louis said, pleased.

The second package was long and flat. Sidney knew it was a book even before he loosened the string. He nodded as he pulled back the brown wrapping paper.

"From Harvard," his father said.

"Yes, I see."

It was a notebook he had kept for an Ethics class at Harvard when he was still an undergraduate. He had no interest whatever in it, but his father was watching him, so he leafed through some of the pages and pretended amazement at what he had written.

"I thought you could use it," Louis said.

"Yes," Sidney said, and nodded.

"Can you use it?"

"I'll find some use for it," Sidney said.

"I found it in the closet," his father said, and seemed to want to say more, but let the sentence trail instead.

"All this stuff," Sidney said, and let his sentence trail as well. He broke the string on the third package. The brown wrapping paper rattled open to reveal a wooden inkstand he had made in a shop class in elementary school. There were two holes for ink bottles, drilled into a solid block of wood that was affixed to a larger, flatter piece of wood. A scalloped bar in front of the inkwells was designed to hold pens. The inkstand was stained walnut. Sidney turned it upside down to its raw, unstained bottom where he had gouged out his name with a knife, S. BRACKMAN, and then filled in the letters with black ink. The date beneath his name was 2/7/25. February 7, 1925. He tried to remember the boy who had made this inkstand, but the image was vague. He turned the stand over in his hands again. Something else to throw in the garbage, he thought.

"You brought that home to your mother," Louis said.

"Yes, I remember."

"It was in the closet."

"I'll take it home with me."

"Sure, I have no use for it," Louis said. "I thought you might like it."

"Sure, I'll take it home."

"Well, how is the trial going?" Louis asked.

"Fine."

"I told all my friends you're in a new trial."

"That's good."

"Is it a murder case?"

"No. Plagiarism."

"What's that?"

"When somebody steals from something that's copyrighted."

"Books?"

"Yes. Or plays. Pop, do you have anything to drink in the house?"

"In the living room, there's something," Louis said. "Don't drink too much."

"No, I won't," Sidney said, and went out of the kitchen and into the darkness of the living room. He snapped on the light and searched in the low cabinet for his father's whiskey supply. There was a partially filled bottle of scotch, and a bottle of banana cordial someone had brought to Louis from Puerto Rico. Eventually, Louis would wrap the cordial in brown paper and present it to Sidney, who would throw it in the garbage the moment he got home. He poured two fingers of scotch into one of the glasses, and then turned off the light and went back into the kitchen.

"You ought to get some bourbon," he said, and went to the refrigerator.

"Isn't there bourbon?"

"No, you've only got a little scotch."

"Well," Louis said, and tilted his head.

Sidney put two ice cubes into his glass, sat at the table with his father, and sipped at the whiskey.

"So what's new?" Louis said.

"I'm getting married," Sidney said. "I think I'm getting married."

"Oh?"

"It's about time, huh?" Sidney said, and smiled at his father, and then took another sip of his scotch. "Forty-eight years old, that's a long time to be single."

"Sure, it's about time," his father said. "Who is the girl?"

"Her name is Charlotte Brown."

"Is she Jewish?"

"No."

His father was silent for a moment. Sidney sipped his drink.

"What is she, then?" his father asked.

"Irish, I think. Or English."

"You don't know?"

"I think she's Irish."

"Charlotte Brown?" his father said. "This doesn't sound Irish to me."

"I think it is."

"She's a nice girl?"

"Yes."

"An older woman?

"Well, she's twenty-seven."

"That's very young, Sidney."

"I know."

"She's pretty?"

"Yes."

"Well," Louis said, and again tilted his head skeptically.

"I'll bring her around someday."

"Yes," his father said, and nodded.

The men were silent. On the stove, the beets were boiling. Sidney finished his drink and went back into the living room for a refill. His father said, "Don't drink too much, Sidney."

"I won't," he answered, and came back into the kitchen. He would take home his father's presents and dump them in the garbage, the inkstand he had made when he was seven, the Chinese bank he had received as a gift when he was ten, and the Harvard notebook from his undergraduate days. He would dump them in the garbage.

"Pop," he said, "why haven't you ever . . ." and stopped.

"Yes?" his father said.

". . . gone back to that doctor on Park Avenue?" Sidney improvised.

"I went."

"You did?"

"Sure. He says it's nothing to worry. It's arthritis, I'll keep taking the cortisone, it isn't God forbid anything worse."

"Well, I'm glad to hear that," Sidney said. "Does the cortisone help?"

"A little."

"Well, that's good."

"Sure."

"Her nickname is Ch-Chickie," Sidney said suddenly.

"What?"

"My f-f-fiancée. Her nickname is Chickie."

"That's a funny name," his father said, and smiled. "Chickie."

"Yeah."

"Your mother, when she was a girl, they used to call her Sarale."

"I know."

"May she rest in peace."

"Mmm," Sidney said. He had finished the second scotch, and he wanted another drink, but he knew his father would frown upon a third. He sat at the kitchen table, jiggling his foot and looking up at the wall clock. It was only six-thirty.

"Do you remember your Aunt Hannah?" Louis asked.

"Yes." He was always asking Sidney if he remembered people he couldn't possibly ever forget. His Aunt Hannah had lived in the apartment next door on Houston Street when he was a boy. He'd spent half his childhood in her kitchen, and now his father asked if he remembered her. How the hell could he possibly ever forget Aunt Hannah?

"Her daughter is going to have a baby," Louis said.

"Another one."

"This is only three."

"I guess it is."

"You should go see your Aunt Hannah every now and then."

"I always mean to."

"Your mother, may she rest in peace, would have liked it."

"Maybe when the trial is finished," Sidney said. "Maybe I'll stop by one day."

"Well, I know you're busy. What did you call it? The trial?"

"Plagiarism."

"That's important?"

"I guess so."

"I'll have to tell my friends."

Yes, you tell them, he thought. Tell them your very important lawyer son is arguing a very important plagiarism case downtown. "There's ten million dollars involved," Sidney said.

Louis whistled softly.

"If we win the case, Carl and I will share four million dollars."

"That's plenty," Louis said.

"Tell your friends," Sidney answered.

He sat in his father's beet-smelling kitchen, and he longed to tell him about Chickie, about the love he felt for her, longed desperately to discuss something *important* with his father for once in his life, not cousin Marvin's idiotic troubles, or Aunt Hannah's third grandchild, but something important to *him,* to Sidney, to your *son,* Pop, to *me.* And he knew in that moment that winning the case would mean nothing to him if he did not also win Chickie. He almost made a bargain with God on the spot. Look, he thought, visualizing himself once again as a sunset-stained rabbi raising his eyes to heaven, Look, God, let me *lose* the case even, I don't *care,* really *I don't care,* just so long as you permit me to win Chickie. The offer startled him, and he revoked it at once because he didn't want God to take him too seriously. And yet, what difference would it make, win or lose, except for the money involved? And was even that important if he could not share the future with Chickie? Would it really matter, win or lose, if . . .

If there was no one there to . . .

Without realizing why, he suddenly said, "Why don't you ever . . ." and hesitated.

"Why don't I ever what?"

"I thought you might like . . ."

"Yes, what?"

Ask him, Sidney thought. At least give him the opportunity.

"Would you like to come down?"

"What?"

"Downtown."

"What do you mean, downtown?"

"The courthouse. The court. Tomorrow."

"What's tomorrow?"

"Friday. I'll be giving my summation. I thought . . ."

"I have to be home to light the *shabiss* candles."

"That's not until sundown. I'll get you home by then."

"How would I get there?"

"By cab. Or I can pick you up, if you like."

"Where is this?"

"Foley Square. Downtown."

"In New York?"

"Yes. I could pick you up in the morning, if you like."

"I have my medicine here," his father said.

"Well, you can take—"

"What time does it start?"

"Ten in the morning."

"The super's coming in tomorrow. To fix the radiator there in the bedroom. It leaks all over the floor."

"I just thought you might like to see . . ."

"Yes?"

". . . a . . . a court case," Sidney said. "Me," he said.

"I saw a court case when Harry Bergner was sued that time."

"I just thought . . ."

"They're all the same, no?"

"Yes, they're all the same," Sidney said. He paused. "I'd like another drink."

"Don't drink too much, Sidney," his father said.

It began raining at half-past seven, and the pressure call to Arthur came not ten minutes after the storm started. He knew at once that it was going to be a pressure call because when he answered, two voices came back at him with "Hello, Arthur," one from Stuart Selig and the other from Oscar Stern on the extension.

"Some storm, huh?" Stuart said.

"Yeah," Arthur said.

"We aren't interrupting anything, are we?" Oscar asked.

"No, I was reading."

"Anything good?" Stuart asked.

"Anything that might make a play?" Oscar asked.

"I don't think so. What's on your mind?"

"We might as well come straight to the point," Stuart said.

"That's right," Oscar said.

"Kent Mercer was up here just a little while ago. He told us he met you for lunch today."

"Yes, we had a long talk," Arthur said.

"According to Kent, you've got some doubts about making these changes Hester wants."

"I'm still thinking it over."

"Well, when do you think you'll know, Arthur? This is Thursday night."

"I know what it is."

"Tomorrow's Friday, Arthur."

"We promised Mitzi we'd let her know by Friday, Arthur."

"We don't want to pressure you . . ."

"That's right."

". . . but you haven't got all the time in the world to make your decision, you know. Maybe you don't have a clear picture of the situation."

"I think Kent gave me a pretty clear picture."

"Did he tell you he's dropping out if you don't make the changes?"

"He hinted it."

"Well, he did more than *hint* it when he was up here. He's the man for your play, Arthur, you realize that, don't you?"

"Yes, but if we have to lose him . . ."

"We *don't* have to lose him," Stuart said.

"That's right," Oscar said.

"We don't have to lose *anybody*. If you agree to make the changes, we'll have one of the best directors in the business and one of the brightest young actresses around, and we'll also get our financing—which is the most important thing."

"You know how much money I'll get if I win this case?" Arthur asked.

"Meantime," Oscar said, "you haven't won it."

"I could produce the play myself, six times over. A *hundred* times over."

"I don't bet on horse races or on trials," Stuart said. "Will you make the changes, or won't you?"

"The Dramatists Guild contract . . ."

"Screw the Dramatists Guild *and* their contract," Stuart said. "Nobody can force you to make the changes, that's true, you're protected. But is the Dramatists Guild going to raise the money for your play?"

"Are *you?*"

"If we sign Hester, yes."

"Guaranteed?"

"Guaranteed. I've been on the phone all day. I've got more than enough promises already."

"That's right."

"Promises aren't cash," Arthur said.

"I can guarantee these promises, Arthur. I'm not exactly new in this business, these are people who've invested with me before. They'll come in if we get Hester."

"She's very hot, Arthur."

"Arthur, we have to know what you plan to do."

"I don't know yet."

"Will you call me later tonight?"

"I may have to sleep on it."

"Do me a favor, don't sleep on it. I want to be able to call Mitzi first thing in the morning and tell her you're eager to get to work on the revisions."

"I'm not."

"*Fake* a little enthusiasm."

"Stuart, I don't like this kind of pressure. I really don't."

"That's right, this is pressure," Oscar said. "We're all under pressure, Arthur, not just you."

"I don't like to make important decisions under pressure."

"Nobody does. But that's the way most important decisions are made."

"We may know about the trial early next week. Can't we—"

"And you may not know for six months."

"It never takes that long."

"It could."

"Anyway, even next week is too late. Arthur, maybe you still don't understand the situation. Hester's going to sign for that Osborne play unless you go along with these changes. Now which is it going to be? Everybody rich and happy, or everybody behaving in a highly unprofessional manner?"

"What's unprofessional about wanting to preserve what I wrote?"

"This is the theater, Arthur. Don't talk like a hick."

"Any play is a collaborative effort, you know that," Oscar said.

"I don't like collaborating with pants pressers."

"What are you talking about?"

"Mitzi Starke is a pants presser. What the hell does she know about playwriting?"

"She doesn't have to know *anything* about playwriting," Stuart said, "as long as she's got clients like Hester Miers."

"If you'd raised the goddamn money, we wouldn't be in this situation," Arthur said angrily.

"We tried our best. And we can still raise it, if you'll compromise a little."

"A little, sure," Arthur said.

"A little, yes. Will you call me later tonight?"

"If I've decided."

"Decide, Arthur," Stuart said.

"Good night, Arthur," Oscar said.

Arthur almost slammed the receiver onto the cradle, but something restrained him. He put it down gently, and then turned from the phone and walked to the rain-streaked window and looked down at the gleaming wet street outside. He went to the closet then, and put on his raincoat and an old rain hat, a battered corduroy he had bought six years ago and perhaps worn as many times since. He looked at the room unseeingly for a moment before turning off the lights, and then went out of the apartment and into the street.

The rain was cold. It fell from the sky in slanting sheets that swept sidewalk and gutter, driven by a sharp wind. He almost changed his mind, and then decided the hell with it and kept walking, the collar of his coat high on the back of his neck, his hat pulled down over his forehead, his hands thrust into his pockets. He did not know where he was going, or why he felt he could think better in the rain than in his apartment, but he continued walking nonetheless, heading west toward Lexington Avenue, and then continuing westward, turning downtown whenever he was stopped by a corner traffic light.

It seemed to him that his decision hinged entirely on the outcome of the trial. If he knew he were positively going to win the case, he could tell them all to go to hell, he would not need anyone's money to produce the play, he could produce the damn thing himself. On the other hand, if he knew for certain that the case was lost, there would be no hope for production unless he were willing to make the changes. Yes, he could take the play around again, but he knew Kent was right on that score, too, a dead duck was a dead duck. He had circulated the play for six months before Selig and Stern optioned it, showing it to most of the theatrical producers in town. It was highly unlikely that anyone would suddenly become interested in it again, not after word went around that they'd had trouble raising the money. Word had a way of getting around in this town, faster than the speed of light. He was willing to bet that Lincoln Center already knew Hester was planning to leave, and exactly why—to star in Arthur Constantine's new play.

If he made the changes.

All you have to do, he thought, is make the changes. It'll be easy to make the changes, God knows you made enough changes when you were working for the Hollywood pants pressers. Out there, anyone was entitled to a suggestion, including the studio typists. He would never forget the day Charlie Mandell asked the *barber* what he thought of a scene they were discussing, right there in Charlie's office, Charlie sitting in his big stuffed green leather chair with the barber's cloth around his neck. And the barber very seriously offered his advice on what he thought would be a better approach to the scene, and Charlie took the suggestion and said, "I think we ought to work it out along those lines. After all, Arthur, these are the people who go to *see* the movies. I'll never sell the little man short." If he made the changes now, he would indeed be selling the little man short because his play was *about* the little man, not about a barber of course, nor even about the little man Charlie Mandell had in mind perhaps, but certainly about a simple ordinary man who happened to be his father. It was an honest play. It was the first honest thing he'd written in a long long while, and now they were asking him to change it, make changes that might not damage its honesty but, yes, he thought, yes. The changes *will* damage the honesty. It will not be the play I wrote anymore.

He had let Freddie Gerard do that to *Catchpole,* well, wait a minute, it wasn't fair to turn on Freddie, if it hadn't been for Freddie the play would never have been produced at all. And yet he *had* allowed Freddie and the director, a man named Fielder Crowell, to turn the play upside down, to rearrange scenes, to emphasize here and to excise there, "This isn't working, Arthur, can you change it to . . . ?" Of course, you can change it to. You can change it to anything. You can bring six hundred pink elephants on stage at any given point, and if you are a skillful enough writer, you can make those elephants seem plausible and reasonable and in fact necessary to plot and theme and character. Yes, you can change it to. You can change a whore to a nun, and a doctor to an Indian chief, you can put this scene at the beginning and that scene at the end, you can change words and lines and speeches, you can rewrite the entire second act in New Haven, and after you've changed everything to, you can change it *back* to again. You can juggle all these bits and pieces in the air like a circus performer and forget exactly what you intended in the first place. You can allow them to march right through the play with mud on their feet, tracking it up while you scurry along behind them trying to wipe up the footprints. Yes, I can change Carol to a social worker who has had one affair, I can change the father to a small business man or a minor executive, I can change the play, I can make it their play, the way I made *Catchpole* their play and therefore nobody's play. And then, maybe years from now, a James Driscoll will step in and *really* finish the job, just the way he did with *Catchpole,* step in and make it not my play, and not their play, but *his* play, steal it right from under my nose, and it'll serve me right because I didn't have the guts to stand behind what I'd written. You want to change it? Fine. Go write your own play. This is my play, and it's going to stay my play.

It's going to stay your *manuscript,* you mean.

Oh sure, very clever, Kent. Go to work on the frightened writer, give me a few good ones right now while I'm up against the ropes. I'm worried about this trial, you see, I really am. I don't know what's happening down there, I haven't heard anyone in these past four days mention the fact that *Catchpole* is worthless so long as *The Paper Dragon* is credited to James Driscoll; that anyone reading my play will say, "Why this was stolen from that novel, what was the name of it, it's a direct steal," instead of the other way around. I've heard a lot of arguments in these past four days about diminishing the value and so on, and I've learned all about Driscoll's creative process, but no one has brought up *my* creative process, the months of hard work I put into that play, the pain each time they asked me for another change, the gradual metamorphosis to what the play became, and the hope, the constant hope that someday someone would recognize what I'd done, but no, not even there, not even in that court of law. It's been Driscoll, Driscoll, Driscoll, *The Paper Dragon* is the glittering success, and *Catchpole* is the shabby little beggar hanging around the fringes of the trial. So get in here, Kent. Get in here with your faggot wrist hanging and tighten your hand into a fist for just a few good ones, a few short sharp ones to the gut. This is a good time to take Constantine. He doesn't know whether he's coming or going, he doesn't know whether to dig one grave or two, let's finish him off once and for all, pow, pow, it's going to stay your *manuscript,* kid, pow, that's the way, it's now or never, kid, wham, again, again, we can't force you to make the changes, zap, whack, bam, but you can't force *us* to produce it, either, you get it, kid? wise up, kid, make the changes, kid, pow.

I don't know, he thought. I just don't know.

If I could climb inside McIntyre's head for just a minute, listen to his thoughts and get some sort of inkling, just a clue is all I need, how can I plan on anything if nothing's sure, if it all depends on the opinion of one man?

Ten million dollars.

Look, Oscar, ten million dollars.

Look, Stuart, the book really *was* stolen from me.

Look, everybody! Look!

He was suddenly chilled to the bone. His face was cold and wet, and his shoes squished water with each step he took. He ran across Sixth Avenue, hurdled the slush against the curb, and spotted a bar in the middle of the block. He walked toward it hastily, glanced through the plate-glass window, and then went inside. Taking a booth near the juke box, he pumped a handful of coins into the machine, and ordered a double scotch.

The city's buildings thrust their broken illumination upward into a sky black with rainclouds, reflected themselves downward again against shining black asphalt. Each brilliant red and green traffic light, each glowing amber street lamp, each twisted tube of orange neon found its echo on the sleek wet surface of the street, so that the city seemed to reverberate with light, seemed to shimmer with light pierced by slanting silver needles of rain. The rain fell remorselessly. It beat noisily upon rooftops and skylights, rattled in gutters and drains, raged in windswept fury across the avenues, hurled its light-smashed slivers against pavement and street. Crumbling pieces of snow splashed away from the banked slush, twisted and whirled like paper boats in the dark curbside torrent, tumbled toward sewer grates, plunged underground in cascades of paper scraps and broken sticks.

They stood in the teeming rain under Jonah's big black umbrella, trying to get a taxi, listening to the irregular beat of the falling drops. There was an insular quality to their corner haven, the secrecy of an attic hiding place. Sally leaned against him, her arm looped through his as they watched the oncoming traffic, Jonah signaling now and again to cabs he thought were free, only to discover they were either carrying passengers or showing their Off Duty signs. But there was no sense of urgency to Jonah's attempts, and Sally exhibited no impatience when, after ten minutes, he still had not succeeded in getting a cab. They began walking idly up Sixth Avenue, looking at the rows of diamond rings in lighted pawnshop windows, stopping to study an old gold locket in one of the smaller antique places, window-shopping cameras and books and phonographs and hardware and records and sewing machines and paint and practical jokes, pausing to study menus taped to restaurant windows, strolling up the avenue as though it were springtime and they were visiting a bazaar.

He had told her at dinner that he'd contacted Santesson late that afternoon and asked him to call off the dogs. He had no doubt now that this was what accounted for the success of the evening, the pleased and somehow flattered smile Sally wore all during the meal, the way she held his arm in easy intimacy now as they walked up the avenue. He could remember walking through the rain with Christie, her hands thrust into the pockets of her white raincoat, a yellow kerchief on her head, the black bangs fringing her brow, her eyes dancing with delight. They had gone to see four movies that day, one at the Roxy, another at the Capitol, a third at the Strand, and the last in a fleabag on 42nd Street, necking furiously in each one. And then they were out in the rain again, and he held her elbow and helped her to pick her delicate way through the puddles, and she said to him quite suddenly, "Jonah, I will never love anyone but you."

And then, one thought linked to the other, one image repeating the other the way the Dunseath looks repeated themselves generation after generation, fading, he thought of Amy. Last week, he had seen a ring in a jewelry shop window on East 61st, a beautiful tiny cameo set with a single diamond. He had known immediately that it would make a perfect Christmas gift for Amy, and would have purchased it on the spot had the shop been open. He had written down the name of the place, and then tucked the card into his wallet, intending to return at the earliest opportunity. But something had always intruded, the ring (he *hoped*) still sat in the jeweler's window, and Amy would be home tomorrow. He wanted to present it to her when he picked her up at the station, a harbinger of the holidays, welcome home, Amy, Merry Christmas, my darling. He would have to pick it up tomorrow, after court broke, there'd still be time. If only life weren't so goddamn cluttered, he thought, if only everything didn't scream at you from a hundred different directions, all the cheap merchandise in these store windows, a thousand shabby Santa Clauses shaking their bells, a million late shoppers rushing past, a lifetime rushing past. He would have to pick up the ring tomorrow, yes, after court broke. They would undoubtedly be out early; the summations would not take that long.

"There's one!" Sally said suddenly.

"Where?"

"There! Quick!"

He saw the cab, and began running for it just as a little man in a dark green trenchcoat leaped off the curb and began signaling wildly to the driver. There was no doubt in Jonah's mind that Sally had seen it first, but even if there had been a question of priority, he did not intend losing the cab. He ran past the little man just as the cab pulled to a stop. Clamping his fingers around the door handle, he said "Sorry," without looking at the man, and then signaled to Sally, who immediately came off the curb to join him.

"This is my taxi," the man said.

"It's my taxi," Jonah said flatly, and held open the door for Sally. The man, he now saw, was perhaps sixty-five years old, and he was drenched to the skin. He stared up at Jonah without rancor, a pleading, frightened look on his wet, red face. He wore rimless glasses, and they were speckled with raindrops. The brim of his hat kept dripping water.

"My wife is waiting there on the sidewalk," the man said lamely.

Jonah did not answer. He hurried Sally into the taxi, slammed the door shut as soon as he was inside, and then gave the driver Sally's address.

"Did you see a woman on the sidewalk?" he asked her.

"No."

"I didn't either."

"I did," the driver said.

"What?" Jonah said.

"Forgive me for living," the driver said, "but there *was* a little old lady huddled in the doorway there near Stern's, that was probably the guy's wife."

"Well, I didn't see her," Jonah said.

"It's none of my business," the driver said, "and I don't

like to get into arguments with passengers, but by rights, this was that guy's cab. If a man signals to you, that's his cab. He gives you a signal, and you give him a signal back. You either wave your hand out the window, or dip your lights, anything to let him know you seen him. That's your contract, mister, that means you ain't gonna pick nobody else up, and he ain't gonna jump in no other cab before you get to him. That's the way it works in this city. You from New York?"

"I'm from New York," Jonah said.

"Then you should know that's the way it works here."

"A new slant on contract law," Jonah said to Sally.

"What was that?" the driver said, glancing over his shoulder.

"Don't you think you ought to watch the road?" Jonah said.

"I'm watching the road fine, thanks. I been driving a taxi for seventeen years, and I never had an accident yet, thank God. Don't worry about my watching the road. That guy signaled to me, and I signaled back, and by rights this was his cab, not that it's any of my business. Also, there *was* a little old lady huddled in the doorway there near Stern's, dripping wet, no matter what you say."

"Look, just drive, will you?" Jonah said, annoyed.

"Forgive me for breathing," the driver said.

Sally cleared her throat.

"But if you think it's fun driving a cab on a rainy night, you ought to try it sometime."

Jonah did not answer. Sally squeezed his hand, and he nodded to her in the darkness of the back seat. The driver was silent for the remainder of the trip downtown. When they reached Sally's building, the fare on the meter was a dollar and ten cents. Jonah tipped the driver a quarter, and got out of the cab to follow Sally, who had taken the umbrella.

"Hey, just a minute, buddy," the driver said.

Jonah hesitated. He ran back to the taxi, stooped to peer through the open front window, and said, "What is it?" The rain was beating down on his head and back. It splashed noisily in the curbside puddles, drummed on the roof of the taxi.

The driver had his hand extended, the dollar bill resting under the dime and the quarter. "You sure you don't need this more than I do?" he asked.

Jonah looked at him steadily.

"Yes, I do," he answered and gingerly picked the quarter from his palm. "Good night," he said politely. He turned away from the cab, and ran through the rain and up the steps to where Sally was wrestling with the umbrella, simultaneously trying to unlock the vestibule door. Behind him, the driver shouted, "What're you, a *wise* guy?" and gunned the taxi away from the curb.

They climbed the four flights to her apartment. Jonah's trouser legs were sticking to him. The shoulders of his raincoat were soaked through to his suit jacket. Sally quickly unlocked the door and said, "You must be drenched," which he acknowledged with a surly nod as they entered the apartment. He took off the dripping raincoat at once, and then removed his jacket and draped it over the living room radiator. His shirt was wet too, clinging to his shoulders and chest. He took off his glasses and dried them briefly on his handkerchief.

"Here," Sally said, "try some of this."

"What is it?"

"Spanish brandy."

Jonah took the extended glass. "Let's drink to the little old lady huddled in the doorway of Stern's," he said.

"It bothers you, doesn't it?" Sally said.

"Yes."

"Then admit it."

"I admit it."

"No, you're joking about it."

"All right, I won't joke about it. It bothers me. It bothers the hell out of me. I don't like the idea of having beat an old lady out of a taxicab. All right? I may be a son of a bitch, but I'm not that ruthless."

"Who says you're a son of a bitch, Jonah?"

"I don't know," he said. He could hear a radio playing somewhere in the building. In the bathroom, the rain drummed noisily on the skylight. "Listen," he said.

"I hear it."

Her head was studiously bent as she poured brandy into her own glass, her light brown hair hanging over one cheek, her eyes intent on the glass and the lip of the bottle. Watching her, he felt curiously relaxed, as though this tiny apartment, the sound of the rain and the distant radio, the feeling of contained heat, this tall and slender girl gracefully putting the cork back into the bottle, all evoked a memory for him that was both comforting and secure. And then, as she turned from the coffee table, head rising, soft brown hair settling gently into place beside the curve of her cheek as though in slow motion, her eyes meeting his, her mouth slowly widening into a smile, everything so slow and easy and tirelessly simple, he remembered the alcohol ring on the bedroom dresser, where Christie's glass of sherry had rested through the night, and the morning had dawned bleakly on the dead and floating fruit flies of their marriage. Without realizing he was about to say it, without recognizing his need to tell her about it, he said "Have you ever been to San Francisco?"

"No," she said. "Whatever made you think of San Francisco?"

"It rained the whole weekend we were there," he said, and shrugged.

She waited. She looked at him expectantly, and waited.

"My partner," he said.

"What?"

"We went to San Francisco together. Have you ever been inside a prison?"

"No."

"You wouldn't like it."

"I guess not."

Silence again, the rain unceasing, the distant radio carrying snatches of melody on the night air, unrecognizable, and still she waited and he thought, What the hell do you want from me? and realized, of course, that she had asked for nothing.

"What is it?" she said.

"What?"

"A . . . a strange look just came over your face."

"No," he said. "Nothing."

"Tell me."

"Nothing," he said.

She nodded, a curious nod that was more like a shrug, and then she sat and crossed her legs, still waiting, knowing he would tell her when he was ready, and wondering if she wanted him to tell her, and remembering the way Hadad had kept referring to him as her boy friend. The internal revenue agent's name had been Ronny, and she'd been very fond of him. Even Gertie had liked him, but of course Gertie didn't know he was married and lived in Scarsdale with his wife and small son. She had not been to bed with a man since she and Ronny ended it in April. She felt no desire now, and yet she knew without question that she would go to bed with Jonah Willow tonight, and she wondered why.

"We were asked to defend a prisoner out there, that's all," Jonah said. "At San Quentin."

"I see."

"He'd killed one of the guards. Said the man had been harassing him."

"Had he?" she asked.

"Who knows? The guard was dead, so we certainly couldn't ask him. Smith maintained—that was his name, Orville Smith—said the guard had made things impossible for him from the moment he arrived. He was serving a life term, you see. He'd murdered his wife and daughter. Killed them with an ax." Jonah paused. "A California firm was handling the case, they called us in to see if we'd be interested. We . . . our firm . . . Raymond's and mine . . . had built a reputation by then and . . . there was a mandatory death penalty involved, you see, if Smith got convicted, that was the law."

"Did you take the case?"

"Well . . . it seemed to me, it seemed to me there *had* been provocation. After all, Smith was pretty much at this fellow's mercy, you know, and had to take his abuse and listen to his remarks. What finally caused him to crack, in fact, was a simple remark, that's all. Smith said the guard called him 'Lizzie' one day, after Lizzie Borden, and that was it. They were in the dining hall, and Smith grabbed his fork and went for the guard's throat and didn't quit until the man was dead. It took four other guards to pull him away, he was a powerful man, six-four, with arms like this."

"Did you take the case, Jonah?"

"I didn't even like the man, I couldn't possibly bring myself to like him and yet . . . I . . . I did feel he had been abused. I tried to explain this to Raymond, why I thought we should take the case. We were sitting on the porch of the guest cottage, Raymond and I, looking out at the rain and the high illuminated walls ot the prison, and Raymond very quietly suggested that maybe I was confusing my private life with my professional life. When I asked him what he meant, he said maybe I was equating the *actual* murder of a wife and child with what was only the *symbolic* murder of a wife and child. Now what's *that* supposed to mean, I said, and he said I'm talking about the divorce, Jonah, and I said, *What* divorce? and he said, *Your* divorce. I'd been divorced that August, you see. Just two months before Raymond and I went to San Quentin together."

"I see."

"He'd always been very fond of Christie. My wife. My former wife."

"I see."

"So . . . so I could understand why he was disturbed about the divorce, and . . . and about Christie drinking and . . . and the things she was doing. He'd known her from . . . from when we were first married you see, when things were very different. But I couldn't understand what any of this had to do with defending Smith, so I . . . I tried to be very calm because Raymond was my closest friend and my partner. . . . I . . . I very calmly explained that I didn't feel any guilt about the failure of my marriage, that Christie had made it virtually impossible to go on living with her, and that we'd both agreed divorce would be best for all parties concerned, including Amy. My daughter. I have a twelve-year-old daughter."

Sally nodded.

"Raymond just said, Sure, Jonah, sure, and then, all of a sudden, he said, I don't want to defend this man. So I . . . I asked him why he didn't want to defend him and he said because Smith is repulsive and rotten and obviously guilty, and I said, Wait a minute, and he said, No, you wait a minute, Jonah, defending that bastard would be contrary to everything I believe about law and justice.

"The rain was coming down, we sat on the porch in those big wicker chairs painted white by the prisoners, and I said, Raymond, you know this man's rights are in danger of being violated, and he said, Don't give me any more of *that* shit, Jonah, all you want is another newspaper headline. And . . . and then he . . . he told me I . . . was nothing but a self-seeking son of a bitch who had never really understood Christie, who had forced her to become what she was by totally ignoring her needs in my ruthless . . . he used that word, ruthless, he said . . . in my ruthless ambition to become the biggest and best-known lawyer in the history of the goddamn profession, that . . . that I was responsible for the divorce and for . . . for ruining a . . . a damn sweet lady."

Jonah's glass was empty.

He put it to his lips, discovered the brandy was gone, and then put the glass down on the table.

"I guess Smith was guilty, Sally, but . . . even if he *had* stabbed that officer in full view of God knows how many men, the thing wasn't premeditated, it wasn't malicious, it *couldn't* have been, it was a spur-of-the-moment act provoked by the guard. Raymond had . . . Raymond had no right to . . . to say the things he said to me.

"But they were said. They were out. And when people pass that certain line, wherever it may be . . ." His voice trailed. "There . . . there are things people say to each other that can never be retracted. Christie and I had said those things, we had hurled all the goddamn filthy words we could think of, we had accused, we had condemned, and it ended." He closed his eyes and sighed. "And then Raymond and I said all there was to say. And there was no going back." He looked up suddenly. "I keep losing partners."

"Maybe you don't need a partner, Jonah."

"Maybe not."

"Did you take the case?"

"Yes. I argued it with everything that was in me, just to prove, just to show Raymond that he was wrong, just to *win* it, and to show him. Mitigating circumstances, I said, provocation, your Honor, here was a man in bondage being tormented by his jailer. We could say, your Honor, we could almost say this security officer was a man seeking his own death, tormenting a convicted murderer. We could in a sense, your Honor, say this man was intent on committing suicide, your Honor, we could say he took his own life. And must we now take yet another life to justify the vagaries of this troubled mind, the labyrinthine motivation of a man intent on suicide? Must we do that, your Honor, to satisfy whatever primitive clamor for blood we recognize within ourselves? When it was all over, they sent him to the gas chamber. Period. I lost."

She suddenly knew why she would allow him to make love to her, knew it even before he said what he said next.

"I'm going to lose this one too, Sally."

"How do you know?"

"Driscoll is guilty."

"That doesn't mean you'll lose."

"Maybe I *want* to lose."

"Will that help?"

"He's guilty," Jonah said. "He sat in that courtroom today and constructed a totally plausible network of deceit, attempting to trace the workings of the mind, something Brackman couldn't *hope* to contradict. Iceman is coal man, and coal man is Colman, and Colman is death, and death is the iceman in *The Iceman Cometh,* expecting us to swallow a literary association test delivered with a straight face. Peter is a phallic reference, and Morley is a Negro he knew as a boy, renamed Christopher in honor of the novelist, and Major Catharine Astor is definitely *not* Constantine's major, and yet Driscoll knew the color of her hair and the minor incident of showing the colonel his medical record, but no this is not the basis for the letter-carrying scene. Nor was the 105th Division based on Constantine's. Then where *did* it come from? How in hell could he have hit upon those identical three digits, and why didn't he have a psychological explanation for *them,* too, the way he had for every other alleged similarity? He slipped the other day when we were having drinks together, he said, 'I won't explain that number,' and then he changed it to 'I can't explain it,' but he meant 'I *won't,*' goddamn it. And the reason he wouldn't is because the number stuck in his head, it remained in his head after he saw Constantine's play—he's been a theatergoer from the time he was twelve, he's probably seen every piece of garbage ever presented on the Broadway stage, he practically admitted as much to me in private. So how *could* he tell us where he got that number, when telling us would have sent the case straight up the chimney?

"He's a lying bastard, and a thief, and I'm defending him."

Sally put down her glass, rose, and walked to where he was standing. Very gently, she put her hands on his shoulders and lifted her face to be kissed. She thought how odd it was that men could talk about losing partners and losing cases and even losing wives, and never once realize what they had really lost. She kissed him and hoped that when he lost this case as well (because he was defending a guilty man he thought was James Driscoll and not himself) perhaps he would remember he had been to bed with her, the way the English teacher in Schenectady would always remember he had been to bed with her.

She knew suddenly that she would not be seeing much of Jonah Willow once the trial ended.

She knew this with certainty, and with sadness, and relief. There were far too many things he was still trying to forget, far too many ghosts in his life; she had no desire to become yet another one of them. She hoped only that he would remember her.

Once she had asked her mother to make believe she was a person, and her mother had said, No, Sally, that coat isn't right for you, take it off.

The rain stopped at midnight, just as they came out of the movie theater and into the street. They walked up Broadway together, Ebie's arm through his, watching the after-theater crowd, relishing the noise and the clamor of New York City, so unlike what they knew in Vermont. Under the marquee of the Astor, a crowd of people in formal wear stood laughing and chatting, trying to get taxis, boisterous and loud, obviously enjoying themselves. The women wore mink coats over flowing gowns of pale blue and lucid pink, corsages pinned to bodice or waist or—as with one pretty brunette in a lustrous dark fur—pinned to her hair, just above the ear. There was a holiday mood outside the hotel and in the lobby as well, where men in dinner jackets told dirty jokes to each other and women laughed raucously with them, and then remembered to blush. A man dressed as Santa Claus, drunk as a lord, came staggering toward the revolving doors, snapping his fingers in time to the music that came from some hidden ballroom. Ebie's face suddenly broke into a grin.

"Listen," she said.

"What is it?"

"Listen."

He could not place the tune. Violins carried it on the noisy lobby air, evoking a mood, frustratingly elusive.

"Come," she said, and suddenly took his hand.

They went through the lobby, searching out the source of the music, following the strains of the orchestra until at last they stood just outside the Rose Room, and nodded to each other like conspirators. She raised her arms, and Driscoll automatically took her hand and cradled her waist, and they began dancing silently in the corridor outside the ballroom.

He felt again the way he'd felt when they were young together, in love together, possessed of a confidence that was now alien to him. She was light in his arms, her feet skimmed over the polished floor. They danced past two old ladies in gloves and hats, who looked at them in wonder. The old ladies delighted him, their looks of astonishment, the way the one in the purple hat opened her eyes wide to express shock, outrage, surprise, wonder, bemusement, even a little touch of wickedness. He wanted to scoop up both old ladies, catch them both in his arms along with Ebie, and dance them down the corridor and out the side door and onto 44th Street and over to Sardi's and maybe clear to the Hudson River and across to Jersey and points west, all the way back to their homes in Albuquerque or Des Moines, and then on past California and across the Pacific to exotic Oriental places that would cause the lady in the purple hat to open her eyes wide again and drop her jaw in shock, outrage, surprise, wonder, bemusement, and wicked glee. He felt, when things were right, as they were now, the same happiness he had known in those years before he left for the Army.

Their feet no longer touched the ground, they seemed to float on air an inch above the floor of the corridor. One of the old ladies was laughing now, all the world loves a lover, a bellhop carrying a wreath of flowers danced out of their way as though he were part of a consuming ballet, the world would soon be dancing with them, people would come out into the streets dancing and singing and shouting their fool heads off because James Randolph Driscoll and Edna Belle Dearborn were in love.

Had been in love, he thought.

As suddenly as they had begun dancing, they stopped.

October, he thought.

Out of breath, Ebie laughed and squeezed his hand.

1950, he thought.

He looked down at her and tried to remember what it had been like before then, and wondered how it could ever be that way again. They walked to the elevators in silence.

I got a medal in October of 1950, he thought, it was pinned right between my eyes, I've been wearing it ever since.

"Oh, my, that was fun," Ebie said.

They entered the waiting car. The doors closed. The elevator streaked up the shaft, cables whining and groaning.

I got my medal for being a nice guy and a fool, he thought, that's what they gave medals for back in those days.

I wrote all about my medal in a book called *The Paper Dragon,* perhaps you've read it, madam. It's about the Korean War, yes, and about this nice young man who is victimized by these horrible people who eventually cause his death, a symbolic death, madam, Oh yes, an *actual* death in the book, but really symbolic—I testified to that effect before the learned and honorable judge today. It is now a matter of record that the death of Lieutenant Alex Cooper, according to his creator (although such status is still in serious doubt), was intended as a symbolic death. If you're ever haggling over that one at a literary tea, just look up the trial record and you'll know the death was supposed to be symbolic. Yes, madam, my medal was delivered in the crisp October, it was a nice medal to receive. I wore it into battle when they came charging across the river, it gave me courage because I didn't give a damn anymore, you see. That's why medals are awarded, to give you courage.

They are all looking for medals in that courtroom, all except me. I got my medal, and I described my medal, and it took every ounce of strength I had, and there's nothing more inside me, nothing left to say or do. I wanted only to die quietly on that farm I bought in Vermont, so why did you have to come along, Mr. Constantine? Why did you have to start this ridiculous suit, opening all the old wounds again, why did you have to do this, Mr. Constantine?

Oh, sure, I can understand. You want a chestful of medals, right? You want all those millions API made on the film, and you want credit for the book as well because you think the book was the medal when it was really only the catalogue description of the medal. The real medal is pinned right here between my eyes, and I'm sure you wouldn't want that, Mr. Constantine, because it has hurt like hell ever since 1950, can't you see the scars, yes, quite painful when it rains. What'll they do if you win this case? Will they have to tell everybody you really wrote *The Paper Dragon?* Will they pull back all the copies and cross out my name, so sorry, put yours in its place? Is that what they do when someone has made a terrible mistake, oh my goodness, we've credited the wrong man with authorship. We gave the medal to the right man, however, and if *The Paper Dragon* is a fairly accurate description of the events leading up to that singular decoration, how then is it possible that the chronicle was stolen? Strange, passing strange indeed.

Do you know what I managed to do in court today?

Under oath?

I managed to tell the truth, and yet *not* tell the truth.

It was quite simple. I could do it with a completely straight face and hardly any increase in my pulse rate. I wouldn't be surprised if I could beat a lie detector test, I'm getting very expert at telling only partial truth. Maybe I'll suggest to his Honorable McIntyre that they give me a lie detector test and ask me if I wrote *The Paper Dragon,* and I will say, Yes, I wrote it, and then they'll ask me if I stole it from Constantine's play, and I'll say, No, I did not steal it from anybody's play, I stole it from in *here,* and in *here,* that's where I stole it. It's a secret I stole from a dying man who has been suffering from a rare incurable malady since October of 1950, that is who I stole it from, whom.

Then how do you account for *this,* sir, and how do you account for *that,* sir, and how do you account for the *fact,* sir, and *tell* us, sir, *tell* us, and I'll partial-truth that infernal machine until it short circuits itself and goes completely out of business, I can beat any machine in the house.

I've already told you once, I told the *world* once, isn't once enough? You know about my medal, what the hell more do you need? Shall I spell it out for you syllable by painful syllable, go over it one more time for the slow ones, cater to the lip readers, spare me, please. Make what you will of it, it's over and done with, the trial is over, the case is closed. I don't even want credit for the book, give the damn book to Constantine, let him go tell his mother *he* wrote it, I don't care.

The elevator doors opened. They stepped out into the corridor and walked to their room. At the door, she hesitated and put her hand on his arm.

"Dris," she said, "there's still a chance."

"For what? The case is closed. Tomorrow they'll make their set speeches, and that'll be that."

"There's something to save," she whispered.

"What's there to save, Ebie?"

"Us."

"Don't make me laugh."

"You thought so once."

"I never thought so."

"When you were discharged, when you came home, you tried to understand."

"I tried to understand for eleven goddamn years. I never could, Ebie. So forget it. I have."

"You haven't forgotten it, you've only exorcised it."

"That's the same thing."

"No. You can't erase something by writing a book about it."

"I wrote a book about the Army in Korea."

"Dris, if you won't tell them the truth, I will." She looked up at him, and he saw that there were tears in her eyes. "I'll tell them about the 105th," she said.

He did not answer her. He stared at her and tried to fathom whether or not there was substance to her threat, but he did not speak.

"I know," she said. "I know it's not a hundred and five."

He kept staring at her.

"I know it's two numbers, Dris. I know it's a ten and a five, and I know *why* and I'll *tell* them why."

"And kill me twice," he said.

"No. And save you once."

He turned away from her and unlocked the door. He hesitated in the doorway, seemed about to say something, and then went into the room instead.

Ebie followed him in soundlessly.

FRIDAY

15

THE DAY WAS COLD and clear.

A brilliant blue sky swept from horizon to horizon beyond the tall courtroom windows, cloudless, reflecting a cold light that caused tabletops and walls, benches and chairs, even pencils lying in repose to leap toward the eye in startling clarity. Each line of the American flag beside the judge's bench seemed inked with a thick pen, its alternating red and white stripes folded in bold black shadows. Driscoll's trained eye followed each wavering dark line, dipped to the point of the flag hanging low, retraced itself upward through crossing draped and overlapping patterns toward the creased blue field and crumpled white stars. He walked behind Ebie to the empty jury box, sat beside her, glanced at Willow, and then turned toward the plaintiff's table, where his eyes met Constantine's.

For a moment, the men almost nodded to each other, almost acknowledged each other's presence. Constantine seemed ready to lift his hand from the table in a short gesture of greeting, Driscoll seemed about to smile in recognition. And then one or another of them, or perhaps both by mutual, silent, and simultaneous consent, snapped the slender thread that hung invisibly in the air between them, severed all communication, and turned once more to the business at hand.

"All rise!" the clerk called, and McIntyre swept from his

chambers, took his seat behind the bench, and signaled for everyone to sit. He was carrying with him the documents submitted to him earlier that morning by both plaintiff and defendants, in which they hoped to show findings of fact and conclusions of law to support their respective cases. He had gone through these briefly in his chambers, and he spread them on the bench top now and looked out over the courtroom, locating Willow and asking, "Are you ready with your argument, Mr. Willow?"

"If your Honor please," Willow said.

"You may proceed."

Willow rose from behind the defense table, a tall and impressive figure in a dignified blue suit, holding his prepared text in his left hand, putting on his glasses as he approached the bench. He glanced at the text for just a moment, and then lowered it, as though he had already committed it to memory and would not have to refer to it again during the course of his summation. He looked up at McIntyre and very softly, so softly that Driscoll could barely hear him from the jury box, said, "If your Honor please, the matter before us these past several days concerns itself solely with whether or not a theft has been committed. The plaintiff has alleged that James Driscoll freely copied from the play *Catchpole* when he was writing his novel *The Paper Dragon*. But the plaintiff has testified that he has no proof, his allegations to the contrary, that Driscoll actually possessed the manuscript or even that he saw the play before writing his book. The entire case, therefore, rests on the alleged similarities between the two works. Now, I know your Honor is familiar with and has certainly studied the record of other cases where plagiarism was claimed. I know, too, that your Honor is aware of the great number of similarities brought before the courts in those other cases, a hundred similarities, two hundred, and in one case something more than four hundred supposed similarities. In most of those cases, however, despite the overwhelming weight of similarities, the courts found *against* a claim of plagiarism. I mention this, your Honor, because the plaintiff's case before us rests on only a very slender body of supposed similarities, all of which are insignificant.

"I do not intend to ask the Court's indulgence while I go over each and every one of these supposedly matching points, your Honor. The plaintiff has put a necessary stress upon them because, lacking any other proof, they are his sole hope of showing theft. But, your Honor, I think we have neglected the fact that most of these similarities—even if they *were* copied—would not form the basis for a plagiarism suit. They are not even copy*right*able, your Honor. An idea is not copyrightable. A theme is not copyrightable. A plot is not copyrightable. Nor is a character copyrightable. The only thing an author may hope to copyright is his manner of expression. Judge Learned Hand has made this abundantly clear in the prevailing cases in this jurisdiction. *Only* the manner of expression can be copyrighted, and *nothing else.*

"Well, your Honor, you have read both play and novel, and you have seen the motion picture—which does not concern us at the moment, but which I believe, by the way, was written and filmed using only the book and related research as sources, and without reference to the play. You have also gone over the charts submitted by the plaintiff, and you have studied the trial transcript and I'm sure you have noted that any of these so-called similarities are due to the fact that both men were dealing with the same subject matter and the same background—the United States Army in time of combat. It would be impossible, your Honor, to present this topic without having similar conflicts springing from the very situation both writers independently chose. One cannot describe a seascape without mentioning the shore or the waves or the sky beyond, and the fact that two authors write of green waves or white foam or wet sand does not indicate one author copied from the other. Such similarities are inevitable.

"The astonishing thing about the plaintiff's claim, of course, is that there is a paucity of even these *non*copyrightable similarities. I can only attribute this to the playwright's poverty of wit, language, insight, and imagination. Your Honor knows that *Catchpole* was badly received by the critics in 1947, and I believe I intimated that the reviews were really devastating, that the play was all but laughed off the stage. The only remarkable thing about this play, in fact, is that it was produced at *all,* and that it managed to sell tickets even for twelve days. I would like to say, incidentally, that Mr. Constantine's testimony concerning the distribution of *free* tickets to Pratt Institute is one area where I can be critical of Mr. Brackman."

"Where does this testimony appear in the record?" McIntyre asked.

"It's in Mr. Constantine's direct, your Honor. I'll find it for you."

Willow walked back to the defense table and leafed through the transcript. Turning toward the bench, he said, "It's on page 11, your Honor." He picked up the bulky transcript and carried it to the bench with him. "He says, 'Yes, sir. There were a series of previews held while we were still rehearsing the play in a loft on Second Avenue.' And when asked which colleges received tickets to these previews, he says, 'C.C.N.Y., Hunter, Brooklyn College, L.I.U., Pratt Institute, and several others.'

"As your Honor knows, the plaintiff was examined at great length before trial by both Mr. Genitori and myself. Never once, your Honor, not once during all those pretrial examinations did he mention preview performances, *or* free tickets, *or* Pratt Institute. And yet, suddenly, we are presented with this startling testimony. And *why* was Pratt Institute so singled out? The answer is simple, your Honor. On the biographical questionnaire Mr. Driscoll sent to Mitchell-Campbell Books, and which was submitted to Mr. Brackman only *after* the pretrial examinations, he mentions that he was a student at Pratt Institute in 1947. So all at once Mr. Constantine remembers that free tickets were distributed to a number of colleges, including Pratt, thereby hoping to establish that Mr. Driscoll at least *could* have seen a performance of the play. I'm surprised, your Honor, I really am surprised that Mr. Brackman permitted his client to testify in such a manner. I'm sure Mr. Brackman did not create this testimony himself, but it was clearly an afterthought and might have been considered more circumspectly by him.

"In the long run, of course, it would not have mattered if a bushel of free tickets went to Pratt, because the play in rehearsal was performed without scenery and would not have afforded Mr. Driscoll the opportunity to see the magic number 105, upon which the plaintiff places such enormous stress—the fingerprints of the thief, Mr. Brackman has repeatedly said. Well, your Honor, we have Mr. Driscoll's testimony that he does not know where the number came from, and that is about as honest an answer as any man can give. He simply does not know. He has also testified that he did not see a performance of that play in 1947 when he was an art student and not at all interested in writing, and he has testified that he did not see a copy of the manuscript until I gave him one several weeks ago. Moreover, the only man who worked with him in an editorial capacity on that book, Mr. Chester Danton, testified that he was abroad in 1947 when the play was produced.

"In his findings of fact, of course, Mr. Brackman emphasizes that there is no claim against Mr. Danton's contributions to the novel. If your Honor please, one of the specific similarities claimed, one of the specific similarities *stressed* by Mr. Constantine in his direct testimony, was the incident of a sniper killing an American soldier. This was supposedly one of the most amazing similarities between the play and the novel. I could understand Mr. Brackman's consternation at discovering the sniper was Mr. *Danton's* idea, a suggestion *he* transmitted to Mr. Driscoll, and *not* Mr. Driscoll's invention at all. I can understand why Mr. Brackman asked during his cross whether Mr. Danton had been trying to mislead him. I can understand all this, your Honor, but the fact remains that the sniper did not appear in the novel as originally submitted to Mitchell-Campbell Books.

"Let us examine that novel for a moment, if we may. I personally, your Honor, have always been fascinated by the creative process, the way in which a writer, a painter, or a composer goes about producing his work. When we strip it of the mystique surrounding it, when we pause to look upon the artist as a man rather than a vague symbol, when we accept the fact that there are no muses involved in honest creation, we must then also see, your Honor, that the true professional is as systematic as an engineer. Richard Strauss, for example, filled dozens of filing cabinets with outlines and ideas, developments of themes, partial scores, all recorded in a unique and personal manner. In much the same way, James Driscoll has provided us with a unique and personal record of the development of his novel, from inception to completion. We have seen his rough outlines and his detailed outlines, we have seen his schedules and his progress reports, his letters to his editor and his agent, as well as reminders to himself, questions he asked, answers he received. We have learned that he would not even write about an operation he had performed a great many times—the disassembly of a rifle—until he had first painstakingly checked on the exact technical language. We have learned that he would not write about the Chinese armies in Korea before learning which of them were in the battle area and in what strength. We have seen the care with which he drew his own map of the patrol route his fictitious squad took into enemy territory. As we go through all this material, your Honor, it becomes crystal clear that here is a man creating his own work, relying upon his own knowledge and background, and supplementing this with meticulous research. This is not the work of a copyist, a plagiarist, a thief. There is no question here, your Honor, but that James Driscoll created *The Paper Dragon* alone, independently, and without reference to any existing work of fiction. In fact, your Honor, I think that even a casual reading of both works clearly indicates that one was not copied from the other.

"Why, then, did I spend so much time during the course of this trial discussing these alleged similarities, some of which the plaintiff himself has labeled 'flimsy and absurd,' when a mere reading shows that there was no plagiarism? Why did I dignify each of these separate charges by examining them with such scrutiny? Why did I amass proof to show Mr.

Driscoll's creative process? I would like to explain, your Honor, lest these co-called similarities seem to take on a significance they do not truly possess.

"There are large sums of money involved here, your Honor. We can suppose without a detailed accounting that the motion picture grossed upwards of ten million dollars, and we have heard testimony to the effect that the novel in its paperback edition alone sold more than two and a half million copies. And whereas it was not mentioned during the trial, I know that the book went into eleven foreign editions, each of which sold extraordinarily well because of the impetus provided by the film. So there is unquestionably a great deal of money involved. But there is more than money, and it is this further consideration that prompted my detailed probing of the similarities, your Honor. I speak now of the reputation of an extremely talented, diligent, and earnest writer, James Driscoll."

He turned to look at the jury box, and Driscoll read his face and his eyes, read them swiftly and in the brief instant it took Willow to glance at him and then turn back toward the judge. But he knew in that single sharp exchange that Willow did not believe a word of what he had just said. The knowledge startled him. He glanced at Ebie and saw that she was sitting with her hands clasped tightly over the pocketbook in her lap, her eyes intent on Willow.

"Now, your Honor, I could easily stress the legal argument, I could easily repeat that even if Mr. Driscoll *had* taken this material he is alleged to have copied, why none of it is copyrightable, the only thing a man may copyright is his manner of expression. And were I to stress the legal argument, and were I to win on that point alone, this would undoubtedly be a victory for Mitchell-Campbell and for Camelot Books, but what about this man James Driscoll? What about this man whose career lies ahead of him, who has written a brilliant first novel, this man who, in Chester Danton's words, 'will go on writing many more excellent books'? What about James Driscoll? Your Honor, we have been asked to believe, for example, that the use of the word

'Loot' when addressing a lieutenant in the United States Army is indicative of copying by this man, James Driscoll. Well, your Honor, I think that this sort of specious reasoning is indicative only of the groundless claim we have before us. We have cited, in our brief, one of Judge Hand's opinions in which he describes an obsessive sort of paranoia that attacks some authors, and I think we have exactly that syndrome here. *Catchpole* was a totally unsuccessful play on a theme which was later successfully explored by James Driscoll in *The Paper Dragon.* It is not difficult to understand how Mr. Constantine, unable to accept the failure of his work, attributed the success of Mr. Driscoll's work to copying. We have this throughout, your Honor. We have Mr. Constantine testifying, for example, that the use of obscenity is common in the armed forces, and then insisting nonetheless that the soldier in his play is a unique creation who must have been stolen by Mr. Driscoll. My friend Mr. Brackman looks troubled, so if your Honor wishes, I'll find the exact place in the transcript . . ."

"I'm not troubled, Mr. Willow. I'm merely very interested in what you're saying."

"Very what?" McIntyre asked.

"Interested, your Honor."

"Well, you looked extremely troubled there for a moment," Willow said. "I'll be happy to find the testimony if . . ."

"He doesn't look at all troubled to me, Mr. Willow," McIntyre said, "but I would like the exact page in the transcript if you have it."

Willow accepted the transcript from his assistant, leafed through it, and said, "It's on page 89, your Honor. This is Mr. Constantine's testimony. 'Question: Do you think they were rarities? Answer: No. Question: They were commonplace? Answer: They were to be found everywhere in the Army.' " Willow looked up from the transcript and said, "You understand, your Honor, that these questions and answers are referring to men using obscene language."

"Yes, I understand that."

"And later, on page 92, I asked Mr. Constantine, 'Yet you still maintain that your character's use of obscenity is unique?' and he replied, 'It is unique, yes.' That's an indication of what we're being asked to accept in this courtroom, your Honor. These clear admissions that the so-called similarities between the two works are really based on common material, and then the stubborn insistence that one work was nonetheless copied from the other. Well, your Honor, that soldier is *not* unique, and we *know* he is not unique. We know, in fact, that a soldier such as this is undoubtedly a commonplace, and it would be very easy to find against the plaintiff on the grounds that the material he claims was copied is not copyrightable material. That would be a perfectly reasonable finding, your Honor, except that it would leave a stain on Mr. Driscoll's character, it would leave a stigma on his career. Such a finding would indicate that he *did* copy from another man, but only material that was in the public domain. And that would be a terrible injustice, your Honor. I ask you, therefore, to consider this in your decision, because I believe with all my heart that James Driscoll has done nothing to warrant this charge of plagiarism. James Driscoll is an artist, your Honor, who wrote a fine book in his own manner and using his own resources. For this, your Honor, we owe him only respect and gratitude."

The courtroom was silent. In the silence, Driscoll looked at Willow, and again knew without doubt that the lawyer had been mouthing words he did not believe. Willow returned the look, and then walked slowly back toward the defense table. Genitori, dressed in his customary pinstriped suit, had already risen, prepared text in hand, and was walking toward the bench. He smiled briefly at no one, cleared his throat, and said, "If your Honor please, concerning the first cause of action against Artists-Producers-International, I can say nothing that Mr. Willow has not already said, and I ask that his argument be adopted as my own. With respect to the cause of action claiming independent infringement, however, I would like to call your Honor's attention to page 127 of the transcript, where I moved for dismissal and assumed arguendo . . ."

Driscoll stopped listening. He was disturbed by what he had detected in Willow's manner, but Ebie's sudden agitation concerned him even more. He knew that she too had sensed the hollowness of Willow's praise—there had never been a time when they both did not react identically and simultaneously to any given stimulus—and he was now troubled to see her fingers working nervously on her handbag, fastening and unfastening the clasp, a small deadly click punctuating Genitori's words, "spend this Court's time in repeating it now," click, "later called Ralph Knowles to the stand," click, "respected and honored director," click, "inconceivable to imagine he had the slightest need for copying any of the plaintiff's paltry work," click.

He did not know what Ebie would do, or even what she *could* do now that the case was officially closed and the arguments begun. He knew only that she was unpredictable, had always been unpredictable, and that she had openly threatened him only the night before. He knew, moreover, and this was what troubled him most, that she was the kind of woman who moved swiftly and directly once she had decided on a course of action. He had learned that in 1950, had learned it once and for all time, and he watched her nervous hands now as they worked the clasp, knowing that her mind was churning with possibilities, listening to each small click with rising anticipation, ". . . the defendant API quite properly replied, Yes, Mr. Edelson and Miss Blake had indeed worked as story editors on those dates," click, "but for the *studio,* you understand," click, "and not in connection with *The Paper Dragon,* which possibility Mr. Knowles put to rout forever when he testified in simple, forceful English that neither Mr. Edelson nor Miss Blake had anything *whatever* to do with the production of his movie," click.

Genitori nodded, and then consulted his text once again, and then said to McIntyre, "I therefore ask you to find, your Honor, that Mr. Ralph Knowles did not see or read the play *Catchpole* before writing his movie, that the motion picture

The Paper Dragon was written and produced independently of that play, and that the claim against Artists-Producers-International should be dismissed. Thank you, your Honor."

Sidney Brackman took a long while getting up from his chair and then moving past Constantine and around the plaintiff's table and into the aisle, where he walked slowly to the front of the courtroom. He turned to look first at Willow, and then at Genitori, and then he looked up at McIntyre and said, "Your Honor, I have been practicing law for twenty-two years now, but there's always something new to learn, I guess. Mr. Willow pointed out to me today, just a few minutes ago, that it was my duty as a lawyer to prevent a witness from giving testimony while he was on the stand under oath. Mr. Willow seems to feel that I permitted testimony which was at best questionable, but I would like to say that Mr. Constantine was *never* asked about preview performances at any time during the pretrial examinations. I can assure Mr. Willow that had the question been asked, it would have been answered honestly, the same way Mr. Constantine has answered every question put to him since this suit began. If Mr. Willow did not think to ask about any performances other than those on Broadway, I do not see why his oversight should then become a reflection on my integrity."

"I assure you, Mr. Brackman, that your integrity is unquestioned," McIntyre said.

"Thank you, your Honor. Thank you, and forgive me for taking the Court's time to clear up this seemingly insignificant matter, but it *was* important to me."

"I understand."

"Thank you. Mr. Willow has also commented on the scarcity of claimed similarities between *Catchpole* and *The Paper Dragon,* pointing out to your Honor that most plagiarism cases will have two hundred, or three hundred, or even four hundred claimed similarities. He also stated that most of these cases were lost by the plaintiff, and I would like to suggest that it was the very weight of the similarities that helped to defeat these claims. When there are so many, your Honor, when every word and every comma becomes a matter for debate, well, obviously the plaintiff is stretching the truth, obviously he is predicating much of his case on sheer imagination. We have not done that here, your Honor. We have claimed only similarities that are plain for all to see. Some of them are less important than others, yes, but they are all pertinent. They are all pertinent because they show that there was copying, and without copying there can be no charge of plagiarism."

"Excuse me one moment, Mr. Brackman," McIntyre said, "but is it your belief that Mr. Driscoll *saw* this play?"

"Your Honor, I know that Mr. Driscoll is now a highly respected writer, and I know that he has been acclaimed as a literary phenomenon, and I know that his novel is still being dissected in the literary journals and, for all I know, being taught in colleges and universities all across these United States of ours. But, your Honor, he was *not* highly respected before he wrote *The Paper Dragon,* he was *not* being lionized, he was in fact totally unknown. By his own admission, he had written only a few unpublished short stories before writing the novel, and he has written *nothing* since. The only reason for his reputation now, in fact, is that he stole another man's work."

"Mr. Brackman, do you think he saw the play?"

"I think he was in possession of it."

"Of what? The play?"

"I think he was in possession of the plaintiff's play, yes."

"Before he wrote his novel?"

"Before he wrote his novel, and perhaps while he was writing his novel."

"I see."

"Your Honor, the evidence cannot show otherwise. Mr. Willow took the time and trouble to amass a great deluge of trivia, a landslide of outlines and letters and maps and what-have-you, but what do these prove? If we believe Mr. Driscoll, then indeed all these collected scraps of paper were the result of personal work habits, and show that he was a diligent man with perhaps an eye on future historians, keeping as it were his own personal time capsule for posterity. But if we do *not* believe Mr. Driscoll, then he was only a clever thief seeking to hide his plagiarism by constructing a supporting body of evidence to substantiate a claim of independent creation."

"I don't wish to interrupt your argument further," McIntyre said, "but I would still like to know whether it is your belief that Mr. Driscoll actually *saw* this play. A minute ago—"

"I don't understand, your Honor."

"Well, you said you thought he possessed a copy of it."

"Yes."

"Do you think he *saw* it as well?"

"Do you mean in performance?"

"Yes," McIntyre said. "Do you think he saw the play on the stage?"

"I don't know."

"Very well."

"He says he did not, your Honor, he has testified to that. He has also testified that he never saw a copy of this play until, when was it, several weeks ago, when Mr. Willow gave him one to read. How then can we explain these similarities—and there are, if your Honor please, exactly twenty-six of them, plus of course the six that were found to exist only between the play and the movie. How do we explain twenty-six concrete and specific similarities between the play *Catchpole* and the novel *The Paper Dragon* unless Mr. Driscoll had access to this play, unless—"

"Mr. Brackman," McIntyre interrupted, "you said earlier that some of these similarities were less important than others. I would—"

"But all pertinent, your Honor. We've set them forth in our brief, and I think we've covered them extensively over the past several days. I certainly don't want to weary you with them again, unless you wish me to do so."

"I merely wanted to know which ones you consider important."

"They are *all* important, your Honor, they are *all* pertinent, including those we concede to be minor. For example, your Honor, we claim that there is a similarity of plot, and then we go on to show exactly how and where the plots are similar, even *identical* in some places. Well, Mr. Willow in his summation said that a plot cannot be copyrighted, and yet one of the cases Mr. Genitori cites in his brief—"

"Yes, Mr. Brackman, I don't think we need belabor the point. If two works have identical plots, even though 'plot' per se is not copyrightable, this would certainly be evidence of copying. Don't you agree, Mr. Willow?"

"Yes, your Honor, *if* the plots were identical."

"Or significantly similar," McIntyre said, and then paused. "Or inexplicably so."

"Yes, your Honor," Willow said.

"So let's not belabor the point."

"By the same token, your Honor," Brackman said, "my opponent has gone to great lengths to show that many of the incidents and events and characters, much of the language, the settings and so forth used in the novel are there only because it happens to be a novel about the United States Army. He says, in effect, that *any* novel about the United States Army, *any* play about the United States Army would necessarily have sergeants in it, or obscenity, or barracks, or what have you. All right, we concede this. Where there's an army, there are necessarily men in uniform, and there are rifles, and battlefields, and enemy soldiers, and wounded men, and nurses, all right, let us say *all* of these things are in the public domain. Nonetheless, your Honor, even material in the public domain may be so combined or compiled as to be copyrightable."

"Yes, I know that, Mr. Brackman. But while we're on this point, I'd like to ask another question. Neither you nor Mr. Willow have said a word about the *differences* between the play and the book, but it strikes me that there are tremendous dissimilarities, and I wonder now whether we shouldn't concern ourselves with these as well. I wonder, in fact, whether we are not *dutybound* to study these dissimilarities in trying to determine whether there was indeed any copying here."

"If your Honor please," Brackman said, "the plaintiff's b-b-b-burden would be to prove th-that the similarities, and not the *dis*similarities, are so overwhelming that, your Honor, that there are enough of them to support a claim of plagiarism."

"Yes, but Mr. Willow admitted for the purposes of argument that even if all these alleged similarities were indeed copied, they would still add up to something too insignificant to be called plagiarism. Wasn't that his point?"

"I believe that was his point," Brackman said.

"Isn't that the point you made, Mr. Willow?"

"It was one of my points, yes, your Honor."

"Your Honor," Brackman said, "I do not believe *any* of these similarities are insignificant, nor do I believe someone can be guilty of just a little plagiarism, in much the same way a woman cannot possibly be just a little pregnant. How many of these similarities need we show before we recognize they cannot all be accidental? How else can we hope to prove plagiarism except by putting the works side by side and saying this corresponds to this, and that corresponds to that? Will the thief oblige us by admitting his theft? Of course not. So how else can we prove this theft, your Honor, except by comparing the works, by locating these seemingly unimportant and insignificant similarities, these so-called coincidences scattered throughout the work, and appearing far too often to be called coincidental? How else, your Honor? By inspecting what is *dissimilar,* as you have suggested? Would this support our claim? No, your Honor. It would only indicate that the work was not copied in its entirety, and that is *not* what we have claimed, nor is it what we have proved here in this Court. We have only proved that *enough* of it was copied to significantly deprive the plaintiff of his rights.

"Mr. Driscoll has claimed, your Honor has heard him testify, that the character Lieutenant Alex Cooper in *The*

Paper Dragon is based upon himself, and yet when asked which specific incidents or events happened to him, James Driscoll, he was hard put to find any such events that were not common to both the book and the play. Lieutenant Cooper was idealistic, yes, but James Driscoll was not. Lieutenant Cooper was single, James Driscoll was not. Lieutenant Cooper had an affair with a nurse, James Driscoll did not. And all down the line, your Honor, we see this same disparity between what *actually* happened to James Driscoll and what happened to the officer supposedly based on himself. Did Mr. Driscoll ever have a man like Colman in his platoon? No. Was there a troublemaker in his platoon? No. Was there a homosexual? No. Was there a murder scheme? No. Was he ever the target of a planned murder? No. He claims first that the book is autobiographical, and then when pressed to tell us just *how* it is autobiographical, he can tell us only that he *invented* most of the incidents.

"I do not think I have to comment on the preposterousness of his Colman-iceman story, or the farfetched allusion to Eugene O'Neill's play, or Mr. Driscoll's insistence that an obviously homosexual character in *Catchpole* was not at all homosexual and was not indeed the basis for the homosexual character in his book. We have Mr. Ralph Knowles's expert testimony—and was it not Mr. Genitori who said he was a highly respected and honored director?—we have his expert testimony that he *did,* in fact, combine two characters in the novel to form the single character of Colman in his film. And *this,* your Honor, is why James Driscoll insisted Colonel Peterson was not a homosexual, only because he knew very well that he *had* taken Peterson and Janus and combined them to form Colman, which process Knowles reversed in making his picture.

"And then, your Honor, we come to what I earlier called the thief's fingerprints and which I still maintain are the fingerprints of a thief, and I refer now to the labeling of the 105th Division."

A silence fell over the courtroom. In the silence, Driscoll heard the click of Ebie's handbag once again, and he turned to look at her and saw that she was straining forward in her seat now, leaning over at a sharp angle, her eyes on Brackman, her mouth drawn into a tight, narrow line.

"The 105th Division," Brackman repeated. "Here, your Honor, I do not think there can be any question whatever of coincidence. No one in this room would be willing to bet even fifty cents on correctly picking the same three digits in sequence, and yet that's exactly what Mr. Driscoll did, he picked three digits at random, one, oh, five, and they just happened to correspond with those same three digits in the play, even though the odds against this happening, as we saw, were a million to one. Now your Honor, that is *too* much to believe, and Mr. Driscoll *knows* it is too much to believe, and so he tells us he does not know how he hit upon those three digits, he *honestly* does not know how they happened to come to him, perhaps on the wings of a muse. Or more likely, your Honor, perhaps as the result of an error, the single error this thief made in his painstaking robbery. After the meticulous compilation of all his covering outlines and plots and maps, after the careful disguising of each and every character and event, here was the one mistake, here was the identifiable—"

Ebie rose.

She rose silently, with both hands tightly clutching her pocketbook, the knuckles white. It seemed for a moment as though she were simply going to leave the courtroom, as though she were unable to listen a moment longer to Brackman's accusations. But she did not move from where she stood in the jury box. She looked up at the judge. Brackman, seeing McIntyre's puzzled frown, stopped speaking and turned to face her.

"Your Honor," she said softly, "may I talk to Mr. Willow?"

Driscoll suddenly put his hand on her shoulder. She looked at him curiously, as though unable to read the gesture, and then turned again to the judge and plaintively inquired, "Your Honor?"

There was, for perhaps thirty seconds, total silence in the courtroom. Brackman did not object, although he was in the middle of his summation and any such interruption was forbidden and in fact unthinkable. Willow made no motion to recess, even though his client's wife had just asked if she could talk to him. The silence was complete, a stunned silence that stifled all action. Like children turning to their father for guidance when one of their peers has unforgivably transgressed, the lawyers looked toward the bench at the front of the courtroom, where McIntyre squinted in consternation, silent himself.

At last he said, "This Court will recess for ten minutes."

They returned to the courtroom at four minutes past eleven. McIntyre called the three attorneys to the bench, where they stood ranged before him, Willow in the center, Brackman and Genitori on either side of him. He fussed about in his chair, making himself comfortable. Then he folded his arms flat on the bench top, leaned forward, and brusquely said, "All right, Mr. Willow, what's this all about?"

"Your Honor," Willow said, "I would like to make application to reopen the case."

"For what purpose?"

"To submit additional testimony."

"Mr. Brackman?"

"Your Honor," Brackman said, "any additional testimony from the defendant at this point, after I've almost completed my summation, could only be injurious to my case. I respectfully submit . . ."

"That may be so, Mr. Brackman. I must say, Mr. Willow, that I have never had anything like this happen to me before."

"I believe we could find precedent for it, your Honor ."

"Yes, I'm sure we could, Mr. Willow," McIntyre said, "especially if we looked at Section 31.45 of the *Cyclopedia of Federal Procedure.*"

"Your Honor, I'm not familiar with that section."

"I *am,* Mr. Willow."

"Forgive me."

"The section states, Mr. Willow—and next time you might wish to consult it before asking that a case be reopened—the section states that even after testimony has been entirely closed, the Court may receive additional evidence in its own discretion."

"Your Honor," Brackman said, "if this were a case before a jury . . ."

"It is not a jury case," McIntyre said, "but even if it were, Mr. Brackman, the Court could in its discretion permit additional testimony."

"I'm sorry, your Honor, I was not aware of that."

"I would like to remind Mr. Willow, however, that such additional testimony cannot be allowed for light reasons, such as to let in cumulative or immaterial evidence."

"Your Honor," Willow said, "I believe this testimony to be exceedingly important, and I know the record would be incomplete without it."

"If your Honor please," Genitori said, "I do not see how in good conscience we can exclude any testimony that may shed light on the matter before us."

"Mr. Brackman?"

"Your Honor, my summation was predicated on what the record already shows. If additional testimony . . ."

"I would have no objection," Willow said, "to Mr. Brackman making a second summation after the new testimony is given."

"Your Honor, I know you can in your discretion—you have just informed me that you can in your discretion reopen the case, but . . ."

"Don't you feel the record should be complete, Mr. Brackman?"

"Indeed, I do, your Honor. But I also feel Mr. Willow should have called all his witnesses when it was time for him to do so, and not—"

"Your Honor, this was unforeseen, and as much a surprise to me as it was to the Court."

"Well," McIntyre said flatly, "I will reopen the case."

"Thank you, your Honor."

"Let the record so indicate. Mr. Brackman, I will allow you to make a new summation later if you so desire."

"Thank you," Brackman said.

"Call your witness, Mr. Willow."

"Edna Belle Driscoll," Willow said.

"Edna Belle Driscoll, please take the stand," the clerk said.

Ebie rose hesitantly, and looked inquiringly at Willow, who nodded. She put her bag down on the bench in the jury box, looked plaintively at her husband, and then walked to where the clerk was waiting with the Bible.

"Edna Belle Driscoll, you do solemnly swear that the testimony you are about to give to the Court in this issue shall be the truth, the whole truth, and nothing but the truth, so help you God?"

"I do," Ebie said.

Her voice was very low. She looked puzzled for a moment as she tried to find the steps leading to the witness stand. When she located them, she moved rapidly to the chair, and then hesitated again before sitting. She looked up at the judge once, and then turned away as Willow approached her.

"Mrs. Driscoll," he said, "are you familiar with the novel *The Paper Dragon?*"

"I am."

"How many times have you read it?"

"Many times. I don't remember the exact number of times."

"Would you say you've read it more than twenty times?"

"Yes."

"From cover to cover?"

"Yes, from cover to cover."

"Then surely you are familiar with the nurse in the book, the woman called Lieutenant Jan Reardon."

"Yes, I'm familiar with her."

"What color hair does Jan Reardon have?"

"Blond."

"Will the record show, your Honor, that Mrs. Driscoll's hair is blond. What color eyes does Jan Reardon have?"

"Blue."

"Will the record show, your Honor, that Mrs. Driscoll's eyes are blue. Where is Jan Reardon from originally, what part of the country?"

"The South."

"Where in the South?"

"Alabama."

"Where are *you* from, Mrs. Driscoll?"

"Alabama."

"Mrs. Driscoll, is Jan Reardon left-handed?"

"Yes."

"Are you left-handed?"

"Yes."

"Does Jan Reardon have a crescent-shaped scar on her thigh?"

"Yes."

"Do you have a similar scar on your thigh?"

"Yes. Yes, I have."

"What was your maiden name?"

"Dearborn."

"Your Honor, may I point out to the Court that the name Reardon with the single exception of the letter *b* contains the exact same letters as are in the name Dearborn, transposed."

"What was that again?" McIntyre said. He picked up a pencil and moved a pad into place before him.

"The name Reardon, your Honor, can be formed by dropping the *b* from Dearborn, and then transposing the letters."

McIntyre wrote silently for a moment, and then studied the pad. "Yes, I see that," he said. "Proceed, Mr. Willow."

"Mrs. Driscoll, can you tell us when and where you first met your husband?"

"At Pratt Institute in 1947."

"Were you a student there at the time?"

"I was."

"How long had you been at the school?"

"A year."

"How long had Mr. Driscoll been there?"

"He had just entered. He was a first-year student."

"And you were an upper classman?"

"Yes, I was in my second year. It was a three-year non-accredited course. The course I was taking."

"So that the relationship between you and your husband, in terms of seniority at least, was similar to the relationship between Lieutenant Alex Cooper and Jan Reardon in the novel *The Paper Dragon?"*

"Yes, it was."

"Was it similar in any other respects?"

"Yes."

"In which respects, Mrs. Driscoll?"

"All of them. Everything."

"Would you explain, please?"

"It was our story."

"Whose story, Mrs. Driscoll?"

"Ours. Dris and me."

"Dris?"

"Yes, my husband."

"Is that what you normally call him?"

"It is what I've always called him."

"What does the nurse call Cooper in *The Paper Dragon?"*

"Coop."

"Your Honor," Brackman said, "I have remained silent until now because I wanted to see where Mr. Willow was heading. It seems to me now that he is introducing Mrs. Driscoll's testimony as that of an expert on the novel *The Paper Dragon,* and I must object to this."

"Your Honor," Willow said, "I am introducing her testimony as that of an expert on what actually happened between her and her husband beginning in the year 1947 and ending in October of 1950. I don't think, your Honor, that I'm going to have to elicit too many responses in order to show what *The Paper Dragon* was all about."

"Overruled. Go on, Mr. Willow."

"If I understand you correctly, Mrs. Driscoll, you are saying that the events in *The Paper Dragon* parallel certain *real* events, is that correct?"

"Yes."

"Can you give us any examples of this?"

"Well . . . for . . . for example when Dris and I first met, we had a fight, not a fight, a sort of an argument. He asked me out and I . . . I thought he was just a fresh kid, he was younger than I, you know, and a first-year student, so I tried to discourage him, but he kept insisting, said he was going to be a famous artist one day, all that sort of thing. And the . . . the same thing happens in the book. When the lieutenant first gets to Korea, he's sort of a . . . a brash person and he tries to get friendly with this nurse, who just refuses his advances. They have this terrible argument, and he tells her she'll be sorry because he's going to be a war hero with the Medal of Honor, you know, he goes on about how he's going to win the Korean war singlehanded, but she still refuses. Then . . . she's sent to Tokyo for a week's leave, and he tries to find her, but he can't until a senior nurse in the book—"

"What's her name?"

"The nurse's? Major Astor. Catharine Astor."

"Is she based on any real person?"

"Yes."

"Who?"

"An older girl at Pratt. Her name was Cathy Ascot, and she told Dris where he could find me. You see, I was sick in bed for a week or so after we met, and Dris didn't know where I lived or anything."

"And in the book?"

"In the book, Coop can't find her because she's in Japan, of course, on leave, and he makes contact with the major who tells him the whole story. Then he gives her a note to pass on to Jan when she gets back. So she's . . . she's instrumental in getting them together, you see. In starting their . . . their romance."

"Is there anything else you can tell us about Cathy Ascot?"

"Yes. She had a broken arm that November. She was always breaking something. She was accident prone."

"Is Major Astor accident prone in the novel?"

"No, but she's always predicting dire happenings and such."

"Are you familiar with the character Peter Colman?"

"I am."

"Is he based on anyone you or your husband knew?"

"He is based on someone we both knew."

"Upon whom is he based?"

"He is based upon a boy who used to live upstairs from us on Myrtle Avenue."

"What was his name?"

"Peter Malcom."

"Your Honor," Willow said, "may I again call the Court's attention to this same device of transposition, where a real name becomes a fictitious name. The letters in both names are almost identical, with the exception of substituting a final *n* for what would have been a final *m*."

"Yes, I see that," McIntyre said. "Please go on."

"Wasn't the fictitious Peter Colman an actor before going into the Army?"

"Yes."

"What was Peter Malcom's profession?"

"He was an actor."

"Now you said that you and your husband lived in the same building with this man . . ."

"Yes. Well, when we got married, Dris moved into my apartment. Peter had always lived upstairs, you see. So Dris knew him, too."

"Was Peter Malcom a homosexual?"

"No, he was not."

"The character Peter Colman in your husband's book is a homosexual. How do you explain this discrepancy?"

"Your Honor," Brackman said, rising, "I don't know what we're doing here, but earlier we allowed Mr. Driscoll to testify concerning the *plaintiff's* intent, and now it seems we are calling upon Mrs. Driscoll to speculate on her *husband's* intent. I don't see how she can possibly explain why or how her husband happened to conceive a character . . ."

"I can tell you *exactly* how," Ebie said.

"Your Honor, I have made an objection," Brackman said.

"Yes, Mr. Brackman. The objection is overruled."

"Mrs. Driscoll?"

"I was going to say . . . I was only going to say that Dris was very jealous of Peter and so he . . . he . . ." Ebie stopped.

"Yes?"

"He first conceived of the character as just a . . . a man, you know, and then later when Mr. Danton suggested the business about the major having been killed, well then it . . . it . . . he decided to make the character less of a man, a homosexual. Because, as I say, he was very jealous of him."

"Does the physical description of Colman in *The Paper Dragon* match the description of Malcom in real life?"

"Exactly."

"In other words, Mrs. Driscoll, is it correct to say that *The Paper Dragon* is based on your husband's courtship of you, and subsequent marriage to you, and his jealousy of a real person you both knew?"

"Yes, and other things as well. His childhood background and the people he knew and thoughts he's had, and expressions he uses, and mannerisms . . . and . . . it's *his* book. It's him."

"Thank you, Mrs. Driscoll."

"Is that all?" Brackman said.

"That's all," Willow said.

Brackman walked slowly toward the witness stand. Ebie was suddenly frightened. Apprehensively, she watched as he moved closer to her, and then turned to look fleetingly at her husband, who was staring straight ahead, looking through the tall windows at the sky beyond.

"Mrs. Driscoll, when did you decide to reveal this information to the Court?" Brackman asked.

"Last night."

"What prompted your decision?"

"I felt that my husband might lose the case unless I spoke up."

"Did you discuss this with Mr. Willow?"

"No."

"You did *not* tell him you wanted to testify?"

"Not until just now. When he asked for the recess."

"I see. Mr. Willow, then, knew nothing of your plans until you surprised us all this morning."

"Yes."

"You did discuss this with your husband, however?"

"Yes."

"What did you say to him?"

"That I would tell."

"Tell what?"

"About . . . the book. Everything."

"And what did he say?"

"He asked me not to."

"Why would he do that?"

"He said the case was closed."

"As indeed it was," Brackman said dryly. "But why would he have objected to you giving testimony that would help him?"

"It was finished in his mind."

"What was finished?"

"The case. It was closed."

"You do feel this testimony will help your husband, don't you?"

"I hope so."

"It certainly won't injure his case, will it?"

"No."

"Then why would he have objected to it?"

"I don't know."

"Perhaps because it makes some of the testimony he gave earlier sound a bit suspect, could that be the reason?"

"Objection, your Honor."

"Sustained."

"Are you aware, Mrs. Driscoll, that your husband earlier

claimed 'Peter' was a phallic reference and that the name 'Colman' was a literary pun on iceman, his mother's iceman, are you aware of that?"

"Yes."

"You were sitting in this courtroom when he gave that testimony, so I'm sure you are aware of it."

"I said I was aware of it."

"Yet your testimony seems in direct contradiction to what your husband swore to. You have just told us that there was a *real* person named Peter Malcom and that your husband based his fictitious character upon this individual."

"Yes."

"Well, Mrs. Driscoll, which of you are we to believe?"

"There *was* a real Peter Malcom. There *is* a real Peter Malcom."

"Then why didn't your husband mention him? Surely the existence of a real man who is so similar to the fictitious character would have been a stronger argument for independent creation than a story about an iceman. You do agree with that, don't you, Mrs. Driscoll?"

"Yes, I do."

"Then why would your husband have—I hesitate to use the word, Mrs. Driscoll, because perjury is a serious charge and a charge that can be prosecuted by the district attorney—why would your husband have *sounded* as though he were trying to, shall I say, *mislead* this Court? Do you think he simply *forgot* about Peter Malcom, the man who lived upstairs?"

"No, but . . ."

"You just testified that he was jealous of him. So how could he have forgotten him?"

"I didn't say he forgot him."

"You *did* say he was jealous of him."

"Yes."

"Why?"

"Because Peter and I were good friends. He was a very troubled person, you see, he was having difficulty getting the kind of acting roles he wanted and . . . we would discuss all this, he would tell me what his ambitions were and . . . and the problems he was having and . . . I would offer encouragement to him . . . I would listen to him."

"So your husband became jealous of him?"

"Yes."

"I see. And that's why he forgot all about him when he was testifying here earlier. Because he was jealous."

"No, he didn't forget all about him. I think it was *both*. I think he really was making a literary pun, in addition to the play on Peter's real name."

"The pun on *The Iceman Cometh,* you mean?"

"Yes."

"The 'Iceman' signifying Death."

"Yes."

"Did Peter Malcom ever try to kill your husband?"

"No."

"Or ever conceive a murder plot against him?"

"No, of course not."

"Yet Peter Colman in the novel does exactly that. In fact, he succeeds in causing the lieutenant's death."

"I know that. I'm quite familiar with the book."

"Since you're so familiar with it, how do you explain it, Mrs. Driscoll?"

"The lieutenant kills *himself*. He sacrifices himself."

"Yes, we all know that. But only because he recognizes Colman's plot."

"Yes."

"But you've just testified that Peter Malcom, the man who is supposedly the source for . . ."

"He *is*."

"Yes, we have your word for that, Mrs. Driscoll, although it does seem to contradict your husband's word on several points. But nonetheless, we *do* have your testimony that this real man Peter Malcom never plotted against your husband's life. Was there ever any trouble between them?"

"Trouble?"

"Yes. Did he and your husband ever fight, or . . ."

"No."

"Or exchange harsh words?"

"No. Dris didn't like him and . . . he . . . he wouldn't have him in the house."

"Did they speak to each other?"

"I don't know. I don't think so."

"Did *you* speak to him?"

"Peter? Yes, of course."

"I see. Even though your husband disliked him?"

"Yes. Peter was . . . I told you. He was a very troubled person. You can't just turn your back on someone, you can't just let them . . . let them get lost or . . . or hurt. You can't just let people die."

"I see." Brackman sighed, walked back to the plaintiff's table, picked up a pencil there, walked to the witness stand again, pursed his lips, looked down at the pencil in his hand, and very quietly said, "Mrs. Driscoll, was there anything in your husband's past to suggest the 105th Division?"

"No," Ebie answered quickly, and then felt she had answered too quickly because Brackman looked up at her sharply, and then smiled.

"Nothing at all?"

"Nothing."

"None of his courses were numbered a hundred and five, were they? Design 105, or Illustration 105, or whatever your husband was studying?"

"No, the courses weren't numbered that way at Pratt."

"Did your husband ever make any reference to having seen a play called *Catchpole?*"

"Certainly not."

"Or to the division insignia in that play?"

"No."

"An insignia with the number 105 in yellow on a black field?"

"No."

"No reference to a hundred and five?"

"No."

"Then where did it come from, Mrs. Driscoll? Was it perhaps the apartment number on Peter Malcom's door?"

"No, he lived in apartment 47."

"Was it *your* apartment number?"

"No."

"Was it your husband's APO number perhaps? When he was overseas?"

"No, it was none of those things."

"Well now, I was really hoping, Mrs. Driscoll, that you could clear up the mystery for us, since you seem to have cleared up so many of the other troubling points. It seems, however, that the thief's fingerprints are still very much in—"

"Don't say that," Ebie warned.

"I beg your pardon, Mrs. Driscoll. But since the theft of another man's work is the matter before this—"

"My husband didn't steal anyone else's work!"

"Then perhaps he may have mentioned to you how he hit upon that number, Mrs. Driscoll, if not by seeing it on the stage?"

"He did not see the play."

"How do you know?"

"He told me."

"Where *did* he get the number, then?"

Ebie hesitated.

"Do you *know,* Mrs. Driscoll?"

"Yes, I know," she whispered.

"What?" the clerk asked. "I'm sorry, I . . ."

"She said, 'Yes, I know,' " Brackman said.

"What?" the clerk said again.

"Yes, she *knows,"* McIntyre said.

"If you indeed know, Mrs. Driscoll," Brackman said wearily, "will you tell us?"

"Yes."

"Please."

"Yes," she repeated, and looked at Driscoll. He was still staring directly ahead of him. "The . . . the number isn't a . . . it isn't a hundred and five."

"Oh? What is it then?"

"Its . . . it's two numbers. It's a ten and . . . and a five."

"I see. It's a ten and a five," Brackman said, and smiled up at the judge. "But not a hundred and five."

"No."

"Mrs. Driscoll, perhaps you'd like to tell us the difference between a ten and a five in sequence, and the number a hundred and five."

"Yes."

"Please."

"The ten and the five are a date."

"What?" Brackman said.

"A date. It's ten slant five."

"I'm not sure I understand you, Mrs. Driscoll," McIntyre said. "By 'ten slant five,' do you mean 'ten *virgule* five?' "

"I don't know what 'virgule' means," Ebie said.

"Well . . ." McIntyre said, and rapidly scribbled onto the pad in front of him. "Is this it?" he asked, and held up the pad for her to see:

10/5

"Yes," Ebie said, "that's it. October 5th."

"October 5th," Brackman said musingly. "Of any particular year, Mrs. Driscoll, or just any year picked at random?"

"1950," Ebie said. She kept watching her husband, but he would not turn to meet her glance.

"October of 1950, I see," Brackman said. "October 5th in the year 1950. And what does that date commemorate? An anniversary, perhaps? Were you married on October 5th?"

"No."

"Did your husband go into the service on October 5th?"

"No."

"Was it your birthday?"

"No."

"Or *his?*"

"No."

"Or Peter's?"

"No."

"Or *anyone's?*"

"No."

"Then *what* was it, Mrs. Driscoll? Why did your husband attach such importance to this number, which you are now telling us is a date, ten virgule five, and not *really* a hundred and five? Perhaps you can tell us."

"October 5th was the date on a . . . a letter."

"What letter?"

"A letter I . . . a letter I wrote to my husband in Korea."

"I see."

"Yes," she said.

"Did you write your husband many letters while he was in Korea?"

"Yes."

"But he took the date from this one letter, is that it?"

"October 5th."

"Yes, that's quite clear. Did you also write to him on October 2nd, perhaps, or October 4th . . ."

"Every day."

"But this particular letter was the one he . . ."

"You . . . you asked if it was an anniversary."

"What?"

"Yes."

"What?"

"It was."

"Oh, it *was* an anniversary, I see. You remember now that it—"

"It was the anniversary of the . . . the death of our marriage," Ebie said, "the death he wrote about in his novel. He . . . he labeled his division the 105th as . . . as another one of his little jokes, a reminder that I had written my letter on the . . . the 5th of October . . . the letter that . . . that told what . . . what . . ."

"I think you have answered the question," Brackman said. He seemed suddenly alarmed. He turned from her swiftly and said, "Your Honor, I have no further—"

"I would like to hear the witness," McIntyre said.

"Your Honor . . ."

"You interrupted the witness before she had concluded her answer, and I would like to hear the rest of that answer now," McIntyre said. "Go on, Mrs. Driscoll."

"Yes," she said and nodded, but remained silent. She kept watching Driscoll, who would not turn to meet her gaze. The courtroom was silent.

"Mrs. Driscoll?"

"I wrote the letter because I loved him," she said. "I wrote it to explain."

She fell silent again. Driscoll did not look at her.

"I wrote and asked him to understand that I was . . . that I was telling him only because I loved him and . . . didn't want a lie between us for the rest of our lives. I asked him to understand."

Her hands were working nervously in her lap now, where only McIntyre could see them. She kept staring intently at her husband, but still he would not look at her. She shook her head as though sorry she had come this far, and then gave a small weary shrug, as though knowing she was committed and would have to go further. Her eyes were suddenly wet. She closed them immediately, and then lowered her head so that the judge would not see her tears. She did not raise her head again until she began speaking once more, and then she did so only to look at her husband. She cried soundlessly while she talked. The tears streamed down her face, but she did not wipe at them. She talked quietly and steadily, and she did not take her eyes from her husband, who never looked at her once during her long unbroken speech.

"I wrote to him because I had to tell him. We had been married that April, you see, and this was only September, the end of September. The truth was terrible, I know that now, I knew it then, I *knew* it was terrible but . . . in his book he described it as a plot to murder him, a theft of his life, his manhood, and it was never any of those things, never anything planned or schemed, only something that . . . one night . . . happened. He might have been able to understand, Dris might have, if only . . . but we had said 'forever' just that April, you see, and then he was gone in June, and this was . . . So how *could* it seem any less awful than it was, how *could* he believe I hadn't wanted it or expected it? I don't know, I don't know. We, . . . were, I was upstairs in his apartment, I shouldn't have been there, I know it, I shouldn't have gone up when he asked me to. But I was lonely, Dris was gone, and he seemed so troubled, so in need. We talked, we . . . no, nothing explains it, nothing *can* explain it. It happened. Maybe I wanted it to happen, maybe Dris was right about that, I don't know. But it happened. I was twenty-two years old, and my husband was fighting a war in Korea, and I . . . I went to bed with Peter Malcom.

"I didn't love him, but I went to bed with him. So simple. So very simple. At first I thought I could live with the idea, forget what I'd done, forget I'd given myself to him. I'd always believed, you see, I'd been taught to believe it wasn't shameful to . . . to love someone. But this wasn't love, no. I couldn't deceive myself into thinking this was anything like love, the only man I ever loved was in Korea. I . . . I continued to write to him, I had to keep writing, my letters to him were the same for almost a week, lie after lie after lie, and then . . . then I couldn't bear it any longer, I knew I had to tell him the truth or allow the lies to destroy our marriage. Instead it was the truth that destroyed it.

"So . . . so you see the ten and the five are the date on that letter, October 5th was when I wrote it, and the man in my husband's book is Peter Malcolm who . . . who made love to me . . . and . . . and . . . and I . . . the nurse in the book is only me, and the . . . the lieutenant is my husband, who . . . who testified in this courtroom yesterday that their love and their future are lost because of a single thoughtless act—isn't that what he said here yesterday?—their love is ruined because of a deception that . . . that causes a man to get killed. That's . . . I don't think that's Mr. Constantine's play. I don't think even Mr. Constantine can believe that's his play. My husband's book, you see, is about . . . about *us,* you see. That's what his book is about. And . . . I . . . I don't think I have anything else to say."

The courtroom was silent.

"Mr. Brackman, do you have any further questions?"

"No questions, your Honor," Brackman said.

Again, there was silence.

"Very well, thank you, Mrs. Driscoll."

Ebie rose, and wiped at her eyes. She looked down when she approached the steps, and then swiftly walked to the jury box. Her husband did not turn toward her as she sat.

"Mr. Brackman," McIntyre said, "I'll allow you to change or add to your summation now if you wish. Or, if you feel you need time for preparation in light of this additional testimony, we can set a date and hear your final argument then."

"I have nothing to add to what I have already said, your Honor."

"Very well. Does *anyone* have anything further to say?"

"If your Honor please," Willow said, "my opponent has suggested that Mr. Driscoll was attempting to mislead this Court. I have no comment to make on that except that I hope in the light of this subsequent testimony, you will take into consideration the personal elements involved. Thank you, your Honor."

"Anything else, gentlemen?" McIntyre asked. "Very well. I'd like to congratulate you on a good trial and argument. I want you to know that despite whatever moments of levity there were during the trial and in some of our discussions, I nonetheless consider this a most serious matter, and not only because of the large sums of money involved. So it's my intention now to reserve decision on the motions and on the entire case until such time as I can render the opinion a case of such gravity warrants. Thank you, gentlemen. I enjoyed it."

The judge rose.

Everyone in the courtroom rose when he did, and then watched in silence as he came from behind the bench. He walked to the door on his right, nodded briefly as it was opened for him, and then went into his chambers.

The door closed gently behind him.

The courtroom was silent.

There was—Arthur and Driscoll felt it simultaneously and with the same intensity—a sense of incompleteness. They both knew, and had known all along, that there would be no decision on the day the trial ended, and perhaps not for weeks afterward. But whereas this sense of an ending delayed, a final result postponed, was something both men had experienced before and knew intimately, they could not accept it *here,* not in the context of an apparatus as structured and as well ordered as the law. They sat in pained silence as though willing the judge to reappear, refusing to accept the knowledge that there would be no decision this day, there would be no victor and no vanquished. Instead, there would be only the same interminable wait that accompanied the production of a play or the publication of a book, the same frustrating delay between completion and inalterable exposure.

The judge did not return.

The door to his chambers remained sealed.

The writers stared at the closed door, each slowly yielding to a rising sense of doubt. No matter *what* Driscoll's wife had been induced to say, Arthur still knew without question that his play had been stolen; and Driscoll knew with equal certainty that he had not stolen it. But what were their respective opinions worth without the corroborating opinion of the judge? In spiraling anxiety, Arthur realized that if the judge decreed his play had not been copied, then the time and energy put into it had been lost, the play was valueless, the play was nothing. And Driscoll similarly realized that if the judge decided against *him,* then whatever he had said in his novel would mean nothing, he would be stripped of ownership, the book might just as well never have been written.

They each knew despair in that moment, a despair that seemed more real to them than anything they had felt during the course of the trial. In near panic, they wondered what they had left unsaid, what they had forgotten to declare, how they could prove to this impartial judge that there was merit to their work, that they were honest men who had honestly delivered, that they could not be summarily dismissed, nor obliterated by decree.

And then despair led inexorably to reason, and they recognized with sudden clarity that the judge's decision would really change nothing. The truth was there in the record to be appreciated or ignored, but it was there nonetheless, and no one's opinion could ever change it. If there was any satisfaction for them that day, it came with the relief this knowledge brought, a relief that was terribly short-lived because it was followed by the cold understanding that even the trial itself had changed nothing. Whatever paper dragons they had fought in this courtroom, the real dragons still waited for them in the street outside, snarling and clawing and spitting fire, fangs sharpened, breath foul, dragons who would devour if they were not ultimately slain.

The two men sat in silence.

Around them, there was not even a semblance of ceremony or ritual consistent with what had gone before. The attorneys were whispering and laughing among themselves, packing their briefcases, the paid mercenaries taking off their armor and putting away their weapons, and hoping to go home to a hot bowl of soup before hiring on again to fight yet another man's battle on yet another day. Genitori shook hands with Willow, and then Kahn shook hands with Willow, and Sheppard shook hands with both attorneys foı API, and then Brackman and his partner walked over to where the defense lawyers stood in a shallow circle and offered his hand first to Willow and then to Genitori, and then introduced all the men to his partner, who beamed in the presence of someone as important as Willow, and then each of the men congratulated each other on how well and nobly the case had been fought, and Brackman said something to Willow off the record, and Willow laughed, and then Genitori told Brackman how wise he was not to have made a second summation, and Brackman in turn complimented Genitori on how expertly he had handled a conceited ass like Ralph Knowles, and they all agreed Knowles had been a very poor witness indeed.

Arthur and Driscoll, apart, watched and said nothing.

Briefcases packed, amenities exchanged, the lawyers again shook hands to show there were no hard feelings between any of them, to assure themselves once again that whatever vile accusations had been hurled in calculated anger within these four walls, they could still express an appreciation of courage and skill, they could still part in the hope that one day they might meet again as battle veterans to reminisce about that terrible week in December when they were fighting a ferocious plagiarism case. And then, because their clients were waiting for the reassuring words that would tide them over through the weeks or perhaps months before the decision came, they moved away from each other cordially and filed out of the courtroom, forming again into two tight, separate groups in the corridor outside, where they talked in low whispers.

They talked only about the trial.

It was easiest to talk about the trial because, for the most part, it had been orderly and serene, moving within the confines of a described pattern toward a conclusion, however delayed. They talked about the trial, and seemed reluctant to leave the corridor, letting several elevators pass them by while they continued to chat, unwilling to make the decisive move that would take them into the next car and then to the street below. Jonah told Genitori and Sheppard that he was positive they had won, positive, and his eyes were glowing even when he sincerely apologized to Driscoll for ever having thought he was guilty. Is that all you have to apologize for? Driscoll asked, and for a moment the corridor went silent, for a moment a pall was cast upon the abounding good fellowship, but only for a moment, only until Jonah grinned and clapped Driscoll on the shoulder and said, Come on, Jimmy, it's all over now, we can all relax. Sheppard grinned too, and chastised himself for having been so stupid, he should have known all along that Mrs. Driscoll was the girl in the book.

He saw the pained expression that crossed Driscoll's face, and fell silent. Genitori swiftly said he too was confident they had won, and then speculated aloud on how much the judge would award them for counsel fees.

Near one of the other elevators, Sidney told Arthur that Mrs. Driscoll's testimony had sounded very phony to him, and probably would not affect the trial in the slightest, the case was still airtight, he was certain the judge would decide in their favor. Arthur nodded, seemingly preoccupied, and when Sidney's partner commented on the fact that he didn't seem terribly elated, Arthur said, Well, I've got my new play to think about, you know. Sidney's partner nodded and said, Of course, of course, and then suddenly remembered he had not called his wife to tell her how the trial had ended. He asked Sidney if he had a dime and while Sidney was fishing in his pocket for one, he said, Isn't there someone you have to call, Sidney? Sidney was silent until he located the coin. Then he handed it to his partner and, with a secret smile, said, Why, no, Carl, there's no one I have to call.

And then all the talking was done, there seemed to be nothing more to say to each other. The afterglow of the trial could no longer warm them, no longer generate a sustaining energy among people who were essentially strangers to each other. They shook hands again, and—still reluctant to get into the elevator that would take them down to the street—broke into smaller groups, lingering in the hallway, Genitori saying he wanted to talk to the clerk before he left, clerks were always infallible indicators of how a trial had gone, and Jonah saying he wanted to go to the men's room, and Sidney telling Arthur to run along, he knew how busy Arthur must be, he would wait for Carl to finish his call. The groups dispersed soundlessly, Driscoll and his wife avoiding Arthur, who took a separate elevator down.

The corridor was empty.

When Genitori came out of the courtroom he told Kahn that the clerk thought McIntyre would find in their favor. Kahn seemed extremely pleased. He confided to Genitori that he had known the plaintiff's case was groundless all along, but that he never ceased to marvel at how the American system worked, a man being able to have his day in court, and to settle his problems there.

God bless America, Genitori said.

16

HE SPENT the afternoon alone.

He was in excellent spirits, walking along Fifth Avenue for a while, his coat open, his muffler loose around his throat, simply walking, and watching everyone, and enjoying himself. Then he sat on one of the benches in Rockefeller Plaza, still watching the people who went by, comparing all the pretty girls to Chickie and deciding, as he had a hundred times before, that he was the luckiest man in the world. He watched the skaters for ten minutes or so, and then crossed over to Saks to listen to the Salvation Army band outside the store, all the while feeling a sense of impending joy, as though his present good mood were only the prelude to something inconceivably better.

He attributed part of his mood to the fact that Christmas was almost here. As a Jew, he had never fully appreciated the religious aspects of the holiday, but he could not deny the excitment that swept over New York at this time each year, nor could he attribute it entirely to the increased activity in the business community, as his father did. Well, his father attributed everything to either good business or bad business, his father was an old *pisher,* and that was all that could be said for him. So he listened to the tinkling of the bells everywhere around him, and the voices singing, and the trumpets and tubas, and the high-heeled rushing click along the sidewalks, and he savored the bite in the air, and knew it was the joyous holiday spirit that accounted for some of his own happiness.

Another part of his happiness, though, had to do with the fact that the trial was over. There was pure relief attached to the completion of any trial, but expecially this one where his opponent had been someone like Jonah Willow; he had to hand it to the bastard, he certainly knew his stuff. As he walked, Sidney still wondered whether Mrs. Driscoll's testimony had really been a surprise. He couldn't believe it hadn't all been carefully planned beforehand by Willow, but my God, what a chance to take, suppose McIntyre had refused to reopen the case? Well, it was finished now, there was nothing to do now but wait for McIntyre's decision which would be God knew when, especially with Christmas just around the corner, and then New Year's, they'd be lucky if they heard before March. In the meantime, he didn't have to worry about preparations, and he didn't have to worry about catching every word Willow said lest he miss an important point that could later trip him up, he didn't have to worry about anything but one thing, and that wasn't bothering him at all. That, in fact, was what accounted for the major part of his joy on this fine December afternoon.

He had put off calling Chickie because he wanted to give her time enough to make her decision, but he knew now, he sensed intuitively that she would marry him. He could not have said how he knew, just a feeling, just a tiny little something inside that told him nothing could go wrong today, everything was being done for the benefit of Sidney Brackman. The beautiful weather, the music in the streets, the city all dressed up in her holiday clothes, this was all for Sidney Brackman who had handled himself pretty well throughout the course of a grueling trial, even if he had to say so himself, right, Sidney? Right, he thought, and looked at his watch, and smiled.

It was close to five o'clock, which meant Chickie would be leaving the office soon, and which meant he should start uptown. He wanted to catch her shortly after she got home, wanted to ask her for her decision, certain he knew what the decision would be—after all, if a girl *isn't* going to marry you, she doesn't say she'll think it over, does she? She just says No, I'm sorry, go peddle your papers. He would kiss her. Very gently. No sex, just a gentle kiss, and he would say Well, darling, now that it's all settled, put on your coat, sweetheart, and we'll stroll right over to Tiffany's and pick out a diamond for you, I'm sure they're open late every night of this wonderful holiday season. And then he would take her to dinner in one of the best restaurants in New York, he'd pick a real fancy one, something very nice and suitable to the occasion, and they would drink champagne and talk quietly about their future plans.

The lights were on in her apartment when he reached the building. He glanced up, smiled, and then went into the foyer and rang the doorbell. Chickie answered his ring immediately, he *knew* it, nothing could go wrong today, everything was perfect and fine and right. He was beginning to think he might even win his cockamamie case, *despite* Mrs. Driscoll's sob story, McIntyre would certainly see through a bleeding heart gambit like that one. He climbed the stairs rapidly, his step light, feeling very young, feeling the way he had in Boston with Rebecca Strauss, wanting to sing, sliding his hand along the banister, tipping his head jauntily, actually humming a little tune inside his head, if you knew Susie, like I know Susie, oh, oh . . .

He knocked on her door.

"Ruth?" she said.

"No," he said. He smiled. "It's me. Sidney."

"Oh. Just a minute, Sidney."

She opened the door immediately. She was wearing black slacks and a black sweater. The sleeves of the sweater were pushed up to her elbows. Her hair was pulled to the back of her neck, tied there with a green ribbon. She was wearing no makeup. She looked beautiful, but she did not look as if she had just got home from the office.

"Come in, Sidney," she said.

There was a curious disorder to the apartment, shoe boxes dumped on the living room floor, pieces of tissue paper trailing through the foyer, jackets and dresses draped over chairs and on the sofa, skirts hanging from doorknobs, blouses laid out in rows on table tops, bras and panties piled in stacks everywhere.

"Some mess, huh?" Chickie said, and smiled.

"Yes," Sidney said, amused. "What are you doing, cleaning out your closets?"

Chickie pecked him on the cheek and said, "Would you like a drink, Sidney?"

"All right," he said. "Where does a man sit in all this . . . this . . ." He gestured helplessly with his open hands, still amused, and feeling that he looked boyish and cute, putting a slightly exaggerated puzzled look on his face and hoping she would kiss him again.

"What can I get you?" she said. "I'm all out of bourbon, but I've got scotch and rye. Choose your poison."

"Well, you certainly sound cheerful," he said, smiling.

"Oh, I *am* very cheerful," she said.

"In that case, I think I'll have one of each, how's that?" he said.

"All right, Mr. Brackman, one of each it is. You asked for it."

"I asked for it, right," Sidney said, and laughed, and watched her as she walked to the bar. "Well, the trial's over," he said, and impulsively clapped his hands together.

"Did you win?"

"Who knows, who cares?" Sidney said. "It's over, and the hell with it."

"That's a good attitude," Chickie said. She was busy at the bar, her back to him.

"Have you made up your mind yet?" he asked, smiling. He knew for certain that her happiness, her cheerfulness, her busy puttering little female motions at the bar were all due to the fact that she had decided to marry him. So he smiled as he asked his question, asked it a trifle coyly and in the same boyish manner he had used when opening his hands wide at the mess in the room, even though she couldn't see him.

"Made up my mind about what?" Chickie said.

"You know," he said, still coyly, still confidently, feeling more and more confident all the time. He took off his hat and sat down on the arm of the big easy chair, avoiding her stacked underwear spread on the chair's seat, certain that Chickie was playing her usual teasing game with him, the game they always played together, and loving her for it. She turned from the bar, carrying a small tray just below her breasts, smiling as she came across the room to him. She offered the tray. There were two glasses on it.

"Scotch and rye," she said, and smiled, and curtsied.

"Thank you, miss," he said, "I think I'll try the scotch first." He lifted the glass and sniffed it. "Ahhh, excellent," he said, and drank. "And now the rye."

"You're going to get sick, Sidney," she warned.

"No, no, this is nothing for an old sailor, nothing at all." He sniffed at the second glass. "Is this any good?" he asked. "How's your rye, miss?"

"How's *your* eye?" Chickie said, and burst out laughing.

"You still haven't answered my question," he said.

"My eye is fine, thank you. Hey, get your hand off there, you fresh thing."

"Oh, excuse me, m'dear," he said, using a W. C. Fields voice, "excuse me, m'little chickadee, wandering hands, bad failing, here we are, let me taste this fine rye whiskey of yours."

He swallowed the second shot, feeling the whiskey burning all the way down to his stomach. "About my question," he said.

"What question?"

"You know."

"Oh," she said. "Yes."

"And, m'dear?"

"Sidney," she said, "I've decided to take a trip to Europe."

"Oh, really?" he said, smiling. "Well, now *that's* an interesting development, m'little chickadee, that's truly a very interesting . . ."

"Really, Sidney," she said.

"What?"

"Really," she said, and she stressed the word so strongly that he knew all at once she was serious. The smiled dropped from his face.

"Wh . . . what do you mean?" he said.

"I'm going to Europe, Sidney. Ruth and I are going to Europe."

"What did you say?"

"I said we're going to Europe. Ruth and I."

"What?"

"Yes, Sidney."

"Europe?"

"Yes, Sidney. Italy and Greece. We're leaving for Rome tomorrow morning, the nine forty-five A.M. flight."

"You're . . . you're joking," he said, knowing she was not, and not at all surprised when she did not answer. "Chickie?"

"Yes?"

"You're joking," he said again.

"No."

"But . . . I thought . . ."

"What did you think, Sidney?"

"That . . . that . . . I don't know."

"You poor dear man," she said, "I'm going to Europe."

"Ch-Ch-Chickie?"

"I'm going to Europe, Sidney."

"But . . ."

"I'm going, Sidney. Really."

"You d-d-didn't tell me."

"I wasn't sure. I had to decide. Now I've decided."

"Wh-wh-what about me?" he asked. "What about me?"

"You poor dear man," she said. "Sidney, I must rush you out now, because you see I've got a million things to do before tomorrow morning."

She caught both his hands in her own, and pulled him gently off the arm of the chair.

"Now put on your hat like a dear man," she said, "and let me get all this packing done. I hate to pack. Don't you hate to pack, Sidney?" She had led him to the door, she was reaching for the doorknob, she was twisting the knob, she was opening the door.

"Chickie, *wait!*" he said sharply.

"Yes, Sidney?"

"I have to . . . Chickie, it's . . . it's im . . . p-p-p-portant to me to . . . Chickie, you've *got* to . . ."

"Sidney, dear," she said, opening the door wide, "what can I say? It's all arranged. Really, Sidney, I'm terribly sorry, but it's all arranged."

"Chickie, I love you," he said.

"Yes."

"I love you."

"Yes, Sidney." She stood silently just inside the open door. "Goodbye, Sidney," she said, easing him into the hallway.

"Chickie . . . what about me?" he asked. "What about me?"

"I hope you win your case," she said, and blew a kiss at him.

The door closed. He heard the lock turning, the tumblers falling.

"What about me?" he said again.

Behind the door, he heard her giggle.

It was 6:10 when Jonah got to Pennsylvania Station.

He did not expect the terminal to be so crowded because by all reasonable standards *next* Friday was to be the start of the Christmas weekend. But he had not counted on the scheduling vagaries of colleges and prep schools; the station was thronged with milling students and excited, waiting parents. There seemed to be an overabundance of servicemen as well, sailors carrying seabags, soldiers lugging duffles, everyone hurrying and intent, worlds colliding, separating, touching, dispersing, touching again, everyone in frantic, busy motion. He asked the man behind the information counter what track the train from Trenton would be on, and was told the train had been in for fifteen minutes already. Shouldering his way through the crowd, he hurried toward the gate.

She was waiting at the entrance.

She was wearing a plaid skirt and a black ski parka. A kookie leather Ringo hat rested lopsidedly on her dark head. She stood with her legs slightly spread, the Dunseath posture, but there was a spring-tight tension in her body, and her eyes flashed searchingly at each passing face. A small suitcase rested near her feet. She was wearing black boots her mother had bought for her at Bendel. He walked up to her swiftly, and she turned to him immediately and mouthed the word "Daddy" soundlessly, and threw herself into his arms. He held her close to him, and closed his eyes, and kissed her cheek and said, "Hello, darling," and she said, "Oh, Daddy, how good to see you," and threw her arms around him again, and kissed him again, and hugged him to her and said, "Do you like my hat?"

"It's lovely," he said, "where'd you get it?"

"It's my roommate's, Yolanda's, did I tell you about Yolanda?"

"I think so. Is this all you have?" he asked, picking up her bag.

"I always travel light," she said, and wiggled her eyebrows, and then laughed, her mother's laugh, her grandmother's laugh, head thrown back, blue eyes flashing. He took her hand in his own, and they hurried through the station. He was tremendously proud of her, aware of her trim good looks, pleased when young college boys turned to look at her, their eyes traveling down over her youthful backside and to her legs. She walked with her mother's loping gait, hips thrust forward, wearing her nutty hat with all the authority of a *Vogue* model, talking to him animatedly as they came out onto Eighth Avenue and tried to find a taxi.

". . . boy had a guitar, he got on at Philadelphia, and we just sang songs and were drinking . . ."

"Drinking? What do you mean?"

"Oh, just a little beer, Daddy, one of the senior boys had a six-pack."

"Honey, you're a little young, don't you think, to be . . ."

"Daddy, he was a senior boy, he must have been seventeen at least."

"I know, honey, but you're only twelve."

"I'll be thirteen in May."

"I know, but still . . ."

"Anyway, I only had a sip. What we did mostly was sing. It was such fun, Daddy, and we got here so *faaaast,* it seemed like no time at all. Have you ever seen such crowds, did you call Mother?"

"Yes, I called her. She's expecting you."

"I know, I spoke to her last night."

"Good."

"Are you going to come up?"

"I don't think so, Amy."

"All right," she said.

In the taxi, she said, "What are you working on now, Daddy?"

"We just concluded a trial today," he said.

"Something good?"

"A plagiarism case."

"Did you win?"

"I think so. We won't know for a while."

"How can you bear waiting?" she said.

"Well, there are always other things coming up. In fact, when I got back to the office today, there was a new case already waiting."

"What kind of a case?"

"An exciting one, I think. A man's been charged with income tax evasion, but he claims he's not *evading* anything, he's simply refusing to pay. He says he will not give money to support an undeclared war, and that unless Congress is allowed to decide whether we should or should not be at war, why then he's being deprived of representation. And without representation . . ."

"No taxation," Amy said, and nodded. "But doesn't *everyone* have to pay income tax?"

"Certainly, honey."

"Then he's guilty. I mean, if he won't pay . . ."

"Well, there are principles involved," Jonah said.

"Will you take the case?"

"I think so. Yes, I think so, honey." He clasped her hand and squeezed it.

"Oh my God, I almost forgot!" Amy said, pulling her hand away and reaching for her suitcase. She unclasped it quickly, burrowed beneath a sweater and a blouse and produced a small slim package wrapped in red and green paper, tied with a bright green bow. He remembered in that instant that he had not yet bought her the ring.

"I got this in New Hope," she said. "Merry Christmas, Daddy."

"Christmas isn't until next week, honey," he said.

"I know, but I wish you'd open it now."

"Shouldn't I wait?"

"Open it, Daddy. Please."

He nodded. Carefully, he slid the bow off the package, and then unwrapped it. It was an address book, black leather, his initials in gold on the cover, J.W.

"It's beautiful," he said.

"Do you like it?"

"Yes, very much."

He knew he should have had the ring to give to her now, knew that this was a very private and personal moment to Amy, this offering of her gift in a taxi speeding to her mother's apartment. He had nothing to offer her in return. He had forgotten to buy the ring, and so he sat and stared at the leather address book with his initials on the cover, J.W., and wondered what he could say, wondered how he could begin to make her understand that he had really intended to have a present for her, to meet her with it at the station, but instead had become involved the moment he got back to the office. Surely she would understand. Surely she would realize that Christmas was still more than a week away, there was still time, wasn't there? Wasn't there still time?

"There's something nice I plan on getting you," he said, and patted her hand.

"Oh, sure, it can wait," Amy said.

"I'll get it to you before Christmas," he said, "don't you worry.

"Oh, sure," Amy said, and was silent. Then, unexpectedly, she shrugged and said, "Christmas is all craparoo, anyway."

He did not call his uncle until eleven o'clock.

He did not know why he was calling, unless it was because he and Ebie were leaving for Vermont in the morning, and Vermont was more distant from Fort Lauderdale than New York City. His uncle's voice was just as he remembered it, gravelly, with a hint of a brogue; he recalled in a rush the living room on West End Avenue, the Chickering piano, his uncle's pink shirts.

"Hello, Uncle Benny," he said, "this is Jimmy."

"Jimmy? Jimbo? Where are you, Jimbo? Are you in Florida?"

"No, no, I'm in New York."

"Hey, Vera, it's my nephew," Uncle Benny shouted. "Hey, how are you, Jimbo?"

"I'm fine, Uncle Benny."

"Good, good. *Vera,*" he shouted, "it's my *nephew!*" To Driscoll, he said, "She's upstairs in bed, Jimbo, hasn't been feeling too well."

"Oh, I'm sorry to hear that."

"Well, it's nothing serious, just a little cold."

"A little cold is what we have in Fort Knox," Driscoll said, and smiled.

"No, that's a little gold," Uncle Benny answered. "What you're thinking of, lad, is a tiny creature in a monster movie."

"No, that's a little ghoul," Driscoll said. "I hate to correct you, Uncle Benny, but I think you mean a small measure of unmitigated nerve."

"Unmitigated nerve?"

"That's right."

"A little *gall!*" Uncle Benny shouted, and burst out laughing. "Ahhh, Jimmy, Jimmy, it's good to hear your voice. How are you, boy? How *are* you?"

"I'm fine."

"And Ebie?"

"Fine. Fine."

"When does the trial start? Is that why you're in New York?"

"Well, yes, but it *ended* today, Uncle Benny."

"It *did?* Did you win?"

"I think so. Yes, I think so."

There was a silence on the line.

"What's the matter, Jimmy?" his uncle asked.

"What do you mean?"

"Why are you calling me at eleven o'clock at night?"

"I just wanted to talk to you, Uncle Benny."

"What about?"

"I just wanted to talk to you."

"Is something wrong?"

"No, no, I just felt I had to talk to someone I . . . someone who . . ."

"Isn't Ebie there?"

"Yes, she's upstairs. In the room. Upstairs."

"I see," Uncle Benny said, and was silent.

Wise old Uncle Benny, he thought, and listened to the crackling silence on the line, the seconds ticking away.

"Uncle Benny," he said at last.

"Yes, Jimmy?"

"I don't know what to do."

"About what?"

"Uncle Benny?"

"Yes?"

"Uncle Benny?"

"Yes, boy, what is it? What is it, Jimbo?"

"Help me."

"How?"

"Help me, Uncle Benny."

"Is it Ebie?"

He nodded, and then realized his uncle could not see him. Very quietly, he said, "Yes, it's Ebie."

"What about her?"

He could not tell him. He sat in the phone booth in the lobby of the hotel, and looked at the receiver clutched tightly in his hand, and could not tell his uncle. The silence lengthened.

"Jimmy?" his uncle said.

"Yes, Uncle Benny."

"Jimmy, whatever it is . . ."

"Yes?"

"Face it. Face it, and it'll vanish."

"Vanish is when you kick somebody out of the kingdom," Driscoll said, and tried a smile.

"No, that's banish," Uncle Benny said automatically, but there was no humor in his voice.

"No, banish are guys who wear masks and go around stealing," Driscoll answered.

"Jim," his uncle said, "don't play games."

"What?" Driscoll said.

"I think you heard me, Jim."

"Yes, but . . ."

"Do you understand me?"

"Uncle Benny, I called because . . ."

"Yes, I know why you called, Jim, now you listen to me, Jim. Where are you?"

"I'm down here. I'm in the lobby. Near the drugstore. Uncle Benny . . ."

"Now you listen to me, Jim, and don't play games, do you hear me? You go right upstairs, do you hear? You go right upstairs and you face whatever it is that's waiting for you there, you face it, Jim, now that's what I'm telling you."

"Yes."

"Do you hear me?"

"Yes."

"All right, that's what you do."

"Yes."

"Good. I've got to go up to Vera now, I think I hear her calling me. Do you understand me, Jim?"

"Yes, Uncle Benny."

"Good. You keep in touch with me."

"Uncle Benny?"

"Yes?"

"Give my regards to Vera."

"I will."

"Uncle Benny?"

"Yes?"

"I . . . I hope she feels better."

"I'm sure she will. Good night, Jim."

"Good night, Uncle Benny."

There was a click on the line.

He stood holding the dead receiver, and then he looked at it in disbelief and slowly replaced it on the hook. Well, that was very helpful, he thought, who the hell called you to play games, Uncle Benny, would you mind telling me? That was really quite helpful, thank you very much, Uncle Benny, I'm certainly glad I called you all the way in Florida to listen to your homespun philosophy. Thank you very much, Uncle Benny, you've certainly set everything right with your words of wisdom, and as a matter of fact I happened to think the banish definition was very good indeed. The phone rang. He lifted the receiver.

"Yes?" he said.

"One moment for additional charges, sir," the operator said.

"Thanks," he said. Additional charges, he thought. That's exactly what I need for a call that I was crazy to make in the first place.

"That'll be thirty-five cents, sir," the operator said.

"Thank you," he said. He dug into his pocket, found a quarter and a dime, and deposited them in the box.

"Thank you, sir," the operator said.

"Sure," he said, and again hung up. He went out of the booth. Tomorrow morning they would leave for Vermont, back to the old hay, alfalfa, and oats, back to the farm he hated, the most insistent crop on which was rocks. What the hell was a city boy doing in Vermont, anyway, how far can you run? Face it, Uncle Benny had said, face it. Thank you, Uncle Benny. Thank you for all the good things if I seem ungrateful now for this singular piece of worthless advice.

She was asleep when he got back to the room, snoring very lightly, his charming wife. He undressed quietly in the dark, and then got under the covers and lay there silently with the green neon Sardi sign illuminating the black windowpane across the room, and Ebie snoring lightly beside him, her body warm, his hand lying close to the curving flank of her naked flesh. She never slept with a stitch on, his sweet Southern flower, never when he first met her and not now either. He wondered if she had slept naked with Peter Malcom, wondered, lightly snoring, and wondered why he did not leave her. Face it. The bed was strange, he did not like hotel rooms. In Vermont, you could hear the mice rattling away the night in the attic. They slept in separate beds in Vermont, twin beds are for Englishmen and other people with severe cramps Uncle Benny had said one night dis*gost*ingly drunk. Face it. He listened to her even breathing, the snoring had stopped now, felt the warmth of her close to him and wondered again why he James Driscoll the Cat did not leave her, sleeping side by side in the Vermont twin beds with the mice racing in the attic, face it, tickytackyticky *tack* their little feet on the ceiling, face it, and then wondered why *she* did not leave him, why Ebie did not leave him.

He touched her shoulder.

She did not stir. He touched her again, more insistently this time. She murmured something in her sleep, and then turned toward him. She sat up. He could not see her face in the darkness.

"Ebie," he whispered.

"What is it?" she said. "What's the matter?"

"Ebie," he said, "do you love me?"

"Yes," she said.

"I'll never understand," he said. "Ebie," he said, "I love you."

"I know."

"I love you very much, Ebie."

"I know."

"But, Ebie, I'll never understand. As long as I live, I will never understand."

"Do you have to?" she asked.

He closed his eyes. "Never understand," he said, "never understand," and was suddenly exhausted. He sighed heavily. As he drifted off into folds of unconsciousness, he thought *Ebie, let's try,* and then was not certain whether he had thought it or said it, and said aloud, certain that he was saying it this time, "Ebie, let's try, Ebie," and sighed again, and said, "I love you, Ebie," and fell into a deep sleep.

He could not seem to get drunk.

He had begun drinking shortly after dinner, sitting in his apartment alone, refusing to answer the telephone because he knew each time it rang that Stuart Selig or Oscar Stern would be on the other end, and he did not know what he wanted to tell them. The bottle of scotch was half empty now, and he still did not know what to do, except sit here alone in his apartment, the way he had been sitting alone in his life from the time he was eighteen and went into the Army, the result of which was *Catchpole.* He could not believe that Driscoll's wife hadn't been coached, could not believe her testimony had not been carefully prepared beforehand, and then sprung by Willow at precisely the right moment, the courtroom magician pulling a rabbit from his tophat, a cuddly Southern bunny with large wet eyes, he could not believe his play had not been stolen.

Well, he thought, it's because I let them do it to me in the first place, I let Freddie and Fielder talk me into making all those changes, I wrecked my own play, and Driscoll stepped in and made a success of it, it's all my own fault when you get right down to it. Which is why I should tell Selig and Stern to go screw, along with Hester Miers and Mitzi Starke, and Walter Kerr thrown in for good measure. Tell them all to go screw, I will not make the changes in my play, I'm going to *win* this damn case and produce the play myself, maybe buy the Helen Hayes, no, not the Helen Hayes, not that jinx Fulton of a theater, I'll buy something nice and cozy and lucky, and maybe I'll buy the *New York Times* as well, how much do you want for your little paper, Mr. Sulzberger?

He was tempted to call Julie in Minnesota, because what they were asking him to do, really, was obliterate his past by obliterating his family, his sister, and by rights she should have something to say about her own demise. He wondered what time it was in Minnesota, and he lifted the telephone receiver from its cradle and when the operator came onto the line, he said, "Operator, I'm thinking of making a long-distance call to Minnesota, can you please tell me what time it is there?"

"Well," the operator said, and hesitated. "Just a moment, sir."

He waited. He owed it to Julie to consult her on her own eradication. Too many things in life got eradicated without consent, what had ever happened to the Sunday feasts at his grandfather's house, who had ever decided *that* issue without a vote?

"Sir?" the operator said.

"Yes?"

"Sir, Minnesota is on Central Standard."

"What does that mean?"

"They're an hour behind us, sir."

"Well, what time is it there?"

"It's almost midnight here, sir, so I would imagine it's almost eleven there."

"I see. Thank you."

"Did you wish to place your call, sir?"

"Well, I don't know yet," he said. "Thank you."

He hung up. Eleven o'clock, he thought. That wasn't

really so late, but Julie probably went to bed early, houseful of kids to get off to school, besides *everybody* probably went to bed early in Minnesota. I really should call her, though, he thought, how can I change her without first getting her permission? They want me to make you a social worker, Julie, he thought, I know you'll get a laugh out of that, it's really pretty comical when you think of it. A social worker who practices the flute in her bedroom next door with the pink curtains on the window and the BEWARE VICIOUS DOG sign tacked crookedly on the white-painted wood, I don't know, Julie.

They told me nothing, Julie.

I thought they'd tell me something in that courtroom.

They told me nothing.

Julie, do you remember once, do you remember when we were walking to the library together one night? and you asked me not to walk quite so fast, my legs aren't as long as *yours,* do you remember that? and I said I'm in a hurry, do you remember? I was in a hurry to get there, Julie, to get where the words were, all the words.

Julie, honey, I never got there.

Julie, they told me nothing, I was hoping they'd tell me something.

Look, we've got to discuss this. Look, what's the sense, we've just got to discuss this.

He reached for the telephone.

What's the sense? he thought.

He waited, his head bent, his hand resting on the telephone. He sighed and lifted the receiver. Rapidly, he dialed. He heard the ringing on the other end, once, twice, and quickly he hung up. He stared at the phone a moment longer, his heart beating wildly, and then he reached for the bottle of scotch and poured himself another drink.

He placed his call at one-thirty A.M. He was very drunk by that time. "Hello!" he shouted into the mouthpiece.

"What? Who's this?"

"Well, I've been sleeping on it," he said.

"What? Who's this?"

"This is Edward Albee. Don't you recognize my voice?"

"Listen, who *is* this?"

"Every writer has a voice, didn't you know that?"

"Arthur?"

"Yes, very good, this is Arthur Miller."

"What is it, Arthur? Are you drunk, Arthur?"

"Why, Stuart, what a thing to say to a man of my talents and respect, what a thing to say. Would you say such a thing to Tenafly New Jersey?"

"I've been trying to get you all day," Stuart said. "Have you decided, Arthur? Is that it?"

"I have decided."

"What have you decided?"

"I have decided to sell out," Arthur said.

"What do you mean?"

"Again," Arthur said.

"I still don't know what you mean."

"I have decided, Stuart, to sell out again. I have decided to sell out because I'm afraid."

"Arthur, that's no attitude to . . ."

"I'm afraid I'll lose the case, Stuart, and I'm afraid if I don't grab Hester then Osborne'll get her, and I'm afraid my sweet little play'll die, Stuart, it'll curl up and die stillborn, never see the light of day, never have a chance to breathe at all. So I'm selling out, I'll do whatever the pants pressers want me to do, make any revisions they want, change little Julie to a whore with a line of sailors waiting outside her bedroom . . ."

"Julie?"

"*Carol,* whatever the hell her name is, who cares?"

"Look, Arthur . . ."

"Tell Mitzi Starke she just bought herself a writer."

"Arthur . . ."

"Tell Hester I'll fit the part to her like a tailored suit from wherever it is fine actresses like Hester Miers buy their tailored suits, tell them they got themselves a tailor, and when I finish the garment they can press it. Tell them."

"Arthur?"

"What?"

"Arthur, are you crying?"

"No," he said.

UNITED STATES DISTRICT COURT
SOUTHERN DISTRICT OF NEW YORK

-- X

ARTHUR NELSON CONSTANTINE,
Plaintiff,

-against-

JAMES DRISCOLL, MITCHELL-CAMPBELL BOOKS, INC., CAMELOT BOOKS, INC., AND ARTISTS-PRODUCERS-INTERNATIONAL,
Defendants.

-- X

BRACKMAN & HARTUNG, of New York, N.Y.
Attorneys for the Plaintiff

SIDNEY BRACKMAN, ESQ., and
CARL HARTUNG, ESQ., of Counsel.

SAMUEL GENITORI, ESQ., and
MICHAEL KAHN, ESQ.,
Attorneys for Defendant Artists-Producers-International

LORRIMER, WILLOW, LEVINE & MAGUIRE, ESQS., of New York, N.Y.
Attorneys for Defendants James Driscoll, Mitchell-Campbell Books, Inc., and Camelot Books, Inc.

JONAH WILLOW, ESQ., and
NORMAN SHEPPARD, ESQ., of Counsel

MC INTYRE, FRANK HARLAN

The plaintiff in this action is Arthur Nelson Constantine, a citizen of New York.[1] He is the author of a play titled "Catchpole," a copy of which was deposited in the Copyright Office in 1947, Certificate of Registration under 17 U.S.C. § 12 issued on August 3, 1947. The play was subsequently produced in New York City and ran for twelve days in October of 1947 at the Fulton Theatre.

James Driscoll,[2] a citizen of New

---

[1] Jurisdictional findings such as this relate to time of action.

[2] Plaintiff did not bring suit against Driscoll. Cross claims against Driscoll, however, have been asserted by Mitchell-Campbell and API should plaintiff recover against them. A cross claim has also been asserted by API against Mitchell-Campbell. All cross claims were deferred by order of this Court, pursuant to Rule 42(b) Fed. Rules Civ. Proc., 29 U.S.C., until defendants' liability has been decided.

York, is the author of a novel titled "The Paper Dragon," published in 1963 by Mitchell-Campbell Books, Inc., a New York corporation. The novel was subsequently filmed by Artists-Producers-International, a Delaware corporation, and put into general release in 1964. At that time, a paperback edition of the book was published by Camelot Books, Inc., a New York corporation.

It is the plaintiff's claim that the novel by James Driscoll and the motion picture written and directed by Ralph Knowles for API were copied from "Catchpole," thereby depriving plaintiff of his rights in the copyrighted composition. An accounting of profits, damages, injunction, and attorneys' fees[3] are sought by the plaintiff.

---

[3] Attorneys' fees under 17 U.S.C. § 116 are sought by defendants inter alia, and consideration was reserved until main issues have been settled.

I

The defendants contend that the plaintiff Constantine forfeited both statutory and common-law copyright by making a "general distribution" of his play prior to its Broadway opening. Since the plaintiff's case is based entirely on copyright law and since such a contention, if valid, would be cause for dismissal, I will consider it before coming to the merits.

Constantine has testified[4] that one hundred and twenty mimeographed copies of his play were distributed to "producers, agents, investors, and anyone interested in the theatre" between January and May of 1947. Earlier findings of this Court with regard to

---

[4] Tr. p. 78

a similar distribution,[5] where a hundred copies of an uncopyrighted work were given "to certain theatrical producers free of charge in an effort to induce them to produce the work," was that such distribution "was not a publication within the meaning of the act." Similarly, in a case[6] where two thousand copies of an unpublished song "were distributed to broadcasting stations and professional musicians for 'plugging' purposes," the Court of Appeals for the District of Columbia would not hold that there had been "such general publication as to vitiate appellant's copyright."

The defendants have cited Judge Palmer's holding, and the affirmation

---

[5] Ilvin v. Avon Publications, 144 F. Supp. 368, 373 (S.D.N.Y. 1956)

[6] Hirshon v. United Artists Corp., 243 F. 2d 640 (D.C. Cir. 1957)

of it by the Court of Appeals for this Circuit,[7] that a distribution of one hundred copies, not limited "as to persons or as to purpose"[8] constitutes a forfeitable publication. But there is every indication in this case that Constantine's distribution of the play "Catchpole" was limited and selective. He sent his play only to theatrical people, and for the sole purpose of generating interest in its possible production. Whether the work was copyrighted under 17 U.S.C. § 12, or uncopyrighted, such restricted distribution would work no forfeiture of the plaintiff's rights.

I therefore find against the defendants' argument.

---

[7] Continental Casualty Co. v. Beardsley, 151 F. Supp. 28 (S.D.N.Y. 1957) modified and affirmed 253 F. 2d 702 (2 Cir. 1958) cert. denied, 358 U.S. 816 (1958).

[8] Ibid., 253 F. 2d at 707.

II

Whereas the plaintiff's first cause of action alleges that Driscoll either possessed a copy of the play or saw it in performance, there is no evidence to support either supposition. Driscoll has denied ever seeing a copy of the play or a performance of it before this action began. When the play was produced on Broadway, he was eighteen years old and studying art at Pratt Institute. His ambition was to become a painter, and although he testified that he later studied writing at New York University, one cannot assume that he had in 1947 already decided on a career in letters.

Lacking forceful evidence of access, therefore, the merits of this case must be decided on the strength of the similarities said to exist between the works.

To support his claim of plagiarism against Driscoll, the plaintiff has prepared and presented to this Court three charts outlining in detail the specific Plot, Character, and Language similarities between the play and the novel. I have studied these charts closely, and I have read both the play and the novel many times, always keeping in mind the alleged similarities. I have also carefully observed and listened to all of the witnesses presented by both sides.

In <u>Holmes</u> v. <u>Hurst</u>, 174 U.S. 82, 86 (1899), it was established that "ideas" per se are not copyrightable, and that "expression" is the only matter susceptible of protection. Whereas it is often extremely difficult to categorize material as either copyrightable or non-copyrightable, there is nonetheless a formidable background of law against which to evaluate the plaintiff's allegation.

I quote Judge Learned Hand:

"...Upon any work, and especially upon a play, a great number of patterns of increasing generality will fit equally well, as more and more of the incident is left out. The last may perhaps be no more than the most general statement of what the play is about, and at times might consist only of its title; but there is a point in this series of abstractions where they are no longer protected, since otherwise the playwright could prevent the use of his 'ideas,' to which, apart from their expression, his property is never extended... Nobody has ever been able to fix that boundary, and nobody ever can...

"...But we do not doubt that two plays may correspond in plot closely enough for infringement. How far that correspondence must go is another matter. Nor need we hold that the same may not be true as to characters, quite independently of the 'plot' proper, though, as far as we know, such a case has never arisen. If 'Twelfth Night' were copyrighted, it is quite possible that a second comer might so closely imitate Sir Toby Belch or Malvolio as to infringe, but it would not be enough that for one of his characters he cast a riotous knight who kept wassail to the discomfort of his household, or a vain and foppish steward who became amorous of his mistress. These would be no more than Shakespeare's 'ideas' in the play, as little capable of monopoly as Einstein's Doctrine of Relativity, or Darwin's theory of the Origin of Species. It follows that the less developed the characters, the less they can be copyrighted; that is the penalty an author must bear for marking them too indistinctly."[9]

---

[9] Nichols v. Universal Pictures Corp., 45 F. 2d 119, 121 (2 Cir.), cert. denied, 282 U.S. 902 (1930)

The Court also remarked:[10]

"A comedy based upon conflicts between Irish and Jews, into which the marriage of their children enters, is no more susceptible of copyright than the outline of 'Romeo and Juliet.'"

Nor have the following plot ideas been held to be protectible:

The anti-Semitic behavior of German students during Hitler's regime.[11]

A new bride brought by her husband to live in the house he once shared with his first wife.[12]

A murder committed in a theatre while a performance of a play was being given.[13]

---

[10] Ibid., 45 F. 2d at 122

[11] Rosen v. Loew's, Inc. 162 F.2d 785, 788 (2 Cir. 1947)

[12] MacDonald v. DuMaurier, 75 F. Supp. 655, 660 (S.D.N.Y. 1948)

[13] Rush v. Oursler, 39 F.2d 468 (S.D.N.Y. 1930)

The plaintiff's alleged similarities were studied against this and other pertinent precedent, in order to determine which were copyrightable "expressions" and which were unprotectible "ideas."

III

The plaintiff's second cause of action alleges that API independently copied from the play "Catchpole." The claim of access gains credibility through API's concession that the play was submitted to them in 1947 before it was produced, and again by the plaintiff when he was an employee of the studio. Infringement, however, cannot be found on the basis of access alone.[14] The motion picture rights to "The Paper Dragon" were purchased

---

[14] Arc Music Corp. v. Lee, 296 F. 2d 186 (2 Cir. 1961)

by API in 1963, and the film version of the novel was written and directed by Ralph Knowles under employment to the studio. He has testified that he used the novel as his primary source, expanding upon it or deleting from it to meet the exigencies of the screen, translating it, in effect, to an entirely different medium. He has also testified that he did additional research on his own, such as reading related articles and books, and visiting various Army bases to refresh his memory on the language and behavior of United States soldiers. He testified that he never read plaintiff's play, either in its full length or in synopsis, and that he never saw a performance of it.

To support the claim against API, plaintiff has supplied the Court with a fourth chart purporting to show additional similarities existing only between the play and the motion picture. I have closely studied this fourth chart, in conjunction with all the others, and I have read the cutting continuity of the film, and I have seen the motion picture at a private screening.

IV

Upon reviewing all of the evidence presented in this case; upon careful study of the play, the novel, and the motion picture; upon close observation of the various witnesses and evaluation of their credibility; upon reference to findings of fact; it is my judgment that the allegations of plagiarism are groundless, and that the claimed similarities are the result of the plaintiff's misled enthusiasm and diligency, "that obsessive conviction, so frequent among authors and composers, that all similarities between their works and any others which appear later must inevitably be ascribed to plagiarism."[15]

<u>Concerning the claim against defendants JAMES DRISCOLL, MITCHELL-CAMPBELL BOOKS, INC. and CAMELOT BOOKS, INC., it is my finding that</u>:

James Driscoll is the sole author of "The Paper Dragon."

"The Paper Dragon" was not copied in whole or in part or in any manner or form from "Catchpole" and does not infringe on the play.

The theme, plot, and characters of "The Paper Dragon" are not similar to the theme, plot, and characters of "Catchpole."

The claimed similarities between the play and the book are either totally absent, non-copyrightable, or the result of a natural and independent development of different works set against a similar background.

---

[15] <u>Deller</u> v. <u>Samuel Goldwyn, Inc.</u>, 150 F. 2d 612, 613 (2 Cir.), <u>cert. denied</u>, 327 U.S. 790 (1945)

I further find that:

The character Alex Cooper in "The Paper Dragon" is based upon James Driscoll.

The character Jan Reardon in "The Paper Dragon" is based upon James Driscoll's wife.

Many other major and minor characters in "The Paper Dragon" are based upon actual individuals James Driscoll has met or known.

The use of the number 105 to designate an Army division in "The Paper Dragon" has as its basis a highly personal event in James Driscoll's life, and was not copied from the plaintiff's play.

Concerning the claim against defendant ARTISTS-PRODUCERS-INTERNATIONAL, it is my finding that:

Neither Ralph Knowles nor API copied

from the plaintiff's play in the preparation, writing, filming, or editing of the motion picture "The Paper Dragon."

The motion picture "The Paper Dragon" does not contain any copyrightable matter that was present in the plaintiff's play.

The motion picture "The Paper Dragon" is adapted solely from Driscoll's novel of the same name.

V

It is therefore my conclusion that there was no plagiarism, that none of the defendants copied from the play "Catchpole," that the plaintiff was not deprived of his rights, and that the defendants are entitled to a judgment dismissing the complaint on the merits. The foregoing shall constitute the Court's findings of fact and conclusion of law in accordance with Fed. Rules Civ. Proc. 52(a), 28 U.S.C. A decree, in accordance with these findings, may be settled on notice.

Frank Harlan McIntyre

U.S.D.J.

Content and organization

An overview of the handbook's contents appears at the front of the book. Briefly, the book divides into the following sections:

- **Chapters 1–5:** The big picture, including rhetoric and the writing process, paragraphs, and document design.
- **Chapters 6–11:** Reading and writing in school, with chapters on academic writing, study skills and exams, critical reading and writing, reading arguments, writing arguments, and reading and using visual arguments.
- **Chapters 12–26:** Sentence basics, including the conventions of English grammar, errors that affect clarity, and techniques of effective sentences.
- **Chapters 27–36**: Punctuation and mechanics (capital letters, underlining, and the like).
- **Chapters 37–41:** Words—how to use them appropriately and precisely, how to look them up, how to spell them.
- **Chapters 42–48:** Research writing, from planning through revising, with help on finding and evaluating electronic sources, a guide to citing sources, and two sample papers.
- **Chapters 49–53:** Writing in the academic disciplines, including literature, the other humanities, the social sciences, and the natural and applied sciences.
- **Chapters 55–57:** Practical information about online writing, business and other public writing, oral presentations, and applying to college.

Recommended usage

The conventions described and illustrated in this handbook are those of standard American English—the label given the dialect used in higher education, business, and the professions. (See also pp. 134–36.) The handbook stresses written standard English, which is more conservative than the spoken dialect in matters of grammar and usage. A great many words and constructions that are widely spoken remain unaccepted in careful writing.

When clear distinctions exist between the language of conversation and that of careful writing, the handbook provides examples of each and labels them *spoken* and *written*. When usage in writing itself varies with the level of formality intended, the handbook labels examples *formal* and *informal*. When usage is mixed or currently changing, the handbook recommends that you choose the more conservative usage because it will be acceptable to all readers.

Companion Web site

The companion Web site offers many resources to help you use the handbook and improve your writing. You can use the site on your own (it is not password protected), or your teacher may direct you to portions of it as part of his or her class assignments.

Go to *ablongman.com/littlebrown,* and click on *The Little, Brown Handbook,* Tenth Edition. You'll see further directions to the following:

- Downloadable checklists and other material from the book.
- The book's exercises in electronic format.
- More than a thousand additional electronic questions.
- Video tutorials that supplement the book's explanations.
- Hundreds of links to other Web sites providing help on the book's topics.
- Sample research papers from various academic disciplines.
- Usage flashcards allowing you to test yourself on tricky words and phrases.

Preface for Teachers

This high school version of *The Little, Brown Handbook* addresses the many needs of writing students and teachers. It is a comprehensive, clear, and accessible guide to a host of writing situations and challenges, from rhetoric and the writing process through grammar and diction to college-entrance exams and essays. Along the way, the handbook gives special attention to academic writing, critical reading and argument, research and documentation, writing about literature and in other disciplines, writing for public audiences, and giving oral presentations.

The Little, Brown Handbook is actually many books in one. The following pages describe its features, including those specifically designed for the high school version.

A guide to academic reading and writing in high school

The handbook gives students a solid foundation in the goals and requirements of reading and writing in academic situations.

- Part 2 covers the skills needed for success in school, with chapters on academic writing, study skills and exams (including essay exams), critical reading and writing, reading arguments critically, writing arguments, and reading and using visual arguments.
- Part 11 covers reading and writing about literature and writing in other humanities, the social sciences, and the natural and applied sciences. Extensive, specially highlighted sections cover documentation in MLA, Chicago, APA, and CSE styles.
- Chapter 57 on applying to college provides tips for taking the SAT, ACT, and AP English exams and for writing an effective college-application essay.

A guide to rhetoric and the writing process

The handbook takes a practical approach to assessing the writing situation, generating ideas, writing the thesis statement, revising, and other elements of the writing process.

- Numerous examples, including a student work-in-progress on Internet communication, illustrate every stage.
- A student paper shows techniques for achieving whole-essay unity and coherence.

- Revising on a word processor, using a spelling checker, and other computer skills are integrated into discussions of revision and editing.
- Extensive material on document design includes help with using illustrations and a section on designing for readers with disabilities.

A guide to research writing

With detailed advice and two sample MLA papers, the handbook attends closely to research writing, keeping pace with changes in its methods and challenges.

- The discussion emphasizes using the library as Web gateway, managing information, evaluating and synthesizing sources, integrating source material, and avoiding plagiarism.
- Guidelines explain how to prepare an annotated bibliography.
- Library subscription services receive close attention. In addition to a detailed, annotated sample search, the text provides help with choosing databases and brainstorming keywords.
- Web logs are covered as possible sources requiring careful evaluation and documentation.
- A discussion of using images as research sources includes a guide to image banks.
- A detailed discussion of evaluating Web sites includes tips for distinguishing scholarly, personal, commercial, and other kinds of sites.
- MLA documentation includes annotated samples of key source types, showing students how to find the bibliographical information needed to cite each type.
- The extensive coverage of documentation in four styles—MLA, Chicago, APA, and CSE—reflects each style's latest version and includes many electronic sources, such as Web logs and multimedia.

A guide to visual literacy

The handbook helps students process visual information and use it effectively in their writing.

- A section on using illustrations includes annotated examples.
- A discussion of viewing images critically uses diverse examples to demonstrate identifying and analyzing visual elements.
- A student paper illustrates a critique of an image.
- A chapter on reading and using visual arguments focuses on images' claims, evidence, assumptions, appeals, and fallacies.
- Illustrations in many of the handbook's student papers show various ways in which visual information can support written ideas.

A guide to usage, grammar, and punctuation

The handbook's core reference material is reliable, accessible, and appropriate for high school students.

- Concise text explains all basic concepts and common errors.
- Annotated examples from across the curriculum represent student academic writing.
- Frequent exercises in connected discourse include end-of-part exercises that combine several kinds of problems. The exercises are also available on the book's companion Web site.

A guide for culturally and linguistically diverse writers

At notes and sections labeled CULTURE LANGUAGE, the handbook provides extensive rhetorical and grammatical help for writers whose first language or dialect is not standard American English.

- Fully integrated coverage, instead of a separate section, means that students can find what they need without having to know which problems they do and don't share with native SAE speakers.
- The "CULTURE LANGUAGE Guide," at the back of the book, orients students with advice on mastering SAE and pulls all the integrated coverage together in one place.

An accessible reference guide

The handbook is designed to be easy to use.

- A clean, uncluttered page design uses color and type clearly to distinguish elements.
- Annotations on both visual and verbal examples directly connect principles and illustrations.
- Dictionary-style headers in the index make it easy to find entries.
- Helpful endpapers offer several paths to the book's content.
- More than 150 boxes provide summaries and checklists of key information.
- A preface just for students outlines the book's contents, details reference aids, and explains the page layout.

An integrated text and Web site

At the start of every handbook chapter, a Web box links students to the book's companion Web site, a powerful open-access resource for students and teachers.

- Most of the handbook's exercises can be completed online. A cross-reference to the Web site appears in the instruction of each dual-format exercise.

- More than a thousand additional self-study questions, keyed to the handbook, provide immediate feedback for every answer.
- Fifteen of the handbook's checklists are available for students to copy and use in generating ideas and revising their work.
- More than thirty video tutorials provide explanations, examples, and tips to help students understand concepts and techniques.
- Hundreds of Web links direct students to helpful sites on the writing process, critical thinking, argument, grammar, research, writing in the disciplines, and more.
- Ten documented student research papers provide examples of writing across the curriculum.
- Usage flashcards allow students to test their knowledge and practice usage.
- The "Instructor's Resources" section provides links to material from the print *Teacher's Resource Manual,* including teaching tips and answers to the handbook's exercises. It also provides lists and summaries from the handbook in transparency and *PowerPoint* format and links to Web sites that are useful to writing teachers.

Supplements

In addition to the companion Web site, a helpful package of supplements accompanies *The Little, Brown Handbook* for both students and teachers.

For students

- *MyCompLab* with the E-book of the college version of *The Little, Brown Handbook* offers comprehensive online resources in grammar, writing, and research in one dynamic, accessible place:

  Grammar resources include *ExerciseZone,* with more than three thousand self-grading practice questions on sentences and paragraphs; and *ESL ExerciseZone*, with more than seven hundred self-grading questions.

  Writing resources include a hundred writing activities involving videos, images, and Web sites; guided assistance through the writing process, with worksheets and exercises; and an extensive collection of sample papers from across the disciplines.

  Research resources include *ResearchNavigator*, which provides help with the research process, the *AutoCite* bibliography maker, and access to *ContentSelect* by EBSCOhost and the subject-search archive of the *New York Times;* and *Avoiding Plagiarism,* which offers tutorials in recognizing plagiarism, paraphrasing, documenting sources in MLA or APA style, and other topics.

  Grade Tracker provides a system for tracking work on the site.

- *The Little, Brown Workbook,* by Donna Gorrell, provides many more exercises and briefer instructional text. A separate answer key is available.

For teachers

All of the following supplements are available to confirmed adopters of *The Little, Brown Handbook*.

- *MyCompLab* offers online resources for teachers on grammar, writing, and research. Accesss to the site is provided upon adoption of *The Little, Brown Handbook*. Each textbook shipment contains an access card (packaged separately) that contains registration instructions and access codes. If the textbook shipment does not include an access card, or if a teacher receives a set of books from another teacher, an access card can be requested by contacting *PHWebAccess@PearsonEd.com*. In subsequent years of an adoption of *The Little, Brown Handbook,* teachers will receive e-mail instructions during the summer to help them set up access to *MyCompLab* for a new class of students.
- *Teacher's Resource Manual to Accompany The Little, Brown Handbook,* High School Version, is a freestanding, two-color paperback that includes answers to the handbook's exercises, essays on teaching, ideas for class discussions and activities, tips for SAT and ACT preparation, and a correlation to AP standards.
- *Diagnostic and Editing Tests and Exercises* are available on reproducible sheets.

Acknowledgments

For this high school version of *The Little, Brown Handbook,* we are grateful to the teachers and educators whose detailed reviews and guidance helped us address the needs of their students: Lisa G. Baker, Wilburton High School; Barbara Bloy, Taft Educational Center; William Bryan Borah, Centreville High School; Brook Bullock, Del City High School; Anne Cognard, Lincoln East High School; Shirley Counsil, Spanish River High School; Cathy A. D'Agostino, New Trier Township High School; Claudia Klein Felske, East Troy High School; Elfie Israel; Stephen Klinge, Archmere Academy; Mary F. McDonald, Enid High School; Gretchen Polnac, Austin High School; Nancy S. Potter, Newport High School; Janice Suppa-Friedman; and Becky Talk, Advanced Placement Strategies.

We are also grateful to the many college instructors who offered suggestions for the handbook's improvement: Dale T. Adams, Lee College; Jonathan Ausubel, Chaffey College; Mark Bernier, Blinn College; Jacqueline A. Blackwell, Thomas Nelson Community College; Winfred P. Bridges, Arkansas State University; Daniel Brigham, University of Colorado, Boulder; Lynnda L. Brown, Tulsa Community

The Little, Brown Handbook

TENTH EDITION

HIGH SCHOOL VERSION

PART 1

The Writing Process

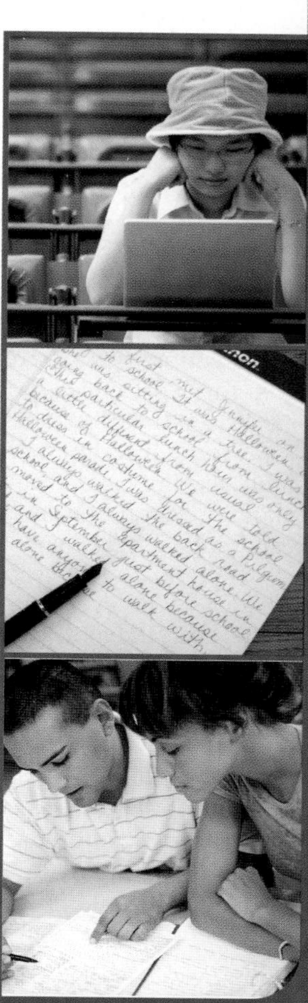

CHAPTER 1

Assessing the Writing Situation

"Writing is easy," snarled the late sportswriter Red Smith. "All you do is sit down at the typewriter and open a vein." Most writers would smile in agreement, and so might you. Like anything worthwhile, writing well takes hard work. This chapter and the next two will show you some techniques that successful writers use to ease the discomfort of writing and produce effective compositions.

1a Understanding how writing happens

Every time you sit down to write, you embark on a **writing process**—the term for all the activities, mental and physical, that go into creating what eventually becomes a finished piece of work. Even for experienced writers the process is usually messy, which is one reason that it is sometimes difficult. Though we may get a sense of ease and orderliness from a well-crafted magazine article, we can safely assume that the writer had to work hard to achieve those qualities, struggling to express half-formed thoughts, shaping and reshaping paragraphs to make a point convincingly.

There is no *one* writing process: no two writers proceed in the same way, and even an individual writer adapts his or her process to the task at hand. Still, most experienced writers pass through overlapping stages:

- **Analyzing the writing situation:** considering subject, purpose, audience, and other elements of the project (pp. 4–17).
- **Developing or planning:** gathering information, focusing on a central theme, and organizing material (pp. 18–46).
- **Drafting:** expressing and connecting ideas (pp. 47–51).
- **Revising and editing:** rethinking and improving structure, content, style, and presentation (pp. 51–67).

http://www.ablongman.com/littlebrown ▶

Visit the companion Web site for more help and additional exercises on the writing situation and the writing process.

The writing process

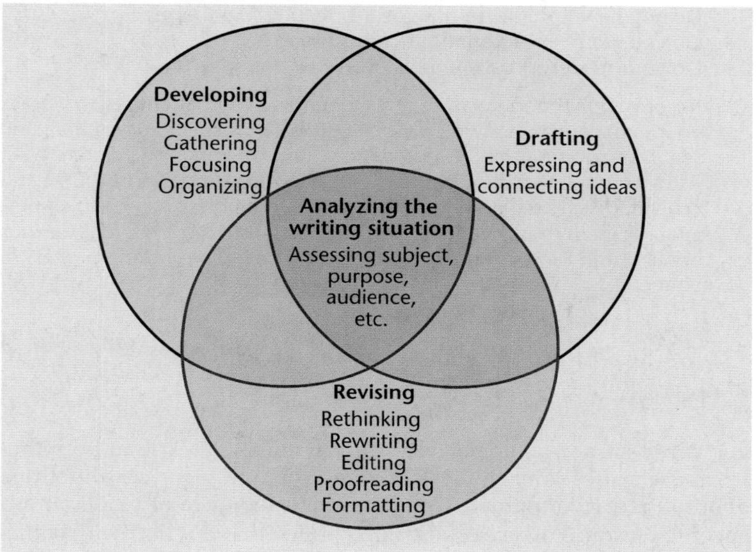

With experience, as you complete varied assignments and try the varied techniques described in this book, you will develop your own basic writing process.

Note Like many others, you may believe that writing is only, or even mainly, a matter of correctness. True, any written message will find a more receptive audience if it is correct in grammar, spelling, and similar matters. But these concerns should come late in the writing process, after you've allowed yourself to discover what you want to say, freeing yourself to make mistakes along the way. As one writer put it, you need to get the clay on the potter's wheel before you can shape it into a bowl, and you need to shape the bowl before you can perfect it. So get your clay on the wheel, and work with it until it looks like a bowl. Then worry about correctness.

EXERCISE 1.1 Starting a writing journal

Recall several writing experiences that you have had—a letter you had difficulty composing, an essay you enjoyed writing, hours spent happily or miserably on a research paper, a posting to an online newsgroup that received a surprising response. What do these experiences reveal to you about writing, particularly your successes and problems with it? Consider the following questions:

Do you like to experiment with language?
Are some kinds of writing easier than others?
Do you have trouble getting ideas or expressing them?
Do you worry about grammar and spelling?
Do your readers usually understand what you mean?

Record your thoughts as part of continuing journal entries that track your experiences as a writer. (See pp. 19–21 on keeping a journal, and see the exercises titled "Considering your past work" in Chapters 1–4.) As you complete writing assignments for your composition course and other courses, keep adding to the journal, noting especially which procedures seem most helpful to you. Your aim is to discover your feelings about writing so that you can develop a dependable writing process of your own.

1b Analyzing the writing situation

Any writing you do for others occurs in a context that both limits and clarifies your choices. You are communicating something about a particular subject to a particular audience of readers for a specific reason. You are establishing yourself as a writer with something to say. You may need to conduct research. You'll be up against a length requirement and a deadline. And you may be expected to present your work in a certain format.

These are the elements of the **writing situation,** and analyzing them at the very start of a project can tell you much about how to proceed. (For more information about these elements, refer to the page numbers given in parentheses.)

Context

- **What is your writing for?** A class in school? Work? Something else? What do you know of the requirements for writing in this context?
- **Will you present your writing on paper, online, or orally?** What does the presentation method require in preparation time, special skills, and use of technology?
- **How much leeway do you have for this writing?** What does the stated or implied assignment tell you?

Subject (pp. 7–9)

- **What does your writing assignment require you to write about?** If you don't have a specific assignment, what subjects might be appropriate for this situation?
- **What interests you about the subject?** What do you already know about it? What questions do you have about it?
- **What does the assignment require you to do with the subject?**

Audience (pp. 10–14)

- **Who will read your writing?**
- **What do your readers already know and think about your subject?** What characteristics—such as education or political views—might influence their response?
- **What do you want readers to do or think after they read your writing?**

Purpose (pp. 15–17)

- **What aim does your assignment specify?** For instance, does it ask you to explain something or argue a point?
- **Why are you writing?**
- **What do you want your work to accomplish?** What effect do you intend it to have on readers?
- **How can you best achieve your purpose?**
- **How do you want to be perceived by readers?** Should they see you as a friend, colleague, expert, or something else?

The rhetorical triangle

The elements of the writing situation listed on these pages contribute to **rhetoric,** a term from the work of the ancient Greek philosopher Aristotle (384–22 BCE). Rhetoric describes how writers and speakers use ideas and language to inform or persuade an audience.

Rhetoric is often drawn as a triangle that represents the three basic elements to be considered in any writing situation:

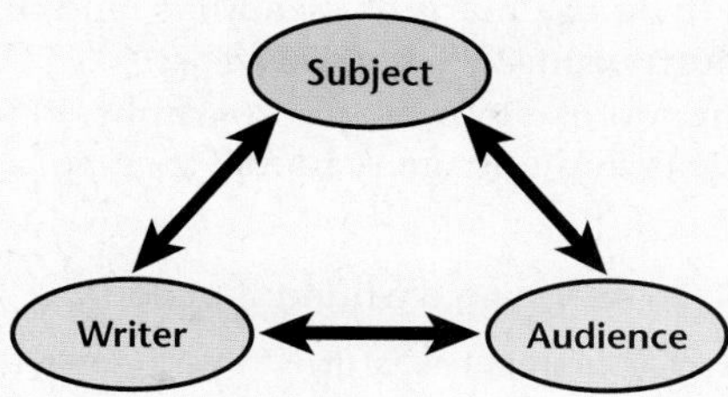

The arrows on the triangle show the interdependence of the three points:

- The **subject** and the evidence the writer uses to address it;
- The **audience** and the ideas, knowledge, beliefs, and attitudes that the writer must take into account;
- The **writer,** who adapts his or her voice to meet the expectations of the audience and the requirements of the subject.

Voice (pp. 13–14)

- **How formal or informal should your writing be,** considering your audience and your purpose?
- **What tone should you use to convey your attitude**—for instance, concerned, forceful, alarmed, pleased, confident?

Research (pp. 560–619)

- **What kinds of evidence will best suit your subject, audience, and purpose?** What combination of facts, examples, and expert opinions will support your ideas?
- **Does your assignment require research?** Will you need to consult sources or conduct interviews, surveys, or experiments?
- **Even if research is not required, what information do you need to develop your subject?** How will you obtain it?
- **What documentation style should you use to cite your sources?** (See pp. 618–19 on source documentation in the academic disciplines.)

Deadline and length

- **When is the assignment due?** How will you apportion the work you have to do in the time available?
- **How long should your writing be?** If no length is assigned, what seems appropriate for your subject, audience, and purpose?

Document design

- **What organization and format does the assignment require?** (See pp. 113–14 on format in the academic disciplines and pp. 738–808 on format in public writing.)
- **How might you use margins, headings, and other elements to achieve your purpose?** (See pp. 118–22.)
- **How might you use graphs, photographs, or other images to support ideas and engage readers?** (See pp. 122–27, 227–31.)

EXERCISE 1.2 Analyzing a writing situation

The following assignment was given in an American history course. What does the assignment specify about the elements of the writing situation? What does it imply? Given this assignment, how would you answer the questions on the previous two pages and above?

Explore the causes of the colonists' victory in the Revolutionary War. First briefly explain the combination of factors that worked in the colonists' favor, and then explain one cause in detail. Quote from contemporary accounts of both colonists and the British to support your claims, and document your sources. Papers should be 3–5 pages, typed.

1c Discovering and limiting a subject

For most writing you do in high school, you will respond to an assignment. The assignment may specify your subject, or it may leave the choice to you. (If you're stuck, you can use the discovery techniques on pp. 18–28 to think of subjects.) Whether the specific subject is assigned or not, it will probably need some thought if it is to achieve these aims:

- **The subject should be suitable for the assignment.**
- **It should be neither too general nor too limited** for the length of project and deadline assigned.
- **It should be something you care about.**

1 Responding to a specific assignment

Many assignments will set boundaries for your subject. For instance, you might be asked to discuss what makes psychotherapy effective, to prepare a lab report on a physics experiment, or to analyze a character in a short story.

Such assignments may seem to leave little room for you to move around, but in fact you'll have several questions to answer:

- **What's wanted from you?** Writing assignments often contain words such as *discuss, describe, analyze, report, interpret, explain, define, argue,* and *evaluate.* These words specify the way you are to approach your subject, what kind of thinking is expected of you, and what your general purpose is. (See pp. 15–17 for more on purpose.)
- **For whom are you writing?** Many assignments will specify or imply your readers, but sometimes you will have to figure out for yourself who your audience is and what it expects from you. (For more on analyzing audience, see pp. 10–14.)
- **What kind of research is required?** Sometimes an assignment specifies the kinds of sources you are expected to consult, and you can use such information to choose your subject. (If you are unsure whether research is required, check with your instructor.)
- **How can you narrow the assigned subject to do it justice in the length and time required?** (See below.)

2 Responding to a general assignment

Many assignments specify features such as length or amount of research, but they leave the choice of subject fairly open—for instance, *Analyze the conflict in one of the short stories we read in this unit* or *Investigate a problem you see in school policy*. When the topic or the approach is more open, consider the following:

- **What subject do you already know something about or have you been wondering about?** College athletic scholarships? A proposed dress code at your school?
- **Have you recently disagreed with someone over a substantial issue?** The change in relations between boys and girls? The methods being used to fight terrorism?
- **What have you read or seen lately?** A shocking book? A violent or funny movie? An effective television commercial?
- **What topic in the reading or class discussion for a course has intrigued you?** A psychological problem such as depression? A literary topic such as plot twists in an author's work?
- **What makes you especially happy or especially angry?** A hobby? The behavior of your friends?
- **Which of your own or others' dislikes and preferences would you like to understand better?** The demand for sport-utility vehicles? A taste for vegetarian cuisine?

Once you have a subject, you'll also need to answer the questions in the bulleted list on the previous page.

3 Narrowing a subject to a question

Whether you arrive at a subject through an assignment or on your own, you will need to narrow it in order to provide the specific details that make writing significant and interesting—all within the assigned length and deadline.

One helpful technique for narrowing a subject is to ask focused questions about it, seeking one that seems appropriate for your assignment and that promises to sustain your interest through the writing process. The following examples illustrate how questioning can scale down broad subjects to specific subjects that are limited and manageable:

Broad subjects	Specific subjects
Communication on the Internet	What are the advantages of online communication? How, if at all, should the government regulate Internet content? How might the Internet contribute to social and economic equality?
Mrs. Mallard in Kate Chopin's "The Story of an Hour"	What changes does Mrs. Mallard undergo? Why does Mrs. Mallard respond as she does to news of her husband's death? What does the story's irony contribute to the character of Mrs. Mallard?
Lincoln's weaknesses as President	What was Lincoln's most significant error as commander-in-chief of the Union army? Why did Lincoln delay emancipating the slaves?

	Why did Lincoln have difficulties controlling his cabinet?
Federal aid to poor school districts	What kinds of schools should be entitled to federal aid?
	How adequate is federal aid to meet the needs of poor districts?
	Why should the federal government aid poor schools more than other schools?

As these examples illustrate, your questions should not lend themselves to yes-or-no answers but should require further thinking.

Here are some guidelines for posing questions:

- **Reread the assignment.** Consider what it tells you about purpose, audience, sources, length, and deadline.
- **Pursue your interests.** If questions don't come easily, try freewriting or brainstorming (pp. 22–23) or use a tree diagram (pp. 37–38).
- **Ask as many questions as you can think of.**
- **Test the question that seems most interesting and appropriate by roughly sketching out the main ideas.** Consider how many paragraphs or pages of specific facts, examples, and other details you would need to pin those ideas down. This thinking should give you at least a vague idea of how much work you'd have to do and how long the resulting paper might be.
- **Break a too-broad question down further, and repeat the previous step.**

The Internet can also help you limit a general subject. On the Web, browse a directory such as *BUBL LINK* (*bubl.ac.uk*). As you pursue increasingly narrow categories, you may find a suitably limited topic.

Don't be discouraged if the perfect question does not come easily or early. You may find that you need to do some planning and writing, exploring different facets of the general subject and pursuing your specific interests, before you hit on the best question. And the question you select may require further narrowing or may shift subtly or even dramatically as you move through the writing process.

EXERCISE 1.3 Narrowing subjects

Following are some general writing assignments. Use the given information and your own interests to pose specific questions for three of these assignments. (You can do this exercise online at *ablongman.com/littlebrown.*)

1. For a composition class, consider how the Internet could alter the experience of popular culture. Length: three pages. Deadline: one week.

2. For a biology class, explain the life cycle of a particular animal or plant species. Deadline: two weeks.
3. For a literature class, respond to a novel or short story you are reading. Length: three pages. Deadline: one week.
4. For a government class, consider possible restrictions on legislators. Length: five pages. Deadline: two weeks.
5. For a journalism class, write a feature story for the town newspaper in which you describe the effects of immigration on your community. Length: two pages. Deadline: unspecified.

EXERCISE 1.4 Considering your past work: Discovering and limiting a subject

Think of something you've recently written—perhaps an application essay, a critical essay, or a research paper. How did your subject evolve from beginning to end? In retrospect, was it appropriate for your writing situation? How, if at all, might it have been modified?

EXERCISE 1.5 Finding and narrowing a subject for your essay

As the first step in developing a three- to four-page essay for the teacher and the other students in your writing class, choose a subject and narrow it. Use the guidelines in the previous section to come up with a question that is suitably interesting, appropriate, and specific.

1d Considering the audience

- **Who are my readers:** teachers, classmates, school population, or a general and unspecified audience?
- **Why will the audience read my writing:** to evaluate or to be informed, entertained, or persuaded?
- **What will readers need from me:** data, experts' views, examples, anecdotes, connections to their interests?
- **What do I want readers to think or do after they read my writing:** change their minds, agree, give credit, laugh, engage in action?
- **How do I want to be perceived by the audience:** as a reporter, an expert, an advocate, or something else?

These questions are central to any writing project, and they will crop up again and again. Except in writing meant only for yourself, you are always trying to communicate with readers—something about a particular subject, for a particular purpose.

Your audience will often be specified or implied in a writing assignment. When you write an editorial for the student newspaper, your audience consists of fellow students. When you write a report on a physics experiment, your audience consists of your physics instructor and perhaps other physicists or your classmates. (See pp. 131–32 for more on audience in academic writing.) Whatever the audience, considering its needs and expectations can help you form or focus a question about your subject, gather answers to the question, and ultimately decide what to say and how to say it.

1 Knowing what readers need

As a reader yourself, you know what readers need:

- **Context:** a link between what they read and their own knowledge and experiences.
- **Predictability:** an understanding of the writer's purpose and how it is being achieved.
- **Information:** the specific facts, examples, and other details that make the subject clear, concrete, interesting, and convincing.
- **Respect:** a sense that the writer respects their values and beliefs, their background, and their intelligence.
- **Voice:** a sense that the writer is a real person.
- **Clarity and correctness:** writing free of unnecessary stumbling blocks and mistakes.

For much academic and public writing, readers have definite needs and expectations. Thus Chapter 6 discusses academic writing in general, Chapters 49–53 discuss writing in various disciplines, and Chapter 55 discusses public writing. Even in these areas, you must make many choices based on audience. In other areas where the conventions of structure and presentation are vaguer, the choices are even more numerous. The box on the next page contains questions that can help you define and make these choices.

2 Appealing to your audience

Your sense of your audience will influence three key elements of what and how you write to appeal to your readers:

- **The specific information you use to gain and keep the attention of readers and guide them to accept your conclusions.** This information may consist of concrete details, facts, examples, or other evidence that makes your ideas clear, supports your assertions, and suits your readers' backgrounds, biases, and special interests. When you provide specific information to reach your readers, you are using a **logical appeal:**

Questions about audience

Identity and expectations

- **Who *are* my readers?**
- **What are my readers' expectations for the kind of writing I'm doing?** Do readers expect features such as a particular organization and format, distinctive kinds of evidence, or a certain style of documenting sources?
- **What do I want readers to know or do after reading my work?** How should I make that clear to them?
- **What is my relationship to my readers?** How formal or informal will they expect me to be? What role and tone should I assume?

Characteristics, knowledge, and attitudes

- **What characteristics of readers are relevant for my subject and purpose?** For instance:

  Age and sex
  Occupation: students, professional colleagues, etc.
  Social or economic role: subject-matter experts, voters, car buyers, potential employers, etc.
  Economic or educational background
  Ethnic background
  Political, religious, or moral beliefs and values
  Hobbies or activities

- **How will the characteristics of readers influence their attitudes toward my subject?**
- **What do readers already know and *not* know about my subject?** How much do I have to tell them?
- **How should I handle any specialized terms?** Will readers know them? If not, should I define them or avoid them?
- **What ideas, arguments, or information might surprise, excite, or offend readers?** How should I handle these points?
- **What misconceptions might readers have of my subject and/or my approach to it?** How can I dispel these misconceptions?

Uses and format

- **What will readers do with my writing?** Should I expect them to read every word from the top, to scan for information, to look for conclusions? Can I help by providing a summary, headings, illustrations, or other aids? (See pp. 113–28 on document design.)

You can download these questions from *ablongman.com/littlebrown*. Save them in a file of their own, duplicate the file for each writing project, and insert appropriate answers between the questions. Print your answers for reference as you develop your paper.

Rhetorical appeals

Rhetoric defines three primary methods of appealing to an audience:

- **Logical appeal,** or **logos:** Appealing to readers' reason through inferences, facts, details, and other evidence.
- **Emotional appeal,** or **pathos:** Appealing to readers' emotions by calling on feelings of empathy, sympathy, anger, fear, and so on.
- **Ethical appeal,** or **ethos:** Appealing to readers by establishing yourself as a trustworthy and credible writer.

A recent survey of juniors and seniors at our school shows that thirty-five percent hold part-time jobs that begin right after the school day ends. [Implies the conclusion that students need quick, individual transportation to get from school to work.]

- **The emotions you try to evoke in your readers.** Depending on your purpose, you may want to use language as well as facts, examples, or other evidence to lead readers to sympathy, anger, fear, or some other emotion. When you appeal to readers in this way, you are using an **emotional appeal:**

Yesterday I saw a student sitting in her car in the middle of the parking lot crying because the lot was full and she knew she would once again be marked tardy. [Readers are likely to feel the student's frustration and fear of punishment.]

- **The role you choose to play in relation to your readers.** The possible roles are many and varied—for instance, scholar, storyteller, guide, reporter, advocate, inspirer—and will depend on your purpose and your attitude toward your topic. In addition, you will want readers to perceive you as reasonable, competent, and trustworthy. When you establish yourself as a believable writer, you are using an **ethical appeal:**

Everybody who must be at the school and begin the day at the same time—staff, faculty, and students—needs and deserves space to park. [Establishes the writer as concerned about equality and fairness.]

For more on appeals, see pages 209–11 and 230–31.

3 Considering your writer's voice

Often you adapt your **writer's voice** to your writing situation. Voice consists in part of the role you choose to play in relation to your readers (see above), but it also consists of the level of formality and the tone of your writing. Tone in writing is like tone of voice in speaking: words and sentence structures on the page convey some of the same information as pitch and volume in the voice. Depending on your writing situation and what you think readers will expect and respond to, your writing may be formal or informal, and your tone may be serious or light, forceful or calm, irritated or cheerful.

Even when you're writing on the same subject, the information you provide, the feelings you tap into, and the role and tone you assume may change substantially for different audiences. Both memos below were written by a student who worked part-time in a small company and wanted to get the company to conserve paper. But the two memos address different readers.

To coworkers

Ever notice how much paper collects in your trash basket every day? Well, most of it can be recycled with little effort, I promise. Basically, all you need to do is set a bag or box near your desk and deposit wastepaper in it. I know, space is cramped in these little cubicles. But what's a little more crowding when the earth's at stake? . . .

Information: how employees could handle recycling; no mention of costs

Feelings: responsibility, helpfulness

Role and tone: cheerful, sympathetic coworker writing informally and personally (*Ever notice; Well; you; I know, space is cramped; what's*)

To management

In my four months here, I have observed that all of us throw out baskets of potentially recyclable paper every day. Considering the drain on our forest resources and the pressure on landfills that paper causes, we could make a valuable contribution to the environmental movement by helping to recycle the paper we use. At the company where I worked before, employees separate clean wastepaper from other trash at their desks. The maintenance staff collects trash in two receptacles, and the trash hauler (the same one we use here) makes separate pickups. I do not know what the hauler charges for handling recyclable material. . . .

Information: specific reasons; view of company as a whole; reference to another company; problem of cost

Feelings: responsibility, concern about cost

Role and tone: thoughtful, respectful employee writing formally and seriously (*Considering the drain; forest resources; valuable contribution;* no *you* or contractions)

Typically for business writing, the information grows more specific and the tone more formal as the rank and number of readers rise.

EXERCISE 1.6 Considering audience

Choose one of the following subjects, and, for each audience specified, ask the questions on page 12. Decide on four points you would make, the role you would assume, and the tone you would adopt for each audience. Then write a paragraph for each based on your decisions. (You can do this exercise online at *ablongman.com/littlebrown.*)

1. The effects of smoking: for elementary school students and for adult smokers
2. Your opposition to a proposed law requiring all bicyclists to wear helmets: for cyclists who oppose the law and for people who favor it
3. Why your school should have a dress code: for your classmates and for the school administrators.

EXERCISE 1.7 Considering your past work: Writing for a specific audience

How did audience figure in a piece of writing you've done in the recent past—perhaps an essay for an application or a paper for a class? How did you decide who your readers were? How and when did your awareness of readers influence your choices as a writer? Consider the evidence you used, the way you presented yourself, and whether you appealed to readers' emotions.

EXERCISE 1.8 Analyzing the audience for your essay

Use the questions on page 12 to determine as much as you can about the probable readers of your essay-in-progress (see Exercise 1.5). What does your analysis reveal about the specific information your readers need? What role do you want to assume, and what tone will best convey your attitude toward your topic?

1e Defining a purpose

When you write, your **purpose** is your chief reason for communicating something about a topic to a particular audience. Purpose thus links both the specific situation in which you are working and the goal you hope to achieve. It is your answer to a potential reader's question, "So what?"

1 Defining a general purpose

Your purpose may fall into one of four general categories: explanation, persuasion, self-expression, or entertainment. These purposes may overlap in a single piece of writing, but usually one predominates. And the dominant purpose will influence your particular slant on your topic, the supporting details you choose, and the language you use.

In high school and public writing, by far the most common purposes are explanation and persuasion:

- **Writing that is mainly explanatory is often called** ***exposition*** (from a Latin word meaning "to explain or set forth"). Using examples, facts, and other evidence, you present an idea about your subject so that readers understand it as you do. Almost any

The general purposes for writing

Purpose for writing	Kinds of writing
To explain or to inform (exposition)	Reports, research papers, essay exams, application letters
To persuade (argument)	Editorials, speeches, opinion papers, proposals
To express feelings or ideas	Journals or diaries, personal narratives, poetry
To entertain	Stories, dialogs, parodies

subject is suitable for exposition: how to pitch a knuckleball, why you want to attend college, the implications of a new discovery in computer science, the interpretation of a short story, the causes of an economic slump. Exposition is the kind of writing encountered most often in newspapers, magazines, and textbooks.

- **Writing that is primarily persuasive is often called *argument*.** Using examples, facts, and other evidence, you support your position on a debatable subject so that readers will at least consider your view and perhaps agree with it or act on it. A newspaper editorial favoring city council reform, a proposal for a new recycling program, a student paper recommending more math and science classes or defending a theory about human psychological development—all these are arguments. (Chapters 9–11 discuss argument in some detail and provide examples.)

2 Defining a specific purpose

Purpose can be conceived more specifically, too, in a way that incorporates your particular subject and the outcome you intend—what you want readers to do or think as a result of reading your writing. Here are some examples of specific purposes:

To explain how Annie Dillard's "Total Eclipse" builds to its climax so that readers appreciate the author's skill

To explain the methods and results of an engineering experiment so that readers understand and accept your conclusions

To explain why the county has been unable to attract new businesses so that readers better understand the local economic slump

To persuade readers to support the school administration's plan for a dress code

To argue against additional regulation of health-maintenance organizations so that readers perceive the disadvantages for themselves

To argue for additional gun-control laws so that readers agree on their necessity

Often, a writing assignment will specify or imply both a general and a specific purpose. Say, for instance, that an English teacher assigns a paper on the use of language in three poems by Emily Dickinson. You know that the purpose is generally to explain, more specifically to show similarities in vocabulary, word order, and tone in the poems. You want readers to come away understanding how Emily Dickinson used language for certain effects in her poems. In addition, you want your teacher to see that you can competently read poetry and write about it. (See p. 132 for more on purpose in academic writing.)

With any writing assignment, try to define your specific purpose as soon as you have formed a question about your subject. Don't worry, though, if you feel uncertain of your purpose at the start. Sometimes you may not discover your purpose until you begin drafting, or you may find that your initial sense of purpose changes as you move through the writing process.

EXERCISE 1.9 Finding purpose in assignments

For each of your questions from Exercise 1.3 (p. 9), suggest a likely general purpose (explanation, persuasion, self-expression, entertainment) and try to define a specific purpose as well. Make audience part of your suggestions: What would you want readers to do or think in each case? (If you completed Exercise 1.3 online, you can add these suggestions to that file.)

EXERCISE 1.10 Considering your past work: Defining a purpose

Look over two or three things you've written in the past year or so. What was your specific purpose in each one? How did the purpose influence your writing? Did you achieve your purpose?

EXERCISE 1.11 Defining a purpose for your essay

For your essay-in-progress, use your thinking so far about topic (Exercise 1.5, p. 10) and audience (Exercise 1.8, p. 15) to define a general and specific purpose for your writing.

CHAPTER 2

Developing and Shaping Ideas

Once you have assessed your writing situation, or even while you're assessing it, you'll begin answering the question you posed about your subject (pp. 8–9). As you generate ideas and information, they in turn may cause you to rephrase your lead question, which will open up new areas to explore. Throughout this stage, you'll bring order to your thoughts, eventually focusing and organizing them so that readers will respond as you intend.

2a Discovering ideas

For some writing projects, you may have little difficulty finding what you have to say about your subject: possible answers to your starting question will tumble forth as ideas on paper or screen. But when you're stuck for what to say, you'll have to coax answers out. Instead of waiting around for inspiration to strike, use a technique to get your mind working. Anything is appropriate: if you like to make drawings or take pictures, for instance, then try that.

The following pages describe some strategies for discovering ideas. These strategies are to be selected from, not followed in sequence: some may help you during early stages of the writing process, even before you're sure of your topic; others may help you later on; and one or two may not help at all. Experiment to discover which strategies work best for you.

Note **Whatever strategy or strategies you use, do your work in writing, not just in your head.** Your work will be retrievable, and the act of writing will help you concentrate and lead you to fresh, sometimes surprising, insights. If you participate in online collaboration to develop subjects, your activities will probably be stored electronically so that you can review and use the work. Ask your instructor how to reach the online files.

http://www.ablongman.com/littlebrown

Visit the companion Web site for more help with discovering and shaping ideas.

Techniques for developing a subject

- Keep a journal (below).
- Observe your surroundings (p. 21).
- Freewrite (p. 22).
- Make a list or brainstorm (p. 23).
- Cluster (p. 24).
- Use the journalist's questions (p. 25).
- Use rhetorical strategies (p. 26).
- Read (p. 27).
- Think critically (p. 28).

CULTURE LANGUAGE The discovery process encouraged here rewards rapid writing without a lot of thinking beforehand about what you will write or how. If your first language is not standard American English, you may find it helpful initially to do this exploratory writing in your native language or dialect and then to translate the worthwhile material for use in your drafts. This process can be productive, but it is extra work. You may want to try it at first and gradually move to composing in standard American English.

1 Keeping a journal

A place to record thoughts and observations, a **journal** can be a good source of ideas for writing. It is a kind of diary, but one more concerned with ideas than with day-to-day events. *Journal* comes from the Latin for "daily," and many journal keepers do write faithfully every day; others make entries less regularly, when the mood strikes or an insight occurs or they have a problem to work out.

Advantages of a journal

Writing in a journal, you are writing to yourself. That means you don't have to worry about main ideas, organization, correct grammar and spelling, or any of the other requirements of writing for others. You can work out your ideas and feelings without the pressure of an audience "out there" who will evaluate your thinking and expression. The freedom and flexibility of a journal can be liberating. Like many others, you may find writing easier, more fun, and more rewarding than you thought possible.

You can keep a journal either on paper (such as a notebook) or on a computer. If you write in the journal every day, or almost, even just for a few minutes, the routine will loosen up your writing muscles and improve your confidence. Indeed, journal keepers often become dependent on the process for the writing practice it gives them, the concentrated thought it encourages, and the connection it fosters between personal, private experience and public information and events.

Usually for the same reasons, teachers sometimes require students to keep journals. The teachers may even collect students' journals to monitor progress, but they read the journals with an understanding of purpose (in other words, they do not evaluate work that was not written to be evaluated), and they usually just credit rather than grade the work.

CULTURE LANGUAGE A journal can be especially helpful if your first language is not standard American English. You can practice writing to improve your fluency, try out sentence patterns, and experiment with vocabulary words. Equally important, you can experiment with applying what you know from experience to what you read and observe.

Uses of a journal

Two uses of a journal are discussed elsewhere in this book: a reading journal, in which you think critically (in writing) about what you read (pp. 153–54, 688–89); and a research journal, in which you record your activities and ideas while you pursue a research project (pp. 561–62). But you can use a journal for other purposes as well. Here are just a few:

- **Prepare for or respond to a class you're taking** by puzzling over a reading or a class discussion.
- **Build ideas for specific writing assignments.**
- **Sketch possible designs for a Web composition.**
- **Explore your reactions to events, trends, or the media.**
- **Confide your hopes.**
- **Write about your own history:** an event in your family's past, a troubling incident in your life, a change you've seen.
- **Analyze a relationship that disturbs you.**
- **Explore your writer's voice by practicing various forms or styles of writing**—for instance, poems or songs, reviews of movies, or reports for TV news.

The writing you produce in your journal will help you learn and grow, and even the personal and seemingly nonacademic entries can supply ideas when you are seeking a subject to write about or are developing an essay. A thought you recorded months ago about a chemistry lab may provide direction for a research paper on the history of science. Two entries about arguments with your brother may suggest what you need to anchor a psychology paper on sibling relations. If you keep your journal on a computer, you can even copy passages from it directly into your drafts.

The following student samples give a taste of journal writing for different purposes. In the first, Charlie Gabnes tries to work out a personal problem with a friend:

> Will's angry outbursts are getting worse—more often, more intense. Beginning to realize it's affecting my feelings for him. He's my best friend, but I feel resentment sometimes, and it's not as easy for me to cool off afterward as for him. Also I'm afraid of him sometimes for fear he'll blow up, so treat him with kid gloves. How do we break this cycle?

In the next example Megan Polanyis ponders something she learned from her biology textbook:

> Ecology and economics have the same root—Greek word for house. Economy = managing the house. Ecology = studying the house. In ecology the house is all of nature, ourselves, the other animals, the plants, the earth, the air, the whole environment. Ecology has a lot to do with economy: study the house in order to manage it.

In the next example Sara Ling responds to an experience. (We'll follow Ling's writing process in this chapter and the next.)

> Had an exchange today on the snowboarding forum with a girl who joined the forum a while ago. She says she signed on at first with a screen name that didn't give away her gender, and she didn't tell anyone she was a girl. She was afraid the guys on the forum might shout her down. She waited until she'd established herself as an experienced snowboarder. Then she revealed her gender, and no one reacted badly. She asked me about my experiences, since my screen name says Sara. Had to admit I'd had problems of the what-does-a-girl-know sort. Wish I'd taken her approach.

2 Observing your surroundings

Sometimes you can find a good subject or good ideas by looking around you, not in the half-conscious way most of us move from place to place in our daily lives but deliberately, all senses alert. On a bus, for instance, are there certain types of passengers? What seems to be on the driver's mind? At school, what are students eating for lunch? Do students moving from class to class look relaxed or stressed?

To get the most from observation, you should have a handheld computer or a notepad and pen handy for taking notes and making sketches. If you have a camera, you may find that the lens sees things your unaided eyes do not notice. (When observing or photographing people, though, keep some distance, take photographs quickly, and avoid staring. Otherwise, your subjects will feel uneasy.) Back at your desk, study your notes, sketches, or photographs for oddities or patterns that you'd like to explore further.

In some academic writing, you'll be expected to formalize observation with surveys, interviews, or experiments. See pages 586 and 733.

3 Freewriting

Writing into a subject

Many writers find subjects or discover ideas by **freewriting:** writing without stopping for a certain amount of time (say, ten minutes) or to a certain length (say, one page). The goal of freewriting is to generate ideas and information from *within* yourself by going around the part of your mind that doesn't want to write or can't think of anything to write. You let words themselves suggest other words. *What* you write is not important; that you *keep* writing is. Don't stop, even if that means repeating the same words until new words come. Don't go back to reread, don't censor ideas that seem dumb or repetitious, and above all don't stop to edit: grammar, punctuation, vocabulary, spelling, and the like are irrelevant at this stage.

The physical act of freewriting may give you access to ideas you were unaware of. For example, the following freewriting by a student, Robert Benday, drew him into the subject of writing as a disguise:

> Write to write. Seems pretty obvious, also weird. What to gain by writing? never anything before. Writing seems always—always—Getting corrected for trying too hard to please the teacher, getting corrected for not trying hard enuf. Frustration, nail biting, sometimes getting carried away making sentences to tell stories, not even true stories, esp. not true stories, that feels like creating something. Writing just pulls the story out of me. The story lets me be someone else, gives me a disguise.

(A later phase of Benday's writing appears on p. 25.)

If you write on a computer, try this technique for moving forward while freewriting: turn off your computer's monitor, or turn its brightness control all the way down so that the screen is dark. The computer will record what you type but keep it from you and thus prevent you from tinkering with your prose. This **invisible writing** may feel uncomfortable at first, but it can free the mind for very creative results. When you've finished freewriting, simply turn the monitor on or turn up the brightness control to read what you've written, and then save or revise it as appropriate. Later, you may be able to transfer some of your freewriting directly into your draft.

CULTURE LANGUAGE Invisible writing can be especially helpful if you are uneasy writing in standard American English and you tend to worry about errors while writing. The blank computer screen leaves you no choice but to explore ideas without giving attention to the way you are expressing them. If you choose to write with the monitor on, concentrate on *what* you want to say, not *how* you are saying it.

Focused freewriting

Focused freewriting is more concentrated: you start with your question about your subject and answer it without stopping for, say, fifteen minutes or one full page. As in all freewriting, you push to bypass mental blocks and self-consciousness, not debating what to say or editing what you've written. With focused freewriting, though, you let the physical act of writing take you into and around your subject.

An example of focused freewriting can be found in the work of Sara Ling, whose journal entry appears on page 21. In a composition course, Ling's instructor had distributed "Welcome to Cyberbia," an essay by M. Kadi about communication on the Internet. The instructor then gave the following assignment:

> M. Kadi's "Welcome to Cyberbia" holds that the Internet will do little to bridge differences among people because its users gravitate toward other users who are like themselves in most respects. More than a decade later, do Kadi's concerns seem valid? Can the Internet serve as a medium for positive change in the way people of diverse backgrounds relate to each other? If so, how? If not, why not? In an essay of 500–700 words, respond to Kadi's essay with a limited and well-supported opinion of your own. The first draft is due Monday, October 31, for class discussion.

On first reading Kadi's essay, Ling had been impressed with its tight logic but had found unconvincing its pessimistic view of the Internet's potential. She reread the essay and realized that some of Kadi's assertions did not correspond to her own Internet experiences. This discovery led Ling to a question: *How might the Internet help to break down barriers between people?* Her focused freewriting began to develop an answer:

> Kadi says we only meet people like ourselves on the Internet, but I've met lots who have very different backgrounds and interests—or "turned out to have" is more like it, since I didn't know anything about them at first. There's the anonymity thing, but Kadi ignores it. You can be anyone or no one. People can get to know me and my ideas without knowing I'm female or Asian American or a student. Then they can find out the facts about me, but the facts will be less likely to get in the way of communication. Communication without set identity, especially physical appearance. This could make for more tolerance of others, of difference.

With this freewriting, Ling moved beyond her initial response to Kadi's essay into her own views of how anonymity on the Internet could improve communication among diverse groups.

4 Making a list

Like focused freewriting, list making requires opening yourself to everything that seems even remotely connected to your topic, without concern for order or repetition or form of expression. You can let your topic percolate for a day or more, recording thoughts on it whenever they occur. (For this approach to work, you need to keep paper or a computer with you at all times.) Or, in a method more akin to

- Where did it happen?
- Why did it happen?
- How did it happen?

These questions can also be useful in probing an essay subject, especially if you are telling a story or examining causes and effects. (See also below and the facing page.)

7 Using rhetorical strategies

Rhetorical strategies—also called **patterns of development**—include narration, definition, comparison and contrast, and classification. They are ways we think about and understand a vast range of subjects, from our own daily experiences to the most complex scientific theories. They also serve as strategies and patterns for writing about these subjects, as illustrated by the discussions and paragraph-length examples on pages 93–102.

To see your subject from many angles and open up ideas about it, you can ask the following questions based on the rhetorical strategies. Not all these questions will be productive, but at least a few should open up new possibilities. (You can download these questions from *ablongman.com/littlebrown*. Save the list in a file of its own, duplicate it for each writing project, and insert appropriate answers between the questions. Print your answers so they're handy as you develop your paper. You can also move passages from the answers directly into your draft.)

How did it happen?

In **narration** you develop the subject as a story, with important events usually arranged chronologically (as they occurred in time): for instance, an exciting basketball game or the steps leading to a war.

How does it look, sound, feel, smell, taste?

In **description** you use sensory details to give a clear impression of a person, place, thing, or feeling, such as a species of animal, a machine, a friend, a building, or an experience.

What are examples of it or reasons for it?

The pattern of **illustration** or **support** suggests development with one or more examples of the subject (one couple's efforts to adopt a child, say, or three states that outlaw Internet gambling) or with the reasons for believing or doing something (three reasons for running for student council, four reasons for increasing federal aid to poor schools).

What is it? What does it encompass, and what does it exclude?

These questions lead to **definition:** specifying what the subject is and is not to give a precise sense of its meaning. Abstract terms—such as *justice, friendship,* and *art*—especially need defining (see p. 184).

What are its parts or characteristics?

Using the pattern of **division** or **analysis,** you separate a subject such as a bicycle or a short story into its elements and examine the relations between elements. The first step in critical thinking, analysis, is also discussed on pages 159–60.

What groups or categories can it be sorted into?

Classification involves separating a large group (such as cars) into smaller groups (subcompact, compact, and so on) based on the characteristics of the individual items (the sizes of the cars). Another example: academic, business, personal, literary, and other types of writing.

How is it like, or different from, other things?

With **comparison and contrast** you point out the similarities and differences between ideas, objects, people, places, and so on: the differences between two similar computer systems, for instance, or the similarities between two opposing political candidates.

Is it comparable to something that is in a different class but more familiar to readers?

This question leads to **analogy,** an extended comparison of unlike subjects. Analogy is often used to explain a topic that may be unfamiliar to readers (for instance, the relation of atoms in a molecule) by reference to a familiar topic (two people slow dancing).

Why did it happen, or what results did it have?

With **cause-and-effect analysis,** you explain why something happened or what its consequences were or will be, or both: the causes of cerebral palsy, the effects of a Supreme Court decision, the causes and effects of a gradual change in the climate.

How do you do it, or how does it work?

In **process analysis** you explain how the subject happens (how a plant grows, how a robot works) or how it is accomplished (how to write an essay).

8 Reading

Many assignments require reading. To respond to M. Kadi's essay about the Internet, for instance, Sara Ling had to digest Kadi's work. Essays on literary works as well as research writing also demand reading. But even when reading is not required by an assignment, it can help you locate or develop your subject by introducing you to ideas you didn't know or expanding on what you do know.

Say you were writing in favor of amateur athletics, a subject to which you had given a lot of thought. You might be inclined to proceed entirely on your own, drawing on facts, examples, and opinions already in your head. But a little digging in sources might open up more. For instance, an article in *Time* magazine could introduce you to an old rule for amateur status, or a comment on a Web log could suggest a pro-amateurism argument that hadn't occurred to you.

People often read passively, absorbing content like blotters, not interacting with it. To read for ideas, you need to be more active, probing text and illustrations with your mind, nurturing any sparks they set off. Always write while you read, taking notes on content and—just as important—on what the content makes you *think*. (See pp. 139–43 for specific guidelines on the process of active reading.)

Note Whenever you use the information or ideas of others in your writing, you must acknowledge your sources in order to avoid the serious offense of plagiarism. (See Chapter 45.)

9 Thinking critically

Even if you do not read for information and ideas on your subject, you can still think critically about it. Critical thinking (discussed on pp. 152–64) can produce creative ideas by leading you to see what is not obvious. It can also lead you systematically to conclusions about your subject.

Sara Ling, writing about communication on the Internet, used the operations of critical thinking to explore her topic:

- **Analysis: What are the subject's elements or characteristics?** Ling looked at the ways Internet users can communicate because of their anonymity.
- **Interpretation: What is the meaning or significance of the elements?** Ling saw that the anonymity of Internet users could help them transcend their physical differences.
- **Synthesis: How do the elements relate to each other, or how does this subject relate to another one?** Ling perceived important and hopeful differences between anonymous Internet communication and face-to-face interaction.
- **Evaluation: What is the value or significance of the subject?** Ling concluded that by making people more tolerant of one another, the Internet could help build community out of diversity.

EXERCISE 2.1 Considering your past work: Developing a topic

In the past how have you generated the ideas for writing? Have you used any of the techniques described on the preceding pages? Have you found the process especially enjoyable or difficult? If some writing tasks were easier than others, what do you think made the difference?

EXERCISE 2.2 Keeping a journal

If you haven't already started a journal on your own or in response to Exercise 1.1 (pp. 3–4), try to do so now. Every day for at least a week, write for at least fifteen minutes about anything on your mind—or consult the list on page 20 for ideas of what to write about. At the end of the week, write about your experience. What did you like about journal writing? What didn't you like? What did you learn about yourself or the world from the writing? How can you use this knowledge?

EXERCISE 2.3 Using freewriting, brainstorming, or clustering

Experiment with freewriting, brainstorming, or clustering. Continue with the subject you selected in Exercise 1.5 (p. 10), or begin with a new subject. Write or draw for at least ten minutes without stopping to reread and edit. (Try using invisible writing as described on p. 22 if you're freewriting or brainstorming on a computer.) When you finish your experiment, examine what you have written for ideas and relationships that could help you develop the subject. What do you think of the technique you tried? Did you have any difficulties with it? Did it help you loosen up and generate ideas?

EXERCISE 2.4 Sending an online query

When you have spent some time developing your subject, consider any doubts you may have or any information you still need. Send an online message to your classmates posing your questions and asking for their advice and insights.

EXERCISE 2.5 Developing your subject

Use at least two of the discovery techniques discussed on the preceding pages to develop the subject you selected in Exercise 1.5 (p. 10). (If you completed Exercise 2.3 above, then use one additional technique.) Later exercises for your essay-in-progress will be based on the ideas you generate in this exercise.

2b Developing a thesis

Your readers will expect an essay you write to be focused on a central idea, or **thesis,** to which all the essay's paragraphs, all its general statements and specific information, relate. The thesis is the controlling idea, the main point, the conclusion you have drawn about the evidence you have accumulated. It is the answer to the question you have been posing about your subject.

A thesis will probably not leap fully formed into your head. You may begin with an idea you want to communicate, but you will need to refine that idea to fit the realities of the paper you write. And often you will have to write and rewrite before you come to a conclusion about what you have. Still, it's wise to try to pin down your thesis when you have a fairly good stock of ideas. Then the thesis can help you start drafting, help keep you focused, and serve as a point of reference when changes inevitably occur.

Question How might the Internet help to break down barriers between people?

Answer Anonymous Internet communication can bypass physical differences.

Question What can be done to relieve students' frustration over parking at our school?

Answer The school must provide adequate parking for students who drive to school.

The next step is to spell out the answer in a sentence that names the topic and makes a claim about it. Creating this sentence may require several drafts.

Sara Ling went through a common process in writing and revising her thesis statement on Internet communication. She first answered her starting question, as shown in the first pair of examples above. Then she tried a statement derived from her answer:

> Internet communication that is anonymous can bypass physical differences.

Ling saw that this statement focused on her starting topic (*Internet communication*) but somewhat buried the crucial quality of anonymity. And the claim lacked significance: So what? Ling first tried to emphasize her intended subject:

> The anonymity of Internet communication . . .

Then she worked on her claim:

> . . . can bypass physical differences, and it could build diversity into community.

This statement said why the subject was significant (*it could build diversity into community*) but the idea was tacked on with *and.* Ling tried again, emphasizing cause and effect:

> Through bypassing physical differences, the unique anonymity of Internet communication could build diversity into community.

For her final revision, Ling responded to a friend's comment that *bypassing physical differences* was too vague. She spelled out her meaning:

> By lowering the barriers of physical appearance, the unique anonymity of Internet communication could build diversity into community.

Often you must deliberately consider your audience as you draft the thesis statement. One student, Ben Nelson, worked on a thesis based on the answer to the question above about the lack of student parking at his school. He arrived fairly easily at his claim that the school needed to provide more parking space for students.

However, to persuade the school administrators to take action, he needed to focus on them as his audience and revise his thesis statement accordingly. In one revision, he addressed the school administrators using a logical appeal:

> Many students who participate in extracurricular activities and hold after-school jobs must drive to school, and they need places to park.

In his second revision, below, Nelson brought in an emotional appeal as well, and he strengthened his writer's voice:

> The school must provide enough parking spaces to accommodate the many students who must drive to school and to protect all students from otherwise dangerous traffic congestion.

As you draft and revise your thesis statement, keep in mind the following:

- **Naming the subject and making a claim about it.**
- **Clearly communicating your subject and claim to your audience.**
- **Establishing your writer's voice.**

Then check your statement against the following questions:

Checklist for revising the thesis statement

- How well does the **subject** of your statement capture the subject of your paper? What **claim** does your statement make about your subject?
- What is the **significance** of the claim? How does it answer "So what?" and convey your purpose?
- How can the claim be **limited** or made more **specific**? Does it state a single idea and clarify the boundaries of the idea?
- How **unified** is the statement? How does each word and phrase contribute to a single idea about the subject?
- What does the thesis statement suggest about your **appeals** to your audience?
- How well does the statement convey your **writer's voice**?

Here are other examples of thesis statements revised to meet the requirements in the box above:

Original	Revised
Seat belts can save lives, but now carmakers are installing air bags. [Not unified: how do the two parts of the sentence relate?]	If drivers had used lifesaving seat belts more often, carmakers might not have needed to install air bags.
Toni Morrison won the Nobel Prize in Literature in 1993. [A	Toni Morrison's 1993 Nobel Prize in Literature, the first

Original	Revised
statement of fact, not a claim about Morrison's work: what is significant about her winning the prize?]	awarded to an African American woman, affirms both the strength of her vivid prose style and the importance of her subject matter.
People should not go on fad diets. [A vague statement that needs limiting with one or more reasons: what's wrong with fad diets?]	Fad diets can be dangerous when they deprive the body of essential nutrients or rely excessively on potentially harmful foods.
Televised sports are different from live sports. [A general statement: how are they different, and why is the difference significant?]	Although television cannot transmit all the excitement of a live game, its close-ups and slow-motion replays reveal much about the players and the strategy of the game.

Note You may sometimes need more than one sentence for your thesis statement, particularly if it requires some buildup:

> Modern English, especially written English, is full of bad habits that interfere with clear thinking. Getting rid of these habits is a first step to political regeneration.
> —Adapted from George Orwell, "Politics and the English Language"

However, don't use this leeway to produce a wordy, general, or disunified statement. The two (or more) sentences must build on each other, and the final sentence must present your key assertion.

EXERCISE 2.6 Evaluating thesis statements

Evaluate the following thesis statements, considering whether each one is sufficiently significant, specific, and unified. Rewrite the statements as necessary to meet these goals.

1. Aggression usually leads to violence, injury, and even death, and we should use it constructively.
2. The religion of Islam is widely misunderstood in the United States.
3. Manners are a kind of social glue.
4. One episode of a radio talk show amply illustrates both the appeal of such shows and their silliness.
5. The poem is about motherhood.

EXERCISE 2.7 Considering your past work: Developing a thesis

Have you been aware in the past of focusing your essays on a central idea, or thesis? Have you found it more efficient to try to pin down your idea early or to let it evolve during drafting? To what extent has a thesis helped or hindered you in shaping your draft?

EXERCISE 2.8 Drafting and revising your own thesis statement

Continuing from Exercise 2.5 (p. 29), write a significant, specific, and unified thesis statement for your essay-in-progress.

2c Organizing ideas

An effective essay has a recognizable shape—an arrangement of parts that guides readers, helping them see how ideas and details relate to each other and contribute to the whole. You may sometimes let an effective organization emerge over one or more drafts. But many writers find that organizing ideas to some extent before drafting can provide a helpful sense of direction, as a map can help a driver negotiate a half-familiar system of roads. If you feel uncertain about the course your essay should follow or have a complicated topic with many parts, devising a shape for your material can clarify your options.

Before you begin organizing your material, look over all the writing you've done so far—freewriting, clustering, notes from reading, whatever. Either on paper or on a computer, pull together a master list of all the ideas and details you think you might want to include. You can add to or subtract from the list as you think about shape.

1 Distinguishing the general and the specific

To organize material for an essay, you need to distinguish general and specific ideas and see the relations between ideas. **General** and **specific** refer to the number of instances or objects included in a group signified by a word. The "ladder" below illustrates a general-to-specific hierarchy.

Most general
↑ life form
plant
flowering plant
rose
American Beauty rose
↓ Uncle Dan's prize-winning American Beauty rose
Most specific

Here are some tips for arranging the ideas in your preliminary writing:

- **Underline, boldface, or circle the most general ideas.** These are the ideas that offer the main support for your thesis statement. They will be more general than the evidence that in turn supports them.

- **Make connections between each general idea and the more specific details that support it.** On paper, start with a fresh sheet, write each general idea down with space beneath it, and add specific information in the appropriate spaces. On a computer, rearrange supporting information under more general points. Your word processor may include a Comment function that allows you to add notes about connections.
- **Respect the meanings of ideas.** Think through the implications of ideas as you sort them. Otherwise, your hierarchies could become jumbled, with *rose,* for instance, illogically subordinated to *animal,* or *life form* somehow subordinated to *rose.*
- **Remove information that doesn't fit.** If you worry about losing deleted information, transfer the notes to a separate sheet of paper or word-processing file.
- **Fill holes where support seems skimpy.** If you recognize a hole but don't know what to fill it with, try using a discovery technique such as freewriting or clustering, or go back to your research sources.
- **Experiment with various arrangements of general ideas and supporting information.** Seek an order that presents your material clearly and logically. On paper, you can cut the master list apart and paste or tape each general idea and its support on a separate piece of paper. Then try different orders for the pages. On a computer, first save the master list and duplicate it. To move material around, select a block of text and either copy and then paste it where you want it or (a little quicker) drag the selected text to where you want it.

2 Choosing an organizing tool

Some writers view outlines as chores and straitjackets, but they need not be dull or confining. There are different kinds of outlines, some more flexible than others. All of them can enlarge and clarify your thinking, showing you patterns of general and specific, suggesting proportions, and highlighting gaps or overlaps in coverage.

Many writers use outlines not only before but also after drafting—to check the underlying structure of the draft when revising it (see p. 52). No matter when it's made, though, an outline can change to reflect changes in your thinking. View any outline you make as a tentative sketch, not as a fixed paint-by-numbers diagram.

A scratch or informal outline

For many essays, especially those with a fairly straightforward structure, a simple listing of ideas and perhaps their support may provide adequate direction for your writing.

A **scratch outline** lists the key points of the paper in the order they will be covered. Here is Sara Ling's scratch outline for her essay on Internet communication:

Thesis statement

By lowering the barriers of physical appearance, the unique anonymity of Internet communication could build diversity into community.

Scratch outline

No fear of prejudgment
  Physical attributes unknown—age, race, gender, etc.
  We won't be shut out because of appearance
Inability to prejudge others
  Assumptions based on appearance
  Meeting of minds only
  Finding shared interests and concerns

Ling put more into this outline than its simplicity might imply, not only working out an order for her ideas but also sketching their implications.

An **informal outline** is usually more detailed than a scratch outline, including key general points and the specific evidence for them. A student's informal outline appears below.

Thesis statement

After Home Inc.'s hiring practices were exposed in the media, the company avoided a scandal with policy changes and a well-publicized outreach to employees and consumers.

Informal outline

Background on scandal
  Previous hiring practices
  Media exposure and public response (brief)
Policy changes
  Application forms
  Interviewing procedures
  Training of personnel
Outreach to employees
  Signs and letters
  Meetings and workshops
Outreach to consumers
  Press conference
  Store signs
  Advertising—print and radio

A tree diagram

In a **tree diagram,** ideas and details branch out in increasing specificity. Like any outline, the diagram can warn of gaps, overlaps, and digressions. But unlike more linear outlines, it can be supplemented and extended indefinitely, so it is easy to alter for new ideas and arrangements discovered during drafting and revision.

Below is a tree diagram by Johanna Abrams, based on her earlier brainstorming about a summer job (p. 24) and the following thesis statement:

Thesis statement

Two months working in a large government agency taught me that an office's pecking order should be respected.

Tree diagram

- Mail-room work
  - Confusion
    - Initials on mail
  - Inefficient, arbitrary procedures
    - Coffee breaks
    - Delivery times
- Mrs. King's behavior
  - Anger and resentment
    - Coldness
    - Meanness
  - Self-protection
    - Rigidity
    - Desperation
- My behavior
  - Busybody
    - Critical
    - Questioning
  - Arrogant
    - Rude
    - No sympathy
- Office/barnyard pecking order
  - Sequence of pecking
  - Effects on lowest chicken
    - Low self-esteem
    - Self-protection
    - Need for power

Each main part of the four-part diagram represents a different general idea about the summer-job experience. Within each part, information grows more specific as it branches downward.

A tree diagram or other visual map can be especially useful for planning a project for the World Wide Web. The diagram can help you lay out the organization of your project and its links and then later can serve as a site map for your readers. (For more on composing for the Web, see pp. 786–92.)

A formal outline

For complex topics requiring complex arrangements of ideas and support, you may want or be required to construct a **formal outline.** More rigidly arranged and more detailed than other outlines, a formal outline not only lays out main ideas and their support but also shows the relative importance of all the essay's elements and how they connect with one another.

Note Because of its structure, a formal outline can be an excellent tool for checking the arrangement of a draft before revising it (see p. 52).

On the basis of her scratch outline (p. 37), Sara Ling prepared this formal outline for her essay on the Internet:

Thesis statement

By lowering the barriers of physical appearance, the unique anonymity of Internet communication could build diversity into community.

Formal outline

I. No fear of being prejudged
   A. Unknown physical attributes
      1. Gender
      2. Age
      3. Race
      4. Style
   B. Freer communication
   C. No automatic rejection
II. Inability to prejudge others
   A. No assumptions based on appearance
      1. Body type
      2. Physical disability
      3. Race
   B. Discovery of shared interests and concerns
      1. Sports and other activities
      2. Family values
      3. Political views
   C. Reduction of physical bias

Ling's outline illustrates several principles of outlining that can help ensure completeness, balance, and clear relationships. (These principles largely depend on distinguishing between the general and the specific. See pp. 35–36.)

Principles of the formal outline

- Labels and indentions indicate order and relative importance.
- Sections and subsections reflect logical relationships.
- Topics of equal generality appear in parallel headings.
- Each subdivision has at least two parts.
- Headings are expressed in parallel grammatical form.
- The introduction and conclusion may be omitted (though not, of course, from the essay).

- **All the outline's parts are systematically indented and labeled.** Roman numerals (I, II) label primary divisions of the essay, indented capital letters (A, B) label secondary divisions, and farther indented Arabic numerals (1, 2) label principal supporting points and examples. A fourth level would be indented farther still and labeled with small letters (a, b). Each succeeding level contains more specific information than the one before it.
- **The outline divides the material into several groups.** An uninterrupted listing of ideas like the one following would indicate a need for tighter, more logical relationships among ideas. (Compare this example with part II of Ling's actual outline.)

```
II. Inability to prejudge others
    A. Body type
    B. Physical disability
    C. Race
    D. Sports and other activities
    E. Family values
    F. Political views
    G. Reduction of physical bias
```

- **Within each part of the outline, distinct topics of equal generality appear in parallel headings,** with the same indention and numbering or lettering. In the following example, points B, C, and D are more specific than point A, not equally general, so they should be subheadings 1, 2, and 3 under it. (See section IIA of Ling's outline.)

```
    A. No assumptions based on appearance
    B. Body type
    C. Physical disability
    D. Race
```

- **All subdivided headings in the outline break into at least two parts** because a topic cannot logically be divided into only one part. The following example violates this principle:

```
    B. Discovery of shared views
        1. Interests and concerns
```

  Any single subdivision should be combined with the heading above it (as in section IIB of Ling's actual outline), matched with another subdivision, or rechecked for its relevance to the heading above it.
- **All headings are expressed in parallel grammatical form** (see pp. 407–11 on parallelism). Ling's is a **topic outline,** in which the headings consist of a noun (*fear, attributes, gender,* and the like) with modifiers (*no, unknown physical, no automatic,* and the like). **In a sentence outline** all headings are expressed as full sentences, as in the following rewrite of part II of Ling's outline.

II. On the Internet, we are unable to prejudge others.
    A. We cannot make common assumptions based on physical appearance.
        1. People with athletic builds must be unintelligent.
        2. People in wheelchairs must be unapproachable or pathetic.
        3. People of other races must hold views different from our own.
    B. We discover shared interests and concerns.
        1. We find common ground in sports and other activities.
        2. We see that we all feel much the same about our families.
        3. We learn the similarities in each other's political views.
    C. The Internet could reduce physical bias in the world.

See page 669 for a complete sentence outline.

- **The outline covers only the body of the essay, omitting the introduction and the conclusion.** The beginning and the ending are important in the essay itself, but you need not include them in the outline unless you are required to do so or anticipate special problems with their organization.

3 Choosing a structure

Introduction, body, and conclusion

Most essays share a basic shape:

- **The *introduction,* usually a paragraph or two, draws readers into the world of the essay.** At a minimum, it announces and clarifies the topic. Often, it ends with the thesis statement, making a commitment that the rest of the essay delivers on. (See pp. 104–08 for more on introductions.)
- **The *body* of the essay develops the thesis and thus fulfills the commitment of the introduction.** The paragraphs in the body develop the general points that support the thesis—the items that would be labeled with Roman numerals and capital letters in a formal outline like the one on page 39. These general points are like the legs of a table supporting the top, the thesis. Each general point may take a paragraph or more, with the bulk of the content providing the details, examples, and reasons (the wood of the table) to support the general point and thus the thesis.
- **The *conclusion* gives readers something to take away from the essay**—a summary of ideas, for instance, or a suggested course of action. (See pp. 108–10 for more on conclusions.)

This basic shape applies mainly to traditional essays. A composition for the World Wide Web probably will have a more flexible structure and will lack a formal conclusion. See pages 786–92 for more on composing for the Web.

CULTURE LANGUAGE If you are not used to reading and writing American academic prose, its pattern of introduction-body-conclusion and the particular schemes discussed below may seem unfamiliar. For instance, instead of introductions that focus quickly on the topic and thesis, you may be used to openings that establish personal connections with readers or that approach the thesis indirectly. And instead of body paragraphs that first emphasize general points and then support those points with specific evidence, you may be used to general statements without support (because writers can assume that readers will supply the evidence themselves) or to evidence without explanation (because writers can assume that readers will infer the general points themselves). When writing American academic prose, you need to take into account readers' expectations for directness and for the statement and support of general points.

Organizing the body by space or time

Two organizational schemes—spatial and chronological—grow naturally out of the topic. A **spatial organization** is especially appropriate for essays that describe a place, an object, or a person. Following the way people normally survey something, you move through space from a chosen starting point to other features of the subject. Describing a building, for instance, you might begin with an impression of the whole, then scan exterior details from top to bottom, and then describe interior spaces.

A **chronological organization** reports events as they occurred in time, usually from first to last. This pattern, like spatial organization, corresponds to readers' own experiences and expectations. It suits an essay in which you do one of the following:

- **Recount a sequence of events,** such as a championship baseball game or the Battle of Gettysburg.
- **Explain a process from beginning to end**—for instance, how to run a marathon or how a tree converts carbon dioxide to oxygen.
- **Explain the causes that led to an effect,** such as the lobbying that helped to push a bill through the legislature. Alternatively,

Schemes for organizing ideas in an essay

- Space
- Time
- Emphasis

General to specific	Increasing importance (climax)
Specific to general	Decreasing familiarity
Problem-solution	Increasing complexity

explain how a cause, such as a flood or a book, had multiple effects.

- **Tell a story about yourself or someone else.**
- **Provide background**—for instance, the making of a film you are analyzing or the procedure used in an experiment you are reporting.

Organizing the body for emphasis

Some organizational schemes must be imposed on ideas and information to aid readers' understanding and achieve a desired emphasis.

General to specific

Two ways of organizing essays depend on the distinction between the general and the specific, discussed on pages 35–36. The **general-to-specific scheme** is common in expository and argumentative essays that start with a general discussion of the main points and then proceed to specific examples, facts, or other evidence. The following thesis statement forecasts a general-to-specific organization:

> As an investment in its own economy, the United States should provide grants to school districts in impoverished areas.

The body of the essay might first elaborate on the basic argument and then provide the supporting data.

Specific to general

Sometimes you may anticipate that readers will not appreciate or agree with your general ideas before they see the support for them—for instance, in an expository essay that presents a unique way of looking at common experience, or in an argumentative essay that takes an unpopular view. In these cases a **specific-to-general scheme** can arouse readers' interest in specific examples or other evidence, letting the evidence build to statements of more general ideas. The following thesis statement could be developed in this way:

> Although most of us are unaware of the public relations campaigns directed at us, they can significantly affect the way we think and live.

The writer might devote most of the essay to a single specific example of a public relations campaign and then explain more generally how the example typifies public relations campaigns.

Problem-solution

Many arguments use a **problem-solution scheme:** first outline a problem that needs solving; then propose a solution. (If the solution involves steps toward a goal, it may be arranged chronologically.) The following thesis statement announces a problem-solution paper:

> To improve the tutoring services, the department should train tutors to work more effectively with groups of students.

Climax

A common scheme in both explanations and arguments is the **climactic organization,** in which ideas unfold in order of increasing drama or importance to a climax. For example, the following thesis statement lists three effects of strip-mining in order of their increasing severity, and the essay would cover them in the same order:

> Strip-mining should be tightly controlled in this region to reduce its pollution of water resources, its destruction of the land, and its devastating effects on people's lives.

As this example suggests, the climactic organization works well in arguments because it leaves readers with the most important point freshest in their minds. In exposition such an arrangement can create suspense and thus hold readers' attention.

Familiarity or complexity

Expository essays can also be arranged to take account of reader's knowledge of the subject. An essay on the effects of air pollution might proceed from **most familiar to least familiar**—from effects readers are likely to know to ones they may not know. Similarly, an explanation of animals' nervous systems might proceed from **simplest to most complex,** so that the explanation of each nervous system provides a basis for readers to understand the more difficult one following.

4 Checking for unity and coherence

In conceiving your organization and writing your essay, you should be aware of two qualities of effective writing that relate to organization: unity and coherence. When you perceive that someone's writing "flows well," you are probably appreciating these two qualities. An essay has **unity** if all its parts relate to and support the thesis statement. Check for unity with these questions:

- **Is each main section relevant to the main idea (thesis) of the essay?**
- **Within main sections, does each example or detail support the principal idea of that section?**

An essay has **coherence** if readers can see the relations among parts and move easily from one thought to the next. Check for coherence with these questions:

- **Do the ideas follow in a clear sequence?**
- **Are the parts of the essay logically connected?**
- **Are the connections clear and smooth?**

A unified and coherent outline will not necessarily guide you to a unified and coherent essay, because so much can change during drafting. Thus you shouldn't be too hard on your outline, in case a seemingly wayward idea proves useful. But do cut obvious digressions and rearrange material that clearly needs moving.

Sample essay

The following essay illustrates some ways of achieving unity and coherence (highlighted in the annotations).

A Picture of Hyperactivity

Hyperactive salespeople improve profits. Hyperactive committee members can run things efficiently. But when children are hyperactive, there are no benefits. A collage of those who must cope with hyperactivity in children—doctors, families, and the children themselves—is a picture of frustration, anger, and loss.

Introduction establishing subject of essay

Thesis statement

The first part of the collage is the doctors. In their terminology, the word hyperactivity has been replaced by ADHD, attention-deficit hyperactivity disorder, to describe children who are abnormally or excessively busy. But doctors do not fully understand the problem, and so they differ over how to treat it. Some recommend a special diet, others recommend behavior-modifying drugs, and still others, who do not consider ADHD a medical problem, recommend psychotherapy. The result is a merry-go-round of tests, often inconclusive, that frustrate doctors and confuse children and their families.

Paragraph idea, linked to thesis statement

Paragraph developed with evidence supporting its idea

For families, the second part of the collage, a diagnosis of ADHD means worry and disruption. Parents are often anxious about doing what's best for their ADHD child, and they are frustrated when the child doesn't improve. They may feel anger that spills over to the child or to the whole family. Siblings can feel jealous of the attention the ADHD child receives, embarrassed by the child's erratic behavior in public, guilty about the jealousy and embarrassment, and above all helpless. As the sister of a child with ADHD, I have felt all of these emotions.

Paragraph idea, linked to thesis statement

Paragraph developed with evidence supporting its idea

The weight of ADHD, however, does not rest on the doctors and families. The darkest part of the collage belongs to the children. From early childhood they may be dragged from doctor to doctor, medicated until they're numb, and constantly discussed by physicians, teachers, neighbors, and even strangers on the street. They may be highly intelligent, but they do poorly in school because of their short attention spans. Their peers dislike them because of their temper and their unwillingness to follow rules. Even their pets mistrust them because of their erratic behavior. They feel isolated and unconfident.

Transition

Paragraph idea, linked to thesis statement

Paragraph developed with evidence supporting its idea

any boundaries between stages at all. Still, your primary goal during the writing process will usually shift from gathering and shaping information to forming connected sentences and paragraphs in a draft and then restructuring and rewriting the draft.

3a Writing the first draft

The only correct drafting style is the one that works for you. Generally, though, the freer and more fluid you are, the better. Some writers draft and revise at the same time, but most let themselves go during drafting and *especially* do not worry about errors. Drafting is the occasion to find and convey meaning through the act of writing. If you fear making mistakes while drafting, that fear will choke your ideas. You draft only for yourself, so errors do not matter. Write freely until you have worked out what you want to say; *then* focus on any mistakes you may have made.

Starting to draft sometimes takes courage, even for seasoned professionals. Students and pros alike find elaborate ways to procrastinate—rearranging shelves, napping, talking with friends. Such procrastination may actually help you if you let ideas for writing simmer at the same time. At some point, though, enough is enough: the deadline looms; you've got to get started. If the blankness still stares back at you, then try one of the following techniques for unblocking.

Ways to start drafting

- **Read over what you've already written**—notes, outlines, and so on. Immediately start your draft with whatever comes to mind.
- **Freewrite** (see p. 22).
- **Write scribbles or type nonsense** until words you can use start coming.
- **Pretend you're writing to a friend about your subject.**
- **Describe an image that represents your subject**—a physical object, a facial expression, two people arguing over something, a giant machine gouging the earth for a mine, whatever.
- **Write a paragraph.** Explain what you think your essay will be about when you finish it.
- **Skip the opening and start in the middle.** Or write the conclusion.
- **Start writing the part that you understand best or feel most strongly about.** Using your outline, divide your essay into chunks—say, one for the introduction, another for the first point, and so on. One of these chunks may call out to be written.

You should find some momentum once you've started writing. If not, however, or if your energy flags, try one or more of the following techniques to keep moving ahead.

Ways to *keep* drafting

- **Set aside enough time for yourself.** For a brief essay, a first draft is likely to take at least an hour or two.
- **Work in a quiet place.**
- **Make yourself comfortable.**
- **If you must stop working, write down what you expect to do next.** Then you can pick up where you stopped with minimal disruption.
- **Be as fluid as possible, and don't worry about mistakes.** Spontaneity will allow your attitudes toward your subject to surface naturally in your sentences, and it will also make you receptive to ideas and relations you haven't seen before. Mistakes will be easier to find and correct later, when you're not also trying to create.
- **Keep going.** Skip over sticky spots; leave a blank if you can't find the right word; put alternative ideas or phrasings in brackets so that you can consider them later without bogging down. If an idea pops out of nowhere but doesn't seem to fit in, quickly jot it down on a separate sheet, or write it into the draft and bracket or boldface it for later attention. You can use an asterisk (*) or some other symbol to mark places where you feel blocked or uncertain. (With a word processor, you can later return to these places by using the Find command to locate the symbol.)
- **Resist self-criticism.** Don't worry about your style, grammar, spelling, punctuation, and the like. Don't worry about what your readers will think. These are very important matters, but save them for revision. On a word processor, help yourself resist self-criticism by turning off automatic spelling- or grammar-checking functions or by trying invisible writing (p. 22).
- **Use your thesis statement and outline** to remind you of your planned purpose, organization, and content.
- **But don't feel constrained by your thesis and outline.** If your writing leads you in a more interesting direction, follow.

If you write on a computer, frequently save the text you're drafting—at least every five or ten minutes and every time you leave the computer. See pages 55–56 for tips on saving documents.

Whether you compose on paper or on a computer, you may find it difficult to tell whether a first draft is finished. The distinction between drafts can be significant because creating text is different from rethinking it and because your instructor may ask you and your classmates to submit your drafts, either on paper or over a

Ways to gain distance from your work

- **Take a break after finishing the draft.** A few hours may be enough; a whole night or day is preferable. The break will clear your mind, relax you, and give you some objectivity.
- **Ask someone to read and react to your draft.** Many writing teachers ask their students to submit their first drafts so that the teacher and, often, the other members of the class can serve as an actual audience to help guide revision. (See also pp. 70–71 on receiving and benefiting from comments.)
- **Type a handwritten draft.** The act of transcription can reveal gaps in content or problems in structure.
- **Print out a word-processed draft.** You'll be able to view all pages of the draft at once, and the different medium can reveal weaknesses you didn't see on screen.
- **Outline your draft.** Highlight the main points supporting the thesis, and write these sentences down separately in outline form. (If you're working on a word processor, you can copy and paste these sentences.) Then examine the outline you've made for logical order, gaps, and digressions. A formal outline can be especially illuminating because of its careful structure. (See pp. 36–41 for a discussion of outlining.)
- **Listen to your draft.** Read the draft out loud to yourself or a relative or classmate, read it into a tape recorder and play the tape, or have someone read the draft to you. Experiencing your words with ears instead of eyes can alter your perceptions.
- **Ease the pressure.** Don't try to re-see everything in your draft at once. Use a checklist like the one on p. 54, making a separate pass through the draft for each item.

2 Revising, then editing

Strictly speaking, revision includes editing—refining the manner of expression to improve clarity or style or to correct errors. In this chapter, though, revision and editing are treated separately to stress their differences: in revision you deal with the underlying meaning and structure of your essay; in editing you deal with its surface. By making separate drafts beyond the first—a revised one and then an edited one—you'll be less likely to waste time tinkering with sentences that you end up cutting, and you'll avoid the temptation to substitute editing for more substantial revision.

The temptation to edit while revising can be especially attractive on a word processor because it's easy to alter copy. Indeed, writers sometimes find themselves editing compulsively, spinning their wheels with changes that cease to have any marked effect on meaning or clarity and that may in fact sap the writing of energy. Planning to revise and then to edit encourages you to look beyond the confines of the screen so that deeper issues of meaning and structure aren't lost to surface matters such as word choice and sentence arrangement.

3 Titling your essay

The revision stage is a good time to consider a title. After drafting, you have a clearer sense of your direction, and the attempt to sum up your essay in a title phrase can help you focus sharply on your topic, purpose, and audience.

Here are suggestions for titling an essay:

- ***A descriptive title* is almost always appropriate and is often expected for academic writing.** It announces the topic clearly, accurately, and as briefly as possible. The final title of Sara Ling's essay—"The Internet: Fragmentation or Community?"—is an example, as are "Images of Lost Identity in *North by Northwest*," "An Experiment in Small-Group Dynamics," "Why Lincoln Delayed Emancipating the Slaves," and "Structure in 'A Rose for Emily.'"
- ***A suggestive title*—the kind often found in popular magazines—may be appropriate for more informal writing.** Examples include "Making Peace" (for an essay on the Peace Corps) and "Anyone for Soup?" (for an essay on working in a soup kitchen). For a more suggestive title, Ling might have chosen "What We Don't Know Can Help Us" or "Secrets of the Internet." Such a title conveys the writer's attitude and main concerns but not the precise topic, thereby pulling readers into the essay to learn more. A source for such a title may be a familiar phrase, a fresh image, or a significant expression from the essay itself.
- **A title tells readers how big the topic is.** For Ling's essay, the title "The Internet" or "Anonymity" would have been too broad, whereas "Lose Your Body" or "Discovering Common Ground" would have been too narrow because each deals with only part of the paper's content.
- **A title should not restate the assignment or the thesis statement**, as in "The Trouble with M. Kadi's Picture of the Internet" or "What I Think About Diversity on the Internet."

For more information on essay titles, see page 356 (avoiding reference to the title in the opening of the paper), 493 (capitalizing words in a title), and 664–65 (the format of a title in the final paper).

4 Using a revision checklist

Set aside at least as much time to revise your essay as you took to draft it. Plan on going through the draft several times to answer

evaluate the kinds of changes you are making. For instance, if during revision you see only minor surface alterations (word substitutions, added punctuation, and the like), then you might consider whether and where to read more deeply for more fundamental changes.

3c Examining a sample revision

In revising her first draft, Sara Ling had the help of her teacher and several of her classmates, to whom she showed the draft as part of her assignment. Based on the revision checklist, she thought that she wanted to stick with her initial purpose and thesis statement and that they had held up well in the draft. But she also knew without being told that her introduction and conclusion were too hurried, that the movement between paragraphs was too abrupt, that the example of the snowboarding forum went on too long, and that the fourth paragraph was thin: she hadn't supplied enough details to support her ideas and convince her readers.

Ling's readers confirmed her self-evaluation. Several, however, raised points that she had not considered, reflected in these comments by classmates:

Comment 1

Why do you say (par. 2) that most people use invented screen names? I don't, and I know other people who don't either. Do you have evidence of how many people use invented names or why they do?

Comment 2

I would have an easier time agreeing with you about the Internet if you weren't quite so gung-ho. For instance, what about the dangers of the Internet, as when adults prey on children or men prey on women? In par. 3, you don't acknowledge that such things can and do happen. Also, is a bias-free world (par. 4) really such a sure thing? People will still meet in person, after all.

At first Ling was tempted to resist these comments because the writers seemed to object to her ideas. But eventually she understood that the comments showed ways she could make the ideas convincing to more readers. The changes took some time, partly because Ling decided to conduct a survey of students in order to test her assumption about people's use of invented screen names.

The following revised draft shows the survey results and Ling's other changes. Ling used the Track Changes function on her word processor, so that deletions are crossed out and additions are in blue. Marginal annotations highlight the main revisions.

The Internet: Fragmentation or Community?

~~Title?~~

Descriptive title names topic and forecasts approach.

We hear all sorts of predictions about how the Internet will enrich our lives and promote equality, tolerance, and thus community in our society. But are these promises realistic? In her 1995 essay "Welcome to Cyberbia," M. Kadi argues that they are not. Instead, she~~In "Welcome to Cyberbia," written in 1995, M. Kadi~~ predicts that the Internet will lead to more fragmentation, not community, ~~in society~~ because users merely ~~people just~~ seek out others ~~like themselves~~ with the same biases, needs, and concerns as their own. The point is an interesting one, ~~B~~but Kadi fails to foresee that ~~how~~ the unique anonymity of Internet communication could actually build diversity into community by lowering the barriers of physical appearance.

Expanded introduction draws readers into Ling's question and summarizes Kadi's essay.

Internet communication can be anonymous on at least two levels. ~~Anonymity on the Internet. It's one of the best things about technology. Most people who communicate online use an invented screen name to avoid revealing personal details such as age, gender, and ethnic background. No one knows~~ The people who communicate with you do not know your age. ~~w~~Whether you're fat or thin or neat or sloppy. What kind of clothes you wear. (Maybe you're not wearing clothes at all). Or anything else about physical appearance. ~~People who know you personally don't even know who you are with an invented screen name.~~ If you use an invented screen name instead of your real name, readers don't even know whatever your name says about you, such as gender or ethnic background.

New transition relates paragraph to thesis statement and smoothes flow.

Blanket assertion is deleted in favor of survey results added later.

Addition clarifies use of invented screen names.

Internet anonymity seems a popular option, judging by the numbers of invented user names seen in online forums. But I thought it would be a good idea to determine the extent of invented user names as well as the reasons for them, so I surveyed seventy-eight students with two questions: (1) Do you ever write with an invented user name when contributing to chat rooms, newsgroups, blogs, and so on? (2) If yes, why do you use an invented name: to protect your privacy, to avoid revealing personal information, or for some other reason? Fig. 1 shows that most of the students do use invented names online. And most do so to protect their privacy or to avoid revealing personal details.

Largest revision presents results of survey conducted to support use of invented screen names.

Users of the Internet clearly value the anonymity it can give them. Twenty students said that they use invented names to mask personal details because they think the details might work against them. One said

New paragraph summarizes survey results and adds examples.

New pie graph presents survey results in an easy-to-read format.

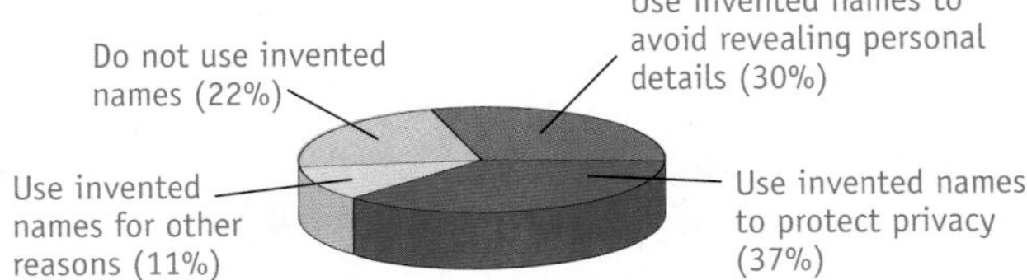

Fig. 1. Use of invented screen names among seventy-eight Internet users.

she is able to participate in a physics discussion list without fear of being ignored by the group's professional physicists. Another said he thinks he can contribute more freely to a political forum because no one knows he's African American. I learned the benefits of anonymity myself when I joined a snowboarding forum using my full name and received hostile

Revisions condense overly long example from Ling's experience.

~~With invented screen names, we can make ourselves known without first being prejudged because of our physical attributes. For example, I participate in a snow-boarding forum that has mostly guys. I didn't realize what I was getting into when I used my full name as my screen name. Before long, I had received unfriendly~~ responses such as "What does a girl know?" and "Why don't you go back to knitting?" I guess I had run into a male prejudice against female snowboarders. However, another girl on the forum had no such problems~~. At first she signed on with a screen name that did not reveal her gender, and no one responded negatively to her messages. When~~ when she ~~had~~ contributed for a while~~,~~ before revealing her gender. ~~she earned respect from the other snowboarders. When she revealed that she was a girl at that point, no one responded negatively in the way I had experienced. She posed at first as someone different from who she really was and could make herself heard.~~

New paragraph acknowledges complexities that were previously ignored.

Granted, concealing or altering identities on the Internet can be a problem, as when adults pose as children to seduce or harm them. These well-publicized occurrences say a great deal about the need to monitor the use of the Internet by children and to be cautious about getting together with Internet correspondents. However, they do not undermine the value of people being able to make themselves heard in situations where normally (in the real world) they would be shut out.

New transition clarifies shift to second main point.

The Internet's anonymity has a flip side too. We cannot be prejudged and

~~W~~we also cannot prejudge others because of their appearance. Often in face-to-face interaction we assume we know things about people just because of the way they look. Someone with an athletic build must be dumb. Someone who is heavy must be uninteresting. Perhaps most significant, someone of another race must have fixed or contrary views about family values, crime, affirmative action, and all sorts of other issues as well. Assumptions like these prevent people from discovering their shared interests and concerns~~,~~. But with ~~and this is particularly true where race is concerned. T~~the anonymity of the Internet, ~~makes~~ such physical barriers to understanding are irrelevant.~~, and only people's minds meet. Because of this, the Internet could create a world free of physical bias.~~

New examples support general statement.

~~Logged on to the Internet we can become more tolerant of others. We can become a community.~~

A world free of physical bias is a long way off, but the more we communicate with just our minds the more likely it is that our minds will find common ground. Logged on, we can become more accepted and accepting, more tolerated and tolerant. We can become a community.

New conclusion qualifies and spells out previously rushed ideas.

Work Cited

Kadi, M. "Welcome to Cyberbia." Utne Reader Mar.-Apr. 1995: 57-59.

New work-cited entry. (See p. 633 on MLA style.)

EXERCISE 3.4 Analyzing a revised draft

Compare Ling's revised draft with her first draft on pages 50–51. Can you see the reasons for most of her changes? Where would you suggest further revisions, and why? (You can do this exercise online at *ablongman.com/littlebrown*.)

EXERCISE 3.5 Considering your past work: Revising

In the past, have you usually revised your drafts extensively? Do you think your writing would benefit from more revision of the sort described in this chapter? Why or why not? Many students who don't revise much explain that they lack the time. Is time a problem for you? Can you think of ways to resolve the problem?

EXERCISE 3.6 Revising your own draft

Revise your own first draft from Exercise 3.3 (p. 51). Use the checklist for revision on page 54 as a guide. Concentrate on purpose, content, and organization, leaving smaller problems for the next draft.

3d Editing the revised draft

Editing for style, clarity, and correctness may come second to more fundamental revision, but it is still very important. A carefully developed essay will fall flat with readers if you overlook awkwardness and errors.

1 Discovering what needs editing

Try these approaches to spot possible flaws in your work:

Ways to find what needs editing

- **Take a break,** even fifteen or twenty minutes, to clear your head.
- **Read the draft *slowly,* and read what you *actually see.*** Otherwise, you're likely to read what you intended to write but didn't.
- **Read as if you are encountering the draft for the first time.** Put yourself in the reader's place.
- **Have a classmate, friend, or relative read your work.** Make sure you understand and consider the reader's suggestions, even if eventually you decide not to take them.
- **Read the draft aloud or, even better, record it.** Listen for awkward rhythms, repetitive sentence patterns, and missing or clumsy transitions.
- **Learn from your own experience.** Keep a record of the problems that others have pointed out in your writing. (See p. 71 for a suggested format.) When editing, check your work against this record.

In your editing, work first for clarity and a smooth movement among sentences and then for correctness. Use the questions in the following checklist to guide your editing, referring to the page numbers in parentheses as needed.

Checklist for editing

Clarity

How well do words and sentences convey their intended meanings? Which words and sentences are confusing? Check especially for these:

Exact language (pp. 520–30)
Parallelism (pp. 407–13)
Clear modifiers (pp. 366–74)
Clear reference of pronouns (pp. 352–60)
Complete sentences (pp. 336–42)
Sentences separated correctly (pp. 344–50)

Effectiveness

How well do words and sentences engage and focus readers? Where does the writing seem wordy, choppy, or dull? Check especially for these:

Emphasis of main ideas (pp. 386–95)
Smooth and informative transitions (pp. 87–90, 110)
Variety in sentence length and structure (pp. 414–21)
Appropriate language (pp. 512–19)
Concise sentences (pp. 531–37)

Correctness

How little or how much do surface errors interfere with clarity and effectiveness? Check especially for these:

Spelling (pp. 544–56)
Pronoun forms, especially subjective (*he, she, they, who*) vs. objective (*him, her, them, whom*) (pp. 269–75)
Verb forms, especially *-s* and *-ed* endings, correct forms of irregular verbs, and appropriate helping verbs (pp. 277–94)
Verb tenses, especially consistency (pp. 294–300, 361–62)
Agreement between subjects and verbs, especially when words come between them or the subject is *each, everyone,* or a similar word (pp. 307–14)
Agreement between pronouns and antecedents, especially when the antecedent contains *or* or the antecedent is *each, everyone, person,* or a similar word (pp. 315–19)
Sentence fragments (pp. 336–42)
Commas, especially with comma splices (pp. 344–49), with *and* or *but* (434), with introductory elements (435–36), with nonessential elements (437–40), and with series (443–45)
Apostrophes in possessives but not plural nouns (*Dave's/witches*) and in contractions but not possessive personal pronouns (*it's/its*) (pp. 463–68)

You can download this checklist from *ablongman.com/littlebrown.* Save the list in a file of its own, duplicate the file for each writing project, and insert appropriate answers between the questions along with notes on specific changes to make.

The second paragraph of Sara Ling's edited draft appears below. One change Ling made throughout the essay shows up here: she resolved an inconsistency in references to *you, people,* and *we,* settling on a consistent *we*. In addition, Ling corrected several sentence fragments in the middle of the paragraph.

Internet communication can be anonymous on at least two levels. The people we~~you~~ communicate with do not know our~~your~~ age~~.~~, ~~W~~whether we're~~you're~~ fat or thin or neat or sloppy~~.~~, ~~W~~what kind of clothes we~~you~~ wear~~.~~ (~~Maybe you're not~~ if we're wearing clothes at all)~~.~~, ~~O~~or anything else about physical appearance. If we~~you~~ use ~~an~~ invented screen names instead of our~~your~~ real names, readers don't even know whatever our~~your~~ names may reveal or suggest ~~says~~ about us~~you~~, such as gender or ethnic background.

2 Editing on a word processor

When you work on a word processor, consider these additional approaches to editing:

- **Don't rely on your word processor's spelling or grammar and style checker to find what needs editing.** See the discussion of these checkers below.
- **If possible, work on a double-spaced paper copy.** Most people find it much harder to spot errors on a computer screen than on paper.
- **Use the Find command to locate and correct your common problems**—certain misspellings, overuse of *there is,* wordy phrases such as *the fact that,* and so on.
- **Resist overediting.** The ease of editing on a computer can lead to rewriting sentences over and over, stealing the life from your prose. If your grammar and style checker contributes to the temptation, consider turning it off.
- **Take special care with additions and omissions.** Make sure you haven't omitted needed words or left in unneeded words.

3 Working with spelling and grammar/style checkers

The spelling checker and grammar and style checker that may come with your word processor can be helpful *if* you work within their limitations. The programs miss many problems and may even flag items that are actually correct. Further, they know nothing of your purpose and your audience, so they cannot make important decisions about your writing. Always use these tools critically:

- **Read your work yourself to ensure that it's clear and error-free.**
- **Consider a checker's suggestions carefully, weighing each one against your intentions.** If you aren't sure whether to accept a checker's suggestion, consult a dictionary, writing handbook, or other source. Your version may be fine.

■ Using a spelling checker

Your word processor's spelling checker can be a great ally: it will flag words that are spelled incorrectly and usually suggest alternative spellings that resemble what you've typed. However, this ally also has the potential to undermine you because of its limitations:

- **The checker may flag a word that you've spelled correctly,** just because the word does not appear in its dictionary.
- **The checker may suggest incorrect alternatives.** In providing a list of alternative spellings for your word, the checker may highlight the one it considers most likely to be correct. You need to verify that this alternative is actually what you intend before selecting it. Consult an online or printed dictionary when you aren't sure of the checker's recommendations.
- **Most important, a spelling checker will not flag words that appear in its dictionary but you have misused.** The jingle in the following screen shot has circulated widely as a warning about spelling checkers (we found it in the *Bulletin of the Missouri Council of Teachers of Mathematics*).

Spelling checker

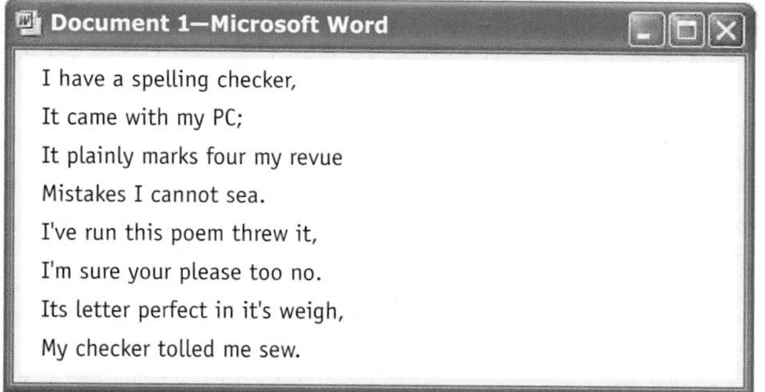

A spelling checker failed to catch any of the thirteen errors in this jingle. Can you spot them?

Using a grammar and style checker

Word processors' grammar and style checkers can flag incorrect grammar or punctuation and wordy or awkward sentences. However, these programs can call your attention only to passages that *may* be faulty. They miss many errors because they are not yet capable of analyzing language in all its complexity (for instance, they can't accurately distinguish a word's part of speech when there are different possibilities, as *light* can be a noun, a verb, or an adjective). And they often question passages that don't need editing, such as an appropriate passive verb or a deliberate and emphatic use of repetition. The screen shot on the next page illustrates the limitations.

You can customize a grammar and style checker to suit your needs and habits as a writer. (Select Options under the Tools menu.) Most checkers allow you to specify whether to check grammar only or grammar and style. Some style checkers can be set to the level of writing you intend, such as formal, standard, and informal. (For

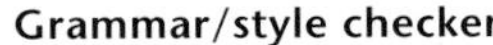

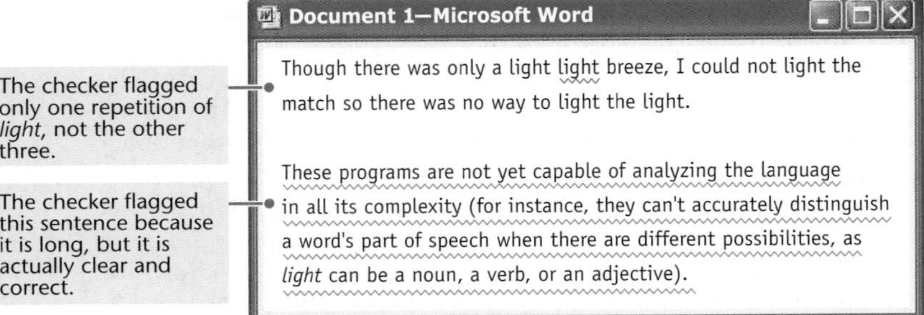

academic writing choose formal.) You can also instruct the checker to flag specific grammar and style problems that tend to occur in your writing, such as mismatched subjects and verbs, apostrophes in plural nouns, overused passive voice, or a confusion between *its* and *it's*.

EXERCISE 3.7 Considering your past work: Editing

How do you find what needs editing in your drafts? What kinds of changes do you make most often? Have you tried focusing on particular kinds of changes, such as correcting mistakes you made in previous writing? If your readers often comment on editing concerns in your work, what can you do to reduce such comments?

EXERCISE 3.8 Editing your own draft

Use the checklist for editing and your own sense of your essay's needs to edit the revised draft of your essay-in-progress.

3e Preparing and proofreading the final draft

After editing your essay, retype or print it once more for submission to your teacher. You may be required to use one of the formats covered in this book: MLA (pp. 664–66) or APA (pp. 755–58). If no format is specified, consult the document-design guidelines in Chapter 5. If you've composed on a word processor, use the Print Preview function under the File menu to check for formatting problems that may not otherwise show up on your screen.

Be sure to proofread the final essay several times to spot and correct errors. To increase the accuracy of your proofreading, you may need to experiment with ways to keep yourself from relaxing into the rhythm and the content of your prose. The box below gives a few tricks, including some used by professional proofreaders.

Techniques for proofreading

- **Read printed copy,** even if you will eventually submit the paper electronically. Most people proofread more accurately when reading type on paper than when reading it on a computer screen. (At the same time, don't view the printed copy as necessarily error-free just because it's clean. Clean-looking copy may still harbor errors.)
- **Read the paper aloud.** Slowly and distinctly pronounce exactly what you see.
- **Place a ruler under each line as you read it.**
- **Read "against copy."** Compare your final draft one sentence at a time against the edited draft you copied it from.
- **Ignore content.** To keep the content of your writing from distracting you while you proofread, read the essay backward, end to beginning, examining each sentence as a separate unit. Or, taking advantage of a computer, isolate each paragraph from its context by printing it on a separate page. (Of course, reassemble the paragraphs before submitting the paper.)

3f Examining a final draft

Sara Ling's final essay begins below, typed in MLA format except for page breaks. Comments in the margins point out key features of the essay's content.

Sara Ling

Mr. Gonzales

Language and Composition, period 3

4 November 2005

The Internet:

Fragmentation or Community?

Descriptive title

We hear all sorts of predictions about how the Internet will enrich our individual lives and promote communication, tolerance, and thus community in our society. But are these promises realistic? In her 1995 essay "Welcome to Cyberbia," M. Kadi argues that they are not. Instead, she predicts that the Internet will lead to more fragmentation, not community, because users merely seek out others with the same biases, concerns, and needs as their own. The point is an interesting one, but Kadi fails to foresee that the unique anonymity of Internet communication could actually build diversity into community by lowering the barriers of physical appearance.

Introduction

Question to be addressed

Summary of Kadi's essay

Thesis statement

consume in there food In addition, these children will be at greater risk for kidney damage, problems with immunity, and other serious imparments. The government bases it's pesticide-safety standards on adults, but childen consume many more the fruits and fruit products likely too contain pestcides.

EXERCISE 3.10 Preparing your final draft

Prepare the final draft of the essay you have been working on throughout Chapters 1–3. Proofread carefully and correct all errors before submitting your essay for review.

3g Giving and receiving comments

1 Working collaboratively

Almost all the writing you do in high school will generate responses from a teacher. In courses that stress writing, you may submit early drafts as well as your final paper, and your readers may include your classmates as well as your teacher. Like Sara Ling's, such courses may feature **collaborative learning,** in which students work together on writing, from completing exercises to commenting on each other's work to producing whole papers. (At more and more schools this group work occurs over a computer network. See pp. 783–86.)

Whether you participate as a writer or as a writing "coach," collaboration can give you experience in reading written work and in reaching readers through writing. You may at first be anxious about criticizing others' work or sharing your own rough drafts, but you'll soon grow to appreciate the interaction and the confidence it gives you in your own reading and writing.

CULTURE LANGUAGE In some cultures writers do not expect criticism from readers, or readers do not expect to think critically about what they read. If critical responses are uncommon in your native culture, collaboration may at first be uncomfortable for you. As a writer, consider that readers are responding to your draft or even your final paper more as an exploration of ideas than as the last word on your subject; then you may be more receptive to readers' suggestions. As a reader, allow yourself to approach a text skeptically, and know that your tactful questions and suggestions will usually be considered appropriate.

2 Responding to the writing of others

If you are the reader of someone else's writing, keep the following principles in mind:

Commenting on others' writing

- **Be sure you know what the writer is saying.** If necessary, summarize the paper to understand its content. (See pp. 141–43.)
- **Address only your most significant concerns with the work.** Use the revision checklist on p. 54 as a guide to what is significant. Unless you have other instructions, ignore mistakes in grammar, punctuation, spelling, and the like. (The temptation to focus on such errors may be especially strong if the writer is less experienced than you are with standard American English.) Emphasizing mistakes will contribute little to the writer's revision.
- **Remember that you are the reader, not the writer.** Don't edit sentences, add details, or otherwise assume responsibility for the paper.
- **Phrase your comments carefully.** Avoid misunderstandings by making sure comments are both clear and respectful. If you are responding on paper or online, not face to face with the writer, remember that the writer has nothing but your written words to go on. He or she can't ask you for immediate clarification and can't infer your attitudes from gestures, facial expressions, and tone of voice.
- **Be specific.** If something confuses you, say *why.* If you disagree with a conclusion, say *why.*
- **Be supportive as well as honest.** Tell the writer what you like about the paper. Word comments positively: instead of *This paragraph doesn't interest me,* say *You have an interesting detail here that I almost missed.* Comment in a way that emphasizes the effect of the work on you, the reader: *This paragraph confuses me because. . . .* And avoid measuring the work against a set of external standards: *This essay is poorly organized. Your thesis statement is inadequate.*
- **While reading, make your comments in writing.** Even if you will be delivering your comments in person later on, the written record will help you recall what you thought.
- **Link comments to specific parts of a paper.** Especially if you are reading the paper on a computer, be clear about what part of the paper each comment relates to. You can embed your comments directly into the paper, distinguishing them with highlighting or color. Or you can use the Comment function of a word processor (see below).

If you are reviewing others' drafts on a word processor, its Comment function will allow you to add comments without inserting words into the document's text. Usually found on the Insert menu, the function creates something like a sticky Post-it note that pops up when readers move their cursors across words you have highlighted. The following screen shot shows one such comment.

An assignment to assemble a writing portfolio will probably also provide guidelines for what to include, how the portfolio will be evaluated, and how (or whether) it will be weighted for a grade. Be sure you understand the purpose of the portfolio and who will read it. For instance, if your writing teacher will be the only reader and her guidelines urge you to show evidence of progress, you might include a paper that took big risks but never entirely succeeded. In contrast, if you don't know all the teachers who will read your work and the guidelines urge you to demonstrate your competence as a writer, you might include only papers that did succeed.

Unless the guidelines specify otherwise, provide error-free copies of your final drafts, label all your samples with your name, and assemble them all in a folder. Add a cover letter or memo that lists the samples, explains why you've included each one, and evaluates your progress as a writer. The self-evaluation involved should be a learning experience for you and will help your teacher assess your development as a writer.

CHAPTER 4

Writing and Revising Paragraphs

A **paragraph** is a group of related sentences set off by a beginning indention or, sometimes, by extra space. For you and your readers, paragraphs provide breathers from long stretches of text and indicate key changes in the development of your thesis. They help to organize and clarify ideas.

In the body of an essay, you may use paragraphs for any of these purposes:

- **To introduce and give evidence for a main point supporting your essay's central idea (its thesis).** See pages 29–34 for a discussion of an essay's thesis.

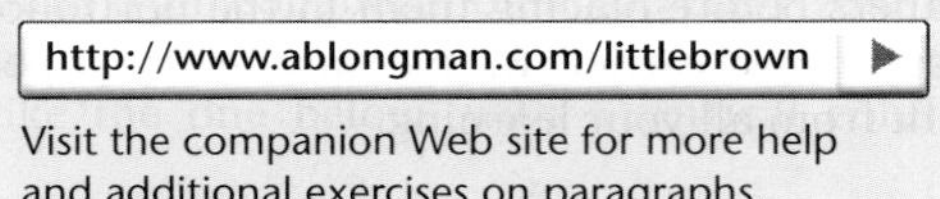

- **Within a group of paragraphs centering on one main point, to develop a key example or other important evidence.**
- **To shift approach**—for instance, from pros to cons, from problem to solution, from questions to answers.
- **To mark movement in a sequence,** such as from one reason or step to another.

In addition, you will use paragraphs for special purposes:

- **To introduce or to conclude an essay.** See pages 104 and 108.
- **To emphasize an important point or to mark a significant transition between points.** See page 110.
- **In dialog, to indicate that a new person has begun speaking.** See pages 110–11.

The following paragraph illustrates simply how an effective body paragraph works to help both writer and reader. The thesis of the essay in which this paragraph appears is that a Texas chili championship gives undue attention to an unpleasant food.

> Some people really like chili, apparently, but nobody can agree how the stuff should be made. C. V. Wood, twice winner at Terlingua, uses flank steak, pork chops, chicken, and green chilis. My friend Hughes Rudd of CBS News, who imported five hundred pounds of chili powder into Russia as a condition of accepting employment as Moscow correspondent, favors coarse-ground beef. Isadore Bleckman, the cameraman I must live with on the road, insists upon one-inch cubes of stew beef and puts garlic in his chili, an Illinois affectation. An Indian of my acquaintance, Mr. Fulton Batisse, who eats chili for breakfast when he can, uses buffalo meat and plays an Indian drum while it's cooking. I ask you.
>
> —Charles Kuralt, *Dateline America*

General statement relating to thesis: announces topic of paragraph

Four specific examples, all providing evidence for general statement

While you are drafting, conscious attention to the requirements of the paragraph may sometimes help pull ideas out of you or help you forge relationships. But don't expect effective paragraphs like Kuralt's to flow from your fingertips while you are grappling with what you want to say. Instead, use the checklist on the next page to guide your revision of paragraphs so that they work to your and your readers' advantage.

Note On the Web the paragraphing conventions described here do not always apply. Web readers sometimes skim text instead of reading word for word, and they are accustomed to embedded links that may take them from the paragraph to another page. Writing

1. Today many black Americans enjoy a measure of economic se- 1
curity beyond any we have known in the history of black America. But 2
if they remain in a nasty blue funk, it's because their very existence
seems an affront to the swelling ranks of the poor. Nor have black intel- 3
lectuals ever quite made peace with the concept of the black bour-
geoisie, a group that is typically seen as devoid of cultural authenticity,
doomed to mimicry and pallid assimilation. I once gave a talk before 4
an audience of black academics and educators, in the course of which I
referred to black middle-class culture. Afterward, one of the academics 5
in the audience, deeply affronted, had a question for me. "Professor 6
Gates," he asked rhetorically, his voice dripping with sarcasm, "what *is*
black middle-class culture?" I suggested that if he really wanted to 7
know, he need only look around the room. But perhaps I should just 8
have handed him a mirror: for just as nothing is more American than
anti-Americanism, nothing is more characteristic of the black bourgeoi-
sie than the sense of shame and denial that the identity inspires.

—Henry Louis Gates, Jr., "Two Nations . . . Both Black"

2. Though they do not know why the humpback whale sings, scien- 1
tists do know something about the song itself. They have measured 2
the length of a whale's song: from a few minutes to over half an hour.
They have recorded and studied the variety and complex arrange- 3
ments of low moans, high squeaks, and sliding squeals that make up
the song. And they have learned that each whale sings in its own 4
unique pattern. —Janet Lieber (student), "Whales' Songs"

EXERCISE 4.2 Revising a paragraph for unity

The following paragraph contains ideas or details that do not support its central idea. Identify the topic sentence in the paragraph and delete the unrelated material. (You can do this exercise online at *ablongman.com/littlebrown.*)

In the southern part of the state, some people still live much as they did a century ago. They use coal- or wood-burning stoves for heating and cooking. Their homes do not have electricity or indoor bathrooms or running water. The towns they live in don't receive adequate funding from the state and federal governments, so the schools are poor and in bad shape. Beside most homes there is a garden where fresh vegetables are gathered for canning. Small pastures nearby support livestock, including cattle, pigs, horses, and chickens. Most of the people have cars or trucks, but the vehicles are old and beat-up from traveling on unpaved roads.

EXERCISE 4.3 Considering your past work: Paragraph unity

For a continuing exercise in this chapter, choose a paper you've written in the past year. Examine the body paragraphs for unity. Do they have clear topic sentences? If not, are the paragraphs' central ideas still clear? Are the paragraphs unified around their central ideas? Should any details be deleted for unity? Should other, more relevant details be added in their stead?

EXERCISE 4.4 Writing a unified paragraph

Develop the following topic sentence into a unified paragraph by using the relevant information in the supporting statements. Delete each statement that does not relate directly to the topic, and then rewrite and combine sentences as appropriate. Place the topic sentence in the position that seems most effective to you. (You can do this exercise online at *ablongman.com/littlebrown*.)

Topic sentence

Mozart's accomplishments in music seem remarkable even today.

Supporting information

Wolfgang Amadeus Mozart was born in 1756 in Salzburg, Austria.
He began composing music at the age of five.
He lived most of his life in Salzburg and Vienna.
His first concert tour of Europe was at the age of six.
On his first tour he played harpsichord, organ, and violin.
He published numerous compositions before reaching adolescence.
He married in 1782.
Mozart and his wife were both poor managers of money.
They were plagued by debts.
Mozart composed over six hundred musical compositions.
His most notable works are his operas, symphonies, quartets, and piano concertos.
He died at the age of thirty-five.

EXERCISE 4.5 Turning topic sentences into unified paragraphs

Develop three of the following topic sentences into detailed and unified paragraphs. (You can do this exercise online at *ablongman.com/littlebrown*.)

1. Men and women are different in at least one important respect.
2. The best Web search engine is [*name*].
3. Fans of ——— music [*country, classical, rock, rap, jazz, or another kind*] come in [*number*] varieties.
4. Professional sports have [*or* have not] been helped by extending the regular season with championship play-offs.
5. Working for good grades can interfere with learning.

4b Achieving paragraph coherence

A paragraph is unified if it holds together—if all its details and examples support the central idea. A paragraph is **coherent** if readers can see *how* the paragraph holds together—how the sentences relate to each other—without having to stop and reread.

Incoherence gives readers the feeling of being yanked around, as the following example shows.

Ways to achieve paragraph coherence

- Organize effectively (p. 81).
- Repeat or restate key words and word groups (p. 85).
- Use parallel structures (p. 85).
- Use pronouns (p. 86).
- Be consistent in nouns, pronouns, and verbs (p. 86).
- Use transitional expressions (p. 87).

> The ancient Egyptians were masters of preserving dead people's bodies by making mummies of them. Mummies several thousand years old have been discovered nearly intact. The skin, hair, teeth, finger- and toenails, and facial features of the mummies were evident. One can diagnose the diseases they suffered in life, such as smallpox, arthritis, and nutritional deficiencies. The process was remarkably effective. Sometimes apparent were the fatal afflictions of the dead people: a middle-aged king died from a blow on the head, and polio killed a child king. Mummification consisted of removing the internal organs, applying natural preservatives inside and out, and then wrapping the body in layers of bandages.

Topic sentence

Sentences related to topic sentence but disconnected from each other

The paragraph as it was actually written appears below. It is much clearer because the writer arranged information differently and also built links into his sentences so that they would flow smoothly:

- After stating the central idea in a topic sentence, the writer moves to two more specific explanations and illustrates the second with four sentences of examples.
- Circled words repeat or restate key terms or concepts.
- Boxed words link sentences and clarify relationships.
- Underlined phrases are in parallel grammatical form to reflect their parallel content.

> The ancient Egyptians were masters of preserving dead people's bodies by (making mummies) of them. [Basically,] (mummification) consisted of removing the internal organs, applying natural preservatives inside and out, and then wrapping the body in layers of bandages. [And] (the process) was remarkably effective.

Topic sentence

Explanation 1: What mummification is

Indeed, mummies several thousand years old have been discovered nearly intact. Their skin, hair, teeth, finger- and toenails, and facial features are still evident. Their diseases in life, such as smallpox, arthritis, and nutritional deficiencies, are still diagnosable. Even their fatal afflictions are still apparent: a middle-aged king died from a blow on the head; a child king died from polio.

Explanation 2: Why the Egyptians were masters

Specific examples of explanation 2

—Mitchell Rosenbaum (student), "Lost Arts of the Egyptians"

Though some of the connections in this paragraph were added in revision, the writer attended to them while drafting as well. Not only superficial coherence but also an underlying clarity of relationships can be achieved by tying each sentence to the one before—generalizing from it, clarifying it, qualifying it, adding to it, illustrating it. Each sentence in a paragraph creates an expectation of some sort in the mind of the reader, a question such as "How was a mummy made?" or "How intact are the mummies?" or "What's another example?" When you recognize these expectations and try to fulfill them, readers are likely to understand relationships without struggle.

1 Organizing the paragraph

The paragraphs on mummies illustrate an essential element of coherence: information must be arranged in an order that readers can follow easily and that corresponds to their expectations. The common organizations for paragraphs correspond to those for entire essays: by space, by time, and for emphasis. (In addition, the rhetorical strategies also suggest certain arrangements. See pp. 93–102.)

Note On a computer you can experiment with different paragraph organizations and emphases. Copy a paragraph, paste the copy into your document, and then try moving sentences around. To evaluate the versions, you'll need to edit each one so that sentences flow smoothly, attending to repetition, parallelism, transitions, and the other techniques discussed in this section.

Organizing by space or time

A paragraph organized **spatially** focuses readers' attention on one point and scans a person, object, or scene from that point. The movement usually parallels the way people actually look at things, from top to bottom, from side to side, from near to far. Virginia Woolf follows the last pattern in the following paragraph:

Problem-solution organization

Even when you do find a newsgroup with apparently useful material, you have no assurance of a correspondent's authority because of e-mail's inherent anonymity. Many people don't cite their credentials. Besides, anyone can pose as an expert. The best information you can get initially is apt to be a reference to something of which you were not aware but can then investigate for yourself. Internet newsgroups can be valuable for that alone. I have been directed to software-problem solutions, owners of out-of-print books, and important people who know nothing about communicating through electronic communities. It is best to start with the assumption that you are conversing with peers, people who know things that you don't, while you probably know things that they don't. Gradually, by trading information, you develop some virtual relationships and can assess the relative validity of your sources. Meanwhile, you will probably have learned a few things along the way.

Topic sentence and clarification: statement of the problem

Solution to the problem

—Adapted from John A. Butler, *Cybersearch*

When your details vary in significance, you can arrange them in a **climactic** order, from least to most important or dramatic:

Climactic organization

Nature has put many strange tongues into the heads of her creatures. There is the frog's tongue, rooted at the front of the mouth so it can be protruded an extra distance for nabbing prey. There is the gecko lizard's tongue, so long and agile that the lizard uses it to wash its eyes. But the ultimate lingual whopper has been achieved in the anteater. The anteater's head, long as it is, is not long enough to contain the tremendous tongue which licks deep into anthills. Its tongue is not rooted in the mouth or throat: it is fastened to the breastbone.

Topic sentence

Least dramatic example

Most dramatic example

—Alan Devoe, "Nature's Utmost"

In other organizations, you can arrange details according to how you think readers are likely to understand them. In discussing the virtues of public television, for instance, you might proceed from **most familiar to least familiar,** from a well-known program your readers have probably seen to less well-known programs they may not have seen. Or in defending the right of government employees to strike, you might arrange your reasons from **simplest to most complex,** from the employees' need to be able to redress grievances to more subtle consequences for relations between employers and employees.

2 Repeating or restating key words

Repeating or restating the important words in a paragraph binds the sentences together and keeps the paragraph's topic uppermost in readers' minds. In the next example, notice how the circled words relate the sentences and stress the important ideas of the paragraph:

> Having listened to both Chinese and English, I also tend to be suspicious of any comparisons between the two languages. Typically, one language—that of the person doing the comparing—is often used as the standard, the benchmark for a logical form of expression. And so the language being compared is always in danger of being judged deficient or superfluous, simplistic or unnecessarily complex, melodious or cacophonous. English speakers point out that Chinese is extremely difficult because it relies on variations in tone barely discernible to the human ear. By the same token, Chinese speakers tell me English is extremely difficult because it is inconsistent, a language of too many broken rules, of Mickey Mice and Donald Ducks.
>
> —Amy Tan, "The Language of Discretion"

This paragraph links sentences through their structure, too, because the subject of each one picks up on key words used earlier:

Sentence 1: Having listened to both Chinese and English, I tend to be suspicious of any comparisons between the two languages.
Sentence 2: Typically, one language . . .
Sentence 3: And so the language . . .
Sentence 4: English speakers . . .
Sentence 5: Chinese speakers . . .

In many incoherent paragraphs, such as the one on mummification on page 80, each sentence subject introduces a topic new to the paragraph so that readers have trouble following the thread. (See pp. 388–89 for more on linking sentences through their subjects.)

3 Using parallel structures

Another way to achieve coherence is through **parallelism**—the use of similar grammatical structures for similar elements of meaning

cold. It spreads. To avoid colds, people should wash their hands often and keep their hands away from their faces.

Medical science has thus succeeded in identifying the hundreds of viruses that can cause the common cold. It has also discovered the most effective means of prevention. One person transmits the cold viruses to another most often by hand. For instance, an infected person covers his mouth to cough. Then he picks up the telephone. Half an hour later, his daughter picks up the same telephone. Immediately afterward, she rubs her eyes. Within a few days, she, too, has a cold. And thus it spreads. To avoid colds, therefore, people should wash their hands often and keep their hands away from their faces.

—Kathleen LaFrank (student), "Colds: Myth and Science"

Transitional expressions (boxed) remove choppiness and spell out relationships

There are scores of transitional expressions on which to draw. The box below shows many common ones, arranged according to the relationships they convey.

Transitional expressions

To add or show sequence

again, also, and, and then, besides, equally important, finally, first, further, furthermore, in addition, in the first place, last, moreover, next, second, still, too

To compare

also, in the same way, likewise, similarly

To contrast

although, and yet, but, but at the same time, despite, even so, even though, for all that, however, in contrast, in spite of, nevertheless, notwithstanding, on the contrary, on the other hand, regardless, still, though, yet

To give examples or intensify

after all, an illustration of, even, for example, for instance, indeed, in fact, it is true, of course, specifically, that is, to illustrate, truly

To indicate place
above, adjacent to, below, elsewhere, farther on, here, near, nearby, on the other side, opposite to, there, to the east, to the left

To indicate time
after a while, afterward, as long as, as soon as, at last, at length, at that time, before, earlier, formerly, immediately, in the meantime, in the past, lately, later, meanwhile, now, presently, shortly, simultaneously, since, so far, soon, subsequently, then, thereafter, until, when

To repeat, summarize, or conclude
all in all, altogether, as has been said, in brief, in conclusion, in other words, in particular, in short, in simpler terms, in summary, on the whole, that is, therefore, to put it differently, to summarize

To show cause or effect
accordingly, as a result, because, consequently, for this purpose, hence, otherwise, since, then, therefore, thereupon, thus, to this end, with this object

Note Draw carefully on the preceding list of transitional expressions because the ones in each group are not interchangeable. For instance, *besides, finally,* and *second* may all be used to add information, but each has its own distinct meaning.

To see where transitional expressions might be needed in your paragraphs, examine the movement from each sentence to the next. (On a computer or on paper, you can highlight the transitional expressions already present and then review the sentences that lack them.) Abrupt changes are most likely to need a transition: a shift from cause to effect, a contradiction, a contrast. You can smooth and clarify transitions *between* paragraphs, too. See pages 110 and 110–12.

CULTURE LANGUAGE If transitional expressions are not common in your native language, you may be tempted to compensate when writing in English by adding them to the beginnings of most sentences. But such explicit transitions aren't needed everywhere, and in fact too many can be intrusive and awkward. When inserting transitional expressions, consider the reader's need for a signal: often the connection from sentence to sentence is already clear from the context, or it can be made clear by relating the content of sentences more closely (see pp. 85–86). When you do need transitional expressions, try varying their positions in your sentences, as shown in the sample paragraph on the facing page.

Punctuating transitional expressions

A transitional expression is usually set off by a comma or commas from the rest of the sentence:

Immediately afterward, she rubs her eyes. Within a few days, she, too, has a cold.

See page 440 for more on this convention and its exceptions.

7 Combining devices to achieve coherence

The devices for achieving coherence rarely appear in isolation in effective paragraphs. As any example in this chapter shows, writers usually combine sensible organization, parallelism, repetition, pronouns, consistency, and transitional expressions to help readers follow the development of ideas.

EXERCISE 4.6 Analyzing paragraphs for coherence

Study the paragraphs by Janet Lieber (p. 78), Hillary Begas (p. 93), and Freeman Dyson (p. 95) for the authors' use of various devices to achieve coherence. Look especially for organization, parallel structures and ideas, repetition and restatement, pronouns, and transitional expressions.

EXERCISE 4.7 Arranging sentences coherently

After the topic sentence (sentence 1), the sentences in the student paragraph below have been deliberately scrambled to make the paragraph incoherent. Using the topic sentence and other clues as guides, rearrange the sentences in the paragraph to form a well-organized, coherent unit. (You can do this exercise online at *ablongman.com/littlebrown*.)

We hear complaints about the Postal Service all the time, but we 1
should not forget what it does *right*. The total volume of mail de- 2
livered by the Postal Service each year makes up almost half
the total delivered in all the world. Its 70,000 employees handle 3
140,000,000,000 pieces of mail each year. And when was the last 4
time they failed to deliver yours? In fact, on any given day the Postal 5
Service delivers almost as much mail as the rest of the world com-
bined. That huge number means over 2,000,000 pieces per employee 6
and over 560 pieces per man, woman, and child in the country.

EXERCISE 4.8 Eliminating inconsistencies

The following paragraph is incoherent because of inconsistencies in person, number, or tense. Identify the inconsistencies and revise the paragraph to give it coherence. (You can do this exercise online at *ablongman.com/littlebrown*.) For further exercises in eliminating inconsistencies, see pages 361, 362–63, and 365.

The Hopi tihu, or kachina likeness, is often called a "doll," but its owner, usually a girl or woman, does not regard them as a plaything. Instead, you treated them as a valued possession and hung them out of the way on a wall. For its owner the tihu represents a connection with the kachina's spirit. They are considered part of the kachina, carrying a portion of the kachina's power.

EXERCISE 4.9 Using transitional expressions

Transitional expressions have been removed from the following paragraph at the numbered blanks. Fill in each blank with an appropriate transitional expression (1) to contrast, (2) to intensify, and (3) to show effect. Consult the list on pages 88–89 if necessary. (You can do this exercise online at *ablongman.com/littlebrown*.)

All over the country, people are swimming, jogging, weightlifting, dancing, walking, playing tennis—doing anything to keep fit. ___(1)___ this school has consistently refused to construct and equip a fitness center. The school has ___(2)___ refused to open existing athletic facilities to all students, not just those playing organized sports. ___(3)___ students have no place to exercise except in their rooms and on dangerous public roads.

EXERCISE 4.10 Considering your past work: Paragraph coherence

Continuing from Exercise 4.3 (p. 78), examine the body paragraphs of your essay to see how coherent they are and how their coherence could be improved. Do the paragraphs have a clear organization? Do you use repetition and restatement, parallelism, pronouns, and transitional expressions to signal relationships? Are the paragraphs consistent in person, number, and tense? Revise two or three paragraphs in ways you think will improve their coherence.

EXERCISE 4.11 Writing a coherent paragraph

Write a coherent paragraph from the following information, combining and rewriting sentences as necessary. First, begin the paragraph with the topic sentence given and arrange the supporting sentences in a climactic order. Then combine and rewrite the supporting sentences, helping the reader see connections by introducing repetition and restatement, parallelism, pronouns, consistency, and transitional expressions. (You can do this exercise online at *ablongman.com/littlebrown*.)

Topic sentence

Hypnosis is far superior to drugs for relieving tension.

Supporting information

Hypnosis has none of the dangerous side effects of the drugs that relieve tension.
Tension-relieving drugs can cause weight loss or gain, illness, or even death.
Hypnosis is nonaddicting.
Most of the drugs that relieve tension do foster addiction.
Tension-relieving drugs are expensive.
Hypnosis is inexpensive even for people who have not mastered self-hypnosis.

EXERCISE 4.12 Turning topic sentences into coherent paragraphs

Develop three of the following topic sentences into coherent paragraphs. Organize your information by space, by time, or for emphasis, as seems most appropriate. Use repetition and restatement, parallelism, pronouns, consistency, and transitional expressions to link sentences. (You can do this exercise online at *ablongman.com/littlebrown*.)

1. The most interesting character in the book [or movie] was ________.
2. Of all my classes, ________ is the one that I think will serve me best throughout life.
3. Although we in the United States face many problems, the one we should concentrate on solving first is ________.
4. The most dramatic building in town is the ________.
5. Children should not have to worry about the future.

4c Developing the paragraph

In an essay that's understandable and interesting to readers, you will provide plenty of solid information to support your general statements. You work that information into the essay through the paragraph, as you build up each point relating to the thesis.

A paragraph may be unified and coherent but still be inadequate if you skimp on details. Take this example:

> Untruths can serve as a kind of social oil when they smooth connections between people. In preventing confrontation and injured feelings, they allow everyone to go on as before.

General statements needing examples to be clear and convincing

This paragraph lacks **development,** completeness. It does not provide enough information for us to evaluate or even care about the writer's assertions.

1 Using specific information

If they are sound, the general statements you make in any writing will be based on what you have experienced, observed, read, and thought. Readers will assume as much and will expect you to provide the evidence for your statements—sensory details, facts, statistics, examples, quotations, reasons. Whatever helps you form your views you need, in turn, to share with readers.

Here is the actual version of the preceding sample paragraph. With examples, the paragraph is more interesting and convincing.

> Untruths can serve as a kind of social oil when they smooth connections between people. Assuring a worried friend that his haircut is

> flattering, claiming an appointment to avoid an aunt's dinner invitation, pretending interest in an acquaintance's children—these lies may protect the liar, but they also protect the person lied to. In preventing confrontation and injured feelings, the lies allow everyone to go on as before.
> —Joan Lar (student), "The Truth of Lies"

Examples specifying kinds of lies and consequences

If your readers often comment that your writing needs more specifics, you should focus on that improvement in your revisions. Try listing the general statements of each paragraph on lines by themselves with space underneath. Then use one of the discovery techniques discussed on pages 18–28 (freewriting, brainstorming, and so on) to find the details to support each sentence. Write these into your draft. If you write on a computer, you can do this revision directly on your draft. First create a duplicate of your draft, and then, working on the copy, separate the sentences and explore their support. Rewrite the supporting details into sentences, reassemble the paragraph, and edit it for coherence.

2 Using rhetorical strategies

If you have difficulty developing an idea or shaping your information, then try asking yourself questions derived from rhetorical strategies, also called patterns of development. (The same strategies can help with essay development, too. See pp. 26–27.)

You can download the following questions from *ablongman .com/littlebrown*. When you're having difficulty with a paragraph, you can duplicate the list and explore answers. You may be able to import what you write directly into your draft.

■ How did it happen? (Narration)

Narration retells a significant sequence of events, usually in the order of their occurrence (that is, chronologically):

> Jill's story is typical for "recruits" to religious cults. She was very lonely in college and appreciated the attention of the nice young men and women who lived in a house near campus. They persuaded her to share their meals and then to move in with them. Between intense bombardments of "love," they deprived her of sleep and sometimes threatened to throw her out. Jill became increasingly confused and dependent, losing touch with any reality besides the one in the group. She dropped out of school and refused to see or communicate with her family. Before long she, too, was preying on lonely college students.
> —Hillary Begas (student), "The Love Bombers"

Important events in chronological order

As this paragraph illustrates, a narrator is concerned not just with the sequence of events but also with their consequence, their importance to the whole. Thus a narrative rarely corresponds to real time; instead, it collapses transitional or background events and focuses on events of particular interest. In addition, writers sometimes rearrange events, as when they simulate the workings of memory by flashing back to an earlier time.

■ How does it look, sound, feel, smell, taste? (Description)

Description details the sensory qualities of a person, place, thing, or feeling. You use concrete and specific words to convey a dominant mood, to illustrate an idea, or to achieve some other purpose. Some description is **subjective:** the writer filters the subject through his or her biases and emotions. In the subjective description by Virginia Woolf on page 82, the *glare* of the walls, the *impenetrable darkness,* the *bulge of a great bowl,* and the *formidable corners and lines* all indicate the author's feelings about what she describes.

In contrast to subjective description, journalists, scientists, and other academic writers often favor description that is **objective,** conveying the subject without bias or emotion:

> Vanessa works in a trendy salon but also cuts hair in her apartment—for a few friends and friends of friends. Her client Lynn sits in a small barber's chair by the window, the place where you'd imagine a breakfast table, a mirror leaning against the wall in front of her. On the floor by the mirror there are a small bowl for Vanessa's dog and a vase with three yellow flowers. Vanessa stands behind Lynn, asking her questions about her hair, chitchatting a little. She keeps her eyes on Lynn's hair as she moves her fingers through it, lifting up, then pulling down one section, then another, then gesturing with her hands around the hair, indicating shape and movement. "How did you like the last haircut?" she asks. How did it handle? Was it easy to manage? What's bugging you now? Does it feel heavy up front? Lynn answers these questions, describing what she wants, relying on adjectives that have more to do with feeling than shape. She wants the cut "freshened," wants it "sassy."
>
> —Mike Rose, *The Mind at Work*

Objective description: specific record of sensory data without interpretation

■ What are examples of it or reasons for it? (Illustration or support)

Some ideas can be developed simply by **illustration or support**—supplying detailed examples or reasons. The writer of the paragraph on lying (pp. 92–93) developed her idea with several specific examples of her general statements. You can also supply a single extended example:

> The language problem that I was attacking loomed larger and larger as I began to learn more. When I would describe in English certain concepts and objects enmeshed in Korean emotion and imagination, I became slowly aware of nuances, of differences between two languages even in simple expression. The remark "Kim entered the house" seems to be simple enough, yet, unless a reader has a clear visual image of a Korean house, his understanding of the sentence is not complete. When a Korean says he is "in the house," he may be in his courtyard, or on his porch, or in his small room! If I wanted to give a specific picture of entering the house in the Western sense, I had to say "room" instead of house—sometimes. I say "sometimes" because many Koreans entertain their guests on their porches and still are considered to be hospitable, and in the Korean sense, going into the "room" may be a more intimate act than it would be in the English sense. Such problems!
>
> —Kim Yong Ik, "A Book-Writing Venture"

Topic sentence (assertion to be illustrated)

Single detailed example

Sometimes you can develop a paragraph by providing your reasons for stating a general idea:

> There are three reasons, quite apart from scientific considerations, that mankind needs to travel in space. The first reason is the need for garbage disposal: we need to transfer industrial processes into space, so that the earth may remain a green and pleasant place for our grandchildren to live in. The second reason is the need to escape material impoverishment: the resources of this planet are finite, and we shall not forgo forever the abundant solar energy and minerals and living space that are spread out all around us. The third reason is our spiritual need for an open frontier: the ultimate purpose of space travel is to bring to humanity not only scientific discoveries and an occasional spectacular show on television but a real expansion of our spirit.
>
> —Freeman Dyson, "Disturbing the Universe"

Topic sentence

Three reasons arranged in order of increasing drama and importance

■ What is it? What does it encompass, and what does it exclude? (Definition)

A **definition** says what something is and is not, specifying the characteristics that distinguish the subject from the other members of its class. You can easily define concrete, noncontroversial terms in a single sentence: *A knife is a cutting instrument* (its class) *with a sharp blade set in a handle* (the characteristics that set it off from, say, scissors or a razor blade). But defining a complicated or controversial topic often requires extended explanation, and you may need to devote a whole paragraph or even an essay to it. Such a definition may provide examples to identify the subject's characteristics. It may also involve other methods of development discussed here, such as classification or comparison and contrast.

The following definition of the word *quality* comes from an essay asserting that "quality in product and effort has become a vanishing element of current civilization":

> In the hope of possibly reducing the hail of censure which is certain to greet this essay (I am thinking of going to Alaska or possibly Patagonia in the week it is published), let me say that quality, as I understand it, means investment of the best skill and effort possible to produce the finest and most admirable result possible. Its presence or absence in some degree characterizes every man-made object, service, skilled or unskilled labor—laying bricks, painting a picture, ironing shirts, practicing medicine, shoemaking, scholarship, writing a book. You do it well or you do it half-well. Materials are sound and durable or they are sleazy; method is painstaking or whatever is easiest. Quality is achieving or reaching for the highest standard as against being satisfied with the sloppy or fraudulent. It is honesty of purpose as against catering to cheap or sensational sentiment. It does not allow compromise with the second-rate.
>
> —Barbara Tuchman, "The Decline of Quality"

General definition

Activities in which quality may figure

Contrast between quality and nonquality

What are its parts or characteristics? (Division or analysis)

Division and **analysis** both involve separating something into its elements, the better to understand it. Here is a simple example:

> A typical daily newspaper compresses considerable information into the top of the first page, above the headlines. The most prominent feature of this space, the newspaper's name, is called the *logo* or *nameplate*. Under the logo and set off by rules is a line of small type called the *folio line*, which contains the date of the issue, the volume and issue numbers, copyright information, and the price. To the right of the logo is a block of small type called a *weather*

The subject being divided

Elements of the subject, arranged spatially

ear, a summary of the day's forecast. And above the logo is a *skyline,* a kind of advertisement in which the paper's editors highlight a special feature of the issue.

—Kansha Stone (student), "Anatomy of a Paper"

Generally, analysis goes beyond simply identifying elements. Often used as a synonym for *critical thinking,* analysis also involves interpreting the elements' meaning, significance, and relationships. You identify and interpret elements according to your particular interest in the subject. (See pp. 158–64 for more on critical thinking and analysis.)

The following paragraph comes from an essay about soap operas. The analytical focus of the whole essay is the way soap operas provide viewers with a sense of community missing from their own lives. The paragraph itself has a narrower focus related to the broader one.

The surface realism of the soap opera conjures up an illusion of "liveness." The domestic settings and easygoing rhythms encourage the viewer to believe that the drama, however ridiculous, is simply an extension of daily life. The conversation is so slow that some have called it "radio with pictures." (Advertisers have always assumed that busy housewives would listen, rather than watch.) Conversation is casual and colloquial, as though one were eavesdropping on neighbors. There is plenty of time to "read" the character's face; close-ups establish intimacy. The sets are comfortably familiar: well-lit interiors of living rooms, restaurants, offices, and hospitals. Daytime soaps have little of the glamour of their prime-time relations. The viewer easily imagines that the conversation is taking place in real time.

—Ruth Rosen, "Search for Yesterday"

Topic and focus: how "liveness" seems an extension of daily life

Elements:
Slow conversation
Casual conversation
Intimate close-ups
Familiar sets
Absence of glamour
Appearance of real time

What groups or categories can it be sorted into? (Classification)

Classification involves sorting many things into groups based on their similarities. Using the pattern, we scan a large group composed of many members that share at least one characteristic—office workers, say—and we assign the members to smaller groups on the basis of some principle—salary, perhaps, or dependence on computers. Here is an example:

In my experience, the parents who hire afternoon sitters for their school-age children tend to fall into one of three groups. The first

Topic sentence

group includes parents who work and want someone to be at home with the children after school. These parents are looking for an extension of themselves, someone who will give the care they would give if they were at home. The second group includes parents who may be home themselves but are too disorganized or too frazzled by their children's demands to handle child care alone. They are looking for an organizer and helpmate. The third and final group includes parents who do not want to be bothered by their children, whether they are home or not. Unlike the parents in the first two groups, who care for their children whenever and however they can, these parents are looking for a substitute for themselves.

—Nancy Whittle (student), "Modern Parenting"

Three groups:
Alike in one way (all hire sitters)
No overlap in groups (each has a different attitude)

Classes arranged in order of increasing drama

How is it like, or different from, other things? (Comparison and contrast)

Asking about similarities and differences leads to **comparison and contrast:** comparison focuses on similarities, whereas contrast focuses on differences. The two may be used separately or together to develop an idea or to relate two or more things. Commonly, comparisons are organized in one of two ways. In the first, **subject by subject,** the two subjects are discussed separately, one at a time:

Consider the differences also in the behavior of rock and classical music audiences. At a rock concert, the audience members yell, whistle, sing along, and stamp their feet. They may even stand during the entire performance. The better the music, the more active they'll be. At a classical concert, in contrast, the better the performance, the more *still* the audience is. Members of the classical audience are so highly disciplined that they refrain from even clearing their throats or coughing. No matter what effect the powerful music has on their intellects and feelings, they sit on their hands.

—Tony Nahm (student), "Rock and Roll Is Here to Stay"

Subjects: rock and classical audiences

Rock audience

Classical audience

In the second comparative organization, **point by point,** the two subjects are discussed side by side and matched feature for feature:

The first electronic computer, ENIAC, went into operation just over fifty years ago, yet the differences between it and today's personal computer are enormous. ENIAC was enormous

Subjects: ENIAC and personal computer

> itself, consisting of forty panels, each two feet wide and four feet deep. Today's notebook PC or Macintosh, by contrast, can fit easily on one's lap. ENIAC had to be configured by hand, with its programmers taking up to two days to reset switches and cables. Today, the average user can change programs in an instant. And for all its size and inconvenience, ENIAC was also slow. In its time, its operating speed of 100,000 pulses per second seemed amazingly fast. However, today's notebook can operate at more than 1 billion pulses per second.
>
> —Shirley Kajiwara (student), "The Computers We Deserve"

Size: ENIAC, personal computer

Ease of programming: ENIAC, personal computer

Speed: ENIAC, personal computer

The following examples show the two organizing schemes in outline form. The one on the left corresponds to the point-by-point paragraph about computers. The one on the right uses the same information but reorganizes it to cover the two subjects separately: first one, then the other.

Point by point

I. Size
  A. ENIAC
  B. Personal computer
II. Ease of programming
  A. ENIAC
  B. Personal computer
III. Speed
  A. ENIAC
  B. Personal computer

Subject by subject

I. ENIAC
  A. Size
  B. Ease of programming
  C. Speed
II. Personal computer
  A. Size
  B. Ease of programming
  C. Speed

Is it comparable to something that is in a different class but more familiar to readers? (Analogy)

Whereas we draw comparisons and contrasts between elements in the same general class (audiences, computers), we link elements in different classes with a special kind of comparison called **analogy.** Most often in analogy we illuminate or explain an unfamiliar, abstract class of things with a familiar and concrete class of things:

> We might eventually obtain some sort of bedrock understanding of cosmic structure, but we will never understand the universe in detail; it is just too big and varied for that. If we possessed an atlas of our galaxy that devoted but a single page to each star system in the Milky Way (so that the sun and all its planets were crammed on one page), that atlas would run to more than ten million volumes of ten thousand pages each. It would take a library the size of

Abstract subject: the universe, specifically the Milky Way

Concrete subject: an atlas

Harvard's to house the atlas, and merely to flip through it, at the rate of a page per second, would require over ten thousand years.

—Timothy Ferris, *Coming of Age in the Milky Way*

■ Why did it happen, or what results did it have? (Cause-and-effect analysis)

When you use analysis to explain why something happened or what is likely to happen, then you are determining causes and effects. **Cause-and-effect analysis** is especially useful in writing about social, economic, or political events or problems. In the next paragraph the author looks at the causes of Japanese collectivism, which he elsewhere contrasts with American individualism:

> The *shinkansen* or "bullet train" speeds across the rural areas of Japan giving a quick view of cluster after cluster of farmhouses surrounded by rice paddies. This particular pattern did not develop purely by chance, but as a consequence of the technology peculiar to the growing of rice, the staple of the Japanese diet. The growing of rice requires the construction and maintenance of an irrigation system, something that takes many hands to build. More importantly, the planting and the harvesting of rice can only be done efficiently with the co-operation of twenty or more people. The "bottom line" is that a single family working alone cannot produce enough rice to survive, but a dozen families working together can produce a surplus. Thus the Japanese have had to develop the capacity to work together in harmony, no matter what the forces of disagreement or social disintegration, in order to survive.
>
> —William Ouchi, *Theory Z*

Effect: pattern of Japanese farming

Causes: Japanese dependence on rice, which requires collective effort

Effect: working in harmony

Cause-and-effect paragraphs tend to focus either on causes, as Ouchi's does, or on effects, as this paragraph does:

> At each step, with every graduation from one level of education to the next, the refrain from bystanders was strangely the same: "Your parents must be so proud of you." I suppose that my parents were proud, although I suspect, too, that they felt more than pride alone as they watched me advance through my education. They seemed to know that my education was separating us from one another, making it difficult to resume familiar intimacies. Mixed with the instincts of parental pride, a certain hurt

Cause: education

Effects:
Pride
Separation
Loss of intimacies
Hurt

also communicated itself—too private ever to be adequately expressed in words, but real nonetheless.

—Richard Rodriguez, "Going Home Again"

- **How does one do it, or how does it work? (Process analysis)**

When you analyze how to do something or how something works, you explain the steps in a **process.** Paragraphs developed by process analysis are usually organized chronologically, as the steps in the process occur. Some process analyses tell the reader how to do a task:

> As a car owner, you waste money when you pay a mechanic to change the engine oil. The job is not difficult, even if you know little about cars. All you need is a wrench to remove the drain plug, a large, flat pan to collect the draining oil, plastic bottles to dispose of the used oil, and fresh oil. First, warm up the car's engine so that the oil will flow more easily. When the engine is warm, shut it off and remove its oil-filler cap (the owner's manual shows where this cap is). Then locate the drain plug under the engine (again consulting the owner's manual for its location) and place the flat pan under the plug. Remove the plug with the wrench, letting the oil flow into the pan. When the oil stops flowing, replace the plug and, at the engine's filler hole, add the amount and kind of fresh oil specified by the owner's manual. Pour the used oil into the plastic bottles and take it to a waste-oil collector, which any garage mechanic can recommend.
>
> —Anthony Andreas (student), "Do-It-Yourself Car Care"

Process: changing oil
Equipment needed
Steps in process

Other process analyses explain how processes are done or how they work in nature. Annie Dillard's paragraph on mangrove islands (p. 82) is one example. Here is another:

> What used to be called "laying on of hands" is now practiced seriously by nurses and doctors. Studies have shown that therapeutic touch, as it is now known, can aid relaxation and ease pain, two effects that may in turn cause healing. A "healer" must first concentrate on helping the patient. Then, hands held a few inches from the patient's body, the healer moves from head to foot. Healers claim that they can detect energy disturbances in the patient that indicate tension, pain, or sickness. With further hand movements, the healer tries to redirect the

Process: therapeutic touch
Benefits
Steps in process

energy. Patients report feeling heat from the healer's hands, perhaps indicating an energy transfer between healer and patient. — How process works

—Lisa Kuklinski (student),
"Old Ways to Noninvasive Medicine"

Diagrams, photographs, and other figures can do much to clarify process analyses. See pages 122–27 for guidelines on creating and clearly labeling figures.

Combining rhetorical strategies

Whatever strategy you choose as the basis for developing a paragraph, others may also prove helpful. Combined strategies have appeared often in this section: Dyson analyzes causes and effects in presenting reasons (p. 95); Tuchman uses contrast to define *quality* (p. 96); Nahm uses description to compare (p. 98); Ouchi uses process analysis to explain causes (p. 100).

3 Checking length

The average paragraph contains between 100 and 150 words, or between four and eight sentences. The actual length of a paragraph depends on the complexity of its topic, the role it plays in developing the thesis of the essay, and its position in the essay. Nevertheless, very short paragraphs are often inadequately developed; they may leave readers with a sense of incompleteness. And very long paragraphs often contain irrelevant details or develop two or more topics; readers may have difficulty following, sorting out, or remembering ideas.

When you are revising your essay, reread the paragraphs that seem very long or very short, checking them especially for unity and adequate development. If the paragraph wanders, cut everything from it that does not support your main idea (such as sentences that you might begin with *By the way*). If it is underdeveloped, supply the specific details, examples, or reasons needed, or try one of the methods of development we have discussed here.

EXERCISE 4.13 Analyzing paragraph development

Examine the paragraph by Henry Louis Gates, Jr. (p. 78) to discover how the author achieves paragraph development. What rhetorical strategy or strategies does the author use? Where does he support general statements with specific evidence?

EXERCISE 4.14 Analyzing and revising skimpy paragraphs

The following paragraphs are not well developed. Analyze them, looking especially for general statements that lack support or leave questions in your mind. Then rewrite one into a well-developed paragraph, supplying your own concrete details or examples. (You can do this exercise online at *ablongman.com/littlebrown.*)

1. One big difference between successful and unsuccessful teachers is the quality of communication. A successful teacher is sensitive to students' needs and excited by the course subject. In contrast, an unsuccessful teacher seems uninterested in students and bored by the subject.

2. Gestures are one of our most important means of communication. We use them instead of speech. We use them to supplement the words we speak. And we use them to communicate some feelings or meanings that words cannot adequately express.

3. I've discovered that a word processor can do much—but not everything—to help me improve my writing. I can easily make changes and try out different versions of a paper. But I still must do the hard work of revising.

EXERCISE 4.15 Considering your past work: Paragraph development

Continuing from Exercises 4.3 (p. 78) and 4.10 (p. 91), examine the development of the body paragraphs in your writing. Where does specific information seem adequate to support your general statements? Where does support seem skimpy? Revise the paragraphs as necessary to make your ideas clearer and more interesting. It may help you to pose the questions on pages 93–101.

EXERCISE 4.16 Writing with rhetorical strategies

Write at least three unified, coherent, and well-developed paragraphs, each one developed with a different strategy. Draw on the topics provided here, or choose your own topics.

1. **Narration**
   An experience of public speaking
   A disappointment
   Leaving home
   Waking up
2. **Description (objective or subjective)**
   Your room
   A crowded or deserted place
   A food
   An intimidating person
3. **Illustration or support**
   Why study
   Having a headache
   The best sports event
   Usefulness or uselessness of a self-help book
4. **Definition**
   Humor
   An adult
   Fear
   Authority
5. **Division or analysis**
   A television news show
   A barn
   A Web site
   A piece of music
6. **Classification**
   Factions in a dispute
   Styles of playing poker
   Types of Web sites
   Kinds of teachers

7. **Comparison and contrast**
   Surfing the Web and watching TV
   AM and FM radio DJs
   High school and college football
   Movies on TV and in a theater
8. **Analogy**
   Taking a test and running a race
   The US Constitution and a building's foundation
   Graduating from high school and being released from prison
9. **Cause-and-effect analysis**
   Connection between tension and anger
   Causes of failing or acing a test
   Connection between credit cards and debt
   Causes of a serious accident
10. **Process analysis**
   Preparing for a job interview
   Setting up a Web log
   Learning to play a musical instrument
   Making a jump shot

4d Writing special kinds of paragraphs

Several kinds of paragraphs do not always follow the guidelines for unity, coherence, development, and length because they serve special functions. These are the essay introduction, the essay conclusion, the transitional or emphatic paragraph, and the paragraph of spoken dialog.

1 Opening an essay

Most of your essays will open with a paragraph that draws readers from their world into your world. A good opening paragraph usually satisfies several requirements:

- **It focuses readers' attention on your subject and arouses their curiosity about what you have to say.**
- **It specifies what your topic is and implies your attitude.**
- **Often it provides your thesis statement.**
- **It is concise and sincere.**

The box on the facing page provides a range of options for achieving these goals.

Note If you are composing on the World Wide Web, you'll want to consider the expectations of Web readers. Your opening page may take the place of a conventional introduction, providing concise text indicating your site's subject and purpose, a menu of its contents, and links to other pages. (See pp. 786–92 for more on composing for the Web.)

CULTURE LANGUAGE The requirements and options for essay introductions may not be what you are used to if your native language is not English. In other cultures, readers may seek familiarity or reassurance

Some strategies for opening paragraphs

- Ask a question.
- Relate an incident.
- Use a vivid quotation.
- Offer a surprising statistic or other fact.
- State an opinion related to your thesis.
- Outline the argument your thesis refutes.
- Provide background.
- Create a visual image that represents your subject.
- Make a historical comparison or contrast.
- Outline a problem or dilemma.
- Define a word central to your subject.
- In some business or technical writing, summarize your paper.

from an author's introduction, or they may prefer an indirect approach to the subject. In academic and business English, however, writers and readers prefer concise, direct expression.

The funnel introduction

One reliably effective introduction forms a kind of funnel:

Funnel introduction

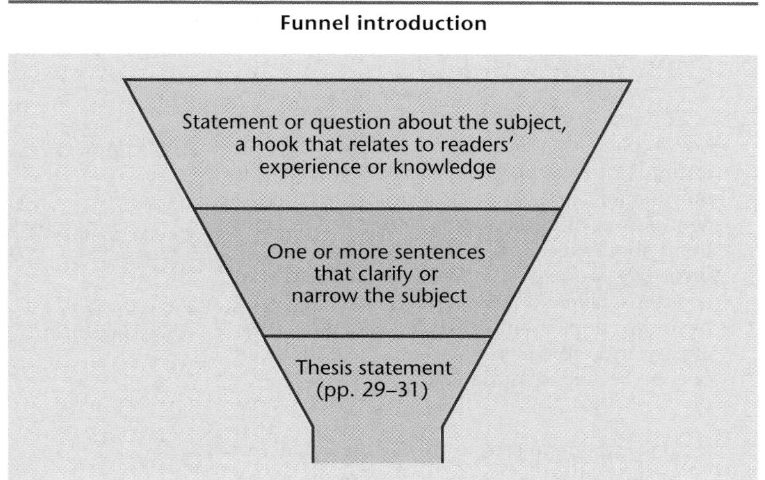

Here are two examples of the funnel introduction:

Can your home or office computer make you sterile? Can it strike you blind or dumb? The answer is: probably not. Nevertheless, reports of side effects relating to computer use should be examined, especially in the area of birth defects, eye complaints, and postural difficulties.

Questions about subject

Clarification of subject: bridge to thesis statement

Although little conclusive evidence exists to establish a causal link between computer use and problems of this sort, the circumstantial evidence can be disturbing. — Thesis statement

—Thomas Hartmann, "How Dangerous Is Your Computer?"

The Declaration of Independence is so widely regarded as a statement of American ideals that its origins in practical politics tend to be forgotten. — Statement about subject

Thomas Jefferson's draft was intensely debated and then revised in the Continental Congress. Jefferson was disappointed with the result. — Clarification of subject: bridge to thesis statement

However, a close reading of both the historical context and the revisions themselves indicates that the Congress improved the document for its intended purpose. — Thesis statement

—Ann Weiss (student), "The Editing of the Declaration of Independence"

Other effective introductions

Several other types of introduction can be equally effective, though they are sometimes harder to invent and control.

Quotation leading into the thesis statement

"It is difficult to speak adequately or justly of London," wrote Henry James in 1881. "It is not a pleasant place; it is not agreeable, or cheerful, or easy, or exempt from reproach. It is only magnificent." — Quotation

Were he alive today, James, a connoisseur of cities, might easily say the same thing about New York or Paris or Tokyo, for the great city is one of the paradoxes of history. — Bridge to thesis statement

In countless different ways, it has almost always been an unpleasant, disagreeable, cheerless, uneasy and reproachful place; in the end, it can only be described as magnificent. — Thesis statement

—*Time*

Incident or image setting up the thesis statement

Canada is pink. I knew that from the map I owned when I was six. On it, New York was green and brown, which was true as far as I could see, so there was no reason to distrust the map maker's portrayal of Canada. When my parents took me across the border and we entered the immigration booth, I looked excitedly for the pink earth. Slowly it dawned on me: this foreign, "different" place was not so different. — Incident from writer's experience

I discovered that the world in my head and the world at my feet were not the same. — Thesis statement

—Robert Ornstein, *Human Nature*

Startling opinion or question

Caesar was right. Thin people need watching. I've been watching them for most of my adult life, and I don't like what I see. When these narrow fellows spring at me, I quiver to my toes. Thin people come in all personalities, most of them menacing. You've got your "together" thin person, your mechanical thin person, your condescending thin person, your tsk-tsk thin person. — Opinion

All of them are dangerous. — Thesis statement

—Suzanne Britt, "That Lean and Hungry Look"

Background, such as a historical comparison

Throughout the first half of this century, the American Medical Association, the largest and most powerful medical organization in the world, battled relentlessly to rid the country of quack potions and cure-alls; and it is the AMA that is generally credited with being the single most powerful force behind the enactment of the early pure food and drug laws. — Historical background

Today, however, medicine's guardian seems to have done a complete about-face and become one of the pharmaceutical industry's staunchest allies—often at the public's peril and expense. — Thesis statement

—Mac Jeffery, "Does Rx Spell Rip-off?"

An effective introductory paragraph need not be long, as the following opener shows:

I've often wondered what goes into a hot dog. Now I know and I wish I didn't. —William Zinsser, *The Lunacy Boom*

Ineffective introductions

When writing and revising an introductory paragraph, avoid the following approaches that are likely to bore readers or make them question your sincerity or control:

Openings to avoid

- **A vague generality or truth.** Don't extend your reach too wide with a line such as *Throughout human history . . .* or *In today's world. . . .* Readers can do without the warm-up.

(continued)

Openings to avoid

(continued)

- **A flat announcement.** Don't start with *The purpose of this essay is . . . , In this essay I will . . .* , or any similar presentation of your intention or topic.
- **A reference to the essay's title.** Don't refer to the title of the essay in the first sentence—for example, *This is a big problem* or *This book is about the history of the guitar.*
- ***According to Webster. . . .*** Don't start by citing a dictionary definition. A definition can be an effective springboard to an essay, but this kind of lead-in has become dull with overuse.
- **An apology.** Don't fault your opinion or your knowledge with *I'm not sure if I'm right, but . . . ; I don't know much about this, but . . .* ; or a similar line.

2 Closing an essay

Most of your compositions will end with a closing statement or conclusion, a signal to readers that you have not simply stopped writing but have actually finished. The conclusion completes an essay, bringing it to a climax while assuring readers that they have understood your intention.

Note Compositions for the Web usually do not provide the kind of closure featured in essays. In fact, you'll need to ensure that your Web pages don't dead-end, leaving the reader stranded without options for moving backward or forward through your material. (For more on Web composition, see pp. 786–92.)

Effective conclusions

An essay conclusion may consist of a single sentence or a group of sentences, usually set off in a separate paragraph. The conclusion may take one or more of the following approaches:

Some strategies for closing paragraphs

- Recommend a course of action.
- Summarize the paper.
- Echo the approach of the introduction.
- Restate your thesis and reflect on its implications.
- Strike a note of hope or despair.
- Give a symbolic or powerful fact or other detail.
- Give an especially compelling example.
- Create an image that represents your subject.
- Use a quotation.

The following paragraph concludes the essay on the Declaration of Independence (the introduction appears on p. 106):

> The Declaration of Independence has come to be a statement of this nation's political philosophy, but that was not its purpose in 1776. Jefferson's passionate expression had to bow to the goals of the Congress as a whole to forge unity among the colonies and to win the support of foreign nations.
>
> —Ann Weiss (student), "The Editing of the Declaration of Independence"

Echo of introduction: contrast between past and present

Restatement and elaboration of thesis

Maxine Hong Kingston uses a different technique—a vivid image—to conclude an essay about an aunt who committed suicide by drowning:

> My aunt haunts me—her ghost drawn to me because now, after fifty years of neglect, I alone devote pages of paper to her, though not origamied into houses and clothes. I do not think she always means me well. I am telling on her, and she was a spite suicide, drowning herself in the drinking water. The Chinese are always very frightened of the drowned one, whose weeping ghost, wet hair hanging and skin bloated, waits silently by the water to pull down a substitute.
>
> —Maxine Hong Kingston, "No Name Woman"

Summary

Image

In the next paragraph the author concludes an essay on environmental protection with a call for action:

> Until we get the answers, I think we had better keep on building power plants and growing food with the help of fertilizers and such insect-controlling chemicals as we now have. The risks are well known, thanks to the environmentalists. If they had not created a widespread public awareness of the ecological crisis, we wouldn't stand a chance. But such awareness by itself is not enough. Flaming manifestos and prophecies of doom are no longer much help, and a search for scapegoats can only make matters worse. The time for sensations and manifestos is about over. Now we need rigorous analysis, united effort and very hard work.
>
> —Peter F. Drucker, "How Best to Protect the Environment"

Summary and opinion

Call for action

Ineffective conclusions

The preceding examples illustrate ways of avoiding several pitfalls of conclusions:

Closings to avoid

- **A repeat of the introduction.** Don't simply replay your introduction. The conclusion should capture what the paragraphs of the body have added to the introduction.
- **A new direction.** Don't introduce a subject different from the one your essay has been about. If you arrive at a new idea, this may be a signal to start fresh with that idea as your thesis.
- **A sweeping generalization.** Don't conclude more than you reasonably can from the evidence you have presented. If your essay is about your frustrating experience trying to clear a parking ticket, you cannot reasonably conclude that *all* local police forces are tied up in red tape.
- **An apology.** Don't cast doubt on your essay. Don't say, *Even though I'm no expert* or *This may not be convincing, but I believe it's true* or anything similar. Rather, to win your readers' confidence, display confidence.

3 Using short emphatic or transitional paragraphs

A short emphatic paragraph can give unusual stress to an important idea, in effect asking the reader to pause and consider before moving on.

> In short, all those who might have taken responsibility ducked it, and catastrophe was inevitable.

A transitional paragraph, because it is longer than a word or phrase and is set off by itself, moves a discussion from one point to another more slowly or more completely than does a single transitional expression or even a transitional sentence attached to a larger paragraph.

> These, then, are the causes of the current contraction in hospital facilities. But how does this contraction affect the medical costs of the government, private insurers, and individuals?
>
> So the debates were noisy and emotion-packed. But what did they accomplish? Historians have identified at least three direct results.

Use transitional paragraphs only to shift readers' attention when your essay makes a significant turn. A paragraph like the following one betrays a writer who is stalling:

> Now that we have examined these facts, we can look at some others that are equally central to an examination of this important issue.

4 Writing dialog

When recording a conversation between two or more people, start a new paragraph for each person's speech. The paragraphing establishes for the reader the point at which one speaker stops talking and another begins.

> The dark shape was indistinguishable. But once I'd flooded him with light, there he stood, blinking.
>
> "Well," he said eventually, "you're a sight for sore eyes. Should I stand here or are you going to let me in?"
>
> "Come in," I said. And in he came.
>
> —Louise Erdrich, *The Beet Queen*

Though dialog appears most often in fictional writing (the source of the preceding example), it may occasionally freshen or enliven narrative or expository essays. (For guidance in using quotation marks and other punctuation in passages of dialog, see pp. 446–48 and 473–74.)

EXERCISE 4.17 Analyzing an introduction and conclusion

Analyze the introductory and concluding paragraphs in the first and final drafts of the student essay in Chapter 3, pages 50–51 and 65–67. What is wrong with the first-draft paragraphs? Why are the final-draft paragraphs better? Could they be improved still further?

EXERCISE 4.18 Considering your past work: Introductions and conclusions

Examine the opening and closing paragraphs of the essay you've been analyzing in Exercises 4.3, 4.10, and 4.15. Do the paragraphs fulfill the requirements and avoid the pitfalls outlined on pages 104–10? Revise them as needed for clarity, conciseness, focus, and interest.

4e Linking paragraphs in the essay

Your paragraphs do not stand alone: each one is a key unit of a larger piece of writing. Though you may draft paragraphs or groups of paragraphs almost as mini-essays, you will eventually need to stitch them together into a unified, coherent, well-developed whole. The techniques parallel those for linking sentences in paragraphs:

- **Make sure each paragraph contributes to your thesis.**
- **Arrange the paragraphs in a clear, logical order.** See pages 35–46 for advice on essay organization.
- **Create links between paragraphs.** Use repetition and restatement to stress and connect key terms, and use transitional expressions and transitional sentences to indicate sequence, direction, contrast, and other relationships.

The essay on pages 45–46 illustrates the first two of these techniques. The following passages from the essay illustrate the third technique, with circled repetitions and restatements, boxed transitional expressions, and transitional sentences noted in annotations.

A Picture of Hyperactivity

Introduction establishing subject and stating thesis

Thesis statement

Hyperactive salespeople improve profits. Hyperactive committee members can run things efficiently. But when children are hyperactive, there are no benefits. A collage of those who must cope with hyperactivity in children—doctors, families, and the children themselves—is a picture of frustration, anger, and loss.

Transitional topic sentence relating to thesis statement

The first part of the collage is the doctors. In their terminology, the word hyperactivity has been replaced by ADHD, attention-deficit hyperactivity disorder, to describe children who are abnormally or excessively busy. . . .

Transitional topic sentence relating to thesis statement

For families, the second part of the collage, a diagnosis of ADHD means worry and disruption. . . .

Transitional sentence

Topic sentence relating to thesis statement

The weight of ADHD, however, does not rest on the doctors and families. The darkest part of the collage belongs to the children. . . .

Transitional sentence into conclusion, restating thesis statement

Taken as a whole, the collage is dark and somber. ADHD is a term with uncertain, unattractive, and bitter associations. But living with my brother, I have also seen a bright spot in the picture. Inside every ADHD child is a loving, trusting, and calm person waiting to be recognized.

EXERCISE 4.19 Analyzing paragraphs in an essay

Analyze the ways in which paragraphs combine in the student essay in Chapter 3, pages 65–67. What techniques does the writer use to link paragraphs to the thesis statement and to each other? Where, if at all, does the writer seem to stray from the thesis or fail to show how paragraphs relate to it? How would you revise the essay to solve any problems it exhibits?

EXERCISE 4.20 Considering your past work: Paragraphs in the essay

Examine the overall effect of the essay you've been analyzing in Exercises 4.3, 4.10, 4.15, and 4.18. Do all the paragraphs relate to your thesis? Are they arranged clearly and logically? How do repetition and restatement, transitional expressions, or transitional sentences connect the paragraphs? Can you see ways to improve the essay's unity, coherence, and development?

CHAPTER 5

Designing Documents

Imaginehowharditwouldbetoreadandwriteiftextlookedlikethis. To make reading and writing easier, we place a space between words. This convention and many others—such as page margins, page numbers, and paragraph breaks—have evolved over time to help writers communicate clearly with readers.

5a Designing academic papers and other documents

The design guidelines offered in this chapter apply to all types of documents, including academic papers, Web sites, business reports, flyers, and newsletters. Each type has specific requirements as well, covered elsewhere in this book.

1 Designing academic papers

Many academic disciplines prefer specific formats for students' papers. This book details two such formats:

- **MLA,** used in English, foreign languages, and some other humanities (pp. 664–66).
- **APA,** used in the social sciences (pp. 755–58).

http://www.ablongman.com/littlebrown

Visit the companion Web site for more help with document design.

Other academic formats can be found in the style guides listed on pages 721, 739, and 767.

The design guidelines in this chapter extend the range of elements and options covered by most academic styles. Your instructors may want you to adhere strictly to a particular style or may allow some latitude in design. Ask them for their preferences.

2 Writing online

In and out of school, you are likely to do a lot of online writing—certainly e-mail and possibly Web logs and other Web sites. The purposes and audiences for online writing vary widely, and so do readers' expectations for its design. Chapter 54 details the approaches you can take in different online writing situations.

3 Designing business documents and other public writing

When you write outside your high school classes, your audience will have certain expectations for how your documents should look and read. Guidelines for such writing appear in the following chapters:

- **Chapter 55 on public writing:** letters, job applications, reports, proposals, flyers, newsletters, brochures.
- **Chapter 56 on oral presentations:** *PowerPoint* slides and other visual aids.

5b Considering principles of design

Most of the principles of design respond to the ways we read. White space, for instance, relieves our eyes and helps to lead us through a document. Groupings or lists help to show relationships. Type sizes, images, and color add variety and help to emphasize important elements.

The sample documents on pages 116–17 illustrate quite different ways one student designed a report for a college marketing course. Even at a glance, the revised document is easier to scan and read. It makes better use of white space, groups similar elements, uses bullets and fonts for emphasis, and more successfully integrates and explains the chart.

As you design your own documents, think about your purpose, the expectations of your readers, and how readers will move through your document. Also consider the following general principles of design, noting how they overlap and support each other.

Principles of document design

- **Create flow** to conduct the reader through the document.
- **Space elements** to give the reader's eye a rest and to focus the reader's attention.
- **Group related elements** in lists or under similar headings.
- **Standardize elements** to match appearance with content and to minimize variations.
- **Emphasize important elements.**

1 Creating flow

Many of the other design principles work in concert with the larger goal of conducting the reader through a document by establishing flow, a pattern for the eye to follow. In text-heavy documents like that on page 117, flow may be achieved mainly with headings, lists, and illustrations. In more visual documents, flow will come from the arrangement and spacing of information as well as from headings.

2 Spacing

The white space on a page eases crowding and focuses readers' attention. On an otherwise full page, just the space indicating paragraphs (an indention or a line of extra space) gives readers a break and reassures them that ideas are divided into manageable chunks.

In papers, reports, and other formal documents, spacing appears mainly in paragraph breaks, in margins, and around headings and lists. In publicity documents, such as flyers and brochures, spacing is usually more generous between elements and helps boxes, headings, and the like pop off the page.

3 Grouping

Grouping information shows relationships visually, reinforcing the sense of the text itself. Here in this discussion, we group the various principles of design under visually identical headings to emphasize them and their similar importance. In the revised design on page 117, the bulleted list details statistics about students' computer use. The list uses similar wording for each item to reinforce

Original design

Runs title and subtitle together. Does not distinguish title from text.

Crowds the page with minimal margins.

Downplays paragraph breaks with small indentions.

Buries statistics in a paragraph. Obscures relationships with non-parallel wording.

Does not introduce the figure, leaving readers to infer its meaning and purpose.

Overemphasizes the figure with large size and excessive white space.

Presents the figure undynamically, flat on.

Does not caption the figure to explain what it shows, offering only a figure number and a partial text explanation.

Ready or Not, Here They Come: College Students and the Internet

College life once meant classrooms of students listening to teachers or groups of students talking over lunch in the union. But the reality today is more complex: students interact with their peers and professors by computer as much as face to face. As these students graduate and enter the workforce, all of society will be affected by their experience.

According to the Pew Internet Research Center (2005), today's college students are practiced computer and Internet users. The Pew Center reports that 20 percent of students in college today started using computers between ages five and eight. By age eighteen all students were using computers. Almost all college students, 86 percent, rely on the Internet, with 66 percent of students using more than one e-mail address. Computer ownership among this group is also very high: 85 percent have purchased or have been given at least one computer.

Students are eager to tap into the Internet's benefits and convenience.

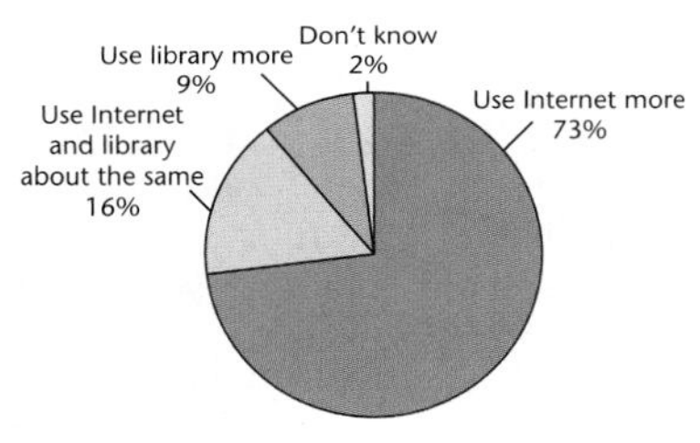

Figure 1

The Internet has eclipsed the library as the site of college students' research, as shown in Figure 1 from the Pew Report. In fact, a mere 9 percent of students

the similarities in the data. Thinking of likely groups as you write can help you organize your material so that it makes sense to you and your readers.

4 Standardizing

As we read a document, the design of its elements quickly creates expectations in us. We assume, for instance, that headings in the same size and color signal information of the same importance or that a list contains items of parallel content. Just as the design creates expectations, so it should fulfill them, treating similar elements similarly. Anticipating design standards as you write a document can help you treat its elements consistently and emphasize the elements you want to draw attention to.

Standardizing also creates clear, uncluttered documents. Even if they are used consistently, too many variations in type fonts and

Revised design

Ready or Not, Here They Come

College Students and the Internet

College life once meant classrooms of students listening to teachers or groups of students talking over lunch in the union. But the reality today is more complex: students interact with their peers and professors by computer as much as face to face. As these students graduate and enter the workforce, all of society will be affected by their experience.

According to the Pew Internet Research Center (2005), today's college students are practiced computer users and Internet users.

- They started young: 20 percent were using computers between ages five and eight, and all were using them by age eighteen.
- They rely on the Internet: 86 percent have used the network, and 66 percent use more than one e-mail address.
- They own computers: 85 percent have purchased or have been given at least one computer.

Students are eager to tap into the Internet's benefits and convenience. Figure 1, from the Pew Report, shows that the Internet has eclipsed the library as the site of college students' research.

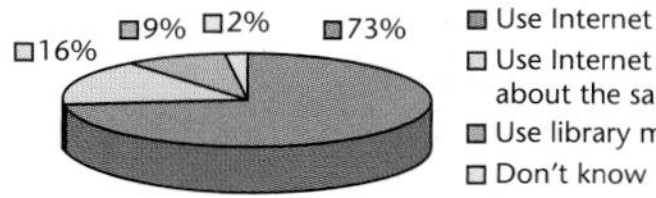

Figure 1. College students' use of the Internet and the library for research

Distinguishes title from subtitle and both from text.

Provides adequate margins.

Emphasizes paragraph breaks with white space.

Groups statistics in a bulleted list set off with white space. Uses parallel wording for parallel information.

Introduces the figure to indicate its meaning and purpose.

Reduces white space around the figure.

Presents the figure to emphasize the most significant segment.

Captions the figure so that it can be read independently from the text.

sizes, colors, indentions, and the like overwhelm readers as they try to determine the significance of the parts. Most formal documents, such as papers and reports, need no more than a single type font for text and headings, with type size and highlighting (such as CAPITAL LETTERS, **boldface**, or *italics*) distinguishing the levels of headings. Publicity documents, such as flyers and brochures, generally employ more variation to arrest readers' attention.

5 Emphasizing

Part of a critical reader's task is to analyze and interpret the meaning of a document, and design helps the reader by stressing what's important. Type fonts and sizes, headings, indentions, color, boxes, white space—all of these establish hierarchies of information, so that the reader almost instinctively grasps what is crucial, what is less so, and what is merely supplementary. In this book, for example, the importance of headings is clear from their size and from the use of decorative elements, such as the boxes around 5c and the heading below; and boxes like the one on page 115 clearly mark summaries and other key information. As you design a document, considering where and how to emphasize elements can actually help you determine your document's priorities.

5c Using the elements of design

Applying the preceding principles involves margins, text, lists, headings, color, and illustrations. You won't use all these elements for every project, and in many writing situations you will be required to follow a prescribed format (see pp. 113–14). If you are addressing readers who have vision disabilities, consider as well the points discussed on pages 127–28.

Note Your word processor may provide wizards or templates for many kinds of documents, such as letters, memos, reports, agendas, résumés, and brochures. **Wizards** guide you through setting up and writing complicated documents. **Templates** are preset forms to which you add your own text, headings, and other elements. Wizards and templates can be helpful, but not if they lead you to create cookie-cutter documents no matter what the writing situation. Always keep in mind that a document should be appropriate for your subject, audience, and purpose.

1 Setting margins

Margins at the top, bottom, and sides of a page help to prevent the pages from overwhelming readers with unpleasant crowding. Most academic and business documents use a minimum one-inch margin on all sides. Publicity documents, such as flyers and brochures, often use narrower margins, compensating with white space between elements.

2 Creating readable text

A document must be readable. You can make text readable by attending to line spacing, type fonts and sizes, highlighting, word spacing, and line breaks.

Line spacing

Most academic documents are double-spaced, with an initial indention for paragraphs, while most business documents are single-spaced, with an extra line of space between paragraphs. Double or triple spacing sets off headings in both. Web sites and publicity documents, such as flyers and brochures, tend to use more line spacing to separate and group distinct parts of the content.

Type fonts and sizes

The readability of text also derives from the type fonts (or faces) and their sizes. For academic and business documents, generally choose a type size of 10 or 12 points, as in these samples:

10-point Courier 10-point Times New Roman
12-point Courier 12-point Times New Roman

Fonts like these and the one you're reading have **serifs**—the small lines finishing the letters, such as the downward strokes on the top of this T. Serif fonts are appropriate for formal writing and are easier for most people to read on paper. **Sans serif** fonts (*sans* means "without" in French) include this one found on many word processors:

10-point Arial 12-point Arial

Sans serif fonts are usually easier to read on a computer screen and are clearer on paper for readers with some vision disabilities (see p. 128).

Your word processor probably offers many decorative fonts as well:

10-point Bodega Sans 10-point Tekton
10-POINT STENCIL *10-point Ruzicka Freehand*
10-point Lucinda Sans *10-point Park Avenue*

Decorative fonts are generally inappropriate in academic and business writing, where letter forms should be conventional and regular. But on some Web sites and in publicity documents, decorative fonts can attract attention, create motion, and reinforce a theme.

Note The point size of a type font is often an unreliable guide to its actual size, as the decorative fonts above illustrate: all the samples are 10 points, but they vary considerably. Before you use a font, print out a sample to be sure it is the size you want.

Highlighting

Within a document's text, underlined, *italic,* **boldface,** or even color type can emphasize key words or sentences. Underlining is rarest these days, having been replaced by italics in all but a few disciplines. (It remains called for in MLA style. See p. 636.) Both academic and business writing sometimes use boldface to give strong emphasis—for instance, to a term being defined—and publicity documents often rely extensively on boldface to draw the reader's eye. Neither academic nor business writing generally uses color within passages of text. In Web and publicity documents, however, color may be effective if the color is dark enough to be readable. (See p. 122 for more on color in document design.)

No matter what your writing situation, use highlighting selectively to complement your meaning, not merely to decorate your work. Many readers consider type embellishments to be distracting.

Word spacing

In most writing situations, follow these guidelines for spacing within and between words:

- **Leave one space between words.**
- **Leave one space after all punctuation, with these exceptions:**

Dash (two hyphens or the so-called em dash on a computer)	`book--its`	`book—its`
Hyphen	`one-half`	
Apostrophe within a word	`book's`	
Two or more adjacent marks	`book.")`	
Opening quotation mark, parenthesis, or bracket	`("book`	`[book`

- **Leave one space before and after an ellipsis mark.** In the examples below, ellipsis marks indicate omissions within a sentence and at the end of a sentence. See pages 486–88 for additional examples.

```
book . . . in
book. . . . The
```

Line breaks

Your word processor will generally insert appropriate breaks between lines of continuous text: it will not, for instance, automatically begin a line with a comma or period, and it will not end a line with an opening parenthesis or bracket. However, you will have to prevent it from breaking a two-hyphen dash or a three-dot ellipsis mark by spacing to push the beginning of each mark to the next line.

When you instruct it to do so (usually under the Tools menu), your word processor will also automatically hyphenate words to prevent very short lines. If you must decide yourself where to break words, follow the guidelines on page 558.

3 Using lists

Lists give visual reinforcement to the relations between like items—for example, the steps in a process or the elements of a proposal. A list is easier to read than a paragraph and adds white space to the page.

When wording a list, work for parallelism among items—for instance, all complete sentences or all phrases (see also p. 410). Set the list with space above and below. Number the items, or mark them with bullets: centered dots or other devices, such as the squares used in the list below about headings. On most word processors you can format a numbered or bulleted list automatically using the Format menu.

4 Using headings

Headings are signposts: they direct the reader's attention by focusing the eye on a document's most significant content. In Web and publicity documents, headings may be decorative as well as functional, capturing the reader's attention with large sizes, lots of white space, and unconventional fonts. In academic and much business writing, however, headings are more purely functional. They break the text into discrete parts, create emphasis, and orient the reader.

When you use headings in academic and business writing, follow these guidelines:

- **Use one, two, or three levels of headings** depending on the needs of your material and the length of your document. Some level of heading every two or so pages will help keep readers on track. (A three-page paper or a one-page letter probably will not need headings.)
- **Create an outline of your document to plan where headings should go.** Reserve the first level of heading for the main points (and sections). Use a second and perhaps a third level of heading to mark subsections of supporting information.
- **Keep headings as short as possible** while making them specific about the material that follows.
- **Word headings consistently**—for instance, all questions (*What Is the Scientific Method?*), all phrases with *-ing* words (*Understanding the Scientific Method*), or all phrases with nouns (*The Scientific Method*).
- **Indicate the relative importance of headings** with type size, positioning, and highlighting, such as capital letters or boldface.

  First-Level Heading

  Second-Level Heading

  Third-Level Heading

  Generally, you can use the same type font and size for headings as for the text.
- **Don't break a page immediately after a heading.** Push the heading to the next page.

Table

A self-explanatory title falls above the table.

Self-explanatory headings label horizontal rows and vertical columns.

The layout of rows and columns is clear: headings align with their data, and numbers align vertically down columns.

Table 1

Percentage of Young Adults Living at Home, 1960-2000

	1960	1970	1980	1990	2000
Males					
Age 18-24	52	54	54	58	57
Age 25-34	9	9	10	15	13
Females					
Age 18-24	35	41	43	48	47
Age 25-34	7	7	7	8	8

Source: Data from United States, Dept. of Commerce, Census Bureau, Census 2000 Summary Tables, 1 July 2002 <http:www.census.gov/servlet/QTTTable?_ts=30543101060>.

3 Using figures

Figures represent data or show concepts visually. They include charts, graphs, and diagrams.

Pie charts

Pie charts show the relations among the parts of a whole. The whole totals 100 percent, and each pie slice is proportional in size to its share of the whole. Use a pie chart when shares, not the underlying data, are your focus.

Pie chart

Color distinguishes segments of the chart. Use distinct shades of gray, black, and white if your paper will not be read in color.

Segment percentages total 100.

Every segment is clearly labeled. You can also use a key, as in the chart on p. 117.

Self-explanatory caption falls below the chart.

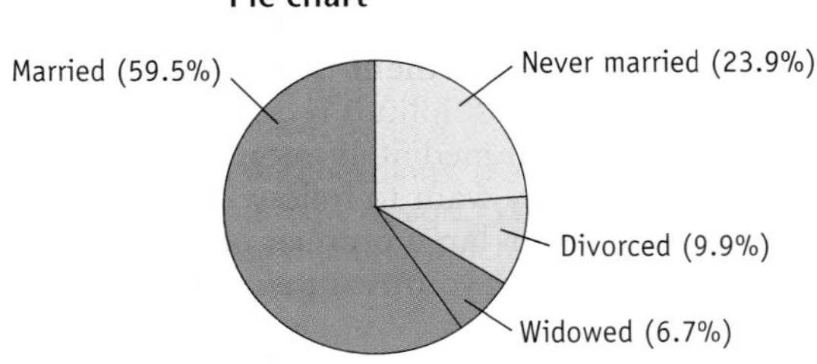

Fig. 1. Marital status in 2004 of adults aged eighteen and over. Data from United States, Dept. of Commerce, Census Bureau, Statistical Abstract of the United States, 2004-05 (Washington, GPO, 2005) no. 30.

Bar charts

Bar charts compare groups or time periods on a measure such as quantity or frequency. Use a bar chart when relative size is your focus.

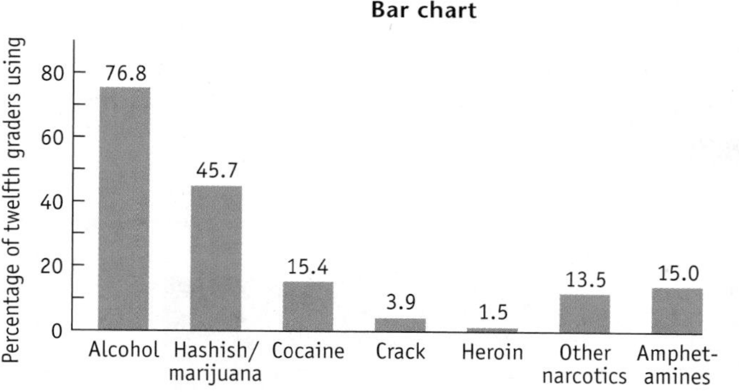

Fig. 2. Lifetime prevalence of use of alcohol, compared with other drugs, among twelfth graders in 2004. Data from Monitoring the Future: A Continuing Study of American Youth, U of Michigan, 12 May 2005, 10 Oct. 2005 <http://www.monitoringthefuture.org/data/data.html>.

Vertical scale shows and clearly labels the values being measured. Zero point clarifies values.

Horizontal scale shows and clearly labels the groups being compared.

Self-explanatory caption falls below the chart.

Line graphs

Line graphs show change over time in one or more subjects. They are an economical and highly visual way to compare many points of data.

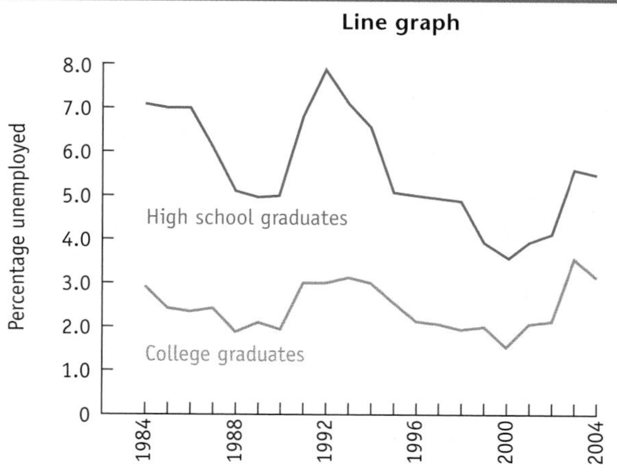

Fig. 3. Unemployent rates of high school graduates and college graduates, 1984–2004. Data from Antony Davies, The Economics of College Tuition, 3 Mar. 2005, 26 June 2005 <http://www.mercatus.org/capitalhill/php?id=420>.

Vertical scale shows and clearly labels the values being measured. Zero point clarifies values.

Color and labels distinguish the subjects being compared. Use dotted and dashed black lines if your paper will not be read in color.

Horizontal scale shows and clearly labels the range of dates.

Self-explanatory caption falls below the graph.

Diagrams

Diagrams show concepts visually, such as the structure of an organization, the way something works or looks, or the relations among subjects. Often, diagrams show what can't be described economically in words. For other examples of diagrams, see pages 3, 105, and 787.

Diagram

Diagram makes concept comprehensible.

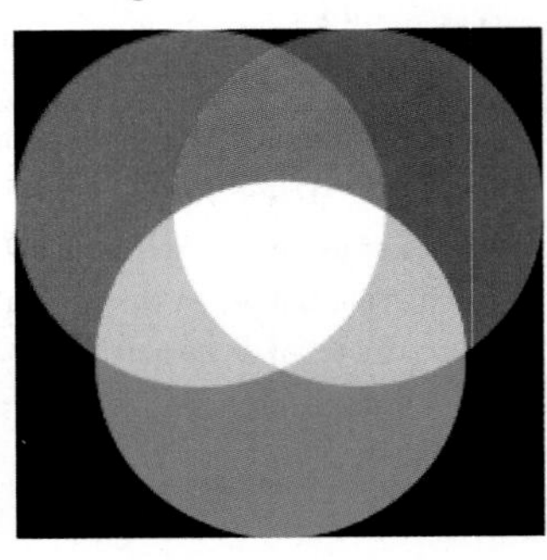

Self-explanatory caption falls below the diagram.

Fig. 4. RGB color theory, applied to televisions and computer monitors, in which all possible colors and white are created from red, green, and blue. From "Color Theory," Wikipedia, 16 July 2005, 2 Aug. 2005 <http://en.wikipedia.org/wiki/Color_theory>.

Photographs and other images

Sometimes you may focus an entire paper on an image such as a photograph, painting, or advertisement (see pp. 176–79). But most commonly you'll use images to add substance to ideas or to enliven them. You might clarify an astronomy paper with a photograph of Saturn (see opposite), add information to an analysis of a novel with a drawing of the author, or capture the theme of a brochure with a cartoon. Images grab readers' attention, so use them carefully to explain, reinforce, or enhance your writing.

One kind of image rarely appears in academic writing: **clip art,** consisting of icons and drawings such as those below from the free site *Barry's Clipart Server* (*http://www.barrysclipart.com/index.php*):

Clip art

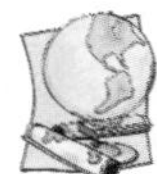

Photograph

Photograph shows subject more economically and dramatically than words could.

Fig. 5. View of Saturn from the Cassini spacecraft, showing the planet and its rings. From United States, National Atmospheric and Space Administration, Jet Propulsion Laboratory, Cassini-Huygens: Mission to Saturn and Titan, 24 Feb. 2005, 26 Apr. 2005 <http://saturn.jpl.nasa.gov/multimedia/images/image-details.cfm?imageID=1398>.

Self-explanatory caption falls below the image.

Many word processors provide files of clip art, and they are also available from CD-ROMs and Web sites (links appear on this book's Web site at *ablongman.com/littlebrown*). Be selective in using these resources: clip art is mostly decorative (which is why it seldom appears in academic and business documents), and an overdecorated document is not only cluttered but unemphatic. In a Web or publicity document, use only clip art that is relevant to your theme and content, directing readers' attention to elements you want to stress.

Note When using an image prepared by someone else—for instance, a photograph or an item of clip art downloaded from the Web—you must verify that the source permits reproduction of the image before you use it. In most documents but especially academic papers, you must also fully cite the source of any borrowed image. See pages 617–18 on copyright issues with Internet sources.

5e Considering readers with disabilities

Your audience may include readers who have low vision, problems with color perception, or difficulties processing visual information. If so, consider adapting your design to meet these readers' needs. Here are a few pointers:

- **Use large type fonts.** Most guidelines call for 14 points or larger.

CHAPTER 6

Writing in Academic Situations

When you write in school, you work within a community of teachers and students who have specific aims and expectations. The basic aim of this community—whether in English, psychology, biology, or some other discipline—is to contribute to and build knowledge through questioning, research, and communication. The differences among disciplines lie mainly in the kinds of questions asked, the kinds of research done to find the answers, and the ways of communicating the answers.

Academic writers communicate using conventional forms, such as case studies, research reports, and reviews of others' writings on a particular subject. Both a discipline's concerns and the kind of writing create the writing situation, which in turn shapes a writer's choice of subject, conception of audience, definition of purpose, choice of structure and content, and even choice of language. This chapter introduces academic writing situations in general. Chapters 50–53 detail the particular goals and expectations of the humanities, the social sciences, and the natural and applied sciences.

6a Becoming an academic writer

As an academic writer, you participate in a discipline community first by studying a subject, acquiring its vocabulary, and learning to express yourself in its ways. As you gain experience and knowledge, you begin to contribute to the community by asking questions and communicating your answers. Such a contribution may seem beyond you at first, as you try to grasp the content of assigned reading and identify important ideas. In any discipline, making the transition to academic writing will be easier if you practice the strategies outlined in the box on the facing page.

http://www.ablongman.com/littlebrown ▶

Visit the companion Web site for more help with academic writing.

Tips for becoming an academic writer

- **Study the course outline, or syllabus, for each class.** This outline lays out the teacher's expectations as well as the course topics, assignments, and deadlines.
- **Do the assigned reading.** You'll gain experience with the discipline's terms and ideas, and you'll become familiar with the kinds of writing expected of you.
- **Participate in class.** Listen carefully, take notes (see p. 139 for tips), ask questions, and join in discussions.
- **Ask questions.** Teachers, advisers, tutors, other students—all can help you.
- **Understand the writing situation posed by each assignment.** Knowing your audience, purpose, options for subjects, and other elements of the situation will help you meet the assignment's expectations. (See pp. 7–8 on analyzing assignments.)

6b Analyzing audience

Some of your writing assignments may specify an identifiable group of readers—for instance, fellow students, the city council, or the editors of a newspaper. Such readers' needs and expectations vary widely; the discussion on pages 10–14 can help you discover what they might be. Many assignments will specify or assume an educated audience or an academic audience. This more general group of readers looks for writing that is clear, balanced, well organized, and well reasoned, among other qualities discussed on page 133. Still other assignments will specify or assume an audience of experts on your subject, readers who look in addition for writing that meets the subject's requirements for claims and evidence, organization, language, format, and other qualities discussed in Chapters 49–53.

Of course, much of your academic writing will have only one reader besides you: the teacher of the class for which you are writing. Teachers fill two main roles as readers:

- **They represent the audience you are addressing.** They may actually be members of the audience, as when you address academic readers or subject experts. Or they may imagine themselves as members of your audience—reading, for instance, as if they sat on the city council. In either case, they're interested in how effectively you write for the audience.
- **They serve as coaches,** guiding you toward achieving the goals of the course and, more broadly, toward the academic aims of building and communicating knowledge.

Like everyone else, teachers have preferences and peeves, but you'll waste time and energy trying to anticipate them. Do attend to written and spoken directions for assignments, of course. But otherwise view your teachers as representatives of the community you are writing for. Their responses will be guided by the community's aims and expectations and by a desire to teach you about them.

6c Determining purpose

For most academic writing, your general purpose will be mainly explanatory or mainly argumentative. That is, you will aim to clarify your subject so that readers understand it as you do, or you will aim to gain readers' agreement with a debatable idea about the subject. (See pp. 15–16 for more on general purposes and Chapters 9–11 for more on argument.) Although the general purpose for writing may not be stated outright in an assignment, it will probably be implied, as you can see in these two abbreviated assignments:

Explanation

Compare the depiction of war in two films viewed this semester, considering plots, characters, dialog, battle scenes, production designs, and other elements of the films.

Argument

What do you see as a theme in the movies of director Steven Spielberg? What belief about the world do his choices of subject and setting convey, either explicitly or implicitly? Support your claim with evidence from at least four of Spielberg's movies, considering plots, characters, dialog, and other elements such as production designs and camera shots.

Your specific purpose—including your subject and how you hope readers will respond—depends on the kind of writing you're doing. In a biology lab report, for instance, you want your readers to understand why you conducted your study, how you conducted it, what the results were, and what their significance is. Not coincidentally, these topics correspond to the major sections of a biology lab report. In following the standard format, you both help to define your purpose and begin to meet the discipline's (and thus your teacher's) expectations.

Your specific purpose will be more complex as well. You take a class to learn about a subject and the ways experts think about it. Your writing, in return, contributes to the discipline through the knowledge you uncover and the lens of your perspective. At the same time, as a student you want to demonstrate your competence with research, evidence, format, and other requirements of the discipline.

6d Choosing structure and content

Many academic writing assignments will at least imply how you should organize your paper and even how you should develop your ideas. Like the biology lab report mentioned earlier, the type of paper required will break into discrete parts, each with its own requirements for content. A common academic writing assignment, the analysis, does not predict definite content but still implies certain requirements: you are asked to make a claim about your subject's meaning or significance, to support the claim with specific evidence, and, often, to show that you understand what others think about the subject. (See Chapter 8 for more on analysis.)

No matter what type of paper an assignment specifies, the broad academic aims of building and exchanging knowledge determine features that are common across disciplines. Follow these general guidelines for your academic writing, supplementing them as indicated with others elsewhere in this book:

- **Develop a central idea or claim, called a *thesis*.** Everything in the paper should relate clearly to this claim. For more on theses, see pages 29–34.
- **State your thesis,** usually near the beginning of the paper.
- **Support the thesis with evidence,** drawn usually from research and sometimes from your own experience. The kinds of evidence will depend on the discipline you're writing in and the type of paper you're doing. For more on evidence in the disciplines, see pages 697–98 (literature), 716–17 (other humanities), 733–34 (social sciences), and 762–63 (natural and applied sciences).
- **Interact with sources.** Do not merely summarize sources but evaluate and synthesize them from your own perspective. For more on using sources, see pages 588–600.
- **Acknowledge sources fully,** using the documentation style appropriate to the discipline. See pages 721, 739, and 767 for lists of disciplines' style guides and pages 624–63 (MLA style for English and some other humanities), 721–22 (Chicago style for history, philosophy, and some other humanities), 739–55 (APA style for the social sciences), and 767–74 (CSE style for the natural and applied sciences).
- **Balance your presentation.** Discuss evidence and opposing views fairly, and take a serious and impartial approach.
- **Organize clearly within the framework of the type of writing you're doing.** Develop your ideas as simply and directly as your purpose and content allow. Clearly relate sentences, paragraphs, and sections so that readers always know where they are in the paper's development.

CULTURE LANGUAGE These features are far from universal. In other cultures, academic writers may be indirect, may expect readers to discover the thesis, or may assume that readers do not require acknowledgment of well-known sources. Recognizing such differences between practices in your native culture and in the United States can help you adapt to US academic writing.

6e Using academic language

American academic writing relies on a dialect called standard American English. The dialect is also used in business, the professions, government, the media, and other sites of social and economic power where people of diverse backgrounds must communicate with one another. It is "standard" not because it is better than other forms of English, but because it is accepted as the common language, much as the dollar bill is accepted as the common currency.

You'll recognize standard American English as the dialect used in this handbook, in magazines and newspapers, and on television news. But you might also notice that the dialect varies a lot, from the formal English of a President's State of the Union address through the middle formality of this handbook to the informal chitchat between anchors on morning TV. Even in academic writing, standard American English allows much room for the writer's own tone and voice, as these passages on the same topic show:

More formal

In *Things Fall Apart,* Chinua Achebe portrays a culture in flux, where ancient rituals of community responsibility and familial loyalty begin to disintegrate. Achebe's central character, a Nigerian tribal chief and a formidable patriarch, finds himself powerless to stop the rising tide of change that floods his home and his village. His son rejects the old traditions, both in the home and among the tribe. Like Shakespeare's King Lear, whose children also confound him, the chief rails against his condition and drifts into madness.

Three complicated sentences

Drawn-out phrasing, such as *finds himself powerless* instead of *can do nothing*

Formal vocabulary, such as *in flux, familial,* and *formidable*

Less formal

Things fall apart in *Things Fall Apart,* by Chinua Achebe. The main character, a Nigerian tribal chief and patriarch, can't stop the world from changing. Even more, he can't count on his son to follow in his footsteps, either at home

Five shorter sentences

More informal phrasing, such as *Things fall apart in . . .* and *can't stop*

or in public. The book echoes Shakespeare's *King Lear.* In both works, rulers with ungrateful children lose their minds in the face of events they can't control.

More informal vocabulary, such as *count on* and *lose their minds*

As different as they are, both examples illustrate several common features of academic language:

- **It follows the conventions of standard American English for grammar and usage.** These conventions are detailed in guides to the dialect, such as this handbook.
- **It uses a standard vocabulary,** not one that only some groups understand, such as slang, an ethnic or regional dialect, or another language. (See pp. 512–14 for more on specialized vocabularies.)
- **It creates some distance between writer and reader with the third person (*he, she, it, they*).** The first person (*I, we*) is sometimes appropriate to express personal opinions or invite readers to think along, but not with a strongly explanatory purpose (*When I read* Things Fall Apart, *I felt sorry for the father*). The second person (*you*) is appropriate only in addressing readers directly (as in this handbook), and even then it may seem condescending or too chummy (*You would feel sorry for the father, too*).
- **It is authoritative and neutral.** In the examples on the facing page, the writers express themselves confidently, not timidly (as in *One comparison that might be considered in this case is with Shakespeare's* King Lear). They also refrain from hostility (*The father deserves to be punished for his stubbornness*) and enthusiasm (*Achebe's tribal chief is a masterpiece of characterization*).

At first, the diverse demands of academic writing may leave you groping for an appropriate voice. In an effort to sound fresh and confident, you may write too casually:

Too casual

The old guy just can't stop the world, and he can't get his son to see things his way.

In an effort to sound "academic," you may produce wordy and awkward sentences:

Wordy and awkward

In *Things Fall Apart,* a culture in the midst of change is portrayed by author Chinua Achebe. Whereas at one time ancient rituals held sway, which included community responsibility and familial loyalty, the culture is now subject to disintegration in the world that exists today. The central character created by Achebe is a Nigerian tribal chief and formidable patriarch who is seen in a condition of powerlessness to stop his home and his village from being flooded by a rising tide of change. [The passive voice in this example, such as *culture . . . is portrayed* and *who is seen*, adds to its wordiness and indirection. See pp. 304–05 for more on verb voice.]

A cure for writing too informally or too stiffly is to read academic writing so that the language and style become familiar and to edit your writing (see pp. 60–62).

CULTURE LANGUAGE If your first language is not English or is an English dialect besides standard American, you know well the power of communicating with others who share your language. Learning to write standard American English in no way requires you to abandon your first language. Like most multilingual people, you are probably already adept at switching between languages as the situation demands—speaking one way with your relatives, say, and another way with an employer. As you practice academic writing, you'll develop the same flexibility with it.

EXERCISE 6.1 Using academic language

Revise the following paragraph to make the language more academic while keeping the factual information the same. (You can do this exercise online at *ablongman.com/littlebrown.*)

If you buy into the stereotype of girls chatting away on their cell phones, you should think again. One of the major wireless companies surveyed 1021 cell phone owners for a period of five years and—surprise!—reported that guys talk on cell phones more than girls do. In fact, guys were way ahead of girls, using an average of 571 minutes a month compared to 424 for girls. That's 35 percent more time on the phone! The survey also asked about conversations on home phones, and while girls still beat the field, the guys are catching up.

EXERCISE 6.2 Considering your past work: Writing in academic situations

Look back at a paper you wrote for one of your high school classes. To what extent does it share the features of academic writing discussed in this chapter? How does it differ? Write a revision plan for making the paper more academic.

EXERCISE 6.3 Considering your native language or dialect

CULTURE LANGUAGE What main similarities and differences do you notice between writing in your native language or dialect and writing for US high school classes? Consider especially audience, purpose, content, structure, and the expression of ideas. Which differences do you think are easiest to bridge? Which are most difficult? Why?

CHAPTER 7

Studying Effectively and Taking Exams

Academic success depends on active, involved learning. If you haven't already, read the previous chapter on academic writing. Use the principles there along with this chapter's practical tips for managing your time, getting the most from your classes and your reading, and taking exams.

7a Managing your time

Planning and pacing your schoolwork and other activities will help you study more efficiently with less stress.

1 Surveying your activities

How do you spend your days? For a week, keep track of all your activities and the time they absorb. How many of the week's 168 hours do you spend eating, sleeping, watching television, talking on the phone, attending classes, studying, working at a job, attending religious services, exercising, commuting, doing laundry, socializing, and so on? How much time can you realistically devote to studying?

2 Scheduling your time

One way to organize your time is to use a calendar that divides each day into waking hours. Block out your activities that occur regularly and at specific times, such as commuting, attending classes, and working. Then fill in the other activities (such as exercise, eating, and studying) that do not necessarily occur at fixed times. Be sure to leave time for relaxing: an unrealistic schedule that assigns all available time to studying will quickly prove too difficult to live by. If you

http://www.ablongman.com/littlebrown ▶

Visit the companion Web site for more help with studying effectively and taking exams.

use a computer regularly, consider keeping your schedule online using a calendar program. Set it to remind you of important due dates.

3 Organizing your workload

Use the syllabuses for your classes to estimate the amount of weekly study time required for each course. Generally, plan on several hours of studying for each class. Block out study periods using these guidelines:

- **Schedule study time close to class time.** You'll study more productively if you review notes, read assigned material, or work on projects shortly after school.
- **Pace assignments.** Plan to start early and work regularly on projects requiring extensive time, such as research papers, so that you will not be overwhelmed near the deadline. (See pp. 560–61 for advice on scheduling research projects.)
- **Adjust the weekly plan as needed to accommodate changes in your workload.** Before each week begins, examine its schedule to be sure you've built in enough time to study for an exam, finish a paper, or meet other deadlines and commitments.

4 Making the most of study time

When you sit down to study, use your time efficiently:

- **Set realistic study goals.** Divide your study sessions into small chunks, each with a short-term goal, such as previewing a textbook chapter or drafting three paragraphs of a paper. Plan breaks, too, so that you can clear your mind, stretch, and refocus on your goals.
- **Tackle difficult homework first.** Resist any urge to put off demanding jobs, such as working on papers, reading textbooks, or doing math problems. Save easy tasks for when you're less alert.
- **Evaluate how you use your study time.** At the end of each week, ask yourself whether you were as productive as you needed to be. If not, what changes can you make to accomplish your goals for the coming week?

7b Listening and taking notes in class

When you begin each class meeting, push aside other concerns so that you can focus and listen. Either on paper or on a computer, record what you hear as completely as possible while sorting out the main ideas from the secondary and supporting ones. Such active note taking will help you understand the teacher's approach to the course and provide you with complete material for later study.

Tips for taking class notes

- **Use your own words.** You will understand and retain the material better if you rephrase it. But use the speaker's words if necessary to catch everything.
- **Leave space in your notes if you miss something.** Teachers usually welcome questions about content but not requests for simple repetition, and it's not fair to distract fellow students during class. Ask someone for the missing information as soon as possible after class.
- **Include any reading content mentioned by your teacher.** Use the notes to integrate all the components of the course—your teacher's views, your own thoughts, and the assigned reading, even if you've already read it.
- **Review your notes shortly after class.** Reinforce your new knowledge when it is fresh by underlining key words and ideas, adding headings and comments in the margins, converting your notes to questions, or outlining the lecture based on your notes. If you don't understand something in the notes, consult a classmate for his or her version.

7c Reading for comprehension

The assigned reading you do for high school classes—such as textbooks, newspaper and journal articles, and works of literature—requires a greater focus on understanding and retention than does the reading you do for entertainment or for practical information. The process discussed here may seem time consuming, but with practice you'll become efficient at it.

Note The following process stresses ways of understanding what you read. In critical reading, covered in the next chapter, you extend this process to analyze and evaluate what you read and see.

1 Writing while reading

Reading for comprehension is an *active* process. Students often believe they are reading actively when they roll a highlighter over the important ideas in a text, but truly engaged reading requires more than that. If you take notes while reading, you "translate" the work into your own words and reconstruct it for yourself.

The substance of your reading notes will change as you preview, read, and summarize. At first, you may jot quick, short notes in the margins, on separate pages, or on a computer. (Use the last two for material you don't own or are reading online.) As you delve into the work, the notes should become more detailed, restating important points, asking questions, connecting ideas. (See p. 155 for an example of a text annotated in this way by a student.) For in-depth critical reading, you may want to keep a reading journal that records both what the work says and what you think about it. (See pp. 155–56.)

2 Previewing

For most course reading, you should **skim** before reading word for word. Skimming gives you an overview of the material that will help you understand any part of it. Your goal is not to comprehend all the details or even the structure of the author's argument. Rather, working as outlined below, aim for a general sense of the length and difficulty of the material, its organization, and its principal ideas.

- **Gauge length and level.** Is the material brief and straightforward enough to read in one sitting, or do you need more time?
- **Examine the title and introduction.** The title and first couple of paragraphs will give you a sense of the topic, the author's approach, and the main ideas. As you read them, ask yourself what you already know about the subject so that you can integrate new information with old.
- **Move from heading to heading.** Viewing the headings as headlines or as the levels of an outline will give you a feeling for which ideas the author sees as primary and which subordinate.
- **Note highlighted words.** You will likely need to learn the meanings of terms in **bold,** *italic,* or color.
- **Slow down for pictures, diagrams, tables, graphs, and other illustrations.** They often contain concentrated information.
- **Read the summary or conclusion.** These paragraphs often recap the main ideas.
- **Think over what you've skimmed.** Try to recall the central idea, or thesis, and the sequence of ideas.

3 Reading

After previewing a text, you can settle into it to learn what it has to say.

First reading

The first time through new material, read as steadily and smoothly as possible, trying to get the gist of what the author is saying.

- **Read in a place where you can concentrate.** Choose a quiet environment away from distractions such as music or talking.
- **Give yourself time.** Rushing yourself or worrying about something else you have to do will prevent you from grasping what you read.
- **Try to enjoy the work.** Seek connections between it and what you already know. Appreciate new information, interesting relationships, forceful writing, humor, good examples.
- **Make notes sparingly during this first reading.** Mark major stumbling blocks—such as a paragraph you don't understand—so that you can try to resolve them before rereading.

CULTURE LANGUAGE If English is not your first language and you come across unfamiliar words, don't stop and look up every one. You will lose more in concentration than you will gain in understanding. Instead, try to guess the meanings of unfamiliar words from their contexts, circle them, and look them up later.

Rereading

After the first reading, plan on at least one other. This time read *slowly*. Your main concern should be to grasp the content and how it is constructed. That means rereading a paragraph if you didn't get the point or using a dictionary to look up words you don't know.

Use your pen, pencil, or keyboard freely to highlight and distill the text:

- **Distinguish main ideas from supporting ideas.** Look for the central idea, or thesis, for the main idea of each paragraph or section, and for the evidence supporting ideas.
- **Learn key terms.** Understand both their meanings and their applications.
- **Discern the connections among ideas.** Be sure you see why the author moves from point A to point B to point C and how those points relate to support the central idea. It often helps to outline the text or summarize it (see below).
- **Add your own comments.** In the margins or separately, note links to other readings or to class discussions, questions to explore further, possible topics for your writing, points you find especially strong or weak. (This last category will occupy much of your time when you are expected to read critically. See pp. 158–64.)

4 Summarizing

A good way to master the content of a text is to **summarize** it: reduce it to its main points, in your own words. Some assignments

Information learned under stress is even harder to apply in stressful situations, such as taking an exam. And the lack of sleep that usually accompanies cramming makes a good performance even more unlikely. If you must cram for a test, face the fact that you can't learn everything. Spend your time reviewing main concepts and facts.

1 Reviewing and memorizing the material

Divide your class notes and reading assignments into manageable units. Reread the material, recite or write out the main ideas and selected supporting ideas and examples, and then skim for an overview. Proceed in this way through all the units of the course, returning to earlier ones as needed to refresh your memory or to relate ideas.

During this stage you should be memorizing what you don't already know by heart. Try these strategies for strengthening your memory:

- **Link new and known information.** For instance, to remember a sequence of four dates in nineteenth-century European history, link the dates to simultaneous and more familiar events in the United States.
- **Create groups of ideas or facts that make sense to you.** For instance, memorize French vocabulary words in related groups, such as words for parts of the body or parts of a house. Keep the groups small: research has shown that we can easily memorize about seven items at a time but have trouble with more.
- **Create narratives and visual images.** You may recall a story or a picture more easily than words. For instance, to remember how the economic laws of supply and demand affect the market for rental housing, you could tie the principles to a narrative about the aftermath of the 1906 San Francisco earthquake, when half the population was suddenly homeless. Or you could visualize a person who has dollar signs for eyes and is converting a spare room into a high-priced rental unit, as many did after the earthquake to meet the new demand for housing.
- **Use *mnemonic devices,* or tricks for remembering.** Say the history dates you want to remember are separated by five years, then four, then nine. By memorizing the first date and recalling $5 + 4 = 9$, you'll have command of all four dates.

2 Organizing summaries of the material

Allow time to reorganize the material in your own way, creating categories that will help you apply the information in various contexts. For instance, in studying for a biology exam, work to understand a process, such as how a plant develops or how photosynthesis occurs. Or in studying for an American government test, explain the structures of the local, state, and federal levels of government. Other useful categories include causes/effects and advantages/disadvantages. Such analytical thinking will improve your mastery of the course material and may even prepare you directly for specific essay questions.

3 Testing yourself

Convert each heading in your notes and class reading into a question. Answer in writing, going back to the class material to fill in what you don't yet know. Be sure you can define and explain all key terms. For subjects that require solving problems (such as mathematics or physics), work out a difficult problem for every type on which you will be tested. For all subjects, focus on the main themes and questions of the course. In a psychology class, for example, be certain you understand principal theories and their implications. In a literature class, test your knowledge of literary movements and genres or the relations among specific works.

When you are satisfied with your preparation, stop studying and get a good night's sleep.

4 Taking essay exams

In writing an essay for an examination, you summarize or analyze a topic, usually in several paragraphs or more and usually within a time limit. An essay question not only tests your knowledge of a subject (as short-answer and objective questions do) but also tests your ability to think critically about what you have learned.

Note For tips on taking the essay portions of the AP, SAT, and ACT exams, see Chapter 57.

Planning your time and your answer

When you first receive an exam, take a few minutes to get your bearings and plan an approach. The time spent will not be wasted.

- **Read the exam all the way through at least once.** Don't start answering any questions until you've seen them all.
- **Weigh the questions.** Determine which questions seem most important, which ones are going to be most difficult for you, and approximately how much time you'll need for each question. (Your teacher may help by assigning a point value to each question as a guide to its importance or by suggesting an amount of time for you to spend on each question.)

Planning continues when you turn to an individual essay question. Resist the temptation to rush right into an answer without some planning, for a few minutes can save you time later and help you produce a stronger essay.

- **Read the question at least twice.** You will be more likely to stick to the question and answer it fully.
- **Examine the words in the question and consider their implications.** Look especially for words such as *describe, define, explain, summarize, analyze, evaluate,* and *interpret,* each of which requires a different kind of response. Here, for example, is an essay question whose key term is *explain:*

  Question

  How did literacy contribute to the abolitionist movement leading up to the Civil War? Explain, using specific examples from your reading.

  See the box opposite, and consult other discussions of such terms on pages 26–27 and 92–102.
- **Make a brief outline of the main ideas you want to cover.** Use the back of the exam sheet or booklet for scratch paper. In the brief outline below, a student planned her answer to the history question above.

  Outline

  1. Literacy among slaves

     Douglass/Jacobs (examples)
     Writings & how they felt about literacy & freedom
  2. White abolitionists & spreading antislavery message
  3. Importance of Uncle Tom's Cabin in changing attitudes

     Popularity
     Lincoln's introduction of Stowe
     Emancipation Proclamation

- **Write a thesis statement for your essay that responds directly to the question and represents your view of the topic.** (If you are unsure of how to write a thesis statement, see pp. 29–34.) Include key phrases that you can expand with supporting evidence for your view. The thesis statement of the student whose outline appears above concisely previews a three-part answer to the sample question:

  Thesis statement

  The abolitionist movement in the years leading up to the Civil War was strengthened by the growth of literacy among black and white Americans, which helped to spread the antislavery message and change public attitudes toward slavery.

Sample instructions for essay examinations

Sample instructions	Key terms	Strategies for answers	Examples of wrong answers
Define *dyslexia* and compare and contrast it with two other learning disabilities.	Define	Specify the meaning of *dyslexia*—distinctive characteristics, ways the impairment works, etc.	Feelings of children with dyslexia. Causes of dyslexia.
	Compare and contrast	Analyze similarities and differences (severity, causes, treatments, etc.).	Similarities without differences, or vice versa.
Analyze the role of Horatio in *Hamlet*.	Analyze	Break Horatio's role into its elements (speeches, relations with other characters, etc.).	Plot summary of *Hamlet*. Description of Horatio's personality.
Explain the effects of the drug Thorazine.	Explain	Set forth the facts and theories objectively.	Argument for or against Thorazine.
	Effects	Analyze the consequences.	Reasons for prescribing Thorazine.
Discuss term limits for elected officials.	Discuss	Explain and compare the main points of view on the issue.	Analysis of one view. Argument for or against one view.
Summarize the process that resulted in the Grand Canyon.	Summarize	Distill the subject to its main points, elements, or steps.	Detailed description of the Grand Canyon.
How do you evaluate the Laffer curve as a predictor of economic growth?	Evaluate	Provide your opinion of significance or value, supported with evidence.	Explanation of the Laffer curve, without evaluation. Comparison of the Laffer curve and another predictor, without evaluation.

Starting the essay

An essay exam does not require a smooth and inviting opening. Instead, begin by stating your thesis immediately and giving an overview of the rest of your essay. Such a capsule version of your answer tells your reader (and grader) generally how much command you have and also how you plan to develop your answer. It also gets you off to a good start.

The opening statement should address the question directly and exactly, as it does in the successful essay answer beginning on the facing page. In contrast, the opening of the unsuccessful essay (opposite) restates the question but does not answer it, nor does the opening provide any sense of the writer's thesis.

Developing the essay

Develop your essay as you would develop any piece of sound academic writing:

- **Observe the methods, terms, or other special requirements of the discipline in which you are writing.**
- **Support your thesis statement with solid generalizations,** each one perhaps the topic sentence of a paragraph.
- **Support each generalization with specific, relevant evidence.**

If you observe a few *don't*s as well, your essay will have more substance:

- **Avoid filling out the essay by repeating yourself.**
- **Avoid other kinds of wordiness that pad and confuse,** whether intentionally or not. (See pp. 531–37.)
- **Avoid resorting to purely subjective feelings.** Keep focused on analysis or whatever is asked of you. (It may help to abolish the word *I* from the essay.)

The following essays illustrate a successful and an unsuccessful answer to the sample essay question on page 146 about literacy and the abolitionist movement. Both answers were written in the allotted time of forty minutes. Marginal comments on each essay highlight their effective and ineffective elements.

Successful essay answer

Introduction answering question and stating thesis

The abolitionist movement in the years leading up to the Civil War was strengthened by the growth of literacy among black and white Americans, which helped to spread the antislavery message and change public attitudes toward slavery.

First main point: literacy among slaves

Although literacy among slaves was largely prohibited in the pre-Civil War South, many slaves learned to read and write. Those who wrote about literacy clearly saw it as related to freedom. For example, Frederick Douglass, author of Narrative of the

Examples

Life of Frederick Douglass, and Harriet Ann Jacobs, author of Incidents in the Life of a Slave Girl, show in their writings the moments of learning to read and write as the moments when they understood the possibilities of freedom. Douglass points out that as he learned to read he began to imagine other worlds and that such imagining allowed him to see himself as an emancipated human being. Jacobs, reading in the attic where she hid until she escaped, came to understand how she might make her way North and become an advocate for those still in slavery.

Second main point: spreading antislavery message

Escaped, literate slaves who went North energized white abolitionists eager to spread the antislavery message. White abolitionists William Lloyd Garrison and Lydia Maria Child embraced Douglass and Jacobs, becoming their champions and citing their writings as examples of the "humanity" of the slave and as evidence of why white Northerners should support the cause of abolition. In the 1830s and 1840s, Garrison introduced Douglass to Northern white audiences, calling on them to listen to Douglass's eloquent speech and to read his powerful writing. Child spoke to audiences of white women in Boston, using Jacobs as an example of a literate Christian woman.

Third main point (with transition *also*): changing attitudes toward slavery

The literacy of white Americans also contributed to the abolitionist movement. When Harriet Beecher Stowe published the novel Uncle Tom's Cabin in 1852, her powerful, dramatic account of slavery fanned the abolitionist sentiment among an increasingly literate population. The novel quickly became extremely popular, so much so that once the Civil War began, soldiers were given copies to carry in their knapsacks. Recognizing the importance of Uncle Tom's Cabin in shaping public attitudes toward slavery, in 1862 Abraham Lincoln introduced Stowe as "the little woman who wrote the book that started this great war." A year later, he issued the Emancipation Proclamation, giving freedom to all slaves.

Examples

Conclusion, restating thesis supported by essay

It's clear that reading and writing—both the literacy of the slaves themselves and the growing literacy of the population at large—had much to do with the progression of the abolitionist movement and ultimate abolition of slavery in the United States.

Unsuccessful essay answer

Introduction, not answering question

Literacy means to be able to read and write. Slaves were not allowed to read and write, but many learned in spite of rules against it. Douglass and Jacobs are two examples of this.

No thesis statement or sense of direction

Irrelevant information

Wheel spinning, discussing literacy but not abolition

In the South, it was illegal to teach a slave to read. Whites were fined or jailed if they were caught teaching slaves to read, and slaves were punished if they were caught with books or paper. Despite this, slaves taught themselves because they knew it was something they needed if they wanted to reach freedom, and they worked hard at figuring out ways to learn their letters and to find materials to write with.

In the North, once abolitionists knew slaves could be readers and writers, they used them to spread the antislavery message. They realized how much the North needed the slaves to join in the

Name dropping without support

Discussion showing familiarity with literacy and abolition but not answering question

fight to abolish slavery. William Lloyd Garrison and Lydia Maria Child are examples of abolitionist writers and speakers who took up the slaves' cause in different ways. Harriet Beecher Stowe's novel Uncle Tom's Cabin provoked reactions from abolitionists and common readers in the North because of how it depicted the demeaning conditions of slavery. The popularity of the novel shows how many more people in the North were learning to read and write as well.

Assertion without support

As mentioned earlier, Jacobs and Douglass were examples of slaves who showed how much literacy changed their lives for the better. They came to the North and became spokespersons for the cause of emancipation, something that finally came to pass when Lincoln issued the Emancipation Proclamation in 1863.

Irrelevant and empty conclusion

Therefore, literacy was extremely important to the cause of abolition. Literacy is just as important today.

Rereading the essay

The time limit on an essay examination does not allow for the careful rethinking and revision you would give an essay or research paper. You need to write clearly and concisely the first time. But try to leave yourself a few minutes after finishing the entire exam for rereading the essay (or essays) and doing touch-ups.

- **Correct mistakes:** illegible passages, misspellings, grammatical errors, and accidental omissions.
- **Verify that your thesis is accurate**—that it is, in fact, what you ended up writing about.
- **Ensure that you have supported all your generalizations.** Cross out irrelevant ideas and details, and add any information that now seems important. (Write on another page, if necessary, keying each addition to the page on which it belongs.)

CHAPTER 8

Forming a Critical Perspective

Throughout high school and beyond, you will be expected to think, read, and write critically. **Critical** here means "skeptical," "exacting," "creative." When you operate critically, you question, test, and build on what others say and what you yourself think. The word *critical* does not mean "negative" in this context: you can think critically about something you like, don't like, or just view neutrally.

You already operate critically every day of your life, as when you probe a friendship ("What did she mean by that?") or when you discuss a movie you just saw ("Don't you think the bad guy was too obvious?"). Such questioning helps you figure out why things happen to you or what your experiences mean.

This chapter introduces more formal methods for thinking and reading critically (next page), viewing images critically (p. 166), and writing critically (p. 172). Learning and applying these methods will both engage you in and prepare you for school courses, career, and life in a democratic society:

- **Teachers and employers will expect you to think critically.** In every field, you will need to assess what you read, see, and hear and to make a good case for your own ideas.
- **Critical thinking helps you understand and express yourself.** With it, you gain insight into your actions and ideas, can weigh them against opposing views, and can persuasively articulate your reasoning and motivations.
- **Your very independence and freedom depend on your ability to think, read, and write critically.** An open democracy allows as much play for stupid and false claims as for sound ones, and the claims that seem sound often conflict with each other. Critical thinking empowers you to decide for yourself what's useful, fair, and wise—and what's not.

http://www.ablongman.com/littlebrown

Visit the companion Web site for more help and additional exercises on critical thinking, reading, and writing.

There's no denying that critical thinking, reading, and writing require discipline and hard work. Besides channeling your curiosity, paying attention, and probing, you will often need to consult experts, interpreting and evaluating their ideas. Such an approach also requires a healthy tolerance for doubt or uncertainty—that feeling you may have when the old rules don't seem to apply or when a change is frightening but still attractive. Out of uncertainty, though, comes creativity—the capacity to organize and generate knowledge, to explain, resolve, illuminate, play. Compared to passive, rote learning, creative work is more involving, more productive, and more enjoyable.

8a Thinking and reading critically

In high school much of your critical thinking will focus on written texts (a short story, a newspaper article, a Web log) or on visual objects (a photograph, a chart, a film). Like all subjects worthy of critical consideration, such works operate on at least three levels: (1) what the creator actually says or shows, (2) what the creator does not say or show but builds into the work (intentionally or not), and (3) what you think. Discovering the first of these levels—reading for comprehension—is discussed in the preceding chapter as part of effective study skills (see pp. 139–41). This chapter builds on the earlier material to help you discover the other two levels. The box below summarizes the reading techniques involved.

The techniques of critical reading are not steps in a firm sequence. You will not use all of them for all the reading you do. On some occasions, even when a close, critical reading is required, you

Techniques of critical reading

For reading a work of literature, which requires a somewhat different approach, see pp. 688–92.

- **Writing:** making notes on your reading throughout the process (next page)
- **Previewing:** getting background; skimming (p. 154)
- **Reading:** interacting with and absorbing the text (pp. 155–56)
- **Summarizing:** distilling and understanding content (p. 158)
- **Forming your critical response** (pp. 158–64)

  Analyzing: separating into parts
  Interpreting: inferring meaning and assumptions
  Synthesizing: reassembling parts; making connections
  Evaluating: judging quality and value

may simply lack the time to preview, read, and reread. (But if your reading time is continually squeezed by your schedule, you may need to rethink your schedule.) On other occasions your reason for reading (your purpose) will determine which techniques you use.

Even a publication like *People* magazine is open to different methods of reading for different purposes:

Purpose	Learn some gossip while filling time in the dentist's office.
Kind of reading	Quick, uncritical
Purpose	Examine *People* as an artifact of our popular culture that reflects and perhaps even molds contemporary values.
Kind of reading	Close, critical

Course assignments, too, differ in their requirements. A book report may require writing, previewing, reading, and summarizing but not intense critical reading. An evaluation of a journal article, in contrast, requires all the techniques discussed here.

CULTURE LANGUAGE The idea of reading critically may require you to make some adjustments if readers in your native culture tend to seek understanding or agreement more than engagement from what they read. Readers of English use texts for all kinds of reasons, including pleasure, reinforcement, information, and many others. But they also read skeptically, critically, to see the author's motives, test their own ideas, and arrive at new knowledge.

1 Writing while reading

Reading a work for comprehension and then for a critical approach is an *active* process. Making notes on what you read involves you by helping you understand how the text works, why, and what you think about it. The notes help you bring to the work your own experiences, knowledge, and questions.

If you own the material you're reading (a book, a photocopy, or a printout), you can make notes in the margins (see p. 155 for an example). If you don't own the material or if your notes won't fit in the margins, make notes separately using pen and paper or your computer. Many readers keep a **reading journal** in which they regularly work out questions and thoughts about what they read. One technique for keeping such a journal is to divide a page or computer screen into two vertical columns, the left side for the work itself, such as summary and questions, and the right side for what the work makes you think, such as agreements or doubts based on your own experiences, comparisons with other works, and ideas for writing. A two-column journal can encourage you to go beyond summarizing what you read to interacting critically with it because the blank right column will beckon you to respond. See the next page for an example of this technique.

Note Whenever you photocopy or download a document or take notes separately from the text you're reading, be sure to record all necessary information about the text's location so that you can find it again and cite it fully if you use it. See page 567 for a list of information to record.

2 Previewing the material

To make the most of your reading, it's worthwhile to skim most texts before reading word for word, forming expectations and even preliminary questions. The preview will make your reading more informed and fruitful.

Use the questions in the box below as a guide to previewing a text.

Questions for previewing a text

- **What kind of work is it?** If the text is nonfiction, is it personal, informative, persuasive, or entertaining? If the text is online, is it fairly static, such as a Web site, or one that changes often, such as a Web log? If the text is literary, determine the **genre:** is it fiction, poetry, drama, or a combination?
- **What is the work's subject and structure?** For nonfiction, follow the steps outlined on page 140 to gauge length and level, read the title and introduction for clues to the topic and main ideas, read the headings, note highlighted words (defined terms), examine illustrations, and read the summary or conclusion. For a literary text, skim several paragraphs or lines to get a feel for the work's subject and the author's writing style.
- **What are the facts of publication?** Does the date of publication suggest currency or datedness? Does the publisher or publication specialize in a particular kind of material—scholarly articles, say, or popular books? For a literary text, what might the publication date tell you about the author's use of language or the work's cultural context? For a Web document, who or what sponsors the site: an individual? a nonprofit organization? an academic institution? a corporation? a government body? (See pp. 592 and 596 on locating the authors of online sources.)
- **What do you know about the author?** Does a biography tell you about the author's publications, interests, biases, and reputation in the field? For an online source, which may be posted by an unfamiliar or anonymous author, what can you gather about the author from his or her words? If possible, trace unfamiliar authors to learn more about them.
- **What is your preliminary response?** What do you already know about the author or the topic? What questions do you have about either the topic or the author's approach to it? What biases of your own might influence your reception of the work—for instance, curiosity, boredom, or an outlook similar or opposed to the author's?

3 Reading

Reading is itself more than a one-step process. You want to understand the first level on which the text operates—what the author actually says—and begin to form your impressions.

A procedure for this stage appears in the preceding chapter (pp. 140–41). To recap: Read once through fairly smoothly, trying to appreciate the work and keeping notes to a minimum. Then read again more carefully, this time making detailed notes, to grasp the ideas and their connections and to pose questions.

Following are examples of active reading from a student, Charlene Robinson. She was responding to Thomas Sowell's "Student Loans," reprinted on the next two pages. First Robinson annotated a photocopy of the essay (the first four paragraphs appear below):

> The first lesson of economics is scarcity: There is never enough of anything to fully satisfy all those who want it.
>
> The first lesson of politics is to disregard the first lesson of economics. When politicians discover some group that is being vocal about not having as much as they want, the "solution" is to give them more. Where do politicians get this "more"? They rob Peter to pay Paul.
>
> After a while, of course, they discover that Peter doesn't have enough. Bursting with compassion, politicians rush to the rescue. Needless to say, they do not admit that robbing Peter to pay Paul was a dumb idea in the first place. On the contrary, they now rob Tom, Dick, and Harry to help Peter.
>
> The latest chapter in this long-running saga is that politicians have now suddenly discovered that many college students graduate heavily in debt. To politicians it follows, as the night follows the day, that the government should come to their rescue with the taxpayers' money.

Basic contradiction between economics and politics

biblical reference?

ironic and dismissive language

politicians = fools? or irresponsible

After reading the text, Robinson wrote about it in the journal she kept on her computer. She divided the journal into two columns, one each for the text and her responses. Here is the portion pertaining to the paragraphs above:

Text	Responses
Economics teaches lessons (1), and politics (politicians) and economics are at odds	Is economics truer or more reliable than politics? More scientific?
Politicians don't accept econ. limits—always trying to satisfy "vocal" voters by giving them what they want (2)	Politicians do spend a lot of our money. Is that what they're elected to do, or do they go too far?
"Robbing Peter to pay Paul" (2)—from the Bible (the Apostles)?	

Text	Responses
Politicians support student loan program with taxpayer funds bec. of "vocal" voters (2-4): another ex. of not accepting econ. limits	I support the loan program, too. Are politicians being irresponsible when they do? (Dismissive language underlined on copy.)

You should try to answer the questions about meaning that you raise in your annotations and your journal, and that may take another reading or some digging in other sources, such as dictionaries and encyclopedias. Recording in your journal what you think the author means will help you build an understanding of the text, and a focused attempt to summarize will help even more (see pp. 141–43 and 158). Such efforts will resolve any confusion you feel, or they will give you the confidence to say that your confusion is the fault of the author, not the reader.

EXERCISE 8.1 Reading

Reprinted below is an essay by Thomas Sowell on the federal government's student-loan program. An economist, Sowell is also a newspaper columnist and the author of many books on economics, politics, and education. This essay appeared in Sowell's collection *Is Reality Optional?*

Read this essay at least twice, until you think you understand what the author is saying. Either on these pages or separately, note your questions and reactions in writing.

Student Loans

The first lesson of economics is scarcity: There is never enough of anything to fully satisfy all those who want it. 1

The first lesson of politics is to disregard the first lesson of economics. When politicians discover some group that is being vocal about not having as much as they want, the "solution" is to give them more. Where do politicians get this "more"? They rob Peter to pay Paul. 2

After a while, of course, they discover that Peter doesn't have enough. Bursting with compassion, politicians rush to the rescue. Needless to say, they do not admit that robbing Peter to pay Paul was a dumb idea in the first place. On the contrary, they now rob Tom, Dick, and Harry to help Peter. 3

The latest chapter in this long-running saga is that politicians have now suddenly discovered that many college students graduate heavily in debt. To politicians it follows, as the night follows the day, that the government should come to their rescue with the taxpayers' money. 4

How big is this crushing burden of college students' debt that we hear so much about from politicians and media deep thinkers? For those students who graduate from public colleges owing money, the debt averages a little under $7,000. For those who graduate from private colleges owing money, the average debt is a little under $9,000. 5

Buying a very modestly priced automobile involves more debt than that. And a car loan has to be paid off faster than the ten years 6 that college graduates get to repay their student loans. Moreover, you have to keep buying cars every several years, while one college education lasts a lifetime.

College graduates of course earn higher incomes than other people. Why, then, should we panic at the thought that they have to repay loans for the education which gave them their opportunities? Even graduates with relatively modest incomes pay less than 10 percent of their annual salary on the loan the first year—with declining percentages in future years, as their pay increases. 7

Political hysteria and media hype may focus on the low-income student with a huge debt. That is where you get your heart-rending stories—even if they are not at all typical. In reality, the soaring student loans of the past decade have resulted from allowing high-income people to borrow under government programs. 8

Before 1978, college loans were available through government programs only to students whose family income was below some cut-off level. That cut-off level was about double the national average income, but at least it kept out the Rockefellers and the Vanderbilts. But, in an era of "compassion," Congress took off even those limits. 9

That opened the floodgates. No matter how rich you were, it still paid to borrow money through the government at low interest rates. The money you had set aside for your children's education could be invested somewhere else, at higher interest rates. Then, when the student loan became due, parents could pay it off with the money they had set aside—pocketing the difference in interest rates. 10

To politicians and the media, however, the rapidly growing loans showed what a great "need" there was. The fact that many students welshed when time came to repay their loans showed how "crushing" their burden of debt must be. In reality, those who welsh typically have smaller loans, but have dropped out of college before finishing. People who are irresponsible in one way are often irresponsible in other ways. 11

No small amount of the deterioration of college standards has been due to the increasingly easy availability of college to people who are not very serious about getting an education. College is not a bad place to hang out for a few years, if you have nothing better to do, and if someone else is paying for it. Its costs are staggering, but the taxpayers carry much of that burden, not only for state universities and city colleges, but also to an increasing extent even for "private" institutions. 12

Numerous government subsidies and loan programs make it possible for many people to use vast amounts of society's resources at low cost to themselves. Whether in money terms or in real terms, federal aid to higher education has increased several hundred percent since 1970. That has enabled colleges to raise their tuition by leaps and bounds and enabled professors to be paid more and more for doing less and less teaching. 13

Naturally all these beneficiaries are going to create hype and hysteria to keep more of the taxpayers' money coming in. But we would be fools to keep on writing blank checks for them. 14

> When you weigh the cost of things, in economics that's called "trade-offs." In politics, it's called "mean-spirited." Apparently, if we just took a different attitude, scarcity would go away. 15
>
> —Thomas Sowell

4 Summarizing

Summarizing a text—distilling it to its essential ideas, in your own words—is an important step for comprehending it and is discussed in detail in the previous chapter (pp. 141–43). Here, we'll look at how Charlene Robinson summarized paragraphs 1–4 of Thomas Sowell's "Student Loans." She first drafted this sentence:

Draft summary

As much as politicians would like to satisfy voters by giving them everything they ask for, the government cannot afford a student loan program.

Rereading the sentence and Sowell's paragraph, Robinson saw that this draft misread the text by asserting that the government cannot afford student loans. She realized that Sowell's point is more complicated than that and rewrote her summary:

Revised summary

As their support of the government's student loan program illustrates, politicians ignore the economic reality that using resources to benefit one group (students in debt) involves taking the resources from another group (taxpayers).

Note Using your own words when writing a summary not only helps you understand the meaning but also constitutes the first step in avoiding plagiarism. The second step is to cite the source when you use it in something written for others. See Chapter 45.

EXERCISE 8.2 Summarizing

Start where Robinson's summary of Thomas Sowell's essay ends (at paragraph 5) to summarize the entire essay. Your summary, in your own words, should not exceed one paragraph. For additional exercises in summarizing, see p. 605.

5 Developing a critical response

Once you've grasped the content of what you're reading—what the author says—then you can turn to understanding what the author does not say outright but suggests or implies or even lets slip. At this stage you are concerned with the purpose or intention of the author and with how he or she carries it out. Depending on what you are reading and why, you may examine evidence, organization, attitude, use of language, and other elements of the text.

Critical thinking and reading consist of four operations: analyzing, interpreting, synthesizing, and (often) evaluating. Although we'll look at them one by one, these operations interrelate and overlap. Indeed, the first three are often combined under the general label *analysis*, and evaluation is sometimes taken for granted as a result of the process.

Guidelines for analysis, interpretation, and synthesis

Guidelines for evaluation appear in the box on p. 164.

- **What is the purpose of your reading?**
- **What questions do you have about the work,** given your purpose?
- **What elements does the most interesting question highlight?** What elements might you ignore as a result?
- **How do you interpret the meaning and significance of the elements?** What are your assumptions about the work? What do you infer about the author's assumptions?
- **What patterns can you see in (or synthesize from) the elements?** How do the elements relate? How does this whole work relate to other works?
- **What do you conclude about the work?** What does this conclusion add to the work?

You can download these guidelines from *ablongman.com/littlebrown*. Create a copy each time you're reading a work critically, and use the questions to prompt your written responses.

In the following pages, we use two quite different examples to show how critical reading can work: *People* magazine and Sowell's "Student Loans."

Analyzing

Analysis is the separation of something into its parts or elements, the better to understand it. To see these elements in what you are reading, begin with a question that reflects your purpose in analyzing the text: why you're curious about it or what you're trying to make out of it. This question will serve as a kind of lens that highlights some features and not others.

Here are some questions you might ask about *People* magazine, listed along with the elements of the magazine that each question highlights:

Questions for analysis	Elements
Does *People* challenge or perpetuate stereotypes?	Stereotypes: explicit and implicit stereotypes or challenges in the magazine
Does the magazine offer positive role models for its readers?	Role models: text and photographs presenting positive or negative role models
Does the magazine's editorial material (articles and accompanying photographs) encourage readers to consume goods and entertainment?	Encouragement of consumption: references to goods and entertainment, focus on consumers, equation of consumption with happiness or success

As these examples show, a question for analysis concentrates your attention on relevant features and eliminates irrelevant features. To answer the question about *People*'s encouragement of consumption, you would focus on items that feature consumption and the products consumed: photographs of designer clothes and celebrities' well-appointed homes, articles on the authors of best-selling books and the stars of new movies. At the same time, you would skip over items that have little or no relevance to consumption, such as uplifting stories about families or the physically challenged.

Analyzing Thomas Sowell's "Student Loans" (pp. 156–58), you might ask these questions:

Questions for analysis	Elements
What is Sowell's attitude toward politicians?	References to politicians: content, words, tone
How does Sowell support his assertions about the loan program's costs?	Support: evidence, such as statistics and examples

A difference in the kinds of questions asked is a key distinction among academic disciplines. A sociologist neatly outlined three disciplines' approaches to poverty:

> Political science does a wonderful job looking at poverty as a policy issue. Economics does an equally wonderful job looking at it from an income-distribution perspective. But sociology asks how people in poverty live and what they aspire to.

Even within disciplines, approaches may differ. The sociologist quoted above may focus on how people in poverty live, but another may be more interested in the effects of poverty on cities or the changes in the poor population over the last fifty years. (See Chapters 49–53 for more on the disciplines' analytical questions.)

Interpreting

Identifying the elements of something is of course only the beginning: you also need to interpret the meaning or significance of the elements and of the whole. Interpretation usually requires you to infer the author's **assumptions**, opinions or beliefs about what is or what could or should be. (**Infer** means to draw a conclusion based on evidence.)

The word *assumption* here has a more specific meaning than it does in everyday usage, where it may stand for expectation ("I assume you'll pay"), speculation ("It was a mere assumption"), or error ("The report was riddled with assumptions"). Defined more strictly as what a person *supposes* to be true, assumptions are unavoidable. We all adhere to certain values and beliefs; we all form opinions. We live our lives by such assumptions.

Though pervasive, assumptions are not always stated outright. Speakers and writers may judge that their audience already understands and accepts their assumptions; they may not even be aware of their assumptions; or they may deliberately refrain from stating their assumptions for fear that the audience will disagree. That is why your job as a critical thinker is to interpret what the assumptions are.

Reasonable inferences

Like an author deciding what to say in an article, the publishers of *People* magazine make assumptions that guide their selection of content for the magazine. One set of assumptions, perhaps the most important, concerns what readers want to see: as a for-profit enterprise, the magazine naturally aims to maintain and even expand its readership (currently about 3.4 million each week). If your analysis of the magazine's editorial material reveals that much of it features consumer products, you might infer the following:

Reasonable — The publishers of *People* assume that the magazine's readers are consumers who want to see and hear about goods and entertainment.

Nowhere in *People* will you find a statement of this assumption, but the evidence implies it.

Similarly, Thomas Sowell's "Student Loans" (pp. 156–58) is based on certain assumptions, some obvious, some not so obvious. If you were analyzing Sowell's attitude toward politicians, as suggested earlier, you would focus on his statements about them. Sowell says that they "disregard the first lesson of economics" (paragraph 2), which implies that they ignore important principles (knowing that Sowell is an economist himself makes this a reasonable assumption on your part). Sowell also says that politicians "rob Peter to pay Paul," are "[b]ursting with compassion," "do not admit

. . . a dumb idea," are characters in a "long-running saga," and arrive at the solution of spending taxes "as the night follows the day"—that is, inevitably (paragraphs 2–4). From these statements and others, you can infer the following:

Reasonable Sowell assumes that politicians become compassionate when a cause is loud and popular, not necessarily just, and they act irresponsibly by trying to solve the problem with other people's (taxpayers') money.

Unreasonable inferences

Interpreting assumptions gives you greater insight into an author's intentions. But it's crucial that inferences fit the evidence of the text, as those above about *People* and Sowell's essay do. Sometimes it's tempting to read too much into the text, as in the next examples:

Faulty *People*'s publishers deliberately skew the magazine's editorial material to promote products on which they receive kickbacks. [The inference is far-fetched, even absurd. It would be reasonable only if there were hard evidence of kickbacks.]

Faulty Sowell thinks that politicians should not be entrusted with running the country. [The inference misreads Sowell. Although he does not outline a solution for politicians' irresponsibility, there's no evidence that he would overhaul our democratic political system.]

Faulty inferences like these are often based on the reader's *own* assumptions about the text or its subject. When thinking and reading critically, you need to look hard at *your* ideas, too.

Synthesizing

If you stopped at analysis and interpretation, critical thinking and reading might leave you with a pile of elements and possible meanings but no vision of the whole. With **synthesis** you make connections among parts *or* among wholes. You create a new whole by drawing conclusions about relationships and implications.

The following conclusion pulls together the earlier analysis of *People* magazine's editorial content and the interpretation of the publisher's assumptions about readers:

Conclusion *People* magazine appeals to its readers' urge to consume by displaying, discussing, and glamorizing consumer goods.

The statement below about Thomas Sowell's essay "Student Loans" connects his assumptions about politicians to a larger idea also implied by the essay:

Conclusion Sowell's view that politicians are irresponsible with taxpayers' money reflects his overall opinion that the laws of economics, not politics, should drive government.

Synthesis may involve working within the text, as in the preceding examples, or it may take you outside the text to the surroundings. (This emphasis is important in research writing, as discussed on pp. 598–99.) The following questions can help you investigate the context of a work:

- **How does the work compare with works by others?** For instance, how does *People*'s juxtaposition of articles and advertisements compare with that in similar magazines, such as *Us Weekly, Entertainment Weekly,* and *Interview*? Or how have other writers responded to Sowell's views on student loans?
- **How does the work fit into the context of other works by the same author or group?** What distinguishes *People* from the many other magazines published by Time Inc., such as *Time* magazine, *Sports Illustrated, Family Circle,* and *Fortune*? How do Sowell's views on student loans typify, or not, the author's other writings on political and economic issues?
- **What cultural, economic, or political forces influence the work?** Why, for instance, are *People* and other celebrity magazines increasingly popular with readers? What other examples might Sowell have given to illustrate his view that economics, not politics, should determine government spending?
- **What historical forces influence the work?** What changes does *People* reflect in how readers choose magazines? How has the indebtedness of college students changed over recent decades?

To create links among the elements of a work or between a work and its context, it helps (again) to write while reading and thinking. The active reading recommended earlier is the place to start, as you note your questions and opinions about the text. You can also create connections with a combination of writing and drawing: start with your notes, expand them as needed to take account of context, and draw connections between related thoughts with lines and arrows. (On a word processor you can use the Highlight function or different colors to link related ideas, or use the Comment function to annotate connections.) You want to open up your thinking, so experiment freely.

With synthesis, you create something different from what you started with. To the supermarket shopper reading *People* while standing in line, the magazine may be entertaining and inconsequential. To you—after a critical reading in which you analyze, interpret, and synthesize—the magazine is (at least in part) a significant vehicle of our consumer culture. The difference depends entirely on the critical reading.

Evaluating

Many critical reading and writing assignments end at analysis, interpretation, and synthesis: you explain your understanding of what the author says and doesn't say. Only if you are expected to **evaluate** the work will you state and defend the judgments you've made about its quality and its significance.

You'll inevitably form judgments while reading the work: *What a striking series of images* or *That just isn't enough evidence.* In evaluating, you collect your judgments, determine that they are generally applicable and are themselves not trivial, and turn them into assertions: *The poet creates fresh, intensely vivid images. The author does not summon the evidence to support his case.* And you support these statements with citations from the text.

Evaluation takes a certain amount of confidence. You may think that you lack the expertise to cast judgment on another's writing, especially if the text is difficult or the author well known. True, the more informed you are, the better a critical reader you are. But conscientious reading and analysis will give you the internal authority to judge a work *as it stands* and *as it seems to you,* against your own unique bundle of experiences, observations, and attitudes.

The box below gives questions that can help you evaluate many kinds of works. There's more on evaluation (including evaluation of online sources) on pages 588–97. For arguments and in academic disciplines, you'll require additional, more specific criteria. See Chapters 9, 11, and 49–53.

Guidelines for evaluation

- **What are your reactions to the work?** What in the work are you responding to?
- **How sound are the work's central idea and evidence?**
- **How well does the author achieve his or her purpose?** How worthwhile is the purpose?
- **How authoritative, trustworthy, and sincere is the author?**
- **How unified and coherent is the work?** Do its parts all support a central idea and clearly relate to one another?
- **What do color, graphics, or (online) sound or video contribute to the work?** Do such elements add meaning or merely decoration?
- **What is the overall quality and significance of the work?**
- **Do you agree or disagree with the work?** Can you support, refute, or extend it?

You can download these guidelines from *ablongman.com/littlebrown.* Create a copy each time you're evaluating a work, and use the questions to prompt your written responses.

EXERCISE 8.3 Thinking critically

Following are some statements about the communications media. Use systematic critical thinking to understand not only what the statement says but also why its author might have said it. As in the example, do your thinking in writing: the act of writing will help you think, and your notes will help you discuss your ideas with your classmates. (You can do this exercise online at *ablongman.com/littlebrown.*)

Example:

Statement: Every year sees the disappearance of more book publishers because the larger companies gobble up the smaller ones.

Analysis: Why did the author make this statement? Certain words reveal the author's purpose: *disappearance of more book publishers; because; larger companies gobble up smaller ones.*

Interpretation: *More* book publishers means others have disappeared. *Because* specifies cause. *Gobble up* implies consumption, predator to prey. Author's assumptions: Large publishers behave like predators. The predatory behavior of large companies causes the disappearance of small companies. The more publishing companies there are, the better.

Synthesis: The author objects to the predatory behavior of large publishing companies, which he or she holds responsible for eliminating small companies and reducing the total number of companies.

Evaluation: This biased statement against large publishers holds them responsible for the shrinking number of book publishers. But are the large companies solely responsible? And why is the shrinking necessarily bad?

1. Newspapers and newsmagazines are better news sources than television because they demand reading, not just viewing.
2. Radio call-in shows are the true democratic forum, giving voice to people of all persuasions.
3. Online communication threatens to undermine our ability to interact face to face.

EXERCISE 8.4 Reading an essay critically

Reread Thomas Sowell's "Student Loans" (pp. 156–58) in order to form your own critical response to it. Follow the guidelines for analysis, interpretation, synthesis, and evaluation in the boxes on pages 159 and 164. Focus on any elements suggested by your question about the text: possibilities are assumptions, evidence, organization, use of language, tone, authority, vision of education or students. Be sure to write while reading and thinking; your notes will help your analysis and enhance your creativity, and they will be essential for writing about the selection (Exercise 8.10, p. 179).

EXERCISE 8.5 Reading a magazine critically

Do your own critical reading of *People* or another magazine. What do you see beyond the obvious? What questions does your reading raise? Let the guidelines on pages 159 and 164 direct your response, and do your work in writing.

8b Viewing images critically

Every day we are bombarded with images—pictures on billboards, commercials on television, graphs and charts in newspapers and textbooks, to name just a few examples. Most images slide by without our noticing them, or so we think. But images, sometimes even more than text, can influence us covertly. Their creators have purposes, some worthy, some not, and understanding those purposes requires critical reading. The method parallels that in the previous section for reading text critically: write while reading, preview, read for comprehension, analyze, interpret, synthesize, and (often) evaluate.

1 Writing while reading an image

Writing as you read an image helps you view it deliberately and record your impressions precisely. If possible, print a copy of the image or scan it into your reading journal so that you can write comments in the image margins. The example on the next page shows how one student, John Latner, annotated an image he was reading.

2 Previewing an image

Your first step in exploring an image is to form initial impressions of the work's origin and purpose and to note distinctive features. This previewing process is like the one for previewing a text (p. 154):

Questions for previewing an image

- **What do you see?** What is most striking about the image? What is its subject? What is the gist of any text or symbols? What is the overall effect of the image?
- **What are the facts of publication?** Where did you first see the image? Do you think the image was created especially for that location or for others as well? What can you tell about when the image was created?
- **What do you know about the person or group that created the image?** For instance, was the creator an artist, scholar, news organization, or corporation? What seems to have been the creator's purpose?
- **What is your preliminary response?** What about the image interests, confuses, or disturbs you? Are the form, style, and subject familiar or unfamiliar? How might your knowledge, experiences, and values influence your reception of the image?

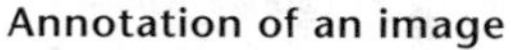

Annotation of an image

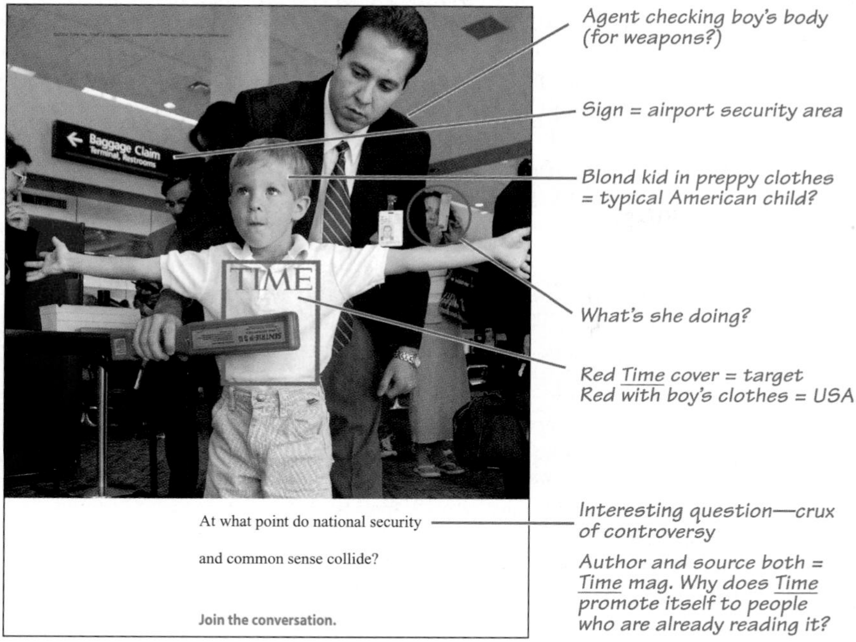

Baggage Claim
Terminal, Restrooms
TIME
At what point do national security and common sense collide?
Join the conversation.
Agent checking boy's body (for weapons?)
Sign = airport security area
Blond kid in preppy clothes = typical American child?
What's she doing?
Red Time cover = target
Red with boy's clothes = USA
Interesting question—crux of controversy
Author and source both = Time mag. Why does Time promote itself to people who are already reading it?

Advertisement appearing in *Time* magazine, October 7, 2002

3 Reading an image

Reading an image requires the same level of concentration as reading a text. Plan to spend more than one session working with the image to absorb its meaning and purpose and then to analyze and maybe challenge its message.

Try to answer the following questions about the image. If some answers aren't clear at this point, skip the question until later.

- **What is the purpose of the image?** Is it mainly explanatory, conveying information, or is it argumentative, trying to convince readers of something or persuade them to act? What information or point of view does it seem intended to get across?
- **Who is the intended audience for the image?** What does the source of the image, including its publication facts, tell about the image creator's expectations for readers' knowledge, interests, and attitudes? What do the features of the image itself add to your impression?

- **What do any words or symbols add to the image?** Whether located on the image or outside it (such as in a caption), do words or symbols add information, focus your attention, or alter your impression of the image?
- **What people, places, things, or action does the image show?** Does the image tell a story? Do its characters or other features tap into your knowledge, or are they unfamiliar?
- **What is the form of the image?** Is it a photograph, advertisement, painting, graph, diagram, cartoon, or something else? How do its content and apparent purpose and audience relate to its form?

In the following journal notes, the student John Latner answered questions like those above about the advertisement for *Time* magazine (previous page) that he had already annotated.

Image details	Responses
Red Time border positioned over boy's chest and around scanning wand	The framing of the wand makes this clearly a story about airport (and homeland) security, not about the boy or the guard.
Boy with blond hair and blue eyes, USA colors in clothes and Time border	The boy is a stereotyped all-American kid, almost doll-like. Most American kids don't look like this, though. How would the ad be different if the kid looked different—with dark skin and dark hair?
Caption asking "At what point do national security and common sense collide?"	The position of the wand seems to imply that the point of collision is in the middle of the boy or maybe the moment when an innocent-looking kid is treated as a security threat. (But aren't there lots of kids throughout history who have become soldiers or were used by adults as weapons? Is it completely illogical to consider kids as potentially dangerous?) "Common sense" seems to mean taking things at face value. Is that the view of people who read Time? Wouldn't it be just the opposite—people buy the mag. because they know there's more to the story than meets the eye? Confusing.

4 Analyzing an image

Elements for analysis

As when analyzing a written work, you analyze an image by identifying its elements. The image elements you might consider appear in the box opposite. Keep in mind that an image is a visual *composition* whose every element likely reflects a deliberate effort to communicate. Still, few images include all the elements, and you can narrow the list further by posing a question about the image you are reading, as illustrated on the next page.

Elements of images

- **Emphasis:** Most images pull your eyes to certain features: a graph line moving sharply upward, a provocative figure, bright color, thick lines, light against shadow, and so on. The cropping of a photograph or, say, the date range in a chart will also reflect what the image creator considers most important.
- **Narration:** Most images tell stories, whether in a sequence (a TV commercial or a graph showing changes over time) or at a single moment (a photograph, a painting, or a pie chart). Sometimes dialog or a title or caption contributes to the story.
- **Point of view:** The image creator influences responses by taking account of both the viewer's physical relation to the image subject—for instance, whether it is seen head-on or from above—and the viewer's assumed attitude toward the subject.
- **Arrangement:** Patterns among colors or forms, figures in the foreground and background, and elements that are juxtaposed or set apart contribute to the image's meaning and effect.
- **Color:** An image's colors can direct the viewer's attention and convey the creator's attitude toward the subject. Color may also suggest a mood, an era, a cultural connection, or another frame for viewing the image.
- **Characterization:** The figures and objects in an image have certain qualities—sympathetic or not, desirable or not, and so on. Their characteristics reflect the roles they play in the image's story.
- **Context:** The source of an image or the background in an image affects its meaning, whether it is a graph from a scholarly journal or a photo of a car on a sunny beach.
- **Tension:** Images often communicate a problem or seize attention with features that seem wrong, such as misspelled or misaligned words, distorted figures, or controversial relations between characters.
- **Allusions:** An **allusion** is a reference to something the audience is likely to recognize and respond to. Examples include a cultural symbol such as a dollar sign, a mythological figure such as a unicorn, or a familiar movie character such as Darth Vader from *Star Wars*.

Question for analysis

As discussed on pages 159–60, you can focus your analysis of elements by framing your main interest in the image as a question. John

Latner concentrated his analysis of the *Time* ad with the question *Does the ad challenge readers to view airport security differently, or does it just reinforce common perceptions?* The question led Latner to focus on certain elements of the ad and to ignore others, as seen in the following entry from his reading journal:

Image elements	**Responses**
Emphasis	The ad foregrounds the boy (especially his eyes looking upward), the security agent, and the familiar Time cover over a scanner like a target around a bull's-eye.
Point of view	We identify with the boy—so innocent and uncomfortable. We identify even more because we're positioned at his eye level. The security agent almost hovers over us, too.
Narration	The collision point of the caption ("At what point do national security and common sense collide?") seems to be the bull's-eye of the scanning wand—treating a boy as a security threat. The ad's commonsense opinion seems to be that airport security procedures are flawed, unfair. But the caption's question mark and "Join the conversation" imply that there may be other views, too.
Color	The boy is much the brightest figure in the image, and his brightness emphasizes his fairness. His clothes are in patriotic colors (white shirt, blue and white pants, red tag on the pants). The Time cover adds more red to the flag colors.
Allusions	The familiar Time cover and the security checkpoint stand out. Also, is there Christian symbolism in the boy's outstretched arms, open hands, and upward gaze—like Christ on the cross?
Characterization	The boy plays the role of unlikely terrorist, maybe even a victim. He is the stereotyped all-American kid, blond, blue-eyed, wholesome. The security agent is the boy's "interrogator"—serious, dark, even menacing.
Tension	The security agent hovering over the boy is disturbing. So are what they're doing and the whole busy scene behind them—bound to evoke a negative response from anyone who's experienced air travel in recent years.

Sample images for analysis

The following images give you a chance to analyze selective elements in two kinds of images, a painting and a page from a Web site. Questions in the annotations can help to open up your thinking.

Elements in a painting

Emphasis: What does light emphasize? Where does the painting guide your eyes next, and how?

Narration: What story does the painting tell? How does it tell the story?

Color: What mood do the colors create? How do they relate to the subject?

Characterization: What role does the central figure play in the story? What other characters can you identify?

Tension: What elements are unexpected, even disturbing?

Liberty's Children, 2002, painting by Ron Oden

Elements of a Web page

Narration: What story is being told by the Web page as a whole and by the chart? Who is telling the story, and why?

Arrangement: How are the bars in the chart organized? What does their arrangement contribute to the story?

Point of view: What can you tell about the intended audience? What is the audience's interest in the story?

Context: How do the CNN source and the page's banner and titles affect the story being told by the chart?

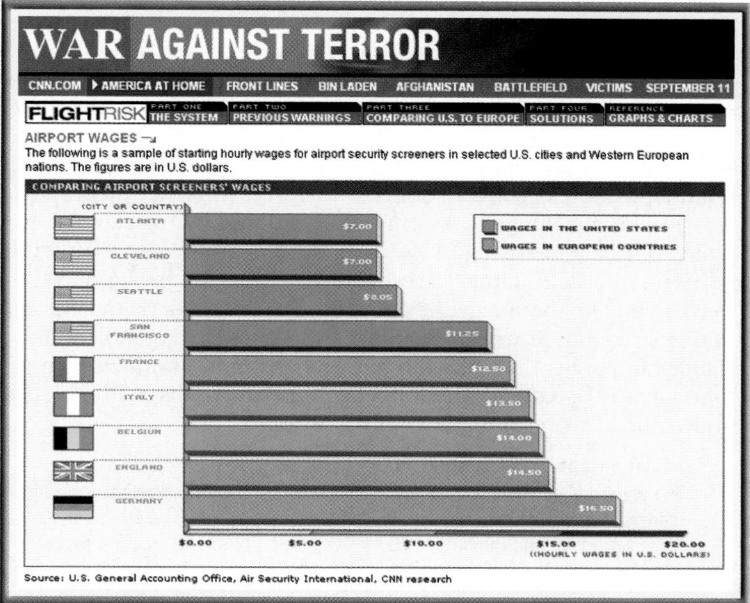

Web page from *CNN.com*, 2001

5 Interpreting an image

The strategies for interpreting an image parallel those for interpreting a written text (pp. 161–62). In this process you look more deeply at the elements, considering them in relation to the image creator's likely assumptions and intentions. You aim to draw reasonable inferences about *why* the image looks as it does. Here's a reasonable inference about the *Time* advertisement on page 167:

Reasonable — The creators of the *Time* ad assume that the magazine's readers are concerned about both national security and the treatment of air travelers.

This inference is supported by the ad's text and photograph: the caption specifically mentions national security, and the photograph clearly emphasizes the experience of air travelers. In contrast, the next inference is *not* reasonable because it leaps to a conclusion that is not supported by the ad:

Faulty — The creators of the *Time* ad assume that the magazine's readers believe airport security checkpoints are unnecessary.

The ad implies that readers may object to some checkpoint procedures, not that they believe the checkpoints themselves are unnecessary.

6 Synthesizing ideas about an image

As discussed on pages 162–63, with synthesis you take analysis and interpretation a step further to consider how a work's elements and underlying assumptions mesh: How do the elements and assumptions relate to one another? What is the overall message of the image? You may also expand your synthesis to view the whole image in a larger context: How does the work compare with works by others? How does the work fit into the context of other works by the same author or group? What cultural, economic, political, or historical forces influence the work?

Placing an image in its context often requires research. For instance, to learn more about the assumptions underlying the *Time* advertisement, John Latner investigated data on the backgrounds and perceptions of the magazine's readers. And to understand the marketing strategies at work in the image, he consulted a book on advertising campaigns that, like the *Time* ad, promote products to people who already use them. The following entry from his reading journal shows the ideas resulting from his synthesis:

Social and political context

The emphasis on the boy plays to two views often held by travelers and Time readers: airport searches needlessly inconvenience people who are highly unlikely to be terrorists, and the better alternative may be profiling, treating people differently on the basis of physical characteristics such as skin and hair color.

"Common sense"
The ad implies certain understandings of readers' "common sense" about national security and airport security: security is a serious issue, many airport procedures are unreasonably broad based and time consuming, and profiling might be used to focus on people who look like terrorists. The ad doesn't challenge these perceptions, but with "Join the conversation" it does suggest that the problem is open to interpretation.

Marketing context
The provocative photograph seems to promise an unconventional perspective on the subject, but the ad mostly reinforces the views assumed to be held by readers. Time's strategy reflects marketing studies: people are more likely to purchase a product that reflects their own opinions and values, even when they're acquiring it to broaden their understanding.

7 Evaluating an image

If your critical reading moves on to evaluation, you'll form judgments about the quality and significance of the image. Questions to ask for evaluation appear in the box on page 164. Briefly: Is the message of the image accurate and fair, or is it distorted and biased? Can you support, refute, or extend the message? Does the image achieve its apparent purpose, and is the purpose worthwhile? How does the image affect you?

See John Latner's paper on pages 177–79 for an evaluation of the *Time* advertisement.

EXERCISE 8.6 Viewing an image critically

Review the list of visual elements on page 169 and then take another close look at the *Time* advertisement on page 167. Using the guidelines on the preceding pages, draw your own conclusions about the ad. Write while reading and thinking to help yourself concentrate and develop ideas. A writing suggestion based on this activity appears in Exercise 8.11, page 179.

EXERCISE 8.7 Viewing an image critically

Select either the painting *Liberty's Children* (p. 171) or the CNN Web page (p. 171) to examine in more detail. Using the guidelines on the preceding pages, read the image methodically and critically. Write down your ideas. A writing suggestion based on this activity appears in Exercise 8.12, page 179.

EXERCISE 8.8 Comparing images critically

Each image in this section—the advertisement, the painting, and the Web page—communicates a perspective on the causes or effects of terrorism in the United States. Using the guidelines on the preceding pages, read these three images as a group, focusing on the story they tell together and on their relative effectiveness in contributing to that story. Write down your responses. A writing suggestion based on this activity appears in Exercise 8.13, page 179.

8c Writing critically

Critical writing, often called *critique,* is largely influenced by the discipline or profession in which it occurs. Thus the topic is covered more extensively in Chapters 10–11 (argument), 50 (literature), 51 (other humanities), 52 (social sciences), and 53 (natural and applied sciences). In this introduction, we'll look at two illustrations, one on a written work and the other on an image.

Note Critical writing is *not* summarizing. You may write a summary to clarify for yourself what an author says or what an image shows, and you may briefly summarize a work in your own larger piece of writing. But your job in critical writing is not just to report; it is to transmit your analysis, interpretation, synthesis, and perhaps evaluation of the text.

1 Writing critically about a text

The following essay by the student Charlene Robinson responds to Thomas Sowell's "Student Loans." Robinson arrived at her response through the process of critical reading outlined in this chapter and then by gathering and organizing her ideas, developing her own central idea (or thesis) about Sowell's text, and drafting and revising until she believed she had supported her central idea.

Robinson does not assume that her readers see the same things in Sowell's essay or share her views, so she offers evidence of Sowell's ideas in the form of direct quotations, summaries, and paraphrases (restatements in her own words). (See pp. 601–05 for more on these techniques.) Robinson then documents these borrowings from Sowell using the style of the Modern Language Association (MLA): the numbers in parentheses are page numbers in the book containing Sowell's essay, listed at the end as a "work cited." (See Chapter 47 for more on MLA style.)

Weighing the Costs

Introduction

Summary of Sowell's essay

In his essay "Student Loans," the economist Thomas Sowell challenges the US government's student-loan program for several reasons: a scarce resource (taxpayers' money) goes to many undeserving students, a high number of recipients fail to repay their loans, and the easy availability of money has led to both lower academic standards and higher college tuitions. Sowell wants his readers to "weigh the costs of things" (133) in order to see, as he does, that the loan program should not receive so much government funding. But does he provide the evidence of cost and other problems to lead the reader to agree with him? The answer is no, because hard evidence is less common than debatable and unsupported assumptions about students, scarcity, and the value of education.

Robinson's critical question

Thesis statement

Sowell's portrait of student-loan recipients is questionable. It is based on averages, some statistical and some not, but averages are often deceptive. For example, Sowell cites college graduates' low average debt of $7,000 to $9,000 (131) without acknowledging the fact that many students' debt is much higher or giving the full range of statistics. Similarly, Sowell dismisses "heart-rending stories" of "the low-income student with a huge debt" as "not at all typical" (132), yet he invents his own exaggerated version of the typical loan recipient: an affluent slacker ("Rockefellers" and "Vanderbilts") for whom college is a "place to hang out for a few years" sponging off the government, while his or her parents clear a profit from making use of the loan program (132). Although such students (and parents) may well exist, are they really typical? Sowell does not offer any data one way or the other—for instance, how many loan recipients come from each income group, what percentage of loan funds go to each group, how many loan recipients receive significant help from their parents, and how many receive none.

First main point

Evidence for first point: paraphrases and quotations from Sowell's text

Evidence for first point: Sowell's omissions

Another set of assumptions in the essay has to do with "scarcity": "There is never enough of anything to fully satisfy all those who want it," Sowell says (131). This statement appeals to readers' common sense, but does the "lesson" of scarcity necessarily apply to the student-loan program? Sowell omits many important figures needed to prove that the nation's resources are too scarce to support the program, such as the total cost of the program, its percentage of the total education budget and the total federal budget, and its cost compared to the cost of defense, Medicare, and other expensive programs. Moreover, Sowell does not mention the interest paid by loan recipients, even though the interest must offset some of the costs of running the program and covering unpaid loans.

Transition to second main point

Second main point

Evidence for second point: Sowell's omissions

The most fundamental and most debatable assumption underlying Sowell's essay is that higher education is a kind of commodity that not everyone is entitled to. In order to diminish the importance of graduates' average debt from education loans, Sowell claims that a car loan will probably be higher (131). This comparison between education and an automobile

Third main point

Evidence for third point: paraphrases and quotations of Sowell's text implies that the two are somehow equal as products and that an affordable higher education is no more a right than a new car is. Sowell also condemns the "irresponsible" students who drop out of school and "the increasingly easy availability of college to people who are not very serious about getting an education" (132). But he overlooks the value of encouraging education, including education of those who don't finish college or who aren't scholars. For many in the United States, education has a greater value than that of a mere commodity like a car. And even from an economic perspective such as Sowell's, the cost to society of an uneducated public needs to be taken into account.

Conclusion

Acknowledgment of Sowell's concerns

Summary of three main points

Return to theme of introduction: weighing costs

Sowell writes with conviction, and his concerns are valid: high taxes, waste, unfairness, declining educational standards, obtrusive government. However, the essay's flaws make it unlikely that Sowell could convince readers who do not already agree with him. He does not support his portrait of the typical loan recipient, he fails to demonstrate a lack of resources for the loan program, and he neglects the special nature of education compared to other services and products. Sowell may have the evidence to back up his assumptions, but by omitting it he himself does not truly weigh the costs of the loan program.

Reference to complete source (in MLA style)

Work Cited

Sowell, Thomas. "Student Loans." Is Reality Optional? and Other Essays. Stanford: Hoover, 1993. 131-33.

—Charlene Robinson (student)

2 Writing critically about an image

The essay below, by the student John Latner, responds to the *Time* magazine advertisement. As you've seen earlier in this chapter, Latner examined the image over several stages, each time discovering more in it and gradually developing his own ideas. In his paper Latner takes pains to be sure that readers will see the image as he does: he reproduces the ad, captions it, and clearly describes its features. He cites his sources using the style of the Modern Language Association (Chapter 47). (All but one of Latner's text citations lack page numbers because the sources themselves are not numbered.)

Note An image is a source just as a written work is, and like a written source it must be acknowledged. Latner cites the *Time* ad both in the image caption and in the list of works cited. If he published his paper online, he would also need to seek the copyright owner's permission to use the image. See pages 615–16 for more about acknowledging sources and pages 617–18 for more about permissions for online publication.

Playing It Safe

Introduction

At first glance, the "Boy at Security" advertisement for Time magazine (fig. 1) is both a humorous and a provocative depiction of a troubling subject: airport security since September 11, 2001. A boy with an angelic face and a nervous expression stands obediently as a security agent passes a large scanner over his chest. The familiar red border and banner of a Time cover surround the scanner, making it the bull's-eye of a target. The caption reads, "At what point do national security and common sense collide?" and then "Join the conversation." This eye-catching ad implies that by reading Time magazine consumers will gain alternative perspectives on important issues. However, a close examination of the ad reveals that it actually reinforces public opinion instead of challenging it.

Description of the image

Thesis statement

Fig. 1. "Boy at Security," an advertisement appearing in Time magazine, promotes the magazine as a source of challenging views on current events. From Time 7 Oct. 2002: 42.

Caption giving the ad's main idea and source

The awkward stance of the boy evokes the common complaint that airport security is intrusive and time consuming (Sharkey). This attitude is encouraged by the cropping of the photograph, which puts the boy at our eye level (increasing our empathy with him) and makes the looming security agent seem intimidating. As the agent does his work, the boy waits uncomfortably and travelers mill around in the background. The ad represents a travel experience that is familiar to the target audience:

First main point

Evidence for first point: news article (Sharkey) and Latner's interpretation of image details

Evidence for first point: survey of magazine's readers

according to a recent survey, the typical Time reader is a white, middle-income adult who takes commercial flights at least yearly (Schulman, Ronca, and Bucuvalas).

Second main point

Evidence for second point: news article

Evidence for second point: Latner's interpretation of image details

The advertisement also taps into a dilemma and debate about airport security. Everyone wants terrorists stopped from boarding airplanes, but many people believe that security procedures go too far by treating all travelers as potential threats, even those who aren't the least bit suspicious (Sharkey). The boy in the ad is a most unlikely terrorist. Besides being quite young, he looks like the stereotype of the all-American child: blond, blue-eyed, neatly dressed in patriotic colors (white shirt and blue and white pants with a red tag). With such a figure at its center, the ad implies and appeals to a preference for profiling travelers—singling people out for suspicion solely because of nationality or physical traits such as skin and hair color. Judging from the public comments in the news media, many Americans, reluctantly or not, favor profiling over the discomfort and inconvenience caused by searching everyone.

Latner's critical question

Evidence for answer: findings of an analyst

Latner's interpretation of source and application to the image

Why would a news magazine print a seemingly provocative ad that actually does little more than appeal to beliefs that its readers already hold? An answer can be found in the research of marketing analyst Marc Gobe, who has found that customers prefer to build long-term relationships with companies that represent their views (32). The intended audience for the Time ad is people who are already reading the magazine. The ad attempts to reinforce the loyalty of these customers by flattering their eagerness for "conversation." The attention-getting image communicates a cutting-edge approach—something to make this magazine seem more interesting than its competitors—but the ad doesn't risk challenging and thus alienating readers.

Conclusion

Possible alternatives to ad's safe approach

Summary and restatement of thesis

If Time truly wanted to demonstrate that it offers rich and diverse opinions on airport security and other issues, it might have juxtaposed two different passengers receiving the same treatment: the seemingly innocent child and someone fitting the profile of a terrorist. Or, to challenge readers' assumptions, the existing photograph might have shown the boy looking defiantly into the camera, raising doubts about his innocence. Either image would have been more thought provoking, but at the risk of disturbing consumers instead of attracting them to the magazine. Ultimately, the Time advertisement achieves its apparent purpose because it creates the illusion of daring without actually taking readers outside their comfort zone.

Works Cited

Gobe, Marc. Citizen Brand. New York: Allworth, 2002.

Schulman, Ronca, and Bucuvalas, Inc. "Time Magazine/SRBI—March 15-17, 2005, Survey." 18 Mar. 2005. 27 May 2005 <http://www.srbi.com/TimePoll-3-18-05b.pdf>.

Sharkey, Joe. "Pants and Profiling: Life on the Front Lines of Checkpoint Security at the Nation's Airports." New York Times on the Web 9 Jan. 2003. 20 May 2005 <http://travel2.nytimes.com/mem/travel/article-page.html?res=9D07E2DE1239>.

Time magazine. Advertisement. Time 7 Oct. 2002: 42.

List of works cited (in MLA style)

—John Latner (student)

EXERCISE 8.9 Responding to critical writing

Read Charlene Robinson's and John Latner's essays carefully. Do you think the authors' critiques are accurate and fair? Are they perceptive? Do the authors provide enough evidence to convince you of their points? Do they miss anything you would have mentioned? Write your responses to one of the essays in a brief critique of your own. (You can do this exercise online at *ablongman.com/littlebrown.*)

EXERCISE 8.10 Writing critically about a text

Write an essay based on your own critical reading of Thomas Sowell's "Student Loans" (Exercise 8.4, p. 165). Your critique may be entirely different from Charlene Robinson's, or you may have developed some of the same points. If there are similarities, they should be expressed and supported in your own way, in the context of your own critical perspective.

EXERCISE 8.11 Writing critically about an image

Write an essay based on your own critical reading of the *Time* advertisement (Exercise 8.6, p. 173). Your critique may be entirely different from John Latner's, or you may have developed some of the same points. If there are similarities, they should be expressed and supported in your own way, in the context of your own critical perspective.

EXERCISE 8.12 Writing critically about an image

Write an essay based on your critical reading of the painting *Liberty's Children* or the CNN Web page (Exercise 8.7, p. 173).

EXERCISE 8.13 Writing critically about several images

Write an essay based on your critical reading and comparison of the three images in this chapter (Exercise 8.8, p. 173).

CHAPTER 9

Reading Arguments Critically

Argument is writing that attempts to open readers' minds to an opinion, change readers' own opinions, or move readers to action. A good argument is neither a cold exercise in logic nor an attempt to beat others into submission. It is a work of negotiation and problem solving in which both writer and reader search for the knowledge that will create common ground between them.

Of course, not all arguments are "good." Whether deliberately or not, some are unclear, incomplete, misleading, or downright false. The negotiation fails; the problem remains unsolved. This chapter will help you read written arguments critically, and the next chapter will help you write effective arguments. After that, in Chapter 11, you'll see how to read and use visual arguments.

CULTURE LANGUAGE The ways of reading and writing arguments described in this chapter and the next may be uncomfortable to you if your native culture approaches such writing differently. In some cultures, for example, a writer is expected to begin indirectly, to avoid asserting his or her opinion outright, or to establish a compromise rather than argue a position. In American academic and business settings, readers and writers look or aim for a well-articulated opinion, evidence gathered from many sources, and a direct and concise argument for the opinion.

9a Recognizing the elements of argument

Few arguments are an easy read. Most demand the attentive critical reading discussed in the previous chapter. (If you haven't read pp. 152–64, you should do so before continuing.) As a reader of argument, your purpose will almost always be the same: you'll want to know whether you should be convinced by the argument. This

http://www.ablongman.com/littlebrown

Visit the companion Web site for more help and additional exercises on reading arguments critically.

purpose focuses your attention on the elements that make an argument convincing, or not.

In a scheme adapted from the work of the British philosopher Stephen Toulmin, an argument has three main elements:

- **Claims:** positive statements that require support. In a written argument the central claim is stated outright in a **thesis statement** (see p. 29). This central claim is what the argument is about. For instance:

  In both its space and its equipment, the school's chemistry classroom is outdated.

  Several minor claims, such as that the present equipment is inadequate, will contribute to the central assertion.
- **Evidence:** the facts, examples, expert opinions, and other information that support the claims. (Toulmin calls evidence *data* or *grounds,* terms that indicate both its specificity and its work as an argument's foundation.) Evidence to support the preceding claim might include the following:

  The present classroom's square feet
  An inventory of equipment
  The testimony of science teachers

  Like the claims, the evidence is always stated outright.
- **Assumptions:** the writer's underlying (and often unstated) beliefs, opinions, principles, or inferences that tie the evidence to the claims. (Toulmin calls these assumptions *warrants:* they justify making the claims on the basis of the evidence provided.) For instance, the following assumption might connect the evidence of professors' testimony with the claim that a new lab is needed:

  Science teachers are the most capable of evaluating the present classroom's quality.

In the following pages, we'll examine each of these elements along with several others: tone and language, reasonableness, and common errors in reasoning. Charlene Robinson's "Weighing the Costs" in the previous chapter (pp. 174–76) provides a good example of critically reading an argument for its claims, evidence, and assumptions.

Note This chapter focuses on reading nonfiction arguments such as those found in speeches, magazines, and books on current issues. Literary works can also be read as arguments in which the author, working from a set of assumptions, tries to persuade readers to accept a point of view by making implicit claims and supporting them with the evidence of character, plot, symbols, and other elements. For more on reading arguments in literary works, see pages 696–97.

Questions for critically reading an argument

- What **claims** does the writer make?
- What kinds and quality of **evidence** does the writer provide to support the claims?
- What **assumptions** underlie the argument, connecting evidence to claims?
- What is the writer's **tone?** How does the writer use **language?**
- Is the writer **reasonable?**
- Is the argument logical? Has the writer committed any **fallacies?**
- Are you convinced by the argument? Why or why not?

You can download these questions from *ablongman.com/littlebrown*. Create a copy for each argument you are reading, and use the questions to prompt your written responses.

9b Testing claims

The claims or assertions in an argument will likely be statements of opinion, fact, belief, or prejudice. It's important to distinguish between the kinds of statements and to analyze the definitions of terms.

1 Recognizing opinions

An **opinion** is a judgment based on facts and arguable on the basis of facts. Reasonable people could and probably do disagree over opinions, and they are potentially changeable: with more facts, a writer might change opinions partly or wholly.

The thesis statement of an effective argument is an opinion, often one of the following:

- **A claim about past or present reality:**

  In both its space and its equipment, the school's chemistry classroom is outdated.

  Academic cheating increases with students' sense of pressure to do well.

- **A claim of value:**

  The new parking fees are unjustified given the lack of student spaces in the lot.

  Computer music pirates undermine the system that encourages the very creation of music.

- **A recommendation for a course of action,** often a solution to a perceived problem:

  The school's outdated chemistry classroom should be replaced incrementally over the next five years.

Schools and businesses can help to resolve the region's traffic congestion by implementing car pools and rewarding participants.

The backbone of an argument consists of specific claims that support the thesis statement. These may be statements of opinion, too, or they may state facts or beliefs.

Opinions do not make arguments by themselves. As a critical reader, you must satisfy yourself that the writer has specified the evidence for the opinions and that the assumptions linking claims and evidence are clear and believable.

2 Recognizing facts

A **fact** may be a verifiable statement—that is, one that can be proved as true:

Last year parking fees increased 16 percent.

Or it may be an inference from verifiable facts:

Over their lifetimes, four-year college graduates earn almost twice as much as high school graduates.

A claim of fact does not work as the thesis of an argument. Although people often dispute facts, they are not fundamentally arguable because ultimately they can be verified. Facts have another important role in argument, providing crucial evidence for other claims (see p. 185).

3 Recognizing beliefs

A **belief** is a conviction based on cultural or personal faith, morality, or values:

Abortion is legalized murder.

Capital punishment is legalized murder.

The primary goal of government should be to provide equality of opportunity for all.

Such statements are often called opinions because they express viewpoints, but they are not based on facts and other evidence. Since they cannot be disproved by facts or even contested on the basis of facts, they cannot serve as the central or supporting claims of an argument. Statements of belief do figure in argument, however: they can serve as a kind of evidence, and they often form the assumptions that link claims and evidence (see pp. 186 and 188–89).

4 Recognizing prejudices

One kind of assertion that has no place in argument is a **prejudice,** an opinion based on insufficient or unexamined evidence:

Women are bad drivers.
Fat people are jolly.
Teenagers are irresponsible.

Unlike a belief, a prejudice is testable: it can be contested and disproved on the basis of facts. Very often, however, we form prejudices or accept them from others—parents, friends, the communications media—without questioning their meaning or testing their truth. Writers who display prejudice do not deserve the confidence and agreement of readers. Readers who accept prejudice are not thinking critically.

When reading arguments that appear online, you should be especially vigilant for claims of belief or prejudice that pose as considered opinions. Anyone with an Internet connection can post anything on the Internet, without passing it through an editorial screening like that undergone by books and articles in journals and magazines. The filtering of such material is entirely up to the reader.

5 Looking for defined terms

In any argument, but especially in arguments about abstract ideas, clear and consistent definition of terms is essential. In the following claim, the writer is not clear about what she means by the crucial term *justice:*

Over the past few decades, justice has deteriorated so badly that it almost does not exist anymore.

The word *justice* is **abstract:** it does not refer to anything specific or concrete and in fact has varied meanings. (The five definitions in *The American Heritage Dictionary* include "the principle of moral rightness" and "the administration and procedure of law.") When the writer specifies her meaning, her assertion is much clearer:

If by *justice* we mean treating people fairly, punishing those who commit crimes, and protecting the victims of those crimes, then justice has deteriorated badly over the past few decades.

Writers who use abstract words such as *justice, equality,* and *maturity* have a responsibility to define them. If the word is important to the argument, such a definition may take an entire paragraph. As a reader you have the obligation to evaluate the writer's definitions before you accept his or her assertions. (See pp. 95–96 for more on definition and a paragraph defining the abstract word *quality*.)

9c Weighing evidence

In argument, evidence demonstrates the validity of the writer's claims. If the evidence is inadequate or questionable, the claims are at best doubtful.

1 Recognizing kinds of evidence

Writers draw on several kinds of evidence to support their claims.

Evidence for argument

- **Facts:** verifiable statements
- **Statistics:** facts expressed in numbers
- **Examples:** specific cases
- **Expert opinions:** the judgments of authorities
- **Appeals to readers' beliefs or needs**

Facts

Facts are statements whose truth can be verified or inferred (see p. 183). Facts employing numbers are **statistics:**

> Of those polled, 62 percent stated a preference for a flat tax.
>
> In 2005 there were 1,370,237 men and women on active duty in the US armed forces.
>
> The average American household consists of 2.58 persons.

Numbers may be implied:

> Earth is closer to the sun than Saturn is.
> The cost of medical care is rising.

Or a fact may involve no numbers at all:

> The city council adjourned without taking a vote.
> The President vetoed the bill.

Examples

Examples are specific instances of the point being made, including historical precedents and personal experiences. The passage below uses a personal narrative as partial support for the claim in the first sentence:

> Besides broadening students' knowledge, service learning can also introduce students to possible careers that they otherwise would have known nothing about. Somewhat reluctantly, I volunteered after school at a daycare center to satisfy the service-learning requirement. But what I learned about child development has led me to consider becoming a child psychologist instead of an engineer.

Expert opinions

Expert opinions are the judgments formed by authorities on the basis of their own examination of the facts. In the following passage the writer cites the opinion of an expert to support the claim in the first sentence:

> Despite the fact that affirmative action places some individuals at a disadvantage, it remains necessary to right the wrongs inflicted historically on whole groups of people. Howard Glickstein, a past director of the US Commission on Civil Rights, maintains that "it simply is not possible to achieve equality and fairness" unless the previous grounds for discrimination (such as sex, race, and national origin) are now considered as grounds for admission to schools and jobs (26).

As this passage illustrates, a citation of expert opinion should always refer the reader to the source, here indicated by author's name and the page number in parentheses, "(26)." Such a citation is also generally accompanied by a reference to the expert's credentials. See pages 608–09 and 618–19.

CULTURE LANGUAGE In some cultures a person with high standing in government, society, or organized religion may be considered an authority on many different subjects. In American academic and business settings, authority tends to derive from study, learning, and experience: the more knowledge a person can demonstrate about a subject, the more authority he or she has. See the next page on relevant evidence.

Appeals to beliefs or needs

An **appeal to beliefs or needs** asks readers to accept an assertion in part because they already accept it as true without evidence or because it coincides with their needs. Each of the following examples combines such an appeal (second sentence) with a summary of factual evidence (first sentence).

> Thus the chemistry classroom is outdated in its equipment. In addition, its shabby, antiquated appearance shames the school, making it seem a second-rate institution. [Appeals to readers' belief that the school is or should be first-rate.]

> That police foot patrollers reduce crime has already been demonstrated. Such officers might also restore our sense that our neighborhoods are orderly, stable places. [Appeals to readers' need for order and stability.]

(For more on beliefs, see p. 183. For more on appeals to emotion, see pp. 209–10).

2 Judging the reliability of evidence

To support claims and convince readers, evidence must be reliable. The tests of reliability for appeals to readers' beliefs and needs are specific to the situation: whether they are appropriate for the argument and correctly gauge how readers actually feel (see pp.

209–10). With the other kinds of evidence, the standards are more general, applying to any argument.

Criteria for weighing evidence

- Is it **accurate:** trustworthy, exact, undistorted?
- Is it **relevant:** authoritative, pertinent, current?
- Is it **representative:** true to context?
- Is it **adequate:** plentiful, specific?

Accuracy

Accurate evidence is true:

- **It is drawn from trustworthy sources.**
- **It is quoted exactly.**
- **It is presented with the original meaning undistorted.**

In an essay favoring gun control, a writer should not rely exclusively on procontrol sources, which are undoubtedly biased. Instead, the writer should also cite anticontrol sources (representing the opposite bias) and neutral sources (attempting to be unbiased). If the writer quotes an expert, the quotation should present the expert's true meaning, not just a few words that happen to support the writer's argument. (As a reader you may have difficulty judging the accuracy of quotations if you are not familiar with the expert's opinions.)

Not just opinions but also facts and examples may be misinterpreted or distorted. Suppose you were reading an argument for extending a three-year-old law allowing the police to stop vehicles randomly as a means of apprehending drunk drivers. If the author cited statistics showing that the number of drunk-driving accidents dropped in the first two years of the law but failed to note that the number rose back to the previous level in the third year, then the evidence would be distorted and thus inaccurate. You or any reader would be justified in questioning the entire argument, no matter how accurate the rest seemed.

Relevance

Relevant evidence pertains to the argument:

- **It comes from sources with authority on the subject.**
- **It relates directly to the point the writer is making.**
- **It is current.**

In an argument against a method of hazardous-waste disposal, a writer should not offer his church minister's opinion as evidence unless she is an authority on the subject and her expertise is up to date.

If she is an authority on Method A and not Method B, the writer should not use her opinion as evidence against Method B. Similarly, the writer's own experience of living near a hazardous-waste site may be relevant evidence *if* it pertains to his thesis. His authority in this case is that of a close observer and a citizen. (See also p. 195 on the fallacy of false authority.)

Representativeness

Representative evidence is true to its context:

- **It reflects the full range of the sample from which it is said to be drawn.**
- **It does not overrepresent any element of the sample.**

In an essay arguing that schools should not open before Labor Day, a writer might say that "the majority of the school's students favor a later starting date." But that writer would mislead readers if the claim were based only on a poll of seniors in an English class. A few class members could not be said to represent the entire student body, particularly students in other grades. To be representative, the poll would have to take in many more students in proportions that reflect the number of students at each grade level.

Adequacy

Adequate evidence is sufficient:

- **It is plentiful enough to support the writer's assertions.**
- **It is specific enough to support the writer's assertions.**

A writer arguing against animal abuse cannot hope to win over readers solely with statements about her personal experiences and claims of her opinions. Her experience may indeed be relevant evidence if, say, she has worked with animals or witnessed animal abuse. And her opinions are indeed important to the argument, so that readers know what she thinks. But even together these are not adequate evidence: they cannot substitute entirely for facts, nonpersonal examples, and the opinions of experts to demonstrate abuse and describe the scope of the problem.

9d Discovering assumptions

Assumptions connect evidence to claims: they are the opinions or beliefs that explain why a particular piece of evidence is relevant to a particular claim. As noted in the preceding chapter on critical thinking, assumptions are not flaws in arguments but necessities:

we all acquire beliefs and opinions that shape our view of the world. Here are some examples that you, or people you know, may hold:

Criminals should be punished.
Hard work is virtuous.
Teachers' salaries are too low.

Assumptions are inevitable in argument, but they aren't neutral. For one thing, an assumption can weaken an argument. Say that a writer claims that real estate development should be prevented in your town. As evidence for this claim, the writer offers facts about past developments that have replaced older buildings. But the evidence is relevant to the claim only if you accept the writer's extreme assumptions that old buildings are always worthy and new development is always bad.

In such a case, the writer's bias may not even be stated. Hence a second problem: in arguments both sound and unsound, assumptions are not always explicit. Following are a claim and evidence forming a reasonable argument. What is the unstated assumption?

Claim

The town should create a plan to manage building preservation and new development.

Evidence

Examples of how such plans work; expert opinions on how and why both preservation and development are needed.

In this instance the assumption is that neither uncontrolled development nor zero development is healthy for the town. If you can accept this assumption, you should be able to accept the writer's claim (though you might still disagree over particulars).

Here are some tips for dealing with assumptions:

Guidelines for analyzing assumptions

- **What are the assumptions underlying the argument?** How does the writer connect claims with evidence?
- **Are the assumptions believable?** Do they express your values? Do they seem true in your experience?
- **Are the assumptions consistent with one another?** Is the argument's foundation solid, not slippery?

9e Watching language, hearing tone

Tone is the expression of the writer's attitudes toward himself or herself, toward the subject, and toward the reader (see pp. 13–14 for a discussion). Tone can tell you quite a bit about the writer's intentions, biases, and trustworthiness. For example:

> Some women cite personal growth as a reason for pursuing careers while raising children. Of course, they are equally concerned with the personal growth of the children they relegate to "child-care specialists" while they work.

In the second sentence this writer is being **ironic,** saying one thing while meaning another. The word *relegate* and the quotation marks with *child-care specialists* betray the writer's belief that working mothers may selfishly neglect their children for their own needs. Irony can sometimes be effective in argument, but here it marks the author as insincere in dealing with the complex issues of working parents and child care.

When reading arguments, you should be alert for the author's language. Look for words that **connote,** or suggest, certain attitudes and evoke certain responses in readers. (Notice your own responses to these word pairs with related meanings but different connotations: *daring/foolhardy, dislike/detest, glad/joyous, angry/rabid, freedom/license.*) Connotative language is no failure in argument; indeed, the strongest arguments use it skillfully to appeal to readers' hearts as well as their minds (see pp. 209–10). But be suspicious if the language runs counter to the substance of the argument.

Look also for evasive words. **Euphemisms,** such as *attack of a sexual nature* for "rape" or *peace-keeping force* for a war-making army, are supposedly inoffensive substitutes for words that may frighten or offend readers (see pp. 515–16). In argument, though, they are sometimes used to hide or twist the truth. An honest, forthright arguer will avoid them.

Finally, watch carefully for sexist, racist, and other biased language that reveals deep ignorance or, worse, entrenched prejudice on the part of the writer. Obvious examples are *broad* for woman and *fag* for homosexual. (See pp. 516–19 for more on such language.)

9f Judging reasonableness

The **reasonableness** of an argument is the sense you get as a reader that the author is fair and sincere. The reasonable writer does not conceal or distort facts, hide prejudices, mask belief as opinion, manipulate you with language, or resort to any of dozens of devices used unconsciously by those who don't know better and deliberately by those who do.

Reasonableness involves all the elements of argument examined so far: claims, evidence, assumptions, and language. In addition, the fair, sincere argument always avoids so-called fallacies (covered in the next section), and it acknowledges the opposition.

Judging whether a writer deals adequately with his or her opposition is a fairly simple matter for the reader of argument. By definition, an arguable issue has more than one side. Even if you have no preconceptions about a subject, you will know that another side exists. If the writer pretends otherwise or dismisses the opposition too quickly, you are justified in questioning the honesty and fairness of the argument. (For the more complicated business of *writing* an acknowledgment of opposing views, see pp. 211–12.)

EXERCISE 9.1 Reading arguments critically

Following are two brief arguments. Though not directly opposed, the two arguments do represent different stances on environmental issues. Read each argument critically, following the process outlined in the previous chapter (pp. 152–64) and answering the questions in the box on page 182 (questions about claims, evidence, assumptions, and the other elements of argument). Develop your responses in writing so that you can refer to them for later exercises and class discussion.

The Environmental Crisis Is Not Our Fault

I am as responsible as most eco-citizens: I bike everywhere; I don't own a car; I recycle newspapers, bottles, cans, and plastics; I have a vegetable garden in the summer; I buy organic products; and I put all vegetable waste into my backyard compost bin, probably the only one in all of Greenwich Village. But I don't at the same time believe that I am saving the planet, or in fact doing anything of much consequence about the various eco-crises around us. What's more, I don't even believe that if "all of us" as individuals started doing the same it would make any but the slightest difference. 1

Leave aside ozone depletion and rain forest destruction—those are patently corporate crimes that no individual actions can remedy to any degree. Take, instead, energy consumption in this country. In the most recent figures, residential consumption was 7.2 percent of the total, commercial 5.5 percent, and industrial 23.3 percent; of the remainder, 27.8 percent was transportation (about one-third of it by private car) and 36.3 percent was electric generation (about one-third for residential use). Individual energy use, in sum, was something like 28 percent of total consumption. Although you and I cutting down on energy consumption would have some small effect (and should be done), it is surely the energy consumption of industry and other large institutions such as government and agribusiness that needs to be addressed first. And it is industry and government that must be forced to explain what their consumption is for, what is produced by it, how necessary it is, and how it can be drastically reduced. 2

The point is that the ecological crisis is essentially beyond "our" control, as citizens or householders or consumers or even voters. It is not something that can be halted by recycling or double-pane insulation. It is the inevitable by-product of our modern industrial civilization, dominated by capitalist production and consumption and serviced and protected by various institutions of government, federal to 3 local. It cannot possibly be altered or reversed by simple individual actions, even by the actions of the millions who take part in Earth Day—even if they all go home and fix their refrigerators and from then on walk to work. Nothing less than a drastic overhaul of this civilization and an abandonment of its ingrained gods—progress, growth, exploitation, technology, materialism, anthropocentricity, and power—will do anything substantial to halt our path to environmental destruction, and it's hard to see how life-style solutions will have an effect on that.

What I find truly pernicious about such solutions is that they get people thinking they are actually making a difference and doing their part to halt the destruction of the earth: "There, I've taken all the bottles to the recycling center and used my string bag at the grocery store; I guess that'll take care of global warming." It is the kind of thing that diverts people from the hard truths and hard choices and hard actions, from the recognition that they have to take on the larger forces of society—corporate and governmental—where true power, and true destructiveness, lie. 4

And to the argument that, well, you have to start somewhere to raise people's consciousness, I would reply that this individualistic approach does not in fact raise consciousness. It does not move people beyond their old familiar liberal perceptions of the world, it does nothing to challenge the belief in technofix or write-your-Congressperson solutions, and it does not begin to provide them with the new vocabulary and modes of thought necessary for a true change of consciousness. We need, for example, to think of recycling centers not as the answer to our waste problems, but as a confession that the system of packaging and production in this society is out of control. Recycling centers are like hospitals; they are the institutions at the end of the cycle that take care of problems that would never exist if ecological criteria had operated at the beginning of the cycle. Until we have those kinds of understandings, we will not do anything with consciousness except reinforce it with the same misguided ideas that created the crisis. 5

—Kirkpatrick Sale

Myths We Wouldn't Miss

There are tall tales and legends. There are fables and apocryphal stories. And there are myths—a number of which we would like to see disappear. Here are some myths that would not be missed: 1

MYTH: Offshore drilling would be an ecological disaster. 2

Truth is, there hasn't been a serious spill in US waters resulting from offshore drilling operations in decades—and even that one, in Santa Barbara Channel in 1969, caused no permanent damage to the environment. 3

This is why we always have such a problem with the reasoning of those who call for moratoriums or outright bans on such activity while the nation continues to import foreign oil. The fact is, oil industry offshore drilling operations cause less pollution than urban runoff, atmospheric phenomena, municipal discharges or natural seeps. 4

Why this nation would choose *not* to drill for oil and *not* to provide the jobs, profits and taxes such activity would mean for the 5

American economy when there are no better alternatives is a mystery we hope puzzles others as much as it does us.

MYTH: America is a profligate waster of energy. 6

The myth makers like to throw around numbers that read like this: 7
with only 5 percent of the world's population, the US uses about 25 percent of the world's energy. But ours is a big country—three thousand miles from one ocean to the next. Transportation accounts for more than 60 percent of US oil use. We could probably cut down if we moved everybody into one corner of the country, but where is the waste?

It certainly isn't the automobiles that are inefficient. They are 8
twice as efficient as the ones we used thirty years ago. If American drivers use more gasoline than their counterparts in Europe and Japan, it may just have something to do with the country's size.

In fact, proof of the country's size may be in our economic out- 9
put—and may also hold a clue as to why we use the energy we do. Despite having only 5 percent of the world's population, America may indeed use 25 percent of the world's energy. However, according to the latest statistics, we also produce about 25 percent of the world's goods and services. Again, where's the waste?

MYTH: Conservation is *the answer* to America's energy problems. 10

No doubt about it, we all need to be careful of the amount of 11
energy we use. But as long as this nation's economy needs to grow, we are going to need energy to fuel that growth.

For the foreseeable future, there are no viable alternatives to petro- 12
leum as the major source of energy, especially for transportation fuels. Let's face it. Over the past thirty years we *have* learned to conserve—in our factories, our homes, our cars. We probably can—and should—do more. But conservation and new exploration should not be mutually exclusive, because even without an increase in energy consumption, we are using up domestic reserves of oil and gas and must replace them. For the good of the economy, those reserves should be replaced with new domestic production, to the extent economically possible. Otherwise, the only solutions would be additional imports or no growth. And stifling growth would be a gross disservice to the people for whom such growth would provide the opportunity for a better life.

Simply put, America is going to need more energy for all its people. 13

And that is no myth. 14

—Oil corporation advertisement

9g Recognizing fallacies

Fallacies—errors in argument—fall into two groups. Some evade the issue of the argument. Others treat the argument as if it were much simpler than it is.

1 Recognizing evasions

The central claim of an argument defines an issue or question: Should real estate development be controlled? Should drug testing be mandatory in the workplace? An effective argument faces the

Checklist of fallacies

Evasions

- **Begging the question:** treating an opinion that is open to question as if it were already proved or disproved.
- **Non sequitur** ("it does not follow"): drawing a conclusion from irrelevant evidence.
- **Red herring:** introducing an irrelevant issue to distract readers.
- **False authority:** citing as expert opinion the views of a person who is not an expert.
- **Inappropriate appeals:**

  Appealing to readers' fear or pity.
  Snob appeal: appealing to readers' wish to be like those who are more intelligent, famous, rich, and so on.
  Bandwagon: appealing to readers' wish to be part of the group.
  Flattery: appealing to readers' intelligence, taste, and so on.
  Argument ad populum ("to the people"): appealing to readers' general values, such as patriotism or love of family.
  Argument ad hominem ("to the man"): attacking the opponent rather than the opponent's argument.

Oversimplifications

- **Hasty generalization (jumping to a conclusion):** asserting an opinion based on too little evidence.
- **Sweeping generalization:** asserting an opinion as applying to all instances when it may apply to some, or to none. **Absolute statements** and **stereotypes** are variations.
- **Reductive fallacy:** generally, oversimplifying causes and effects.
- **Post hoc fallacy:** assuming that *A* caused *B* because *A* preceded *B*.
- **Either/or fallacy (false dilemma):** reducing a complicated question to two alternatives.
- **False analogy:** exaggerating the similarities in an analogy or ignoring key differences.

central issue squarely with relevant opinions, beliefs, and evidence. An ineffective argument dodges the issue.

Begging the question

A writer **begs the question** by treating an opinion that is open to question as if it were already proved or disproved. (In essence, the writer begs readers to accept his or her ideas from the start.)

> The school's library expenses should be reduced by cutting subscriptions to useless periodicals. [Begged questions: Are some of the library's periodicals useless? Useless to whom?]
>
> We should stop looking for the "real" Shakespeare and concentrate on understanding his plays. [Begged questions: Does research into Shakespeare's life preclude interpreting the plays? Is there merit in researching Shakespeare's life?]

Non sequitur

A **non sequitur** occurs when no logical relation exists between two or more connected ideas. In Latin *non sequitur* means "it does not follow." In the sentences below, the second thought does not follow from the first:

> She uses a wheelchair, so she must be unhappy. [The second clause does not follow from the first.]
>
> Kathleen Newsome should be mayor because she has the best-run campaign organization. [Shouldn't support for a candidate be based on his or her qualities, not the campaign's organization?]

Red herring

A **red herring** is literally a kind of fish that might be drawn across a path to distract a bloodhound from a scent it's following. In argument, a red herring is an irrelevant issue intended to distract readers from the relevant issues. The writer changes the subject rather than pursue the argument.

> A school free-speech code is essential to protect students, who already have enough problems with academic pressure. [Academic pressure and speech codes are different subjects. What protections do students need that a speech code will provide?]
>
> How can anyone claim that *King Lear* is a great play when there is evidence that Shakespeare did not write it? [Questions about Shakespeare's authorship do not diminish the play, which needs to be considered on its own merits.]

False authority

Arguments often cite as evidence the opinions of people who are experts on the subject (see pp. 185–86). But writers use **false authority** when they cite as an expert someone whose expertise is doubtful or nonexistent.

> My uncle, a medical doctor, has read *The Scarlet Letter* and considers Roger Chillingworth a reasonable portrait of a physician in colonial America. [Is the uncle an expert in colonial medicine?]
>
> According to Helen Liebowitz, the Food and Drug Administration has approved sixty dangerous drugs in the last two years alone. [Who is Helen Liebowitz? On what authority does she make this claim?]

Inappropriate appeals

Appeals to readers' emotions are common in effective arguments. But such appeals must be relevant and must supplement rather than substitute for facts, examples, and other evidence.

Writers sometimes ignore the question with **appeals to readers' fear or pity.**

By electing Susan Clark to the city council, you will prevent the city's economic collapse. [Trades on people's fears. Can Clark singlehandedly prevent economic collapse? Is collapse even likely?]

She should not have to pay taxes, because she is an aged widow with no friends or relatives. [Appeals to people's pity. Should age and loneliness, rather than income, determine a person's tax obligation?]

Sometimes writers ignore the question by appealing to readers' sense of what other people believe or do. One approach is **snob appeal,** inviting readers to accept an assertion in order to be identified with others they admire.

As any literate person knows, James Joyce is the best twentieth-century novelist. [But what qualities of Joyce's writing make him a superior novelist?]

Tiger Woods has an account at Big City Bank, and so should you. [A celebrity's endorsement of course does not automatically guarantee the worth of a product, a service, an idea, or anything else.]

A similar tactic invites readers to accept an assertion because everybody else does. This is the **bandwagon approach.**

As everyone knows, marijuana use leads to heroin addiction. [What is the evidence?]

Yet another diversion involves **flattery** of readers, in a way inviting them to join in a conspiracy.

We all understand our school's problems well enough to see the disadvantages of such a policy. [What are the disadvantages of the policy?]

The **argument ad populum** ("argument to the people") asks readers to accept a conclusion based on shared values or even prejudices and nothing else.

Any truly patriotic American will support the President's action. [But why is the action worth taking?]

One final and very common kind of inappropriate emotional appeal addresses *not* the pros and cons of the issue itself but the real or imagined negative qualities of the people who hold the opposing view. This kind of argument is called **ad hominem,** Latin for "to the man."

One of the scientists has been treated for emotional problems, so his pessimism about nuclear waste merits no attention. [Do the scientist's previous emotional problems invalidate his current views?]

2 Recognizing oversimplifications

To **oversimplify** is to conceal or ignore complexities in a vain attempt to create a neater, more convincing argument than reality allows.

Hasty generalization

A **hasty generalization,** also called **jumping to a conclusion,** is a claim based on too little evidence or on evidence that is unrepresentative. (See also p. 188.)

> It is disturbing that several of the youths who shot up schools were users of violent video games. Obviously, these games can breed violence, and they should be banned. [A few cases do not establish the relation between the games and violent behavior. Most youths who play violent video games do not behave violently.]

> From the way it handled this complaint, we can assume that the consumer protection office has little intention of protecting consumers. [One experience with the office does not demonstrate its intention or overall performance.]

Sweeping generalization

Whereas a hasty generalization comes from inadequate evidence, a **sweeping generalization** probably is not supportable at all. One kind of sweeping generalization is the **absolute statement** involving words such as *all, always, never,* and *no one* that allow no exceptions. Rarely can evidence support such terms. Moderate words such as *some, sometimes, rarely,* and *few* are more reasonable.

Another common sweeping generalization is the **stereotype,** a conventional and oversimplified characterization of a group of people.

> People who live in cities are unfriendly.
> Californians are fad-crazy.
> Women are emotional.
> Men can't express their feelings.

(See also pp. 516–19 on sexist and other biased language.)

Reductive fallacy

The **reductive fallacy** oversimplifies (or reduces) the relation between causes and their effects. The fallacy (sometimes called **oversimplification**) often involves linking two events as if one caused the other directly, whereas the causes may be more complex or the relation may not exist at all. For example:

> Poverty causes crime. [If so, then why do people who are not poor commit crimes? And why aren't all poor people criminals?]

> The better a school's athletic facilities are, the worse its academic programs are. [The sentence assumes a direct cause-and-effect link between athletics and scholarship.]

Post hoc fallacy

Related to the reductive fallacy is the assumption that because *A* preceded *B,* then *A* must have caused *B.* This fallacy is called in

Latin *post hoc, ergo propter hoc,* meaning "after this, therefore because of this," or the **post hoc fallacy** for short.

> In the two months since he took office, Mayor Holcomb has allowed crime in the city to increase 12 percent. [The increase in crime is probably attributable to conditions existing before Holcomb took office.]
>
> The town council erred in permitting the adult bookstore to open, for shortly afterward two women were assaulted. [It cannot be assumed without evidence that the women's assailants visited or were influenced by the bookstore.]

Either/or fallacy

In the **either/or fallacy** (also called **false dilemma**), the writer assumes that a complicated question has only two answers, one good and one bad, both bad, or both good.

> City police officers are either brutal or corrupt. [Most city police officers are neither.]
>
> Conflicts in novels are between characters or within a character's own mind. [Conflicts are not necessarily one or the other.]

False analogy

An **analogy** is a comparison between two essentially unlike things for the purpose of definition or illustration. In arguing by analogy, a writer draws a likeness between things on the basis of a single shared feature and then extends the likeness to other features. For instance, the "war on drugs" equates a battle against a foe with a program to eradicate (or at least reduce) sales and use of illegal drugs. Both involve an enemy, a strategy of overpowering the enemy, a desired goal, officials in uniform, and other similarities.

Analogy can only illustrate a point, never prove it: just because things are similar in one respect, they are not *necessarily* alike in other respects. In the fallacy called **false analogy,** the writer assumes such a complete likeness. Here is the analogy of the war on drugs taken to its false extreme:

> To win the war on drugs, we must wage more of a military-style operation. Prisoners of war are locked up without the benefit of a trial by jury, and drug dealers should be, too. Soldiers shoot their enemy on sight, and officials who encounter big drug operations should, too. Military traitors may be executed, and corrupt law enforcers could be, too.

Literary analysis sometimes uses false analogies, too. In an attempt to connect with a current cultural issue, the following passage blurs the focus on Gatsby and loses the point.

> Gatsby is clearly a dreamer. He lives in a world that he has crafted from his desire to possess Daisy, the object of his obsession. His quest

is like that of corporate executives who lie and cheat to gain the objects of their obsessions—yachts, mansions, companies, and more money. Like the executives, who are punished by the legal system, Gatsby was punished to the full extent of the moral law.

EXERCISE 9.2 Analyzing advertisements

Leaf through a magazine or watch commercial television for half an hour, looking for advertisements that attempt to sell a product not on the basis of its worth but by snob appeal, flattery, or other inappropriate appeals to emotions. Be prepared to discuss the advertisers' techniques. (See Chapter 11, pp. 230–31, if you need help analyzing the appeals in images.)

EXERCISE 9.3 Identifying and revising fallacies

Fallacies tend to appear together, as each of the following sentences illustrates. Identify at least one fallacy in each sentence. Then revise the sentences to make them more reasonable. (You can do this exercise online at *ablongman.com/littlebrown.*)

1. The American government can sell nuclear technology to non-nuclear nations, so why can't individuals, who after all have a God-given right to earn a living as they see fit?
2. A successful marriage demands a maturity that no one under twenty-five possesses.
3. Students' persistent complaints about the grading system prove that it is unfair.
4. People watch television because they are too lazy to talk or read or because they want mindless escape from their lives.
5. Racial tension is bound to occur when people with different backgrounds are forced to live side by side.

EXERCISE 9.4 Identifying fallacies in arguments

Analyze the two arguments on pages 191–93 for fallacies. To what extent do any fallacies weaken either argument? Explain.

EXERCISE 9.5 Identifying fallacies online

At *groups.yahoo.com*, find a conversation about drug testing in the workplace, environmental pollution, violence in the media, or any other subject that interests you and that is debatable. Read through the arguments made in the conversation, noting the fallacies you see. List the fallacious statements as well as the types of fallacies they illustrate, keeping in mind that a given statement may illustrate more than a single type.

CHAPTER 10

Writing an Argument

In one way or another, most writing attempts to persuade readers. The author of a research report wants readers to view the findings as significant. The author of a literary analysis wants readers to accept his or her insights into a work. Even the author of a novel wants readers to see the depicted characters or situations in a certain way.

Argument is a special kind of persuasion, a deliberate and straightforward attempt to make a claim, develop it with evidence, and convince readers to agree or to act. In composing an argument, you try to clarify an issue or solve a problem by finding the common ground between you and your readers. Using critical thinking, you develop and test your own ideas. Using a variety of techniques, you engage readers in an attempt to narrow the distance between your views and theirs.

This chapter introduces the process and techniques of composing a written argument. The next chapter discusses the use of images, such as photographs and charts, as an effective tool for argument.

10a Finding a subject

An argument subject must be arguable—that is, reasonable people will disagree over it and be able to support their positions with evidence. This sentence implies the *do*s and *don't*s listed below.

Tests for an argument subject

A good subject:

- Concerns a matter of opinion—a conclusion drawn from evidence.
- Can be disputed: others might take a different position.
- *Will* be disputed: it is controversial.
- Is something you care about and know about or want to research.
- Is narrow enough to argue in the space and time available.

http://www.ablongman.com/littlebrown ▶

Visit the companion Web site for more help and additional exercises on writing arguments.

A bad subject:

- Cannot be disputed because it concerns a fact, such as the distance to Saturn or the functions of the human liver.
- Cannot be disputed because it concerns a personal preference or belief, such as a liking for a certain vacation spot or a moral commitment to vegetarianism.
- *Will not* be disputed because few if any disagree over it—the virtues of a secure home, for instance.

Additional help on subjects for writing appears earlier in this book:

- **Working with a specific assignment,** page 7.
- **Working with a general assignment,** pages 7–8.
- **Narrowing a subject to a question,** pages 8–9.

CULTURE LANGUAGE Choosing a subject for argument may seem difficult if you're not familiar with what people in the United States find debatable. One way to find a subject is to scout online discussion groups, such as those listed at *groups.yahoo.com,* for subjects on which there is a range of opinion. Another approach is to read a newspaper every day for at least a week, looking for issues that involve or interest you. Following the development of the issues in articles, editorials, and letters to the editor will give you a sense of how controversial they are, what the positions are, and what your position might be.

EXERCISE 10.1 Finding a subject for argument

Explain why each subject below is or is not appropriate for argument. Refer to the box on the previous page if you need help. (You can do this exercise online at *ablongman.com/littlebrown.*)

1. Granting of athletic scholarships to first-year college students
2. Care of automobile tires
3. Censoring the Web sites of hate groups
4. History of the town park
5. Housing for the homeless
6. Billboards in urban residential areas or in rural areas
7. Animal testing for cosmetics research
8. Cats versus dogs as pets
9. Ten steps in recycling wastepaper
10. Benefits of having siblings

10b Conceiving a thesis statement

The **thesis** is the main idea of your paper (see pp. 29–34). In an argument the **thesis statement** makes the claim that you want your readers to accept or act on. Here are two thesis statements on the same subject:

The end of Dickens's novel fails because of its predictability.

If one scene were left out, readers would be happily surprised by the end of Dickens's novel instead of bored by its predictability.

Your thesis statement must satisfy the same requirements as your subject (see the box on the previous two pages). But it must also specify the basis for your claim. In both of the preceding thesis statements, the writer makes clear that the judgment of Dickens's ending is based on its predictability.

EXERCISE 10.2 Conceiving a thesis statement

For each subject in Exercise 10.1 that you deemed arguable, draft a tentative thesis statement that specifies the basis for an argument. If you prefer, choose five arguable subjects of your own and draft a thesis statement for each one. One thesis statement should interest you enough to develop into a complete argument in later exercises.

10c Analyzing your purpose and your audience

Your purpose in argument is, broadly, to engage readers in order to convince them of your position or persuade them to act. But arguments have more specific purposes as well, such as the following:

To strengthen the commitment of existing supporters
To win new supporters from the undecided or uninformed
To get the opposition to reconsider
To inspire supporters to act
To deter the undecided from acting

It's no accident that each of these purposes characterizes the audience (*existing supporters, the undecided,* and so on). In argument, even more than in other kinds of writing, achieving your purpose depends on the response of your readers, so you need a sense of who they are and where they stand. The "Questions About Audience" on page 12 can help you identify readers' knowledge, beliefs, and other pertinent information. In addition, you need to know how readers stand on your subject—not only whether they agree or disagree generally, but also which specific assertions and which appeals they will find more or less convincing. (For more on appeals in argument, see pp. 209–11.)

Your purpose can help you fill in this information. If you decide to address supporters or opponents, you essentially select readers with certain inclinations and ignore other readers who may tune in. If you decide to win new supporters from those who are undecided on your topic, you'll have to imagine skeptical readers who will be convinced only by an argument that is detailed, logical, and fair. Like you when you read an argument critically, these skeptical readers seek to be reasoned with, not manipulated into a position or hammered over the head.

EXERCISE 10.3 Analyzing purpose and audience

Specify a purpose and likely audience for the thesis statement you chose to develop in Exercise 10.2. What do purpose and audience suggest about the way you should develop the argument?

10d Using reason

As a reader of argument, you seek evidence for the writer's claims and clear reasoning about the relationship of evidence to claims. As a writer of argument, you seek to provide what the reader needs in a way that furthers your case.

The thesis of your argument is a conclusion you reach by reasoning about evidence. Two common processes of reasoning are induction and deduction—methods of thinking that you use all the time even if you don't know their names. You can think of induction and deduction as two different ways of moving among claims, evidence, and assumptions—the elements of argument derived from Stephen Toulmin's work and discussed on pages 180–81.

1 Reasoning inductively

When you're about to buy a used car, you consult friends, relatives, and consumer guides before deciding what kind of car to buy. Using **inductive reasoning,** you make specific observations about cars (your evidence) and you induce, or infer, a **generalization** (or claim) that Model X is the most reliable. Writing a paper on the effectiveness of print advertising, you might also use inductive reasoning:

First analyze statistics on advertising in print and in other media (evidence).
Then read comments by advertisers and publishers (more evidence).
Finally, form a conclusion that print is the most cost-effective advertising medium (generalization).

This reasoning builds from the evidence to the claim, with assumptions connecting evidence to claim. By predicting something about the unknown based on what you know, you create new knowledge out of old.

The more evidence you accumulate, the more probable it is that your generalization is true. Note, however, that absolute certainty is not possible. At some point you must *assume* that your evidence justifies your generalization, for yourself and your readers. Most errors

Inductive reasoning

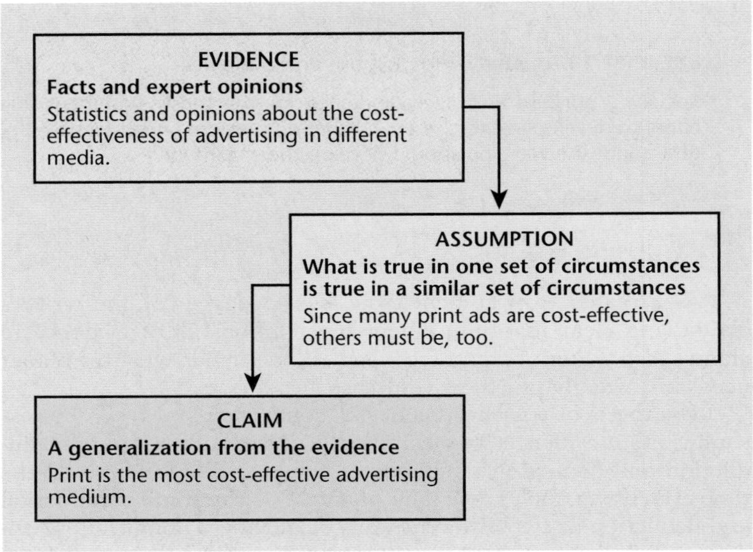

EVIDENCE
Facts and expert opinions
Statistics and opinions about the cost-effectiveness of advertising in different media.

↓

ASSUMPTION
What is true in one set of circumstances is true in a similar set of circumstances
Since many print ads are cost-effective, others must be, too.

↓

CLAIM
A generalization from the evidence
Print is the most cost-effective advertising medium.

in inductive reasoning involve oversimplifying either the evidence or the generalization. See pages 193–99 on fallacies.

2 Reasoning deductively

You use **deductive reasoning** when you proceed from your generalization that Model X is the most reliable used car to your own specific circumstances (you want to buy a used car) to the conclusion (or claim) that you should buy a Model X car. Like induction, deduction uses the elements of argument—claims, evidence, and assumptions—but with it you apply old information to new.

■ The deductive syllogism

The conventional way of displaying a deductive argument is in a **syllogism:**

Premise: All human beings are mortal. [A generalization, fact, principle, or belief that you assume to be true.]
Premise: I am a human being. [New information: a specific case of the first premise.]
Conclusion: Therefore, I am mortal.

As long as the premises of a syllogism are true, the conclusion derives logically and certainly from them. If you want the school

Deductive reasoning

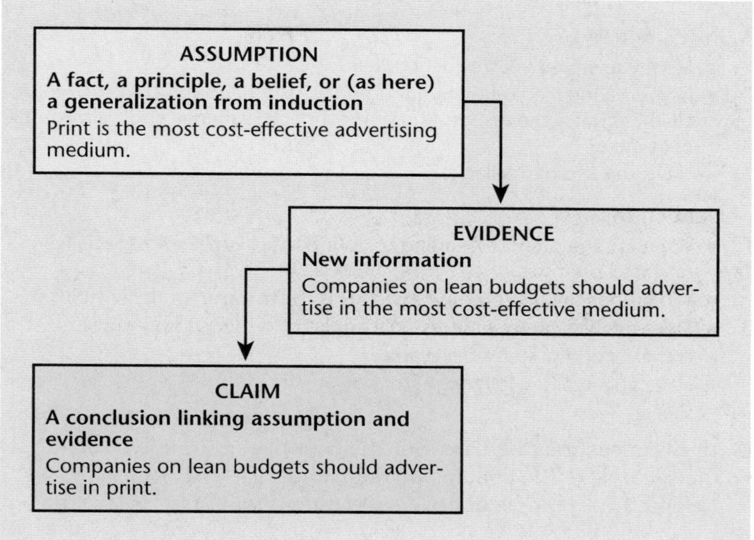

administration not to raise fees for participation in the debate team, your deductive argument might be expressed in this syllogism:

> **Premise:** The administration should not raise fees on student activities that have had no increase in expenses.
> **Premise:** The debate team's expenses have not increased.
> **Conclusion:** Therefore, the administration should not raise fees for the debate team.

The force of deductive reasoning depends on the reliability of the premises and the care taken to apply them in drawing conclusions. The reasoning process is **valid** if the premises lead logically to the conclusion. It is **true** if the premises are believable.

■ Problems with syllogisms

Sometimes the reasoning in a deductive argument is true because the premises are believable, but it is *not* valid because the conclusion doesn't derive logically from the premises:

> **Premise:** The administration should not raise fees on student activities that have had no increase in expenses.
> **Premise:** The soccer team is a student activity.
> **Conclusion:** Therefore, the administration should not raise fees for the soccer team.

Tests for inductive and deductive reasoning

Induction

- Have you stated your evidence clearly?
- Is your evidence complete enough and good enough to justify your claim? What is the assumption that connects evidence and claim? Is it believable?
- Have you avoided fallacies?

Deduction

- What are the premises leading to your conclusion? Look especially for unstated premises.
- What does the first premise assume? Is the assumption believable?
- Does the first premise necessarily apply to the second premise?
- Is the second premise believable?
- Have you avoided fallacies?

Both premises may be true, but the first does not *necessarily* apply to the second, so the conclusion is invalid.

Sometimes, too, deductive reasoning is valid but *not* true:

> **Premise:** All high school administrators are indifferent to students' needs.
> **Premise:** The administration of Central High is a high school administration.
> **Conclusion:** Therefore, the administration of Central High is indifferent to students' needs.

This syllogism is valid but useless: the first premise is an untrue assumption, so the entire argument is untrue. Invalid and untrue syllogisms underlie many of the fallacies discussed on pages 193–99.

A particular hazard of deductive reasoning is the **unstated premise:** the basic assumption linking evidence and conclusion is not stated but implied. Here the unstated premise is believable and the argument is reasonable:

> Ms. Stein has worked with drug addicts for fifteen years, so she knows a great deal about their problems. [Unstated premise: Anyone who has worked fifteen years with drug addicts knows about their problems.]

But when the unstated premise is wrong or unfounded, the argument is false. For example:

> Since Jane Lightbow is a senator, she must receive money illegally from lobbyists. [Unstated premise: All senators receive money illegally from lobbyists.]

To avoid such false conclusions, you may be tempted to make your claims sound more reasonable. But even a conclusion that sounds reasonable must be supportable. For instance, changing *must* to *might* modifies the unstated assumption about Senator Lightbow:

> Since Jane Lightbow is a senator, she might receive money illegally from lobbyists. [Unstated premise: *Some* senators receive money illegally from lobbyists.]

But it does not necessarily follow that Senator Lightbow is one of the "some." The sentence, though logical, is not truly reasonable unless evidence demonstrates that Senator Lightbow should be linked with illegal activities.

EXERCISE 10.4 Reasoning inductively

Study the facts below and then evaluate each of the numbered conclusions following them. Which of the generalizations are reasonable given the evidence, and which are not? Why? (You can do this exercise online at *ablongman.com/littlebrown.*)

In 2004–05 each American household viewed an average of 50 hours and 12 minutes of television, DVDs, or videos weekly.

Each individual viewed an average of 30 hours and 23 minutes per week.

Those viewing the most television per week (43 hours and 6 minutes) were women over age 55.

Those viewing the least television per week (19 hours and 17 minutes) were children ages 6 to 11.

Households earning under $30,000 a year watched an average of 53 hours and 19 minutes a week.

Households earning more than $60,000 a year watched an average of 48 hours and 7 minutes a week.

1. Households with incomes under $30,000 tend to watch more television than average.
2. Women watch more television than men.
3. Nonaffluent people watch less television than affluent people.
4. Women over age 55 tend to watch more television than average.
5. Children watch less television than critics generally assume.

EXERCISE 10.5 Reasoning deductively

Convert each of the following statements into a syllogism. (You may have to state unstated assumptions.) Use the syllogism to evaluate both the validity and the truth of the statement. (You can do this exercise online at *ablongman.com/littlebrown.*)

> *Example:*
> DiSantis is a banker, so he does not care about the poor.

Premise: Bankers do not care about the poor.
Premise: DiSantis is a banker.
Conclusion: Therefore, DiSantis does not care about the poor.

The statement is untrue because the first premise is untrue.

1. The mayor opposed pollution controls when he was president of a manufacturing company, so he may not support new controls or vigorously enforce existing ones.
2. Information on corporate Web sites is unreliable because the sites are sponsored by for-profit entities.
3. Schroeder is a good artist because she trained at Parsons, like many other good artists.
4. Wealthy athletes who use their resources to help others deserve our particular appreciation.
5. Jimson is clearly a sexist because she has hired only one woman.

10e Using evidence

Whether your argument is reasonable or not depends heavily on the evidence you marshal to support it. The kinds of evidence and the criteria for evaluating evidence are discussed in detail on pages 184–88. Finding evidence is discussed under research writing on pages 569–87. Evaluating sources of evidence, including online sources, is discussed under research writing on pages 588–97.

The kind and quantity of evidence you use should be determined by your purpose, your subject, and the needs of your audience. Some arguments, such as an appeal for volunteer help in a soup kitchen, will rely most heavily on examples (including perhaps a narrative of your own experience) and on appeals to readers' beliefs. Other arguments, such as a proposal for mandatory side air bags in cars, will rely much more on statistics and expert opinions. Most arguments, including these, will mingle facts, examples, expert opinions, and appeals to readers' beliefs and needs.

In using evidence for argument, you'll need to be especially wary of certain traps that carelessness or zeal can lure you into. These are listed in the following box.

Responsible use of evidence

- **Don't distort.** You mislead readers when you twist evidence to suit your argument—for instance, when you claim that crime in your city occurs five times more often than it did in 1955, without mentioning that the population is also seven times larger.

- **Don't stack the deck.** Ignoring damning evidence is like cheating at cards. You must deal forthrightly with the opposition. (See pp. 211–12.)
- **Don't exaggerate.** Watch your language. Don't attempt to manipulate readers by characterizing your own evidence as *pure* and *rock-solid* and the opposition's as *ridiculous* and *half-baked.* Make the evidence speak for itself.
- **Don't oversimplify.** Avoid forcing the evidence to support more than it can. (See also pp. 196–99.)
- **Don't misquote.** When you cite experts, quote them accurately and fairly.

EXERCISE 10.6 Using reason and evidence in your argument

Develop the structure and evidence for the argument you began in Exercises 10.2 and 10.3 (pp. 202 and 203). (You may want to begin drafting at this stage.) Is your argument mainly inductive or mainly deductive? Use the box on page 206 to test the reasoning of the argument. Use the boxes on page 187 and above to test your evidence.

10f Reaching your readers

To reach your readers in argument, you appeal directly to their reason and emotions, you present yourself as someone worth heeding, and you account for views opposing your own.

1 Appealing to readers

In forming convictions about arguable issues, we generally interpret the factual evidence through the filter of our values, beliefs, tastes, desires, and feelings. You may object to placing the new town dump in a particular wooded area because the facts suggest that the site is not large enough and that prevailing winds will blow odors back through the town. But you may also have fond memories of playing in the wooded area as a child, feelings that color your interpretation of the facts and strengthen your conviction that the dump should be placed elsewhere. Your conviction is partly rational, because it is based on evidence, and partly emotional, because it is also based on feelings.

Logical and emotional appeals

Almost all arguments combine logical and emotional appeals. **Logical appeals** (called *logos* in classical rhetoric) stem from reasoning logically between evidence and claims. **Emotional appeals** (*pathos*) tap into readers' beliefs and feelings. The following passages, all arguing the same view on the same subject, illustrate how either a primarily logical or a primarily emotional appeal may be weaker than an approach that uses both:

> Logical appeal
>
> Advertising should show more physically challenged people. The millions of disabled Americans have considerable buying power, yet so far advertisers have made no attempt to tap that power. [Appeals to the logic of financial gain.]
>
> Emotional appeal
>
> Advertising should show more physically challenged people. By keeping the physically challenged out of the mainstream depicted in ads, advertisers encourage widespread prejudice against disability, prejudice that frightens and demeans those who hold it. [Appeals to the sense of fairness, open-mindedness.]
>
> Logical and emotional appeals
>
> Advertising should show more physically challenged people. The millions of disabled Americans have considerable buying power, yet so far advertisers have made no attempt to tap that power. Further, by keeping the physically challenged out of the mainstream depicted in ads, advertisers encourage widespread prejudice against disability, prejudice that frightens and demeans those who hold it.

The third passage, in combining both kinds of appeal, gives readers both logical and emotional bases for agreeing with the writer.

For an emotional appeal to be successful, it must be appropriate for the audience and the argument:

- **It must not misjudge readers' actual feelings.**
- **It must not raise emotional issues that are irrelevant to the claims and the evidence.** See pages 95–96 for a discussion of specific inappropriate appeals, such as the bandwagon approach.

One further caution: Photographs and other images can reinforce your claims with a strong emotional appeal, but they must be relevant to your claims, and you must explain their relevance in your text and captions. See pages 230–31 for more on the appeals in images.

Ethical appeal

A third kind of approach to readers is the **ethical appeal** (*ethos*): the sense you give of being a competent, fair, trustworthy person. A sound argument backed by ample evidence—a logical appeal—will convince readers of your knowledge and reasonableness. (So will your acknowledging the opposition. See the next page.) Appropriate emotional appeals will demonstrate that you share readers' beliefs and needs. An argument that is concisely written and correct in grammar, spelling, and other matters will underscore your competence. In addition, a sincere and even tone will assure readers that you are a balanced person who wants to reason with them.

A sincere and even tone need not exclude language with emotional appeal—words such as *frightens* and *demeans* at the end of the third example on the previous page. But avoid certain forms of expression that will mark you as unfair:

- **Insulting words,** such as *idiotic* or *fascist.*
- **Biased language,** such as *rednecks* or *fags.* (See pp. 516–19.)
- **Sarcasm**—for instance, using the phrase *What a brilliant idea* to indicate contempt for the idea and its originator.
- **Exclamation points!** They'll make you sound shrill!

See also pages 189–90 on tone.

2 Answering opposing views

A good test of your fairness in argument is how you handle possible objections. Assuming your thesis is indeed arguable, then others can marshal their own evidence to support a different view or views. You need to find out what these other views are and what the support is for them. Then, in your argument, you need to address these views directly and fairly. It's not a mark of weakness or failure to admit that the opposition's arguments have validity. Indeed, by showing yourself to be honest and fair, you strengthen your ethical appeal and thus your entire argument.

The following paragraph illustrates one way to answer opposing views:

> The athletic director at Springfield University argues against reducing university support for athletic programs on the grounds that they make money that goes toward academic programs. It is true that the surpluses from the football and basketball programs have gone into the general university fund, and some of that money may have made it into academic departments (the fund's accounting methods make it impossible to say for sure). But the athletic director misses the point. The problem is not that the athletic programs may cost more than they take in but that they demand too much to begin with. For an institution that hopes to become first-rate academically, too many facilities, too much money, too much energy, and too many people are tied up in the effort to produce championship sports teams.
>
> —William Hoving (student), "Scholarship Versus Gamesmanship"

Statement of opposing view

Concession that opposing view is partly valid

Demonstration that opposing view is irrelevant

This example takes a traditional approach to addressing the opposition. The author states the opposing view and grants validity to the point that surpluses from certain athletic programs have been channeled into the university's general fund. Following that concession, he then argues that the opposing view is less compelling than his own because the athletic programs demand resources that would be better used on academic programs.

A somewhat different approach to addressing the opposition, developed by the psychologist Carl Rogers, emphasizes the search for common ground in argument. Throughout a Rogerian argument, you stress points of agreement between your position and the opposition's—conceding the opposing views immediately, stating the situations in which opposing views might be valid, and suggesting new points of agreement.

Whether you're writing a traditional or a Rogerian argument, spend some time developing a comprehensive list of views that might oppose yours. You'll find them in your research, by talking to friends and classmates, and by critically thinking about your own ideas. You can also look for a range of views in a discussion group that deals with your subject. A place to start is the archive at *groups.yahoo.com*.

EXERCISE 10.7 Identifying appeals

Identify each passage below as primarily a logical appeal or primarily an emotional appeal. Which passages make a strong ethical appeal as well? (You can do this exercise online at *ablongman.com/littlebrown.*)

1. Web surfing may contribute to the global tendency toward breadth rather than depth of knowledge. Using those most essential of skills—pointing and clicking—our brightest minds may now never encounter, much less read, the works of Plato, Shakespeare, and Darwin.
2. Thus the data collected by these researchers indicate that a mandatory sentence for illegal possession of handguns may lead to reduction in handgun purchases.
3. Most broadcasters worry that further government regulation of television programming could breed censorship—certainly, an undesirable outcome. Yet most broadcasters also accept that children's television is a fair target for regulation.
4. Anyone who cherishes life in all its diversity could not help being appalled by the mistreatment of laboratory animals. The so-called scientists who run the labs are misguided.
5. Many experts in constitutional law have warned that the rule violates the right to free speech. Yet other experts have viewed the rule, however regretfully, as necessary for the good of the community as a whole.

EXERCISE 10.8 Reaching your readers

Continuing your argument-in-progress from Exercise 10.6 (p. 209), analyze whether your claims are logical or emotional and whether the mix is appropriate for your audience and argument. Analyze your ethical appeal, too, considering whether it can be strengthened. Then make a list of possible opposing views. Think freely at first, not stopping to censor views that seem far-fetched or irrational. When your list is complete, decide which views must be taken seriously and why, and develop a response to each one.

10g Organizing your argument

All arguments include the same parts, but depending on the type of argument the organization can vary:

- **Introduction:** Commonly, the introduction establishes the significance of the subject or the scope of the problem, provides the background, and usually includes the thesis statement. However, if you think your readers may have difficulty accepting your thesis statement before they see at least some support for it, then it may come later in the paper. A Rogerian argument uses the introduction to emphasize the common ground between writer and readers, saving the thesis for the conclusion.
- **Body:** The body paragraphs state and develop the claims supporting the thesis, using clearly relevant evidence. The arrangement of the claims and their position relative to the response to opposing views can vary widely. See below.
- **Response to opposing views:** The response to opposing views details and addresses those views, finding common ground, demonstrating the argument's greater strengths, or conceding the opponent's points. For some arguments, readers will be satisfied to see opposing views dealt with at the end. For others, each claim will invite its own objections, and those opposing views will need to be addressed claim by claim. In a Rogerian argument, a concession to opposing views appears right after the introduction, before the claims get underway, in order to establish common ground.
- **Conclusion:** The conclusion completes the argument. Often it restates the thesis, summarizes the supporting claims, and makes a final appeal to readers. In a Rogerian argument, the conclusion states the thesis as a solution, giving ground and inviting the audience to do the same.

For more on introductions and conclusions, see pages 104–10.

You may want to experiment with various organizations—for instance, trying out your strongest claims first or last in the body,

Organizing an argument's body and response to opposing views

A common scheme	A variation
Claim 1 and evidence	Claim 1 and evidence
Claim 2 and evidence	Response to opposing views
Claim X and evidence	Claim 2 and evidence
Response to opposing views	Response to opposing views
	Claim X and evidence
	Response to opposing views

The Rogerian scheme	The problem-solution scheme
Concession to opposing views	The problem: claims and evidence
Claim 1 and evidence	The solution: claims and evidence
Claim 2 and evidence	Response to opposing views
Claim X and evidence	

stating claims outright or letting the evidence build to them, answering the opposition near the beginning or near the end or claim by claim. You can do this experimentation on paper, of course, but it's easier on a computer. Try rearranging your outline as described on page 36. Or try rearranging your draft (work with a copy) by cutting and pasting parts of it for different emphases.

EXERCISE 10.9 Organizing your argument

Continuing from Exercise 10.8 (p. 213), develop a structure for your argument. Consider especially how you will introduce it, how you will arrange your claims, where you will place your responses to opposing views, and how you will conclude.

10h Revising your argument

When you revise your argument, do it in at least two stages—revising underlying meaning and structure, and editing more superficial elements. The checklists on pages 54 and 60–61 can be a guide. Supplement them with the checklist below, which encourages you to think critically about your own argument.

Checklist for revising an argument

Thesis

- What is your thesis? Where is it stated?
- In what ways is your thesis statement an arguable claim?

Reasoning

- If your thesis derives from induction, where have you related the evidence to your generalization?
- If your thesis derives from deduction, is your syllogism both true and valid?
- Have you avoided fallacies in reasoning?

Evidence

- Where have you provided the evidence readers need?
- Where might your evidence not be accurate, relevant, representative, or adequate? (Answer this question from the point of view of a neutral or even skeptical reader.)

Appeals

- Where have you considered readers' probable beliefs and values?
- How are your rational appeals and emotional appeals appropriate for your readers?
- What is your ethical appeal? How can you improve it?

Opposing views

- What opposing views have you answered?
- How successfully have you conceded or refuted opposing views? (Again, consider the neutral, skeptical, or hostile reader.)

Organization

- Will readers be able to follow your argument? How clearly does it move from one point to the next?
- How appropriate is your organization given the likely views of your readers?

You can download this checklist from *ablongman.com/littlebrown*. Create a copy and answer the questions for each argument you write.

EXERCISE 10.10 Writing and revising your argument

Draft and revise the argument you have developed in the exercises in this chapter. Use the revision checklists on page 54 and above to review your work.

10i Examining a sample argument

The following essay by the student Craig Holbrook illustrates the principles discussed in this chapter. As you read the essay, notice especially the organization; the relation of claims and supporting evidence (including illustrations); the mix of logical, emotional, and ethical appeals; and the ways he responds to opposing views.

TV Can Be Good for You

Introduction

Identification of prevailing view

Disagreement with prevailing view

Thesis statement making three claims for television

Television wastes time, pollutes minds, destroys brain cells, and turns some viewers into murderers. Thus runs the prevailing talk about the medium, supported by serious research as well as simple belief. But television has at least one strong virtue, too, which helps to explain its endurance as a cultural force. It provides replacement voices that ease loneliness, spark healthful laughter, and even educate young children.

Background for claim 1: effects of loneliness

Evidence for effects of loneliness

Most people who have lived alone understand the curse of silence, when the only sound is the buzz of unhappiness or anxiety inside one's own head. Although people of all ages who live alone can experience intense loneliness, the elderly are especially vulnerable to solitude. For example, they may suffer increased confusion or depression when left alone for long periods but then rebound when they have steady companionship (Bondevik and Skogstad 329-30).

Evidence for effects of television on loneliness

Statement of claim 1

A study of elderly men and women in New Zealand found that television can actually serve as a companion by assuming "the role of social contact with the wider world," reducing "feelings of isolation and loneliness because it directs viewers' attention away from themselves" ("Television Programming"). (See fig. 1.) Thus television's replacement voices can provide comfort because they distract from a focus on being alone.

Illustration supporting claim 1

Fig. 1. Television can be a source of companionship for people whose living situations and limited mobility leave them lonely. Photograph by Jean Michel Foujols, Corbis image 42-15243193, 13 June 2005 <http://pro.corbis.com>.

The absence of real voices can be most damaging when it means a lack of laughter. Here, too, research shows that television can have a positive effect on health. Laughter is one of the most powerful calming forces available to human beings, proven in many studies to reduce heart rate, lower blood pressure, and ease other stress-related ailments (Burroughs, Mahoney, and Lippman 172; Griffiths 18). (See fig. 2.) Television offers plenty of laughter: the recent listings for a single Friday night included more than twenty comedy programs running on the networks and on basic cable.

Background for claim 2: effects of laughter

Evidence for effects of laughter

Evidence for comedy on television

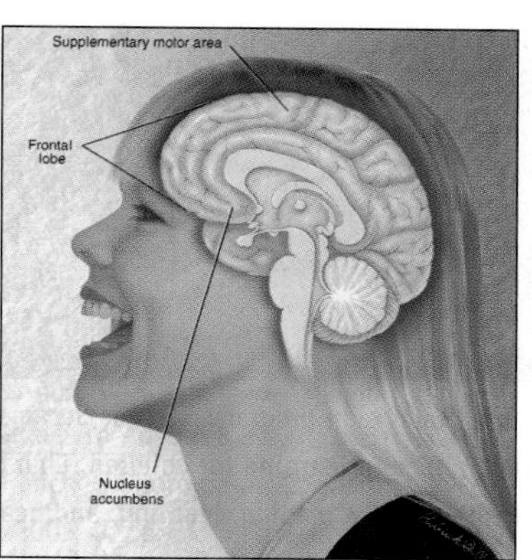

Illustration supporting healthful effects of laughter

Fig. 2. According to the Society for Neuroscience, the process of understanding and being amused by something funny stimulates at least three main areas of the brain. The society makes no recommendation about TV watching, but other studies show the healthful effects of the activity. Illustration by Lydia Kibiuk from Society for Neuroscience, Brain Briefings, Dec. 2001, 12 June 2005 <http://apu.sfn.org/BrainBriefings/bb_humor.htm>.

A study reported in a health magazine found that laughter inspired by television and video is as healthful as the laughter generated by live comedy. Volunteers laughing at a video comedy routine "showed significant improvements in several immune functions, such as natural killer-cell activity" (Laliberte 78). Further, the effects of the comedy were so profound that "merely anticipating watching a funny video improved mood, depression, and anger as much as two days beforehand" (Laliberte 79). Clearly, television's replacement voices can have healthful effects by causing laughter.

Evidence for effects of laughter in response to television

Statement of claim 2

EXERCISE 10.11 Critically reading an argument

Analyze the construction and effectiveness of the preceding essay by answering the following questions. (You can do this exercise online at *ablongman.com/littlebrown*.)

1. Where does Holbrook make claims related to his thesis statement, and where does he provide evidence to support the claims?
2. Where does Holbrook appeal primarily to reason, and where does he appeal primarily to emotion? What specific beliefs and values of readers does he appeal to?
3. How would you characterize Holbrook's ethical appeal?
4. How effective do you find the illustrations as support for Holbrook's claims? What appeals do they make? (For an analysis of Holbrook's first illustration, see p. 231.)
5. What objections to his argument does Holbrook anticipate? How does he respond to them?
6. How effective do you find this argument? To what extent does Holbrook convince you that television has virtues? Do some claims seem stronger or weaker than others? Does Holbrook respond adequately to objections?
7. Write a critical evaluation of "TV Can Be Good for You." First summarize Holbrook's views. Then respond to those views by answering the questions posed in number 6 above.

CHAPTER 11

Reading and Using Visual Arguments

Visual arguments use images to engage and convince readers. Visual arguments can be strong because their claims are immediate and often emotional. Advertisements often provide the most vivid and memorable examples, but writers in almost every academic field support their claims with images. In this chapter you'll learn how to read visual arguments critically (opposite) and how to use images to strengthen your own arguments (p. 227).

http://www.ablongman.com/littlebrown ▶

Visit the companion Web site for more help with reading and using visual arguments.

Note This chapter builds on the previous three, which discuss forming a critical perspective (including viewing images critically), reading an argument critically, and writing an argument. If you haven't already done so, read those chapters before this one.

11a Reading visual arguments critically

Chapter 9 explains the three main elements of any argument: claims, evidence, and assumptions. To read visual arguments critically, you'll analyze all three elements.

1 Testing claims

Claims are positive statements that require support (see pp. 181, 182–84). In a visual argument, claims may be made by composition as well as by content, with or without accompanying words. Here are a few examples of visual claims:

Image A magnetic sticker shaped like a ribbon and decorated with the colors and symbols of the American flag, positioned prominently on a car.

Claim I support American troops overseas, and you should, too.

Image A photograph framing hundreds of chickens crammed into small cages, resembling familiar images of World War II concentration camps.

Claim Commercial poultry-raising practices are cruel and unethical.

Image A chart with dramatically contrasting bars that represent the optimism, stress, and weight reported by people before and after they participated in a program of daily walking.

Claim Daily exercise leads to a healthier and happier life.

Image A cartoon featuring affluent-looking young adults on an affluent-looking college campus, conversing and frowning sadly as they gaze downhill at rough-looking teens in a dilapidated schoolyard. The caption reads, "Yes, it's sad what's happening to schools today. But everyone knows that throwing money at the problem isn't the solution."

Claim Better funding makes for better schools.

The image opposite is one of a series of advertisements featuring unnamed but well-known people as milk drinkers. The celebrity here is Oscar de la Hoya, a boxing champion. The advertisement makes several claims both in the photograph and in the text.

2 Weighing evidence

The kinds of evidence provided in images parallel those found in written arguments (see pp. 184–86):

Claims in an image

Image claim: Cool, tough men drink milk.

Image claim: Attractive people drink milk.

Image claim: Athletes drink milk.

Image claim: It's patriotic to drink milk.

Text claim: Milk is a good source of nutrition, helping to build muscles.

Advertisement by the Milk Processor Education Program

- **Facts** can be verified by observation or research. In visual arguments they may be data, as in a graph showing a five-year rise in oil prices. Or they may be inferences drawn from data, as in the statement in the preceding ad that milk provides "high-quality protein for your muscles without the fat." Sometimes images serve as facts themselves, objects that are analyzed in accompanying writing, as the milk ad is examined by this text or as the ad from *Time* magazine is examined by John Latner in the essay on pages 177–79.
- **Examples** illustrate and reinforce a point. Visual arguments often focus on an instance of the argument's claims, as Oscar de la Hoya does in the milk ad. Another ad might feature multiple images as examples: a Sizzler TV commercial, for instance, shows a sequence of luscious-looking foods to be had at the restaurant. An image might also illustrate a claim made in accompanying writing, as, again, the milk ad does in this text.

- **Expert opinions** are the findings of subject-matter authorities based on their research and experience. A visual argument might present a chart from an expert showing a trend in, say, unemployment among high school graduates. The familiar TV ad that features a doctor recommending a particular medicine to a patient offers the doctor as an expert.
- **Appeals to beliefs or needs** reinforce readers' values or truths. Many visual arguments make such appeals by depicting how things clearly ought to be (an antidrug ad featuring a teenager who is confidently refusing peer pressure) or, in contrast, by showing how things clearly should not be (a Web site for an antihunger campaign featuring images of emaciated children).

The evidence in a visual argument should be judged by the same criteria as that in a written argument (pp. 186–88):

- **Is the evidence accurate?** Images can be manipulated just as words can, and like words they should be analyzed for their fairness, precision, and trustworthiness. For example, a graph claiming to show changes in students' living expenses between 1995 and 2005 should identify the source and purpose of the research, supply data for all the years, and clarify the definition of *living expenses*.
- **Is the evidence relevant and adequate?** An image should pertain to the claims made in the larger argument and should sufficiently demonstrate its own claims. In an article on eating disorders, for instance, relevant and adequate images might include a medical diagram showing the liver damage from malnutrition and a photograph of a frail-bodied person suffering from anorexia. However, a photograph of a skinny model or actor would be neither relevant nor adequate, merely sensationalistic, unless the subject had publicly confirmed that his or her low weight resulted from an eating disorder.
- **Does the evidence represent the context?** Representative visual evidence reflects the full range of the sample it's drawn from and does not overrepresent or hide important elements of the subject. For example, a photographic essay claiming to document the poor working conditions of migrant farm workers might reasonably include images of one worker's scarred hands and another worker suffering from heat prostration. But to be representative, the essay would also need to illustrate the full range of migrant workers' experiences.

The annotations on the following pie chart demonstrate a way to analyze the evidence in a visual argument—even when, as in this case, the image comes from a highly reputable source. (The Social Science Data Analysis Network is a scholarly organization.)

Evidence in a visual argument

Accuracy: Trustworthy because based on data from the US Census, but perhaps somewhat distorted by the census's reliance on information volunteered by respondents

Relevance and adequacy: Shows incomes, as claimed, but the data are not immediately current because the US Census is conducted only every ten years

Representativeness: Fully representative of the census sample, with no distortion of particular segments (e.g., by emphasizing some pie slices over others)

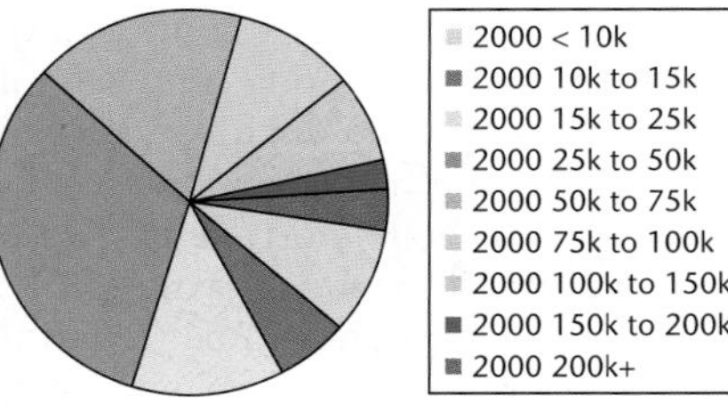

Fig. 1. Household incomes in the United States, based on data from the 2000 US Census, from Social Science Data Analysis Network, CensusScope, 15 Oct. 2005 <http://www.censusscope.org/us/chart_income.html>.

3 Discovering assumptions

Like a written argument, a visual argument is based on **assumptions**—the creator's ideas, often unstated, about why the evidence relates to the claims (see pp. 188–89). In visual arguments many assumptions involve the creator's beliefs about the audience, as detailed below. The examples analyze the milk ad on page 222, featuring the boxer Oscar de la Hoya.

- **Who readers are and where they will see the argument.** The de la Hoya ad first appeared in sports magazines, so the advertiser could assume readers who are interested in sports and athletes.
- **What readers already know about the subject.** To sports fans, de la Hoya would be a familiar subject. The advertiser presumably considers readers less familiar with the benefits of milk or with its appeal to celebrities like de la Hoya.
- **How familiar readers are with the purpose, format, and style of the argument.** With nearly two hundred print and TV ads since 1994, the milk-mustache campaign has become a fixture of US popular culture. Each new ad fits into the framework established by its predecessors.
- **Whether readers are likely to lean toward the argument's claims.** The advertiser clearly assumes that the endorsement of a sports star like de la Hoya will carry weight with readers. At the same time, it seems to assume that the benefits of milk still need selling to readers.
- **What kinds of information, ideas, and images readers will find persuasive.** The advertiser seems to assume that a strictly

factual claim about the health benefits of milk would not be persuasive enough to readers, so it shows that admirable people like de la Hoya consume milk. The photograph of de la Hoya emphasizes qualities that the advertiser presumably thinks will appeal to readers: fitness, toughness, directness, and even (in the robe draped over the boxer's shoulders) patriotism.

4 Recognizing fallacies

Fallacies, or errors in argument, are sometimes accidental, but they are often used deliberately to manipulate readers' responses. All the fallacies of written arguments discussed on pages 193–99 appear in visual arguments as well. Here we'll focus on examples of the two main categories.

- **Evasions attempt to deflect the reader from the central claim of the argument.** One evasion is **snob appeal,** inviting readers to think or be like someone they admire. Look again at the de la Hoya milk ad on page 222. Like all celebrity ads in the milk-mustache campaign, this one appeals to the reader's wish to emulate a famous person. If you drink milk, the ad says subtly, you too may become fit, skillful, and direct (notice that de la Hoya looks unguardedly into the camera). The ad does have some substance in its specific and verifiable claim that milk contains "high-quality protein for your muscles without the fat," but de la Hoya himself, with his milk mustache, makes a stronger claim.
- **Oversimplifications imply that subjects are less complex than they are.** Two examples are the **either/or fallacy,** which asserts that a complicated situation has only two sides worth

Fallacies in a visual argument

The Electoral College vote in the 2004 US Presidential election: red states for Bush, blue states for Kerry

Either/or fallacy: Solid colors implying that all of the voters in each state chose either the Republican or the Democratic candidate, when every state had voters for both candidates and for candidates from other political parties

Sweeping generalization: Strong contrast implying that voters' concerns were unconflicted and were represented by a single vote

considering, and the **sweeping generalization**, which asserts that a single view applies to all instances when it may apply only to some, or to none. Both fallacies appear in the map on the previous page, which represents the Electoral College vote in the 2004 US Presidential election: red for states won by Republican George W. Bush, blue for states won by Democrat John F. Kerry. The colors represent majority votes and Electoral College, not popular, votes. Still, the colors have been used to characterize the political and social preferences of each state's entire population and to reinforce stereotypes about rural vs. urban, heartland vs. coastal, and conservative vs. liberal citizens.

EXERCISE 11.1 Reading a visual argument critically

The image below is an e-card found on the Web site of Big Brothers Big Sisters of America, a community organization that brings children and mentors together. The organization invites site visitors to send its cards "to encourage friends and family members to support Big Brothers Big Sisters." Examine the card's visual argument closely, and jot down your answers to the following questions. (You can do this exercise online at *ablongman.com/littlebrown.*)

1. Who appears to be the intended audience? What aspects of the text and photograph seem best suited to that audience?
2. What can you tell about Big Brothers Big Sisters from this e-card?
3. What claims does the image make?
4. What evidence supports the claims? How effective is it?
5. What assumptions underlie the argument, connecting evidence to claims?
6. How does the visual organization (cropping of the photograph, placement of the text) make the argument more or less effective?
7. Is the argument persuasive to you? Why or why not?

E-card from the Web site of
Big Brothers Big Sisters of America

EXERCISE 11.2 Identifying fallacies in visual arguments

Locate a current or historical source with extreme views on a subject, such as the Web site of an outspoken political commentator, a sensationalist tabloid newspaper, or a collection of wartime propaganda (from any nation or era). Photocopy or print an image that seems especially ripe with fallacies and, referring to the complete list of fallacies on p. 194, find as many as possible in the image. The following sites can help you begin your search:

Political commentators

Al Franken: *shows.airamericaradio.com/alfrankenshow*
Rush Limbaugh: *rushlimbaugh.com/home/today.guest.html*

Tabloids

National Enquirer (US): *nationalenquirer.com*
Daily Mail (Great Britain): *http://www.dailymail.co.uk/pages/live/dailymail/home.html?in_page_id=1766*

World War II propaganda

Northwestern University library (American images): *http://www.library.northwestern.edu/govpub/collections/wwii-posters*
Calvin College (German images): *http://www.calvin.edu/academic/cas/gpa*

11b Using visual arguments effectively

Chapter 10 explains how you can use written argument to convince readers of your claims and perhaps move them to take action. Weaving images into an argument can strengthen it *if* the images are well chosen to provide evidence and make appropriate appeals.

Note Any visual you include in a paper requires the same detailed citation as a written source. If you plan to publish your argument online, you will also need to seek permission from the author. See pages 615–18 for more on acknowledging sources and obtaining permissions.

1 Choosing images

You can wait until you've drafted an argument before concentrating on what images to include. This approach keeps your focus on the research and writing needed to craft the best argument from sources. But you can also begin thinking visually at the beginning of a project, as you might if your initial interest in the subject was sparked by a compelling image. Either way, ask yourself some basic questions as you consider visual options:

- **Which parts of your argument can use visual reinforcement?** What can be explained better visually than verbally? Can a graph or chart present data compactly and interestingly? Can a photograph appeal effectively to readers' beliefs and values?

- **What are the limitations or requirements of your writing situation?** What do the type of writing you're doing and its format allow? Look through examples of similar writing to gauge the kinds of illustrations readers will expect.
- **What kinds of visuals are readily available on your subject?** As you researched your subject, what images seemed especially effective? What sources have you not yet explored? Tips for locating images, whether printed or online, appear on pages 584–86.
- **Should you create original images tailored to your argument?** Instead of searching for existing images, would your time be better spent taking your own photographs or generating visual explanations, such as diagrams, charts, and graphs? Tips for creating images appear on pages 122–27.

2 Using images as evidence

An image can attract readers' attention, but if it stops there it will amount to mere decoration or, worse, it will distract readers from the substance of your argument. When you use images as *evidence* for your argument, you engage readers both intellectually and visually.

The images used as evidence in visual arguments fall into four general categories:

- **Artifacts serving as the subject of the argument,** such as a painting or advertisement you are analyzing. (See pp. 176–79 for an example.)
- **Visual records of a subject or incident,** such as a historical photograph or a seismic record of an earthquake tremor.
- **Visual explanations of a concept or trend,** such as a diagram of the human respiratory system or a graph of financial data.
- **Visual examples of claims made in the argument,** such as a photograph of a school building abandoned after funding shortfalls or a screen shot of a Web pop-up advertisement.

To make an image work hard as evidence, be sure it relates directly to a point in your argument, adds to that point, and gives readers something to think about. Always include a caption that explicitly ties the image to your text, so that readers don't have to puzzle out your intentions, and that provides source information. Number images in sequence (Fig. 1, Fig. 2, and so on), and refer to them by number at the appropriate points in your text. (See Chapter 5, pp. 122–27, for more on captioning and numbering illustrations.)

The images below and on the next page illustrate approaches to using visual evidence in an argument with the following thesis: *Television shows focusing on cosmetic procedures are encouraging women to opt for such procedures in order to conform to a particular standard of beauty.*

Images as evidence

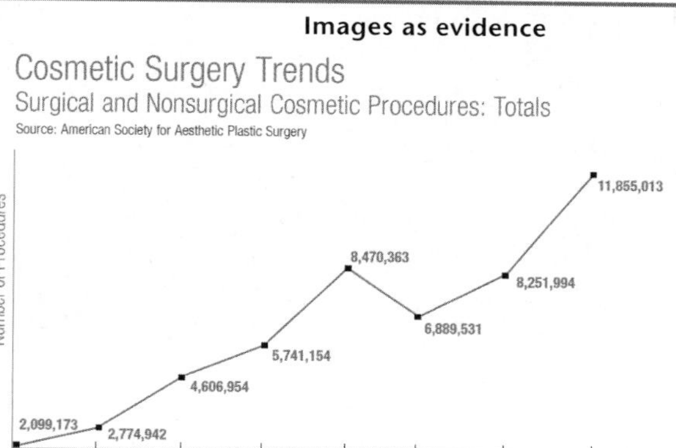

Graph from a reputable source providing a visual explanation of the overall increase in cosmetic procedures

Fig. 1. Numbers of cosmetic procedures performed in the United States, 1997-2004. In 2004 such procedures increased 44 percent. Graph from American Society for Aesthetic Plastic Surgery, <u>2004 Cosmetic Surgery National Data Bank: Statistics</u>, 3 June 2005 <http://www.surgery.org/press/statistics-2004.php>.

Caption explaining the graph and highlighting the 2004 increase, the most relevant to the paper's claims

A decorative image that sensationalizes but does not illuminate the argument

Fig. 2. A participant on the television show <u>Extreme Makeover</u>, from Walt Disney Internet Group, ABC, <u>Extreme Makeover</u>, 2005, 30 May 2005 <http://abc.go.com/primetime/extrememakeover/index.html>.

An uninformative caption that neither tells how to view the image nor links the image to the argument's claims

Images as evidence

Before and after images providing both a visual record and visual examples of the argument's claims

Caption explaining the images and the woman's cosmetic treatments, tying the images to the text of the paper

Fig. 2. Before and after images of a participant on the television show Extreme Makeover. In addition to the change in personal style implied by the change in clothes, hairdo, and body language, this participant also underwent nose surgery, a brow lift, eye surgery, dental work, liposuction, and breast augmentation. Photographs from Walt Disney Internet Group, ABC, Extreme Makeover, 2005, 30 May 2005 <http://abc.go.com/primetime/extrememakeover/index.html>.

3 Considering images' appeals to readers

Images can help to strengthen your argument's appeals to readers. The appeals are discussed in detail on pages 11–13 and 209–11. The summary below suggests how they apply to images:

- **Logical appeals target readers' capacity for reasoning rationally.** Images can strengthen the evidence for an argument if they come from reliable sources, present information fairly and accurately, and relate clearly to the paper's claims.
- **Emotional appeals tap into readers' beliefs and feelings.** Images can appeal to a host of ideas and emotions, including patriotism, curiosity, moral values, sympathy, and anger. Any such appeal should correctly gauge readers' beliefs and feelings and should be clearly relevant to the argument.
- **Ethical appeals show readers that you are a competent, fair, and trustworthy source of information.** Images make ethical appeals largely by making appropriate logical and emotional appeals. In addition, they can show that you are aware of readers'

knowledge, prove your seriousness, and demonstrate your neutrality.

To see how all three appeals can work in images, look again at a photograph used in the sample argument paper on pages 216–19. This image illustrates the writer's claim that television can ease loneliness.

Appeals in an image

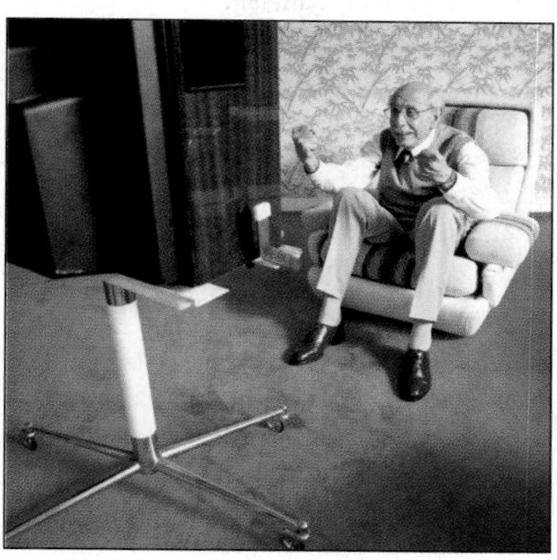

Logical appeal: Backs up the writer's claim that TV can ease loneliness: the man appears to live alone (only one chair is visible) and is interacting enthusiastically with the TV

Emotional appeal: Reinforces the benefits of TV watching: the man's isolation may be disturbing, but his excitement is pleasing

Ethical appeal: Conveys the writer's competence through the appropriateness of the image for the point being made

Fig. 1. Television can be a source of companionship for people whose living situations and limited mobility leave them lonely. Photograph by Jean Michel Foujols, Corbis image 42-15243193, 13 June 2005 <http://pro.corbis.com>.

EXERCISE 11.3 Brainstorming images for a visual argument

Working on your own or with others in a small group, apply the four questions for choosing images (pp. 227–28) to the argument subjects below. Which subject would most likely benefit from images? Which would be most difficult to illustrate? Why? (You can do this exercise online at *ablongman.com/littlebrown.*)

1. A program to help senior citizens adopt and care for a pet would improve seniors' lives and benefit the community.
2. Smoking cigarettes is a good way to meet interesting people.
3. Today's military-recruitment advertising targets certain kinds of people more than others.
4. Our school needs a better recycling program.
5. Listening to music while studying helps one retain crucial information.

EXERCISE 11.4 Filling gaps in a visual argument

Take another look at the graph on page 229 and the paired photographs on page 230, taken from a paper claiming that TV makeover shows encourage women to have cosmetic procedures in order to conform to a particular beauty standard. What additional images might bolster the argument? Consider especially how you might supplement the graph to connect the increase in cosmetic procedures with the growing popularity of TV makeover shows that feature such procedures.

EXERCISE 11.5 Revising an oversimplified visual argument

The red and blue map on page 225 comes from *Maps and Cartograms of the 2004 US Presidential Election Results* at *www-personal.umich.edu/~mejn/election.* Visit the site to see illustrations that capture more of the complexity of the 2004 election. Then write a brief visual argument based on one of the other images. Alternatively, write a brief argument about the original red and blue map, explaining its flaws. (Remember to include and cite in your paper any image you discuss.)

EXERCISE 11.6 Creating a deliberately bad visual argument

Purposely breaking the rules of argument can be fun and illuminating, building your knowledge about what works best and why. Using one of the topics listed in Exercise 11.3 or a new one, create a visual argument and an accompanying paragraph of text that deliberately antagonize readers instead of appealing to them. Do your best to do your worst: instead of demonstrating logic, use flawed reasoning or confusing examples; instead of appealing to readers' values and emotions, let your argument be boring or hostile; instead of communicating your credibility and expertise, display ignorance or ineptness.

EXERCISE 11.7 Revising an ineffective visual argument

Locate an ineffective visual argument, and use the guidelines on pages 230–31 to improve its likely appeal to readers. If your classmates completed Exercise 11.6, you could revise another student's deliberately bad argument.

PART 3

Grammatical Sentences

CHAPTER 12

Understanding Sentence Grammar

Grammar describes how language works. Following the rules of standard English grammar is what allows you to communicate with others across barriers of personality, region, class, or ethnic origin. If you are a native English speaker, you follow these rules mostly unconsciously. But when you're trying to improve your ability to communicate, it can help to make the rules conscious and learn the language used to describe them.

Grammar reveals a lot about a sentence, even if you don't know the meanings of all the words:

The rumfrums prattly biggled the pooba.

You don't know what this sentence means, but you can infer that some things called *rumfrums* did something to a *pooba*. They *biggled* it, whatever that means, in a *prattly* way. Two grammatical cues, especially, make this sentence like *The students easily passed the test:*

- **Word forms.** The ending *-s* means more than one *rumfrum*. The ending *-ed* means that *biggled* is an action that happened in the past. The ending *-ly* means that *prattly* probably describes *how* the *rumfrums biggled.*
- **Word order.** *Rumfrums biggled pooba* resembles a common sequence in English: something (*rumfrums*) performed some action (*biggled*) to or on something else (*pooba*). Since *prattly* comes right before the action, it probably describes the action.

This chapter explains how such structures work and shows how practicing with them can help you communicate more effectively.

Note Grammar and style checkers can both offer assistance and cause problems as you compose sentences. Look for the cautions and tips for using such checkers in this and the next five parts

http://www.ablongman.com/littlebrown

Visit the companion Web site for more help and additional exercises on sentence grammar.

of this book. For more information about grammar and style checkers, see pages 63–64.

12a Understanding the basic sentence

The **sentence** is the basic unit of thought. Its grammar consists of words with specific forms and functions arranged in specific ways.

1 Identifying subjects and predicates

Most sentences make statements. First the **subject** names something; then the **predicate** makes an assertion about the subject or describes an action by the subject.

Subject	Predicate
Art	thrives.

The **simple subject** consists of one or more nouns or pronouns, whereas the **complete subject** also includes any modifiers. The **simple predicate** consists of one or more verbs, whereas the **complete predicate** adds any words needed to complete the meaning of the verb plus any modifiers.

Sometimes, as in the short example *Art thrives,* the simple and complete subject and predicate are the same. More often, they are different:

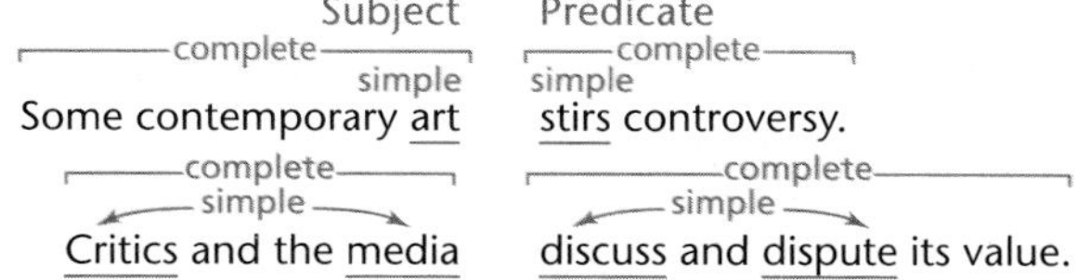

In the second example, the simple subject and simple predicate are both **compound:** in each, two words joined by a coordinating conjunction (*and*) serve the same function.

Note If a sentence contains a word group such as *that makes it into established museums* or *because viewers finally agree about its quality,* you may be tempted to mark the subject and verb in the word group as the subject and verb of the sentence. But these word groups are subordinate clauses, made into modifiers by the words they begin with: *that* and *because.* See pages 254–55 for more on subordinate clauses.

CULTURE LANGUAGE The subject of an English sentence may be a noun (*art*) or a pronoun that refers to the noun (*it*), but not both. (See p. 237.)

Faulty	Some art it stirs controversy.
Revised	Some art stirs controversy.

Tests to find subjects and predicates

The tests below use the following example:

Art that makes it into museums has often survived controversy.

Identify the subject.

- **Ask *who* or *what* is acting or being described in the sentence.**

Complete subject	art that makes it into museums

- **Isolate the sample subject by deleting modifiers**—words or word groups that don't name the actor of the sentence but give information about it. In the example, the word group *that makes it into museums* does not name the actor but modifies it.

Simple subject	art

Identify the predicate.

- **Ask what the sentence asserts about the subject:** what is its action, or what state is it in? In the example, the assertion about *art* is that it *has often survived controversy*.

Complete predicate	has often survived controversy

- **Isolate the verb, the simple predicate, by changing the time of the subject's action**. The simple predicate is the word or words that change as a result.

Example	Art . . . has often survived controversy.
Present	Art . . . often survives controversy.
Future	Art . . . often will survive controversy.
Simple predicate	has survived

2 Identifying the basic words: Nouns and verbs

The following five simple sentences consist almost entirely of two quite different kinds of words:

Subject	Predicate
The earth	trembled.
The earthquake	destroyed the city.
The result	was chaos.
The government	sent the city aid.
The citizens	considered the earthquake a disaster.

The words in the subject position name things, such as *earth, earthquake,* and *government.* In contrast, the words in the predicate position express states or actions, such as *trembled, destroyed,* and *sent.*

These two groups of words work in different ways. *Citizen* can become *citizens,* but not *citizened. Destroyed* can become *destroys,*

The parts of speech

Nouns name persons, places, things, ideas, or qualities: *Roosevelt, girl, Kip River, coastline, Koran, table, strife, happiness.* (See below.)

Pronouns usually substitute for nouns and function as nouns: *I, you, he, she, it, we, they, myself, this, that, who, which, everyone.* (See p. 239.)

Verbs express actions, occurrences, or states of being: *run, bunt, inflate, become, be.* (See the next page.)

Adjectives describe or modify nouns or pronouns: *gentle, small, helpful.* (See p. 244.)

Adverbs describe or modify verbs, adjectives, other adverbs, or whole groups of words: *gently, helpfully, almost, really, someday.* (See p. 244.)

Prepositions relate nouns or pronouns to other words in a sentence: *about, at, down, for, of, with.* (See p. 247.)

Conjunctions link words, phrases, and clauses. **Coordinating conjunctions** and **correlative conjunctions** link words, phrases, or clauses of equal importance: *and, but, or, nor; both . . . and, not only . . . but also, either . . . or.* (See pp. 261–62.) **Subordinating conjunctions** introduce subordinate clauses and link them to main clauses: *although, because, if, whenever.* (See p. 255.)

Interjections express feeling or command attention, either alone or in a sentence: *hey, oh, darn, wow.*

but not *destroyeds.* Grammar reflects such differences by identifying the **parts of speech** or **word classes** shown in the box above. Except for *the* and *a,* which simply point to and help identify the words after them, the five sentences about the earthquake consist entirely of nouns and verbs.

Nouns

Meaning

Nouns name. They may name a person (*Hilary Duff, Jesse Jackson, astronaut*), a thing (*chair, book, Mt. Rainier*), a quality (*pain, mystery, simplicity*), a place (*city, Washington, ocean, Red Sea*), or an idea (*reality, peace, success*).

Form

Most nouns form the **possessive** to indicate ownership or source. Singular nouns usually add an apostrophe plus *-s* (*Auden's poems*); plural nouns usually add just an apostrophe (*citizens' rights*).

Nouns also change form to distinguish between singular (one) and plural (more than one). Most nouns add *-s* or *-es* for the plural: *earthquake, earthquakes; city, cities.* Some nouns have irregular plurals: *woman, women; child, children.*

EXERCISE 12.3 Using nouns and verbs

Identify each of the following words as a noun, as a verb, or as both. Then create sentences of your own, using each word in each possible function. (You can do this exercise online at *ablongman.com/littlebrown*.)

Example:
fly
Noun and verb.
The fly sat on the meat loaf. [Noun.] The planes fly low. [Verb.]

1. wish
2. tie
3. swing
4. mail
5. spend
6. label
7. door
8. company
9. whistle
10. glue

3 Forming sentence patterns with nouns and verbs

English builds all sentences on the five basic patterns shown in the box on the facing page. As the diagrams indicate, the patterns differ in their predicates because the relation between the verb and the remaining words is different.

CULTURE LANGUAGE The word order in English sentences may not correspond to word order in the sentences of your native language. English, for instance, strongly prefers subject first, then verb, then any other words, whereas some other languages prefer the verb first. The main exceptions to the word patterns discussed below appear on pages 265–66. See also pages 366–72 on positioning modifiers in sentences.

Pattern 1: The earth trembled.

In the simplest pattern the predicate consists only of the verb. Verbs in this pattern do not require following words to complete their meaning and thus are called **intransitive** (from Latin words meaning "not passing over").

Subject	Predicate
	Intransitive verb
The earth	trembled.
The hospital	may close.

Pattern 2: The earthquake destroyed the city.

In pattern 2 the predicate consists of a verb followed by a noun that identifies who or what receives the action of the verb. This noun is a **direct object.** Verbs that require direct objects to complete their meaning are called **transitive** ("passing over"): the verb transfers the action from subject to object.

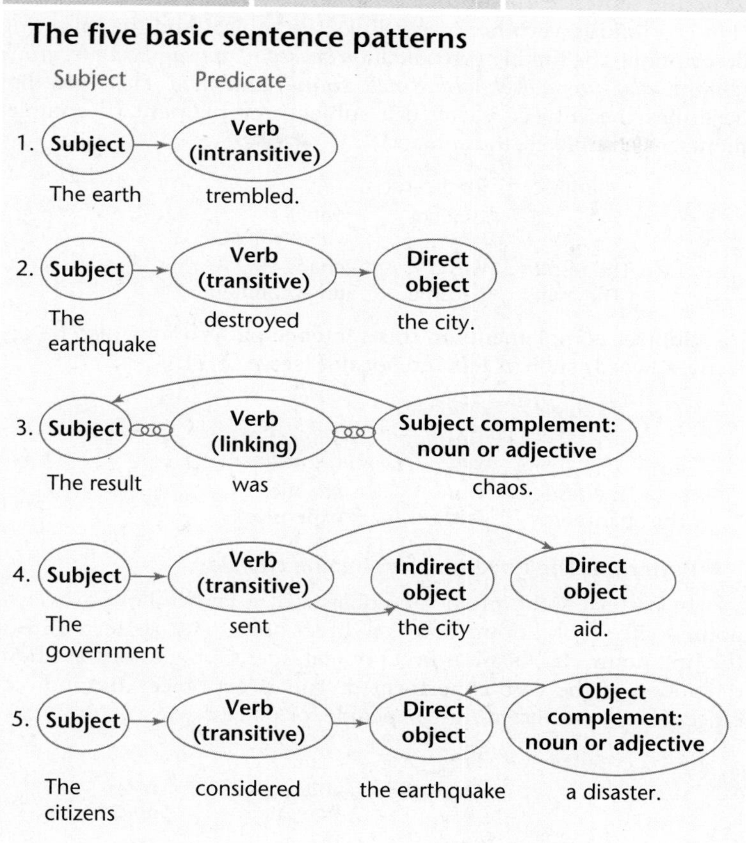

Subject	Predicate	
	Transitive verb	*Direct object*
The earthquake	destroyed	the city.
Education	opens	doors.

CULTURE LANGUAGE The distinction between transitive verbs and intransitive verbs like those in pattern 1 is important because only transitive verbs may be used in the passive voice (*The city was destroyed*). (See p. 304.) Your dictionary says whether a verb is transitive or intransitive. Some verbs (*begin, learn, read, write,* and others) are both.

Pattern 3: The result was chaos.

In pattern 3 the predicate also consists of a verb followed by a noun, but here the noun renames or describes the subject. We could write the sentence *The result* = *chaos*. The verb serving as an equal sign is a **linking verb** because it links the subject and the following description. The linking verbs include *be, seem, appear, become, grow, remain, stay, prove, feel, look, smell, sound,* and *taste*. The word that describes the subject is called a **subject complement** (it complements, or completes, the subject).

Subject	Predicate	
	Linking verb	*Subject complement*
The result	was	chaos.
The man	became	an accountant.

Subject complements in this sentence pattern may also be adjectives, words such as *tall* and *hopeful* (see p. 242):

Subject	Predicate	
	Linking verb	*Subject complement*
The result	was	chaotic.
The apartments	seem	expensive.

■ Pattern 4: The government sent the city aid.

In pattern 4 the predicate consists of a verb followed by two nouns. The second noun, *aid,* is a direct object (see pattern 2). But the first noun, *city,* is an **indirect object,** identifying to or for whom the action of the verb is performed. The direct object and indirect object refer to different things, people, or places.

Subject	Predicate		
	Transitive verb	*Indirect object*	*Direct object*
The government	sent	the city	aid.
One company	offered	its employees	bonuses.

A number of verbs can take indirect objects, including those above and *allow, bring, buy, deny, find, get, leave, make, pay, read, sell, show, teach,* and *write*.

CULTURE LANGUAGE With some verbs expressing action done to or for someone, the indirect object must be turned into a phrase beginning with *to* or *for*. These verbs include *admit, announce, demonstrate, explain, introduce, mention, prove, recommend, say,* and *suggest*. The *to* or *for* phrase then falls after the direct object.

Faulty	The manual explains workers the new procedure.
Revised	The manual explains the new procedure to workers.

■ Pattern 5: The citizens considered the earthquake a disaster.

In pattern 5, as in pattern 4, the predicate consists of a verb followed by two nouns. But in pattern 5 the first noun is a direct object and the second noun renames or describes it. Here the second noun is an **object complement** (it complements, or completes, the object):

Subject	Predicate		
	Transitive verb	*Direct object*	*Object complement*
The citizens	considered	the earthquake	a disaster.
The class	elected	Joan O'Day	president.

Like a subject complement (pattern 3), an object complement may be a noun or an adjective, as below:

Subject	Predicate		
	Transitive verb	*Direct object*	*Object complement*
The citizens	considered	the earthquake	disastrous.
Success	makes	some people	nervous.

EXERCISE 12.4 Identifying sentence patterns

In the following sentences, identify each verb as intransitive, transitive, or linking. Then identify each direct object (DO), indirect object (IO), subject complement (SC), and object complement (OC). (You can do this exercise online at *ablongman.com/littlebrown*.)

Example:

Children give (transitive verb) their parents (IO) both headaches (DO) and pleasures (DO).

1. Many people find New York City exciting.
2. Tourists flock there each year.
3. Often they visit Times Square first.
4. The square's lights are astounding.
5. The flashing signs sell visitors everything from TVs to underwear.

EXERCISE 12.5 Creating sentences

Create sentences by using each of the following verbs in the pattern indicated. (For the meanings of the abbreviations, see the directions for Exercise 12.4.) You may want to change the form of the verb. (You can do this exercise online at *ablongman.com/littlebrown*.)

Example:

give (S-V-IO-DO)
Sam gave his brother a birthday card.

1. laugh (S-V)
2. elect (S-V-DO-OC)
3. steal (S-V-DO)
4. catch (S-V-DO)
5. bring (S-V-IO-DO)
6. seem (S-V-SC)
7. call (S-V-DO-OC)
8. become (S-V-SC)
9. buy (S-V-IO-DO)
10. study (S-V)

12b Expanding the basic sentence with single words

Most of the sentences we read, write, or speak are more complex and also more informative and interesting than those examined so far. Most sentences contain one or more of the following: (1) modifying words (discussed here); (2) word groups, called phrases and clauses (p. 246); and (3) combinations of two or more words or word groups of the same kind (p. 260).

1 Using adjectives and adverbs

The simplest expansion of sentences occurs when we add modifying words to describe or limit the nouns and verbs. Modifying words add details:

Recently, the earth trembled.
The earthquake nearly destroyed the old city.
The federal government soon sent the city aid.
The grant was a very generous one but disappeared too quickly.

The underlined words represent two different parts of speech:

- **Adjectives** describe or modify nouns and pronouns. They specify which one, what quality, or how many.

old city (adjective noun) generous one (adjective pronoun) two pears (adjective noun)

- **Adverbs** describe or modify verbs, adjectives, other adverbs, and whole groups of words. They specify when, where, how, and to what extent.

An *-ly* ending often signals an adverb, but not always: *friendly* is an adjective; *never, not,* and *always* are adverbs. The only way to tell whether a word is an adjective or an adverb is to determine what it modifies.

Adjectives and adverbs appear in three forms:

- The **positive** form is the basic form, the one listed in the dictionary: *good, green, angry; badly, quickly, angrily.*
- The **comparative** form indicates a greater degree of the quality named by the word: *better, greener, angrier; worse, more quickly, more angrily.*

- The **superlative** form indicates the greatest degree of the quality named: *best, greenest, angriest; worst, most quickly, most angrily.*

(For further discussion of these forms, see p. 324.)

2 Using other words as modifiers

Nouns and special forms of verbs may sometimes serve as modifiers of other nouns. In combinations such as *office buildings, Thanksgiving prayer,* and *shock hazard,* the first noun modifies the second. In combinations such as *singing birds, corrected papers,* and *broken finger,* the first word is a verb form modifying the following noun. (These modifying verb forms are discussed in more detail on pp. 249–52.) Again, the part of speech to which we assign a word always depends on its function in a sentence.

EXERCISE 12.6 Identifying and using adjectives and adverbs

Identify the adjectives and adverbs in the following sentences. Then use each sentence as a model for creating a sentence of your own. (You can do this exercise online at *ablongman.com/littlebrown.*)

Example:

The red (adjective) barn sat uncomfortably (adverb) among modern (adjective) buildings.

Sample imitation: The little girl complained loudly to her busy mother.

1. The blue water glistened in the hot afternoon sunlight.
2. Happily, children dipped their toes in the cool lake.
3. Excitedly, some of the children hopped into the water.
4. Cautious parents watched from their shady porches.
5. The children played contentedly until the day finally ended.

EXERCISE 12.7 Using verb forms as modifiers

Use each of the following verb forms to modify a noun in a sentence of your own. (You can do this exercise online at *ablongman.com/littlebrown.*)

Example:

smoking
Only a smoking cigar remained.

1. scrambled
2. twitching
3. rambling
4. typed
5. painted
6. written
7. charging
8. ripened
9. known
10. driven

Life on a raft was an opportunity for adventure.
adjective phrase adjective phrase

Huck Finn rode the raft by choice.
adverb phrase

CULTURE LANGUAGE The meanings and idiomatic uses of English prepositions can be difficult to master; most must be memorized or looked up in a dictionary. (A list of dictionaries for English as a second language appears on p. 539.) See pages 293–94 for the uses of prepositions in two-word verbs such as *look after* and pages 525–27 for the uses of prepositions in idioms.

Punctuating prepositional phrases

Since a prepositional phrase lacks a subject and a predicate, it should not be punctuated as a complete sentence. If it is, the result is a **sentence fragment** (Chapter 17):

Fragment Toward the sun.

The phrase must be attached to another group of words containing both a subject and a predicate:

Revised The plane turned toward the sun.

A prepositional phrase that introduces a sentence is set off with punctuation, usually a comma, unless it is short (see pp. 435–36):

According to the newspaper and other sources, the governor has reluctantly decided to veto the bill.

In 1865 the Civil War finally ended.

A prepositional phrase that interrupts or concludes a sentence is *not* set off with punctuation when it is essential to the meaning of the word or words it modifies (see p. 437):

The announcement of a tuition increase surprised no one.

Students expected new fees for the coming year.

When an interrupting or concluding prepositional phrase is *not* essential to meaning, but merely adds information to the sentence, then it *is* set off with punctuation, usually a comma or commas (see p. 437):

The governor, according to the newspaper and other sources, has reluctantly decided to veto the bill.

As all the preceding examples illustrate, a preposition and its object are not separated by a comma.

EXERCISE 12.9 Identifying prepositional phrases

Identify the prepositional phrases in the following passage. Indicate whether each phrase functions as an adjective or as an adverb, and name the word that the phrase modifies. (You can do this exercise online at *ablongman.com/littlebrown.*)

Example:

After an hour I finally arrived at the home of my professor.

On July 3, 1863, at Gettysburg, Pennsylvania, General Robert E. Lee gambled unsuccessfully for a Confederate victory in the American Civil War. Called Pickett's Charge, the battle was one of the most disastrous conflicts of the war. Confederate and Union forces faced each other on parallel ridges separated by almost a mile of open fields. After an artillery bombardment of the Union position, about 12,000 Confederate infantry marched toward the Union ridge. The Union guns had been silent but suddenly roared, mowing the approaching Confederates. Within an hour, perhaps half of the Confederate soldiers lay wounded or dead.

EXERCISE 12.10 Sentence combining: Prepositional phrases

To practice writing sentences with prepositional phrases, combine each group of sentences below into one sentence that includes one or two prepositional phrases. You will have to add, delete, and rearrange words. Some items have more than one possible answer. (You can do this exercise online at *ablongman.com/littlebrown.*)

Example:

I will start working. The new job will pay the minimum wage.

I will start working at a new job for the minimum wage.

1. The slow loris protects itself well. Its habitat is Southeast Asia. It possesses a poisonous chemical.
2. To frighten predators, the loris exudes the chemical. The chemical comes from a gland. The gland is on the loris's upper arm.
3. The loris's chemical is highly toxic. The chemical is not like a skunk's spray. Even small quantities of the chemical are toxic.
4. A tiny dose can affect a human. The dose would get in the mouth. The human would be sent into shock.
5. Predators probably can sense the toxin. They detect it at a distance. They use their nasal organs.

2 Using verbals and verbal phrases

Verbals are special verb forms such as *smoking* or *hidden* or *to win* that can function as nouns (*smoking is dangerous*) or as modifiers (*the hidden money, the urge to win*).

Note A verbal *cannot* stand alone as the complete verb in the predicate of a sentence. For example, *The man smoking* and *The* *money hidden* are not sentences but sentence fragments (see p. 336). Any verbal must combine with a helping verb to serve as the predicate of a sentence: *The man was smoking. The money is hidden.*

Because verbals cannot serve alone as sentence predicates, they are sometimes called **nonfinite verbs** (in essence, they are "unfinished"). **Finite verbs,** in contrast, can make an assertion or express a state of being without a helping verb (they are "finished"). Either of the two tests below can distinguish finite and nonfinite verbs.

Tests for finite and nonfinite verbs (verbals)

Test 1 Does the word require a change in form when a third-person subject changes from singular to plural?

Yes Finite verb: *It sings. They sing.*

No Nonfinite verb (verbal): *bird singing, birds singing*

Test 2 Does the word require a change in form to show the difference in present, past, and future?

Yes Finite verb: *It sings. It sang. It will sing.*

No Nonfinite verb (verbal): *The bird singing is/was/will be a robin.*

There are three kinds of verbals: participles, gerunds, and infinitives.

Participles

All verbs have two participle forms, a present and a past. The **present participle** consists of the dictionary form of the verb plus the ending *-ing: beginning, completing, hiding.* The **past participle** of most verbs consists of the dictionary form plus *-d* or *-ed: believed, completed.* Some common verbs have an irregular past participle, such as *begun* or *hidden.* (See pp. 280–82.)

Both present and past participles function as adjectives to modify nouns and pronouns:

Shopping malls sometimes frustrate shoppers.

Shoppers may feel trapped.

CULTURE LANGUAGE For English verbs expressing feeling, the present and past participles have different meanings: *It was a boring lecture. The bored students slept.* See pages 327–28.

Gerunds

Gerund is the name given to the *-ing* form of the verb when it serves as a noun:

subject

Strolling through stores can exhaust the hardiest shopper.

object

Many children learn to hate shopping.

Present participles and gerunds can be distinguished *only* by their function in a sentence. If the *-ing* form functions as an adjective (*a teaching degree*), it is a present participle. If the *-ing* form functions as a noun (*Teaching is difficult*), it is a gerund.

CULTURE LANGUAGE In English, always use a gerund, not any other verb form, as the object of a preposition: *Diners are prohibited from smoking.* See also the culture-language note below.

Infinitives

The **infinitive** is the *to* form of the verb, the dictionary form preceded by the infinitive marker *to: to begin, to hide, to run.* Infinitives may function as adjectives, nouns, or adverbs:

adjective

The question to answer is why shoppers endure mall fatigue.

noun

The solution for mall fatigue is to leave.

adverb

Still, shoppers find it difficult to quit.

CULTURE LANGUAGE Infinitives and gerunds may follow some English verbs and not others and may differ in meaning after a verb: *The singer stopped to sing. The singer stopped singing.* (See pp. 290–92.)

Verbal phrases

Participles, gerunds, and infinitives—like other verb forms—may take subjects, objects, or complements, and they may be modified by adverbs. The verbal and all the words immediately related to it make up a **verbal phrase.** With verbal phrases, we can create concise sentences packed with information.

Like participles, **participial phrases** always serve as adjectives, modifying nouns or pronouns:

Buying things, most shoppers feel themselves in control.

They make selections determined by personal taste.

Gerund phrases, like gerunds, always serve as nouns:

subject

Shopping for clothing and other items satisfies personal needs.

object of preposition

Malls are good at creating such needs.

Infinitive phrases may serve as nouns, adverbs, or adjectives:

sentence subject — subject complement
To design a mall is to create an artificial environment.
noun phrase — noun phrase

Malls are designed to make shoppers feel safe.
adverb phrase

The environment supports the impulse to shop for oneself.
adjective phrase

Note When an infinitive or infinitive phrase serves as a noun after verbs such as *hear, help, let, make, see,* and *watch,* the infinitive marker *to* is omitted: *We all heard her tell* [not *to tell*] *the story.*

Punctuating verbals and verbal phrases

Verbal phrases punctuated as complete sentences are sentence fragments (Chapter 17). A complete sentence must contain a subject and a finite verb (p. 250):

Fragment	Treating the patients kindly.
Revised	She treats the patients kindly.

A verbal or verbal phrase serving as a modifier is almost always set off with a comma when it introduces a sentence (see p. 435):

To pay tuition, some students work at two jobs.

A modifying verbal or verbal phrase that interrupts or concludes a sentence is *not* set off with punctuation when it is essential to the meaning of the word or words it modifies (see p. 437):

Jobs paying well are hard to find.

When an interrupting or concluding verbal modifier is *not* essential to meaning but merely adds information to the sentence, it *is* set off with punctuation, usually a comma or commas (see p. 437):

One good job, paying twelve dollars an hour, was filled in fifteen minutes.

EXERCISE 12.11 Identifying verbals and verbal phrases

The following sentences contain participles, gerunds, and infinitives as well as participial, gerund, and infinitive phrases. First identify each verbal or verbal phrase. Then indicate whether it is used as an adjective, an adverb, or a noun. (You can do this exercise online at *ablongman.com/littlebrown.*)

Example:

adjective — adverb
Laughing, the talk-show host prodded her guest to speak.

1. Written in 1850 by Nathaniel Hawthorne, *The Scarlet Letter* tells the story of Hester Prynne.
2. Shunned by the community, Hester endures her loneliness.
3. Hester is humble enough to withstand her Puritan neighbors' cutting remarks.
4. Despite the cruel treatment, the determined young woman refuses to leave her home.
5. By living a life of patience and unselfishness, Hester eventually becomes the community's angel.

EXERCISE 12.12 Sentence combining: Verbals and verbal phrases

To practice writing sentences with verbals and verbal phrases, combine each of the following pairs of sentences into one sentence. You will have to add, delete, change, and rearrange words. Each item has more than one possible answer. (You can do this exercise online at *ablongman.com/littlebrown.*)

Example:

My father took pleasure in mean pranks. For instance, he hid the neighbor's cat.

My father took pleasure in mean pranks such as hiding the neighbor's cat.

1. Air pollution is a health problem. It affects millions of Americans.
2. The air has been polluted mainly by industries and automobiles. It contains toxic chemicals.
3. Environmentalists pressure politicians. They think politicians should pass stricter laws.
4. Many politicians waver. They are not necessarily against environmentalism.
5. The problems are too complex. They cannot be solved easily.

3 Using absolute phrases

Absolute phrases consist of a noun or pronoun and a participle, plus any modifiers:

absolute phrase
Many ethnic groups, their own place established, are making way for new arrivals.

absolute phrase — absolute phrase
Their native lands left behind, an uncertain future looming, immigrants face many obstacles.

These phrases are called *absolute* (from a Latin word meaning "free") because they have no specific grammatical connection to a noun, verb, or any other word in the rest of the sentence. Instead, they modify the entire rest of the sentence, adding information.

Notice that absolute phrases, unlike participial phrases, always contain a subject. Compare the following sentences:

participial phrase

For many immigrants learning English, the language introduces American culture.

absolute phrase

The immigrants having learned English, their opportunities widen.

We often omit the participle from an absolute phrase when it is some form of *be,* such as *being* or *having been:*

absolute phrase

Two languages [being] at hand, bilingual citizens in fact have many cultural and occupational advantages.

Punctuating absolute phrases

Absolute phrases are always set off from the rest of the sentence with punctuation, usually a comma or commas (see also pp. 442–43):

Their future more secure**,** these citizens will make room for new arrivals.

These citizens**,** their future more secure**,** will make room for new arrivals.

EXERCISE 12.13 Sentence combining: Absolute phrases

To practice writing sentences with absolute phrases, combine each pair of sentences below into one sentence that contains an absolute phrase. You will have to add, delete, change, and rearrange words. (You can do this exercise online at *ablongman.com/littlebrown.*)

Example:

The flower's petals wilted. It looked pathetic.
Its petals wilted, the flower looked pathetic.

1. Geraldine Ferraro's face beamed. She enjoyed the crowd's cheers after her nomination for Vice President.
2. A vacancy had occurred. Sandra Day O'Connor was appointed the first female Supreme Court justice.
3. Her appointment was confirmed. Condoleezza Rice became the first female national security adviser.
4. The midterm elections were over. Nancy Pelosi was elected the first female minority leader of the House of Representatives.
5. The election was won. Elizabeth Dole was a US senator from North Carolina.

4 Using subordinate clauses

A **clause** is any group of words that contains both a subject and a predicate. There are two kinds of clauses, and the distinction between them is important:

- **A *main* or *independent clause* makes a complete statement and can stand alone as a sentence:** *The sky darkened.*

- A *subordinate* or *dependent clause* is just like a main clause except that it begins with a subordinating word: *when the sky darkened; because he wants it; whoever calls.* The subordinating word reduces the clause to a single part of speech—an adjective, an adverb, or a noun—that supports the idea in a main clause. Because it only modifies or names something, a subordinate clause cannot stand alone as a sentence (see the discussion of punctuation on p. 257). (The word *subordinate* means "secondary" or "controlled by another." It comes from the Latin *sub,* "under," and *ordo,* "order.")

The following examples show the differences between main and subordinate clauses:

The school teaches parents. [main clause] It is unusual. [main clause]

Because the school teaches parents, [subordinate clause] it is unusual. [main clause]

Some parents avoid their children's schools. [main clause] They are often illiterate. [main clause]

Parents who are illiterate often avoid their children's schools. [main clause; "who are illiterate" = subordinate clause]

Two kinds of subordinating words introduce subordinate clauses: subordinating conjunctions and relative pronouns.

Subordinating conjunctions

Subordinating conjunctions, like prepositions, never change form in any way. In the following box they are arranged by the relationships they signal. (Some fit in more than one group.)

Common subordinating conjunctions

Cause or effect	Condition	Comparison or contrast	Space or time
as	even if	as	after
because	if	as if	as long as
in order that	if only	as though	before
since	provided	rather than	now that
so that	since	than	once
Concession	unless	whereas	since
although	when	whether	till
as if	whenever	while	until
even if	whether	Purpose	when
even though		in order that	whenever
though		so that	where
		that	wherever
			while

CULTURE LANGUAGE Subordinating conjunctions convey their meaning without help from other function words, such as the coordinating conjunctions *and, but, for,* and *so* (p. 261).

Faulty Even though the parents are illiterate, but their children may read well. [*Even though* and *but* have the same meaning, so both are not needed.]

Revised Even though the parents are illiterate, their children may read well.

■ **Relative pronouns**

Unlike subordinating conjunctions, **relative pronouns** usually act as subjects or objects in their own clauses, and two of them (*who* and *whoever*) change form accordingly (see pp. 273–75).

Relative pronouns

which	what	who (whose, whom)
that	whatever	whoever (whomever)

■ **Subordinate clauses**

Subordinate clauses function as adjectives, adverbs, or nouns.

Adjective clauses

Adjective clauses modify nouns and pronouns. They usually begin with the relative pronoun *who, whom, whose, which,* or *that,* although a few adjective clauses begin with *when* or *where* (standing for *in which, on which,* or *at which*). The pronoun is the subject or object of the clause it begins. The clause ordinarily falls immediately after the noun or pronoun it modifies:

Parents who are illiterate often have bad memories of school.

Schools that involve parents are more successful with children.

One school, which is open year-round, helps parents learn to read.

The school is in a city where the illiteracy rate is high.

Adverb clauses

Like adverbs, **adverb clauses** modify verbs, adjectives, other adverbs, and whole groups of words. They usually tell how, why, when, where, under what conditions, or with what result. They always begin with subordinating conjunctions.

The school began teaching parents when adult illiteracy gained national attention.

At first the program was not as successful as its founders had hoped.

Because it was directed at people who could not read, advertising had to be inventive.

Noun clauses

Noun clauses function as subjects, objects, and complements in sentences. They begin with *that, what, whatever, who, whom, whoever, whomever, when, where, whether, why,* or *how*. Unlike adjective and adverb clauses, noun clauses *replace* a word (a noun) within a clause; therefore, they can be difficult to identify.

sentence subject
Whether the program would succeed depended on door-to-door advertising.

object of verb
Teachers explained in person how the program would work.

object of preposition
A few parents were anxious about what their children would think.

Elliptical clauses

A subordinate clause that is grammatically incomplete but clear in meaning is an **elliptical clause** (*ellipsis* means "omission"). The meaning of the clause is clear because the missing element can be supplied from the context. Most often the elements omitted are the pronouns *that, which,* and *whom* or the predicate from the second part of a comparison.

Skepticism and fear were among the feelings [that] the parents voiced.
The parents knew their children could read better than they [could read].

Punctuating subordinate clauses

Subordinate clauses punctuated as complete sentences are sentence fragments (Chapter 17). Though a subordinate clause contains a subject and a predicate and thus resembles a complete sentence, it also begins with a subordinating word that makes it into an adjective, adverb, or noun. A single part of speech cannot stand alone as a complete sentence.

Fragment Because a door was ajar.
Revised A door was ajar.
Revised The secret leaked because a door was ajar.

A subordinate clause serving as an adverb is almost always set off with a comma when it introduces a sentence (see p. 435):

Although the project was almost completed, it lost its funding.

A modifying subordinate clause that interrupts or concludes a main clause is *not* set off with punctuation when it is essential to the meaning of the word or words it modifies (see p. 437):

> The woman who directed the project lost her job.
>
> The project lost its funding because it was not completed on time.

When an interrupting or concluding subordinate clause is *not* essential to meaning, but merely adds information to the sentence, it *is* set off with punctuation, usually a comma or commas (see p. 437):

> The project lost its funding, although it was almost completed.
>
> The director, who holds a PhD, sought new funding.

EXERCISE 12.14 Identifying subordinate clauses

Identify the subordinate clauses in the following sentences. Then indicate whether each is used as an adjective, an adverb, or a noun. If the clause is a noun, indicate what function it performs in the sentence. (You can do this exercise online at *ablongman.com/littlebrown.*)

> *Example:*
>
> The article explained how one could build an underground house. [Object of *explained.*] (noun)

1. Scientists who want to catch the slightest signals from space use extremely sensitive receivers.
2. Even though they have had to fight for funding, these scientists have persisted in their research.
3. The research is called SETI, which stands for Search for Extraterrestrial Intelligence.
4. The theory is that intelligent beings in space are trying to get in touch with us.
5. The challenge is to guess what frequency these beings would use to send signals.

EXERCISE 12.15 Sentence combining: Subordinate clauses

To practice writing sentences with subordinate clauses, combine each pair of main clauses into one sentence. Use either subordinating conjunctions or relative pronouns as appropriate, referring to the lists on pages 255 and 256 if necessary. You will have to add, delete, and rearrange words. Each item has more than one possible answer. (You can do this exercise online at *ablongman.com/littlebrown.*)

> *Example:*
>
> She did not have her tire irons with her. She could not change her bicycle tire.
>
> Because she did not have her tire irons with her, she could not change her bicycle tire.

1. Moviegoers expect something. Movie sequels should be as exciting as the original films.

2. A few sequels are good films. Most are poor imitations of the originals.
3. A sequel to a blockbuster film arrives in the theater. Crowds quickly line up to see it.
4. Viewers pay to see the same villains and heroes. They remember these characters fondly.
5. Afterward, viewers often grumble about filmmakers. The filmmakers rehash tired plots and characters.

5 Using appositives

An **appositive** is usually a noun that renames another noun nearby, most often the noun just before the appositive. (The word *appositive* derives from a Latin word that means "placed near to" or "applied to.") An appositive phrase includes modifiers as well.

> Bizen ware, a dark stoneware, has been produced in Japan since the fourteenth century.

> The name Bizen comes from the location of the kilns used to fire the pottery.

All appositives can replace the words they refer to: *A dark stoneware has been produced in Japan.*

Appositives are often introduced by words and phrases such as *or, that is, such as, for example,* and *in other words:*

> Bizen ware is used in the Japanese tea ceremony, that is, the Zen Buddhist observance that links meditation and art.

Appositives are economical alternatives to adjective clauses containing a form of *be,* as shown in the next example.

> Bizen ware, [which is] a dark stoneware, has been produced in Japan since the fourteenth century.

Although most appositives are nouns that rename other nouns, they may also be and rename other parts of speech, such as the verb *thrown* in the sentence below:

> The pottery is thrown, or formed on a potter's wheel.

Punctuating appositives

Appositives punctuated as complete sentences are sentence fragments (see Chapter 17). To correct such fragments, you can usually connect the appositive to the main clause containing the word referred to:

Fragment	An exceedingly tall man with narrow shoulders.
Revised	He stood next to a basketball player, an exceedingly tall man with narrow shoulders.

An appositive is *not* set off with punctuation when it is essential to the meaning of the word it refers to (see pp. 439–40):

The verb *howl* comes from the Old English verb *houlen*.

When an appositive is *not* essential to the meaning of the word it refers to, it *is* set off with punctuation, usually a comma or commas (see pp. 439–40):

An aged elm, the tree was struck by lightning.
The tree, an aged elm, was struck by lightning.
Lightning struck the tree, an aged elm.

A nonessential appositive is sometimes set off with a dash or dashes, especially when it contains commas (see p. 482):

Three people—Will, Erica, and Alex—object to the new procedure.

A concluding appositive is sometimes set off with a colon (see p. 479):

Two principles guide the judge's decisions: justice and mercy.

EXERCISE 12.16 Sentence combining: Appositives

To practice writing sentences with appositives, combine each pair of sentences into one sentence that contains an appositive. You will have to delete and rearrange words. Some items have more than one possible answer. (You can do this exercise online at *ablongman.com/littlebrown.*)

Example:

The largest land animal is the elephant. The elephant is also one of the most intelligent animals.

The largest land animal, the elephant, is also one of the most intelligent animals.

1. Some people perform amazing feats when they are very young. These people are geniuses from birth.
2. John Stuart Mill was a British philosopher. He had written a history of Rome by age seven.
3. Two great artists began their work at age four. They were Paul Klee and Gustav Mahler.
4. Mahler was a Bohemian composer of intensely emotional works. He was also the child of a brutal father.
5. Paul Klee was a Swiss painter. As a child he was frightened by his own drawings of devils.

12d Compounding words, phrases, and clauses

A **compound construction** combines words that are closely related and equally important. It makes writing clearer and more economical because it pulls together linked information.

Headaches can be controlled by biofeedback. Heart rate can be controlled by biofeedback.

compound subject
Headaches and heart rate can be controlled by biofeedback.

Without medication, biofeedback cures headaches. It steadies heart rate. It lowers blood pressure. It relaxes muscles.

compound predicate
Without medication, biofeedback cures headaches, steadies heart rate, lowers blood pressure, and relaxes muscles.

1 Using coordinating conjunctions and correlative conjunctions

Two kinds of words create compound constructions: coordinating and correlative conjunctions. **Coordinating conjunctions** are few and do not change form. In the following box the relationship that each conjunction signals appears in parentheses.

Coordinating conjunctions

and (*addition*)	nor (*alternative*)	for (*cause*)	yet (*contrast*)
but (*contrast*)	or (*alternative*)	so (*effect*)	

To remember the coordinating conjunctions, use the word *fanboys: for, and, nor, but, or, yet, so.*

The coordinating conjunctions *and, but, nor,* and *or* always connect words or word groups of the same kind—that is, two or more nouns, verbs, adjectives, adverbs, phrases, subordinate clauses, or main clauses:

Biofeedback or simple relaxation can relieve headaches.
Biofeedback is effective but costly.
Relaxation also works well, and it is inexpensive.

The conjunctions *for* and *so* connect only main clauses. *For* indicates cause; *so* indicates effect.

Biofeedback can be costly, for the training involves technical equipment and specialists.

Relaxation can be difficult to learn alone, so some people do seek help from specialists.

Some coordinating conjunctions pair up with other words to form **correlative conjunctions.** In the following box the relationship each conjunction signals appears in parentheses.

Common correlative conjunctions

both . . . and (*addition*)
not only . . . but also (*addition*)
not . . . but (*substitution*)
either . . . or (*alternative*)
neither . . . nor (*negation*)
whether . . . or (*alternative*)
as . . . as (*comparison*)

> Both biofeedback and relaxation can relieve headaches.
>
> The techniques require neither psychotherapy nor medication.
>
> The headache sufferer learns not only to recognize the causes of headaches but also to control those causes.

Punctuating compounded words, phrases, and clauses

Two words, phrases, or subordinate clauses that are connected by a coordinating conjunction are *not* separated by a comma (see p. 451):

> The library needs renovation and rebuilding.
>
> The work will begin after the spring term ends but before the fall term begins.

When two *main* clauses are joined into one sentence with a coordinating conjunction, a comma precedes the conjunction (see p. 434):

> The project will be lengthy, and everyone will suffer some inconvenience.

When two main clauses are joined *without* a coordinating conjunction, they must be separated with a semicolon to avoid the error called a comma splice (see p. 344):

> The work cannot be delayed; it's already overdue.

In a series of three or more items, commas separate the items, with *and* usually preceding the last item (see p. 443):

> The renovated library will feature new study carrels, new shelving, and a larger reference section.

Semicolons sometimes separate the items in a series if they are long or contain commas (see p. 459).

A comma also separates two or more adjectives when they modify a noun equally and are not joined by a coordinating conjunction (see p. 444):

> Cracked, crumbling walls will be repaired.

The comma does *not* separate adjectives when the one nearer the noun is more closely related to it in meaning (see p. 444):

New reading lounges will replace the old ones.

2 Using conjunctive adverbs

One other kind of connecting word, called a **conjunctive adverb,** relates only main clauses, not words, phrases, or subordinate clauses. In the following box the conjunctive adverbs are arranged by the relationships they signal.

Common conjunctive adverbs

Addition	Emphasis	Comparison or contrast	Cause or effect	Time
also	certainly	however	accordingly	finally
besides	indeed	in comparison	as a result	meanwhile
further	in fact	in contrast	consequently	next
furthermore	still	instead	hence	now
in addition	undoubtedly	likewise	similarly	then
incidentally		nevertheless	therefore	thereafter
moreover		nonetheless	thus	
		otherwise		

It's important to distinguish between conjunctive adverbs and conjunctions (coordinating and subordinating) because they demand different punctuation (see the next page). Conjunctive adverbs are *adverbs:* they describe the relation of ideas in two clauses, and, like most adverbs, they can move around in their clause:

Relaxation techniques have improved; however, few people know them.

Relaxation techniques have improved; few people know them, however.

In contrast, conjunctions bind two clauses into a single grammatical unit, and they cannot be moved:

Although few people know them, relaxation techniques have improved. [The subordinating conjunction can't be moved: *Few people know them although, relaxation techniques have improved.*]

Relaxation techniques have improved, but few people know them. [The coordinating conjunction can't be moved: *Relaxation techniques have improved, few people know them but.*]

Note Some connecting words have more than one use. *After, until,* and some other words may be either prepositions or subordinating conjunctions. Some prepositions, such as *behind* and *in,* can serve also as adverbs, as in *He trailed behind.* And some conjunctive adverbs, particularly *however,* may also serve simply as adverbs in sentences such as *However much the books cost, we must have them.* Again, the part of speech of a word depends on its function in a sentence.

Punctuating sentences containing conjunctive adverbs

Because the two main clauses related by a conjunctive adverb remain independent units, they must be separated by a semicolon (see p. 255). If they are separated by a comma, the result is a comma splice (Chapter 18):

Comma splice	Interest rates rose, therefore, real estate prices declined.
Revised	Interest rates rose; therefore, real estate prices declined.

A conjunctive adverb is almost always set off from its clause with a comma or commas (see p. 440):

The decline was small; however, some investors were badly hurt.
The decline was small; some investors, however, were badly hurt.

EXERCISE 12.17 Sentence combining: Compound constructions

To practice compounding words, phrases, and clauses, combine each of the following pairs of sentences into one sentence that is as short as possible without altering meaning. Use an appropriate connecting word of the type specified in parentheses, referring to the lists on pages 262–63 as necessary. You will have to add, delete, and rearrange words, and you may have to change or add punctuation. (You can do this exercise online at *ablongman.com/littlebrown.*)

Example:

The encyclopedia had some information. It was not detailed enough. (*Conjunctive adverb.*)

The encyclopedia had some information; however, it was not detailed enough.

1. All too often people assume that old age is not a productive time. Many people in their nineties have had great achievements. (*Conjunctive adverb.*)
2. In his nineties the philosopher Bertrand Russell spoke vigorously for international peace. He spoke for nuclear disarmament. (*Correlative conjunction.*)
3. Grandma Moses did not retire to an easy chair. She began painting at age seventy-six and was still going at one hundred. (*Conjunctive adverb.*)
4. The British general George Higginson published his memoirs after

he was ninety. The British archaeologist Margaret Murray published her memoirs after she was ninety. (*Coordinating conjunction.*)

5. The architect Frank Lloyd Wright designed his first building at age twenty. He designed his last building at age ninety. (*Coordinating conjunction.*)

12e Changing the usual word order

So far, all the examples of basic sentence grammar have been similar: the subject of the sentence comes first, naming the performer of the predicate's action, and the predicate comes second. This arrangement describes most English sentences, but four kinds of sentences change the order.

Questions

In most questions the verb or part of it precedes the subject:

verb subject verb
Have interest rates been rising?

verb subject verb
Did rates rise?

verb subject verb
Why did rates rise today?

subject verb
What is the answer? [Normal subject-verb order.]

Commands

In commands the subject *you* is omitted:

verb
Think of the options.

verb
Watch the news.

Passive sentences

Generally, the subject performs the action of a verb in the **active voice**. But sometimes the subject *receives* the action of a verb in the **passive voice**:

Active — subject verb
Kyong wrote the paper.

Passive — subject verb
The paper was written by Kyong.

See pages 304–05 for more on forming the passive voice, and see page 305 on overuse of the passive voice.

Sentences with postponed subjects

The subject follows the predicate in two sentence patterns. The normal order may be reversed for emphasis:

Henry comes here. [Normal order.]
Here comes Henry. [Reversed order.]

Or the word *there* or *it* may postpone the subject:

verb subject
There will be eighteen people attending the meeting.

verb subject
It was surprising that Marinetti was nominated.

There and *it* in such sentences are called **expletives.** Expletive sentences have their uses, but they can also be wordy and unemphatic (see p. 536).

CULTURE LANGUAGE When you use an expletive construction, be careful to include *there* or *it*. Only commands and some questions can begin with verbs.

Faulty No one predicted the nomination. Were no polls showing Marinetti ahead.

Revised No one predicted the nomination. There were no polls showing Marinetti ahead.

EXERCISE 12.18 Forming questions and commands

Form a question and a command from the following noun and verb pairs. (You can do this exercise online at *ablongman.com/littlebrown.*)

Example:
wood, split
Did you split all this wood?
Split the wood for our fire.

1. water, boil
2. music, stop
3. table, set
4. dice, roll
5. telephone, use

EXERCISE 12.19 Rewriting passives and expletives

Rewrite each passive sentence below as active, and rewrite each expletive construction to restore normal subject-predicate order. (For additional exercises with the passive voice and with expletives, see pp. 305–06, 388, and 537–38.) (You can do this exercise online at *ablongman .com/littlebrown.*)

Example:
All the trees in the park were planted by the city.
The city planted all the trees in the park.

1. The screenplay for *Monster's Ball* was cowritten by Milo Addica and Will Rokos.
2. The film was directed by Marc Foster.
3. There was only one performance in the movie that received an Academy Award.
4. It was Halle Berry who won the award for best actress.
5. Berry was congratulated by the press for being the first African American to win the award.

12f Classifying sentences

We describe and classify sentences in two different ways: by function (statement, question, command, exclamation, and so on) or by structure. Four basic sentence structures are possible: simple, compound, complex, and compound-complex. Each structure gives different emphasis to the sentence's main idea or ideas and to any supporting information.

1 Writing simple sentences

A **simple sentence** consists of a single main clause and no subordinate clause:

main clause
Last summer was unusually hot.

main clause
The summer made many farmers leave the area for good or reduced them to bare existence.

2 Writing compound sentences

A **compound sentence** consists of two or more main clauses and no subordinate clause. The clauses may be joined by a coordinating conjunction and a comma, by a semicolon alone, or by a conjunctive adverb and a semicolon.

main clause — main clause
Last July was hot, but August was even hotter.

main clause — main clause
The hot sun scorched the earth; the lack of rain killed many crops.

3 Writing complex sentences

A **complex sentence** contains one main clause and one or more subordinate clauses:

main clause — subordinate clause
Rain finally came, although many had left the area by then.

main clause — subordinate clause
Those who remained were able to start anew because the government
subordinate clause
came to their aid.

Notice that length does not determine whether a sentence is complex or simple; both kinds can be short or long.

4 Writing compound-complex sentences

A **compound-complex sentence** has the characteristics of both the compound sentence (two or more main clauses) and the complex sentence (at least one subordinate clause):

subordinate clause / main clause

Even though government aid finally came, many people had already been reduced to poverty, and others had been forced to move.

main clause

EXERCISE 12.20 Identifying sentence structures

Mark the main clauses and subordinate clauses in the following sentences. Identify each sentence as simple, compound, complex, or compound-complex. (You can do this exercise online at *ablongman .com/littlebrown.*)

Example:

main clause / subordinate clause

The police began patrolling more often when crime in the neighborhood increased. [Complex sentence.]

1. Joseph Pulitzer endowed the Pulitzer Prizes.
2. Pulitzer, incidentally, was the publisher of the New York newspaper *The World.*
3. Although the first prizes were for journalism and letters only, Pulitzers are now awarded in music and other areas.
4. For example, Berke Breathed won for his *Bloom County* comic strip, and Roger Reynolds won for his musical composition *Whispers Out of Time.*
5. Although only one prize is usually awarded in each category, in 1989 Taylor Branch's *Parting the Waters* won a history prize, and it shared the honor with James M. McPherson's *Battle Cry of Freedom.*

EXERCISE 12.21 Sentence combining: Sentence structures

Combine each set of simple sentences below to produce the kind of sentence specified in parentheses. You will have to add, delete, change, and rearrange words. (You can do this exercise online at *ablongman.com/littlebrown.*)

Example:

The traffic passed the house. It never stopped. (*Complex.*)
The traffic that passed the house never stopped.

1. Recycling takes time. It reduces garbage in landfills. (*Compound.*)
2. People begin to recycle. They generate much less trash. (*Complex.*)
3. White tissues and paper towels biodegrade more easily than dyed ones. People still buy dyed papers. (*Complex.*)
4. The cans are aluminum. They bring recyclers good money. (*Simple.*)
5. Environmentalists have hope. Perhaps more communities will recycle newspaper and glass. Many citizens refuse to participate. (*Compound-complex.*)

CHAPTER 13

Case of Nouns and Pronouns

Case is the form of a noun or pronoun that shows the reader how it functions in a sentence—that is, whether it functions as a subject, as an object, or in some other way. As shown in the box on the next page, only *I, we, he, she, they,* and *who* change form for each case. Thus these pronouns are the focus of this chapter.

The **subjective case** generally indicates that the word is a subject or a subject complement. (See pp. 235 and 241–42.)

> [subject] She and Novick discussed the proposal.
>
> The proposal ignores many [subject] who need help.
>
> The disgruntled planners were [subject complement] she and Novick.

The **objective case** generally indicates that the word is the object of a verb or preposition. (See pp. 240–43 and 247.)

> The proposal disappointed [object of verb] her and Novick.
>
> A colleague [object of verb] whom they respected let [object of verb] them down.
>
> Their opinion of [object of preposition] him suffered.

The **possessive case** generally indicates ownership or source:

> Her counterproposal is in preparation.
> Theirs is the more defensible position.
> The problem is not his.

Do not use an apostrophe to form the possessive of personal pronouns: *yours* (not *your's*); *theirs* (not *their's*). (See p. 467. See also p. 463 for the possessive forms of nouns, which do use apostrophes.)

http://www.ablongman.com/littlebrown 

Visit the companion Web site for more help and additional exercises on noun and pronoun case.

Case forms of nouns and pronouns

	Subjective	Objective	Possessive
Nouns	boy	boy	boy's
	Jessie	Jessie	Jessie's
Personal pronouns			
Singular			
1st person	I	me	my, mine
2nd person	you	you	your, yours
3rd person	he	him	his
	she	her	her, hers
	it	it	its
Plural			
1st person	we	us	our, ours
2nd person	you	you	your, yours
3rd person	they	them	their, theirs
Relative and interrogative pronouns			
	who	whom	whose
	whoever	whomever	—
	which, that, what	which, that, what	—
Indefinite pronouns			
	everybody	everybody	everybody's

Note Grammar and style checkers may flag some problems with pronoun case, but they will also miss a lot. For instance, one checker spotted the error in *We asked whom would come* (should be *who would come*), but it overlooked *We dreaded them coming* (should be *their coming*).

CULTURE LANGUAGE In standard American English, *-self* pronouns do not change form to show function. Their only forms are *myself, yourself, himself, herself, itself, ourselves, yourselves, themselves.* Avoid nonstandard forms such as *hisself, ourself,* and *theirselves.*

13a Use the subjective case for compound subjects and for subject complements.

In compound subjects use the same pronoun form you would use if the pronoun stood alone as a subject:

subject
She and Novick will persist.

The others may lend their support when she and Novick [subject] get a hearing.

If you are in doubt about the correct form, try the test in the box below.

After a linking verb, such as a form of *be,* a pronoun renaming the subject (a subject complement) should be in the subjective case:

The ones who care most are she and Novick. [subject complement]

It was they [subject complement] whom the mayor appointed.

If this construction sounds stilted to you, use the more natural order: *She and Novick are the ones who care most. The mayor appointed them.*

A test for case forms in compound constructions

1. **Identify a compound construction** (one connected by *and, but, or, nor*).

   [He, Him] and [I, me] won the prize.
   The prize went to [he, him] and [I, me].

2. **Write a separate sentence for each part of the compound.**

   [He, Him] won the prize. [I, Me] won the prize.
   The prize went to [he, him]. The prize went to [I, me].

3. **Choose the pronouns that sound correct.**

   He won the prize. I won the prize. [Subjective.]
   The prize went to him. The prize went to me. [Objective.]

4. **Put the separate sentences back together.**

   He and I won the prize.
   The prize went to him and me.

13b Use the objective case for compound objects.

In compound objects use the same pronoun form you would use if the pronoun stood alone as an object:

The mayor nominated Zhu and him. [direct object]

The mayor gave Zhu and him [indirect object] awards.

Credit goes equally to them and the mayor. [object of preposition]

If you are in doubt about the correct form, try the test in the box above.

EXERCISE 13.1 Choosing between subjective and objective pronouns

From the pairs in brackets, select the appropriate subjective or objective pronoun(s) for each of the following sentences. (You can do this exercise online at *ablongman.com/littlebrown*.)

Example:

"Between you and [I, me]," the seller said, "this deal is a steal."
"Between you and me," the seller said, "this deal is a steal."

1. Lisa and [I, me] were competing for places on the relay team.
2. The fastest runners at our school were [she, her] and [I, me], so [we, us] expected to make the team.
3. [She, Her] and [I, me] were friends but also intense rivals.
4. The time trials went badly, excluding both [she, her] and [I, me] from the team.
5. Next season we are determined to earn at least one place between [she, her] and [I, me].

13c Use the appropriate case when the plural pronoun *we* or *us* occurs with a noun.

Whether to use *we* or *us* with a noun depends on the use of the noun:

object of preposition

Freezing weather is welcomed by us skaters.

subject

We skaters welcome freezing weather.

13d In appositives the case of a pronoun depends on the function of the word described or identified.

object of verb — appositive identifies object

The class elected two representatives, DeShawn and me.

subject — appositive identifies subject

Two representatives, DeShawn and I, were elected.

If you are in doubt about case in an appositive, try the sentence without the word the appositive identifies: *The class elected DeShawn and me. DeShawn and I were elected.*

EXERCISE 13.2 Choosing between subjective and objective pronouns

From the pairs in brackets, select the appropriate subjective or objective pronoun for each of the following sentences. (You can do this exercise online at *ablongman.com/littlebrown*.)

Example:

Convincing [we, us] veterans to vote yes will be difficult.
Convincing us veterans to vote yes will be difficult.

1. Obtaining enough protein is important to [we, us] vegetarians.
2. Instead of obtaining protein from meat, [we, us] vegetarians get our protein from other sources.
3. Jeff claims to know only two vegetarians, Helena and [he, him], who avoid all animal products, including milk.
4. Some of [we, us] vegetarians eat fish, which is a good source of protein.
5. [We, Us] vegetarians in my family, my parents and [I, me], drink milk and eat fish.

13e The case of a pronoun after *than* or *as* in a comparison depends on the meaning.

When a pronoun follows *than* or *as* in a comparison, the case of the pronoun indicates what words may have been omitted. When the pronoun is subjective, it must serve as the subject of an omitted verb:

Some critics like Glass more than he [does]. (he: subject)

When the pronoun is objective, it must serve as the object of an omitted verb:

Some critics like Glass more than [they like] him. (him: object)

13f Use the objective case for pronouns that are subjects or objects of infinitives.

The school asked him to speak. (him: subject of infinitive)

Students chose to invite him. (him: object of infinitive)

13g The case of the pronoun *who* depends on its function in its clause.

To choose between *who* and *whom, whoever* and *whomever,* you need to figure out whether the word serves as a subject or as an object. Use *who* where you would use *he* or *she*—all ending in vowels. Use *whom* where you would use *him* or *her*—all ending in consonants.

2. They may not hear important instructions and information from teachers. Teachers may speak softly.
3. Classmates may not be audible. The teacher calls on those classmates.
4. Some hearing-impaired children may work harder to overcome their disability. These children get a lot of encouragement at home.
5. Some hearing-impaired children may take refuge in fantasy friends. They can rely on these friends not to criticize or laugh.

13h Ordinarily, use a possessive pronoun or noun immediately before a gerund.

A **gerund** is the *-ing* form of a verb (*running, sleeping*) used as a noun (p. 250). Like nouns, gerunds are commonly preceded by possessive nouns and pronouns: *our vote* (noun), *our voting* (gerund).

The coach disapproved of their lifting weights.

The coach's disapproving was a surprise.

A noun or pronoun before an *-ing* verb form is not always possessive. Sometimes the *-ing* form will be a present participle modifying the preceding word:

Everyone had noticed him weightlifting. [Emphasis on *him*.]
objective pronoun — participle

Everyone had noticed his weightlifting. [Emphasis on the activity.]
possessive pronoun — gerund

Note that a gerund usually is not preceded by the possessive when the possessive would create an awkward construction:

Awkward	A rumor spread about everybody's on the team wanting to quit.
Less awkward	A rumor spread about everybody on the team wanting to quit.
Better	A rumor spread that everybody on the team wanted to quit.

EXERCISE 13.5 Revising: Case

Revise all inappropriate case forms in the following paragraph, and explain the function of each case form. (You can do this exercise online at *ablongman.com/littlebrown*.)

Written four thousand years ago, *The Epic of Gilgamesh* tells of the friendship of Gilgamesh and Enkidu. Gilgamesh was a bored king who his people thought was too harsh. Then he met Enkidu, a wild man whom had lived with the animals in the mountains. Immediately, him and Gilgamesh wrestled to see whom was more powerful. After hours of struggle, Enkidu admitted that Gilgamesh was stronger than him. Now the friends needed adventures worthy of the two strongest men on earth. Gilgamesh said, "Between you and I, mighty deeds will be accomplished, and our fame will be everlasting." Among their acts, Enkidu and him defeated a giant bull, Humbaba, and cut down the bull's cedar forests. Them bringing back cedar logs to Gilgamesh's treeless land won great praise from the people. When Enkidu died, Gilgamesh mourned his death, realizing that no one had been a better friend than him. When Gilgamesh himself died many years later, his people raised a monument praising Enkidu and he for their friendship and their mighty deeds of courage.

Note See page 333 for an exercise involving case along with other aspects of grammar.

CHAPTER 14

Verbs

The verb is the most complicated part of speech in English, changing form to express a wide range of information.

Verb Forms

All verbs except *be* have five basic forms. The first three are the verb's **principal parts.**

- **The *plain form* is the dictionary form of the verb.** When the subject is a plural noun or the pronoun *I, we, you,* or *they,* the plain form indicates action that occurs in the present, occurs habitually, or is generally true.

A few artists live in town today.
They hold classes downtown.

http://www.ablongman.com/littlebrown

Visit the companion Web site for more help and additional exercises on verb forms.

Terms used to describe verbs

Tense

The time of the verb's action—for instance, present (*kick*), past (*kicked*), future (*will kick*). (See p. 294.)

Mood

The attitude of the verb's speaker or writer—the difference, for example, in *I kick the ball, Kick the ball,* and *I suggest that you kick the ball.* (See p. 301.)

Voice

The distinction between the **active,** in which the subject performs the verb's action (*I kick the ball*), and the **passive,** in which the subject is acted upon (*The ball is kicked by me*). (See p. 308.)

Person

The verb form that reflects whether the subject is speaking (*I/we kick the ball*), spoken to (*You kick the ball*), or spoken about (*She kicks the ball*). (See p. 308.)

Number

The verb form that reflects whether the subject is singular (*The girl kicks the ball*) or plural (*Girls kick the ball*). (See p. 310.)

- **The *past-tense form* indicates that the action of the verb occurred before now.** It usually adds *-d* or *-ed* to the plain form, although some irregular verbs form it in other ways (see p. 280).

  Many artists lived in town before this year.
  They held classes downtown. [Irregular verb.]

- **The *past participle* is the same as the past-tense form, except in most irregular verbs.** It combines with forms of *have* or *be* (*has climbed, was created*), or by itself it modifies nouns and pronouns (*the sliced apples*).

  Artists have lived in town for decades.
  They have held classes downtown. [Irregular verb.]

- **The *present participle* adds *-ing* to the verb's plain form.** It combines with forms of *be* (*is buying*), modifies nouns and pronouns (*the boiling water*), or functions as a noun (*Running exhausts me*).

  A few artists are living in town today.
  They are holding classes downtown.

- **The *-s form* ends in *-s* or *-es*.** When the subject is a singular noun, a pronoun such as *everyone,* or the personal pronoun *he, she,* or *it,* the *-s* form indicates action that occurs in the present, occurs habitually, or is generally true.

The artist lives in town today.
She holds classes downtown.

The verb *be* has eight forms rather than the five forms of most other verbs:

Plain form	be		
Present participle	being		
Past participle	been		
	I	*he, she, it*	*we, you, they*
Present tense	am	is	are
Past tense	was	was	were

CULTURE LANGUAGE If standard American English is not your native language or dialect, you may have difficulty with verbs' *-s* forms (including those for *be: is, was*) or with the forms that indicate time (such as the past-tense form). See pages 284–85 and 297–98, respectively, for more on these forms.

Helping verbs

Helping verbs, also called **auxiliary verbs,** combine with some verb forms to indicate time and other kinds of meaning, as in *can run, was sleeping, had been* eaten. These combinations are **verb phrases.** Since the plain form, present participle, or past participle in any verb phrase always carries the principal meaning, it is sometimes called the **main verb.**

Verb phrase	
Helping	*Main*
Artists can	train others to draw.
The techniques have	changed little.

These are the most common helping verbs:

be able to	had better	must	used to
be supposed to	have to	ought to	will
can	may	shall	would
could	might	should	

Forms of *be:* be, am, is, are, was, were, been, being
Forms of *have:* have, has, had, having
Forms of *do:* do, does, did

CULTURE LANGUAGE The helping verbs of standard American English may be problematic if you are used to speaking another language or dialect. See pages 285–89 for more on helping verbs.

14a Use the correct forms of regular and irregular verbs.

Most verbs are **regular;** that is, they form their past tense and past participle by adding *-d* or *-ed* to the plain form.

Plain form	Past tense	Past participle
live	lived	lived
act	acted	acted

Since the past tense and past participle are created in the same way, the forms of regular verbs do not often cause problems in speech and writing (but see p. 284).

About two hundred English verbs are **irregular;** that is, they form their past tense and past participle in some irregular way.

Plain form	Past tense	Past participle
begin	began	begun
break	broke	broken
sleep	slept	slept

You can see the difference between a regular and an irregular verb in these examples:

Plain form	Today the birds twitter. Today the birds sing.
Past tense	Yesterday the birds twittered. Yesterday the birds sang.
Past participle	In the past the birds have twittered. In the past the birds have sung.

Check a dictionary under the plain form if you have any doubt about a verb's principal parts. If no other forms are listed, the verb is regular: both the past tense and the past participle add *-d* or *-ed* to the plain form. If the verb is irregular, the dictionary will list the plain form, the past tense, and the past participle in that order (*go, went, gone*). If the dictionary gives only two forms (as in *think, thought*), then the past tense and the past participle are the same.

CULTURE LANGUAGE Some English dialects use distinctive verb forms that differ from those of standard American English: for instance, *drug* for *dragged, growed* for *grew, come* for *came,* or *went* for *gone.* In situations requiring standard American English, use the forms in the list opposite or in a dictionary.

Note A grammar and style checker may flag incorrect forms of irregular verbs, but it may also fail to do so. For example, a checker flagged *The runner stealed second base* (*stole* is correct) but not *The*

Principal parts of common irregular verbs

Plain form	Past tense	Past participle
arise	arose	arisen
become	became	become
begin	began	begun
bid	bid	bid
bite	bit	bitten, bit
blow	blew	blown
break	broke	broken
bring	brought	brought
burst	burst	burst
buy	bought	bought
catch	caught	caught
choose	chose	chosen
come	came	come
cut	cut	cut
dive	dived, dove	dived
do	did	done
draw	drew	drawn
dream	dreamed, dreamt	dreamed, dreamt
drink	drank	drunk
drive	drove	driven
eat	ate	eaten
fall	fell	fallen
find	found	found
flee	fled	fled
fly	flew	flown
forget	forgot	forgotten, forgot
freeze	froze	frozen
get	got	got, gotten
give	gave	given
go	went	gone
grow	grew	grown
hang (suspend)	hung	hung
hang (execute)	hanged	hanged
hear	heard	heard
hide	hid	hidden
hold	held	held
keep	kept	kept
know	knew	known
lay	laid	laid
lead	led	led
leave	left	left
lend	lent	lent
let	let	let
lie	lay	lain

(continued)

Principal parts of common irregular verbs

(continued)

Plain form	Past tense	Past participle
lose	lost	lost
pay	paid	paid
prove	proved	proved, proven
ride	rode	ridden
ring	rang	rung
rise	rose	risen
run	ran	run
say	said	said
see	saw	seen
set	set	set
shake	shook	shaken
shrink	shrank, shrunk	shrunk, shrunken
sing	sang, sung	sung
sink	sank, sunk	sunk
sit	sat	sat
sleep	slept	slept
slide	slid	slid
speak	spoke	spoken
spring	sprang, sprung	sprung
stand	stood	stood
steal	stole	stolen
swim	swam	swum
swing	swung	swung
take	took	taken
teach	taught	taught
tear	tore	torn
throw	threw	thrown
wear	wore	worn
write	wrote	written

runner had steal second base (*stolen* is correct). When in doubt about the forms of irregular verbs, refer to the preceding list, consult a dictionary, or consult the links at this book's companion Web site (*ablongman.com/littlebrown*).

EXERCISE 14.1 Using irregular verbs

For each irregular verb in brackets, give either the past tense or the past participle, as appropriate, and identify the form you used. (You can do this exercise online at *ablongman.com/littlebrown*.)

Example:

Though we had [hide] the cash box, it was [steal].

Though we had hidden the cash box, it was stolen. [Two past participles.]

1. The world population has [grow] by two-thirds of a billion people in less than a decade.
2. In 2000 it [break] the 6 billion mark.
3. Experts have [draw] pictures of a crowded future.
4. They predict that the world population may have [slide] up to as much as 10 billion by the year 2050.
5. Though the food supply [rise] in the last decade, the share to each person [fall].

14b Distinguish between *sit* and *set*, *lie* and *lay*, and *rise* and *raise*.

The forms of *sit* and *set, lie* and *lay,* and *rise* and *raise* are easy to confuse:

Plain form	Past tense	Past participle
sit	sat	sat
set	set	set
lie	lay	lain
lay	laid	laid
rise	rose	risen
raise	raised	raised

In each of these confusing pairs, one verb is **intransitive** (it does not take an object) and one is **transitive** (it does take an object). (See pp. 240–43 for more on this distinction.)

Intransitive

The patients lie in their beds. [*Lie* means "recline" and takes no object.]

Visitors sit with them. [*Sit* means "be seated" or "be located" and takes no object.]

Patients' temperatures rise. [*Rise* means "increase" or "get up" and takes no object.]

Transitive

Orderlies lay the dinner trays on tables. [*Lay* means "place" and takes an object, here *trays*.]

Orderlies set the trays down. [*Set* means "place" and takes an object, here *trays*.]

Nursing aides raise the shades. [*Raise* means "lift" or "bring up" and takes an object, here *shades*.]

EXERCISE 14.2 Distinguishing *sit/set, lie/lay, rise/raise*

Choose the correct verb from the pair given in brackets. Then supply the past tense or past participle, as appropriate. (You can do this exercise online at *ablongman.com/littlebrown.*)

Example:

After I washed all the windows, I [lie, lay] down the squeegee and then I [sit, set] the table.

After I washed all the windows, I laid down the squeegee and then I set the table.

1. Yesterday afternoon the child [lie, lay] down for a nap.
2. The child has been [rise, raise] by her grandparents.
3. Most days her grandfather has [sit, set] with her, reading her stories.
4. She has [rise, raise] at dawn most mornings.
5. Her toys were [lie, lay] out on the floor.

14c Use the *-s* and *-ed* forms of the verb when they are required. CULTURE LANGUAGE

Speakers of some English dialects and nonnative speakers of English sometimes omit the *-s* and *-ed* verb endings when they are required in standard American English.

Note A grammar and style checker will flag many omitted *-s* and *-ed* endings from verbs, such as in *he ask* and *was ask*. But it will miss many omissions, too.

Required *-s* ending

Use the *-s* form of a verb when *both* of these situations hold:

- **The subject is a singular noun (*boy*), an indefinite pronoun (*everyone*), or *he, she,* or *it*.** These subjects are **third person,** used when someone or something is being spoken about.
- **The verb's action occurs in the present.**

The letter asks [not ask] for a quick response.
Delay costs [not cost] money.

Be especially careful with the *-s* forms of *be* (*is*), *have* (*has*), and *do* (*does, doesn't*). These forms should always be used to indicate present time with third-person singular subjects.

The company is [not be] late in responding.
It has [not have] problems.
It doesn't [not don't] have the needed data.
The contract does [not do] depend on the response.

In addition, *be* has an *-s* form in the past tense with *I* and with third-person singular subjects:

The company was [not were] in trouble before.

I, you, and plural subjects do *not* take the *-s* form of verbs:

I am [not is] a student.
You are [not is] also a student.
They are [not is] students, too.

- **Required *-ed* or *-d* ending**

The *-ed* or *-d* verb form is required in *any* of these situations:

- **The verb's action occurred in the past:**

Yesterday the company asked [not ask] for more time.

- **The verb form functions as a modifier:**

The data concerned [not concern] should be retrievable.

- **The verb form combines with a form of *be* or *have:***

The company is supposed [not suppose] to be the best.
It has developed [not develop] an excellent reputation.

Watch especially for a needed *-ed* or *-d* ending when it isn't pronounced clearly in speech, as in *asked, discussed, mixed, supposed, walked,* and *used.*

EXERCISE 14.3 Using *-s* and *-ed* verb endings

CULTURE LANGUAGE Supply the correct form of each verb in brackets. Be careful to include *-s* and *-ed* (or *-d*) endings where they are needed for standard English. (You can do this exercise online at *ablongman.com/littlebrown.*)

A teacher sometimes [ask] too much of a student. In high school I was once [punish] for being sick. I had [miss] some school, and I [realize] that I would fail a test unless I had a chance to make up the classwork. I [discuss] the problem with the teacher, but he said I was [suppose] to make up the work while I was sick. At that I [walk] out of the class. I [receive] a failing grade then, but it did not change my attitude. Today I still balk when a teacher [make] unreasonable demands or [expect] miracles.

14d Use helping verbs with main verbs appropriately. CULTURE LANGUAGE

Helping verbs combine with main verbs to form verb phrases (see p. 279).

Note Grammar and style checkers often spot omitted helping verbs and incorrect main verbs with helping verbs, but sometimes they do not. A checker flagged *Many been fortunate* and *She working* but overlooked other examples on the following pages, such as *The conference will be occurred.*

1 Use helping verbs when they are required.

Standard American English requires helping verbs in certain situations:

- **The main verb ends in *-ing:***

  Researchers are conducting fieldwork all over the world. [Not Researchers conducting. . . .]

- **The main verb is *been* or *be:***

  Many have been fortunate in their discoveries. [Not Many been. . . .]
  Some could be real-life Indiana Joneses. [Not Some be. . . .]

- **The main verb is a past participle, such as *talked, begun,* or *thrown.***

  Their discoveries were covered in newspapers and magazines. [Not Their discoveries covered. . . .]

  Often the researchers have done TV interviews. [Not the researchers done. . . .]

In every example above, omitting the helping verb would create an incomplete sentence, or **sentence fragment** (see Chapter 17). In a complete sentence, some part of the verb (helping or main) must be capable of changing form to show changes in time: *I run, I ran; you are running, you were running* (see p. 337). But a present participle (*conducting*), an irregular past participle (*been*), and the infinitive *be* cannot change form in this way. They need helping verbs to work as sentence verbs.

2 Combine helping verbs and main verbs appropriately for your meaning.

Helping verbs and main verbs combine into verb phrases in specific ways.

Note The main verb in a verb phrase (the one carrying the main meaning) does not change to show a change in subject or time: *she has sung, you had sung.* Only the helping verb may change.

- **Form of *be* + present participle**

The **progressive tenses** indicate action in progress (see p. 297). Create them with *be, am, is, are, was, were,* or *been* followed by the main verb's present participle:

She is working on a new book.

Be and *been* always require additional helping verbs to form the progressive tenses:

can	might	should	} be working	have	} been working
could	must	will		has	
may	shall	would		had	

When forming the progressive tenses, be sure to use the *-ing* form of the main verb:

Faulty Her ideas are grow more complex. She is developed a new approach to ethics.

Revised Her ideas are growing more complex. She is developing a new approach to ethics.

Form of *be* + past participle

The **passive voice** of the verb indicates that the subject *receives* the action of the verb (see p. 304). Create the passive voice with *be, am, is, are, was, were, being,* or *been* followed by the main verb's past participle:

Her latest book was completed in four months.

Be, being, and *been* always require additional helping verbs to form the passive voice:

have	} been completed	am	was	} being completed
has		is	were	
had		are		

will be completed

Be sure to use the main verb's past participle for the passive voice:

Faulty Her next book will be publish soon.

Revised Her next book will be published soon.

Note Only transitive verbs may form the passive voice:

Faulty A philosophy conference will be occurred in the same week. [*Occur* is not a transitive verb.]

Revised A philosophy conference will occur in the same week.

See pages 304–05 for advice on when to use and when to avoid the passive voice.

Forms of *have*

Four forms of *have* serve as helping verbs: *have, has, had, having.* One of these forms plus the main verb's past participle creates one of the **perfect tenses,** those expressing action completed before another specific time or action (see p. 296):

> Some students have complained about the laboratory.
> Others had complained before.

Will and other helping verbs sometimes accompany forms of *have* in the perfect tenses:

> Several more students will have complained by the end of the week.

Forms of do

Do, does, and *did* have three uses as helping verbs, always with the plain form of the main verb:

- **To pose a question:** *How did the trial end?*
- **To emphasize the main verb:** *It did end eventually.*
- **To negate the main verb, along with *not* or *never*:** *The judge did not withdraw.*

Be sure to use the main verb's plain form with any form of *do:*

Faulty	The judge did remained in court.
Revised	The judge did remain in court.

Modals

The modal helping verbs include *can, could, may,* and *might,* along with several two- and three-word combinations, such as *have to* and *be able to.* (See p. 279 for a list of helping verbs.) Use the plain form of the main verb with a modal unless the modal combines with another helping verb (usually *have*):

Faulty	The equipment can detects small vibrations. It should have detect the change.
Revised	The equipment can detect small vibrations. It should have detected the change.

Modals convey various meanings, with these being most common:

- **Ability:** *can, could, be able to*

  The equipment can detect small vibrations. [Present.]

  The equipment could detect small vibrations. [Past.]

  The equipment is able to detect small vibrations. [Present. Past: was able to. Future: will be able to.]

- **Possibility:** *could, may, might, could/may/might have* + past participle

  The equipment could fail. [Present.]
  The equipment may fail. [Present or future.]

The equipment might fail. [Present or future.]
The equipment may have failed. [Past.]

- **Necessity or obligation:** *must, have to, be supposed to*

  The lab must purchase a backup. [Present or future.]

  The lab has to purchase a backup. [Present or future. Past: had to.]

  The lab will have to purchase a backup. [Future.]

  The lab is supposed to purchase a backup. [Present. Past: was supposed to.]

- **Permission:** *may, can, could*

  The lab may spend the money. [Present or future.]
  The lab can spend the money. [Present or future.]
  The lab could spend the money. [Present or future, more tentative.]
  With budget approval, the lab could have spent the money. [Past.]

- **Intention:** *will, shall, would*

  The lab will spend the money. [Future.]

  Shall we offer advice? [Future. Use *shall* for questions requesting opinion or consent.]

  We would have offered advice. [Past.]

- **Request:** *could, can, would*

  Could [or can or would] you please obtain a bid? [Present or future.]

- **Advisability:** *should, had better, ought to, should have* + past participle

  You should obtain three bids. [Present or future.]
  You had better obtain three bids. [Present or future.]
  You ought to obtain three bids. [Present or future.]
  You should have obtained three bids. [Past.]

- **Past habit:** *would, used to*

  In years past we would obtain five bids.
  We used to obtain five bids.

EXERCISE 14.4 Using helping verbs

CULTURE LANGUAGE Add helping verbs in the following sentences where they are needed for standard English. (You can do this exercise online at *ablongman.com/littlebrown*.)

Example:

The story been told for many years.
The story has been told for many years.

1. Each year thousands of new readers been discovering Agatha Christie's mysteries.

Noun or pronoun + infinitive

Some verbs may be followed by an infinitive alone or by a noun or pronoun and an infinitive. The presence of a noun or pronoun changes the meaning.

ask	dare	need	wish
beg	expect	promise	would like
choose	help	want	

He expected to watch.
He expected his workers to watch.

Some verbs *must* be followed by a noun or pronoun before an infinitive:

admonish	encourage	oblige	require
advise	forbid	order	teach
allow	force	permit	tell
cause	hire	persuade	train
challenge	instruct	remind	urge
command	invite	request	warn
convince			

He instructed his workers to watch.

Do not use *to* before the infinitive when it follows one of these verbs and a noun or pronoun:

feel	make ("force")
have	see
hear	watch
let	

He let his workers learn by observation.

EXERCISE 14.6 Revising: Verbs plus gerunds or infinitives

CULTURE LANGUAGE Revise the following sentences so that gerunds or infinitives are used correctly with verbs. Mark the number preceding any sentence that is already correct. (You can do this exercise online at *ablongman.com/littlebrown.*)

Example:

A politician cannot avoid to alienate some voters.
A politician cannot avoid alienating some voters.

1. A program called HELP Wanted tries to encourage citizens take action on behalf of American competitiveness.
2. Officials working on this program hope improving education for work.
3. American businesses find that their workers need learning to read.
4. In the next ten years the United States expects facing a shortage of 350,000 scientists.
5. HELP Wanted suggests creating a media campaign.

14f Use the appropriate particles with two-word verbs. CULTURE LANGUAGE

Standard American English includes some verbs that consist of two words: the verb itself and a **particle,** a preposition or adverb that affects the meaning of the verb. For example:

Look up the answer. [Research the answer.]
Look over the answer. [Examine the answer.]

The meanings of these two-word verbs are often quite different from the meanings of the individual words that make them up. (There are some three-word verbs, too, such as *put up with* and *run out of.*)

A dictionary of English as a second language will define two-word verbs and say whether the verb may be separated in a sentence, as explained below. (See p. 539 for a list of ESL dictionaries.) A grammar and style checker will recognize few if any misuses of two-word verbs.

Note Many two-word verbs are more common in speech than in more formal academic or business writing. For formal writing, consider using *research* instead of *look up, examine* or *inspect* instead of *look over.*

Inseparable two-word verbs

Verbs and particles that may not be separated by any other words include the following:

call on	go out with	run across	stay away
catch on	go over	run into	stay up
come across	grow up	run out of	take care of
get along	keep on	speak up	turn out
get up	look for	speak with	turn up at
give in	look into	stand up	work for
go on	play around		

Faulty Children grow quickly up.
Revised Children grow up quickly.

Separable two-word verbs

Most two-word verbs that take direct objects may be separated by the object:

Parents help out their children.
Parents help their children out.

If the direct object is a pronoun, the pronoun *must* separate the verb from the particle:

Faulty Parents help out them.
Revised Parents help them out.

ally depends on meaning. You'll have to proofread carefully yourself to catch errors in tense or tense sequence.

CULTURE LANGUAGE In standard American English, a verb conveys time and sequence through its form. In some other languages and English dialects, various markers besides verb form may indicate the time of a verb. For instance, in African American dialect *I be attending class on Friday* means that the speaker attends class every Friday. To a speaker of standard American English, however, the sentence may be unclear: last Friday? this Friday? every Friday? The intended meaning must be indicated by verb tense: *I attended class on Friday. I will attend class on Friday. I attend class on Friday.*

14g Use the appropriate tense to express your meaning.

Many errors in verb tense are actually errors in verb form like those discussed earlier. Still, the present tense, the perfect tenses, and the progressive tenses can cause problems.

1 Observe the special uses of the present tense.

Most academic and business writing uses the past tense (*the rebellion occurred*), but the present tense has several distinctive uses:

Action occurring now

She understands the problem.
We define the problem differently.

Habitual or recurring action

Banks regularly undergo audits.
The audits monitor the banks' activities.

A general truth

The mills of the gods grind slowly.
The earth is round.

Discussion of literature, film, and so on (see also p. 700)

Huckleberry Finn has adventures we all envy.
In that article, the author examines several causes of crime.

Future time

Next week we draft a new budget.
Funding ends in less than a year.

(In the last two examples, time is really indicated by *Next week* and *in less than a year*.)

2 Observe the uses of the perfect tenses.

The perfect tenses generally indicate action completed before another specific time or action. (The term *perfect* derives from the Latin *perfectus,* "completed.") The present perfect tense also indicates action begun in the past and continued into the present. The perfect tenses consist of a form of *have* plus the verb's past participle.

> present perfect
> The dancer has performed here only once. [The action is completed at the time of the statement.]

> present perfect
> Critics have written about the performance ever since. [The action began in the past and continues now.]

> past perfect
> The dancer had trained in Asia before his performance. [The action was completed before another past action.]

> future perfect
> He will have performed here again by next month. [The action begins now or in the future and will be completed by a specified time in the future.]

CULTURE LANGUAGE With the present perfect tense, the words *since* and *for* are followed by different information. After *since,* give a specific point in time: *The United States has been a member of the United Nations since 1945.* After *for,* give a span of time: *The United States has been a member of the United Nations for many decades.*

3 Observe the uses of the progressive tenses. CULTURE LANGUAGE

The progressive tenses indicate continuing (therefore progressive) action. In standard American English the progressive tenses consist of a form of *be* plus the verb's *-ing* form (present participle). (The words *be* and *been* must be combined with other helping verbs. See pp. 286–87.)

> present progressive
> The economy is improving.

> past progressive
> Last year the economy was stagnating.

> future progressive
> Economists will be watching for signs of growth.

> present perfect progressive
> The government has been expecting an upturn.

> past perfect progressive
> Various indicators had been suggesting improvement.

> future perfect progressive
> By the end of this month, investors will have been pushing the markets up for half a year.

Note Verbs that express unchanging states (especially mental states) rather than physical actions do not usually appear in the progressive tenses. These verbs include *adore, appear, believe, belong, care, doubt, hate, have, hear, imagine, know, like, love, mean, need, own, prefer, realize, remember, see, sound, taste, think, understand,* and *want.*

Faulty She is wanting to study ethics.
Revised She wants to study ethics.

14h Use the appropriate sequence of verb tenses.

The term **sequence of tenses** refers to the relation between the verb tense in a main clause and the verb tense in a subordinate clause or phrase. The tenses should change when necessary to reflect changes in actual or relative time. (For a discussion of tense shifts—changes *not* required by meaning—see pp. 361–62.)

1 Use the appropriate tense sequence with infinitives.

The **present infinitive** is the verb's plain form preceded by *to*. It indicates action *at the same time* as or *later* than that of the verb:

verb: present perfect — infinitive: present
She would have liked to see [not to have seen] change before now.

The verb's **perfect infinitive** consists of *to have* followed by the past participle, as in *to have talked, to have won.* It indicates action *earlier* than that of the verb:

verb: present — infinitive: perfect
Other researchers would like [not would have liked] to have seen change as well.

2 Use the appropriate tense sequence with participles.

The present participle shows action occurring *at the same time* as that of the verb:

participle: present — verb: past perfect
Testing a large group, the researcher had posed multiple-choice questions.

The past participle and the present perfect participle show action occurring *earlier* than that of the verb:

participle: past — verb: past
Prepared by earlier failures, she knew not to ask open questions.

participle: present perfect — verb: past
Having tested many people, she understood the process.

3 Use the appropriate tense sequence with the past or past perfect tense.

When the verb in the main clause is in the past or past perfect tense, the verb in the subordinate clause must also be past or past perfect:

main clause: past — subordinate clause: past

The researchers discovered that people varied widely in their knowledge of public events.

main clause: past — subordinate clause: past perfect

The variation occurred because respondents had been born in different decades.

main clause: past perfect — subordinate clause: past

None of them had been born when Warren G. Harding was President.

Exception Always use the present tense for a general truth, such as *The earth is round:*

main clause: past — subordinate clause: present

Most understood that popular Presidents are not necessarily good Presidents.

4 Use the appropriate tense sequence in conditional sentences.

A **conditional sentence** states a factual relation between cause and effect, makes a prediction, or speculates about what might happen. Such a sentence usually contains a subordinate clause beginning with *if, when,* or *unless* along with a main clause stating the result. The three kinds of conditional sentences use distinctive verbs.

Factual relation

Statements linking factual causes and effects use matched tenses in the subordinate and main clauses:

subordinate clause: present — main clause: present

When a voter casts a ballot, he or she has complete privacy.

subordinate clause: past — main clause: past

When voters registered in some states, they had to pay a poll tax.

Prediction

Predictions generally use the present tense in the subordinate clause and the future tense in the main clause:

subordinate clause: present — main clause: future

Unless citizens regain faith in politics, they will not vote.

Sometimes the verb in the main clause consists of *may, can, should,* or *might* plus the verb's plain form: *If citizens regain faith, they may vote.*

Speculation

The verbs in speculations depend on whether the linked events are possible or impossible. For possible events in the present, use the past tense in the subordinate clause and *would, could,* or *might* plus the verb's plain form in the main clause:

subordinate clause: past — main clause: *would* + verb

If voters had more confidence, they would vote more often.

Always use *were* in the subordinate clause, even when the subject is *I, he, she, it* or a singular noun. (See p. 302 for more on this distinctive verb form.)

subordinate clause: past — main clause: *would* + verb

If the voter were more confident, he or she would vote more often.

For impossible events in the present—events that are contrary to fact—use the same forms as above (including the distinctive *were* when applicable):

subordinate clause: past — main clause: *might* + verb

If Lincoln were alive, he might inspire confidence.

For impossible events in the past, use the past perfect tense in the subordinate clause and *would, could,* or *might* plus the present perfect tense in the main clause:

subordinate clause: past perfect — main clause: *might* + present perfect

If Lincoln had lived past the Civil War, he might have helped stabilize the country.

EXERCISE 14.8 Adjusting tense sequence: Past or past perfect tense

The tenses in each sentence below are in correct sequence. Change the tense of one verb as instructed. Then change the tense of infinitives, participles, and other verbs to restore correct sequence. Some items have more than one possible answer. (You can do this exercise online at *ablongman.com/littlebrown.*)

Example:

Delgado will call when he reaches his destination. (*Change will call to called.*)

Delgado called when he reached [or had reached] his destination.

1. Diaries that Adolf Hitler is supposed to have written have surfaced in Germany. (*Change have surfaced to had surfaced.*)
2. Many people believe that the diaries are authentic because a well-known historian has declared them so. (*Change believe to believed.*)
3. However, the historian's evaluation has been questioned by other authorities, who call the diaries forgeries. (*Change has been questioned to was questioned.*)
4. They claim, among other things, that the paper is not old enough to have been used by Hitler. (*Change claim to claimed.*)
5. Eventually, the doubters will win the debate because they have the best evidence. (*Change will win to won.*)

EXERCISE 14.9 Revising: Tense sequence with conditional sentences

Supply the appropriate tense for each verb in brackets below. (You can do this exercise online at *ablongman.com/littlebrown.*)

Example:

If Babe Ruth or Jim Thorpe [be] athletes today, they [remind] us that even sports heroes must contend with a harsh reality.

If Babe Ruth or Jim Thorpe were athletes today, they might [or could or would] remind us that even sports heroes must contend with a harsh reality.

1. When an athlete [turn] professional, he or she [commit] to a grueling regimen of mental and physical training.
2. If athletes [be] less committed, they [disappoint] teammates, fans, and themselves.
3. If professional athletes [be] very lucky, they [play] until age forty.
4. Unless an athlete [achieve] celebrity status, he or she [have] few employment choices after retirement.
5. If professional sports [be] less risky, athletes [have] longer careers and more choices after retirement.

Mood

Mood in grammar is a verb form that indicates the writer's or speaker's attitude toward what he or she is saying. The **indicative mood** states a fact or opinion or asks a question:

The theater needs help. [Opinion.]
The ceiling is falling in. [Fact.]
Will you contribute to the theater? [Question.]

The **imperative mood** expresses a command or gives a direction. It omits the subject of the sentence, *you:*

Help the theater. [Command.]
Send contributions to the theater. [Direction.]

The **subjunctive mood** expresses a suggestion, a requirement, or a desire, or it states a condition that is contrary to fact (that is, imaginary or hypothetical). The subjunctive mood uses distinctive verb forms.

- **Suggestion or requirement:** plain form with all subjects.

http://www.ablongman.com/littlebrown ▶

Visit the companion Web site for more help and additional exercises on verb mood.

Voice

The **voice** of a verb tells whether the subject of the sentence performs the action (**active voice**) or is acted upon (**passive voice**). In the passive voice, the actual actor may be named in a prepositional phrase (such as *by the city*) or may be omitted.

CULTURE LANGUAGE A passive verb always consists of a form of *be* plus the past participle of the main verb: *rents are controlled.* Other helping verbs must also be used with *be, being,* and *been: rents have been controlled.* Only a transitive verb (one that takes an object) may be used in the passive voice. (See p. 287.)

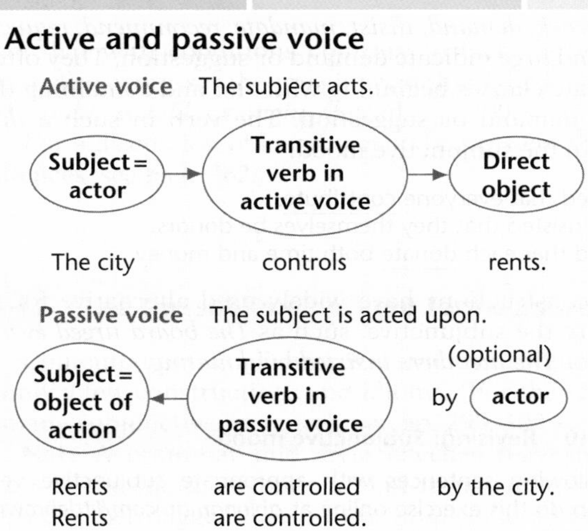

Converting active to passive

To change a transitive verb from active to passive voice, convert either an indirect object or a direct object into the subject of the sentence, and use the passive verb form:

	subject	transitive verb	indirect object	direct object
Active	The city	gives	tenants	leases.
	new subject	passive verb	direct object	
Passive	Tenants	are given	leases.	
	new subject	passive verb	indirect object	old subject
	Leases	are given	tenants	by the city.

http://www.ablongman.com/littlebrown

Visit the companion Web site for more help and additional exercises on verb voice.

Converting passive to active

To change a passive verb to active, name the verb's actor as the subject, use an active verb form, and convert the old subject into an object:

	subject	passive verb	
Passive	Tenants	are protected	by leases.
	new subject	active verb	old subject = object
Active	Leases	protect	tenants.

14j Generally, prefer the active voice. Use the passive voice when the actor is unknown or unimportant.

Because the passive omits or de-emphasizes the actor (the performer of the verb's action), it can deprive writing of vigor and is often vague or confusing. The active voice is usually stronger, clearer, and more forthright.

Weak passive: The Internet is used for research by many scholars, and its expansion to the general public has been criticized by some.

Strong active: Many scholars use the Internet for research, and some have criticized its expansion to the general public.

The passive voice is useful in two situations: when the actor is unknown and when the actor is unimportant or less important than the object of the action.

> The Internet was established in 1969 by the US Department of Defense. The network has now been extended internationally to governments, foundations, corporations, educational institutions, and private individuals. [In the first sentence the writer wishes to stress the Internet rather than the Department of Defense. In the second sentence the actor is unknown or too complicated to name.]
>
> After the solution had been cooled to 10°C, the acid was added. [The person who cooled and added, perhaps the writer, is less important than the facts that the solution was cooled and acid was added. Passive sentences are common in scientific writing. See p. 764.]

Except in such situations, however, you should prefer the active voice in your writing.

Note Most grammar and style checkers can be set to spot the passive voice. (See p. 63.) But the checkers will flag appropriate passives as well, such as when the actor is unknown.

EXERCISE 14.11 Converting between active and passive voices

To practice using the two voices of the verb, convert the following sentences from active to passive or from passive to active. (In converting from passive to active, you may have to add a subject for the new sentence.) Which version of each sentence seems more effective, and why? (You can do this exercise online at *ablongman.com/littlebrown.*) For additional exercises with the passive voice, see pages 266 and 388.

Example:

The aspiring actor was discovered in a nightclub.
A talent scout discovered the aspiring actor in a nightclub.

1. When the Eiffel Tower was built in 1889, it was thought by the French to be ugly.
2. At that time many people still resisted industrial technology.
3. The tower's naked steel construction epitomized this technology.
4. Beautiful ornament was expected to grace fine buildings.
5. Further, the tower could not even be called a building because it had no solid walls.

EXERCISE 14.12 Revising: Verb forms, tense, mood

Mark all the verbs and verbals in the following paragraph and correct their form, tense, or mood if necessary. (You can do this exercise online at *ablongman.com/littlebrown.*)

For centuries the natives of Melanesia, a group of islands laying northeast of Australia, have practice an unusual religion. It began in the eighteenth century when European explorers first have visited the islands. The natives were fascinated by the rich goods or "cargo" possessed by the explorers. They saw the wealth as treasures of the gods, and cargo cults eventually had arised among them. Over the centuries some Melanesians turned to Christianity in the belief that the white man's religion will bring them the white man's treasures. During World War II, US soldiers, having arrived by boat and airplane to have occupied some of the islands, introduced new and even more wonderful cargo. Even today some leaders of the cargo cults insist that the airplane is worship as a vehicle of the Melanesians' future salvation.

Note See page 333 for an exercise involving verbs along with other aspects of grammar.

CHAPTER 15

Agreement

Agreement helps readers understand the relations between elements in a sentence. Subjects and verbs agree in number and person:

> More Japanese Americans live in Hawaii and California than elsewhere.
> (subject: Japanese Americans; verb: live)

> Daniel Inouye was the first Japanese American in Congress.
> (subject: Daniel Inouye; verb: was)

Pronouns and their **antecedents**—the words they refer to—agree in person, number, and gender:

> Inouye makes his home in Hawaii.
> (antecedent: Inouye; pronoun: his)

> Hawaiians value his work for them.
> (antecedent: Hawaiians; pronoun: them)

15a Make subjects and verbs agree in number.

Most subject-verb agreement problems arise when endings are omitted from subjects or verbs or when the relation between sentence parts is uncertain.

Note A grammar and style checker will catch many simple errors in subject-verb agreement, such as *Addie and John is late,* and some more complicated errors, such as *Is Margaret and Tom going with us?* (should be *are* in both cases). But a checker failed to flag *The old group has gone their separate ways* (should be *have*) and offered a wrong correction for *The old group have gone their separate ways,* which is already correct.

1 The *-s* and *-es* endings work differently for nouns and verbs.

An *-s* or *-es* ending does opposite things to nouns and verbs: it usually makes a noun *plural,* but it always makes a present-tense

http://www.ablongman.com/littlebrown

Visit the companion Web site for more help and additional exercises on subject-verb and pronoun-antecedent agreement.

Person and number in subject-verb agreement

	Number	
Person	*Singular*	*Plural*
First	I eat.	We eat.
Second	You eat.	You eat.
Third	He/she/it eats.	They eat.
	The bird eats.	Birds eat.

verb *singular.* Thus a singular noun as subject will not end in *-s,* but its verb will. A plural noun as subject will end in *-s,* but its verb will not. **Between them, subject and verb use only one *-s* ending.**

Singular	Plural
The boy plays.	The boys play.
The bird soars.	The birds soar.

The only exceptions to these rules involve the nouns that form irregular plurals, such as *child/children, woman/women.* The irregular plural still requires a plural verb: The *children play.*

CULTURE LANGUAGE If your first language or dialect is not standard American English, subject-verb agreement may be problematic, especially for these reasons:

- **Some English dialects follow different rules for subject-verb agreement,** such as omitting the *-s* ending for singular verbs or using the *-s* ending for plural verbs.

Nonstandard	The voter resist change.
Standard	The voter resists change.
Standard	The voters resist change.

  The verb *be* changes spelling for singular and plural in both present and past tenses. (See also p. 278.)

Nonstandard	Taxes is high. They was raised just last year.
Standard	Taxes are high. They were raised just last year.

  Have also has a distinctive *-s* form, *has:*

Nonstandard	The new tax have little chance of passing.
Standard	The new tax has little chance of passing.

- **Some other languages change all verb phrases to match their subjects,** but in English only the helping verbs *be, have,* and *do* change for different subjects. The modal helping verbs—*can, may, should, will,* and others—do not change:

Nonstandard The tax mays pass next year.
Standard The tax may pass next year.

The main verb in a verb phrase also does not change for different subjects:

Nonstandard The tax may passes next year.
Standard The tax may pass next year.

2 Subject and verb should agree even when other words come between them.

When the subject and verb are interrupted by other words, make sure the verb agrees with the subject:

A catalog of courses and requirements often baffles [not baffle] students.

The requirements stated in the catalog are [not is] unclear.

Note Phrases beginning with *as well as, together with, along with,* and *in addition to* do not change the number of the subject:

The president, as well as the deans, has [not have] agreed to revise the catalog.

If you really mean *and* in such a sentence, use it. Then the subject is compound, and the verb should be plural: *The president and the deans have agreed to revise the catalog.*

3 Subjects joined by *and* usually take plural verbs.

Two or more subjects joined by *and* usually take a plural verb, whether one or all of the subjects are singular:

Frost and Roethke were contemporaries.

Frost, Roethke, Stevens, and Pound are among the great American poets.

Exceptions When the parts of the subject form a single idea or refer to a single person or thing, they take a singular verb:

Avocado and bean sprouts is a California sandwich.

When a compound subject is preceded by the adjective *each* or *every,* the verb is usually singular:

Each man, woman, and child has a right to be heard.

All of the money is reserved for emergencies.

All of the funds are reserved for emergencies.

The word referred to by the pronoun may also be implied:

All are planning to attend. [*All* implies "all the people."]

All is lost. [*All* implies "everything."]

CULTURE LANGUAGE See page 332 for the distinction between *few* ("not many") and *a few* ("some").

6 Collective nouns take singular or plural verbs depending on meaning.

A **collective noun** has singular form but names a group of individuals or things—for example, *army, audience, committee, crowd, family, group, team.* As a subject, a collective noun may take a singular or plural verb, depending on the context. When the group acts as one unit, use a singular verb:

The group agrees that action is necessary.

But when considering the group's members as individuals who act separately, use the plural form of the verb:

The old group have gone their separate ways.

The collective noun *number* may be singular or plural. Preceded by *a,* it is plural; preceded by *the,* it is singular.

A number of people are in debt.

The number of people in debt is very large.

CULTURE LANGUAGE In English some noncount nouns (nouns that don't form plurals) are collective nouns because they name groups: for instance, *furniture, clothing, mail.* These noncount nouns usually take singular verbs: *Mail arrives daily.* But some of these nouns take plural verbs, including *clergy, military, people, police,* and any collective noun that comes from an adjective, such as *the poor, the rich, the young, the elderly.* If you mean one representative of the group, use a singular noun such as *police officer* or *poor person.*

7 The verb agrees with the subject even when the normal word order is inverted.

Inverted subject-verb order occurs mainly in questions and in constructions beginning with *there* or *it* and a form of *be:*

Nonstandard The tax mays pass next year.
Standard The tax may pass next year.

The main verb in a verb phrase also does not change for different subjects:

Nonstandard The tax may passes next year.
Standard The tax may pass next year.

2 Subject and verb should agree even when other words come between them.

When the subject and verb are interrupted by other words, make sure the verb agrees with the subject:

A catalog of courses and requirements often baffles [not baffle] students.

The requirements stated in the catalog are [not is] unclear.

Note Phrases beginning with *as well as, together with, along with,* and *in addition to* do not change the number of the subject:

The president, as well as the deans, has [not have] agreed to revise the catalog.

If you really mean *and* in such a sentence, use it. Then the subject is compound, and the verb should be plural: *The president and the deans have agreed to revise the catalog.*

3 Subjects joined by *and* usually take plural verbs.

Two or more subjects joined by *and* usually take a plural verb, whether one or all of the subjects are singular:

Frost and Roethke were contemporaries.

Frost, Roethke, Stevens, and Pound are among the great American poets.

Exceptions When the parts of the subject form a single idea or refer to a single person or thing, they take a singular verb:

Avocado and bean sprouts is a California sandwich.

When a compound subject is preceded by the adjective *each* or *every,* the verb is usually singular:

Each man, woman, and child has a right to be heard.

Summary of subject-verb agreement

- **Basic subject-verb agreement** (p. 307):

Singular	Plural
The kite flies.	The kites fly.

- **Words between subject and verb** (p. 309):

  The kite with two tails flies badly. The tails of the kite compete.

- **Subjects joined by *and*** (p. 309):

  The kite and the bird are almost indistinguishable.

- **Subjects joined by *or* or *nor*** (below):

  The kite or the bird dives. Kites or birds fill the sky.

- **Indefinite pronouns as subjects** (opposite):

  No one knows. All the spectators wonder.

- **Collective nouns as subjects** (p. 312):

  A flock appears. The flock disperse.

- **Inverted word order** (p. 312):

  Is the kite or the bird blue? Are the kite and the bird both blue?

- **Linking verbs** (p. 313):

  The kite is a flier and a dipper.

- ***Who, which, that* as subjects** (p. 313):

  The kite that flies longest wins. Kites that fall lose.

- **Subjects with plural form and singular meaning** (p. 314):

  Aeronautics plays a role in kite flying.

- **Titles and words named as words** (p. 314):

  Kite Dynamics is one title. *Vectors* is a key word.

But a compound subject *followed* by *each* takes a plural verb:

> The man and the woman each have different problems.

4 When parts of a subject are joined by *or* or *nor*, the verb agrees with the nearer part.

When all parts of a subject joined by *or* or *nor* are singular, the verb is singular; when all parts are plural, the verb is plural.

> Either the painter or the carpenter knows the cost.

The cabinets or the bookcases are too costly.

When one part of the subject is singular and the other plural, avoid awkwardness by placing the plural part closer to the verb so that the verb is plural:

Awkward Neither the owners nor the contractor agrees.

Revised Neither the contractor nor the owners agree.

When the subject consists of nouns and pronouns of different person requiring different verb forms, the verb agrees with the nearer part of the subject. Reword if this construction is awkward:

Awkward Either Juarez or I am responsible.

Revised Either Juarez is responsible, or I am.

5 With an indefinite pronoun, use a singular or plural verb as appropriate.

An **indefinite pronoun** is one that does not refer to a specific person or thing. Most indefinite pronouns take a singular verb, but some take a plural verb and some take a singular *or* a plural verb.

Common indefinite pronouns

Singular			Singular or plural	Plural
anybody	everyone	no one	all	both
anyone	everything	nothing	any	few
anything	much	one	more	many
each	neither	somebody	most	several
either	nobody	someone	some	
everybody	none	something		

The singular indefinite pronouns refer to a single unspecified person or thing, and they take a singular verb:

Something smells. Neither is right.

The plural indefinite pronouns refer to more than one unspecified thing, and they take a plural verb:

Both are correct. Several were invited.

The other indefinite pronouns take a singular or a plural verb depending on whether the word they refer to is singular or plural. The word may be stated in the sentence:

All of the money is reserved for emergencies.

All of the funds are reserved for emergencies.

The word referred to by the pronoun may also be implied:

All are planning to attend. [*All* implies "all the people."]

All is lost. [*All* implies "everything."]

CULTURE LANGUAGE See page 332 for the distinction between *few* ("not many") and *a few* ("some").

6 Collective nouns take singular or plural verbs depending on meaning.

A **collective noun** has singular form but names a group of individuals or things—for example, *army, audience, committee, crowd, family, group, team.* As a subject, a collective noun may take a singular or plural verb, depending on the context. When the group acts as one unit, use a singular verb:

The group agrees that action is necessary.

But when considering the group's members as individuals who act separately, use the plural form of the verb:

The old group have gone their separate ways.

The collective noun *number* may be singular or plural. Preceded by *a,* it is plural; preceded by *the,* it is singular.

A number of people are in debt.

The number of people in debt is very large.

CULTURE LANGUAGE In English some noncount nouns (nouns that don't form plurals) are collective nouns because they name groups: for instance, *furniture, clothing, mail.* These noncount nouns usually take singular verbs: *Mail arrives daily.* But some of these nouns take plural verbs, including *clergy, military, people, police,* and any collective noun that comes from an adjective, such as *the poor, the rich, the young, the elderly.* If you mean one representative of the group, use a singular noun such as *police officer* or *poor person.*

7 The verb agrees with the subject even when the normal word order is inverted.

Inverted subject-verb order occurs mainly in questions and in constructions beginning with *there* or *it* and a form of *be:*

Is voting a right or a privilege?

Are a right and a privilege the same thing?

There are differences between them.

In constructions beginning with *there,* you may use *is* before a compound subject when the first element in the subject is singular:

There is much work to do and little time to do it.

Word order may sometimes be inverted for emphasis. The verb still agrees with its subject:

From the mountains comes an eerie, shimmering light.

8 A linking verb agrees with its subject, not the subject complement.

A linking verb such as *is* or *are* should agree with its subject, usually the first element in the sentence, not with the noun or pronoun serving as a subject complement (see p. 242):

The child's sole support is her court-appointed guardians.

Her court-appointed guardians are the child's sole support.

9 *Who, which,* and *that* take verbs that agree with their antecedents.

When used as subjects, *who, which,* and *that* refer to another word in the sentence, called the **antecedent.** The verb agrees with the antecedent:

Mayor Garber ought to listen to the people who work for her.

Bardini is the only aide who has her ear.

Agreement problems often occur with relative pronouns when the sentence includes *one of the* or *the only one of the:*

Bardini is one of the aides who work unpaid. [Of the aides who work unpaid, Bardini is one.]

Bardini is the only one of the aides who knows the community. [Of the aides, only one, Bardini, knows the community.]

CULTURE LANGUAGE In phrases like those above beginning with *one of the,* be sure the noun is plural: *Bardini is one of the aides* [not *aide*] *who work unpaid.*

10 Nouns with plural form but singular meaning take singular verbs.

Some nouns with plural form (that is, ending in *-s*) are usually regarded as singular in meaning. They include *athletics, economics, mathematics, measles, mumps, news, physics, politics,* and *statistics,* as well as place names such as *Athens, Wales,* and *United States.*

After so long a wait, the news has to be good.

Statistics is required of psychology majors.

A few of these words take plural verbs only when they describe individual items rather than whole bodies of activity or knowledge: *The statistics prove him wrong.*

Measurements and figures ending in *-s* may also be singular when the quantity they refer to is a unit:

Three years is a long time to wait.

Three-fourths of the library consists of reference books.

11 Titles and words named as words take singular verbs.

When your sentence subject is the name of a corporation, the title of a work (such as a book), or a word you are defining or describing, the verb should be singular even if the name, title, or word is plural:

Hakada Associates is a new firm.

Dream Days remains a favorite book.

Folks is a down-home word for *people.*

EXERCISE 15.1 Revising: Subject-verb agreement

Revise the verbs in the following sentences as needed to make subjects and verbs agree in number. If the sentence is already correct as given, circle the number preceding it. (You can do this exercise online at *ablongman.com/littlebrown.*)

Example:

Each of the job applicants type sixty words per minute.
Each of the job applicants types sixty words per minute.

1. Weinstein & Associates are a consulting firm that try to make businesspeople laugh.
2. Statistics from recent research suggests that humor relieves stress.
3. Reduced stress in businesses in turn reduce illness and absenteeism.

4. Reduced stress can also reduce friction within an employee group, which then work more productively.
5. In special conferences held by one consultant, each of the participants practice making the others laugh.
6. One consultant to many companies suggest cultivating office humor with practical jokes such as a rubber fish in the water cooler.
7. When employees or their manager regularly post cartoons on the bulletin board, office spirit usually picks up.
8. When someone who has seemed too easily distracted is entrusted with updating the cartoons, his or her concentration often improves.
9. In the face of levity, the former sourpuss becomes one of those who hides bad temper.
10. Every one of the consultants caution, however, that humor has no place in life-affecting corporate situations such as employee layoffs.

15b Make pronouns and their antecedents agree in person, number, and gender.

The **antecedent** of a pronoun is the noun or other pronoun to which the pronoun refers.

Homeowners fret over their tax bills.
antecedent — pronoun

Its constant increases make the tax bill a dreaded document.
pronoun — antecedent

Since a pronoun derives its meaning from its antecedent, the two must agree in person, number, and gender.

Person, number, and gender in pronoun-antecedent agreement

	Number	
Person	*Singular*	*Plural*
First	*I*	*we*
Second	*you*	*you*
Third	*he, she, it,* indefinite pronouns, singular nouns	*they,* plural nouns
Gender		
Masculine	*he,* nouns naming males	
Feminine	*she,* nouns naming females	
Neuter	*it,* all other nouns	

Note Grammar and style checkers cannot help with agreement between pronoun and antecedent because they cannot recognize the intended relation between the two.

CULTURE LANGUAGE The gender of a pronoun should match its antecedent, not a noun that the pronoun may modify: *Sara Young invited her* [not *his*] *son to join the company's staff.* Also, nouns in English have only neuter gender unless they specifically refer to males or females. Thus nouns such as *book, table, sun,* and *earth* take the pronoun *it.*

Summary of pronoun-antecedent agreement

- **Basic pronoun-antecedent agreement:**

  Old Faithful spews its columns of water, each of them over 115 feet high.

- **Antecedents joined by *and*** (below):

  Old Faithful and Giant are geysers known for their height.

- **Antecedents joined by *or* or *nor*** (opposite):

  Either Giant or Giantess ejects its column the highest.

- **Indefinite words as antecedents** (opposite):

  Each of the geysers has its own personality. Each person who visits has his or her memories.

- **Collective nouns as antecedents** (p. 318):

  A crowd amuses itself watching Old Faithful. The crowd go their separate ways.

1 Antecedents joined by *and* usually take plural pronouns.

Two or more antecedents joined by *and* usually take a plural pronoun, whether one or all of the antecedents are singular:

Mr. Bartos and I cannot settle our dispute.

The dean and my adviser have offered their help.

Exceptions When the compound antecedent refers to a single idea, person, or thing, then the pronoun is singular:

My friend and adviser offered her help.

When the compound antecedent follows *each* or *every*, the pronoun is singular:

> Every girl and woman took her seat.

2 When parts of an antecedent are joined by *or* or *nor*, the pronoun agrees with the nearer part.

When the parts of an antecedent are connected by *or* or *nor*, the pronoun should agree with the part closer to it:

> Tenants or owners must present their grievances.

> Either the tenant or the owner will have her way.

When one subject is plural and the other singular, the sentence will be awkward unless you put the plural one second:

Awkward	Neither the tenants nor the owner has yet made her case.
Revised	Neither the owner nor the tenants have yet made their case.

3 With an indefinite word as antecedent, use a singular or plural pronoun as appropriate.

Indefinite words do not refer to any specific person or thing. They include **indefinite pronouns** such as *anyone, everybody,* and *no one* (see p. 311 for a list). They also include **generic nouns,** or singular nouns that refer to typical members of a group, as in *The individual has rights* or *The job requires a person with computer skills.* Most indefinite pronouns and all generic nouns are singular in meaning. When they serve as antecedents of pronouns, the pronouns should be singular.

> Everyone on the women's team now has her own locker.
> indefinite pronoun

> Every person on the women's team now has her own locker.
> generic noun

Five indefinite pronouns—*all, any, more, most, some*—may be singular or plural in meaning depending on what they refer to:

> Few women athletes had changing spaces, so most had to change in their rooms.

> Most of the changing space was dismal, its color a drab olive green.

Four indefinite pronouns—*both, few, many, several*—are always plural in meaning:

> Few realize how their athletic facilities have changed.

Most agreement problems arise with the singular indefinite words. We often use these words to mean something like "many" or "all" rather than "one" and then refer to them with plural pronouns, as in *Everyone has their own locker* or *A person can padlock their locker*. Often, too, we mean indefinite words to include both masculine and feminine genders and thus resort to *they* instead of the **generic *he***—the masculine pronoun referring to both genders, as in *Everyone deserves his privacy*. (For more on the generic *he*, which many readers view as sexist, see p. 518.)

Although some experts accept *they, them,* and *their* with singular indefinite words, most do not, and many teachers and employers regard the plural as incorrect. To be safe, work for agreement between singular indefinite words and the pronouns that refer to them. You have several options:

Ways to correct agreement with indefinite words

- **Change the indefinite word to a plural, and use a plural pronoun to match:**

  Faulty Every athlete deserves their privacy.
  Revised Athletes deserve their privacy.

- **Rewrite the sentence to omit the pronoun:**

  Faulty Everyone is entitled to their own locker.
  Revised Everyone is entitled to a locker.

- **Use *he or she* (*him or her, his or her*) to refer to the indefinite word:**

  Faulty Now everyone has their private space.
  Revised Now everyone has his or her private space.

  However, used more than once in several sentences, *he or she* quickly becomes awkward. (Many readers do not accept the alternative *he/she*.) In most cases, using the plural or omitting the pronoun will not only correct agreement problems but also create more readable sentences.

4 Collective noun antecedents take singular or plural pronouns depending on meaning.

Collective nouns such as *army, committee, family, group,* and *team* have singular form but may be referred to by singular or plural pronouns, depending on the meaning intended. When the group acts as a unit, the pronoun is singular:

The committee voted to disband itself.

When the members of the group act separately, the pronoun is plural:

The old group have gone their separate ways.

In the last example, note that the verb and pronoun are consistent in number (see also pp. 360–61).

Inconsistent	The old group has gone their separate ways.
Consistent	The old group have gone their separate ways.

CULTURE LANGUAGE In standard American English, collective nouns that are noncount nouns (they don't form plurals) usually take singular pronouns: *The mail sits in its own basket.* A few noncount nouns take plural pronouns, including *clergy, military, people, police, the rich,* and *the poor: The police support their unions.* (See also p. 312.)

EXERCISE 15.2 Revising: Pronoun-antecedent agreement

Revise the following sentences so that pronouns and their antecedents agree in person and number. Some items have more than one possible answer. Try to avoid the generic *he* (see opposite). If you change the subject of a sentence, be sure to change verbs as necessary for agreement. If the sentence is already correct as given, mark the number preceding it. (You can do this exercise online at *ablongman.com/littlebrown*.)

Example:

Each of the Boudreaus' children brought their friends to the party.

All of the Boudreaus' children brought their friends to the party. *Or:* Each of the Boudreaus' children brought friends to the party. *Or:* Each of the Boudreaus' children brought his or her friends to the party.

1. Each girl raised in a Mexican American family in the Rio Grande Valley of Texas hopes that one day they will be given a *quinceañera* party for their fifteenth birthday.
2. Such celebrations are very expensive because it entails a religious service followed by a huge party.
3. A girl's immediate family, unless they are wealthy, cannot afford the party by themselves.
4. The parents will ask each close friend or relative if they can help with the preparations.
5. Surrounded by her family and attended by her friends and their escorts, the *quinceañera* is introduced as a young woman eligible for Mexican American society.

EXERCISE 15.3 Adjusting for agreement

In the sentences below, subjects agree with verbs and pronouns agree with antecedents. Make the change specified in parentheses after each sentence, and then revise the sentence as necessary to maintain agreement. Some items have more than one possible answer. (You can do this exercise online at *ablongman.com/littlebrown*.)

Example:

The student attends weekly conferences with her teacher. (*Change The student to Students.*)

Students *attend* weekly conferences with their teacher.

1. A biologist wishes to introduce captive red wolves into the Smoky Mountains in order to increase the wild population of this endangered species. (*Change A biologist to Biologists.*)
2. When freed, the wolf naturally has no fear of humans and thus is in danger of being shot. (*Change wolf to wolves.*)
3. The first experiment to release the wolves was a failure. (*Change experiment to experiments.*)
4. Now researchers pen the wolf puppy in the wooded area that will eventually be its territory. (*Change puppy to puppies.*)
5. The wolf has little contact with people, even its own keeper, during the year of its captivity. (*Change wolf to wolves.*)

EXERCISE 15.4 Revising: Agreement

Revise the sentences in the following paragraphs to correct errors in agreement between subjects and verbs or between pronouns and their antecedents. Try to avoid the generic *he*. (You can do this exercise online at *ablongman.com/littlebrown*.)

The writers Richard Rodriguez and Maxine Hong Kingston, despite their differences, shares one characteristic: their parents was immigrants to California. A frequent theme of their writings are the difficulties of growing up with two languages and two cultures.

A child whose first language is not English is often ridiculed because they cannot communicate "properly." Rodriguez learned Spanish at home, but at school everyone expected him to use their language, English. He remembers his childish embarrassment because of his parents' poor English. College and graduate school, which usually expands one's knowledge, widened the gap between Rodriguez and his Latino culture. His essays suggests that he lost a part of himself, a loss that continue to bother him.

Kingston spoke Chinese at home and also learned her first English at school. She sometimes write of these experiences, but more often she write to recover and preserve her Chinese culture. *The Woman Warrior,* which offer a blend of autobiography, family history, and mythic tales, describe the struggle of Kingston's female relatives. *China Men* focus on Kingston's male ancestors; each one traveled to Hawaii or California to make money for their wife back in China. Kingston's work, like Rodriguez's essays, reflect the tension and confusion that the child of immigrants often feel when they try to blend two cultures.

Note See page 333 for an exercise involving agreement along with other aspects of grammar.

CHAPTER 16

Adjectives and Adverbs

Adjectives and adverbs are modifiers that describe, restrict, or otherwise qualify the words to which they relate.

Functions of adjectives and adverbs

Adjectives modify nouns:	serious student
pronouns:	ordinary one
Adverbs modify verbs:	warmly greet
adjectives:	only three people
adverbs:	quite seriously
phrases:	nearly to the edge of the cliff
clauses:	just when we arrived
sentences:	Fortunately, she is employed.

Many of the most common adjectives are familiar one-syllable words such as *bad, strange, large,* and *wrong.* Many others are formed by adding endings such as *-al, -able, -ful, -less, -ish, -ive,* and *-y* to nouns or verbs: *optional, fashionable, beautiful, fruitless, selfish, expressive, dreamy.*

Most adverbs are formed by adding *-ly* to adjectives: *badly, strangely, largely, beautifully.* But note that we cannot depend on *-ly* to identify adverbs, since some adjectives also end in *-ly* (*fatherly, lonely*) and since some common adverbs do not end in *-ly* (*always,*

http://www.ablongman.com/littlebrown 

Visit the companion Web site for more help and additional exercises on adjectives and adverbs.

EXERCISE 16.1 Revising: Adjectives and adverbs

Revise the following sentences so that adjectives and adverbs are used appropriately. If any sentence is already correct as given, mark the number preceding it. (You can do this exercise online at *ablongman .com/littlebrown*.)

Example:

The announcer warned that traffic was moving very slow.
The announcer warned that traffic was moving very slowly.

1. King George III of England declared Samuel Johnson suitably for a pension.
2. Johnson was taken serious as a critic and dictionary maker.
3. Thinking about his meeting with the king, Johnson felt proudly.
4. Johnson was relieved that he had not behaved badly in the king's presence.
5. After living cheap for over twenty years, Johnson finally had enough money from the pension to eat and dress good.

16d Use the comparative and superlative forms of adjectives and adverbs appropriately.

Adjectives and adverbs can show degrees of quality or amount with the endings *-er* and *-est* or with the words *more* and *most* or *less* and *least*. Most modifiers have three forms:

Positive The basic form listed in the dictionary	Comparative A greater or lesser degree of the quality	Superlative The greatest or least degree of the quality
Adjectives		
red	redder	reddest
awful	more/less awful	most/least awful
Adverbs		
soon	sooner	soonest
quickly	more/less quickly	most/least quickly

If sound alone does not tell you whether to use *-er/-est* or *more/most,* consult a dictionary. If the endings can be used, the dictionary will list them. Otherwise, use *more* or *most.*

1 Use the correct forms of irregular adjectives and adverbs.

Certain adjectives and adverbs are irregular: they change the spelling of their positive form to show comparative and superlative degrees.

Degrees of irregular adjectives and adverbs

Positive	Comparative	Superlative
Adjectives		
good	better	best
bad	worse	worst
little	littler, less	littlest, least
many, some, much	more	most
Adverbs		
well	better	best
badly	worse	worst

2 Use either *-er/-est* or *more/most,* not both.

A double comparative or double superlative combines the *-er* or *-est* ending with the word *more* or *most.* It is redundant.

> Chang was the wisest [not most wisest] person in town.
> He was smarter [not more smarter] than anyone else.

3 Use the comparative for comparing two things and the superlative for comparing three or more things.

> It is the shorter of her two books. [Comparative.]
> *The Yearling* is the most popular of the six books. [Superlative.]

In conversation the superlative form is often used to compare only two things: *When two people argue, the angriest one is usually wrong.* But the distinction between the forms should be observed in writing.

4 Use comparative or superlative forms only for modifiers that can logically be compared.

Some adjectives and adverbs cannot logically be compared—for instance, *perfect, unique, dead, impossible, infinite.* These absolute words can be preceded by adverbs like *nearly* and *almost* that mean "approaching," but they cannot logically be modified by *more* or *most* (as in *most perfect*). This distinction is sometimes ignored in speech, but it should always be made in writing:

> Not He was the most unique teacher we had.
> But He was a unique teacher.

EXERCISE 16.2 Revising: Comparatives and superlatives

Revise the sentences below so that the comparative and superlative forms of adjectives and adverbs are appropriate for formal usage. Mark the number preceding any sentence that is already correct. (You can do this exercise online at *ablongman.com/littlebrown*.)

Example:

Finishing high school and working at two jobs was the most impossible thing I ever did.

Finishing high school and working at two jobs was impossible [or the hardest thing I ever did].

1. Charlotte was the older of the three Brontë sisters, all of whom were novelists.
2. Some readers think Emily Brontë's *Wuthering Heights* is the most saddest novel they have ever read.
3. Of the other two sisters, Charlotte and Anne, Charlotte was probably the more talented.
4. Critics still argue about whether Charlotte or Emily wrote more better.
5. Certainly this family of women novelists was the most unique.

16e Watch for double negatives.

In a **double negative** two negative words such as *no, not, none, neither, barely, hardly,* or *scarcely* cancel each other out. Some double negatives are intentional: for instance, *She was not unhappy* indicates with understatement that she was indeed happy. But most double negatives say the opposite of what is intended: *Zoey did not feel nothing* asserts that Zoey felt other than nothing, or something. For the opposite meaning, one of the negatives must be eliminated or changed to a positive: *She felt nothing* or *She did not feel anything.*

Faulty The IRS cannot hardly audit all tax returns. None of its audits never touch many cheaters.

Revised The IRS cannot audit all tax returns. Its audits never touch many cheaters.

EXERCISE 16.3 Revising: Double negatives

Identify and revise the double negatives in the following paragraph. Each error may have more than one correct revision. (You can do this exercise online at *ablongman.com/littlebrown*.)

Interest in books about the founding of the United States seems to vary with the national mood. Americans show hardly no interest in books about the founders when things are going well in the United States. However, when Americans can't barely agree on major issues, sales of books about the Revolutionary War era increase. During such periods, one cannot go to no bookstore without seeing several new volumes about John Adams, Thomas Jefferson, and other founders. When Americans feel they don't have nothing in common, their increased interest in the early leaders may reflect a desire for unity.

16f Use nouns sparingly as modifiers.

We often use one noun to modify another. For example:

child care flood control security guard

Such phrases can be both clear and concise, but overuse of noun modifiers can lead to flat, even senseless, writing. To avoid awkwardness or confusion, observe two principles. First, prefer possessives or adjectives as modifiers:

Not A student takes the state medical board exams to become a dentist technician.

But A student takes the state medical board's exams to become a dental technician.

Second, use only short nouns as modifiers and use them only in two- or three-word sequences:

Confusing Minimex maintains a plant employee relations improvement program.

Revised Minimex maintains a program for improving relations among plant employees.

16g Distinguish between present and past participles as adjectives. CULTURE LANGUAGE

Both present participles and past participles may serve as adjectives: *a burning building, a burned building.* As in the examples, the two participles usually differ in the time they indicate.

But some present and past participles—those derived from verbs expressing feeling—can have altogether different meanings. The present participle modifies something that causes the feeling: *That was a frightening storm* (the storm frightens). The past participle modifies something that experiences the feeling: *They quieted the frightened horses* (the horses feel fright).

The following participles are among those likely to be confused:

amazing/amazed
amusing/amused
annoying/annoyed
astonishing/astonished
boring/bored
confusing/confused
depressing/depressed
embarrassing/embarrassed
exciting/excited
exhausting/exhausted

fascinating/fascinated
frightening/frightened
frustrating/frustrated
interesting/interested
pleasing/pleased
satisfying/satisfied
shocking/shocked
surprising/surprised
tiring/tired
worrying/worried

EXERCISE 16.4 Revising: Present and past participles

CULTURE LANGUAGE Revise the adjectives in the following sentences as needed to distinguish between present and past participles. If the sentence is already correct as given, mark the number preceding it. (You can do this exercise online at *ablongman.com/littlebrown.*)

Example:

The subject was embarrassed to many people.
The subject was embarrassing to many people.

1. Several critics found Alice Walker's *The Color Purple* to be a fascinated book.
2. One confused critic wished that Walker had deleted the scenes set in Africa.
3. Another critic argued that although the book contained many depressed episodes, the overall impact was excited.
4. Since other readers found the book annoyed, this critic pointed out its many surprised qualities.
5. In the end most critics agreed that the book was a satisfied novel.

16h Use *a, an, the,* and other determiners appropriately. CULTURE LANGUAGE

Determiners are special kinds of adjectives that mark nouns because they always precede nouns. Some common determiners are *a, an,* and *the* (called **articles**) and *my, their, whose, this, these, those, one, some,* and *any*. They convey information to readers—for instance, by specifying who owns what, which one of two is meant, or whether a subject is familiar or unfamiliar.

Native speakers of standard American English can rely on their intuition when using determiners, but speakers of other languages and dialects often have difficulty with them. In standard English the use of determiners depends on the context they appear in and the kind of noun they precede:

- A **proper noun** names a particular person, place, or thing and begins with a capital letter: *February, Joe Allen, Red River.* Most proper nouns are not preceded by determiners.
- A **count noun** names something that is countable in English and can form a plural: *girl/girls, apple/apples, child/children.* A singular count noun is always preceded by a determiner; a plural count noun sometimes is.

- A **noncount noun** names something not usually considered countable in English, and so it does not form a plural. A noncount noun is sometimes preceded by a determiner. Here is a sample of noncount nouns, sorted into groups by meaning:

  Abstractions: confidence, democracy, education, equality, evidence, health, information, intelligence, knowledge, luxury, peace, pollution, research, success, supervision, truth, wealth, work

  Food and drink: bread, candy, cereal, flour, meat, milk, salt, water, wine

  Emotions: anger, courage, happiness, hate, joy, love, respect, satisfaction

  Natural events and substances: air, blood, dirt, gasoline, gold, hair, heat, ice, oil, oxygen, rain, silver, smoke, weather, wood

  Groups: clergy, clothing, equipment, furniture, garbage, jewelry, junk, legislation, machinery, mail, military, money, police, vocabulary

  Fields of study: architecture, accounting, biology, business, chemistry, engineering, literature, psychology, science

A dictionary of English as a second language will tell you whether a noun is a count noun, a noncount noun, or both. (See p. 539 for recommended dictionaries.)

Note Many nouns can be both count and noncount nouns:

The library has a room for readers. [*Room* is a count noun meaning "walled area."]

The library has room for reading. [*Room* is a noncount noun meaning "space."]

Partly because the same noun may fall into different groups, grammar and style checkers are unreliable guides to missing or misused articles and other determiners. For instance, a checker flagged the omitted *a* before *Scientist* in *Scientist developed new processes;* it did not flag the omitted *a* before *new* in *A scientist developed new process;* and it mistakenly flagged the correctly omitted article *the* before *Vegetation* in *Vegetation suffers from drought.*

1 Use *a, an,* and *the* where they are required.

With singular count nouns

A or *an* precedes a singular count noun when the reader does not already know its identity, usually because you have not mentioned it before:

A local scientist developed a process to strengthen metals. [*Scientist* and *process* are being introduced for the first time.]

The precedes a singular count noun that has a specific identity for the reader, for one of the following reasons:

- You have mentioned the noun before:

  A local scientist developed a process to strengthen metals. The scientist patented the process. [*Scientist* and *process* were identified in the preceding sentence.]

- You identify the noun immediately before or after you state it:

  The most productive laboratory is the chemistry group at the local university. [*Most productive* identifies *laboratory. At the local university* identifies *chemistry group.* And *local university* is a shared facility.]

- The noun names something unique—the only one in existence:

  The sun rises in the east. [*Sun* and *east* are unique.]

- The noun names an institution or facility that is shared by the community of readers:

  Many men and women aspire to the presidency. [*Presidency* is a shared institution.]

  The fax machine has changed business communication. [*Fax machine* is a shared facility.]

The is not used before a singular noun that names a general category:

> Sherman said that war is hell. [*War* names a general category.]
> The war in Croatia left many dead. [*War* names a specific war.]

With plural count nouns

A or *an* never precedes a plural noun. *The* does not precede a plural noun that names a general category. *The* does precede a plural noun that names specific representatives of a category.

> Men and women are different. [*Men* and *women* name general categories.]
>
> The women formed a team. [*Women* refers to specific people.]

With noncount nouns

A or *an* never precedes a noncount noun. *The* does precede a noncount noun when it names specific representatives of a general category:

> Vegetation suffers from drought. [*Vegetation* names a general category.]
>
> The vegetation in the park withered or died. [*Vegetation* refers to specific plants.]

With proper nouns

A or *an* never precedes a proper noun. *The* generally does not precede a proper noun:

> Garcia lives in Boulder.

There are exceptions, however. For instance, we generally use *the* before plural proper nouns (*the Murphys, the Boston Celtics*) and the names of groups and organizations (*the Department of Justice, the Sierra Club*), ships (*the Lusitania*), oceans (*the Pacific*), mountain ranges (*the Alps*), regions (*the Middle East*), rivers (*the Mississippi*), and some countries (*the United States, the Sudan*).

2 Use other determiners appropriately.

The uses of English determiners besides articles also depend on context and kind of noun. The following determiners may be used as indicated with singular count nouns, plural count nouns, or noncount nouns.

- **With any kind of noun (singular count, plural count, noncount)**

  my, our, your, his, her, its, their
  possessive nouns (*boy's, boys'*)
  whose, which(ever), what(ever)
  some, any, the other
  no

  Their account is overdrawn. [Singular count.]
  Their funds are low. [Plural count.]
  Their money is running out. [Noncount.]

- **Only with singular nouns (count and noncount)**

  this, that

  This account has some money. [Count.]
  That information may help. [Noncount.]

- **Only with noncount nouns and plural count nouns**

  most, enough, other, such, all, all of the, a lot of

  Most money is needed elsewhere. [Noncount.]
  Most funds are committed. [Plural count.]

- **Only with singular count nouns**

  one, every, each, either, neither, another

  One car must be sold. [Singular count.]

- **Only with plural count nouns**

  these, those
  both, many, few, a few, fewer, fewest, several
  two, three, and so forth

  Two cars are unnecessary. [Plural count.]

Note *Few* means "not many" or "not enough." *A few* means "some" or "a small but sufficient quantity."

Few committee members came to the meeting.
A few members can keep the committee going.

Do not use *much* with a plural count noun:

Many [not Much] members want to help.

- **Only with noncount nouns**

much, more, little, a little, less, least, a large amount of

Less luxury is in order. [Noncount.]

Note *Little* means "not many" or "not enough." *A little* means "some" or "a small but sufficient quantity."

Little time remains before the conference.

The members need a little help from their colleagues.

Do not use *many* with a noncount noun:

Much [not Many] work remains.

EXERCISE 16.5 Revising: Articles

CULTURE LANGUAGE For each blank below, indicate whether *a, an, the,* or no article should be inserted. (You can do this exercise online at *ablongman .com/littlebrown.*)

From _____ native American Indians who migrated from _____ Asia 20,000 years ago to _____ new arrivals who now come by _____ planes, _____ United States is _____ nation of foreigners. It is _____ country of immigrants who are all living under _____ single flag.

Back in _____ seventeenth and eighteenth centuries, at least 75 percent of the population came from _____ England. However, between 1820 and 1975 more than 38 million immigrants came to this country from elsewhere in _____ Europe. Many children of _____ immigrants were self-conscious and denied their heritage; many even refused to learn _____ native language of their parents and grandparents. They tried to "Americanize" themselves. The so-called Melting Pot theory of _____ social change stressed _____ importance of blending everyone together into _____ kind of stew. Each nationality would contribute its own flavor, but _____ final stew would be something called "American."

This Melting Pot theory was never completely successful. In the last half of the twentieth century, _____ ethnic revival changed _____ metaphor. Many people now see _____ American society as _____ mosaic. Americans are once again proud of their heritage, and _____ ethnic differences make _____ mosaic colorful and interesting.

EXERCISE 16.6 Revising: Adjectives and adverbs

Revise the following paragraph so that it conforms to formal usage of adjectives and adverbs. (You can do this exercise online at *ablongman .com/littlebrown.*)

Americans often argue about which professional sport is better: basketball, football, or baseball. Basketball fans contend that their sport offers more action because the players are constant running and shooting. Because it is played indoors in relative small arenas, basketball allows fans to be more closer to the action than the other sports do. Fans point to how graceful the players fly through the air to the hoop. Football fanatics say they don't hardly stop yelling once the game begins. They cheer when their team executes a real complicated play good. They roar more louder when the defense stops the opponents in a goal-line stand. They yell loudest when a fullback crashes in for a score. In contrast, the supporters of baseball believe that it might be the most perfect sport. It combines the one-on-one duel of pitcher and batter struggling valiant with the tight teamwork of double and triple plays. Because the game is played slow and careful, fans can analyze and discuss the manager's strategy. Besides, they don't never know when they might catch a foul ball as a souvenir. However, no matter what the sport, all fans feel happily only when their team wins!

EXERCISE ON CHAPTERS 13–16 Revising: Grammatical sentences

The paragraphs below contain errors in pronoun case, verb forms, subject-verb agreement, pronoun-antecedent agreement, and the forms of adjectives and adverbs. Revise the paragraphs to correct the errors. (You can do this exercise online at *ablongman.com/littlebrown.*)

Occasionally, musicians become "crossover artists" whom can perform good in more than one field of music. For example, Wynton and Branford Marsalis was train in jazz by their father, the great pianist Ellis Marsalis. Both of the sons has became successful classical artists. Branford's saxophone captures the richness of pieces by Ravel and Stravinsky. Wynton's albums of classical trumpet music from the Baroque period has brung him many awards. Still, if he was to choose which kind of music he likes best, Wynton would probable choose jazz. In contrast to the Marsalises, Yo-Yo Ma and Jean-Pierre Rampal growed up studying classical music. Then in the 1980s they was invited by Claude Bolling, a French pianist, to record Bolling's jazz compositions. In fact, Rampal's flute blended with Bolling's music so good that the two men have did three albums.

Such crossovers are often more harder for vocalists. Each type of music has their own style and feel that is hard to learn. For example, Luciano Pavarotti and Kiri te Kanawa, two great opera performers, have sang popular music and folk songs in concerts and on albums. On each occasion, their technique was the most perfect, yet each

CHAPTER 17

Sentence Fragments

A **sentence fragment** is part of a sentence that is set off as if it were a whole sentence by an initial capital letter and a final period or other end punctuation. Although writers occasionally use fragments deliberately and effectively (see p. 343), readers perceive most fragments as serious errors because, expecting complete sentences, they find partial sentences distracting or confusing. (Before reading further, you may find it helpful to review pp. 235–43 and 254–58 on sentences and clauses.)

Complete sentence versus sentence fragment

A **complete sentence** or **main clause**

- contains a subject and a verb (*The wind blows*)
- and is not a subordinate clause (beginning with a word such as *because* or *who*).

A **sentence fragment**

- lacks a verb (*The wind blowing*)
- or lacks a subject (*And blows*)
- or is a subordinate clause not attached to a complete sentence (*Because the wind blows*).

Note A grammar and style checker can spot many but not all sentence fragments, and it may flag sentences that are actually correct commands, such as *Continue reading.*

17a Test your sentences for completeness, and revise any fragments.

The following three tests will help you determine whether a word group punctuated as a sentence is actually a complete sentence.

http://www.ablongman.com/littlebrown ▶

Visit the companion Web site for more help and additional exercises on sentence fragments.

If the word group does not pass *all three* tests, it is a fragment and needs to be revised.

Tests for complete sentences

Perform *all three* of the following tests to be sure your sentences are complete.

1. Find the verb.
2. Find the subject.
3. Make sure the clause is not subordinate.

Test 1: Find the verb.

Look for a verb in the group of words. If you do not have one, the word group is a fragment:

Fragment Uncountable numbers of sites on the World Wide Web.

Revised Uncountable numbers of sites make up the World Wide Web.

Any verb form you find must be a **finite verb,** one that changes form as indicated below. A verbal does not change; it cannot serve as a sentence verb without the aid of a helping verb.

	Finite verbs in complete sentences	Verbals in sentence fragments
Singular	The network grows.	The network growing.
Plural	Networks grow.	Networks growing.
Present	The network grows.	The network growing.
Past	The network grew.	
Future	The network will grow.	

CULTURE LANGUAGE Some languages allow forms of *be* to be omitted as helping or linking verbs. But English requires stating forms of *be:*

Fragments The network growing. It already larger than its developers anticipated.

Revised The network is growing. It is already larger than its developers anticipated.

Test 2: Find the subject.

If you find a finite verb, look for its subject by asking *who* or *what* performs the action or makes the assertion of the verb. The subject of the sentence will usually come before the verb. If there is no subject, the word group is probably a fragment:

Fragment And has great popular appeal.

Revised And the Web has great popular appeal.

In one kind of complete sentence, a command, the subject *you* is understood: [*You*] *Experiment with the Web.*

CULTURE LANGUAGE Some languages allow the omission of the sentence subject, especially when it is a pronoun. But in English, except in commands, the subject is always stated:

Fragments	Web shopping is expanding dramatically. Is threatening traditional stores.
Revised	Web shopping is expanding dramatically. It is threatening traditional stores.

- **Test 3: Make sure the clause is not subordinate.**

A subordinate clause usually begins with a subordinating word:

Subordinating conjunctions			Relative pronouns	
after	once	until	that	who/whom
although	since	when	which	whoever/whomever
as	than	where		whose
because	that	whereas		
if	unless	while		

(See p. 255 for a longer list of subordinating conjunctions.)

Subordinate clauses serve as parts of sentences (nouns or modifiers), not as whole sentences:

Fragment	When the government devised the Internet.
Revised	The government devised the Internet.
Revised	When the government devised the Internet, no expansive computer network existed.

Fragment	The reason that the government devised the Internet.
Revised	The reason that the government devised the Internet was to provide secure links among departments and defense contractors.

Note Questions beginning with *how, what, when, where, which, who, whom, whose,* and *why* are not sentence fragments: *Who was responsible? When did it happen?*

- **Revising sentence fragments**

Almost all sentence fragments can be corrected in one of two ways, the choice depending on the importance of the information in the fragment:

- **Rewrite the fragment as a complete sentence,** giving the information in the fragment the same importance as that in other complete sentences:

Fragment	A major improvement of the Internet occurred with the World Wide Web. Which allows users to move easily between sites.

Revised A major improvement of the Internet occurred with the World Wide Web. It allows users to move easily between sites.

Two main clauses may be separated by a semicolon instead of a period (see p. 455).

- **Combine the fragment with a main clause,** subordinating the information in the fragment to the information in the main clause:

Fragment The Web is easy to use. Loaded with links and graphics.

Revised The Web, loaded with links and graphics, is easy to use.

Punctuating corrected fragments

In the preceding example, commas separate the inserted phrase from the rest of the sentence because the phrase is not essential to the meaning of any word in the main clause but simply adds information (see p. 437). When a phrase or subordinate clause *is* essential to the meaning of a word in the main clause, a comma or commas do *not* separate the two elements:

Fragment With the links, users can move to other Web sites. That they want to consult.

Revised With the links, users can move to other Web sites that they want to consult.

Sometimes a fragment may be combined with the main clause using a colon or a dash (see pp. 479 and 482, respectively):

Fragment The Web connects sites from all over the Internet. Different databases, different software, different machines.

Revised The Web connects sites from all over the Internet: different databases, different software, different machines.

Fragment The Web is a boon to student researchers. A vast and accessible library.

Revised The Web is a boon to student researchers—a vast and accessible library.

EXERCISE 17.1 Identifying and revising sentence fragments

Apply the tests for completeness to each of the following word groups. If a word group is a complete sentence, mark the number preceding it. If it is a sentence fragment, revise it in two ways: by making it a complete sentence, and by combining it with a main clause written from the information given in other items. (You can do this exercise online at *ablongman.com/littlebrown.*)

Example:

And could not find his money. [The word group has a verb (*could . . . find*) but no subject.]

Revised into a complete sentence: And he could not find his money.

Combined with a new main clause: He was lost and could not find his money.

1. In an interesting article about vandalism against works of art.
2. The motives of the vandals varying widely.
3. Those who harm artwork are usually angry.
4. But not necessarily at the artist or the owner.
5. For instance, a man who hammered at Michelangelo's *Pietà*.
6. And knocked off the Virgin Mary's nose.
7. Because he was angry at the Roman Catholic Church.
8. Which knew nothing of his grievance.
9. Although many damaged works can be repaired.
10. Usually even the most skillful repairs are forever visible.

17b A subordinate clause is not a complete sentence.

Subordinate clauses contain both subjects and verbs, but they always begin with a subordinating conjunction (*although, if,* and so on) or a relative pronoun (*who, which, that*). (See pp. 254–55.) Subordinate clauses serve as nouns or modifiers, but they cannot stand alone as complete sentences.

To correct a subordinate clause set off as a sentence, combine it with the main clause or remove or change the subordinating word to create a main clause.

Fragment	Many pine trees bear large cones. Which appear in August.
Revised	Many pine trees bear large cones, which appear in August.
Revised	Many pine trees bear large cones. They appear in August.

17c A verbal phrase or a prepositional phrase is not a complete sentence.

A **verbal phrase** consists of an infinitive (*to choose*), a past participle (*chosen*), or a present participle or gerund (*choosing*) together with any objects and modifiers it may have (see p. 251). A verbal phrase is a noun or modifier and cannot serve as the verb in a complete sentence:

Fragment	For many of the elderly, their house is their only asset. Offering some security but no income.
Revised	For many of the elderly, their house is their only asset, offering some security but no income.

Revised For many of the elderly, their house is their only asset. It offers some security but no income.

A **prepositional phrase** is a modifier consisting of a preposition (such as *in, on, to,* and *with*) together with its object and any modifiers (see p. 247). A prepositional phrase cannot stand alone as a complete sentence:

Fragment In a squeeze between a valuable asset and little income. Eventually many elderly people sell their homes.

Revised In a squeeze between a valuable asset and little income, eventually many elderly people sell their homes.

Revised Many elderly people are in a squeeze between a valuable asset and little income. Eventually they may sell their homes.

CULTURE LANGUAGE Some English prepositions consist of two or three words: *as well as, along with, in addition to, on top of,* and others. Don't let prepositions of more than one word mislead you into writing sentence fragments.

Fragment In today's retirement communities, the elderly may have health care, housekeeping, and new friends. As well as financial security.

Revised In today's retirement communities, the elderly may have health care, housekeeping, and new friends, as well as financial security.

17d Any word group lacking a subject or a verb or both is not a complete sentence.

We often follow a noun with a modifier. No matter how long the noun and its modifier are, they cannot stand alone as a sentence:

Fragments People waving flags and cheering. Lined the streets for the parade.

Revised People waving flags and cheering lined the streets for the parade.

Fragment Veterans who fought in Vietnam. They are finally being honored.

Revised Veterans who fought in Vietnam are finally being honored.

Appositives are nouns, or nouns and their modifiers, that rename or describe other nouns (see p. 259). They cannot stand alone as sentences:

Fragment	When I was a child, my favorite adult was an old uncle. A retired sea captain who always told me long stories of wild adventures in faraway places.
Revised	When I was a child, my favorite adult was an old uncle, a retired sea captain who always told me long stories of wild adventures in faraway places.

Compound predicates are predicates made up of two or more verbs and their objects, if any (see p. 260). A verb or its object cannot stand alone as a sentence:

Fragment	Uncle Marlon drew out his tales. And embellished them.
Revised	Uncle Marlon drew out his tales and embellished them.
Fragment	He described characters he had met. And storms at sea.
Revised	He described characters he had met and storms at sea.

Note Beginning a sentence with a coordinating conjunction such as *and* or *but* can lead to a sentence fragment. Check every sentence you begin with a coordinating conjunction to be sure it is complete.

EXERCISE 17.2 Revising: Sentence fragments

Correct any sentence fragment below either by combining it with a main clause or by making it a main clause. If an item contains no sentence fragment, mark the number preceding it. (You can do this exercise online at *ablongman.com/littlebrown.*)

Example:

Jujitsu is good for self-protection. Because it enables one to overcome an opponent without the use of weapons.

Jujitsu is good for self-protection because it enables one to overcome an opponent without the use of weapons.

1. Human beings who perfume themselves. They are not much different from other animals.
2. Animals as varied as insects and dogs release *pheromones*. Chemicals that signal other animals.
3. Human beings have a diminished sense of smell. And do not consciously detect most of their own species' pheromones.
4. The human substitute for pheromones may be perfumes. Especially musk and other fragrances derived from animal oils.
5. Some sources say that humans began using perfume to cover up the smell of burning flesh. During sacrifices to the gods.
6. Perfumes became religious offerings in their own right. Being expensive to make, they were highly prized.
7. The earliest historical documents from the Middle East record the use of fragrances. Not only in religious ceremonies but on the body.

8. In the nineteenth century chemists began synthesizing perfume oils. Which previously could be made only from natural sources.
9. The most popular animal oil for perfume today is musk. Although some people dislike its heavy, sweet odor.
10. Synthetic musk oil would help conserve a certain species of deer. Whose gland is the source of musk.

17e Be aware of the acceptable uses of incomplete sentences.

A few word groups lacking the usual subject-predicate combination are not sentence fragments because they conform to the expectations of most readers. They include exclamations (*Oh no!*); questions and answers (*Where next? To Kansas.*); and commands (*Move along. Shut the window.*). Another kind of incomplete sentence, occurring in special situations, is the transitional phrase (*So much for the causes, now for the results. One final point.*).

Experienced writers sometimes use sentence fragments when they want to achieve a special effect. Such fragments appear more in informal than in formal writing. Unless you are experienced and thoroughly secure in your own writing, you should avoid all fragments and concentrate on writing clear, well-formed sentences.

EXERCISE 17.3 Revising: Sentence fragments

Revise the following paragraph to eliminate sentence fragments by combining them with main clauses or rewriting them as main clauses. (You can do this exercise online at *ablongman.com/littlebrown.*)

Baby red-eared slider turtles are brightly colored. With bold patterns on their yellowish undershells. Which serve as a warning to predators. The bright colors of skunks and other animals. They signal that the animals will spray nasty chemicals. In contrast, the turtle's colors warn largemouth bass. That the baby turtle will actively defend itself. When a bass gulps down a turtle. The feisty baby claws and bites. Forcing the bass to spit it out. To avoid a similar painful experience. The bass will avoid other baby red-eared slider turtles. The turtle loses its bright colors as it grows too big. For a bass's afternoon snack.

Note See page 383 for an exercise involving sentence fragments along with comma splices, fused sentences, and other sentence errors.

CHAPTER 18

Comma Splices and Fused Sentences

A sentence or main clause contains at least a subject and a predicate, which together express a complete thought (see p. 235). We can separate two consecutive main clauses in one of four ways:

- **With a period:**

  The ship was huge. Its mast stood eighty feet high.

- **With a semicolon:**

  The ship was huge; its mast stood eighty feet high.

- **With a comma preceding a coordinating conjunction** that joins the clauses and specifies the relation between them:

  The ship was huge, and its mast stood eighty feet high.

- **With a colon** when the second clause explains the first (see p. 479):

  The ship was huge: its mast stood eighty feet high.

The period, semicolon, or colon alone or the comma plus coordinating conjunction signals readers that one main clause (complete thought) is ending and another is beginning.

The comma splice and the fused sentence deprive readers of this signal and often force them to reread for sense. In a **comma splice** the two main clauses are joined (or spliced) *only* with a comma, not with a coordinating conjunction as well.

Comma splice
The ship was huge, its mast stood eighty feet high.

In a **fused sentence** no punctuation or coordinating conjunction appears between the main clauses.

http://www.ablongman.com/littlebrown ▶

Visit the companion Web site for more help and additional exercises on comma splices and fused sentences.

Situations that may produce comma splices and fused sentences

- **The first clause is negative; the second, positive:**

Splice Petric is not a nurse, she is a doctor.
Revised Petric is not a nurse; she is a doctor.

- **The second clause amplifies or illustrates the first:**

Fused She did well in high school her average was 3.9.
Revised She did well in high school: her average was 3.9.

- **The second clause contains a conjunctive adverb or other transitional expression, such as *however* or *for example*** (see p. 348)**:**

Splice She had intended to become a biologist, however, medicine seemed more exciting.
Revised She had intended to become a biologist; however, medicine seemed more exciting.

- **The subject of the second clause repeats or refers to the subject of the first clause:**

Fused Petric is an internist she practices in Topeka.
Revised Petric is an internist. She practices in Topeka.

- **Splicing or fusing is an attempt to link related ideas or to smooth choppy sentences:**

Splice She is very committed to her work, she devotes almost all her time to patient care.
Revised Because she is very committed to her work, she devotes almost all her time to patient care.
Revised She is so committed to her work that she devotes almost all her time to patient care.

- **Words identifying the speaker divide a quotation between two complete sentences.** (See p. 446 for the punctuation to use in this case.)

Splice "Medicine is a human frontier," Petric says, "The boundaries are unknown."
Revised "Medicine is a human frontier," Petric says. "The boundaries are unknown."

Fused sentence
The ship was huge its mast stood eighty feet high.

Exception Experienced writers sometimes use a comma without a coordinating conjunction between very brief main clauses that are grammatically parallel:

subordinate clause. (See p. 255 for a list of subordinating conjunctions and pp. 400–04 for more on subordination.) Subordination is often more effective than forming separate sentences because it defines the relation between ideas more precisely:

Comma splice	The vitamins are adequate, the flavor is deficient.
Revised	The vitamins are adequate**.** The flavor is deficient. [Both ideas receive equal weight.]
Improved	Even though the vitamins are adequate**,** the flavor is deficient. [Emphasis on the second idea.]

18b Separate main clauses related by *however, for example,* and so on.

Two kinds of words that are not conjunctions describe how one main clause relates to another:

- **Conjunctive adverbs,** such as *consequently, finally, hence, however, indeed, therefore,* or *thus.* (See p. 263 for a longer list.)
- Other **transitional expressions,** such as *even so, for example, in fact, of course, to the right,* and *to this end.* (See pp. 88–89 for a longer list.)

When two main clauses are related by a conjunctive adverb or a transitional expression, they must be separated by a period or by a semicolon. The adverb or expression is also generally set off by a comma or commas (see p. 439):

Comma splice	Most Americans refuse to give up unhealthful habits, consequently our medical costs are higher than those of many other countries.
Revised	Most Americans refuse to give up unhealthful habits**.** Consequently**,** our medical costs are higher than those of many other countries.
Revised	Most Americans refuse to give up unhealthful habits**;** consequently**,** our medical costs are higher than those of many other countries.

Conjunctive adverbs and transitional expressions are different from coordinating conjunctions (*and, but,* and so on) and subordinating conjunctions (*although, because,* and so on):

- **Unlike conjunctions, conjunctive adverbs and transitional expressions do not join two clauses into a grammatical unit.** They merely describe the way two clauses relate in meaning.
- **Unlike conjunctions, conjunctive adverbs and transitional expressions can be moved within a clause** (see also p. 263). No

matter where in the clause an adverb or expression falls, though, the clause must be separated from another main clause by a period or semicolon.

Comma splice

The increased time devoted to watching television is not the only cause of the decline in reading ability, however, it is one of the important causes.

Period

The increased time devoted to watching television is not the only cause of the decline in reading ability. However, it is one of the important causes.

Semicolon

The increased time devoted to watching television is not the only cause of the decline in reading ability; however, it is one of the important causes.

The increased time devoted to watching television is not the only cause of the decline in reading ability; it is, however, one of the important causes.

EXERCISE 18.1 Identifying and revising comma splices

Correct each comma splice below in *two* of the ways described on pages 346–48. If an item contains no comma splice, mark the number preceding it. (You can do this exercise online at *ablongman.com/littlebrown*.)

Example:

Carolyn still had a headache, she could not get the child-proof cap off the aspirin bottle.

Carolyn still had a headache because she could not get the child-proof cap off the aspirin bottle. [Subordination.]

Carolyn still had a headache, for she could not get the child-proof cap off the aspirin bottle. [Coordinating conjunction.]

1. Money has a long history, it goes back at least as far as the earliest records.
2. Many of the earliest records concern financial transactions, indeed, early history must often be inferred from commercial activity.
3. Every known society has had a system of money, though the objects serving as money have varied widely.
4. Sometimes the objects have had real value, in modern times, however, their value has been more abstract.
5. Cattle, fermented beverages, and rare shells have served as money, each one had actual value for the society.

Fused Sentences

18c Combine two main clauses only with an appropriate conjunction or punctuation mark between them.

When two main clauses are joined without a word to connect them or a punctuation mark to separate them, the result is a **fused sentence.** Fused sentences can rarely be understood on first reading, and they are never acceptable in standard written English.

Fused Our foreign policy is not well defined it confuses many countries.

Fused sentences may be corrected in the same ways as comma splices. See pages 346–48.

Separate sentences

Our foreign policy is not well defined. It confuses many countries.

Comma and coordinating conjunction

Our foreign policy is not well defined, and it confuses many countries.

Semicolon

Our foreign policy is not well defined; it confuses many countries.

Subordinating conjunction

Because our foreign policy is not well defined, it confuses many countries.

EXERCISE 18.2 Identifying and revising fused sentences

Revise each of the fused sentences below in *two* of the four ways shown above. (You can do this exercise online at *ablongman.com/littlebrown.*)

Example:

Tim was shy he usually refused invitations.
Tim was shy, so he usually refused invitations.
Tim was shy; he usually refused invitations.

1. Throughout history money and religion were closely linked there was little distinction between government and religion.
2. The head of state and the religious leader were often the same person all power rested in one ruler.
3. These powerful leaders decided what objects would serve as money their backing encouraged public faith in the money.
4. Coins were minted of precious metals the religious overtones of money were then strengthened.

5. People already believed the precious metals to be divine their use in money intensified its allure.

EXERCISE 18.3 Sentence combining: Comma splices and fused sentences

Combine each pair of sentences below into one sentence without creating a comma splice or fused sentence. Combine sentences by (1) supplying a comma and coordinating conjunction, (2) supplying a semicolon, or (3) subordinating one clause to the other. You will have to add, delete, or change words as well as punctuation. (You can do this exercise online at *ablongman.com/littlebrown*.)

Example:

The sun sank lower in the sky. The colors gradually faded.

As the sun sank lower in the sky, the colors gradually faded. [The first clause is subordinated to the second.]

1. The exact origin of paper money is unknown. It has not survived as coins, shells, and other durable objects have.
2. Perhaps goldsmiths were also bankers. Thus they held the gold of their wealthy customers.
3. The goldsmiths probably gave customers receipts for their gold. These receipts were then used in trade.
4. The goldsmiths were something like modern-day bankers. Their receipts were something like modern-day money.
5. The goldsmiths became even more like modern-day bankers. They began issuing receipts for more gold than they actually held in their vaults.

EXERCISE 18.4 Revising: Comma splices and fused sentences

Identify and revise the comma splices and fused sentences in the following paragraph. (You can do this exercise online at *ablongman.com/littlebrown*.)

All those parents who urged their children to eat broccoli were right, the vegetable really is healthful. Broccoli contains sulforaphane, moreover, this mustard oil can be found in kale and Brussels sprouts. Sulforaphane causes the body to make an enzyme that attacks carcinogens, these substances cause cancer. The enzyme speeds up the work of the kidneys then they can flush harmful chemicals out of the body. Other vegetables have similar benefits however, green, leafy vegetables like broccoli are the most efficient. Thus wise people will eat their broccoli it could save their lives.

Note See page 383 for an exercise involving comma splices and fused sentences along with other sentence errors.

CHAPTER 19

Pronoun Reference

A **pronoun** such as *it* or *they* derives its meaning from its **antecedent,** the noun it substitutes for. Therefore, a pronoun must refer clearly and unmistakably to its antecedent in order for the meaning to be clear. A sentence such as *Jim told Mark he was not invited* is not clear because the reader does not know whether *he* refers to Jim or to Mark.

One way to make pronoun reference clear is to ensure that the pronoun and antecedent agree in person, number, and gender (see p. 315). The other way is to ensure that the pronoun refers unambiguously to a single, close, specific antecedent.

Note Grammar and style checkers cannot recognize unclear pronoun reference. For instance, a checker did not spot any of the problems in Exercise 19.2 on page 358.

CULTURE LANGUAGE An English pronoun does need a clear antecedent nearby, but don't use both a pronoun and its antecedent as the subject of the same sentence or clause: *Jim* [not *Jim he*] *told Mark to go alone.* (See also pp. 377–78.)

19a Make a pronoun refer clearly to one antecedent.

When either of two nouns can be a pronoun's antecedent, the reference will not be clear:

Confusing Emily Dickinson is sometimes compared with Jane Austen, but she was quite different.

Revise such a sentence in one of two ways:

- **Replace the pronoun with the appropriate noun:**

Clear Emily Dickinson is sometimes compared with Jane Austen, but Dickinson [or Austen] was quite different.

http://www.ablongman.com/littlebrown

Visit the companion Web site for more help and additional exercises on pronoun reference.

Principal causes of unclear pronoun reference

- **More than one possible antecedent** (facing page and below):

Confusing	To keep birds from eating seeds, soak them in blue food coloring.
Clear	To keep birds from eating seeds, soak the seeds in blue food coloring.

- **Antecedent too far away** (p. 354):

Confusing	Employees should consult with their supervisor who require personal time.
Clear	Employees who require personal time should consult with their supervisor.

- **Antecedent only implied** (p. 355):

Confusing	Many children begin reading on their own by watching television, but this should probably be discounted in government policy.
Clear	Many children begin reading on their own by watching television, but such self-instruction should probably be discounted in government policy.

See also pages 356–58.

- **Avoid repetition by rewriting the sentence.** If you use the pronoun, make sure it has only one possible antecedent:

Clear	Despite occasional comparison, Emily Dickinson and Jane Austen were quite different.
Clear	Though sometimes compared with her, Emily Dickinson was quite different from Jane Austen.

Sentences that report what someone said, using verbs such as *said* or *told,* often require direct rather than indirect quotation:

Confusing	Juliet Noble told Ashley Torre that she was next in line for the job.
Clear	Juliet Noble told Ashley Torre, "I am next in line for the job."
Clear	Juliet Noble told Ashley Torre, "You are next in line for the job."

Note Avoid the awkward device of using a pronoun followed by the appropriate noun in parentheses, as in the following example:

Weak	Noble and Torre had both hoped for the job, so she (Noble) was disappointed.
Improved	Noble was disappointed because she and Torre had both hoped for the job.

19b Place a pronoun close enough to its antecedent to ensure clarity.

A clause beginning *who, which,* or *that* generally should fall immediately after the word to which it refers:

Confusing	Kara found a lamp in the attic that her aunt had used.
Clear	In the attic Kara found a lamp that her aunt had used.

Even when only one word could possibly serve as the antecedent of a pronoun, the relationship between the two may still be unclear if they are widely separated:

Confusing	Jane Austen had little formal education but was well educated at home. Far from living an isolated life in the English countryside, the Austens were a large family with a wide circle of friends who provided entertainment and cultural enrichment. They also provided material for her stories.
Clear	Jane Austen had little formal education but was well educated at home. Far from living an isolated life in the English countryside, the Austens were a large family with a wide circle of friends who provided entertainment and cultural enrichment. They also provided material for Jane Austen's stories.

EXERCISE 19.1 Revising: Ambiguous and remote pronoun reference

Rewrite the following sentences to eliminate unclear pronoun reference. If you use a pronoun in your revision, be sure that it refers to only one antecedent and that it falls close enough to its antecedent to ensure clarity. (You can do this exercise online at *ablongman.com/littlebrown.*)

Example:

Sam found an old gun in the rotting shed that was just as his grandfather had left it.

In the rotting shed Sam found an old gun that was just as his grandfather had left it.

1. There is a difference between the heroes of the twentieth century and the heroes of earlier times: they have flaws in their characters.

2. Sports fans still admire Pete Rose, Babe Ruth, and Joe Namath even though they could not be perfect.
3. Fans liked Rose for having his young son serve as batboy when he was in Cincinnati.
4. The reputation Rose earned as a gambler and tax evader may overshadow his reputation as a ballplayer, but it will survive.
5. Rose amassed an unequaled record as a hitter, using his bat to do things no one else has ever done. It stands even though Rose was banned from baseball.

19c Make a pronoun refer to a specific antecedent, not an implied one.

A pronoun should refer to a specific noun or other pronoun. The reader can only guess at the meaning of a pronoun when its antecedent is implied by the context, not stated outright.

1 Use *this, that, which,* and *it* cautiously.

The most common kind of implied reference occurs when the pronoun *this, that, which,* or *it* refers to a whole idea or situation described in the preceding clause, sentence, or even paragraph. Such reference, often called **broad reference,** is acceptable only when the pronoun refers clearly to the entire preceding clause. In the following sentence, *which* could not possibly refer to anything but the whole preceding clause:

> I can be kind and civil to people, which is more than you can.
> —George Bernard Shaw

But if a pronoun might confuse a reader, you should avoid using it or provide an appropriate noun:

Confusing — The British knew little of the American countryside, and they had no experience with the colonists' guerilla tactics. This gave the colonists an advantage.

Clear — The British knew little of the American countryside, and they had no experience with the colonists' guerilla tactics. This ignorance and inexperience gave the colonists an advantage.

2 Implied nouns are not clear antecedents.

A noun may be implied in some other word or phrase, as *happiness* is implied in *happy, driver* is implied in *drive*, and *mother* is implied in *mother's*. But a pronoun cannot refer clearly to an implied noun, only to a specific, stated one:

Confusing	Cohen's report brought her a lawsuit.
Clear	Cohen was sued over her report.
Confusing	Her reports on psychological development generally go unnoticed outside it.
Clear	Her reports on psychological development generally go unnoticed outside the field.

3 Titles of papers are not clear antecedents.

The title of a paper is entirely separate from the paper itself, so a pronoun should not be used in the opening sentence of a paper to refer to the title:

Title	How to Row a Boat
Not	This is not as easy as it looks.
But	Rowing a boat is not as easy as it looks.

19d Use *it* and *they* to refer only to definite antecedents.

Although common in speech, using *it* and *they* to refer to indefinite antecedents is inappropriate in writing.

Confusing	In Chapter 4 of this book, it describes the early flights of the Wright brothers.
Clear	Chapter 4 of this book describes the early flights of the Wright brothers.
Confusing	Even in reality TV shows, they present a false picture of life.
Clear	Even reality TV shows present a false picture of life.

19e Use *you* only to mean "you, the reader."

You should clearly mean "you, the reader." The context must be appropriate for such a meaning:

Inappropriate	In the fourteenth century you had to struggle simply to survive.
Revised	In the fourteenth century one [or a person] had to struggle simply to survive.

Writers sometimes drift into *you* because *one, a person, the individual,* or a similar indefinite word can be difficult to sustain. Sentence after sentence, the indefinite word may sound stuffy, and it requires the sexist *he* or the awkward *he or she* for pronoun-antecedent agreement (see pp. 317–18). To avoid these difficulties, try using plural nouns and pronouns:

Original	In the fourteenth century one had to struggle simply to survive.
Revised	In the fourteenth century people had to struggle simply to survive.

19f Use the pronoun *it* only one way in a sentence.

We use *it* idiomatically in expressions such as *It is raining.* We use *it* to postpone the subject in sentences such as *It is true that more jobs are available to women today.* And we use *it* as a personal pronoun in sentences such as *Nicole wanted the book, but she couldn't find it.* All these uses are standard, but two of them in the same passage can confuse the reader:

Confusing	It is true that the Constitution sets limits, but it is also flexible.
Clear	The Constitution does set limits, but it is also flexible.

19g Use *who, which,* and *that* for appropriate antecedents.

The relative pronouns *who, which,* and *that* commonly refer to persons, animals, or things. *Who* refers most often to persons but may also refer to animals that have names:

Dorothy is the girl who visits Oz.
Her dog, Toto, who accompanies her, gives her courage.

Which refers to animals and things:

The Orinoco River, which is 1600 miles long, flows through Venezuela into the Atlantic Ocean.

That refers to animals and things and occasionally to persons when they are collective or anonymous:

The rocket that failed cost millions.
Infants that walk need constant tending.

(See also p. 439 for the use of *which* and *that* in nonessential and essential clauses.)

Shifts like those in the first draft are likely to occur while you are trying to piece together meaning during drafting. But during editing you should make your sentences consistent in grammatical elements.

Note Grammar and style checkers cannot recognize most shifts in sentences. Proofread your work on your own, looking carefully for inconsistencies.

20a Keep a sentence or related sentences consistent in person and number.

Person in grammar refers to the distinction among the person talking (first person), the person spoken to (second person), and the person, object, or concept being talked about (third person). **Number** refers to the distinction between one (singular) and more than one (plural).

Shifts in person

Most shifts in person occur because we can refer to people in general, including our readers, either in the third person (*a person, one; people, they*) or in the second person (*you*):

People should not drive when they have been drinking.
One should not drive when he or she has been drinking.
You should not drive when you have been drinking.

Although any one of these possibilities is acceptable in an appropriate context, a mixture of them is inconsistent:

Inconsistent	If a person works hard, you can gain satisfaction.
Revised	If you work hard, you can gain satisfaction.
Revised	If a person works hard, he or she can gain satisfaction.
Better	If people work hard, they can gain satisfaction.

Shifts in number

Inconsistency in number occurs most often between a pronoun and its antecedent (see p. 315):

Inconsistent	If a student does not understand a problem, they should consult the teacher.
Revised	If a student does not understand a problem, he or she should consult the teacher.
Better	If students do not understand a problem, they should consult the teacher.
Or	A student who does not understand a problem should consult the teacher.

Note Generic nouns and most indefinite pronouns take singular pronouns with a definite gender: *he, she,* or *it.* When we use a generic noun like *student* or *person* or an indefinite pronoun like *everyone* or *each,* we often mean to include both males and females. To indicate this meaning, use *he or she* rather than *he* (as in the first of the preceding revisions) or, better still, rewrite in the plural or rewrite to avoid the pronoun (as in the second and third of the revisions). See page 318 for more discussion and examples.

Inconsistency in number can also occur between other words (usually nouns) that relate to each other in meaning.

Inconsistent	All the boys have a good reputation.
Revised	All the boys have good reputations.

The consistency in the revised sentence is called **logical agreement** because the nouns are consistent (the *boys* have *reputations,* not a single *reputation*).

EXERCISE 20.1 Revising: Shifts in person and number

Revise the following sentences to make them consistent in person and number. (You can do this exercise online at *ablongman.com/littlebrown.*)

Example:

A plumber will fix burst pipes, but they won't repair waterlogged appliances.

Plumbers will fix burst pipes, but they won't repair waterlogged appliances.

1. When a taxpayer is waiting to receive a tax refund from the Internal Revenue Service, you begin to notice what time the mail carrier arrives.
2. If the taxpayer does not receive a refund check within six weeks of filing a return, they may not have followed the rules of the IRS.
3. If a taxpayer does not include a Social Security number on a return, you will have to wait for a refund.
4. When taxpayers do not file their return early, they will not get a refund quickly.
5. If one makes errors on the tax form, they might even be audited, thereby delaying a refund even longer.

20b Keep a sentence or related sentences consistent in tense and mood.

Shifts in tense

Within a sentence or from one sentence to another, certain changes in tense may be required to indicate changes in actual or relative time (see p. 298). The following changes are necessary:

Ramon will graduate from high school thirty-one years after his father arrived in the United States.

But changes that are not required by meaning distract readers. Unnecessary shifts between past and present in passages narrating a series of events are particularly confusing:

Inconsistent — Immediately after Booth shot Lincoln, Major Rathbone threw himself upon the assassin. But Booth pulls a knife and plunges it into the major's arm.

Revised — Immediately after Booth shot Lincoln, Major Rathbone threw himself upon the assassin. But Booth pulled a knife and plunged it into the major's arm.

Use the present tense consistently to describe what an author has written, including the action in literature or a film:

Inconsistent — The main character in the novel suffers psychologically because he has a clubfoot, but he eventually triumphed over his disability.

Revised — The main character in the novel suffers psychologically because he has a clubfoot, but he eventually triumphs over his disability.

Shifts in mood

Shifts in the mood of verbs occur most frequently in directions when the writer moves between the imperative mood (*Unplug the appliance*) and the indicative mood (*You should unplug the appliance*). (See p. 301.) Directions are usually clearer and more concise in the imperative, as long as its use is consistent:

Inconsistent — Cook the mixture slowly, and you should stir it until the sugar is dissolved.

Revised — Cook the mixture slowly, and stir it until the sugar is dissolved.

EXERCISE 20.2 Revising: Shifts in tense and mood

Revise the following sentences to make them consistent in tense and mood. (You can do this exercise online at *ablongman.com/littlebrown*.)

Example:

Lynn ran to first, rounded the base, and keeps running until she slides into second.

Lynn ran to first, rounded the base, and kept running until she slid into second.

1. When your cholesterol count is too high, adjusting your diet and exercise level reduced it.

2. After you lowered your cholesterol rate, you decrease the chances of heart attack and stroke.
3. First eliminate saturated fats from your diet; then you should consume more whole grains and raw vegetables.
4. To avoid saturated fats, substitute turkey and chicken for beef, and you should use cholesterol-free salad dressing and cooking oil.
5. A regular program of aerobic exercise, such as walking or swimming, improves your cholesterol rate and made you feel much healthier.

20c Keep a sentence or related sentences consistent in subject and voice.

When a verb is in the **active voice,** the subject names the actor: *Linda passed the peas.* When a verb is in the **passive voice,** the subject names the receiver of the action: *The peas were passed* [*by Linda*]. (See pp. 304–05.)

A shift in voice may sometimes help focus the reader's attention on a single subject, as in *The candidate campaigned vigorously and was nominated on the first ballot.* However, most shifts in voice also involve shifts in subject. They are unnecessary and confusing.

Inconsistent — Internet newsgroups cover an enormous range of topics for discussion. Forums for meeting people with like interests are provided in these groups.

Revised — Internet newsgroups cover an enormous range of topics for discussion and provide forums for meeting people with like interests.

EXERCISE 20.3 Revising: Shifts in subject and voice

Make the following sentences consistent in subject and voice. (You can do this exercise online at *ablongman.com/littlebrown.*)

Example:

At the reunion they ate hot dogs and volleyball was played.
At the reunion they ate hot dogs and played volleyball.

1. If students learn how to study efficiently, much better grades will be made on tests.
2. Conscientious students begin to prepare for tests immediately after the first class is attended.
3. Before each class all reading assignments are completed, and the students outline the material and answer any study questions.
4. In class they listen carefully and good notes are taken.
5. Questions are asked by the students when they do not understand the teacher.

20d Keep a quotation or a question consistently direct or indirect.

Direct quotations or questions report the exact words of a quotation or question:

> "I am the greatest," bragged Muhammad Ali.
> In his day few people asked, "Is he right?"

Indirect quotations or questions report that someone said or asked something, but not in the exact words:

> Muhammad Ali bragged that he was the greatest.
> In his day few people asked whether he was right.

Shifts between direct and indirect quotations or questions are difficult to follow.

Shift in quotation	Kapek reported that the rats avoided the maze and "as of this writing, none responds to conditioning."
Revised (indirect)	Kapek reported that the rats avoided the maze and that as of his writing none responded to conditioning.
Revised (direct)	Kapek reported, "The rats avoid the maze. As of this writing, none responds to conditioning."
Shift in question	The reader wonders whether the experiment failed or did it perhaps succeed?
Revised (indirect)	The reader wonders whether the experiment failed or whether it perhaps succeeded.
Revised (direct)	Did the experiment fail? Or did it perhaps succeed?

For more on quotations, see pages 446–48 (commas with signal phrases such as *she said*), 471–77 (quotation marks), and 607–10 (integrating quotations into your writing). For more on questions, see pages 429–30.

EXERCISE 20.4 Revising: Shifts in direct and indirect quotations and questions

Revise each of the following sentences twice, once to make it consistently direct, once to make it consistently indirect. You will have to guess at the exact wording of direct quotations and questions that are now stated indirectly. (You can do this exercise online at *ablongman.com/littlebrown.*)

Example:

We all wonder what the next decade will bring and will we thrive or not?

Direct: What will the next decade bring? Will we thrive or not?

Indirect: We all wonder what the next decade will bring and whether we will thrive or not.

1. One anthropologist says that the functions of marriage have changed and "nowhere more dramatically than in industrialized cultures."
2. The question even arises of whether siblings may marry and would the union be immoral?
3. The author points out, "Sibling marriage is still illegal everywhere in the United States" and that people are still prosecuted under the law.
4. She says that incest could be considered a universal taboo and "the questions asked about the taboo vary widely."
5. Some ask is the taboo a way of protecting the family or whether it may be instinctive.

EXERCISE 20.5 Revising: Shifts

Revise the following paragraph to eliminate unnecessary shifts in person, number, tense, mood, and voice. (You can do this exercise online at *ablongman.com/littlebrown.*)

Driving in snow need not be dangerous if you practice a few rules. First, one should avoid fast starts, which prevent the wheels from gaining traction and may result in the car's getting stuck. Second, drive more slowly than usual, and you should pay attention to the feel of the car: if the steering seemed unusually loose or the wheels did not seem to be grabbing the road, slow down. Third, avoid fast stops, which lead to skids. One should be alert for other cars and intersections that may necessitate that the brakes be applied suddenly. If you need to slow down, the car's momentum can be reduced by downshifting as well as by applying the brakes. When braking, press the pedal to the floor only if you have antilock brakes; otherwise, the pedal should be pumped in short bursts. If you feel the car skidding, the brakes should be released and the wheel should be turned into the direction of the skid, and then the brakes should be pressed or pumped again. If one repeated these motions, the skid would be stopped and the speed of the car would be reduced.

Note See page 383 for an exercise involving shifts along with sentence fragments, comma splices, and other sentence errors.

EXERCISE 21.2 Using limiting modifiers

Use each of the following limiting modifiers in two versions of the same sentence. (You can do this exercise online at *ablongman.com/littlebrown.*)

Example:
only
He is the only one I like. He is the one only I like.

1. almost
2. even
3. hardly
4. simply
5. nearly

21c Make each modifier refer to only one grammatical element.

A modifier can modify only *one* element in a sentence—the subject, the verb, or some other element. A **squinting modifier** seems confusingly to refer to either of two words:

Squinting Snipers who fired on the soldiers often escaped capture.

Clear Snipers who often fired on the soldiers escaped capture.

Clear Snipers who fired on the soldiers escaped capture often.

When an adverb modifies an entire main clause, as in the last example, it can usually be moved to the beginning of the sentence: *Often, snipers who fired on the soldiers escaped capture.*

EXERCISE 21.3 Revising: Squinting modifiers

Revise each sentence twice so that the squinting modifier applies clearly first to one element and then to the other. (You can do this exercise online at *ablongman.com/littlebrown.*)

Example:
The work that he hoped would satisfy him completely frustrated him.
The work that he hoped would completely satisfy him frustrated him.
The work that he hoped would satisfy him frustrated him completely.

1. People who sunbathe often can damage their skin.
2. Sunbathers who apply a sunscreen frequently block some of the sun's harmful ultraviolet rays.
3. Men and women who lie out in the sun often have leathery, dry skin.
4. Doctors tell sunbathers when they are older they risk skin cancer.
5. People who stay out of the sun usually will have better skin and fewer chances of skin cancer.

21d Keep subjects, verbs, and objects together.

English sentences tend to move from subject to verb to object. The movement is so familiar that modifiers between these elements can be awkward.

A subject and verb may be separated by an adjective that modifies the subject: *Kuwait, which has a population of 1.3 million, is a rich nation.* But an adverb of more than a word usually stops the flow of the sentence:

subject — adverb — verb

Awkward Kuwait, after the first Gulf War ended in 1991, began returning to normal.

adverb — subject verb

Revised After the first Gulf War ended in 1991, Kuwait began returning to normal.

Even a one-word adverb will be awkward between a verb and its object:

verb — adverb object

Awkward The war had damaged badly many of Kuwait's oil fields.

verb — object

Revised The war had badly damaged many of Kuwait's oil fields.

adverb

21e Keep parts of infinitives or verb phrases together.

An **infinitive** consists of the marker *to* plus the plain form of a verb: *to produce, to enjoy.* The two parts of the infinitive are widely regarded as a grammatical unit that should not be split:

infinitive

Awkward The weather service expected temperatures to not rise.

infinitive

Revised The weather service expected temperatures not to rise.

A split infinitive may sometimes be natural and preferable, though it may still bother some readers:

infinitive

Several US industries expect to more than triple their use of robots.

Here the split infinitive is more economical than the alternatives, such as *Several US industries expect to increase their use of robots by more than three times.*

A **verb phrase** consists of a helping verb plus a main verb, as in *will call, was going, had been writing* (see p. 279). A single-word adverb may be inserted after the helping verb in a verb phrase (or the first helping verb if more than one): *Scientists have lately been using spacecraft to study the sun.* But when longer adverbs interrupt verb phrases, the result is almost always awkward:

helping verb — adverb — main verb

Awkward The spacecraft *Ulysses* will after traveling close to the sun report on the sun's energy fields.

adverb — verb phrase

Revised After traveling close to the sun, the spacecraft *Ulysses* will report on the sun's energy fields.

CULTURE LANGUAGE In an English question, place a one-word adverb after the first helping verb and the subject:

helping verb — subject — adverb — rest of verb phrase

Will spacecraft ever be able to leave the solar system?

EXERCISE 21.4 Revising: Separated sentence parts

Revise the following sentences to connect separated parts (subject-predicate, verb-object, verb phrase, infinitive). (You can do this exercise online at *ablongman.com/littlebrown*.)

Example:

Most children have by the time they are seven lost a tooth.
By the time they are seven, most children have lost a tooth.

1. Myra Bradwell founded in 1868 the *Chicago Legal News*.
2. Bradwell was later denied, although she had qualified, admission to the Illinois Bar Association.
3. In an attempt to finally gain admission to the bar, she carried the case to the Supreme Court, but the justices decided against her.
4. Bradwell was determined that no other woman would, if she were qualified, be denied entrance to a profession.
5. The Illinois legislature finally passed, in response to Bradwell's persuasion, a bill ensuring that no one on the basis of gender would be restricted from a profession.

21f Position adverbs with care. CULTURE LANGUAGE

A few adverbs are subject to conventions that can trouble non-native speakers of English.

Adverbs of frequency

Adverbs of frequency include *always, never, often, rarely, seldom, sometimes,* and *usually*. They appear at the beginning of a sentence, before a one-word verb, or after the helping verb in a verb phrase:

verb phrase — adverb

Awkward Robots have put sometimes humans out of work.

Revised   Robots have sometimes put humans out of work. (helping verb: have; adverb: sometimes; main verb: put)

Revised   Sometimes robots have put humans out of work. (adverb: Sometimes; verb phrase: have put)

Adverbs of frequency always follow the verb *be:*

Awkward   Robots often are helpful to workers. (adverb: often; verb: are)

Revised   Robots are often helpful to workers. (verb: are; adverb: often)

Adverbs of degree

Adverbs of degree include *absolutely, almost, certainly, completely, especially, extremely, hardly,* and *only.* They fall just before the word modified (an adjective, another adverb, sometimes a verb).

Awkward   Robots have been useful especially in making cars. (adjective: useful; adverb: especially)

Revised   Robots have been especially useful in making cars. (adverb: especially; adjective: useful)

Adverbs of manner

Adverbs of manner include *badly, beautifully, openly, sweetly, tightly, well,* and others that describe how something is done. They usually fall after the verb:

Awkward   Robots smoothly work on assembly lines. (adverb: smoothly; verb: work)

Revised   Robots work smoothly on assembly lines. (verb: work; adverb: smoothly)

The adverb *not*

When the adverb *not* modifies a verb, place it after the helping verb (or the first helping verb if more than one):

Awkward   Robots do think not. (helping verb: do; main verb: think)

Revised   Robots do not think. (helping verb: do; main verb: think)

Place *not* after a form of *be: Robots are not thinkers.*

When *not* modifies another adverb or an adjective, place it before the other modifier: *Robots are not sleek machines.*

21g Arrange adjectives appropriately. CULTURE LANGUAGE

English follows distinctive rules for arranging two or three adjectives before a noun. (A string of more than three adjectives before a noun is rare.) The order depends on the meaning of the adjectives, as indicated in the following table:

Determiner	Opinion	Size or shape	Color	Origin	Material	Noun used as adjective	Noun
many						state	**laws**
	striking		green	Thai			**birds**
a	fine			German			**camera**
this		square			wooden		**table**
all						business	**reports**
the			blue		litmus		**paper**

See page 444 for guidelines on punctuating two or more adjectives before a noun.

EXERCISE 21.5 Revising: Placement of adverbs and adjectives

CULTURE LANGUAGE Revise the sentences below to correct the positions of adverbs or adjectives. If a sentence is already correct as given, circle the number preceding it. (You can do this exercise online at *ablongman .com/littlebrown*.)

Example:

Gasoline high prices affect usually car sales.
High gasoline prices usually affect car sales.

1. Some years ago Detroit cars often were praised.
2. Luxury large cars especially were prized.
3. Then a serious oil shortage led drivers to value small foreign cars that got good mileage.
4. When gasoline ample supplies returned, consumers bought again American large cars.
5. However, the large cars not were luxury sedans but vans and sport-utility vehicles.

Dangling Modifiers

21h Relate dangling modifiers to their sentences.

A **dangling modifier** does not sensibly modify anything in its sentence:

Dangling Passing the building, the vandalism became visible.

Dangling modifiers usually introduce sentences, contain a verb form, and imply but do not name a subject: in the preceding example, the implied subject is the someone or something passing the building. Readers assume that this implied subject is the same as the subject of the sentence (*vandalism* in the example). When it is not, the modifier "dangles" unconnected to the rest of the sentence.

Certain modifiers are the most likely to dangle:

- **Participial phrases:**

Dangling Passing the building, the vandalism became visible.

Revised As we passed the building, the vandalism became visible.

- **Infinitive phrases:**

Dangling To understand the causes, vandalism has been extensively investigated.

Revised To understand the causes, researchers have extensively investigated vandalism.

- **Prepositional phrases in which the object of the preposition is a gerund:**

Dangling After studying the problem, vandals are now thought to share certain characteristics.

Revised After studying the problem, researchers think that vandals share certain characteristics.

- **Elliptical clauses in which the subject and perhaps the verb are omitted:**

Dangling When destructive, researchers have learned that vandals are more likely to be in groups.

Revised When vandals are destructive, researchers have learned, they are more likely to be in groups.

Dangling modifiers are especially likely when the verb in the main clause is in the **passive voice** instead of the **active voice**, as in *vandalism has been investigated* and *vandals are thought*. (See pp. 304–05 for more on the passive voice.)

Note A modifier may be dangling even when the sentence elsewhere contains a word the modifier might seem to describe, such as *vandals* below:

Dangling When destructive, researchers have learned that vandals are more likely to be in groups.

In addition, a dangling modifier may fall at the end of a sentence:

Dangling The vandalism was visible passing the building.

CHAPTER 22

Mixed and Incomplete Sentences

Mixed Sentences

A **mixed sentence** contains two or more parts that are incompatible—that is, the parts do not fit together. The misfit may be in grammar or in meaning.

Note Grammar and style checkers may recognize a simple mixed construction such as *reason is because,* but they will fail to flag most mixed sentences.

22a Untangle sentences that are mixed in grammar.

Sentences mixed in grammar combine two or more incompatible grammatical structures.

1 Make sure subject and verb fit together grammatically.

A mixed sentence may occur when you start a sentence with one plan and end it with another:

Mixed — By paying more attention to impressions than facts [modifier (prepositional phrase)] leads [verb] us to misjudge others.

Revised — By paying more attention to impressions than facts, [modifier (prepositional phrase)] we misjudge [subject + verb] others.

Revised — Paying more attention to impressions than facts [subject (gerund phrase)] leads [verb] us to misjudge others.

http://www.ablongman.com/littlebrown

Visit the companion Web site for more help and an additional exercise on mixed and incomplete sentences.

subject — modifier (adjective clause)

Mixed The fact that someone may be considered guilty just for associating with someone guilty.

subject verb

Revised The fact is that someone may be considered guilty just for associating with someone guilty.

subject — verb —

Revised Someone may be considered guilty just for associating with someone guilty.

In some mixed sentences the grammar is so jumbled that the writer has little choice but to start over:

Mixed My long-range goal is through law school and government work I hope to help people deal with those problems we all deal with more effectively.

Possible My long-range goal is to go to law school and then work in government so that I can help people deal more effectively with problems we all face.

Mixed sentences are especially likely on a computer when you connect parts of two sentences or rewrite half a sentence but not the other half. Mixed sentences may also occur when you don't focus your sentences on the subject and verb so that these elements carry the principal meaning. (See pp. 386–88.) If you need help identifying the subject and verb, see pages 235–38.

2 State parts of sentences, such as subjects, only once. CULTURE LANGUAGE

In some languages other than English, certain parts of sentences may be repeated. These include the subject in any kind of clause or an object or adverb in an adjective clause. In English, however, these parts are stated only once in a clause.

■ Repetition of subject

You may be tempted to restate a subject as a pronoun before the verb. But the subject needs stating only once in its clause.

Faulty The liquid it reached a temperature of 180°F.
Revised The liquid reached a temperature of 180°F.

Faulty Gases in the liquid they escaped.
Revised Gases in the liquid escaped.

■ Repetition in an adjective clause

Adjective clauses begin with *who, whom, whose, which, that, where,* and *when* (see p. 256). The beginning word replaces another word: the subject (*He is the person who called*), an object of a verb or preposition (*He is the person whom I mentioned*), or a preposition and pronoun (*He knows the office where [in which] the conference will occur*).

Do not state the word that *who, whom,* and so on replace in an adjective clause:

Faulty — The technician *whom* the test depended on her was burned. [*Whom* should replace *her*.]

Revised — The technician whom the test depended on was burned.

Adjective clauses beginning with *where* or *when* do not need an adverb such as *there* or *then:*

Faulty — Gases escaped at a moment when the technician was unprepared then.

Revised — Gases escaped at a moment when the technician was unprepared.

22b Match subjects and predicates in meaning.

In a sentence with mixed meaning, the subject is said to be or do something it cannot logically be or do. Such a mixture is sometimes called **faulty predication** because the predicate conflicts with the subject.

■ Illogical equation with *be*

When a form of *be* connects a subject and a word that describes the subject (a complement), the subject and complement must be logically related:

Mixed — A compromise between the city and the country would be the ideal place to live.

Revised — A community that offered the best qualities of both city and country would be the ideal place to live.

■ *Is when, is where*

Definitions require nouns on both sides of *be.* Definition clauses beginning with *when* or *where* are common in speech but should be avoided in writing:

Mixed — An examination is when you are tested on what you know.

Revised — An examination is a test of what you know.

■ *Reason is because*

The commonly heard construction *reason is because* is redundant since *because* means "for the reason that":

Mixed The reason the temple requests donations is because the school needs expansion.

Revised The reason the temple requests donations is that the school needs expansion.

Revised The temple requests donations because the school needs expansion.

Other mixed meanings

Mismatched subjects and predicates are not confined to sentences with *be:*

Mixed The use of emission controls was created to reduce air pollution.

Revised Emission controls were created to reduce air pollution.

EXERCISE 22.1 Revising: Sentences mixed in grammar or meaning

Revise the following sentences so that their parts fit together both in grammar and in meaning. Each item has more than one possible answer. (You can do this exercise online at *ablongman.com/littlebrown.*)

Example:

When they found out how expensive pianos are is why they were discouraged.

They were discouraged because they found out how expensive pianos are.

When they found out how expensive pianos are, they were discouraged.

1. A hurricane is when the winds in a tropical depression rotate counterclockwise at more than seventy-four miles per hour.
2. Because hurricanes can destroy so many lives and so much property is why people fear them.
3. Through high winds, storm surge, floods, and tornadoes is how a hurricane can kill thousands of people.
4. Many scientists observe that hurricanes in recent years they have become more ferocious and destructive.
5. However, in the last half-century, with improved communications systems and weather satellites have made hurricanes less deadly.

EXERCISE 22.2 Revising: Repeated sentence parts

CULTURE LANGUAGE Revise the following sentences to eliminate any unnecessary repetition of sentence parts. (You can do this exercise online at *ablongman.com/littlebrown.*)

Example:

Over 79 percent of Americans they have heard of global warming.
Over 79 percent of Americans have heard of global warming.

1. Global warming it is caused by the gradual erosion of the ozone layer that protects the earth from the sun.
2. Scientists who study this problem they say that the primary causes of erosion are the use of fossil fuels and the reduction of forests.
3. Many nonscientists they mistakenly believe that aerosol spray cans are the primary cause of erosion.
4. One scientist whom others respect him argues that Americans have effectively reduced their use of aerosol sprays.
5. He argues that we will stop global warming only when the public learns the real causes then.

Incomplete Sentences

The most serious kind of incomplete sentence is the fragment (see Chapter 17). But sentences are also incomplete when they omit one or more words needed for clarity.

Note Grammar and style checkers will not flag most kinds of incomplete sentences discussed in this section.

22c Omissions from compound constructions should be consistent with grammar or idiom.

In both speech and writing, we commonly omit words not necessary for meaning, such as those in brackets in the following examples. Notice that all the sentences contain compound constructions (see p. 260):

By 2010 automobile-emission standards will be tougher, and by 2015 [automobile-emission standards will be] tougher still.

Some cars will run on electricity and some [will run] on methane or another alternative fuel.

Environmentalists have hopes for alternative fuels and [for] public transportation.

Such omissions are possible only when you omit words that are common to all the parts of a compound construction. When the parts differ in either grammar or idiom, all words must be included in all parts:

One new car gets eighty miles per gallon of gasoline; some old cars get as little as five miles per gallon. [One verb is singular, the other plural.]

Environmentalists were invited to submit proposals and were eager to do so. [Each *were* has a different grammatical function: the first is a helping verb; the second is a linking verb.]

They believe in and work for fuel conservation. [Idiom requires different prepositions with *believe* and *work*.]

In the sentence *My brother and friend moved to Dallas,* the omission of *my* before *friend* indicates that *brother* and *friend* are the same person. If two different persons are meant, the modifier or article must be repeated: *My brother and my friend moved to Dallas.*

(See pp. 407–10 for a list of English idioms with prepositions and pp. 525–27 for a discussion of grammatical parallelism.)

22d All comparisons should be complete and logical.

Comparisons make statements about the relation between two or more things, as in *Dogs are more intelligent than cats.*

1 State a comparison fully enough to ensure clarity.

Unclear Automakers worry about their industry more than environmentalists.

Clear Automakers worry about their industry more than environmentalists do.

Clear Automakers worry about their industry more than they worry about environmentalists.

2 The items being compared should in fact be comparable.

Illogical The cost of an electric car is greater than a gasoline-powered car. [Illogically compares a cost and a car.]

Revised The cost of an electric car is greater than the cost of [or that of] a gasoline-powered car.

3 Use *any* or *any other* appropriately in comparisons.

Comparing a person or thing with all others in the same group creates two units: (1) the individual person or thing and (2) all *other* persons or things in the group. The two units need to be distinguished:

Illogical Los Angeles is larger than any city in California. [Since Los Angeles is itself a city in California, the sentence seems to say that Los Angeles is larger than itself.]

Logical Los Angeles is larger than any other city in California.

Comparing a person or thing with the members of a *different* group assumes separate units to begin with. The two units do not need to be distinguished with *other:*

Illogical Los Angeles is larger than any other city in Canada. [The cities in Canada constitute a group to which Los Angeles does not belong.]

Logical Los Angeles is larger than any city in Canada.

sustained her. Roosevelt and Adams were stricken with polio when they were adults; Itzhak Perlman when a child. He was unable to play sports, instead he studied the violin, now many think he is greater than any violinist in the world.

Like Perlman, many physically challenged individuals turn to the arts. Perhaps the reason is because the joy of artistic achievement compensates for other pleasures they cannot experience. Stevie Wonder, José Feliciano, and Andrea Bocelli all express, through their music, their souls. Although unable to see physically, their music reveals truly how well they see. Hearing impairment struck Ludwig van Beethoven and Marlee Matlin it did not stop them from developing their talents. Already a successful composer, many of Beethoven's most powerful pieces were written after he became deaf. Similarly, Matlin has had excellent acting roles in movies, plays, and television programs, indeed she won an Oscar for *Children of a Lesser God*. She encourages others to develop their ability, and many hearing-impaired actors have been inspired by her.

PART 5

Effective Sentences

CHAPTER 23
Emphasizing Ideas

CHAPTER 24
Using Coordination and Subordination

CHAPTER 25
Using Parallelism

CHAPTER 26
Achieving Variety

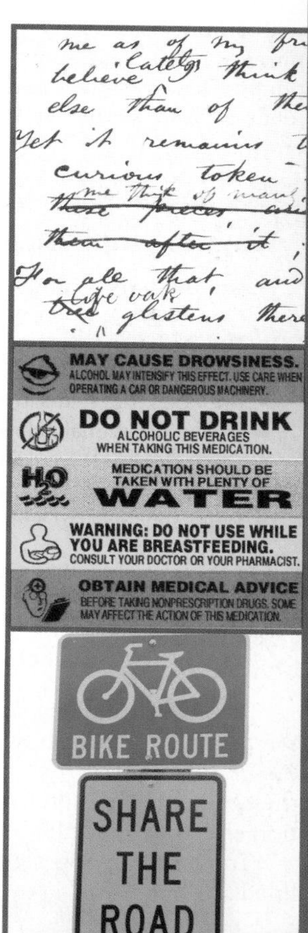

CHAPTER 23

Emphasizing Ideas

When you emphasize the main ideas in your sentences, you hold and channel readers' attention.

Note Many grammar and style checkers can spot some problems with emphasis, such as nouns made from verbs, passive voice, wordy phrases, and long sentences that may also be flabby and unemphatic. However, the checkers cannot help you identify the important ideas in your sentences or whether those ideas receive appropriate emphasis.

Ways to emphasize ideas

- Use the subjects and verbs of sentences to state key actors and actions (below).
- Use the beginnings and endings of sentences to pace and stress information (p. 388).
- Arrange series items in order of increasing importance (p. 389).
- Use an occasional balanced sentence (p. 391).
- Carefully repeat key words and phrases (p. 392).
- Set off important ideas with punctuation (p. 393).
- Write concisely (p. 394).

23a Using subjects and verbs effectively

The heart of every sentence is its subject, which usually names the actor, and its verb, which usually specifies the subject's action: *Children* [subject] *grow* [verb]. When these elements do not identify the sentence's key actor and action, readers must find that information elsewhere and the sentence may be wordy and unemphatic.

In the following sentences, the subjects and verbs are underlined.

http://www.ablongman.com/littlebrown

Visit the companion Web site for more help and additional exercises on emphasis.

Unemphatic The intention of the company was to expand its workforce. A proposal was also made to diversify the backgrounds and abilities of employees.

These sentences are unemphatic because their key ideas do not appear in their subjects and verbs. Revised, the sentences are not only clearer but more concise:

Revised The company intended to expand its workforce. It also proposed to diversify the backgrounds and abilities of employees.

The constructions below usually drain meaning from a sentence's subject and verb.

Nouns made from verbs

Nouns made from verbs can obscure the key actions of sentences and add words. These nouns include *intention* (from *intend*), *proposal* (from *propose*), *decision* (from *decide*), *expectation* (from *expect*), *persistence* (from *persist*), *argument* (from *argue*), and *inclusion* (from *include*).

Unemphatic After the company made a decision to hire more disabled workers, its next step was the construction of wheelchair ramps and other facilities.

Revised After the company decided to hire more disabled workers, it next constructed wheelchair ramps and other facilities.

Weak verbs

Weak verbs, such as *made* and *was* in the unemphatic sentence above, tend to stall sentences just where they should be moving and often bury key actions:

Unemphatic The company is now the leader among businesses in complying with the 1990 Americans with Disabilities Act. Its officers make speeches on the act to business groups.

Revised The company now leads other businesses in complying with the 1990 Americans with Disabilities Act. Its officers speak on the act to business groups.

Passive voice

Verbs in the passive voice state actions received by, not performed by, their subjects. Thus the passive de-emphasizes the true actor of the sentence, sometimes omitting it entirely. Generally, prefer the active voice, in which the subject performs the verb's action. (See also pp. 304–05.)

Unemphatic	The 1990 law is seen by most businesses as fair, but the costs of complying have sometimes been exaggerated.
Revised	Most businesses see the 1990 law as fair, but some opponents have exaggerated the costs of complying.

EXERCISE 23.1 Revising: Emphasis of subjects and verbs

Rewrite the following sentences so that their subjects and verbs identify their key actors and actions. (You can do this exercise online at *ablongman.com/littlebrown*.)

Example:

The issue of students making a competition over grades is a reason why their focus on learning may be lost.

Students who compete over grades may lose their focus on learning.

1. The work of many heroes was crucial in helping to emancipate the slaves.
2. The contribution of Harriet Tubman, an escaped slave herself, included the guidance of hundreds of other slaves to freedom on the Underground Railroad.
3. A return to slavery was risked by Tubman or possibly death.
4. During the Civil War she was also a carrier of information from the South to the North.
5. After the war needy former slaves were helped by Tubman's raising of money for refugees.

23b Using sentence beginnings and endings

Readers automatically seek a writer's principal meaning in the main clause of a sentence—essentially, in the subject that names the actor and the verb that usually specifies the action (see the preceding pages). Thus you can help readers understand your intended meaning by controlling the information in your subjects and the relation of the main clause to any modifiers attached to it.

Old and new information

Generally, readers expect the beginning of a sentence to contain information that they already know or that you have already introduced. They then look to the sentence ending for new information. In the unemphatic passage below, the second and third sentences both begin with new topics, while the old topics appear at the ends of the sentences. The pattern of the passage is A→B. C→B. D→A.

Unemphatic	Education (A) almost means controversy (B) these days, with rising costs and constant complaints about its inade-

quacies. But the value [C] of schooling should not be obscured by the controversy [B]. The single best means [D] of economic advancement, despite its shortcomings, remains education [A].

In the more emphatic revision, old information begins each sentence and new information ends the sentence. The passage follows the pattern A→B. B→C. A→D.

Revised — Education [A] almost means controversy [B] these days, with rising costs and constant complaints about its inadequacies. But the controversy [B] should not obscure the value [C] of schooling. Education [A] remains, despite its shortcomings, the single best means of economic advancement [D].

■ Cumulative and periodic sentences

You can call attention to information by placing it first or last in a sentence, reserving the middle for incidentals:

Unemphatic — Education remains the single best means of economic advancement, despite its shortcomings. [Emphasizes shortcomings.]

Revised — Despite its shortcomings, education remains the single best means of economic advancement. [Emphasizes advancement more than shortcomings.]

Revised — Education remains, despite its shortcomings, the single best means of economic advancement. [De-emphasizes shortcomings.]

Many sentences begin with the main clause and then add more modifiers to explain, amplify, or illustrate it. Such sentences are called **cumulative** (because they accumulate information as they proceed) or **loose** (because they are not tightly structured). They parallel the way we naturally think.

Cumulative — Education has no equal in opening minds, instilling values, and creating opportunities.

Cumulative — Most of the Great American Desert is made up of bare rock, rugged cliffs, mesas, canyons, mountains, separated from one another by broad flat basins covered with sunbaked mud and alkali, supporting a sparse and measured growth of sagebrush or creosote or saltbush, depending on location and elevation.

—Edward Abbey

The opposite kind of sentence, called **periodic**, saves the main clause until just before the end (the period) of the sentence. Everything before the main clause points toward it.

Periodic In opening minds, instilling values, and creating opportunities, education has no equal.

Periodic With people from all over the world—Korean grocers, Jamaican cricket players, Vietnamese fishers, Haitian cabdrivers, Chinese doctors—the American mosaic is continually changing.

The periodic sentence creates suspense for readers by reserving important information for the end. But readers should already have an idea of the sentence's subject—because it was discussed or introduced in the preceding sentence—so that they know what the opening modifiers describe. A variation of the periodic sentence names the subject at the beginning, follows it with a modifier, and then completes the main clause:

> Dick Hayne, who works in jeans and loafers and likes to let a question cure in the air for a while before answering it, bears all the markings of what his generation used to call a laid-back kind of guy.
>
> —George Rush

EXERCISE 23.2 Sentence combining: Beginnings and endings

Locate the main idea in each group of sentences below. Then combine each group into a single sentence that emphasizes that idea by placing it at the beginning or the end. For sentences 2–5, determine the position of the main idea by considering its relation to the previous sentences: if the main idea picks up a topic that's already been introduced, place it at the beginning; if it adds new information, place it at the end. (You can do this exercise online at *ablongman.com/littlebrown.*)

Example:

The storm blew roofs off buildings. It caused extensive damage. It knocked down many trees. It severed power lines.

Main idea at beginning: The storm caused extensive damage, blowing roofs off buildings, knocking down many trees, and severing power lines.

Main idea at end: Blowing roofs off buildings, knocking down many trees, and severing power lines, the storm caused extensive damage.

1. Pat Taylor strode into the room. The room was packed. He greeted students called "Taylor's Kids." He nodded to their parents and teachers.
2. This was a wealthy Louisiana oilman. He had promised his "Kids" free college educations. He was determined to make higher education available to all qualified but disadvantaged students.

3. The students welcomed Taylor. Their voices joined in singing. They sang "You Are the Wind Beneath My Wings." Their faces beamed with hope. Their eyes flashed with self-confidence.
4. The students had thought a college education was beyond their dreams. It seemed too costly. It seemed too demanding.
5. Taylor had to ease the costs and the demands of getting to college. He created a bold plan. The plan consisted of scholarships, tutoring, and counseling.

23c Arranging parallel elements effectively

Series

With parallelism, you use similar grammatical structures for ideas linked by *and, but,* and similar words: *Blustery winds and upturned leaves often signal thunderstorms.* (See Chapter 25.) In addition, you should arrange the parallel ideas in order of their importance:

Unemphatic — The storm ripped the roofs off several buildings, killed ten people, and knocked down many trees in town. [Buries the most serious damage—deaths—in the middle.]

Emphatic — The storm knocked down many trees in town, ripped the roofs off several buildings, and killed ten people. [Arranges items in order of increasing importance.]

You may want to use an unexpected item at the end of a series for humor or for another special effect:

> Early to bed and early to rise makes a man healthy, wealthy, and dead.
> —James Thurber

But be careful not to use such a series carelessly. The following series seems thoughtlessly random rather than intentionally humorous:

Unemphatic — The painting has subdued tone, intense feeling, and a length of about three feet.

Emphatic — The painting, about three feet long, has subdued tone and intense feeling.

Balanced sentences

A sentence is **balanced** when its clauses are parallel—that is, matched in grammatical structure (Chapter 25). When used carefully, balanced sentences can be especially effective in alerting readers to a strong comparison between two ideas. Read the following examples aloud to hear their rhythm.

> The fickleness of the women I love is equalled only by the infernal constancy of the women who love me. —George Bernard Shaw

In a pure balanced sentence two main clauses are exactly parallel: they match item for item.

> Scratch a lover, and find a foe. —Dorothy Parker

But the term is commonly applied to sentences that are only approximately parallel or that have only some parallel parts:

> If thought corrupts language, language can also corrupt thought. —George Orwell

> As the traveler who has once been from home is wiser than he who has never left his own doorstep, so a knowledge of one other culture should sharpen our ability to scrutinize more steadily, to appreciate more lovingly, our own. —Margaret Mead

EXERCISE 23.3 Revising: Series and balanced elements

Revise the following sentences so that elements in a series or balanced elements are arranged to give maximum emphasis to main ideas. (You can do this exercise online at *ablongman.com/littlebrown.*)

Example:

The campers were stranded without matches, without food or water, and without a tent.

The campers were stranded without matches, without a tent, and without food or water.

1. Remembering her days as a "conductor" on the Underground Railroad made Harriet Tubman proud, but she got angry when she remembered her years as a slave.
2. Tubman wanted freedom regardless of personal danger, whereas for her husband, John, personal safety was more important than freedom.
3. Tubman proved her fearlessness in many ways: she led hundreds of other slaves to freedom, she was a spy for the North during the Civil War, and she disobeyed John's order not to run away.
4. To conduct slaves north to freedom, Tubman risked being returned to slavery, being hanged for a huge reward, and being caught by Southern patrollers.
5. After the war Tubman worked tirelessly for civil rights and women's suffrage; raising money for homes for needy former slaves was something else she did.

23d Repeating ideas

Repetition of words and phrases often clutters and weakens sentences, as discussed on page 535. But carefully planned repetition can be an effective means of emphasis. Such repetition often combines with parallelism. It may occur in a series of sentences (see p. 85) or in a series of words, phrases, or clauses within a sentence, as in the following examples:

> There is something uneasy in the Los Angeles air this afternoon, some unnatural stillness, some tension. —Joan Didion

> We have the tools, all the tools—we are suffocating in tools—but we cannot find the actual wood to work or even the actual hand to work it. —Archibald MacLeish

23e Separating ideas

When you save important information for the end of a sentence, you can emphasize it even more by setting it off from the rest of the sentence, as in the second example below:

> Mothers and housewives are the only workers who do not have regular time off, so they are the great vacationless class.

> Mothers and housewives are the only workers who do not have regular time off. They are the great vacationless class. —Anne Morrow Lindbergh

You can vary the degree of emphasis by varying the extent to which you separate one idea from the others. A semicolon provides more separation than a comma, and a period provides still more separation. Compare the following sentences:

> Most of the reading which is praised for itself is neither literary nor intellectual, but narcotic.

> Most of the reading which is praised for itself is neither literary nor intellectual; it is narcotic.

> Most of the reading which is praised for itself is neither literary nor intellectual. It is narcotic. —Donald Hall

Sometimes a dash or a pair of dashes will isolate and thus emphasize a part of a statement (see also pp. 482–83):

> His schemes were always elaborate, ingenious, and exciting—and wholly impractical.

> Athletics—that is, winning athletics—has become a profitable university operation.

EXERCISE 23.4 Emphasizing with repetition or separation

Emphasize the main idea in each of the following sentences or groups of sentences by following the instructions in parentheses: either combine sentences so that parallelism and repetition stress the main idea, or place the main idea in a separate sentence. Each item has more than one possible answer. (You can do this exercise online at *ablongman.com/littlebrown*.)

Example:

I try to listen to other people's opinions. When my mind is closed, I find that other opinions open it. And they can change my mind when it is wrong. (*Parallelism and repetition.*)

I try to listen to other people's opinions, for they can open my mind when it is closed and they can change my mind when it is wrong.

1. One of the few worthwhile habits is daily reading. One can read for information. One can read for entertainment. Reading can give one a broader view of the world. (*Parallelism and repetition.*)
2. Reading introduces new words. One encounters unfamiliar styles of expression through reading. (*Parallelism and repetition.*)
3. Students who read a great deal will more likely write vividly, coherently, and grammatically, for they will have learned from other authors. (*Separation.*)
4. Reading gives knowledge. One gets knowledge about other cultures. One will know about history and current events. One gains information about human nature. (*Parallelism and repetition.*)
5. As a result of reading, writers have more resources and more flexibility, and thus reading creates better writers. (*Separation.*)

23f Being concise

Conciseness—brevity of expression—aids emphasis no matter what the sentence structure. Unnecessary words detract from necessary words. They clutter sentences and obscure ideas.

Weak — In my opinion the competition in the area of grades is distracting. It distracts many students from their goal, which is to obtain an education that is good. There seems to be a belief among a few students that grades are more important than what is measured by them.

Emphatic — The competition for grades distracts many students from their goal of obtaining a good education. A few students seem to believe that grades are more important than what they measure.

Techniques for tightening sentences are listed in the box opposite. Some of these techniques appear earlier in this chapter. All of them are covered in Chapter 39 on writing concisely.

EXERCISE 23.5 Revising: Conciseness

Revise the following sentences to make them more emphatic by eliminating wordiness. (You can do this exercise online at *ablongman.com/littlebrown.*)

Ways to achieve conciseness

- **Make the subject and verb of each sentence identify its actor and action** (pp. 386, 532):

  Avoid nouns made from verbs.
  Use strong verbs.
  Rewrite the passive voice as active.

- **Cut or shorten empty words or phrases** (p. 533):

  Shorten filler phrases, such as *by virtue of the fact that.*
  Cut all-purpose words, such as *area, factor.*
  Cut unneeded qualifiers, such as *in my opinion, for the most part.*

- **Cut unnecessary repetition** (p. 535).
- **Reduce clauses to phrases and phrases to single words** (p. 536).
- **Avoid constructions beginning with *there is* or *it is*** (p. 536).
- **Combine sentences** (p. 537).
- **Cut or rewrite jargon** (p. 537).

Example:

The problem in this particular situation is that we owe more money than we can afford under present circumstances.

The problem is that we owe more money than we can afford.

1. As far as I am concerned, customers who are dining out in restaurants in our country must be wary of suggestive selling, so to speak.
2. In suggestive selling, diners are asked by the waiter to buy additional menu selections in addition to what was ordered by them.
3. For each item on the menu, there is another food that will naturally complement it.
4. For example, customers will be presented with the question of whether they want to order french fries along with a sandwich or whether they want to order a salad along with a steak dinner.
5. Due to the fact that customers often give in to suggestive selling, they often find that their restaurant meals are more costly than they had intended to pay.

EXERCISE 23.6 Revising: Emphasizing ideas

Drawing on the advice in this chapter, rewrite the following paragraph to emphasize main ideas and to de-emphasize less important information. (You can do this exercise online at *ablongman.com/littlebrown.*)

In preparing pasta, there is a requirement for common sense and imagination rather than for complicated recipes. The key to success in this area is fresh ingredients for the sauce and perfectly cooked pasta.

The sauce may be made with just about any fresh fish, meat, cheese, herb, or vegetable. As for the pasta itself, it may be dried or fresh, although fresh pasta is usually more delicate and flavorful, as many experienced cooks find. Dried pasta is fine with zesty sauces; with light oil and cream sauces fresh pasta is the best choice. There is a difference in the cooking time for dried and fresh pasta, with dried pasta taking longer. It is important that the cook follow the package directions and that the pasta be tested before the cooking time is up. The pasta is done when the texture is neither tough nor mushy but *al dente,* or "firm to the bite," according to the Italians, who ought to know.

Note See page 422 for an exercise involving emphasis along with parallelism and other techniques for effective sentences.

CHAPTER 24

Using Coordination and Subordination

When clearly written, your sentences show the relations between ideas and stress the more important ideas over the lesser ones. Two techniques can help you achieve such clarity:

- ***Coordination* shows that two or more elements in a sentence are equally important in meaning.** You signal coordination with words such as *and, but,* and *or.*

  equally important

  Car insurance is costly, but health insurance seems a luxury.

- ***Subordination* shows that some elements in a sentence are less important than other elements for your meaning.** Usually, the main idea appears in the main clause, and supporting information appears in single words, phrases, and subordinate clauses.

http://www.ablongman.com/littlebrown

Visit the companion Web site for more help and additional exercises on coordination and subordination.

less important (subordinate clause) — more important (main clause)
Because accidents and thefts occur frequently, car insurance is costly.

Note Grammar and style checkers may spot some errors in punctuating coordinated and subordinated elements, and they can flag long sentences that may contain excessive coordination or subordination. But otherwise they provide little help because they cannot recognize the relations among ideas in sentences.

24a Coordinating to relate equal ideas

By linking equally important information, you can emphasize the relations for readers. Compare the passages below:

String of simple sentences

We should not rely so heavily on oil. Coal and uranium are also overused. We have a substantial energy resource in the moving waters of our rivers. Smaller streams add to the total volume of water. The resource renews itself. Oil and coal are irreplaceable. Uranium is also irreplaceable. The cost of water does not increase much over time. The costs of coal, oil, and uranium rise dramatically.

Ideas coordinated

We should not rely so heavily on oil, coal, and uranium, for we have a substantial energy resource in the moving waters of our rivers and streams. Oil, coal, and uranium are irreplaceable and thus subject to dramatic cost increases; water, however, is self-renewing and more stable in cost.

Ways to coordinate information in sentences

- **Link main clauses with a comma and a coordinating conjunction:** *and, but, or, nor, for, so, yet* (p. 434).

  Independence Hall in Philadelphia is now restored, but fifty years ago it was in bad shape.

- **Relate main clauses with a semicolon alone or a semicolon and a conjunctive adverb:** *however, indeed, thus,* etc. (pp. 455, 457).

  The building was standing; however, it suffered from neglect.

- **Within clauses, link words and phrases with a coordinating conjunction:** *and, but, or, nor* (p. 261).

  The people and officials of the nation were indifferent to Independence Hall or took it for granted.

- **Link main clauses, words, or phrases with a correlative conjunction:** *both . . . and, not only . . . but also,* etc. (p. 262).

  People not only took the building for granted but also neglected it.

The information in both passages is essentially the same, but the second is shorter and considerably easier to read and understand because it links coordinate ideas with the underlined words.

Punctuating coordinated words, phrases, and clauses

Most coordinated words, phrases, and subordinate clauses are not punctuated with commas (see p. 450). The exceptions are items in a series and coordinate adjectives:

> We rely heavily on coal, oil, and uranium. [A series; see p. 443.]
> Dirty, unhealthy air is one result. [Coordinate adjectives; see p. 444.]

In a sentence consisting of two main clauses, punctuation depends on whether a coordinating conjunction, a conjunctive adverb, or no connecting word links the clauses:

> Oil is irreplaceable, but water is self-renewing. [See p. 434.]
> Oil is irreplaceable; however, water is self-renewing. [See p. 457.]
> Oil is irreplaceable; water is self-renewing. [See p. 455.]

1 Using coordination effectively

A string of coordinated elements—especially main clauses—creates the same effect as a string of simple sentences: it obscures the relative importance of ideas and details.

> Excessive coordination — The weeks leading up to the resignation of President Richard Nixon were eventful, and the Supreme Court and the Congress closed in on him, and the Senate Judiciary Committee voted to begin impeachment proceedings, and finally the President resigned on August 9, 1974.

Such a passage needs editing to stress the important points (underlined below) and to de-emphasize the less important information:

> Revised — The weeks leading up to the resignation of President Richard Nixon were eventful, as the Supreme Court and the Congress closed in on him and the Senate Judiciary Committee voted to begin impeachment proceedings. Finally, the President resigned on August 9, 1974.

2 Coordinating logically

Coordinated sentence elements should be logically equal and related, and the relation between them should be the one expressed by the connecting word. If either principle is violated, the result is **faulty coordination.**

Faulty John Stuart Mill was a nineteenth-century utilitarian, and he believed that actions should be judged by their usefulness or by the happiness they cause. [The two clauses are not separate and equal: the second expands on the first by explaining what a utilitarian such as Mill believed.]

Revised John Stuart Mill, a nineteenth-century utilitarian, believed that actions should be judged by their usefulness or by the happiness they cause.

Faulty Mill is recognized as a utilitarian, and he did not found the utilitarian school of philosophy. [The two clauses seem to contrast, requiring *but* or *yet* between them.]

Revised Mill is recognized as a utilitarian, but he did not found the utilitarian school of philosophy.

EXERCISE 24.1 Sentence combining: Coordination

Combine sentences in the following passages to coordinate related ideas in the ways that seem most effective to you. You will have to supply coordinating conjunctions or conjunctive adverbs and the appropriate punctuation. (You can do this exercise online at *ablongman .com/littlebrown.*)

1. Many chronic misspellers do not have the time to master spelling rules. They may not have the motivation. They may rely on dictionaries to catch misspellings. Most dictionaries list words under their correct spellings. One kind of dictionary is designed for chronic misspellers. It lists each word under its common *misspellings*. It then provides the correct spelling. It also provides the definition.
2. Henry Hudson was an English explorer. He captained ships for the Dutch East India Company. On a voyage in 1610 he passed by Greenland. He sailed into a great bay in today's northern Canada. He thought he and his sailors could winter there. The cold was terrible. Food ran out. The sailors mutinied. The sailors cast Hudson adrift in a small boat. Eight others were also in the boat. Hudson and his companions perished.

EXERCISE 24.2 Revising: Excessive or faulty coordination

Revise the following sentences to eliminate excessive or faulty coordination. Relate ideas effectively by adding or subordinating information or by forming more than one sentence. Each item has more than one possible answer. (You can do this exercise online at *ablongman.com/ littlebrown*.)

Example:

My dog barks, and I have to keep her inside.

Because my dog's barking disturbs my neighbors, I have to keep her inside.

1. Often soldiers admired their commanding officers, and they gave them nicknames, and these names frequently contained the word "old," but not all of the commanders were old.
2. General Thomas "Stonewall" Jackson was also called "Old Jack," and he was not yet forty years old.
3. Another Southern general in the Civil War was called "Old Pete," and his full name was James Longstreet.
4. The Union general Henry W. Halleck had a reputation as a good military strategist, and he was an expert on the work of a French military authority, Henri Jomini, and Halleck was called "Old Brains."
5. General William Henry Harrison won the Battle of Tippecanoe, and he received the nickname "Old Tippecanoe," and he used the name in his presidential campaign slogan "Tippecanoe and Tyler, Too," and he won the election in 1840, but he died of pneumonia a month after taking office.

24b Subordinating to distinguish main ideas

With **subordination** you use words or word groups to indicate that some ideas in a sentence are less important than the idea in the main clause. In the following sentence, it is difficult to tell what is most important:

Excessive coordination	Computer prices have dropped, and production costs have dropped more slowly, and computer manufacturers have had to contend with shrinking profits.

The following revision places the point of the sentence (shrinking profits) in the main clause and reduces the rest of the information to a modifier (underlined):

Revised	<u>Because production costs have dropped more slowly than prices,</u> computer manufacturers have had to contend with shrinking profits.

No rules can specify what information in a sentence you should make primary and what you should subordinate; the decision will depend on your meaning. But, in general, you should consider using subordinate structures for details of time, cause, condition, concession, purpose, and identification (size, location, and the like). You can subordinate information with the structures listed in the box opposite.

In general, the shorter a subordinate structure is, the less emphasis it has. The following examples show how subordinate structures may convey various meanings with various weights. (Some appropriate subordinating words for each meaning appear in parentheses.)

Ways to subordinate information in sentences

- **Use a subordinate clause beginning with a subordinating conjunction:** *although, because, if, whereas,* etc. (p. 255).

  Although some citizens had tried to rescue Independence Hall, they had not gained substantial public support.

- **Use a subordinate clause beginning with a relative pronoun:** *who, whoever, which, that* (p. 256).

  The first strong step was taken by the federal government, which made the building a national monument.

- **Use a phrase** (p. 246).

  Like most national monuments, Independence Hall is protected by the National Park Service. [Prepositional phrase.]

  Protecting many popular tourist sites, the service is a highly visible government agency. [Verbal phrase.]

- **Use an appositive** (p. 259).

  The National Park Service, a branch of the Department of Interior, also runs Yosemite and other wilderness parks.

- **Use a modifying word.**

  At the red brick Independence Hall, park rangers give guided tours and protect the irreplaceable building from vandalism.

Space or time (*after, before, since, until, when, while; at, in, on, until*)

The mine explosion killed six workers. The owners adopted safety measures.

After the mine explosion killed six workers, the owners adopted safety measures. [Subordinate clause.]

After six deaths in a mine explosion, the owners adopted safety measures. [Prepositional phrases.]

Cause or effect (*as, because, since, so that; because of, due to*)

Jones had been without work for six months. He was having trouble paying his bills.

Because Jones had been without work for six months, he was having trouble paying his bills. [Subordinate clause.]

Having been jobless for six months, Jones could not pay his bills. [Verbal phrase.]

Condition (*if, provided, since, unless, whenever; with, without*)

Forecasters predict a mild winter. Farmers hope for an early spring.

Whenever forecasters predict a mild winter, farmers hope for an early spring. [Subordinate clause.]

Such sentences usually have more than one idea that deserves a main clause, so they are best revised by sorting their details into more than one sentence:

> Revised Struck by one of the worst hurricanes in three decades, the boats at the dock were ripped from their moorings. The owners were unprepared because the weather service had said that storms at this time of year blow out to sea.

A common form of excessive subordination occurs with a string of adjective clauses, each beginning with *which, who,* or *that:*

> Stringy The company opened a new plant outside Louisville, which is in Kentucky and which is on the Ohio River, which forms the border between Kentucky and Ohio.

To revise such sentences, recast some of the subordinate clauses as other kinds of modifying structures:

> Revised The company opened a new plant outside Louisville, Kentucky, a city across the Ohio River from Ohio.

EXERCISE 24.3 Sentence combining: Subordination

Combine each of the following pairs of sentences twice, each time using one of the subordinate structures in parentheses to make a single sentence. You will have to add, delete, change, and rearrange words. (You can do this exercise online at *ablongman.com/littlebrown.*)

Example:

During the late eighteenth century, workers carried beverages in brightly colored bottles. The bottles had cork stoppers. (*Clause beginning that. Phrase beginning with.*)

During the late eighteenth century, workers carried beverages in brightly colored bottles that had cork stoppers.

During the late eighteenth century, workers carried beverages in brightly colored bottles with cork stoppers.

1. The bombardier beetle sees an enemy. It shoots out a jet of chemicals to protect itself. (*Clause beginning when. Phrase beginning seeing.*)
2. The beetle's spray is very potent. It consists of hot and irritating chemicals. (*Phrase beginning consisting. Phrase beginning of.*)
3. The spray's two chemicals are stored separately in the beetle's body and mixed in the spraying gland. The chemicals resemble a nerve-gas weapon. (*Phrase beginning stored. Clause beginning which.*)
4. The tip of the beetle's abdomen sprays the chemicals. The tip revolves like a turret on a World War II bomber. (*Phrase beginning revolving. Phrase beginning spraying.*)
5. The beetle defeats most of its enemies. It is still eaten by spiders and birds. (*Clause beginning although. Phrase beginning except.*)

EXERCISE 24.4 Revising: Subordination

Rewrite the following paragraph in the way you think most effective to subordinate the less important ideas to the more important ones. Use subordinate clauses, phrases, and single words as you think appropriate. (You can do this exercise online at *ablongman.com/littlebrown*.)

Fewer students entering college are planning to major in the liberal arts. I mean by "liberal arts" such subjects as history, English, and the social sciences. Students think a liberal arts degree will not help them get jobs. They are wrong. They may not get practical, job-related experience from the liberal arts, but they will get a broad education, and it will never again be available to them. Many employers look for more than a technical, professional education. They think such an education can make an employee's views too narrow. The employers want open-minded employees. They want employees to think about problems from many angles. The liberal arts curriculum instills such flexibility. The flexibility is vital to the health of our society.

EXERCISE 24.5 Revising: Faulty or excessive subordination

Revise the following sentences to eliminate faulty or excessive subordination. Correct faulty subordination by reversing main and subordinate structures. Correct excessive subordination by coordinating equal ideas or by making separate sentences. (You can do this exercise online at *ablongman.com/littlebrown*.)

Example:

Terrified to return home, he had driven his mother's car into a cornfield.

Having driven his mother's car into a cornfield, he was terrified to return home.

1. Genaro González is blessed with great writing talent, which means that his novel *Rainbow's End* and his story collection *Only Sons* have been published.
2. He loves to write, although he has also earned a doctorate in psychology.
3. His first story, which reflects his consciousness of his Aztec heritage and place in the world, is titled "Un Hijo del Sol."
4. González, who writes equally well in English and Spanish, received a large fellowship that enabled him to take a leave of absence from the University of Texas–Pan American, where he teaches psychology, so that he could write without worrying about an income.
5. González wrote the first version of "Un Hijo del Sol" while he was a sophomore at Pan American, which is in the Rio Grande valley of southern Texas, which González calls "el Valle" in the story.

24c Choosing clear connectors

Most connecting words signal specific and unambiguous relations; for instance, *but* clearly indicates contrast, and *because* clearly indicates cause. A few connectors, however, require careful use, either because they are ambiguous in many contexts or because they are often misused.

1 Using *as* and *while* clearly

The subordinating conjunction *as* can indicate several relations, including comparison and time:

Comparison	The technicians work quickly, as they are required to do.
Time	One shift starts as the other stops.

Avoid using *as* to indicate cause. It is unclear.

Unclear	As the experiment was occurring, the laboratory was sealed. [Time or cause intended?]
Revised	When the experiment was occurring, the laboratory was sealed. [Time.]
Revised	Because the experiment was occurring, the laboratory was sealed. [Cause.]

The subordinating conjunction *while* can indicate either time or concession. Unless the context makes the meaning of *while* unmistakably clear, choose a more exact connector:

Unclear	While technicians work in the next room, they cannot hear the noise. [Time or concession intended?]
Revised	When technicians work in the next room, they cannot hear the noise. [Time.]
Revised	Although technicians work in the next room, they cannot hear the noise. [Concession.]

2 Using *as* and *like* correctly

The use of *as* as a substitute for *whether* or *that* is considered nonstandard (it does not conform to spoken and written standard English):

Nonstandard	They are not sure as the study succeeded.
Revised	They are not sure whether [or that] the study succeeded.

Although the preposition *like* is often used as a conjunction in informal speech and in advertising (*Dirt-Away works like a soap should*), writing generally requires the conjunction *as, as if, as though,* or *that:*

Speech	It seemed like it did succeed.
Writing	It seemed as if [or as though or that] it did succeed.

EXERCISE 24.6 Revising: Coordination and subordination

The following paragraph consists entirely of simple sentences. Use coordination and subordination to combine sentences in the ways you think most effective to emphasize main ideas. (You can do this exercise online at *ablongman.com/littlebrown.*)

Sir Walter Raleigh personified the Elizabethan Age. That was the period of Elizabeth I's rule of England. The period occurred in the last half of the sixteenth century. Raleigh was a courtier and poet. He was also an explorer and entrepreneur. Supposedly, he gained Queen Elizabeth's favor. He did this by throwing his cloak beneath her feet at the right moment. She was just about to step over a puddle. There is no evidence for this story. It does illustrate Raleigh's dramatic and dynamic personality. His energy drew others to him. He was one of Elizabeth's favorites. She supported him. She also dispensed favors to him. However, he lost his queen's goodwill. Without her permission he seduced one of her maids of honor. He eventually married the maid of honor. Elizabeth died. Then her successor imprisoned Raleigh in the Tower of London. Her successor was James I. The king falsely charged Raleigh with treason. Raleigh was released after thirteen years. He was arrested again two years later on the old treason charges. At the age of sixty-six he was beheaded.

Note See page 422 for an exercise involving coordination and subordination along with parallelism and other techniques for effective sentences.

CHAPTER 25

Using Parallelism

Parallelism is a similarity of grammatical form between two or more elements.

The air is dirtied by || factories belching smoke
and || cars spewing exhaust.

Parallel structure reinforces and highlights a close relation between compound sentence elements, whether words, phrases, or clauses.

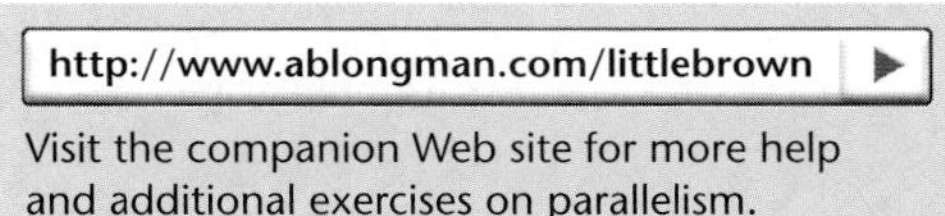
http://www.ablongman.com/littlebrown

Visit the companion Web site for more help and additional exercises on parallelism.

The principle underlying parallelism is that form should reflect meaning: since the parts of compound constructions have the same function and importance, they should have the same grammatical form.

Note A grammar and style checker cannot recognize problems with parallelism because it cannot recognize the relations among ideas.

25a Using parallelism for coordinate elements

Use parallelism in all the situations illustrated in the box on the facing page.

Note Parallel elements match each other in structure, but they do not always match word for word:

The pioneers passed || through the town
and || into the vast, unpopulated desert.

1 Using parallelism for elements linked by coordinating conjunctions

The coordinating conjunctions *and, but, or, nor,* and *yet* always signal a need for parallelism:

The industrial base was shifting and shrinking.

Politicians rarely acknowledged the problem or proposed alternatives.

Industrial workers were understandably disturbed that they were losing their jobs and that no one seemed to care.

If sentence elements linked by coordinating conjunctions are not parallel in structure, the resulting sentence will be awkward and distracting:

Nonparallel Three reasons why steel companies kept losing money were that their plants were inefficient, high labor costs, and foreign competition was increasing.

Revised Three reasons why steel companies kept losing money were inefficient plants, high labor costs, and increasing foreign competition.

All the words required by idiom or grammar must be stated in compound constructions (see also p. 260).

Nonparallel Given training, workers can acquire the skills and interest in other jobs. [*Skills* and *interest* require different prepositions, so both must be stated.]

Revised Given training, workers can acquire the skills for and interest in other jobs.

Patterns of parallelism

- **Use parallel structures for elements connected by coordinating conjunctions** (*and, but, or,* etc.) **or correlative conjunctions** (*both . . . and, neither . . . nor,* etc.):

  In 1988 a Greek cyclist, backed up by || engineers,
physiologists,
and || athletes,
broke the world's record for human flight
with neither || a boost
nor || a motor.

- **Use parallel structures for elements being compared or contrasted:**

  || Pedal power
rather than || horse power
propelled the plane.

- **Use parallel structures for lists, outlines, or headings:**

  The four-hour flight was successful because
|| (1) the cyclist was very fit,
|| (2) he flew a straight course over water,
and || (3) he kept the aircraft near the water's surface.

Often, the same word must be repeated to avoid confusion:

Confusing: Thoreau stood up for his principles by not paying his taxes and spending a night in jail. [Did he spend a night in jail or not?]

Revised: Thoreau stood up for his principles by not paying his taxes and by spending a night in jail.

Be sure that clauses beginning *who* or *which* are coordinated only with other *who* or *which* clauses, even when the pronoun is not repeated:

Nonparallel: Thoreau is the nineteenth-century essayist who retired to the woods and he wrote about nature.

Revised: Thoreau is the nineteenth-century essayist who retired to the woods and [who] wrote about nature.

2 Using parallelism for elements linked by correlative conjunctions

Correlative conjunctions are pairs of connectors. For example:

both . . . and	neither . . . nor	not only . . . but also
either . . . or	not . . . but	whether . . . or

1. The ancient Greeks celebrated four athletic contests: the Olympic Games at Olympia, the Isthmian Games were held near Corinth, at Delphi the Pythian Games, and the Nemean Games were sponsored by the people of Cleonae.
2. Each day of the games consisted of either athletic events or holding ceremonies and sacrifices to the gods.
3. In the years between the games, competitors were taught wrestling, javelin throwing, and how to box.
4. Competitors participated in running sprints, spectacular chariot and horse races, and running long distances while wearing full armor.
5. The purpose of such events was developing physical strength, demonstrating skill and endurance, and to sharpen the skills needed for war.
6. Events were held for both men and for boys.
7. At the Olympic Games the spectators cheered their favorites to victory, attended sacrifices to the gods, and they feasted on the meat not burned in offerings.
8. The athletes competed less to achieve great wealth than for gaining honor both for themselves and their cities.
9. Of course, exceptional athletes received financial support from patrons, poems and statues by admiring artists, and they even got lavish living quarters from their sponsoring cities.
10. With the medal counts and flag ceremonies, today's Olympians sometimes seem to be proving their countries' superiority more than to demonstrate individual talent.

25b Using parallelism to increase coherence

Effective parallelism will enable you to combine in a single, well-ordered sentence related ideas that you might have expressed in separate sentences. Compare the following three sentences with the original single sentence written by H. L. Mencken:

> Slang originates in the effort of ingenious individuals to make the language more pungent and picturesque. They increase the store of terse and striking words or widen the boundaries of metaphor. Thus a vocabulary for new shades and differences in meaning is provided by slang.

> Slang originates in the effort of ingenious individuals to make the language more pungent and picturesque—to increase the store of terse and striking words, to widen the boundaries of metaphor, and to provide a vocabulary for new shades and differences in meaning.
>
> —H. L. Mencken

Parallel structure works as well to emphasize the connections among related sentences in a paragraph:

> *Lewis Mumford stands* high in the company of this century's sages. A scholar of cosmic cultural reach and conspicuous public conscience,

a distinguished critic of life, arts, and letters, an unequaled observer of cities and civilizations, *he is* secure in the modern pantheon of great men. *He is* also an enigma and an anachronism. A legend of epic proportions in intellectual and academic circles, *he is* surprisingly little known to the public.

—Ada Louise Huxtable

Here, Huxtable tightly binds her sentences with two layers of parallelism: the subject-verb patterns of all four sentences (italic and underlined) and the appositives of the second and fourth sentences (underlined). (See pp. 85–86 for another illustration of parallelism among sentences.)

EXERCISE 25.3 Sentence combining: Parallelism

Combine each group of sentences below into one concise sentence in which parallel elements appear in parallel structures. You will have to add, delete, change, and rearrange words. Each item has more than one possible answer. (You can do this exercise online at *ablongman.com/littlebrown.*)

Example:

The new process works smoothly. It is efficient, too.
The new process works smoothly and efficiently.

1. People can develop post-traumatic stress disorder (PTSD). They develop it after experiencing a dangerous situation. They will also have felt fear for their survival.
2. The disorder can be triggered by a wide variety of events. Combat is a typical cause. Similarly, natural disasters can result in PTSD. Some people experience PTSD after a hostage situation.
3. PTSD can occur immediately after the stressful incident. Or it may not appear until many years later.
4. Sometimes people with PTSD will act irrationally. Moreover, they often become angry.
5. Other symptoms include dreaming that one is reliving the experience. They include hallucinating that one is back in the terrifying place. In another symptom one imagines that strangers are actually one's former torturers.

EXERCISE 25.4 Revising: Parallelism

Revise the following paragraph to create parallelism wherever it is required for grammar or for coherence. (You can do this exercise online at *ablongman.com/littlebrown.*)

The great white shark has an undeserved bad reputation. Many people consider the great white not only swift and powerful but also to be a cunning and cruel predator on humans. However, scientists claim that the great white attacks humans not by choice but as a result of chance. To a shark, our behavior in the water is similar to that of porpoises, seals, and sea lions—the shark's favorite foods. These sea mammals are both agile enough and can move fast enough to evade the shark. Thus the shark must attack with swiftness and noiselessly to surprise the prey and giving it little chance to escape. Humans become the shark's victims not because the shark has any preference or hatred of humans but because humans can neither outswim nor can they outmaneuver the shark. If the fish were truly a cruel human-eater, it would prolong the terror of its attacks, perhaps by circling or bumping into its intended victims before they were attacked.

Note See page 422 for an exercise involving parallelism along with other techniques for effective sentences.

CHAPTER 26

Achieving Variety

In a paragraph or an essay, each sentence stands in relation to those before and after it. To make sentences work together effectively, you need to vary their length, structure, and word order to reflect the importance and complexity of ideas. Variety sometimes takes care of itself, but you can practice established techniques for achieving varied sentences:

Ways to achieve variety among sentences

- Vary the length and structure of sentences so that important ideas stand out (opposite).
- Vary the beginnings of sentences with modifiers, transitional words and expressions, and occasional expletive constructions (p. 417).
- Occasionally, invert the normal order of subject, verb, and object or complement (p. 420).
- Occasionally, use a command, question, or exclamation (p. 420).

A series of similar sentences will prove monotonous and ineffective, as the following passage illustrates.

http://www.ablongman.com/littlebrown ▶

Visit the companion Web site for more help and an additional exercise on sentence variety.

> Ulysses S. Grant and Robert E. Lee met on April 9, 1865. Their meeting place was the parlor of a modest house at Appomattox Court House, Virginia. They met to work out the terms for the surrender of Lee's Army of Northern Virginia. One great chapter of American life ended with their meeting, and another began. Grant and Lee were bringing the Civil War to its virtual finish. Other armies still had to surrender, and the fugitive Confederate government would struggle desperately and vainly. It would try to find some way to go on living with its chief support gone. Grant and Lee had signed the papers, however, and it was all over in effect.

These eight sentences are all between twelve and sixteen words long (counting initials and dates), they are about equally detailed, and they all begin with the subject. We get a sense of names, dates, and events but no immediate sense of how they relate or what is most important.

Now compare the preceding passage with the actual passage written by Bruce Catton. Here the four sentences range from eleven to fifty-five words, and only one sentence begins with its subject:

> When Ulysses S. Grant and Robert E. Lee met in the parlor of a modest house at Appomattox Court House, Virginia, on April 9, 1865, to work out the terms for the surrender of Lee's Army of Northern Virginia, a great chapter in American life came to a close, and a great new chapter began.
>
> These men were bringing the Civil War to its virtual finish. To be sure, other armies had yet to surrender, and for a few days the fugitive Confederate government would struggle desperately and vainly, trying to find some way to go on living now that its chief support was gone. But in effect it was all over when Grant and Lee signed the papers.
>
> —Bruce Catton, "Grant and Lee"

Suspenseful periodic sentence (p. 390) focuses attention on meeting; details of place, time, and cause are in opening subordinate clause

Short sentence sums up

Cumulative sentence (p. 389) reflects lingering obstacles to peace

Short final sentence indicates futility of further struggle

The rest of this chapter suggests how you can vary your sentences for the kind of interest and clarity achieved by Catton.

Note Some grammar and style checkers will flag long sentences, and you can check for appropriate variety in a series of such sentences. But generally these programs cannot help you see where variety may be needed because they cannot recognize the relative importance and complexity of your ideas.

26a Varying sentence length and structure

The sentences of a stylistically effective essay will vary most obviously in their length and the arrangement of main clauses and modifiers. The variation in length and structure makes writing both readable and clear.

1 Varying length

In most contemporary writing, sentences vary from about ten to about forty words. When sentences are all at one extreme or the other, readers may have difficulty focusing on main ideas and seeing the relations among them:

- **Long sentences.** If most of your sentences contain thirty-five words or more, your main ideas may not stand out from the details that support them. Break some of the long sentences into shorter, simpler ones.
- **Short sentences.** If most of your sentences contain fewer than ten or fifteen words, all your ideas may seem equally important and the links between them may not be clear. Try combining them with coordination (p. 397) and subordination (p. 400) to show relationships and to stress main ideas over supporting information.

2 Rewriting strings of brief and simple sentences

A series of brief and simple sentences is both monotonous and hard to understand because it forces the reader to sort out relations among ideas. If you find that you depend on brief, simple sentences, work to increase variety by combining some of them into longer units that emphasize and link important ideas while de-emphasizing incidental information. (See Chapter 24.)

The following examples show how a string of simple sentences can be revised into an effective piece of writing:

Monotonous — The moon is now drifting away from the earth. It moves away at the rate of about one inch a year. This movement is lengthening our days. They increase a thousandth of a second every century. Forty-seven of our present days will someday make up a month. We might eventually lose the moon altogether. Such great planetary movement rightly concerns astronomers, but it need not worry us. It will take 50 million years.

Revised — The moon is now drifting away from the earth <u>about one inch a year</u>. <u>At a thousandth of a second every century</u>, this movement is lengthening our days. Forty-seven of our present days will someday make up a month, <u>if we don't eventually lose the moon altogether</u>. Such great planetary movement rightly concerns astronomers, but it need not worry us. It will take 50 million years.

In the revision, underlining indicates subordinate structures that were simple sentences in the original. With five sentences instead of the original eight, the revision emphasizes the moon's movement, our lengthening days, and the enormous span of time involved.

3 Rewriting strings of compound sentences

Compound sentences are usually just simple sentences linked with conjunctions. Thus a series of them will be as weak as a series of brief, simple sentences, especially if the clauses of the compound sentences are all about the same length:

Monotonous — Physical illness may involve more than the body, for the mind may also be affected. Disorientation is common among sick people, but they are often unaware of it. They may reason abnormally, or they may behave immaturely.

Revised — Physical illness may involve the mind as well as the body. Though often unaware of it, sick people are commonly disoriented. They may reason abnormally or behave immaturely.

The first passage creates a seesaw effect. The revision, with some main clauses shortened or changed into modifiers (underlined), is both clearer and more emphatic. (See p. 398 for more on avoiding excessive coordination.)

EXERCISE 26.1 Revising: Varied sentence structures

Rewrite the following paragraph to increase variety so that important ideas receive greater emphasis than supporting information does. You will have to change some main clauses into modifiers and then combine and reposition the modifiers and the remaining main clauses. (You can do this exercise online at *ablongman.com/littlebrown*.)

Charlotte Perkins Gilman was a leading intellectual in the women's movement during the first decades of the twentieth century. She wrote *Women and Economics.* This book challenged Victorian assumptions about differences between the sexes, and it explored the economic roots of women's oppression. Gilman wrote little about gaining the vote for women, but many feminists were then preoccupied with this issue, and historians have since focused their analyses on this issue. As a result, Gilman's contribution to today's women's movement has often been overlooked.

26b Varying sentence beginnings

An English sentence often begins with its subject, which generally captures old information from a preceding sentence (see pp. 388–89):

The defendant's lawyer was determined to break the prosecution's witness. She relentlessly cross-examined the stubborn witness for a week.

However, an unbroken sequence of sentences beginning with the subject quickly becomes monotonous, as shown by the unvaried passage on Grant and Lee that opened this chapter (p. 415). You can vary this subject-first pattern by adding modifiers or other elements before the subject.

Note The final arrangement of sentence elements should always depend on two concerns: the relation of a sentence to those preceding and following it and the emphasis required by your meaning.

Adverb modifiers

Adverbs modify verbs, adjectives, other adverbs, and whole clauses. They can often fall in a variety of spots in a sentence. Consider these different emphases:

For a week, the defendant's lawyer relentlessly cross-examined the stubborn witness.

Relentlessly, the defendant's lawyer cross-examined the stubborn witness for a week.

Relentlessly, for a week, the defendant's lawyer cross-examined the stubborn witness.

Notice that the last sentence, with both modifiers at the beginning, is periodic and thus highly emphatic (see p. 390).

CULTURE LANGUAGE In standard American English, placing certain adverb modifiers at the beginning of a sentence requires you to change the normal subject-verb order as well. The most common of these modifiers are negatives, including *seldom, rarely, in no case, not since,* and *not until.*

Faulty	Seldom [adverb] a witness [subject] has held [verb phrase] the stand for so long.
Revised	Seldom [adverb] has [helping verb] a witness [subject] held [main verb] the stand for so long.

Adjective modifiers

Adjectives, modifying nouns and pronouns, may include participles and participial phrases, as in *flying geese* or *money well spent* (see pp. 249–52). These modifiers may sometimes fall at the beginning of a sentence to postpone the subject:

The witness was exhausted from his testimony, and he did not cooperate.

Exhausted from his testimony, the witness did not cooperate.

Coordinating conjunctions and transitional expressions

When the relation between two successive sentences demands, you may begin the second with a coordinating conjunction such as *and* or *but* (p. 261) or with a transitional expression such as *first, for instance, however,* or *therefore* (pp. 88–89).

> The witness had expected to be dismissed after his first long day of cross-examination. But he was not.
>
> The price of clothes has risen astronomically in recent years. For example, a cheap cotton shirt that once cost $6 now costs $25.

Occasional expletive constructions

An expletive construction—*it* or *there* plus a form of *be*—may occasionally be useful to delay and thus emphasize the subject of the sentence:

> His judgment seems questionable, not his desire.
> It is his judgment that seems questionable, not his desire.

However, expletive constructions are more likely to flatten writing by adding extra words. You should use them rarely, only when you can justify doing so. (See also p. 536.)

EXERCISE 26.2 Revising: Varied sentence beginnings

Follow the instructions in parentheses to revise each group of sentences below: either create a single sentence that begins with an adverb or adjective modifier, or make one sentence begin with an appropriate connector. (You can do this exercise online at *ablongman.com/littlebrown.*)

> *Example:*
> The *Seabird* took first place. It moved quickly in the wind. (*One sentence with adjective modifier beginning moving.*)
> Moving quickly in the wind, the *Seabird* took first place.

1. Some people are champion procrastinators. They seldom complete their work on time. (*Two sentences with transitional expression.*)
2. Procrastinators may fear criticism. They may fear rejection. They will delay completing an assignment. (*One sentence with adverb modifier beginning if.*)
3. Procrastinators often desire to please a boss or a teacher. They fear failure so much that they cannot do the work. (*Two sentences with coordinating conjunction.*)
4. Procrastination seems a hopeless habit. It is conquerable. (*One sentence with adverb modifier beginning although.*)
5. Teachers or employers can be helpful. They can encourage procrastinators. They can give procrastinators the confidence to do good work on time. (*One sentence with adjective modifier beginning helpfully encouraging.*)

EXERCISE 26.3 Revising: Varied sentence beginnings

Revise the following paragraph to vary sentence beginnings by using each of the following at least once: an adverb modifier, an adjective modifier, a coordinating conjunction, and a transitional expression. (You can do this exercise online at *ablongman.com/littlebrown.*)

Scientists in Egypt dug up 40-million-year-old fossil bones. They had evidence of primitive whales. The whale ancestors are called mesonychids. They were small, furry land mammals with four legs. These limbs were complete with kneecaps, ankles, and little toes. Gigantic modern whales have tiny hind legs inside their bodies and flippers instead of front legs. Scientists are certain that these two very different creatures share the same family tree.

26c Inverting the normal word order

The word order of subject, verb, and object or complement is strongly fixed in English (see pp. 240–43). Thus an inverted sentence can be emphatic:

> Voters once had some faith in politicians, and they were fond of incumbents. But now all politicians, especially incumbents, voters seem to detest. [The object *all politicians* precedes the verb *detests.*]

Inverting the normal order of subject, verb, and complement can be useful in two successive sentences when the second expands on the first:

> Critics have not been kind to Presidents who have tried to apply the ways of private business to public affairs. Particularly explicit was the curt verdict of one critic of President Hoover: Mr. Hoover was never President of the United States; he was four years chairman of the board.
>
> —Adapted from Emmet John Hughes, "The Presidency vs. Jimmy Carter"

Inverted sentences used without need are artificial. Avoid descriptive sentences such as *Up came Ben and down went Katie's spirits.*

26d Mixing types of sentences

Most written sentences make statements. Occasionally, however, questions, commands, or exclamations may enhance variety.

Questions may set the direction of a paragraph, as in *What does a detective do?* or *How is the percentage of unemployed workers calculated?* More often, though, the questions used in exposition or argument do not require answers but simply emphasize ideas that readers can be expected to agree with. Such **rhetorical questions** are illustrated in the following passage:

> Another word that has ceased to have meaning due to overuse is *attractive. Attractive* has become verbal chaff. Who, by some stretch of language and imagination, cannot be described as attractive? And just what is it that attractive individuals are attracting? —Diane White

Commands occur frequently in an explanation of a process, particularly in directions, as this passage on freewriting illustrates:

> The idea is simply to write for ten minutes (later on, perhaps fifteen or twenty). Don't stop for anything. Go quickly, without rushing. Never stop to look back, to cross something out, to wonder how to spell something, to wonder what word or thought to use, or to think about what you are doing. —Peter Elbow

Notice that the authors of these examples use questions and commands to achieve some special purpose. Variety occurs because a particular sentence type is effective for the context, not because the writer set out to achieve variety for its own sake.

EXERCISE 26.4 Writing varied sentences

Imagine that you are writing an essay on a transportation problem at your school. Practice varying sentences by composing a sentence or passage to serve each purpose listed below. (You can do this exercise online at *ablongman.com/littlebrown.*)

1. Write a question that could open the essay.
2. Write a command that could open the essay.
3. Write an exclamation that could open the essay.
4. For the body of the essay, write an appropriately varied paragraph of at least five sentences, including at least one short and one long sentence beginning with the subject; at least one sentence beginning with an adverb modifier; at least one sentence beginning with a coordinating conjunction or transitional expression; and one rhetorical question or command.

EXERCISE 26.5 Analyzing variety

Examine the following paragraph for sentence variety. By analyzing your own response to each sentence, try to explain why the author wrote each short or long sentence, each cumulative or periodic sentence, each sentence beginning with its subject or beginning some other way, and each question. (You can do this exercise online at *ablongman.com/littlebrown.*)

That night in my rented room, while letting the hot water run over my can of pork and beans in the sink, I opened [H. L. Mencken's] *A Book of Prefaces* and began to read. I was jarred and shocked by the style, the clear, clean, sweeping sentences. Why did he write like that?

And how did one write like that? I pictured the man as a raging demon, slashing with his pen, consumed with hate, denouncing everything American, extolling everything European or German, laughing at the weaknesses of people, mocking God, authority. What was this? I stood up, trying to realize what reality lay behind the meaning of the words. Yes, this man was fighting, fighting with words. He was using words as a weapon, using them as one would use a club. Could words be weapons? Well, yes, for here they were. Then, maybe, perhaps, I could use them as a weapon? No. It frightened me. I read on and what amazed me was not what he said, but how on earth anybody had the courage to say it. —Richard Wright, *Black Boy*

EXERCISE 26.6 Revising: Variety

The following paragraph consists entirely of simple sentences that begin with their subjects. As appropriate, use the techniques discussed in this chapter to vary sentences. Your goal is to make the paragraph more readable and make its important ideas stand out clearly. You will have to delete, add, change, and rearrange words. (You can do this exercise online at *ablongman.com/littlebrown.*)

The Italian volcano Vesuvius had been dormant for many years. It then exploded on August 24 in the year AD 79. The ash, pumice, and mud from the volcano buried two busy towns. Herculaneum is one. The more famous is Pompeii. Both towns lay undiscovered for many centuries. Herculaneum and Pompeii were discovered in 1709 and 1748, respectively. The excavation of Pompeii was the more systematic. It was the occasion for initiating modern methods of conservation and restoration. Herculaneum was simply looted of its most valuable finds. It was then left to disintegrate. Pompeii appears much as it did before the eruption. A luxurious house opens onto a lush central garden. An election poster decorates a wall. A dining table is set for breakfast.

EXERCISE ON CHAPTERS 23–26 Revising: Effective sentences

Revise the paragraphs below to emphasize main ideas, de-emphasize supporting information, and achieve a pleasing, clear variety in sentences. As appropriate, employ the techniques discussed in Chapters 23–26, such as using subjects and verbs effectively, subordinating and coordinating, creating parallelism, and varying sentence beginnings. Edit the finished product for punctuation. (You can do this exercise online at *ablongman.com/littlebrown.*)

Modern Americans owe many debts to Native Americans. Several pleasures are among the debts. Native Americans originated two fine junk foods. They discovered popcorn. Potato chips were also one of their contributions.

The introduction of popcorn to the European settlers came from Native Americans. Massasoit provided popcorn at the first Thanksgiving feast. The Aztecs offered popcorn to the Spanish explorer Hernando Cortés. The Aztecs wore popcorn necklaces. So did the natives of the West Indies. There were three ways that the Native Americans popped the corn. First, they roasted an ear over fire. The ear was skewered on a stick. They ate only some of the popcorn. They ate the corn that fell outside the flames. Second, they scraped the corn off the cob. The kernels would be thrown into the fire. Of course, the fire had to be low. Then the popped kernels that did not fall into the fire were eaten. The third method was the most sophisticated. It involved a shallow pottery vessel. It contained sand. The vessel was heated. The sand soon got hot. Corn kernels were stirred in. They popped to the surface of the sand and were eaten.

A Native American chef was responsible for devising the crunchy potato chip. His name was George Crum. In 1853 Crum was cooking at Moon Lake Lodge. The lodge was in Saratoga Springs, New York. Complaints were sent in by a customer. The man thought Crum's french-fried potatoes were too thick. Crum tried a thinner batch. These were also unsuitable. Crum became frustrated. He deliberately made the potatoes thin and crisp. They could not be cut with a knife and fork. Crum's joke backfired. The customer raved about the potato chips. The chips were named Saratoga Chips. Soon they appeared on the lodge's menu. They also appeared throughout New England. Crum later opened his own restaurant. Of course, he offered potato chips.

Now all Americans munch popcorn in movies. They crunch potato chips at parties. They gorge on both when alone and bored. They can be grateful to Native Americans for these guilty pleasures.

CHAPTER 27

End Punctuation

End punctuation marks—the period, the question mark, and the exclamation point—signal the ends of sentences.

Note A grammar checker may flag missing question marks after direct questions or incorrect combinations of marks (such as a question mark and a period at the end of a sentence), but it cannot do much else.

27a Use periods after most sentences and with some abbreviations.

1 Use a period to end a statement, mild command, or indirect question.

Statements

These are exciting and trying times.
The airline went bankrupt.

Mild commands

Please do not smoke.
Think of the possibilities.

If you are unsure whether to use an exclamation point or a period after a command, use a period. The exclamation point should be used only rarely (see p. 431).

An **indirect question** reports what someone has asked but not in the form or exact words of the original:

Indirect questions

Students sometimes wonder whether their teachers read the papers they write.

Abused children eventually stop asking why they are being punished.

http://www.ablongman.com/littlebrown

Visit the companion Web site for more help and an additional exercise on end punctuation.

CULTURE LANGUAGE In standard American English, an indirect question uses the wording and subject-verb order of a statement: *The reporter asked why the negotiations failed*, not *why did the negotiations fail.*

2 Use periods with some abbreviations.

Use periods with abbreviations that consist of or end in small letters. Otherwise, omit periods from abbreviations.

Dr.	Mr., Mrs.	e.g.	Feb.	ft.
St.	Ms.	i.e.	p.	a.m., p.m.
PhD	BC, BCE	USA	IBM	AM, PM
BA	AD, CE	US	USMC	AIDS

Note When a sentence ends in an abbreviation with a period, don't add a second period: *My first class is at 8 a.m.*

See also pages 502–05 on uses of abbreviations in writing.

EXERCISE 27.1 Revising: Periods

Revise the following sentences so that periods are used correctly. (You can do this exercise online at *ablongman.com/littlebrown*.)

Example:

Several times I wrote to ask when my subscription ended?
Several times I wrote to ask when my subscription ended.

1. The teacher asked when Plato wrote *The Republic*?
2. Give the date within one century
3. The exact date is not known, but it is estimated at 370 BCE
4. Dr Arn will lecture on Plato at 7:30 p.m..
5. The area of the lecture hall is only 1600 sq ft

27b Use question marks after direct questions and sometimes to indicate doubt.

1 Use a question mark with a direct question.

What is the difference between these two people?
Will economists ever really understand the economy?

After an indirect question, use a period: *The senator asked why the bill had passed.* (See opposite.)

Questions in a series are each followed by a question mark:

The officer asked how many times the suspect had been arrested. Three times? Four times? More than that?

The use of capital letters for questions in a series is optional (see p. 493).

Note Question marks are never combined with other question marks, exclamation points, periods, or commas:

Faulty "What is the point?," readers ask.
Revised "What is the point**?**" readers ask.

2 Use a question mark within parentheses to indicate doubt about a number or date.

The Greek philosopher Socrates was born in 470 (**?**) BC and died in 399 BC from drinking poison after having been condemned to death.

Note Don't use a question mark within parentheses to express sarcasm or irony. Express these attitudes through sentence structure and word choice. (See Chapters 23 and 38.)

Faulty Stern's friendliness (?) bothered Crane.
Revised Stern's insincerity bothered Crane.

EXERCISE 27.2 Revising: Question marks

Revise the following sentences so that question marks (along with other punctuation marks) are used correctly. (You can do this exercise online at *ablongman.com/littlebrown*.)

Example:
"When will it end?," cried the man dressed in rags.
"When will it end**?**" cried the man dressed in rags.

1. In Homer's *Odyssey*, Odysseus took seven years to travel from Troy to Ithaca. Or was it eight years. Or more?
2. Odysseus must have wondered whether he would ever make it home?
3. "What man are you and whence?," asks Odysseus's wife, Penelope.
4. Why does Penelope ask, "Where is your city? Your family?"?
5. Penelope does not recognize Odysseus and asks who this stranger is?

27c Use an exclamation point after an emphatic statement, interjection, or command.

No**!** We must not lose this election**!**
Come here immediately**!**

Follow mild interjections and commands with commas or periods, as appropriate:

No**,** the response was not terrific**.**
To prolong your car's life, change its oil regularly**.**

Use exclamation points sparingly, not to express sarcasm, irony, or amazement. Rely on sentence structure and word choice to express these attitudes. (See Chapters 23 and 38.)

Faulty After traveling 4.4 billion miles through space, *Voyager 2* was off-target by 21 miles (!).

Revised After traveling 4.4 billion miles through space, *Voyager 2* was off-target by a mere 21 miles.

Relying on the exclamation point for emphasis is like crying wolf: the mark loses its power to impress the reader. Frequent exclamation points can also make writing sound overemotional:

Overused exclamation points

Our city government is a mess! After just six months in office, the mayor has had to fire four city officials! In the same period the city councilors have done nothing but argue! And city services decline with each passing day!

Note Exclamation points are never combined with other exclamation points, question marks, periods, or commas:

Faulty "This will not be endured!," he roared.

Revised "This will not be endured**!**" he roared.

EXERCISE 27.3 Revising: Exclamation points

Revise the following sentences so that exclamation points (along with other punctuation marks) are used correctly. If a sentence is punctuated correctly as given, mark the number preceding it. (You can do this exercise online at *ablongman.com/littlebrown.*)

Example:

"Well, now!," he said loudly.
"Well, now**!**" he said loudly.

1. As the firefighters moved their equipment into place, the police shouted, "Move back!".
2. A child's cries could be heard from above: "Help me. Help."
3. When the child was rescued, the crowd called "Hooray."
4. The rescue was the most exciting event of the day!
5. Let me tell you about it.

EXERCISE 27.4 Revising: End punctuation

Insert appropriate punctuation (periods, question marks, or exclamation points) where needed in the following paragraph. (You can do this exercise online at *ablongman.com/littlebrown.*)

When visitors first arrive in Hawaii, they often encounter an unexpected language barrier Standard English is the language of business and government, but many of the people speak Pidgin English Instead of an excited "Aloha" the visitors may be greeted with an excited

Pidgin "Howzit" or asked if they know "how fo' find one good hotel" Many Hawaiians question whether Pidgin will hold children back because it prevents communication with the *haoles,* or Caucasians, who run businesses Yet many others feel that Pidgin is a last defense of ethnic diversity on the islands To those who want to make standard English the official language of the state, these Hawaiians may respond, "Just 'cause I speak Pidgin no mean I dumb" They may ask, "Why you no listen" or, in standard English, "Why don't you listen"

Note See page 490 for a punctuation exercise combining periods with other marks of punctuation.

CHAPTER 28

The Comma

Commas usually function within sentences to separate elements (see the box on the next page). Omitting needed commas or inserting needless ones can confuse the reader:

Comma needed	Though very tall Abraham Lincoln was not an overbearing man.
Revised	Though very tall, Abraham Lincoln was not an overbearing man.
Unneeded commas	The hectic pace of Beirut, broke suddenly into frightening chaos when the city became, the focus of civil war.
Revised	The hectic pace of Beirut broke suddenly into frightening chaos when the city became the focus of civil war.

Note Grammar and style checkers will ignore many comma errors. For example, a checker failed to catch the missing commas in *The boat ran aground and we were stranded* and in *We cooked lasagna spinach and apple pie.* At the same time the checker overlooked the misused commas in *The trip was short but, the weather was perfect* and *The travelers were tempted by, the many shops, and varied restaurants.*

http://www.ablongman.com/littlebrown

Visit the companion Web site for more help and additional exercises on the comma.

Principal uses of the comma

- **Separate main clauses linked by a coordinating conjunction** (next page):

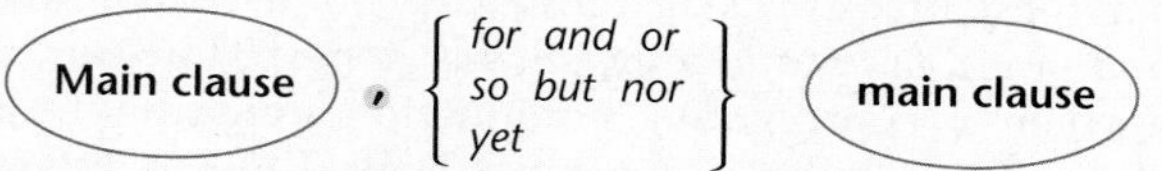

The building is finished, but it has no tenants.

- **Set off most introductory elements** (p. 435):

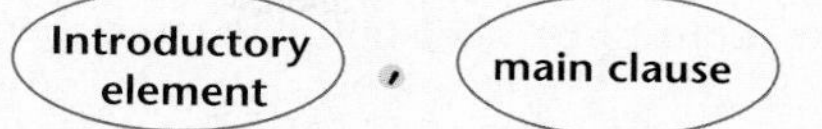

Unfortunately, the only tenant pulled out.

- **Set off nonessential elements** (p. 437):

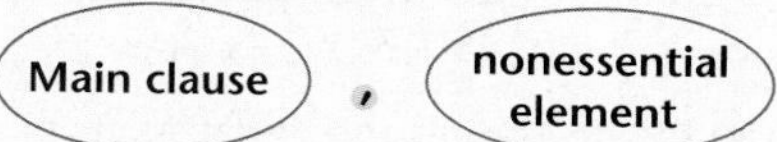

The empty building symbolizes a weak local economy, which affects everyone.

The primary cause, the decline of local industry, is not news.

- **Separate items in a series** (p. 443):

. . . item 1 , item 2 , { and / or } item 3 . . .

The city needs healthier businesses, new schools, and improved housing.

- **Separate coordinate adjectives** (p. 444):

A tall, sleek skyscraper is not needed.

Other uses of the comma:

Set off absolute phrases (p. 442).
Set off phrases expressing contrast (p. 443).
Separate parts of dates, addresses, long numbers (p. 445).
Separate quotations and signal phrases (p. 446).
Prevent misreading (p. 449).

See also page 450 for when *not* to use the comma.

28a Use a comma before *and, but,* or another coordinating conjunction linking main clauses.

The coordinating conjunctions are *and, but, or, nor, for, so,* and *yet*. When these link words or phrases, do not use a comma: *Dugain plays and sings Irish and English folk songs*. However, *do* use a comma when a coordinating conjunction joins main clauses. A **main clause** has a subject and a predicate (but no subordinating word at the beginning) and makes a complete statement (see p. 254).

> Caffeine can keep coffee drinkers alert, and it may elevate their mood.
>
> Caffeine was once thought to be safe, but now researchers warn of harmful effects.
>
> Coffee drinkers may suffer sleeplessness, for the drug acts as a stimulant to the nervous system.

Note Do not add a comma *after* a coordinating conjunction between main clauses (see also pp. 450–51):

> Not Caffeine increases the heart rate, and, it constricts blood vessels.
>
> But Caffeine increases the heart rate, and it constricts blood vessels.

Exceptions When the main clauses in a sentence are very long or grammatically complicated, or when they contain internal punctuation, a semicolon before the coordinating conjunction will clarify the division between clauses (see p. 459):

> Caffeine may increase alertness, elevate mood, and provide energy; but it may also cause irritability, anxiety, stomach pains, and other ills.

When main clauses are very short and closely related in meaning, you may omit the comma between them as long as the resulting sentence is clear:

> Caffeine helps but it also hurts.

If you are in doubt about whether to use a comma in such a sentence, use it. It will always be correct.

EXERCISE 28.1 Punctuating linked main clauses

Insert a comma before each coordinating conjunction that links main clauses in the following sentences. (You can do this exercise online at *ablongman.com/littlebrown*.)

Example:

I would have attended the concert and the reception but I had to baby-sit for my niece.

I would have attended the concert and the reception, but I had to baby-sit for my niece.

1. Parents once automatically gave their children the father's surname but some no longer do.
2. Instead, they bestow the mother's name for they believe that the mother's importance should be recognized.
3. The child's surname may be just the mother's or it may link the mother's and the father's with a hyphen.
4. Sometimes the first and third children will have the mother's surname and the second child will have the father's.
5. Occasionally the mother and father combine parts of their names and a new hybrid surname is born.

EXERCISE 28.2 Sentence combining: Linked main clauses

Combine each group of sentences below into one sentence that contains only two main clauses connected by the coordinating conjunction in parentheses. Separate the main clauses with a comma. You will have to add, delete, and rearrange words. (You can do this exercise online at *ablongman.com/littlebrown*.)

Example:

The circus had come to town. The children wanted to see it. Their parents wanted to see it. (*and*)

The circus had come to town, and the children and their parents wanted to see it.

1. Parents were once legally required to bestow the father's surname on their children. These laws have been contested in court. They have been found invalid. (*but*)
2. Parents may now give their children any surname they choose. The arguments for bestowing the mother's surname are often strong. They are often convincing. (*and*)
3. Critics sometimes question the effects of unusual surnames on children. They wonder how confusing the new surnames will be. They wonder how fleeting the surnames will be. (*or*)
4. Children with surnames different from their parents' may suffer embarrassment. They may suffer identity problems. Giving children their father's surname is still very much the norm. (*for*)
5. Hyphenated names are awkward. They are also difficult to pass on. Some observers think they will die out in the next generation. Or they may die out before. (*so*)

28b Use a comma to set off most introductory elements.

An introductory element modifies a word or words in the main clause that follows. These elements are usually set off from the rest of the sentence with a comma:

Subordinate clause (p. 254)

Even when identical twins are raised apart, they grow up very like each other.

Because they are similar, such twins interest scientists.

essential, such an element is *not* set off with commas. The element *is* essential, but punctuation is *not.*

Meaning and context

The same element in the same sentence may be essential or nonessential depending on your intended meaning and the context in which the sentence appears. For example, look at the second sentence in each of the following passages:

Essential

Not all the bands were equally well received, however. The band playing old music held the audience's attention. The other groups created much less excitement. [*Playing old music* identifies a particular band.]

Nonessential

A new band called Fats made its debut on Saturday night. The band**,** playing old music**,** held the audience's attention. If this performance is typical, the group has a bright future. [*Playing old music* adds information about a band already named.]

Punctuation of interrupting nonessential elements

When a nonessential element falls in the middle of a sentence, be sure to set it off with a pair of commas, one *before* and one *after* the element. Dashes or parentheses may also set off nonessential elements (see pp. 482 and 484).

A test for essential and nonessential elements

1. **Identify the element.**

   Hai Nguyen who emigrated from Vietnam lives in Denver.
   Those who emigrated with him live elsewhere.

2. **Remove the element. Does the fundamental meaning of the sentence change?**

   Hai Nguyen lives in Denver. ***No.***
   Those live elsewhere. ***Yes.*** [Who are *Those?*]

3. **If *no,* the element is *nonessential* and should be set off with punctuation.**

   Hai Nguyen**,** who emigrated from Vietnam**,** lives in Denver.

   If *yes,* the element is *essential* and should *not* be set off with punctuation.

   Those who emigrated with him live elsewhere.

1 Use a comma or commas to set off nonessential clauses and phrases.

Clauses and phrases serving as adjectives and adverbs may be either nonessential or essential. In the following examples the underlined clauses and phrases are nonessential: they could be omitted without changing the meaning of the words they modify.

Nonessential

Elizabeth Blackwell was the first woman to graduate from an American medical school, in 1849.

She was a medical pioneer, helping to found the first medical college for women.

She taught at the school, which was affiliated with the New York Infirmary.

Blackwell, who published books and papers on medicine, practiced pediatrics and gynecology.

She moved to England in 1869, when she was forty-eight.

Note Most adverb clauses are essential because they describe conditions necessary to the main clause. They are set off by a comma only when they introduce sentences (see p. 435) and when they are truly nonessential, adding incidental information (as in the last example above) or expressing a contrast beginning *although, even though, though, whereas,* and the like.

In the following sentences, the underlined elements limit the meaning of the words they modify. Removing the elements would leave the meaning too general.

Essential

The history of aspirin began with the ancient Greeks.

Physicians who sought to relieve their patients' pains recommended chewing willow bark.

Willow bark contains a chemical that is similar to aspirin.

Note Whereas both nonessential and essential clauses may begin with *which,* only essential clauses begin with *that.* Some writers prefer *that* exclusively for essential clauses and *which* exclusively for nonessential clauses. See the Glossary of Usage, page 851, for advice on the use of *that* and *which.*

2 Use a comma or commas to set off nonessential appositives.

An **appositive** is a noun or noun substitute that renames another noun just before it. (See p. 259.) Many appositives are nonessential; thus they are set off, usually with commas.

Nonessential

Toni Morrison's fifth novel, Beloved, won the Pulitzer Prize in 1988.
Morrison, a native of Ohio, won the Nobel Prize in 1993.

Take care *not* to set off essential appositives; like other essential elements, they limit or define the word to which they refer.

Essential

Morrison's novel *The Bluest Eye* is about an African American girl who longs for blue eyes.

The critic Michiko Kakutani says that Morrison's work "stands radiantly on its own as an American epic."

3 Use a comma or commas to set off transitional or parenthetical expressions.

Transitional expressions

Transitional expressions form links between ideas. They include conjunctive adverbs such as *however* and *moreover* as well as other words or phrases such as *for example* and *of course*. (See pp. 88–89 for a list of transitional words and phrases.) Transitional expressions are nonessential, so set them off with a comma or commas:

American workers, for example, receive fewer holidays than European workers do.

When a transitional expression links main clauses, precede it with a semicolon and follow it with a comma. (See p. 457.)

European workers often have long paid vacations; indeed, they may receive a full month.

Note The conjunctions *and, but,* and *yet* are sometimes used as transitional expressions but are not followed by commas (see p. 450). Nor are commas required after some transitional expressions that we read without pauses, such as *also, hence, next, now,* and *thus.* A few transitional expressions, notably *therefore* and *instead,* do not need commas when they fall inside or at the ends of clauses.

American workers thus put in more work days. But the days themselves may be shorter.

Parenthetical expressions

Parenthetical expressions provide comments, explanations, digressions, or other supplementary information not essential to meaning—for example, *fortunately, unfortunately, all things considered, to be frank, in other words.* Set parenthetical expressions off with commas:

Few people would know, or even guess, the most celebrated holiday on earth.

That holiday is, surprisingly, New Year's Day.

(Dashes and parentheses may also set off parenthetical expressions. See pp. 482 and 484, respectively.)

4 Use a comma or commas to set off *yes* and *no,* tag questions, words of direct address, and mild interjections.

Yes and *no*

Yes, the editorial did have a point.
No, that can never be.

Tag questions

Beatriz should be allowed to vote, should she not?
They don't stop to consider others, do they?

Direct address

Cody, please bring me the newspaper.
With all due respect, sir, I will not do that.

Mild interjections

Well, you will never know who did it.
Oh, they forgot all about the science fair.

(You may want to use an exclamation point to set off a forceful interjection. See p. 430.)

EXERCISE 28.5 Punctuating essential and nonessential elements

Insert commas in the following sentences to set off nonessential elements, and delete any commas that incorrectly set off essential elements. If a sentence is correct as given, mark the number preceding it. (You can do this exercise online at *ablongman.com/littlebrown.*)

Example:

Our language has adopted the words, *garage* and *fanfare,* from the French.

Our language has adopted the words *garage* and *fanfare* from the French.

1. Italians insist that Marco Polo the thirteenth-century explorer did not import pasta from China.
2. Pasta which consists of flour and water and often egg existed in Italy long before Marco Polo left for his travels.
3. A historian who studied pasta says that it originated in the Middle East in the fifth century.
4. Most Italians dispute this account although their evidence is shaky.

5. Wherever pasta originated, the Italians are now the undisputed masters, in making and cooking it.
6. Marcella Hazan, who has written several books on Italian cooking, insists that homemade and hand-rolled pasta is the best.
7. Most cooks must buy dried pasta lacking the time to make their own.
8. The finest pasta is made from semolina, a flour from hard durum wheat.
9. Pasta manufacturers choose hard durum wheat, because it makes firmer cooked pasta than common wheat does.
10. Pasta, made from common wheat, tends to get soggy in boiling water.

EXERCISE 28.6 Sentence combining: Essential and nonessential elements

Combine each pair of sentences below into one sentence that uses the element described in parentheses. Insert commas as appropriate. You will have to add, delete, change, and rearrange words. Some items have more than one possible answer. (You can do this exercise online at *ablongman.com/littlebrown*.)

Example:

Mr. Ward's oldest sister helped keep him alive. She was a nurse in the hospital. (*Nonessential clause beginning who.*)

Mr. Ward's oldest sister, who was a nurse in the hospital, helped keep him alive.

1. American colonists first imported pasta from the English. The English had discovered it as tourists in Italy. (*Nonessential clause beginning who.*)
2. The English returned from their grand tours of Italy. They were called macaronis because of their fancy airs. (*Essential phrase beginning returning.*)
3. A hair style was also called macaroni. It had elaborate curls. (*Essential phrase beginning with.*)
4. The song "Yankee Doodle" refers to this hairdo. It reports that Yankee Doodle "stuck a feather in his cap and called it macaroni." (*Essential clause beginning when.*)
5. The song was actually intended to poke fun at unrefined American colonists. It was a creation of the English. (*Nonessential appositive beginning a creation.*)

28d Use a comma or commas to set off absolute phrases.

An **absolute phrase** modifies a whole main clause rather than any word in the clause, and it usually consists of at least a participle (such as *done* or *having torn*) and its subject (a noun or pronoun). (See p. 253.) Absolute phrases can occur at almost any point in the sentence, and they are always set off by a comma or commas:

Household recycling having succeeded, the city now wants to extend the program to businesses.

Many businesses, their profits already squeezed, resist recycling.

28e Use a comma or commas to set off phrases expressing contrast.

The essay needs less wit, more pith.
The substance, not the style, is important.
Substance, unlike style, cannot be faked.

Note Writers often omit commas around contrasting phrases beginning with *but: A full but hazy moon shone down.*

EXERCISE 28.7 Punctuating absolute phrases and phrases of contrast

Insert commas in the following sentences to set off absolute phrases and phrases of contrast. (You can do this exercise online at *ablongman.com/littlebrown.*)

Example:

The recording contract was canceled the band having broken up.
The recording contract was canceled, the band having broken up.

1. Prices having risen rapidly the government debated a price freeze.
2. A price freeze unlike a rise in interest rates seemed a sure solution.
3. The President would have to persuade businesses to accept a price freeze his methods depending on their resistance.
4. No doubt the President his advisers having urged it would first try a patriotic appeal.
5. The President not his advisers insisted on negotiations with businesses.

28f Use commas between items in a series and between coordinate adjectives.

1 Use commas between words, phrases, or clauses forming a series.

Place commas between all elements of a **series**—that is, three or more items of equal importance:

Anna Spingle married at the age of seventeen, had three children by twenty-one, and divorced at twenty-two.

She worked as a cook, a baby-sitter, and a crossing guard.

Some writers omit the comma before the coordinating conjunction in a series (*Breakfast consisted of coffee, eggs and kippers*). But the final comma is never wrong, and it always helps the reader see the last two items as separate:

Confusing Spingle's new job involves typing, filing and answering correspondence.

Clear Spingle's new job involves typing, filing, and answering correspondence.

Exception When items in a series are long and grammatically complicated, they may be separated by semicolons. When the items contain commas, they must be separated by semicolons. (See p. 259.)

2 Use commas between two or more adjectives that equally modify the same word.

When two or more adjectives modify the same word equally, they are said to be **coordinate.** The adjectives may be separated either by *and* or by a comma, as in the following examples.

Spingle's scratched and dented car is old, but it gets her to work.
She has dreams of a sleek, shiny car.

Adjectives are not coordinate—and should *not* be separated by commas—when the one nearer the noun is more closely related to the

Punctuating two or more adjectives

1. **Identify the adjectives.**

   She was a faithful sincere friend.
   They are dedicated volunteer tutors.

2. **Can the adjectives be reversed without changing meaning?**

   She was a sincere faithful friend. ***Yes.***
   They are volunteer dedicated tutors. ***No.***

3. **Can the word *and* be inserted between the adjectives without changing meaning?**

   She was a faithful and sincere friend. ***Yes.***
   They are dedicated and volunteer tutors. ***No.***

4. **If *yes* to both questions, the adjectives *are* coordinate and *should* be separated by a comma.**

   She was a faithful, sincere friend.

   If *no* to both questions, the adjectives are *not* coordinate and should *not* be separated by a comma.

   They are dedicated volunteer tutors.

noun in meaning. In each of the next examples, the second adjective and the noun form a unit that is modified by the first adjective:

Spingle's children work at various part-time jobs.
They all expect to go to a nearby community college.

See the box above for a test to use in punctuating adjectives.

Note Numbers are not coordinate with other adjectives:

Faulty Spingle has three, teenaged children.
Revised Spingle has three teenaged children.

Do not use a comma between the final adjective and the noun:

Faulty The children hope to achieve good, well-paying, jobs.
Revised The children hope to achieve good, well-paying jobs.

EXERCISE 28.8 Punctuating series and coordinate adjectives

Insert commas in the following sentences to separate coordinate adjectives or elements in series. Mark the number preceding each sentence whose punctuation is already correct. (You can do this exercise online at *ablongman.com/littlebrown*.)

Example:

Quiet by day, the club became a noisy smoky dive at night.
Quiet by day, the club became a noisy, smoky dive at night.

1. Shoes with high heels originated to protect feet from the mud garbage and animal waste in the streets.
2. The first known high heels worn strictly for fashion appeared in the sixteenth century.
3. The heels were worn by men and made of colorful silk brocades soft suedes or smooth leathers.
4. High-heeled shoes received a boost when the short powerful King Louis XIV of France began wearing them.
5. Eventually only wealthy fashionable French women wore high heels.

28g Use commas according to convention in dates, addresses, place names, and long numbers.

Use commas to separate most parts of dates, addresses, and place names: *June 20, 1950; 24 Fifth Avenue, Suite 601; Cairo, Illinois.* Within a sentence, any element preceded by a comma should be followed by a comma as well, as in the examples below:

Dates

July 4, 1776, is the date the Declaration of Independence was signed.

The bombing of Pearl Harbor on Sunday, December 7, 1941, prompted American entry into World War II.

Do not use commas between the parts of a date in inverted order: *Their anniversary on 15 December 2005 was their fiftieth.* You need not use commas in dates consisting of a month or season and a year: *For the United States the war ended in August 1945.*

Addresses and place names

Columbus, Ohio, is the state capital and the location of Ohio State University.

The population of Garden City, Long Island, New York, is 30,000.

Use the address 220 Cornell Road, Woodside, California 94062, for all correspondence.

Do not use a comma between a state and a zip code.

Long numbers

Use the comma to separate the figures in long numbers into groups of three, counting from the right. With numbers of four digits, the comma is optional.

A kilometer is 3,281 feet [or 3281 feet].
The new assembly plant cost $7,535,000 to design and build.

CULTURE LANGUAGE Usage in American English differs from that in some other languages and dialects, which use a period, not a comma, to separate the figures in long numbers.

EXERCISE 28.9 Punctuating dates, addresses, place names, numbers

Insert commas as needed in the following sentences.

Example:

The house cost $27000 fifteen years ago.
The house cost $27,000 fifteen years ago.

1. The festival will hold a benefit dinner and performance on March 10 2006 in Asheville.
2. The organizers hope to raise more than $100000 from donations and ticket sales.
3. Performers are expected from as far away as Milan Italy and Kyoto Japan.
4. All inquiries sent to Mozart Festival PO Box 725 Asheville North Carolina 28803 will receive a quick response.
5. The deadline for ordering tickets by mail is Monday December 3 2005.

28h Use commas with quotations according to standard practice.

The words *he said, she writes,* and so on identify the source of a quotation. These **signal phrases** may come before, after, or in the middle of the quotation. A signal phrase must always be separated from the quotation by punctuation, usually a comma or commas.

Note Additional issues with quotations are discussed elsewhere in this book:

- **Using quotation marks conventionally,** pages 470–77.
- **Choosing and transcribing quotations from sources,** pages 603–05.
- **Integrating source material into your text,** pages 607–10.
- **Acknowledging the sources of quotations to avoid plagiarism,** pages 615–16 and 618–19.
- **Formatting long prose quotations and poetry quotations** in MLA style, pages 665–66; and APA style, pages 757–58.

1 Ordinarily, use a comma with a signal phrase before or after a quotation.

Eleanor Roosevelt said, "You must do the thing you think you cannot do."

"Knowledge is power," writes Francis Bacon.

Exceptions Do not use a comma when a signal phrase follows a quotation ending in an exclamation point or a question mark:

"Michael!" Mrs. Harrison called.
"Why must I come home?" he asked.

Do not use commas with a quotation introduced by *that* or with a quotation that is integrated into your sentence structure:

James Baldwin insists that "one must never, in one's life, accept . . . injustices as commonplace."

Baldwin thought that the violence of a riot "had been devised as a corrective" to his own violence.

Use a colon instead of a comma between a signal phrase and a quotation when the signal phrase is actually a complete sentence and the quotation is very formal or longer than a sentence.

The Bill of Rights is unambiguous: "Congress shall make no law respecting an establishment of religion, or prohibiting the free exercise thereof."

2 With an interrupted quotation, precede the signal phrase with a comma and follow it with the punctuation required by the quotation.

Quotation

"The shore has a dual nature, changing with the swing of the tides."

Signal phrase

"The shore has a dual nature," observes Rachel Carson, "changing with the swing of the tides." [The signal phrase interrupts the quotation at a comma and thus ends with a comma.]

Quotation

"However mean your life is, meet it and live it; do not shun it and call it hard names."

Signal phrase

"However mean your life is, meet it and live it," Thoreau advises in *Walden*; "do not shun it and call it hard names." [The signal phrase interrupts the quotation at a semicolon and thus ends with a semicolon.]

Quotation

"This is the faith with which I return to the South. With this new faith we will be able to hew out of the mountain of despair a stone of hope."

Signal phrase

"This is the faith with which I return to the South," Martin Luther King, Jr., proclaimed. "With this new faith we will be able to hew out of the mountain of despair a stone of hope." [The signal phrase interrupts the quotation at the end of a sentence and thus ends with a period.]

Note Using a comma instead of a semicolon or a period after the Thoreau and King signal phrases would result in the error called a comma splice: two main clauses separated only by a comma. (See pp. 344–49.)

3 Place commas that follow quotations within quotation marks.

"Death is not the greatest loss in life," claims Norman Cousins.

"The greatest loss," Cousins says, "is what dies inside us while we live."

EXERCISE 28.10 Punctuating quotations

Insert commas or semicolons in the following sentences to correct punctuation with quotations. Mark the number preceding any sentence whose punctuation is already correct. (You can do this exercise online at *ablongman.com/littlebrown*.)

Example:

The shoplifter declared "I didn't steal anything."

The shoplifter declared, "I didn't steal anything."

1. The writer and writing teacher Peter Elbow proposes an "open-ended writing process" that "can change you, not just your words."
2. "I think of the open-ended writing process as a voyage in two stages" Elbow says.
3. "The sea voyage is a process of divergence, branching, proliferation, and confusion" Elbow continues "the coming to land is a process of convergence, pruning, centralizing, and clarifying."
4. "Keep up one session of writing long enough to get loosened up and tired" advises Elbow "long enough in fact to make a bit of a voyage."
5. "In coming to new land" Elbow says "you develop a new conception of what you are writing about."

28i Use commas to prevent misreading.

In some sentences words may run together in unintended and confusing ways unless a comma separates them:

Confusing Soon after the business closed its doors.
Clear Soon after, the business closed its doors.

Always check whether a comma added to prevent misreading might cause some other confusion or error. In the first example below, the comma prevents *pasta* and *places* from running into each other as *pasta places*, but it separates the subject (*historian*) and the verb (*places*). The revision solves both problems.

Faulty A historian who studied pasta, places its origin in the Middle East.

Revised A historian who studied pasta says that it originated in the Middle East.

EXERCISE 28.11 Punctuating to prevent misreading

Insert commas in the following sentences to prevent misreading. (You can do this exercise online at *ablongman.com/littlebrown.*)

Example:

To Laura Ann symbolized decadence.
To Laura, Ann symbolized decadence.

1. Though happy people still have moments of self-doubt.
2. In research subjects have reported themselves to be generally happy people.
3. Among those who have life has included sufferings as well as joys.
4. Of fifty eight subjects reported bouts of serious depression.
5. For half the preceding year had included at least one personal crisis.

28j Use commas only where required.

Commas can make sentences choppy and even confusing if they are used more often than needed. The main misuses of commas are summarized in the box opposite.

1 Delete any comma after a subject or a verb.

Commas interrupt the movement from subject to verb to object or complement, as in the following faulty examples.

Faulty The returning soldiers, received a warmer welcome than they expected. [Separation of subject and verb.]

Revised The returning soldiers received a warmer welcome than they expected.

Faulty They had chosen, to fight for their country. [Separation of verb *chosen* and object *to fight*.]

Revised They had chosen to fight for their country.

Exception Use commas between subject, verb, and object or complement only when other words between these elements require punctuation:

Americans, who are preoccupied with other sports, have only recently developed an interest in professional soccer. [Commas set off a nonessential clause.]

2 Delete any comma that separates a pair of words, phrases, or subordinate clauses joined by a coordinating conjunction.

When linking elements with *and, or,* or another coordinating conjunction, do not use a comma unless the elements are main clauses (see p. 434):

Faulty Banks could, and should help older people manage their money. [Compound helping verb.]

Revised Banks could and should help older people manage their money.

Faulty Older people need special assistance because they live on fixed incomes, and because they are not familiar with new accounts, and rates. [Compound subordinate clauses *because . . . because* and compound object of preposition *with*.]

Revised Older people need special assistance because they live on fixed incomes and because they are not familiar with new accounts and rates.

Principal misuses of the comma

- **Don't use a comma after a subject or verb:**

  Faulty Anyone with breathing problems, should not exercise during smog alerts.

  Revised Anyone with breathing problems should not exercise during smog alerts.

- **Don't separate a pair of words, phrases, or subordinate clauses joined by *and, or,* or *nor*:**

  Faulty Asthmatics are affected by ozone, and sulfur oxides.

  Revised Asthmatics are affected by ozone and sulfur oxides.

- **Don't use a comma after *and, but, although, because,* or another conjunction:**

  Faulty Smog is dangerous and, sometimes even fatal.

  Revised Smog is dangerous and sometimes even fatal.

- **Don't set off essential elements:**

  Faulty Even people, who are healthy, should be careful.

  Revised Even people who are healthy should be careful.

  Faulty Bruce Springsteen's song, "Born in the USA," became an anthem.

  Revised Bruce Springsteen's song "Born in the USA" became an anthem.

- **Don't set off a series:**

  Faulty Cars, factories, and even bakeries, contribute to smog.

  Revised Cars, factories, and even bakeries contribute to smog.

- **Don't set off an indirect quotation:**

  Faulty Experts say, that the pollutant ozone is especially damaging.

  Revised Experts say that the pollutant ozone is especially damaging.

Faulty Banks, and community groups can assist the elderly, and eliminate the confusion they often feel. [Compound subject and compound predicate.]

Revised Banks and community groups can assist the elderly and eliminate the confusion they often feel.

3 Delete any comma after a conjunction.

The coordinating conjunctions (*and, but,* and so on) and the subordinating conjunctions (*although, because,* and so on) are not followed by commas:

Ellis Island New York reopened for business in 1990 but now the customers are tourists not immigrants. This spot which lies in New York Harbor was the first American soil seen, or touched by many of the nation's immigrants. Though other places also served as ports of entry for foreigners none has the symbolic power of, Ellis Island. Between its opening in 1892 and its closing in 1954, over 20 million people about two-thirds of all immigrants were detained there before taking up their new lives in the United States. Ellis Island processed over 2000 newcomers a day when immigration was at its peak between 1900 and 1920.

As the end of a long voyage and the introduction to the New World Ellis Island must have left something to be desired. The "huddled masses" as the Statue of Liberty calls them indeed were huddled. New arrivals were herded about kept standing in lines for hours or days yelled at and abused. Assigned numbers they submitted their bodies to the pokings and proddings of the silent nurses and doctors, who were charged with ferreting out the slightest sign of sickness, disability or insanity. That test having been passed the immigrants faced interrogation by an official through an interpreter. Those, with names deemed inconveniently long or difficult to pronounce, often found themselves permanently labeled with abbreviations, of their names, or with the names, of their hometowns. But, millions survived the examination humiliation and confusion, to take the last short boat ride to New York City. For many of them and especially for their descendants Ellis Island eventually became not a nightmare but the place where life began.

Note See page 490 for a punctuation exercise combining commas with other marks of punctuation.

CHAPTER 29

The Semicolon

The semicolon separates equal and balanced sentence elements, usually main clauses (opposite through p. 458), and sometimes items in series (p. 459).

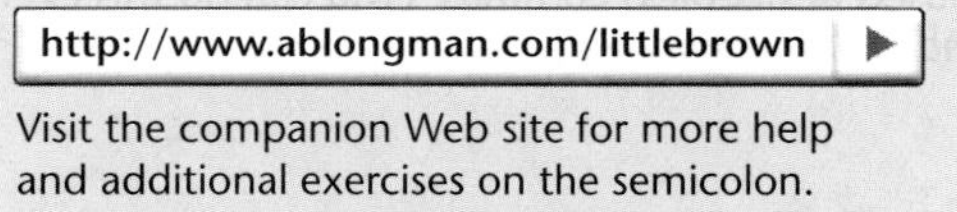

Note A grammar and style checker can spot a few errors in the use of semicolons. For example, a checker suggested using a semicolon after *perfect* in *The set was perfect, the director had planned every detail,* thus correcting a comma splice. But it missed the incorrect semicolon in *The set was perfect; deserted streets, dark houses, and gloomy mist* (a colon would be correct; see p. 479).

29a Use a semicolon between main clauses not joined by *and, but,* or another coordinating conjunction.

Main clauses contain a subject and a predicate and do not begin with a subordinating word (see p. 254). When you join two main clauses in a sentence, you have two primary options for separating them:

- **Insert a comma and a coordinating conjunction:** *and, but, or, nor, for, so, yet.* (See p. 234.)

  The drug does little to relieve symptoms**,** and it can have side effects.

- **Insert a semicolon:**

  The side effects are not minor**;** some leave the patient quite ill.

Note If you do not link main clauses with a coordinating conjunction and you separate them only with a comma or with no punctuation at all, you will produce a comma splice or a fused sentence. (See Chapter 18.)

EXERCISE 29.1 Punctuating between main clauses

Insert semicolons to separate main clauses in the following sentences. (You can do this exercise online at *ablongman.com/littlebrown.*)

Example:

One man at the auction bid prudently another spent his bank account.

One man at the auction bid prudently**;** another spent his bank account.

1. More and more musicians are playing computerized instruments more and more listeners are worrying about the future of acoustic instruments.
2. The computer is not the first new technology in music the pipe organ and saxophone were also technological breakthroughs in their day.
3. Musicians have always experimented with new technology audiences have always resisted the experiments.

Distinguishing the comma, the semicolon, and the colon

The *comma* chiefly separates both equal and unequal sentence elements.

- It separates main clauses when they are linked by a coordinating conjunction (p. 434):

  An airline once tried to boost sales by advertising the tense alertness of its crews, but nervous fliers did not want to hear about pilots' sweaty palms.

- It separates subordinate information that is part of or attached to a main clause, such as an introductory element or a nonessential modifier (pp. 435, 437):

  Although the airline campaign failed, many advertising agencies, including some clever ones, copied its underlying message.

The *semicolon* chiefly separates equal and balanced sentence elements. Often the first clause creates an expectation, and the second clause fulfills the expectation.

- It separates complementary main clauses that are *not* linked by a coordinating conjunction (previous page):

  The airline campaign had highlighted only half the story; the other half was buried in the copy.

- It separates complementary main clauses that are related by a conjunctive adverb or other transitional expression (opposite):

  The campaign should not have stressed the pilots' insecurity; instead, the campaign should have stressed the improved performance resulting from that insecurity.

The *colon* chiefly separates unequal sentence elements.

- It separates a main clause from a following explanation or summary, which may or may not be a main clause (pp. 479–80):

  Many successful advertising campaigns have used this message: the anxious seller is harder working and smarter than the competitor.

4. Most computer musicians are not merely following the latest fad they are discovering new sounds and new ways to manipulate sound.
5. Few musicians have abandoned acoustic instruments most value acoustic sounds as much as electronic sounds.

EXERCISE 29.2 Sentence combining: Related main clauses

Combine each set of three sentences below into one sentence containing only two main clauses, and insert a semicolon between the clauses. You will have to add, delete, change, and rearrange words. Most items have more than one possible answer. (You can do this exercise online at *ablongman.com/littlebrown.*)

Example:

The painter Andrew Wyeth is widely admired. He is not universally admired. Some critics view his work as sentimental.

The painter Andrew Wyeth is widely but not universally admired**;** some critics view his work as sentimental.

1. Electronic instruments are prevalent in jazz. They are also prevalent in rock music. They are less common in classical music.
2. Jazz and rock change rapidly. They nourish experimentation. They nourish improvisation.
3. Traditional classical music does not change. Its notes and instrumentation were established by a composer. The composer was writing decades or centuries ago.
4. Contemporary classical music not only can draw on tradition. It also can respond to innovations. These are innovations such as jazz rhythms and electronic sounds.
5. Much contemporary electronic music is more than just one type of music. It is more than just jazz, rock, or classical. It is a fusion of all three.

29b Use a semicolon between main clauses related by *however, for example,* and so on.

Two kinds of words can relate main clauses: **conjunctive adverbs,** such as *consequently, hence, however, indeed,* and *thus* (see p. 263), and other **transitional expressions,** such as *even so, for example,* and *of course* (see pp. 88–89). When either of these connects two main clauses, the clauses should be separated by a semicolon:

An American immigrant, Levi Strauss, invented blue jeans in the 1860s**;** eventually, his product clothed working men throughout the West.

The position of the semicolon between main clauses never changes, but the conjunctive adverb or transitional expression may move around within a clause. The adverb or expression is usually set off with a comma or commas (see p. 438):

Blue jeans have become fashionable all over the world**;** however**,** the American originators still wear more jeans than anyone else.

Blue jeans have become fashionable all over the world**;** the American originators**,** however**,** still wear more jeans than anyone else.

Its mobility distinguishes a conjunctive adverb or transitional expression from other connecting words, such as coordinating and subordinating conjunctions. See pages 263–64 on this distinction.

Note If you use a comma or no punctuation at all between main clauses connected by a conjunctive adverb or transitional expression, you will produce a comma splice or a fused sentence. (See Chapter 18.)

EXERCISE 29.3 Punctuating main clauses related by conjunctive adverbs or transitional expressions

Insert a semicolon in each of the following sentences to separate main clauses related by a conjunctive adverb or transitional expression. Also insert a comma or commas where needed to set off the adverb or expression. (You can do this exercise online at *ablongman.com/littlebrown.*)

Example:

He knew that tickets for the concert would be scarce therefore he arrived at the box office hours before it opened.

He knew that tickets for the concert would be scarce**;** therefore**,** he arrived at the box office hours before it opened.

1. Music is a form of communication like language the basic elements however are not letters but notes.
2. Computers can process any information that can be represented numerically as a result they can process musical information.
3. A computer's ability to process music depends on what software it can run it must moreover be connected to a system that converts electrical vibration into sound.
4. Computers and their sound systems can produce many different sounds indeed the number of possible sounds is infinite.
5. The powerful music computers are very expensive therefore they are used only by professional musicians.

EXERCISE 29.4 Sentence combining: Main clauses related by conjunctive adverbs or transitional expressions

Combine each set of three sentences below into one sentence containing only two main clauses. Connect the clauses with the conjunctive adverb or transitional expression in parentheses, and separate them with a semicolon. Be sure the adverbs and expressions are punctuated appropriately. You will have to add, delete, change, and rearrange words. Each item has more than one possible answer. (You can do this exercise online at *ablongman.com/littlebrown.*)

Example:

The Albanians censored their news. We got little news from them. And what we got was unreliable. (*therefore*)

The Albanians censored their news**;** therefore**,** the little news we got from them was unreliable.

1. Most music computers are too expensive for the average consumer. Digital keyboard instruments can be inexpensive. They are widely available. (*however*)

2. Inside the keyboard is a small computer. The computer controls a sound synthesizer. The instrument can both process and produce music. (*consequently*)
3. The person playing the keyboard presses keys or manipulates other controls. The computer and synthesizer convert these signals. The signals are converted into vibrations and sounds. (*immediately*)
4. The inexpensive keyboards can perform only a few functions. To the novice computer musician, the range is exciting. The range includes drum rhythms and simulated instruments. (*still*)
5. Would-be musicians can orchestrate whole songs. They start from just the melody lines. They need never again play "Chopsticks." (*thus*)

29c Use a semicolon to separate main clauses if they are complicated or contain commas, even with a coordinating conjunction.

We normally use a comma with a coordinating conjunction such as *and* or *but* between main clauses (see p. 434). But a semicolon makes a sentence easier to read when the main clauses contain commas or are grammatically complicated:

> By a conscious effort of the mind, we can stand aloof from actions and their consequences**;** and all things, good and bad, go by us like a torrent. —Henry David Thoreau

> I doubt if the texture of Southern life is any more grotesque than that of the rest of the nation, but it does seem evident that the Southern writer is particularly adept at recognizing the grotesque**;** and to recognize the grotesque, you have to have some notion of what is not grotesque and why. —Flannery O'Connor

29d Use semicolons to separate items in a series if they are long or contain commas.

We normally use commas to separate items in a series (see p. 443). But when the items are long or internally punctuated, semicolons help readers identify the items:

> The custody case involved Amy Dalton, the child**;** Ellen and Mark Dalton, the parents**;** and Ruth and Hal Blum, the grandparents.

> One may even reasonably advance the claim that the sort of communication that really counts, and is therefore embodied into permanent records, is primarily written**;** that "words fly away, but written messages endure," as the Latin saying put it two thousand years ago**;** and that there is no basic significance to at least fifty percent of the oral interchange that goes on among all sorts of persons, high and low. —Mario Pei

EXERCISE 29.5 Punctuating long main clauses and series items

Substitute semicolons for commas in the following sentences to separate main clauses or series items that are long or contain commas. (You can do this exercise online at *ablongman.com/littlebrown.*)

Example:

He debated whether to attend college in San Francisco, which was temperate but far from his parents, New York City, which was exciting but expensive, or Atlanta, which was close to home but already familiar.

He debated whether to attend college in San Francisco, which was temperate but far from his parents; New York City, which was exciting but expensive; or Atlanta, which was close to home but already familiar.

1. The Indian subcontinent is separated from the rest of the world by clear barriers: the Bay of Bengal and the Arabian Sea to the east and west, respectively, the Indian Ocean to the south, and 1600 miles of mountain ranges to the north.
2. In the north of India are the world's highest mountains, the Himalayas, and farther south are fertile farmlands, unpopulated deserts, and rain forests.
3. India is a nation of ethnic and linguistic diversity, with numerous religions, including Hinduism, Islam, and Christianity, with distinct castes and ethnic groups, and with sixteen languages, including the official Hindi and the "associate official" English.
4. Between the seventeenth and nineteenth centuries, the British colonized most of India, taking control of government, the bureaucracy, and industry, and they assumed a social position above all Indians.
5. During British rule the Indians' own unresolved differences and their frustrations with the British erupted in violent incidents such as the Sepoy Mutiny, which began on February 26, 1857, and lasted two years, the Amritsar Massacre on April 13, 1919, and violence between Hindus and Muslims during World War II that resulted in the separation of Pakistan from India.

29e Use the semicolon only where required.

Semicolons do not separate unequal sentence elements and should not be overused.

1 Delete or replace any semicolon that separates a subordinate clause or a phrase from a main clause.

The semicolon does not separate subordinate clauses from main clauses or phrases from main clauses:

Faulty Pygmies are in danger of extinction; because of encroaching development.

Revised Pygmies are in danger of extinction because of encroaching development.

Faulty According to African authorities; only about 35,000 Pygmies exist today.

Revised According to African authorities, only about 35,000 Pygmies exist today.

Note Many readers regard a phrase or subordinate clause set off with a semicolon as a kind of sentence fragment. (See Chapter 17.)

2 Delete or replace any semicolon that introduces a series or explanation.

Colons and dashes, not semicolons, introduce series, explanations, and so forth. (See p. 479.)

Faulty Teachers have heard all sorts of reasons why students do poorly; psychological problems, family illness, too much work, too little time.

Revised Teachers have heard all sorts of reasons why students do poorly: psychological problems, family illness, too much work, too little time.

Revised Teachers have heard all sorts of reasons why students do poorly—psychological problems, family illness, too much work, too little time.

3 Use the semicolon sparingly.

Use the semicolon only occasionally. Many semicolons in a passage, even when they are required by rule, often indicate repetitive sentence structure. To revise a passage with too many semicolons, you'll need to restructure your sentences, not just remove the semicolons. (See Chapter 26 for tips on varying sentences.)

Semicolon overused

The Make-a-Wish Foundation helps sick children; it grants the wishes of children who are terminally ill. The foundation learns of a child's wish; the information usually comes from parents, friends, or hospital staff; the wish may be for a special toy, a trip to the circus, or a visit to Disneyland. The foundation grants some wishes with its own funds; for other wishes it appeals to those who have what the child desires.

Revised

The Make-a-Wish Foundation grants the wishes of children who are terminally ill. From parents, friends, or hospital staff, the foundation learns of a child's wish for a special toy, a trip to the circus, or a visit to Disneyland. It grants some wishes with its own funds; for other wishes it appeals to those who have what the child desires.

EXERCISE 29.6 Revising: Misused or overused semicolons

Revise the following sentences to eliminate misused or overused semicolons, substituting other punctuation as appropriate. (You can do this exercise online at *ablongman.com/littlebrown.*)

Example:

The doctor gave everyone the same advice; get exercise.
The doctor gave everyone the same advice**:** get exercise.

1. The main religion in India is Hinduism; a way of life as well as a theology and philosophy.
2. Unlike Christianity and Judaism; Hinduism is a polytheistic religion; with deities numbering in the hundreds.
3. Hinduism is unlike many other religions; it allows its creeds and practices to vary widely from place to place and person to person. Other religions have churches; Hinduism does not. Other religions have principal prophets and holy books; Hinduism does not. Other religions center on specially trained priests or other leaders; Hinduism promotes the individual as his or her own priest.
4. In Hindu belief there are four types of people; reflective, emotional, active, and experimental.
5. Each type of person has a different technique for realizing the true, immortal self; which has infinite existence, infinite knowledge, and infinite joy.

EXERCISE 29.7 Revising: Semicolons

Insert semicolons in the following paragraph wherever they are needed. Eliminate any misused or needless semicolons, substituting other punctuation as appropriate. (You can do this exercise online at *ablongman.com/littlebrown.*)

The set, sounds, and actors in the movie captured the essence of horror films. The set was ideal; dark, deserted streets, trees dipping their branches over the sidewalks, mist hugging the ground and creeping up to meet the trees, looming shadows of unlighted, turreted houses. The sounds, too, were appropriate, especially terrifying was the hard, hollow sound of footsteps echoing throughout the film. But the best feature of the movie was its actors; all of them tall, pale, and thin to the point of emaciation. With one exception, they were dressed uniformly in gray and had gray hair. The exception was an actress who dressed only in black; as if to set off her pale yellow, nearly white, long hair; the only color in the film. The glinting black eyes of another actor stole almost every scene, indeed, they were the source of all the film's mischief.

Note See page 490 for a punctuation exercise combining semicolons with other marks of punctuation.

CHAPTER 30

The Apostrophe

Unlike other punctuation marks, which separate words, the apostrophe (') appears as *part* of a word to indicate possession or the omission of one or more letters.

Note Grammar and style checkers have mixed results in recognizing apostrophe errors. For instance, most flag missing apostrophes in contractions (as in *isnt*), but many cannot distinguish between *its* and *it's, their* and *they're, your* and *you're, whose* and *who's*. The checkers can identify some apostrophe errors in possessives but will overlook others and may flag correct plurals. Instead of relying on your checker, try using your computer's Search or Find function to hunt for all words you have ended in *-s*. Then check each one to ensure that you have used apostrophes correctly.

30a Use the apostrophe to indicate the possessive case for nouns and indefinite pronouns.

In English the **possessive case** shows ownership or possession of one person or thing by another. Possession may be shown with an *of* phrase (*the hair of the dog*); or it may be shown with the addition of an apostrophe and, usually, an *-s* (*the dog's hair*).

Note Apostrophes are easy to misuse. Always check your drafts to ensure the following:

- **Every word ending in *-s* neither omits a needed apostrophe nor adds an unneeded one.**
- **The apostrophe or apostrophe-plus-*s*** is an *addition*. Before this addition, always spell the name of the owner or owners without dropping or adding letters: *girls* becomes *girls'*, not *girl's*.

1 Add -'s to singular nouns and indefinite pronouns.

Bill Boughton**'s** skillful card tricks amaze children.

Anyone**'s** eyes would widen. [Indefinite pronoun.]

Most tricks will pique an adult**'s** curiosity, too.

Visit the companion Web site for more help and additional exercises on the apostrophe.

Example:

The [men] blood pressures were higher than the [women].

The men**'s** blood pressures were higher than the women**'s**.

1. In the myths of the ancient Greeks, the [goddesses] roles vary widely.
2. [Demeter] responsibility is the fruitfulness of the earth.
3. [Athena] role is to guard the city of Athens.
4. [Artemis] function is to care for wild animals and small children.
5. [Athena and Artemis] father, Zeus, is the king of the gods.
6. Even a single [goddess] responsibilities are often varied.
7. Over several [centuries] time, Athena changes from a [mariner] goddess to the patron of crafts.
8. Athena is also concerned with fertility and with [children] well-being, since [Athens] strength depended on a large and healthy population.
9. Athena often changes into [birds] forms.
10. In [Homer] *Odyssey* she assumes a [sea eagle] form.
11. In ancient Athens the myths of Athena were part of [everyone] knowledge and life.
12. A cherished myth tells how Athena fights to retain possession of her [people] land when the god Poseidon wants it.
13. [Athena and Poseidon] skills are different, and each promises a special gift to the Athenians.
14. At the [contest] conclusion, Poseidon has given water and Athena has given an olive tree, for sustenance.
15. The other gods decide that the [Athenians] lives depend more on Athena than on Poseidon.

30b Delete or replace any apostrophe in a plural noun, a singular verb, or a possessive personal pronoun.

Not all words ending in -*s* take an apostrophe. Three kinds of words are especially likely to attract unneeded apostrophes.

Plural nouns

Form most plural nouns by adding -*s* or -*es* (*boys, Smiths, families, Joneses*). Never add an apostrophe to form the plural:

Faulty The unleashed dog's began traveling in a pack.
Revised The unleashed dogs began traveling in a pack.

Faulty The Jones' and Bass' were feuding.
Revised The Jones**es** and Bass**es** were feuding.

Singular verbs

Do not add an apostrophe to present-tense verbs used with *he, she, it,* and other third-person singular subjects. These verbs always end in -*s* but *never* with an apostrophe:

Faulty The subway break's down less often now.
Revised The subway breaks down less often now.

Faulty It run's more reliably.
Revised It runs more reliably.

Possessive personal pronouns

His, hers, its, ours, yours, theirs, and *whose* are possessive forms of the pronouns *he, she, it, we, you, they,* and *who.* They do not take apostrophes:

Faulty The credit is her's not their's.
Revised The credit is hers, not theirs.

The personal pronouns are often confused with contractions, such as *it's, you're,* and *who's.* See below.

EXERCISE 30.2 Distinguishing between plurals and possessives

Supply the appropriate form—possessive or plural—of each word given in brackets. Some answers require apostrophes, and some do not. (You can do this exercise online at *ablongman.com/littlebrown.*)

Example:

A dozen Hawaiian [shirt], each with [it] own loud design, hung in the window.

A dozen Hawaiian shirts, each with its own loud design, hung in the window.

1. Demeter may be the oldest of the Greek [god], older than Zeus.
2. Many prehistoric [culture] had earth [goddess] like Demeter.
3. In myth she is the earth mother, which means that the responsibility for the fertility of both [animal] and [plant] is [she].
4. The [goddess] festival came at harvest time, with [it] celebration of bounty.
5. The [people] [prayer] to Demeter thanked her for grain and other [gift].

30c Use an apostrophe to indicate the omission in a standard contraction.

it is, it has	it's	let us	let's
he is	he's	does not	doesn't
she is	she's	were not	weren't
they are	they're	class of 2009	class of '09
you are	you're	of the clock	o'clock
who is, who has	who's	madam	ma'am

Contractions are common in speech and in informal writing. They may also be used to relax style in more formal kinds of writing, as they are in this handbook. But be aware that many people disapprove of contractions in any kind of formal writing.

Note Contractions are easily confused with the possessive personal pronouns:

Contraction	Possessive pronoun
it's	its
they're	their
you're	your
who's	whose

Faulty Legislators know their going to have to cut the budget to eliminate it's deficit.

Revised Legislators know they're going to have to cut the budget to eliminate its deficit.

If you tend to confuse these forms, search for both spellings throughout your drafts. Then test for correctness:

- **Use an apostrophe when you intend the word to contain the sentence verb *is*, *are*, or *has*,** as in *It is [It's] a shame, It has [It's] happened, They are [They're] to blame, You are [You're] right, Who is [Who's] coming? Who has [Who's] responded?*
- **Don't use an apostrophe when you intend the word to indicate possession,** as in *Its tail was wagging, Their car broke down, Your eyes are blue, Whose book is that?*

EXERCISE 30.3 Forming contractions

Form contractions from each set of words below. Use each contraction in a complete sentence. (You can do this exercise online at *ablongman .com/littlebrown*.)

Example:

we are: we're
We're open to ideas.

1. she would
2. could not
3. they are
4. he is
5. do not
6. she will
7. hurricane of 1962
8. is not
9. it is
10. will not

EXERCISE 30.4 Revising: Contractions and personal pronouns

Revise the following sentences to correct mistakes in the use of contractions and personal pronouns. Mark the number preceding any sentence that is already correct. (You can do this exercise online at *ablongman.com/littlebrown*.)

Example:

The agencies give they're employees their birthdays off.
The agencies give their employees their birthdays off.

1. In Greek myth the goddess Demeter has a special fondness for Eleusis, near Athens, and it's people.
2. She finds rest among the people and is touched by their kindness.
3. Demeter rewards the Eleusians with the secret for making they're land fruitful.
4. The Eleusians begin a cult in honor of Demeter, whose worshiped in secret ceremonies.
5. Its unknown what happened in the ceremonies, for no participant ever revealed their rituals.

30d Increasingly, the apostrophe does not mark plural abbreviations, dates, and words or characters named as words.

You'll sometimes see apostrophes used to form the plurals of abbreviations (*BA's*), dates (*1900's*), and words or characters named as words (*but*'s). However, most current style guides do not recommend the apostrophe in these cases.

BAs	PhDs
1990s	2000s

The sentence has too many buts [or *buts*].
Two 3s [or *3*s] end the zip code.

Note Underline or italicize a word or character named as a word (see p. 500), but not the added *-s*.

EXERCISE 30.5 Revising: Apostrophes

In the following paragraph correct any mistakes in the use of the apostrophe or any confusion between contractions and possessive personal pronouns. (You can do this exercise online at *ablongman.com/littlebrown.*)

Landlocked Chad is among the worlds most troubled countries. The people's of Chad are poor: they're average per capita income equals just over $1000 a year. Less than half of Chads population is literate, and every five hundred people must share only two teacher's. The natural resources of the nation have never been plentiful, and now, as it's slowly being absorbed into the growing Sahara Desert, even water is scarce. Chads political conflicts go back to the nineteenth century, when the French colonized the land by brutally subduing it's people. The rule of the French—who's inept government of the colony did nothing to ease tensions among racial, tribal, and religious group's—ended with independence in 1960. But since then the Chadians experience has been one of civil war and oppression, and their also threatened with invasions from they're neighbors.

Note See page 490 for a punctuation exercise involving apostrophes along with other marks of punctuation.

CHAPTER 31

Quotation Marks

Quotation marks—either double (" ") or single (' ')—mainly enclose direct quotations from speech and from writing. The chart on the next two pages summarizes this use and the combination of quotation marks with commas, ellipsis marks, and other punctuation. Additional information on using quotations appears elsewhere in this book:

- **Using commas with signal phrases introducing quotations,** pages 446–48.
- **Using brackets and the ellipsis mark to indicate changes in quotations,** pages 485–88.
- **Quoting sources versus paraphrasing or summarizing them,** pages 601–05.
- **Integrating quotations into your text,** pages 607–10.
- **Acknowledging the sources of quotations to avoid plagiarism,** pages 615–16 and 618–19.
- **Formatting long prose quotations and poetry quotations** in MLA style, pages 665–66; and APA style, pages 757–58.

Note Always use quotation marks in pairs, one at the beginning of a quotation and one at the end. Most grammar and style checkers will help you use quotation marks in pairs by flagging a lone mark. Most checkers can also be set to ignore other marks of

http://www.ablongman.com/littlebrown ▶

Visit the companion Web site for more help and additional exercises on quotation marks.

Handling quotations from speech or writing

Direct and indirect quotation

Direct quotation

According to Lewis Thomas, **"**We are, perhaps uniquely among the earth's creatures, the worrying animal. We worry away our lives.**"**

Do not use quotation marks with a direct quotation that is set off from your text. See pages 665–66 (MLA style) and 757–58 (APA style).

Quotation within quotation

Quoting a phrase by Lewis Thomas, the author adds, **"**We are **'**the worrying animal.**'"**

Indirect quotation

Lewis Thomas says that human beings are unique among animals in their worrying.

Quotation marks with other punctuation marks

Commas and periods

Human beings are the "worrying animal**,"** says Thomas.
Thomas calls human beings "the worrying animal**."**

Semicolons and colons

Machiavelli says that "the majority of men live content"**;** in contrast, Thomas calls us "the worrying animal."

Thomas believes that we are "the worrying animal"**:** we spend our lives afraid and restless.

Question marks, exclamation points, dashes

When part of your own sentence:

Who said that human beings are "the worrying animal"**?**
Imagine saying that we human beings "worry away our lives"**!**
Thomas's phrase—"the worrying animal"—seems too narrow.

When part of the original quotation:

"Will you discuss this with me**?"** she asked.
"I demand that you discuss this with me**!"** she yelled.
"Please, won't you—" She paused.

Altering quotations

Brackets for additions

"We **[**human beings**]** worry away our lives," says Thomas.

Brackets for altered capitalization

"**[**T**]**he worrying animal" is what Thomas calls us. He says that "**[**w**]**e worry away our lives."

(continued)

"What shall I call you? Your name?" Andrews whispered rapidly, as with a high squeak the latch of the door rose.

"Elizabeth," she said. "Elizabeth."

—Graham Greene, *The Man Within*

Note When you quote a single speaker for more than one paragraph, put quotation marks at the beginning of each paragraph but at the end of only the last paragraph. The absence of quotation marks at the end of each paragraph but the last tells readers that the speech is continuing.

31d Put quotation marks around the titles of works that are parts of other works.

Use quotation marks to enclose the titles of works that are published or released within larger works: see the box below. As in the second article title in the box, use single quotation marks for a quotation within a quoted title, and enclose all punctuation in the title within the quotation marks. Use underlining or italics for all other titles, such as books, plays, periodicals, and movies. (See p. 499.)

Titles to be enclosed in quotation marks

Other titles should be underlined or italicized. (See p. 499.)

Songs
"Lucy in the Sky with Diamonds"
"America the Beautiful"

Short poems
"Stopping by Woods on a Snowy Evening"
"Sunday Morning"

Articles in periodicals
"Comedy and Tragedy Transposed"
"Does 'Scaring' Work?"

Essays
"Politics and the English Language"
"Joey: A 'Mechanical Boy'"

Short stories
"The Battler"
"The Gift of the Magi"

Page or document on a Web site
"Readers' Page" (on site Friends of Prufrock)

Episodes of television and radio programs
"The Mexican Connection" (on 60 Minutes)
"Cooking with Clams" (on Eating In)

Subdivisions of books
"Voyage to the Houyhnhnms" (Part IV of Gulliver's Travels)
"The Mast Head" (Chapter 35 of Moby-Dick)

Note Some academic disciplines do not require quotation marks for titles within source citations. See pages 743–44 (APA style) and 769–70 (CSE style).

EXERCISE 31.2 Quoting titles

Insert quotation marks as needed for titles in the following sentences. If quotation marks should be used instead of underlining, insert them. (You can do this exercise online at *ablongman.com/littlebrown.*)

Example:

She published an article titled Marriage in Grace Paley's An Interest in Life.

She published an article titled "Marriage in Grace Paley's 'An Interest in Life.'"

1. In Chapter 8, titled How to Be Interesting, the author explains the art of conversation.
2. The Beatles' song Let It Be reminds Martin of his uncle.
3. The article that appeared in Mental Health was titled Children of Divorce Ask, "Why?"
4. In the encyclopedia the discussion under Modern Art fills less than a column.
5. One prizewinning essay, Cowgirls on Wall Street, first appeared in Entrepreneur magazine.

31e Quotation marks may be used to enclose words used in a special sense.

On movie sets movable "wild walls" make a one-walled room seem four-walled on film.

Writers often put quotation marks around a word they are using with irony—that is, with a different or even opposite meaning than usual:

With all the "compassion" it could muster, the agency turned away two-thirds of those seeking help. —Joan Simonson

Readers quickly tire of such irony, though, so use it sparingly. Prefer language that expresses your meaning exactly. (See Chapter 38.)

Note For words you are defining, use underlining or italics. (See p. 500.)

31f Use quotation marks only where they are required.

Don't use quotation marks in the titles of your papers unless they contain or are themselves direct quotations:

Not “The Death Wish in One Poem by Robert Frost”
But The Death Wish in One Poem by Robert Frost
Or The Death Wish in “Stopping by Woods on a Snowy Evening”

Don’t use quotation marks to enclose common nicknames or technical terms that are not being defined:

Not As President, “Jimmy” Carter preferred to use his nickname.
But As President, Jimmy Carter preferred to use his nickname.

Not “Mitosis” in a cell is fascinating to watch.
But Mitosis in a cell is fascinating to watch.

Don’t use quotation marks in an attempt to justify or apologize for slang and trite expressions that are inappropriate to your writing. If slang is appropriate, use it without quotation marks.

Not We should support the President in his “hour of need” rather than “wimp out” on him.
But We should give the President the support he needs rather than turn away like cowards.

(See pp. 514 and 529 for more on slang and trite expressions.)

31g Place other punctuation marks inside or outside quotation marks according to standard practice.

The position of another punctuation mark inside or outside a closing quotation mark depends on what the other mark is, whether it appears in the quotation, and whether a source citation immediately follows the quotation.

1 Place commas and periods inside quotation marks.

Commas or periods fall *inside* closing quotation marks, even when (as in the third example) single and double quotation marks are combined:

Swift uses irony in his essay “A Modest Proposal.”

Many first-time readers are shocked to see infants described as “delicious.”

“‘A Modest Proposal,’” writes one critic, “is so outrageous that it cannot be believed.”

(See pp. 446–50 for the use of commas, as in the preceding example, to separate a quotation from a signal phrase such as *writes one critic*.)

Exception When a parenthetical source citation immediately follows a quotation, place any period or comma *after* the citation:

One critic calls the essay "outrageous" (Olms 26).

Partly because of "the cool calculation of its delivery" (Olms 27), Swift's satire still chills a modern reader.

See page 630 for more on placing parenthetical citations.

2 Place colons and semicolons outside quotation marks.

Some years ago the slogan in elementary education was "learning by playing"; now educators are concerned with basic skills.

We all know what is meant by "inflation": more money buys less.

3 Place dashes, question marks, and exclamation points inside quotation marks only if they belong to the quotation.

When a dash, question mark, or exclamation point is part of the quotation, put it *inside* quotation marks. Don't use any other punctuation such as a period or comma:

"But must you—" Marcia hesitated, afraid of the answer.

"Go away!" I yelled.

Did you say, "Who is she?" [When both your sentence and the quotation would end in a question mark or exclamation point, use only the mark in the quotation.]

When a dash, question mark, or exclamation point applies only to the larger sentence, not to the quotation, place it *outside* quotation marks—again, with no other punctuation:

One evocative line in English poetry—"After many a summer dies the swan"—comes from Alfred, Lord Tennyson.

Who said, "Now cracks a noble heart"?

The woman called me "stupid"!

EXERCISE 31.3 Revising: Quotation marks

The underlined words in the following sentences are titles or direct quotations. Remove incorrect underlining, and insert quotation marks. Be sure that other marks of punctuation are correctly placed inside or outside the quotation marks. (You can do this exercise online at *ablongman.com/littlebrown*.)

Example:

The award-winning essay is <u>Science and Values</u>.

The award-winning essay is "Science and Values."

1. In the title essay of her book <u>The Death of the Moth and Other Essays</u>, Virginia Woolf describes the last moments of a <u>frail and diminutive body</u>.

2. An insect's death may seem insignificant, but the moth is, in Woolf's words, life, a pure bead.
3. The moth's struggle against death, indifferent, impersonal, is heroic.
4. Where else but in such a bit of life could one see a protest so superb?
5. At the end Woolf sees the moth lying most decently and uncomplainingly composed; in death it finds dignity.

EXERCISE 31.4 Revising: Quotation marks

Insert quotation marks as needed in the following paragraph. (You can do this exercise online at *ablongman.com/littlebrown*.)

In one class we talked about a passage from I Have a Dream, the speech delivered by Martin Luther King, Jr., on the steps of the Lincoln Memorial on August 28, 1963:

> When the architects of our republic wrote the magnificent words of the Constitution and the Declaration of Independence, they were signing a promissory note to which every American was to fall heir. This note was a promise that all men would be guaranteed the unalienable rights of life, liberty, and the pursuit of happiness.

What did Dr. King mean by this statement? the teacher asked. Perhaps we should define promissory note first. Then she explained that a person who signs such a note agrees to pay a specific sum of money on a particular date or on demand by the holder of the note. One student suggested, Maybe Dr. King meant that the writers of the Constitution and Declaration promised that all people in America should be equal. He and over 200,000 people had gathered in Washington, DC, added another student. Maybe their purpose was to demand payment, to demand those rights for African Americans. The whole discussion was an eye opener for those of us (including me) who had never considered that those documents make promises that we should expect our country to fulfill.

Note See page 490 for a punctuation exercise involving quotation marks along with other marks of punctuation.

CHAPTER 32

Other Punctuation Marks

This chapter covers the colon (below), the dash (p. 482), parentheses (p. 484), brackets (p. 485), the ellipsis mark (p. 486), and the slash (p. 489).

Note Many grammar and style checkers will flag a lone parenthesis or bracket so that you can match it with another parenthesis or bracket. But most checkers cannot recognize other misuses of the marks covered here and instead simply ignore the marks.

32a Use the colon to introduce and to separate.

The colon is mainly a mark of introduction: it signals that the words following will explain or amplify. The colon also has several conventional uses, such as in expressions of time.

In its main use as an introducer, a colon is *always* preceded by a complete **main clause**—one containing a subject and a predicate and not starting with a subordinating word (see p. 254 for more on main clauses). A colon may or may not be followed by a main clause. This is one way the colon differs from the semicolon (see the box on the next page). The colon is interchangeable with the dash, though the dash is more informal and more abrupt (see p. 482).

Note Don't use a colon more than once in a sentence. The sentence should end with the element introduced by the colon.

1 Use a colon to introduce a concluding explanation, series, appositive, or long or formal quotation.

Depending on your preference, a complete sentence *after* the colon may begin with a capital letter or a small letter. Just be consistent throughout an essay.

> **http://www.ablongman.com/littlebrown ▶**
>
> Visit the companion Web site for more help and additional exercises on the colon, the dash, parentheses, brackets, the ellipsis mark, and the slash.

Distinguishing the colon and the semicolon

- **The *colon* is a mark of introduction that separates elements of *unequal* importance**, such as statements and explanations or introductions and quotations. The first element must be a complete main clause; the second element need not be. (See below.)

  The business school caters to working students: it offers special evening courses in business writing, finance, and management.

  The school has one goal: to train students to be responsible, competent businesspeople.

- **The *semicolon* separates elements of *equal* importance,** almost always complete main clauses. (See p. 454.)

  Few enrolling students know exactly what they want from the school; most hope generally for a managerial career.

Explanation

Soul food is a varied cuisine: it includes spicy gumbos, black-eyed peas, and collard greens.

Soul food has a deceptively simple definition: African American ethnic cooking.

Sometimes a concluding explanation is preceded by *the following* or *as follows* and a colon:

A more precise definition might be the following: ingredients, cooking methods, and dishes originating in Africa, brought to the New World by black slaves, and modified or supplemented in the Caribbean and the American South.

Series (p. 443)

At least three soul food dishes are familiar to most Americans: fried chicken, barbecued spareribs, and sweet potato pie.

Appositive (p. 259)

Soul food has one disadvantage: fat.

Certain expressions commonly introduce appositives, such as *namely* and *that is*. These expressions should *follow* the colon: *Soul food has one disadvantage: namely, fat.*

Long or formal quotation

The comma generally separates a signal phrase from a quotation (see p. 446). But when you introduce a long or formal quotation with a complete sentence, use a colon instead:

One soul food chef has a solution: "Soul food doesn't have to be greasy to taste good. Instead of using ham hocks to flavor beans, I use smoked turkey wings. The soulful, smoky taste remains, but without all the fat of pork."

2 Use a colon to separate titles and subtitles and the subdivisions of time.

Titles and subtitles	Time
*Charles Dickens**:** An Introduction to His Novels*	1**:**30 AM
*Eros and Civilization**:** An Inquiry into Freud*	12**:**26 PM

3 Use the colon only where required.

Use the colon only at the *end* of a main clause. Do not use it directly after a verb or preposition.

Not Two critically acclaimed movies directed by Steven Spielberg are: *Schindler's List* and *Saving Private Ryan*.

But Two critically acclaimed movies directed by Steven Spielberg are *Schindler's List* and *Saving Private Ryan*.

Not Shakespeare had the qualities of a Renaissance thinker, such as: humanism and an interest in Greek and Roman literature.

But Shakespeare had the qualities of a Renaissance thinker, such as humanism and an interest in Greek and Roman literature.

EXERCISE 32.1 Revising: Colons

Insert colons as needed in the following sentences, or delete colons that are misused. (You can do this exercise online at *ablongman.com/littlebrown*.)

Example:

Mix the ingredients as follows sift the flour and salt together, add the milk, and slowly beat in the egg yolk.

Mix the ingredients as follows**:** sift the flour and salt together, add the milk, and slowly beat in the egg yolk.

1. In remote areas of many developing countries, simple signs mark human habitation a dirt path, a few huts, smoke from a campfire.
2. In the built-up sections of industrialized countries, nature is all but obliterated by signs of human life, such as: houses, factories, skyscrapers, and highways.
3. The spectacle makes many question the words of Ecclesiastes 1.4 "One generation passeth away, and another cometh; but the earth abideth forever."
4. Yet many scientists see the future differently they hold that human beings have all the technology necessary to clean up the earth and restore the cycles of nature.
5. All that is needed is: a change in the attitudes of those who use technology.

32b Use a dash to indicate shifts in tone or thought and to set off some sentence elements.

The dash is mainly a mark of interruption: it signals an insertion or break.

Note In your papers, form a dash with two hyphens (--), or use the character called an em dash on your word processor. Do not add extra space around or between the hyphens or around the em dash.

1 Use a dash or dashes to indicate shifts and hesitations.

Shift in tone

The novel—if one can call it that—appeared in 2004.

Unfinished thought

If the book had a plot—but a plot would be conventional.

Hesitation in dialog

"I was worried you might think I had stayed away because I was influenced by—" He stopped and lowered his eyes.

Astonished, Howe said, "Influenced by what?"

"Well, by—" Blackburn hesitated and for an answer pointed to the table. —Lionel Trilling

2 Use a dash or dashes to emphasize nonessential elements.

Dashes may be used in place of commas or parentheses to set off and emphasize nonessential elements. (See the box on the facing page.) Dashes are especially useful when these elements are internally punctuated. Be sure to use a pair of dashes when the element interrupts a main clause.

Appositive (p. 259)

The qualities Monet painted—bright sunlight, rich shadows, deep colors—abounded near the rivers and gardens he used as subjects.

Modifier

Though they are close together—separated by only a few blocks—the two neighborhoods could be in different countries.

Parenthetical expression (p. 484)

At any given time there exists an inventory of undiscovered embezzlement in—or more precisely not in—the country's businesses and banks. —John Kenneth Galbraith

3 Use a dash to set off introductory series and concluding series and explanations.

Introductory series

Shortness of breath, skin discoloration or the sudden appearance of moles, persistent indigestion, the presence of small lumps—all these may signify cancer.

Distinguishing dashes, commas, and parentheses

Dashes, commas, and parentheses may all set off nonessential elements.

- ***Dashes* give the information the greatest emphasis** (facing page):

  Many students—including some on the advisory board—disapprove of the new dress code.

- ***Commas* are less emphatic** (p. 437):

  Many students, including some on the advisory board, disapprove of the new dress code.

- ***Parentheses* are the least emphatic,** signaling that the information is just worth a mention (next page):

  Many students (including some on the advisory board) disapprove of the new dress code.

A dash sets off concluding series and explanations more informally and more abruptly than a colon does (see p. 480):

Concluding series

The patient undergoes a battery of tests—CAT scan, bronchoscopy, perhaps even biopsy.

Concluding explanation

Many patients are disturbed by the CAT scan—by the need to keep still for long periods in an exceedingly small space.

4 Use the dash only where needed.

Don't use the dash when commas, semicolons, and periods are more appropriate. And don't use too many dashes. They can create a jumpy or breathy quality in writing.

Not In all his life—eighty-seven years—my great-grandfather never allowed his picture to be taken—not even once. He claimed the "black box"—the camera—would steal his soul.

But In all his eighty-seven years my great-grandfather did not allow his picture to be taken even once. He claimed the "black box"—the camera—would steal his soul.

EXERCISE 32.2 Revising: Dashes

Insert dashes as needed in the following sentences. (You can do this exercise online at *ablongman.com/littlebrown.*)

Example:

What would we do if someone like Adolf Hitler that monster appeared among us?

What would we do if someone like Adolf Hitler—that monster—appeared among us?

1. The movie-theater business is undergoing dramatic changes changes that may affect what movies are made and shown.
2. The closing of independent theaters, the control of theaters by fewer and fewer owners, and the increasing ownership of theaters by movie studios and distributors these changes may reduce the availability of noncommercial films.
3. Yet at the same time the number of movie screens is increasing primarily in multiscreen complexes so that smaller films may find more outlets.
4. The number of active movie screens that is, screens showing films or booked to do so is higher now than at any time since World War II.
5. The biggest theater complexes seem to be something else as well art galleries, amusement arcades, restaurants, spectacles.

32c Use parentheses to enclose parenthetical expressions and labels for lists within sentences.

Parentheses *always* come in pairs: one before and one after the punctuated material.

1 Use parentheses to enclose parenthetical expressions.

Parenthetical expressions include explanations, digressions, and examples that may be helpful or interesting but are not essential to meaning. They are emphasized least when set off with a pair of parentheses instead of commas or dashes. (See the box on p. 483.)

The population of Philadelphia **(**now about 1.5 million**)** has declined since 1950.

Ariel **(**published in 1965**)** contains Sylvia Plath's last poems.

Note Don't put a comma before a parenthetical expression enclosed in parentheses:

Not Philadelphia's population compares with Houston's, (just over 1.6 million).

But Philadelphia's population compares with Houston's (just over 1.6 million).

A comma, semicolon, or period falling after a parenthetical expression should be placed *outside* the closing parenthesis:

Philadelphia has a larger African American population (nearly 40 percent**),** while Houston has a larger Latino population (nearly 28 percent**).**

When it falls between other complete sentences, a complete sentence enclosed in parentheses has a capital letter and end punctuation:

In general, coaches will tell you that scouts are just guys who can't coach. (But then, so are brain surgeons**.)** —Roy Blount

2 Use parentheses to enclose labels for lists within sentences.

Outside the Middle East, the countries with the largest oil reserves are (1) Venezuela (63 billion barrels), (2) Russia (57 billion barrels), and (3) Mexico (51 billion barrels).

When you set a list off from your text, do not enclose such labels in parentheses.

EXERCISE 32.3 Revising: Parentheses

Insert parentheses as needed in the following sentences. (You can do this exercise online at *ablongman.com/littlebrown.*)

Example:

Shoppers can find good-quality, inexpensive furniture for example, desks, tables, chairs, sofas, even beds in junk stores.

Shoppers can find good-quality, inexpensive furniture (for example, desks, tables, chairs, sofas, even beds) in junk stores.

1. Many of those involved in the movie business agree that multiscreen complexes are good for two reasons: 1 they cut the costs of exhibitors, and 2 they offer more choices to audiences.
2. Those who produce and distribute films and not just the big studios argue that the multiscreen theaters give exhibitors too much power.
3. The major studios are buying movie theaters to gain control over important parts of the distribution process what gets shown and for how much money.
4. For twelve years 1938–50 the federal government forced the studios to sell all their movie theaters.
5. But because they now have more competition television and DVD players, for instance, the studios are permitted to own theaters.

32d Use brackets within quotations to indicate your own comments or changes.

Brackets have specialized uses in mathematical equations, but their main use for all kinds of writing is to indicate that you have altered a quotation. If you need to explain, clarify, or correct the words of the writer you quote, place your additions in a pair of brackets:

"That Texaco station [just outside Chicago] is one of the busiest in the nation," said a company spokesperson.

Use brackets if you need to alter the capitalization of a quotation so that it will fit into your sentence. (See also p. 493.)

"[O]ne of the busiest in the nation" is how a company spokesperson described the station.

You may also use a bracketed word or words to substitute for parts of a quotation that would otherwise be unclear. In the following sentence, the bracketed word substitutes for *they* in the original:

"Despite considerable achievements in other areas, [humans] still cannot control the weather and probably will never be able to do so."

See page 607 for additional examples of using brackets with quotations.

The word *sic* (Latin for "in this manner") in brackets indicates that an error in the quotation appeared in the original and was not made by you. When following MLA style, do not underline or italicize *sic* in brackets. Most other styles—including Chicago, APA, and CSE—do italicize *sic*.

According to the newspaper report, "The car slammed thru [sic] the railing and into oncoming traffic."

Don't use *sic* to make fun of a writer or to note errors in a passage that is clearly nonstandard or illiterate.

Note Always acknowledge the sources of quotations in order to avoid plagiarism. (See pp. 615–16 and 618–19.)

32e Use the ellipsis mark to indicate omissions from quotations and pauses in speech.

The **ellipsis mark** consists of three spaced periods (. . .). It usually indicates an omission from a quotation, although it may also show an interruption in dialog.

Note Additional issues with quotations are discussed elsewhere in this book:

- **Integrating source material into your text,** pages 607–10.
- **Acknowledging the sources of quotations to avoid plagiarism,** pages 615–16 and 618–19. See also example 3 on the facing page.

1 The ellipsis mark substitutes for omissions from quotations.

When you omit a part of a quotation, show the omission with an ellipsis mark. All the following examples quote from the passage below about environmentalism.

Original quotation

"At the heart of the environmentalist world view is the conviction that human physical and spiritual health depends on sustaining the planet in a relatively unaltered state. Earth is our home in the full, genetic sense, where humanity and its ancestors existed for all the millions of years of their evolution. Natural ecosystems—forests, coral reefs, marine blue waters—maintain the world exactly as we would wish it to be maintained. When we debase the global environment and extinguish the variety of life, we are dismantling a support system that is too complex to understand, let alone replace, in the foreseeable future." —Edward O. Wilson, "Is Humanity Suicidal?"

1. Omission of the middle of a sentence

"Natural ecosystems . . . maintain the world exactly as we would wish it to be maintained."

2. Omission of the end of a sentence, without source citation

"Earth is our home. . . ." [The sentence period, closed up to the last word, precedes the ellipsis mark.]

3. Omission of the end of a sentence, with source citation

"Earth is our home . . ." (Wilson 27). [The sentence period follows the source citation.]

4. Omission of parts of two or more sentences

Wilson writes, "At the heart of the environmentalist world view is the conviction that human physical and spiritual health depends on sustaining the planet . . . where humanity and its ancestors existed for all the millions of years of their evolution."

5. Omission of one or more sentences

As Wilson puts it, "At the heart of the environmentalist world view is the conviction that human physical and spiritual health depends on sustaining the planet in a relatively unaltered state. . . . When we debase the global environment and extinguish the variety of life, we are dismantling a support system that is too complex to understand, let alone replace, in the foreseeable future."

6. Omission from the middle of a sentence through the end of another sentence

"Earth is our home. . . . When we debase the global environment and extinguish the variety of life, we are dismantling a support system that is too complex to understand, let alone replace, in the foreseeable future."

7. Omission of the beginning of a sentence, leaving a complete sentence

a. Bracketed capital letter

"[H]uman physical and spiritual health," Wilson writes, "depends on sustaining the planet in a relatively unaltered state." [No ellipsis mark is needed because the brackets around the *H* indicate that the letter was not capitalized originally and thus that the beginning of the sentence has been omitted.]

b. Small letter

According to Wilson, "human physical and spiritual health depends on sustaining the planet in a relatively unaltered state." [No ellipsis mark is needed because the small *h* indicates that the beginning of the sentence has been omitted.]

c. Capital letter from the original

Hami comments, ". . . Wilson argues eloquently for the environmentalist world view." [An ellipsis mark is needed because the quoted part of the sentence begins with a capital letter and it is not clear that the beginning of the original sentence has been omitted.]

8. Use of a word or phrase

Wilson describes the earth as "our home." [No ellipsis mark needed.]

Note the following features of the examples:

- **Use an ellipsis mark when it is not otherwise clear that you have left out material from the source,** as when you omit one or more sentences (examples 5 and 6) or when the words you quote form a complete sentence that is different in the original (examples 1–4 and 7c).
- **You don't need an ellipsis mark when it is obvious that you have omitted something,** such as when capitalization indicates omission (examples 7a and 7b) or when a phrase clearly comes from a larger sentence (example 8).
- **Place as ellipsis mark after a sentence period *except* when a parenthetical source citation follows the quotation,** as in example 3. Then the sentence period falls after the citation.

If you omit one or more lines of poetry or paragraphs of prose from a quotation, use a separate line of ellipsis marks across the full width of the quotation to show the omission:

In "Song: Love Armed" from 1676, Aphra Behn contrasts two lovers' experiences of a romance:

> Love in fantastic triumph sate,
>   Whilst bleeding hearts around him flowed,
>
> . . . .
>
> But my poor heart alone is harmed,
>   Whilst thine the victor is, and free. (lines 1-2, 15-16)

(See pp. 665–66 for the format of displayed quotations like this one. And see p. 629 on the source-citation form illustrated here.)

2 The ellipsis mark indicates pauses or unfinished statements.

When writing dialog or when writing informally (not in academic writing), you can show hesitation or interruption with an ellipsis mark instead of a dash (p. 482).

"I wish . . ." His voice trailed off.

EXERCISE 32.4 Using ellipsis marks

Use ellipsis marks and any other needed punctuation to follow the numbered instructions for quoting from the following paragraph. (You can do this exercise online at *ablongman.com/littlebrown.*)

Women in the sixteenth and seventeenth centuries were educated in the home and, in some cases, in boarding schools. Men were educated at home, in grammar schools, and at the universities. The universities were closed to female students. For women, "learning the Bible," as Elizabeth Joceline puts it, was an impetus to learning to read. To be able to read the Bible in the vernacular was a liberating experience that freed the reader from hearing only the set passages read in the church and interpreted by the church. A Protestant woman was expected to read the scriptures daily, to meditate on them, and to memorize portions of them. In addition, a woman was expected to instruct her entire household in "learning the Bible" by holding instructional and devotional times each day for all household members, including the servants.

—Charlotte F. Otten, *English Women's Voices, 1540–1700*

1. Quote the fifth sentence, but omit everything from *that freed the reader* to the end.
2. Quote the fifth sentence, but omit the words *was a liberating experience that.*
3. Quote the first and sixth sentences.

32f Use the slash between options, between lines of poetry, and in electronic addresses.

Option

I don't know why some teachers oppose pass/fail courses.

Between options, the slash is not surrounded by extra space.

Note The options *and/or* and *he/she* should be avoided. (See the Glossary of Usage, pp. 837 and 844.)

Poetry

Many readers have sensed a reluctant turn away from death in Frost's lines "The woods are lovely, dark and deep, / But I have promises to keep" (13–14).

When you run lines of poetry into your text, separate them with a slash surrounded by space. (See pp. 665–66 for more on quoting poetry.)

Electronic address

http://www.stanford.edu/depts/spc/spc.html

EXERCISE 32.5 Revising: Colons, dashes, parentheses, brackets, ellipsis marks, slashes

Insert colons, dashes, parentheses, brackets, ellipsis marks, or slashes as needed in the following paragraph. When different marks would be appropriate in the same place, be able to defend the choice you make. (You can do this exercise online at *ablongman.com/littlebrown.*)

"Let all the learned say what they can, 'Tis ready money makes the man." These two lines of poetry by the Englishman William Somerville 1645–1742 may apply to a current American economic problem. Non-American investors with "ready money" pour some of it as much as $1.3 trillion in recent years into the United States. The investments of foreigners are varied stocks and bonds, savings deposits, service companies, factories, art works, even the campaigns of political candidates. Proponents of foreign investment argue that it revives industry, strengthens the economy, creates jobs more than 3 million, they say, and encourages free trade among nations. Opponents discuss the risks of heavy foreign investment it makes the American economy vulnerable to outsiders, sucks profits from the country, and gives foreigners an influence in governmental decision making. On both sides, it seems, "the learned say 'Tis ready money makes the man or country." The question is, whose money?

EXERCISE ON CHAPTERS 27–32 Revising: Punctuation

The following paragraphs are unpunctuated except for end-of-sentence periods. Insert periods, commas, semicolons, apostrophes, quotation marks, colons, dashes, or parentheses where they are required. When different marks would be appropriate in the same place, be able to defend the choice you make. (You can do this exercise online at *ablongman.com/littlebrown.*)

Brewed coffee is the most widely consumed beverage in the world. The trade in coffee beans alone amounts to well over $6000000000 a year and the total volume of beans traded exceeds 4250000 tons a year. Its believed that the beverage was introduced into Arabia in the fifteenth century AD probably by Ethiopians. By the middle or late sixteenth century the Arabs had introduced the beverage to the Europeans who at first resisted it because of its strong flavor and effect as a mild stimulant. The French Italians and other Europeans incorporated coffee into their diets by the seventeenth century the English however preferred tea which they were then importing from India. Since America was colonized primarily by the English Americans also preferred tea. Only after the Boston Tea Party 1773 did Americans begin drinking coffee in large quantities. Now though the US is one of the top coffee-consuming countries consumption having been spurred on by familiar advertising claims Good till the last drop Rich hearty aroma Always rich never bitter.

Produced from the fruit of an evergreen tree coffee is grown primarily in Latin America southern Asia and Africa. Coffee trees require a hot climate high humidity rich soil with good drainage and partial shade consequently they thrive on the east or west slopes of tropical volcanic mountains where the soil is laced with potash and drains easily. The coffee beans actually seeds grow inside bright red berries. The berries are picked by hand and the beans are extracted by machine leaving a pulpy fruit residue that can be used for fertilizer. The beans are usually roasted in ovens a chemical process that releases the beans essential oil caffeol which gives coffee its distinctive aroma. Over a hundred different varieties of beans are produced in the world each with a different flavor attributable to three factors the species of plant *Coffea arabica* and *Coffea robusta* are the most common and the soil and climate where the variety was grown.

PART 7

Mechanics

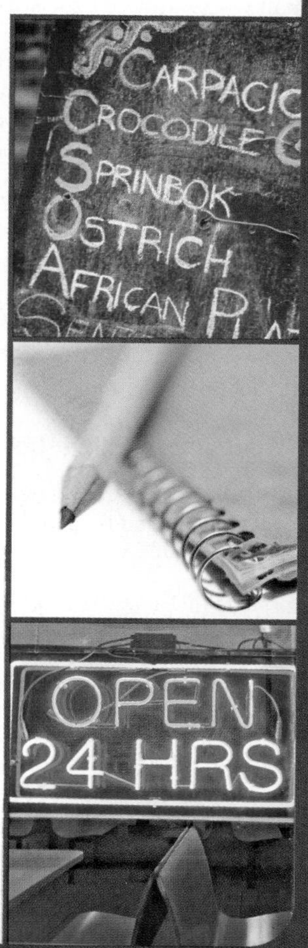

CHAPTER 33

Capitals

Generally, capitalize a word only when a dictionary or conventional use says you must. Consult one of the style guides listed on pages 739 and 767 for special uses of capitals in the social, natural, and applied sciences.

Note A grammar and style checker will flag overused capital letters and missing capitals at the beginnings of sentences. It will also spot missing capitals at the beginnings of proper nouns and adjectives—*if* the nouns and adjectives are in the checker's dictionary. For example, a checker caught *christianity* and *europe* but not *china* (for the country) or *Stephen king.*

CULTURE LANGUAGE Conventions of capitalization vary from language to language. English, for instance, is the only language to capitalize the first-person singular pronoun (*I*), and its practice of capitalizing proper nouns but not most common nouns also distinguishes it from some other languages.

33a Capitalize the first word of every sentence.

Every writer should own a good dictionary.
Will inflation be curbed?
Watch out!

When quoting other writers, you must either reproduce the capital letters beginning their sentences or indicate with brackets that you have altered the source. Whenever possible, integrate the quotation into your own sentence so that its capital letters coincide with your own:

"Psychotherapists often overlook the benefits of self-deception," the author argues.

The author argues that "the benefits of self-deception" are not always recognized by psychotherapists.

http://www.ablongman.com/littlebrown

Visit the companion Web site for more help and an additional exercise on capital letters.

If you need to alter the capitalization in the source, indicate the change with brackets (see p. 485):

> "[T]he benefits of self-deception" are not always recognized by psychotherapists, the author argues.
>
> The author argues that "[p]sychotherapists often overlook the benefits of self-deception."

Note Capitalization of questions in a series is optional. Both examples below are correct:

> Is the population a hundred? Two hundred? More?
> Is the population a hundred? two hundred? more?

Also optional is capitalization of the first word in a complete sentence after a colon (see p. 479).

33b Capitalize most words in titles and subtitles of works.

Within your text, capitalize all the words in a title *except* the following: articles (*a, an, the*), *to* in infinitives, and connecting words (prepositions and coordinating and subordinating conjunctions) of fewer than five letters. Capitalize even these short words when they are the first or last word in a title or when they fall after a colon or semicolon.

> *The Sound and the Fury*
> "Courtship Through the Ages"
> *A Diamond Is Forever*
> "Knowing Whom to Ask"
> *Learning from Las Vegas*
> "The Truth About AIDS"
> *Management: A New Theory*
> "Once More to the Lake"
> *An End to Live For*
> "Power: How to Get It"
> *File Under Architecture*
> *Only when I Laugh*

Always capitalize the prefix or first word in a hyphenated word within a title. Capitalize the second word only if it is a noun or an adjective or is as important as the first word.

> "Applying Stage Make-up"
> *The Pre-Raphaelites*
> *Through the Looking-Glass*

Note The style guides of the academic disciplines have their own rules for capitals in titles. For instance, MLA style for English and some other humanities capitalizes all subordinating conjunctions but no prepositions. In addition, APA style for the social sciences and CSE style for the sciences capitalize only the first word and proper names in book and article titles within source citations. See pages 743–44 (APA) and 769–70 (CSE).

33c Always capitalize the pronoun *I* and the interjection *O*. Capitalize *oh* only when it begins a sentence.

I love to stay up at night, but, oh, I hate to get up in the morning.

He who thinks himself wise, O heavens, is a great fool.
—Voltaire

33d Capitalize proper nouns, proper adjectives, and words used as essential parts of proper nouns.

Proper nouns name specific persons, places, and things: *Shakespeare, California, World War I.* **Proper adjectives** are formed from some proper nouns: *Shakespearean, Californian.*

1 Capitalize proper nouns and proper adjectives.

Capitalize all proper nouns and proper adjectives but not the articles (*a, an, the*) that precede them.

Proper nouns and adjectives to be capitalized

Specific persons and things

Stephen King	the Leaning Tower of Pisa
Napoleon Bonaparte	Boulder Dam
Doris Lessing	the Empire State Building

Specific places and geographical regions

New York City	the Mediterranean Sea
China	Lake Victoria
Europe	the Northeast, the South
North America	the Rocky Mountains

But: northeast of the city, going south

Days of the week, months, holidays

Monday	Yom Kippur
May	Christmas
Thanksgiving	Columbus Day

Historical events, documents, periods, movements

World War II	the Middle Ages
the Vietnam War	the Age of Reason
the Boston Tea Party	the Renaissance
the Treaty of Ghent	the Great Depression
the Constitution	the Romantic Movement
the Bill of Rights	the Cultural Revolution

Government offices or departments and institutions

House of Representatives	Polk Municipal Court
Department of Defense	Warren County Hospital
Appropriations Committee	Northeast High School

Political, social, athletic, and other organizations and associations and their members

Democratic Party, Democrats	Rotary Club, Rotarians
Sierra Club	League of Women Voters
Girl Scouts of America, Scout	Boston Celtics
B'nai B'rith	Chicago Symphony Orchestra

Races, nationalities, and their languages

Native American	Germans
African American	Swahili
Caucasian	Italian

But: blacks, whites

Religions and their followers

Christianity, Christians	Judaism, Orthodox Jews
Protestantism, Protestants	Hinduism, Hindus
Catholicism, Catholics	Islam, Muslims

Religious terms for the sacred

God	Buddha
Allah	the Bible [*but* biblical]
Christ	the Koran, the Qur'an

Note Follow your own preference in capitalizing *he, his,* or *him* when referring to God or Allah.

2 Capitalize common nouns used as essential parts of proper nouns.

Common nouns name general classes of persons, places, or things, and they generally are not capitalized. However, capitalize the common nouns *street, avenue, park, river, ocean, lake, company, college, county,* and *memorial* when they are part of proper nouns naming specific places or institutions:

Main Street	Lake Superior
Central Park	Ford Motor Company
Mississippi River	Madison College
Pacific Ocean	George Washington Memorial

3 Capitalize trade names.

Trade names identify individual brands of certain products. When a trade name loses its association with a brand and comes to refer to a product in general, it is not capitalized. Refer to a dictionary for current usage when you are in doubt about a name.

Scotch tape
Chevrolet
Xerox
Bunsen burner

But: nylon, thermos

33e Capitalize most titles of persons only when they precede proper names.

Professor Otto Osborne
Doctor Jane Covington
Governor Ella Moore

Otto Osborne, a professor of English
Jane Covington, a medical doctor
Ella Moore, the governor

Not The Senator supported the bill.
But The senator supported the bill.
Or Senator Carmine supported the bill.

Exception Many writers capitalize a title denoting very high rank even when it follows a proper name or is used alone:

Ronald Reagan, past President of the United States
the Chief Justice of the United States Supreme Court

33f Avoid common misuses of capital letters.

1 Use small letters for common nouns replacing proper nouns.

Not I am determined to take a World History class before I graduate from High School.

But I am determined to take a world history class before I graduate from high school.

Or I am determined to take World History I before I graduate from Grimsley High School.

2 Capitalize compass directions only when they refer to specific geographical areas.

The storm blew in from the northeast and then veered south along the coast. [Here *northeast* and *south* refer to general directions.]

Students from the South have trouble adjusting to the Northeast's bitter winters. [Here *South* and *Northeast* refer to specific regions.]

3 Use small letters for the names of seasons or the names of academic years or terms.

spring
summer
autumn
fall quarter
senior year
winter term

4 Capitalize the names of relationships only when they form part of or substitute for proper names.

my mother
my uncle Brad
the father of my friend
Brad's brother

I remember how Dad scolded us.
Aunt Annie and Uncle Jake died within two months of each other.

5 Use capitals according to convention in online communication.

Online messages written in all-capital letters or with no capital letters are difficult to read. Further, messages in all-capital letters may be considered rude. Use capital letters according to rules 33a–33f in all your online communication.

EXERCISE 33.1 Revising: Capitals

Capitalize words as necessary in the following sentences, or substitute small letters for unnecessary capitals. Consult a dictionary if you are in doubt. If the capitalization in a sentence is already correct, mark the number preceding the sentence. (You can do this exercise online at *ablongman.com/littlebrown*.)

Example:

The first book on the reading list is mark twain's *a connecticut yankee in king arthur's court.*

The first book on the reading list is Mark Twain's *A Connecticut Yankee in King Arthur's Court.*

1. San Antonio, texas, is a thriving city in the southwest.
2. The city has always offered much to tourists interested in the roots of spanish settlement of the new world.
3. The alamo is one of five Catholic Missions built by Priests to convert native americans and to maintain spain's claims in the area.
4. But the alamo is more famous for being the site of an 1836 battle that helped to create the republic of Texas.
5. Many of the nearby Streets, such as Crockett street, are named for men who gave their lives in that Battle.
6. The Hemisfair plaza and the San Antonio river link new tourist and convention facilities developed during mayor Cisneros's terms.
7. Restaurants, Hotels, and shops line the River. the haunting melodies of "Una paloma blanca" and "malagueña" lure passing tourists into Casa rio and other excellent mexican restaurants.
8. The university of Texas at San Antonio has expanded, and a Medical Center has been developed in the Northwest part of the city.
9. Sea World, on the west side of San Antonio, entertains grandparents, fathers and mothers, and children with the antics of dolphins and seals.

10. The City has attracted high-tech industry, creating a corridor of economic growth between san antonio and austin and contributing to the texas economy.

Note See page 509 for an exercise involving capitals along with underlining or italics and other mechanics.

CHAPTER 34

Underlining or Italics

Underlining and *italic type* indicate the same thing: the word or words are being distinguished or emphasized. If you underline two or more words in a row, underline the space between the words, too: Criminal Statistics: Misuses of Numbers.

Note A grammar and style checker cannot recognize problems with underlining or italics. Use the guidelines in this chapter to edit your work.

34a Use underlining or italics consistently and appropriately for your writing situation.

Italic type is now used almost universally in business and academic writing. Still, some academic style guides, notably the *MLA Handbook,* continue to prefer underlining, especially in source citations. Ask your teacher for his or her own preference. (We use underlining for the examples in this chapter because it is easier to see than italics.)

Use either italics or underlining consistently throughout a document. For instance, if you are writing an English paper and following MLA style for underlining in source citations, use underlining in the body of your paper as well.

http://www.ablongman.com/littlebrown

Visit the companion Web site for more help and an additional exercise on underlining or italics.

34b Underline or italicize the titles of works that appear independently.

Within your text, underline or italicize the titles of works that are published, released, or produced separately from other works (see the box below). Use quotation marks for all other titles (see p. 474).

Titles to be underlined or italicized

Other titles should be placed in quotation marks. (See p. 474.)

Books
War and Peace
Psychology: An Introduction

Plays
Hamlet
The Phantom of the Opera

Computer software
Microsoft Internet Explorer
Acrobat Reader

Web sites
Google
Friends of Prufrock

Pamphlets
The Truth About Alcoholism
Plants of the Desert

Long musical works
Tchaikovsky's *Swan Lake*
The Beatles' *Revolver*
But: Symphony in C

Television and radio programs
All Things Considered
NBC Sports Hour

Long poems
Beowulf
Paradise Lost

Periodicals
Time
Boston Globe
Yale Law Review

Published speeches
Lincoln's *Gettysburg Address*
Pericles's *Funeral Oration*

Movies, DVDs, and videos
Schindler's List
How to Relax

Works of visual art
Michelangelo's *David*
Picasso's *Guernica*

Note Underline or italicize marks of punctuation only when they are part of the title: *Did you read Catch-22?* (not *Catch-22*?). In titles of newspapers underline or italicize the name of the city only when it is part of the title:

New York Times Manchester *Guardian*

When giving the title of a periodical in your text, you need not capitalize, underline, or italicize the article *the,* even if it is part of the title: *She has the New York Times delivered to her in Japan.*

Exceptions Legal documents, the Bible, the Koran, and their parts are generally not underlined or italicized:

Not They registered their *deed*.
But They registered their deed.

Not We studied the *Book of Revelation* in the *Bible*.
But We studied the Book of Revelation in the Bible.

Many sciences do not use underlining or italics for some or all titles within source citations. (See pp. 769–74 on CSE style.)

34c Underline or italicize the names of ships, aircraft, spacecraft, and trains.

Queen Elizabeth 2	*Orient Express*	*Apollo XI*
Challenger	*Spirit of St. Louis*	*Montrealer*

34d Underline or italicize foreign words and phrases that have not been absorbed into English.

English has adopted many foreign words and phrases—such as the French "bon voyage"—and these need not be underlined or italicized. Do underline or italicize words considered foreign, consulting a dictionary if needed.

> The scientific name for the brown trout is *Salmo trutta*. [The Latin scientific names for plants and animals are always underlined or italicized.]
>
> What a life he led! He was a true *bon vivant*.
>
> The Latin *De gustibus non est disputandum* translates roughly as "There's no accounting for taste."

34e Underline or italicize words or characters named as words.

Use underlining or italics to indicate that you are citing a character or word as a word rather than using it for its meaning. Words you are defining fall under this convention:

> The word *syzygy* refers to a straight line formed by three celestial bodies, as in the alignment of the earth, sun, and moon.
>
> Some people say *th*, as in *thought*, with a faint *s* or *f* sound.
>
> Carved into the column, twenty feet up, was a mysterious *7*.

34f Occasionally, underlining or italics may be used for emphasis.

Underlining or italics can stress an important word or phrase, especially in reporting how someone said something:

"Why on earth would you do that?" she cried.

But use such emphasis very rarely. Excessive underlining or italics will make your writing sound immature or hysterical:

> The settlers had no firewood and no food. Many of them starved or froze to death that first winter.

34g In online communication, use alternatives for underlining or italics.

Electronic mail and other forms of online communication sometimes do not allow underlining or italics for the purposes described in this chapter. On Web sites, for instance, underlining often indicates a link to another site.

To distinguish elements that usually require underlining or italics, type an underscore before and after the element: *Measurements coincide with those in _Joule's Handbook_.* You can also emphasize words with asterisks: *I *will not* be able to attend.*

Avoid using all-capital letters for emphasis. (See also p. 497.)

EXERCISE 34.1 Revising: Underlining or italics

Underline or italicize words and phrases as needed in the following sentences, or circle any words or phrases that are underlined unnecessarily. Note that some highlighting is correct as given. (You can do this exercise online at *ablongman.com/littlebrown.*)

Example:

Of Hitchcock's movies, Psycho is the scariest.
Of Hitchcock's movies, Psycho is the scariest.

1. Of the many Vietnam veterans who are writers, Oliver Stone is perhaps the most famous for writing and directing the films Platoon and Born on the Fourth of July.
2. Tim O'Brien has written short stories for Esquire, GQ, and Massachusetts Review.
3. Going After Cacciato is O'Brien's dreamlike novel about the horrors of combat.
4. The word Vietnam is technically two words (Viet and Nam), but most American writers spell it as one word.
5. American writers use words or phrases borrowed from Vietnamese, such as di di mau ("go quickly") or dinky dau ("crazy").
6. Philip Caputo's gripping account of his service in Vietnam appears in the book A Rumor of War.
7. Caputo's book was made into a television movie, also titled A Rumor of War.
8. David Rabe's plays—including The Basic Training of Pavlo Hummel, Streamers, and Sticks and Bones—depict the effects of the war not only on the soldiers but on their families.

9. Called the poet laureate of the Vietnam war, Steve Mason has published two collections of poems: Johnny's Song and Warrior for Peace.
10. The Washington Post published rave reviews of Veteran's Day, an autobiography by Rod Kane.

Note See page 509 for an exercise involving underlining or italics along with capitals and other mechanics.

CHAPTER 35

Abbreviations

The following guidelines on abbreviations pertain to the text of a nontechnical document. All academic disciplines use abbreviations in source citations, and much technical writing, such as in the sciences and engineering, uses many abbreviations in the document text. For the requirements of the discipline you are writing in, consult one of the style guides listed on pages 721 (humanities), 739 (social sciences), and 767 (natural and applied sciences).

Usage varies, but writers increasingly omit periods from abbreviations that consist of or end in capital letters: *US, BA, USMC, PhD.* See page 429 on punctuating abbreviations.

Note A grammar and style checker may flag some abbreviations, such as *ft.* (for *foot*) and *st.* (for *street*). A spelling checker will flag abbreviations it does not recognize. But neither checker can tell you whether an abbreviation is appropriate for your writing situation or will be clear to your readers.

35a Use standard abbreviations for titles immediately before and after proper names.

Before the name	After the name
Dr. James Hsu	James Hsu, MD
Mr., Mrs., Ms., Hon., St., Rev., Msgr., Gen.	DDS, DVM, PhD, EdD, OSB, SJ, Sr., Jr.

http://www.ablongman.com/littlebrown

Visit the companion Web site for more help and an additional exercise on abbreviations.

Abbreviations for nontechnical writing

- Titles before or after proper names: *Dr. Jorge Rodriguez; Jorge Rodriguez, PhD.*
- Familiar abbreviations and acronyms: *USA, AIDS.*
- *BC, BCE, AD, CE, AM, PM, no.,* and *$* with dates and numbers.
- *I.e., e.g.,* and other Latin abbreviations within parentheses and in source citations.
- *Inc., Bros., Co.,* and *&* with names of business firms.

Use abbreviations such as *Rev., Hon., Prof., Rep., Sen., Dr.,* and *St.* (for *Saint*) only if they appear with a proper name. Spell them out in the absence of a proper name:

Not We learned to trust the Dr.
But We learned to trust the doctor.
Or We learned to trust Dr. Kaplan.

The abbreviations for academic degrees—*PhD, MA, BA,* and the like—may be used without a proper name: *My brother took seven years to get his PhD. It will probably take me just as long to earn my BA.*

35b Familiar abbreviations and acronyms are acceptable in most writing.

An **acronym** is an abbreviation that spells a pronounceable word, such as WHO, NATO, and AIDS. These and other abbreviations that use initials are acceptable in most writing as long as they are familiar to readers. Abbreviations of two or more words written in all capital letters may be written without periods (see p. 429):

Institutions	LSU, UCLA, TCU
Organizations	CIA, FBI, YMCA, AFL-CIO
Corporations	IBM, CBS, ITT
People	JFK, LBJ, FDR
Countries	US, USA

Note If a name or term (such as *operating room*) appears often in a piece of writing, then its abbreviation (*OR*) can cut down on extra words. Spell out the full term at its first appearance, give its abbreviation in parentheses, and use the abbreviation from then on.

2. About 65 mill. yrs. ago, a comet or asteroid crashed into the earth.
3. The result was a huge crater about 10 km. (6.2 mi.) deep in the Gulf of Mex.
4. Sharpton's new measurements suggest that the crater is 50 pct. larger than scientists previously believed.
5. Indeed, 20-yr.-old drilling cores reveal that the crater is about 186 mi. wide, roughly the size of Conn.
6. The space object was traveling more than 100,000 m.p.h. and hit earth with the impact of 100 to 300 million megatons of TNT.
7. On impact, 200,000 cubic km. of rock and soil were vaporized or thrown into the air.
8. That's the equivalent of 2.34 bill. cubic ft. of matter.
9. The impact would have created 400-ft. tidal waves across the Atl. Ocean, temps. higher than 20,000 degs., and powerful earthquakes.
10. Sharpton theorizes that the dust, vapor, and smoke from this impact blocked the sun's rays for mos., cooled the earth, and thus resulted in the death of the dinosaurs.

Note See page 509 for an exercise involving abbreviations along with capitals and other mechanics.

CHAPTER 36

Numbers

This chapter addresses the use of numbers (numerals versus words) in the text of a document. All disciplines use many more numerals in source citations.

Note Grammar and style checkers will flag numerals beginning sentences and can be customized to ignore or to look for numerals (see p. 63). But they can't tell you whether numerals or spelled-out numbers are appropriate for your writing situation.

http://www.ablongman.com/littlebrown

Visit the companion Web site for more help and an additional exercise on numbers.

36a Use numerals according to standard practice in the field you are writing in.

Always use numerals for numbers that require more than two words to spell out:

The leap year has 366 days.
The population of Minot, North Dakota, is about 32,800.

In nontechnical academic writing, spell out numbers of one or two words:

Twelve nations signed the treaty.

The ball game drew forty-two thousand people. [A hyphenated number may be considered one word.]

In much business writing, use numerals for all numbers over ten (*five reasons, 11 participants*). In technical academic and business writing, such as in science and engineering, use numerals for all numbers over ten, and use numerals for zero through nine when they refer to exact measurements (*2 liters, 1 hour*). (Consult one of the style guides listed on pp. 739 and 767 for more details.)

Note Use a combination of numerals and words for round numbers over a million: *26 million, 2.45 billion.* And use either all numerals or all words when several numbers appear together in a passage, even if convention would require a mixture:

Inconsistent	The satellite Galatea is about twenty-six thousand miles from Neptune. It is 110 miles in diameter and orbits Neptune in just over ten hours.
Revised	The satellite Galatea is about 26,000 miles from Neptune. It is 110 miles in diameter and orbits Neptune in just over 10 hours.

CULTURE LANGUAGE In American English a comma separates the numerals in long numbers (*26,000*), and a period functions as a decimal point (*2.06*).

36b Use numerals according to convention for dates, addresses, and other information.

Even when a number requires one or two words to spell out, we conventionally use numerals in the following situations:

Days and years

June 18, 2000 AD 12 456 BCE 1999

Exception The day of a month may be expressed in words when it is not followed by a year (*June fifth; October first*).

Pages, chapters, volumes, acts, scenes, lines	Decimals, percentages, and fractions
Chapter 9, page 123 *Hamlet,* act 5, scene 3, lines 35–40	22.5 48% (*or* 48 percent) 3½
Addresses	**Scores and statistics**
RD 2 419 Stonewall Street Washington, DC 20036	21 to 7 a mean of 26 a ratio of 8 to 1
Exact amounts of money	**The time of day**
$4.50 $3.5 million (*or* $3,500,000)	9:00 AM 2:30 PM

Exceptions Round dollar or cent amounts of only a few words may be expressed in words: *seventeen dollars; fifteen hundred dollars; sixty cents.* When the word *o'clock* is used for the time of day, also express the number in words: *two o'clock* (not *2 o'clock*).

36c Always spell out numbers that begin sentences.

For clarity, spell out any number that begins a sentence. If the number requires more than two words, reword the sentence so that the number falls later and can be expressed as a numeral:

Not 3.7 billion people live in Asia.
But The population of Asia is 3.7 billion.

EXERCISE 36.1 Revising: Numbers

Revise the following sentences so that numbers are used appropriately for nontechnical writing. Mark the number preceding any sentence in which numbers are already used appropriately. (You can do this exercise online at *ablongman.com/littlebrown.*)

Example:

Christina paid two hundred five dollars for used scuba gear.
Christina paid $205 for used scuba gear.

1. The planet Saturn is nine hundred million miles, or nearly one billion five hundred million kilometers, from the sun.
2. A year on Saturn equals almost thirty of our years.
3. Thus, Saturn orbits the sun only two and four-tenths times during the average human life span.
4. It travels in its orbit at about twenty-one thousand six hundred miles per hour.

5. 15 to 20 times denser than Earth's core, Saturn's core measures 17,000 miles across.
6. The temperature at Saturn's cloud tops is minus one hundred seventy degrees Fahrenheit.
7. In nineteen hundred thirty-three, astronomers found on Saturn's surface a huge white spot 2 times the size of Earth and 7 times the size of Mercury.
8. Saturn's famous rings reflect almost seventy percent of the sunlight that approaches the planet.
9. The ring system is almost forty thousand miles wide, beginning 8800 miles from the planet's visible surface and ending forty-seven thousand miles from that surface.
10. Saturn generates about one hundred thirty trillion kilowatts of electricity.

EXERCISE ON CHAPTERS 33–36 Revising: Mechanics

Revise the paragraphs below to correct any errors in the use of capital letters, underlining or italics, abbreviations, and numbers. (For abbreviations and numbers follow standard practice for nontechnical writing.) Consult a dictionary as needed. (You can do this exercise online at *ablongman.com/littlebrown.*)

According to many sources—e.g., the Cambridge Ancient History and Gardiner's Egypt of the Pharaohs—the ancient egyptians devoted much attention to making Life more convenient and pleasurable for themselves.

Our word pharaoh for the ancient egyptian rulers comes from the egyptian word pr'o, meaning "great house." Indeed, the egyptians placed great emphasis on family residences, adding small bedrms. as early as 3500 yrs. bce. By 3000 bce, the egyptians made ice through evaporation of water at night and then used it to cool their homes. About the same time they used fans made of palm fronds or papyrus to cool themselves in the day. To light their homes, the egyptians abandoned the animal-fat lamps Humans had used for 50 thousand yrs. Instead, around 1300 bce the people of Egt. devised the 1st oil lamps.

egyptians found great pleasure in playing games. Four thousand three hundred yrs. ago or so they created one of the oldest board games known. the game involved racing ivory or stone pieces across a papyrus playing board. By three thousand bce, egyptian children played marbles with semi-precious stones, some of which have been found in gravesites at nagada, EG. Around one thousand three hundred sixty bce, small children played with clay rattles covered in silk and shaped like animals.

To play the game of love, egyptian men and women experimented with cosmetics applied to skin and eyelids. kohl, history's first eyeliner, was used by both sexes to ward off evil. 5000 yrs. ago egyptians wore wigs made of vegetable fibers or human hair. In 9 hundred bce, queen

Isimkheb wore a wig so heavy that she needed assistance in walking. To adjust their make-up and wigs, egyptians adapted the simple metal mirrors devised by the sumerians in the bronze age, ornamenting them with carved handles of ivory, gold, or wood. Feeling that only those who smelled sweet could be attractive, the egyptians made deodorants from perfumed oils, e.g., cinnamon and citrus.

PART 8

Effective Words

CHAPTER 37

Using Appropriate Language

Appropriate language suits your writing situation—your subject, purpose, and audience. Like everyone, you vary your words depending on the context in which you are speaking and writing. Look, for example, at the underlined words in these two sentences:

> Some patients decide to bag counseling because their shrinks seem strung out.
>
> Some patients decide to abandon counseling because their therapists seem disturbed.

The first sentence might be addressed to friends in casual conversation. The second is more suitable for an academic audience.

The more formal language of the second example is typical of **standard American English.** This is the dialect of English normally expected and used in school, business, government, the professions, and the communications media. (For more on its role in academic writing, see pp. 134–36.)

The vocabulary of standard American English is huge, allowing expression of an infinite range of ideas and feelings; but it does exclude words that only some groups of people use, understand, or find inoffensive. Some of those more limited vocabularies should be avoided altogether; others should be used cautiously and in special situations, as when aiming for a special effect with an audience you know will appreciate it. Whenever you doubt a word's status, consult a dictionary (see p. 538).

Note Many grammar and style checkers can be set to flag potentially inappropriate words (see p. 63), such as nonstandard dialect, slang, colloquialisms, and gender-specific terms (*manmade, mailman*). However, the checker can flag only words listed in its dictionary of questionable words. For example, a checker flagged *businessman* as potentially sexist in *A successful businessman puts clients*

http://www.ablongman.com/littlebrown

Visit the companion Web site for more help and additional exercises on appropriate language.

Language in academic and public writing

Always appropriate

Standard American English

Sometimes appropriate

Regional words and expressions
Slang
Colloquial language
Neologisms
Technical language
Euphemisms

Rarely or never appropriate

Nonstandard dialect
Double talk
Pretentious writing
Biased language: sexist, racist, ethnocentric, etc.

first, but the checker did not flag *his* in *A successful businessperson listens to his clients.* If you use a checker to review your language, you'll need to determine whether a flagged word is or is not appropriate for your writing situation.

37a Revising nonstandard dialect CULTURE LANGUAGE

Like many countries, the United States consists of scores of regional, social, and ethnic groups with their own distinct dialects, or versions of English. Standard American English is one of these dialects, and so are Black English, Appalachian English, Creole, and the English of coastal Maine. All the dialects of English share many features, but each also has its own vocabulary, pronunciation, and grammar.

If you speak a dialect of English besides standard American English, be careful about using your dialect in situations where standard English is the norm, such as in academic or public writing. Dialects are not wrong in themselves, but forms imported from one dialect into another may still be perceived as unclear or incorrect. When you know standard English is expected in your writing, edit to eliminate expressions in your dialect that you know (or have been told) differ from standard English. These expressions may include *theirselves, hisn, them books,* and others labeled "nonstandard" by a dictionary. They may also include verb forms, as discussed on pages 280–94. For help identifying and editing nonstandard language, see "CULTURE LANGUAGE Guide" inside the back cover of this book.

Your participation in the community of standard English does not require you to abandon your own dialect. You may want to use it in writing you do for yourself, such as journals, notes, and drafts, which should be composed as freely as possible. You may want to quote it in an academic paper, as when analyzing or reporting conversation in dialect. And, of course, you will want to use it with others who speak it.

37b Using regionalisms only when appropriate

Regionalisms are expressions or pronunciations peculiar to a particular area. Southerners may say they *reckon*, meaning "think" or "suppose." People in Maine invite their Boston friends to come *down* rather than *up* (north) to visit. New Yorkers stand *on* rather than *in* line for a movie.

Regional expressions are appropriate in writing addressed to local readers and may lend realism to regional description, but they should be avoided in writing intended for a general audience.

37c Using slang only when appropriate

All groups of people—from musicians and computer scientists to vegetarians and golfers—create novel and colorful expressions called **slang.** The following quotation, for instance, is from an essay on the slang of "skaters" (skateboarders):

> Curtis slashed ultra-punk crunchers on his longboard, while the Rubeman flailed his usual Gumbyness on tweaked frontsides and lofty fakie ollies.
> —Miles Orkin, "Mucho Slingage by the Pool"

Among those who understand it, slang may be vivid and forceful. It often occurs in dialog, and an occasional slang expression can enliven an informal essay. Some slang, such as *dropout* (*She was a high school dropout*), has proved so useful that it has passed into the general vocabulary.

But most slang is too flippant and imprecise for effective communication, and it is generally inappropriate for academic or business writing. Notice the gain in seriousness and precision achieved in the following revision:

Slang Many students start out pretty together but then get weird.

Revised Many students start out with clear goals but then lose their direction.

37d Using colloquial language only when appropriate

Colloquial language designates the words and expressions appropriate to everyday spoken language. Regardless of our backgrounds and how we live, we all try to *get along with* each other. We play with *kids*, *go crazy* for something, and in our worst moments try to *get back at* someone who has made us do the *dirty work*.

When you write informally, colloquial language may be appropriate to achieve the casual, relaxed effect of conversation. An occasional colloquial word dropped into otherwise more formal writing can also help you achieve a desired emphasis. But colloquial language does not provide the exactness needed in more formal academic, public, and professional writing. In such writing you should generally avoid any words and expressions labeled "informal" or "colloquial" in your dictionary. Take special care to avoid **mixed diction,** a combination of standard and colloquial words:

Mixed diction — According to a Native American myth, the Great Creator had a dog hanging around with him when he created the earth.

Revised — According to a Native American myth, the Great Creator was accompanied by a dog when he created the earth.

37e Revising neologisms

Neologisms are words created (or coined) so recently that they have not come into established use. An example is *prequel* (made up of *pre-*, meaning "before," and the ending of *sequel*), a movie or book that takes the story of an existing movie or book back in time. Some neologisms do become accepted as part of our general vocabulary—*motel,* coined from *motor* and *hotel,* is an example. But most neologisms pass quickly from the language. Unless such words serve a special purpose in your writing and are sure to be understood by your readers, you should avoid them.

37f Using technical words with care

All disciplines and professions rely on special words or give common words special meanings. Chemists speak of *esters* and *phosphatides,* geographers and mapmakers refer to *isobars* and *isotherms,* and literary critics write about *motifs* and *subtexts.* Such technical language allows specialists to communicate precisely and economically with other specialists who share their vocabulary. But without explanation these words are meaningless to nonspecialists. When you are writing for nonspecialists, avoid unnecessary technical terms and carefully define terms you must use.

37g Revising indirect or pretentious writing

In most writing, small, plain, and direct words are preferable to big, showy, or evasive words. Avoid euphemisms, double talk, and pretentious writing.

A **euphemism** is a presumably inoffensive word that a writer or speaker substitutes for a word deemed potentially offensive or too blunt, such as *passed away* for "died." Euphemisms appear whenever a writer or speaker wants to bury the truth, as when a governor mentions the *negative growth* (meaning "decline") in her state. Use euphemisms only when you know that blunt, truthful words would needlessly hurt or offend members of your audience.

A kind of euphemism that deliberately evades the truth is **double talk** (also called **doublespeak** or **weasel words**): language intended to confuse or to be misunderstood. Today double talk is unfortunately common in politics and advertising—the *revenue enhancement* that is really a tax, the *biodegradable* bags that last decades. Double talk has no place in honest writing.

Euphemism and sometimes double talk seem to keep company with fancy writing. Any writing that is more elaborate than its subject requires will sound **pretentious**—that is, excessively showy. Choose your words for their exactness and economy. The big, ornate word may be tempting, but pass it up. Your readers will be grateful.

Pretentious: To perpetuate our endeavor of providing funds for our elderly citizens as we do at the present moment, we will face the exigency of enhanced contributions from all our citizens.

Revised: We cannot continue to fund Social Security and Medicare for the elderly unless we raise taxes.

37h Revising sexist and other biased language

Even when we do not mean it to, our language can reflect and perpetuate hurtful prejudices toward groups of people, especially racial, ethnic, religious, age, and sexual groups. Such biased language can be obvious—words such as *nigger, whitey, mick, kike, fag, dyke,* and *broad.* But it can also be subtle, generalizing about groups in ways that may be familiar but that are also inaccurate or unfair. For instance, people with physical disabilities are as varied a group as any other: the only thing they have in common is some form of impairment. To assume that people with disabilities share certain attitudes (shyness, helplessness, victimization, whatever) is to disregard the uniqueness of each person.

Biased language reflects poorly on the user, not on the person or persons whom it mischaracterizes or insults. Unbiased language does not submit to false generalizations. It treats people as individuals and labels groups as they wish to be labeled.

1 Avoiding stereotypes of race, ethnicity, religion, age, and other characteristics

A **stereotype** is a generalization based on poor evidence, a kind of formula for understanding and judging people simply because of their membership in a group:

Men are uncommunicative.
Women are emotional.
Liberals want to raise taxes.
Conservatives are affluent.

At best, stereotypes betray an uncritical writer, one who is not thinking beyond notions received from others. Worse, they betray a writer who does not mind hurting others or even *wants* to hurt others.

In your writing, be alert for any general statements about people based on only one or a few characteristics. Be especially cautious about substituting such statements for the evidence you should be providing instead.

Stereotype	Elderly drivers should have their licenses limited to daytime driving. [Implies that all elderly people are poor night drivers.]
Revised	Drivers with impaired night vision should have their licenses limited to daytime driving.

Some stereotypes have become part of the language, but they are still potentially offensive.

Stereotype	The administrators are too blind to see the need for a new gymnasium.
Revised	The administrators do not understand the need for a new gymnasium.

2 Avoiding sexist language

Among the most subtle and persistent biased language is that expressing narrow ideas about men's and women's roles, position, and value in society. This **sexist language** distinguishes needlessly between men and women in such matters as occupation, ability, behavior, temperament, and maturity. Like other stereotypes, it can wound or irritate readers, and it indicates the writer's thoughtlessness or unfairness. The following box suggests some ways of eliminating sexist language.

Eliminating sexist language

- **Avoid demeaning and patronizing language**—for instance, identifying women and men differently or trivializing either gender:

Sexist	Dr. Keith Kim and Lydia Hawkins wrote the article.
Revised	Dr. Keith Kim and Dr. Lydia Hawkins wrote the article.
Revised	Keith Kim and Lydia Hawkins wrote the article.
Sexist	Ladies are entering formerly male occupations.
Revised	Women are entering formerly male occupations.

(continued)

Eliminating sexist language

(continued)

- **Avoid occupational or social stereotypes,** assuming that a role or profession is exclusively male or female:

  Sexist The considerate doctor commends a nurse when she provides his patients with good care.

  Revised The considerate doctor commends a nurse who provides good care for patients.

- **Avoid referring needlessly to gender:**

  Sexist Marie Curie, a woman chemist, discovered radium.
  Revised Marie Curie, a chemist, discovered radium.

  Sexist The patients were tended by a male nurse.
  Revised The patients were tended by a nurse.

- **Avoid using *man* or words containing *man* to refer to all human beings.** Here are a few alternatives:

businessman	businessperson
chairman	chair, chairperson
congressman	representative in Congress, legislator
craftsman	craftsperson, artisan
layman	layperson
mankind	humankind, humanity, human beings, people
policeman	police officer
salesman	salesperson, sales representative

  Sexist Man has not reached the limits of social justice.
  Revised Humankind [or Humanity] has not reached the limits of social justice.

  Sexist The furniture consists of manmade materials.
  Revised The furniture consists of synthetic materials.

- **Avoid the generic *he*,** the male pronoun used to refer to both genders. (See also pp. 317–18.)

  Sexist The newborn child explores his world.
  Revised Newborn children explore their world. [Use the plural for the pronoun and the word it refers to.]
  Revised The newborn child explores the world. [Avoid the pronoun altogether.]
  Revised The newborn child explores his or her world. [Substitute male and female pronouns.]

Use the last option sparingly—only once in a group of sentences and only to stress the singular individual.

CULTURE LANGUAGE Forms of address vary widely from culture to culture. In some cultures, for instance, one refers to all older women as if they were married, using the equivalent of the title *Mrs.* Usage in the United States is changing toward making no assumptions about marital status, rank, or other characteristics—for instance, using the title *Ms.* for a woman unless she is known to prefer *Mrs.* or *Miss.*

3 Using appropriate labels

We often need to label groups: *swimmers, politicians, mothers, Christians, westerners, students.* But labels can be shorthand stereotypes that slight the person labeled and ignore the preferences of the group members themselves. Showing sensitivity when applying labels reveals that you are alert to readers' needs and concerns. Although sometimes dismissed as "political correctness," such sensitivity hurts no one and helps gain your readers' trust and respect.

- **Avoid labels that (intentionally or not) disparage the person or group you refer to.** A person with emotional problems is not a *mental patient.* A person with cancer is not a *cancer victim.* A person using a wheelchair is not *wheelchair-bound.*
- **Use names for racial, ethnic, and other groups that reflect the preferences of each group's members,** or at least many of them. Examples of current preferences include *African American* or *black, latino/latina* (for Americans and American immigrants of Spanish-speaking descent), and *people with disabilities* (rather than *the handicapped*). But labels change often. To learn how a group's members wish to be labeled, ask them directly, attend to usage in reputable periodicals, or check a recent dictionary.

A helpful reference for appropriate labels is *Guidelines for Bias-Free Writing,* by Marilyn Schwartz and the Task Force on Bias-Free Language of the Association of American University Presses.

EXERCISE 37.1 Revising: Appropriate words

Rewrite the following sentences as needed for standard American English. Consult a dictionary to determine whether particular words are appropriate and to find suitable substitutes. (You can do this exercise online at *ablongman.com/littlebrown.*)

Example:

If negotiators get hyper during contract discussions, they may mess up chances for a settlement.

If negotiators become excited or upset during contract discussions, they may harm chances for a settlement.

1. Acquired immune deficiency syndrome (AIDS) is a major deal all over the world.

2. The disease gets around primarily by sexual intercourse, exchange of bodily fluids, shared needles, and blood transfusions.
3. Those who think the disease is limited to homos, druggies, and foreigners are quite mistaken.
4. Stats suggest that in the United States one in every five hundred college kids carries the virus.
5. A person with AIDS does not deserve to be subjected to exclusionary behavior or callousness on the part of his fellow citizens. Instead, he has the necessity for all the compassion, medical care, and financial assistance due those who are in the extremity of illness.
6. An AIDS victim often sees a team of doctors or a single doctor with a specialized practice.
7. The doctor may help his patients by obtaining social services for them as well as by providing medical care.
8. The AIDS sufferer who loses his job may need public assistance.
9. For someone who is very ill, a full-time nurse may be necessary. She can administer medications and make the sick person as comfortable as possible.
10. Some people with AIDS have insurance, but others lack the bread for premiums.

CHAPTER 38

Using Exact Language

To write clearly and effectively, you will want to find the words that fit your meaning exactly and convey your attitude precisely. Don't worry too much about choosing exact words while you are drafting an essay. If the right word doesn't come to you, leave a blank. Revision (p. 51) or editing (p. 60) is the stage to consider tone, specificity, and precision.

Note A grammar and style checker can provide some help with inexact language. For instance, you can set it to flag commonly confused words (such as *continuous/continual*), misused prepositions in idioms (such as *accuse for* instead of *accuse of*), and

http://www.ablongman.com/littlebrown

Visit the companion Web site for more help and additional exercises on exact language.

clichés. (See p. 63 on setting a checker.) But the checker can flag only words stored in its dictionary. It can't help you at all with inappropriate connotation, excessive abstraction, or other problems discussed in this chapter.

38a Using the right word for your meaning

Precisely expressing your meaning requires understanding both the denotations and the connotations of words. A word's **denotation** is the thing or idea it refers to, the meaning listed in the dictionary without reference to the emotional associations it may arouse in a reader. Using words according to their established denotations is essential if readers are to grasp your meaning. Here are a few guidelines:

- **Become acquainted with a dictionary.** Consult it whenever you are unsure of a word's meaning.
- **Distinguish between similar-sounding words that have widely different denotations:**

  Inexact Older people often suffer infirmaries [places for the sick].
  Exact Older people often suffer infirmities [disabilities].

  Some words, called **homonyms** (from the Greek meaning "same name"), sound exactly alike but differ in meaning: for example, *principal/principle* or *rain/reign/rein.* (See pp. 545–46 for a list of commonly confused homonyms.)
- **Distinguish between words with related but distinct denotations:**

  Inexact Television commercials continuously [unceasingly] interrupt programming.
  Exact Television commercials continually [regularly] interrupt programming.

In addition to their emotion-free denotations, many words also carry related meanings that evoke specific feelings. These **connotations** can shape readers' responses and are thus a powerful tool for writers. (At the same time they are a potential snare for readers. See pp. 189–90.) Some connotations are personal: the word *dog,* for instance, may have negative connotations for the letter carrier who has been bitten three times. Usually, though, people agree about connotations. The following word pairs are just a few of many that have related denotations but very different connotations:

pride: sense of self-worth
vanity: excessive regard for oneself

firm: steady, unchanging, unyielding
stubborn: unreasonable, bullheaded

enthusiasm: excitement
mania: excessive interest or desire

statesman or *stateswoman:* responsible, high-minded public servant
politician: self-serving elected official

quiet: peacefully silent
taciturn: stubbornly silent

Understanding connotation is especially important in choosing among **synonyms,** words with approximately, but often not exactly, the same meanings. For instance, *cry* and *weep* both denote the shedding of tears, but *cry* more than *weep* connotes a sobbing sound accompanying the tears. *Sob* itself connotes broken, gasping crying, with tears, whereas *wail* connotes sustained sound, perhaps without tears.

Several resources can help you track down words with the exact connotations you want:

- **A standard dictionary distinguishes among synonyms.** See page 541 for an example.
- **A dictionary of synonyms lists and defines synonyms in groups.** See page 540 for a title.
- **A thesaurus lists synonyms but does not distinguish among them.** See page 540 for a title.

Note Because a thesaurus lacks definitions, it can only suggest possibilities. You will still need a dictionary to discover words' exact denotations and connotations.

EXERCISE 38.1 Revising: Denotation

Revise any underlined word below that is not used according to its established denotation. Circle any word used correctly. Consult a dictionary if you are uncertain of a word's precise meaning. (You can do this exercise online at *ablongman.com/littlebrown.*)

Example:

Sam and Dave are going to Bermuda and Hauppauge, respectfully, for spring vacation.

Sam and Dave are going to Bermuda and Hauppauge, respectively, for spring vacation.

1. Maxine Hong Kingston was rewarded many prizes for her first two books, *The Woman Warrior* and *China Men.*
2. Kingston sites her mother's tales about ancestors and ancient Chinese customs as the sources of these memoirs.
3. In her childhood Kingston was greatly effected by her mother's tale about a pregnant aunt who was ostracized by villagers.
4. The aunt gained avengeance by drowning herself in the village's water supply.
5. Kingston decided to make her nameless relative infamous by giving her immortality in *The Woman Warrior.*

EXERCISE 38.2 Considering the connotations of words

Fill the blank in each sentence below with the most appropriate word from the list in parentheses. Consult a dictionary to be sure of your choice. (You can do this exercise online at *ablongman.com/littlebrown.*)

Example:

Channel 5 ________ Oshu the winner before the polls closed. (*advertised, declared, broadcast, promulgated*)

Channel 5 declared Oshu the winner before the polls closed.

1. AIDS is a serious health ________. (*problem, worry, difficulty, plight*)
2. Once the virus has entered the blood system, it ________ T-cells. (*murders, destroys, slaughters, executes*)
3. The ________ of T-cells is to combat infections. (*ambition, function, aim, goal*)
4. Without enough T-cells, the body is nearly ________ against infections. (*defenseless, hopeless, desperate*)
5. To prevent exposure to the disease, one should be especially ________ in sexual relationships. (*chary, circumspect, cautious, calculating*)

38b Balancing the abstract and concrete, the general and specific

To understand a subject as you understand it, your readers need ample guidance from your words. When you describe a building as *beautiful* and nothing more, you force readers to provide their own ideas of what makes a building beautiful. If readers bother (and they may not), they surely will not conjure up the image you had in mind. Use words to tell readers what you want them to know, that the beautiful building is *a sleek, silver skyscraper with blue-tinted windows,* for instance, or *a Victorian brick courthouse with tall, arched windows.*

Clear, exact writing balances abstract and general words, which outline ideas and objects, with concrete and specific words, which sharpen and solidify.

- **Abstract words** name qualities and ideas: *beauty, inflation, management, culture, liberal.* **Concrete words** name things we can know by our five senses of sight, hearing, touch, taste, and smell: *sleek, humming, brick, bitter, musty.*
- **General words** name classes or groups of things, such as *buildings, weather,* or *birds,* and include all the varieties of the class. **Specific words** limit a general class, such as *buildings,* by naming a variety, such as *skyscraper, Victorian courthouse,* or *hut.*

Note that *general* and *specific* are relative terms: the same word may be more general than some words but more specific than others:

Abstract and general words are useful in the broad statements that set the course for your writing:

> The wild horse in America has a romantic history.
>
> We must be free from government interference in our affairs.
>
> Relations between the sexes today are only a little more relaxed than they were in the past.

But the sentences following these would have to develop the ideas with concrete and specific details. When your meaning calls for an abstract or general word, make sure you define it, explain it, and narrow it. Look at how concrete and specific information turns vague sentences into exact ones in the examples below:

> Vague The size of his hands made his smallness real. [How big were his hands? How small was he?]
>
> Exact Not until I saw his delicate, doll-like hands did I realize that he stood a full head shorter than most other men.
>
> Vague The long flood caused a lot of awful destruction in the town. [How long did the flood last? What destruction did it cause? Why was the destruction awful?]
>
> Exact The flood waters, which rose swiftly and then stayed stubbornly high for days, made life a misery for the hundreds who had to evacuate their ruined homes and stores.

Note You can use your computer's Find function to help you find and revise abstract and general words that you tend to overuse. Examples of such words might include *nice, interesting, things, very, good, a lot, a little,* and *some.*

EXERCISE 38.3 Revising: Concrete and specific words

Make the following paragraph vivid by expanding the sentences with appropriate details of your own choosing. Substitute concrete and specific words for the abstract and general ones that are underlined. (You can do this exercise online at *ablongman.com/littlebrown.*)

I remember clearly how awful I felt the first time I attended Mrs. Murphy's second-grade class. I had recently moved from a small town in Missouri to a crowded suburb of Chicago. My new school looked big from the outside and seemed dark inside as I walked down the long corridor toward the classroom. The class was noisy as I neared the door; but when I entered, everyone became quiet and looked at me. I felt uncomfortable and wanted a place to hide. However, in a loud voice Mrs. Murphy directed me to the front of the room to introduce myself.

EXERCISE 38.4 Using concrete and specific words

For each abstract or general word below, give at least two other words or phrases that illustrate increasing specificity or concreteness. Consult a dictionary as needed. Use the most specific or concrete word from each group in a sentence of your own. (You can do this exercise online at *ablongman.com/littlebrown*.)

Example:
awake, watchful, vigilant
Vigilant guards patrol the buildings.

1. fabric
2. delicious
3. car
4. narrow-minded
5. reach (*verb*)
6. green
7. walk (*verb*)
8. flower
9. serious
10. pretty
11. teacher
12. nice
13. virtue
14. angry
15. crime

38c Using idioms

Idioms are expressions in any language whose meanings cannot be determined simply from the words in them or whose component words cannot be predicted by any rule of grammar; often, they violate conventional grammar. Examples of English idioms include *put up with, plug away at,* and *make off with.*

Idiomatic combinations of verbs or adjectives and prepositions can be confusing for both native and nonnative speakers of English. A number of these pairings are listed in the box below.

Idioms with prepositions

abide by a rule
abide in a place or state
accords with
according to
accuse of a crime
adapt from a source
adapt to a situation
afraid of
agree on a plan as a group
agree to someone else's plan
agree with a person
angry with
aware of
based on
capable of
certain of
charge for a purchase
charge with a crime
concur in an opinion
concur with a person
contend for a principle
contend with a person
dependent on
differ about or over a question
differ from in some quality
differ with a person
disappointed by or in a person
disappointed in or with a thing

(continued)

Idioms with prepositions
(continued)

familiar with
identical with or to
impatient for a raise
impatient with a person
independent of
infer from
inferior to
involved in a task
involved with a person
oblivious of or to one's surroundings
oblivious of something forgotten
occupied by a person
occupied in study
occupied with a thing
opposed to
part from a person
part with a possession
prior to
proud of
related to
rewarded by the judge
rewarded for something done
rewarded with a gift
similar to
superior to
wait at a place
wait for a train, a person
wait on a customer

CULTURE LANGUAGE If you are learning standard American English, you are justified in stumbling over its prepositions: their meanings can shift depending on context, and they have many idiomatic uses. In mastering the prepositions of standard English, you probably can't avoid memorization. But you can help yourself by memorizing related groups, such as the following.

_At, in,_ or _on_ in expressions of time

- Use *at* before actual clock time: *at 8:30.*
- Use *in* before a month, year, century, or period: *in April, in 2007, in the twenty-first century, in the next month.*
- Use *on* before a day or date: *on Tuesday, on August 3, on Labor Day.*

_At, in,_ or _on_ in expressions of place

- Use *at* before a specific place or address: *at the school, at 511 Iris Street.*
- Use *in* before a place with limits or before a city, state, country, or continent: *in the house, in a box, in Oklahoma City, in China, in Asia.*
- Use *on* to mean "supported by" or "touching the surface of": *on the table, on Iris Street, on page 150.*

For or _since_ in expressions of time

- Use *for* before a period of time: *for an hour, for two years.*
- Use *since* before a specific point in time: *since 1999, since the war began.*

A dictionary of English as a second language is the best source for the meanings of prepositions; see the recommendations on page 539. In addition, some references focus on prepositions. See, for instance, volume 1 (*Verbs with Prepositions and Particles*) of the *Oxford Dictionary of Current Idiomatic English.*

EXERCISE 38.5 Using prepositions in idioms

Insert the preposition that correctly completes each idiom in the following sentences. Consult the box on the previous page or a dictionary as needed. (You can do this exercise online at *ablongman.com/littlebrown.*)

Example:

I disagree _______ many feminists who say women should not be homemakers.

I disagree with many feminists who say women should not be homemakers.

1. As Mark and Lana waited _______ the justice of the peace, they seemed oblivious _______ the other people in the lobby.
2. But Mark inferred _______ Lana's glance at a handsome man that she was no longer occupied _______ him alone.
3. Angry _______ Lana, Mark charged her _______ not loving him enough to get married.
4. Impatient _______ Mark's childish behavior, Lana disagreed _______ his interpretation of her glance.
5. They decided that if they could differ so violently _______ a minor incident, they should part _______ each other.

38d Using figurative language

Figurative language (or a **figure of speech**) departs from the literal meanings (the denotations) of words. It is common in speech. Having *slept like a log,* you may get up to find it *raining cats and dogs* and have to *run like the wind* to get to school on time.

The rapid exchange of speech leaves little time for inventiveness, and most figures of daily conversation, like those above, are worn and hackneyed. Writing gives you time to reject the tired figure and to search out fresh, concrete words and phrases that capture meaning precisely and feelingly:

Literal	As I try to write, I can think of nothing to say.
Figurative	As I try to write, my mind is a slab of black slate.

The following are some common figures of speech. (Others appear in the Glossary of Terms, pp. 836–52.)

- **Simile and metaphor** compare two things of different classes, often one abstract and the other concrete. A **simile** makes the comparison explicit and usually begins with *like* or *as:*

38e Using fresh, not trite, expressions

Trite expressions, or **clichés,** are phrases so old and so often repeated that they have become stale. They include the following:

acid test
add insult to injury
better late than never
beyond the shadow of a doubt
brought back to reality
cold, hard facts
cool as a cucumber
crushing blow
easier said than done
face the music
flat as a pancake
green with envy
hard as a rock
heavy as lead
hit the nail on the head
hour of need
ladder of success
moving experience
needle in a haystack
point with pride
ripe old age
shoulder the burden
smart as a whip
sneaking suspicion
sober as a judge
stand in awe
strong as an ox
thin as a rail
tired but happy
tried and true
untimely death
wise as an owl

Besides these old phrases, stale writing may also depend on fashionable words that are losing their effect: for instance, *lifestyle, enhance, excellent, fantastic,* and *caring.*

Many of these expressions were once fresh and forceful, but constant use has dulled them. They, in turn, will dull your writing by suggesting that you have not thought about what you are saying and have resorted to the easiest phrase.

Clichés may slide into your drafts while you are trying to express your meaning. In editing, then, be wary of any expression you have heard or used before. Substitute fresh words of your own or restate the idea in plain language.

Trite: A healthful lifestyle enhances your ability to go for the gold, allows you to enjoy life to the fullest, and helps you live to a ripe old age.

Revised: Living healthfully helps you perform well, enjoy life thoroughly, and live long.

EXERCISE 38.8 Revising: Trite expressions

Revise the following sentences to eliminate trite expressions. (You can do this exercise online at *ablongman.com/littlebrown.*)

Example:

The basketball team had almost seized victory, but it faced the test of truth in the last quarter of the game.

The basketball team seemed about to win, but the real test came in the last quarter of the game.

1. The disastrous consequences of the war have shaken the small nation to its roots.
2. Prices for food have shot sky high, and citizens have sneaking suspicions that others are making a killing on the black market.
3. Medical supplies are so few and far between that even civilians who are as sick as dogs cannot get treatment.
4. With most men fighting or injured or killed, women have had to bite the bullet and bear the men's burden in farming and manufacturing.
5. Last but not least, the war's heavy drain on the nation's pocketbook has left the economy in a shambles.

CHAPTER 39

Writing Concisely

Concise writing makes every word count. Conciseness is not the same as mere brevity: detail and originality should not be cut along with needless words. Rather, the length of an expression should be appropriate to the thought.

You may find yourself writing wordily when you are unsure of your subject or when your thoughts are tangled. It's fine, even necessary, to stumble and grope while drafting. But you should straighten out your ideas and eliminate wordiness during revision and editing.

Note Any grammar and style checker will identify at least some wordy structures, such as repeated words, weak verbs, passive voice, and *there is* and *it is* constructions. But a checker can't identify all potentially wordy structures, nor can it tell you whether a structure is appropriate for your ideas.

CULTURE LANGUAGE As you'll see in the examples that follow, wordiness is not a problem of incorrect grammar. A sentence may be perfectly grammatical but still contain unneeded words that interfere with your idea.

http://www.ablongman.com/littlebrown 

Visit the companion Web site for more help and additional exercises on writing concisely.

Ways to achieve conciseness

Wordy (87 words)

The highly pressured nature of critical-care nursing is due to the fact that the patients have life-threatening illnesses. Critical-care nurses must have possession of steady nerves to care for patients who are critically ill and very sick. The nurses must also have possession of interpersonal skills. They must also have medical skills. It is considered by most health-care professionals that these nurses are essential if there is to be improvement of patients who are now in critical care from that status to the status of intermediate care.

- Focus on subject and verb, and cut or shorten empty words and phrases.
- Avoid nouns made from verbs.
- Cut unneeded repetition.
- Combine sentences.
- Change passive voice to active voice.
- Eliminate *there is* constructions.
- Cut unneeded repetition, and reduce clauses and phrases.

Concise (37 words)

Critical-care nursing is highly pressured because the patients have life-threatening illnesses. Critical-care nurses must possess steady nerves and interpersonal and medical skills. Most health-care professionals consider these nurses essential if patients are to improve to intermediate care.

39a Focusing on the subject and verb

Using the subjects and verbs of your sentences for the key actors and actions will reduce words and emphasize important ideas. (See pp. 386–88 for more on this topic.)

Wordy The reason why most of the country shifts to daylight savings time is that winter days are much shorter than summer days.

Concise Most of the country shifts to daylight savings time because winter days are much shorter than summer days.

Focusing on subjects and verbs will also help you avoid several other causes of wordiness (also discussed further on pp. 386–88):

Nouns made from verbs

Wordy The occurrence of the winter solstice, the shortest day of the year, is an event occurring about December 22.

Concise The winter solstice, the shortest day of the year, occurs about December 22.

Weak verbs

Wordy The earth's axis has a tilt as the planet is in orbit around the sun so that the northern and southern hemispheres are alternately in alignment toward the sun.

Concise The earth's axis tilts as the planet orbits the sun so that the northern and southern hemispheres alternately align toward the sun.

Passive voice

Wordy During its winter the northern hemisphere is tilted farthest away from the sun, so the nights are made longer and the days are made shorter.

Concise During its winter the northern hemisphere tilts away from the sun, making the nights longer and the days shorter.

See also pages 304–05 on changing the passive voice to the active voice, as in the example above.

39b Cutting or shortening empty words and phrases

Empty words and phrases walk in place, gaining little or nothing in meaning. When you cut or shorten them, your writing will move faster and work harder.

Many empty phrases can be cut entirely:

all things considered
as far as I'm concerned
for all intents and purposes
for the most part
in a manner of speaking
in my opinion
last but not least
more or less

Wordy As far as I am concerned, discrimination against women still exists in medicine for all intents and purposes.

Revised Discrimination against women still exists in medicine.

Other empty words can be cut along with some words around them:

angle
area
aspect
case
character
element
factor
field
kind
manner
nature
situation
thing
type

Wordy The type of large expenditures on advertising that manufacturers must make is a very important aspect of the cost of detergents.

Concise Manufacturers' large advertising expenditures increase the cost of detergents.

Still other empty phrases can be reduced from several words to a single word:

For	Substitute
at all times	always
at the present time	now
at this point in time	now
in today's society	now
in the nature of	like
for the purpose of	for
in order to	to
until such time as	until
for the reason that	because
due to the fact that	because
because of the fact that	because
by virtue of the fact that	because
despite the fact that	although
in the event that	if
by means of	by
in the final analysis	finally

Wordy At this point in time, the software is expensive due to the fact that it has no significant competition.

Revised The software is expensive now because it has no significant competition.

EXERCISE 39.1 Revising: Subjects and verbs; empty words and phrases

Revise the following sentences to achieve conciseness by focusing on subjects and verbs and by cutting or reducing empty words and phrases. (You can do this exercise online at *ablongman.com/littlebrown.*) See also page 388 for an additional exercise in focusing on subjects and verbs.

Example:

I am making college my destination because of many factors, but most of all because of the fact that I want a career in medicine.

I am going to college mainly because I want a career in medicine.

1. *Gerrymandering* refers to a situation in which the lines of a voting district are redrawn so that a particular party or ethnic group has benefits.
2. The name is a reference to the fact that Elbridge Gerry, the governor of Massachusetts in 1812, redrew voting districts in Essex County.
3. On the map one new district was seen to resemble something in the nature of a salamander.
4. Upon seeing the map, a man who was for all intents and purposes a critic of Governor Gerry's administration cried out, "Gerrymander!"
5. At the present time, changes may be made in the character of a district's voting pattern by a political group by gerrymandering to achieve the exclusion of rival groups' supporters.

39c Cutting unnecessary repetition

Planned repetition and restatement can make writing more coherent (p. 85) or emphatic (pp. 392–93). But unnecessary repetition weakens sentences:

Wordy — Many unskilled workers without training in a particular job are unemployed and do not have any work.

Concise — Many unskilled workers are unemployed.

The use of one word two different ways within a sentence is confusing:

Confusing — Preschool instructors play a role in the child's understanding of male and female roles.

Clear — Preschool instructors contribute to the child's understanding of male and female roles.

The simplest kind of useless repetition is the phrase that says the same thing twice. In the following examples, the unneeded words are underlined:

biography of his life
circle around
consensus of opinion
continue on
cooperate together
few in number
final completion
frank and honest exchange
the future to come
habitual custom
important [basic] essentials
large in size
puzzling in nature
repeat again
return again
revert back
square [round] in shape
surrounding circumstances

CULTURE LANGUAGE Phrases like those above are redundant because the main word already implies the underlined word or words. The repetition is not emphatic but tedious. A dictionary will tell you what meanings a word implies. *Assassinate,* for instance, means "murder someone well known," so the following sentence is redundant: *Julius Caesar was assassinated and killed.*

EXERCISE 39.2 Revising: Unnecessary repetition

Revise the following sentences to achieve conciseness. Concentrate on eliminating repetition and redundancy. (You can do this exercise online at *ablongman.com/littlebrown.*)

Example:

Because the circumstances surrounding the cancellation of classes were murky and unclear, the editor of the student newspaper assigned a staff reporter to investigate and file a report on the circumstances.

Because the circumstances leading to the cancellation of classes were unclear, the editor of the student newspaper assigned a staffer to investigate and report the story.

1. Some Vietnam veterans coming back to the United States after their tours of duty in Vietnam had problems readjusting again to life in America.
2. Afflicted with post-traumatic stress disorder, a psychological disorder that sometimes arises after a trauma, some veterans had psychological problems that caused them to have trouble holding jobs and maintaining relationships.
3. Some who used to use drugs in Vietnam could not break their drug habits after they returned back to the United States.
4. The few veterans who committed crimes and violent acts gained so much notoriety and fame that many Americans thought all veterans were crazy, insane maniacs.
5. As a result of such stereotyping of Vietnam-era veterans, veterans are included in the same antidiscrimination laws that protect other victims of discrimination.

39d Reducing clauses to phrases, phrases to single words

Modifiers—subordinate clauses, phrases, and single words—can be expanded or contracted depending on the emphasis you want to achieve. (See pp. 256–58 on phrases and clauses and 400–03 on working with modifiers.) When editing your sentences, consider whether any modifiers can be reduced without loss of emphasis or clarity:

Wordy The Channel Tunnel, which runs between Britain and France, bores through a bed of solid chalk that is twenty-three miles across.

Concise The Channel Tunnel between Britain and France bores through twenty-three miles of solid chalk.

39e Eliminating *there is* and *it is* constructions

You can postpone the sentence subject with the words *there is* (*there are, there was, there were*) and *it is* (*it was*). (See p. 266.) These constructions can be useful to emphasize the subject (as when introducing it for the first time) or to indicate a change in direction. But often they just add words and create limp sentences:

Wordy There were delays and cost overruns that plagued construction of the Channel Tunnel. It is the expectation of investors to earn profits at last, now that there are trains passing daily through the tunnel.

Concise Delays and cost overruns plagued construction of the Channel Tunnel. Investors expect to earn profits at last, now that trains pass daily through the tunnel.

39f Combining sentences

Often the information in two or more sentences can be combined into one tight sentence:

Wordy — An unexpected problem with the Channel Tunnel is stowaways. The stowaways are mostly illegal immigrants. They are trying to smuggle themselves into England. They cling to train roofs and undercarriages.

Concise — An unexpected problem with the Channel Tunnel is stowaways, mostly illegal immigrants who are trying to smuggle themselves into England by clinging to train roofs and undercarriages.

A number of exercises in this handbook give you practice in sentence combining. For a list, see "Sentence combining" in this book's index.

39g Rewriting jargon

Jargon can refer to the special vocabulary of any discipline or profession (see p. 515). But it has also come to describe vague, inflated language that is overcomplicated, even incomprehensible. When it comes from government or business, we call it *bureaucratese*.

Jargon — The weekly social gatherings stimulate networking by members of management from various divisions, with the aim of developing contacts and maximizing the flow of creative information.

Translation — The weekly parties give managers from different divisions a chance to meet and to share ideas.

EXERCISE 39.3 Revising: Conciseness

Rewrite each passage below into a single concise sentence, using the techniques described in this chapter. (You can do this exercise online at *ablongman.com/littlebrown.*)

Example:

He was taking some exercise in the park. Then several thugs were suddenly ahead of him in his path.

He was exercising [or jogging or strolling] in the park when several thugs suddenly loomed in his path.

1. Chewing gum was originally introduced to the United States by Antonio López de Santa Anna. He was the Mexican general.
2. After he had been defeated by the Texans in 1845, the general, who was exiled, made the choice to settle in New York.
3. A piece of chicle had been stashed by the general in his baggage. Chicle is the dried milky sap of the Mexican sapodilla tree.

4. There was more of this resin brought into the country by Santa Anna's friend Thomas Adams. Adams had a plan to make rubber.
5. The plan failed. Then the occasion arose for Adams to get a much more successful idea on the basis of the use to which the resin was put by General Santa Anna. That is, Adams decided to make a gum that could be chewed.

EXERCISE 39.4 Revising: Conciseness

Make the following passage as concise as possible. Be merciless. (You can do this exercise online at *ablongman.com/littlebrown.*)

At the end of a lengthy line of reasoning, he came to the conclusion that the situation with carcinogens [cancer-causing substances] should be regarded as similar to the situation with the automobile. Instead of giving in to an irrational fear of cancer, we should consider all aspects of the problem in a balanced and dispassionate frame of mind, making a total of the benefits received from potential carcinogens (plastics, pesticides, and other similar products) and measuring said total against the damage done by such products. This is the nature of most discussions about the automobile. Instead of responding irrationally to the visual, aural, and air pollution caused by automobiles, we have decided to live with them (while simultaneously working to improve on them) for the benefits brought to society as a whole.

CHAPTER 40

Using Dictionaries

A dictionary can answer most questions about words. This chapter shows you how to choose a dictionary that suits your purpose and how to read a dictionary without difficulty.

40a Choosing a dictionary

1 Abridged dictionaries

Abridged dictionaries are the most practical for everyday use. Often called desk dictionaries because of their convenient size, they

http://www.ablongman.com/littlebrown ▶

Visit the companion Web site for links to online dictionaries and other language resources.

usually list 150,000 to 200,000 words and concentrate on fairly common words and meanings.

The American Heritage College Dictionary
Merriam-Webster's Collegiate Dictionary
The Random House Webster's College Dictionary
Webster's New World College Dictionary

Most of these dictionaries are available both in print and on CD-ROM, and some are available online (visit *ablongman.com/littlebrown* for links). Your computer may include a dictionary that you can customize with words or meanings it does not cover. With an electronic dictionary, as with a print dictionary, you can look up words as you write, checking spellings, meanings, synonyms, and other information.

CULTURE LANGUAGE If English is not your first language, you probably should have a dictionary prepared especially for ESL students in addition to one of the dictionaries listed above. The dictionaries listed below give much more information on such matters as count versus noncount nouns, prepositions with verbs and adjectives, and other concerns of ESL students.

COBUILD English Language Dictionary
Longman Dictionary of Contemporary English. Longman Dictionary of American English is the American version.
Oxford Advanced Learner's Dictionary. Oxford Dictionary of American English is the American version.

2 Unabridged dictionaries

Unabridged dictionaries are the most scholarly and comprehensive of all dictionaries, sometimes consisting of many volumes. They emphasize the history of words and the variety of their uses. An unabridged dictionary is useful when you are studying a word in depth, reading or writing about the literature of another century, or looking for a quotation containing a particular word. The following unabridged dictionaries are available at most libraries.

The Oxford English Dictionary, 20 volumes
The Random House Webster's Unabridged Dictionary
Webster's Third New International Dictionary of the English Language

3 Special dictionaries

Special dictionaries limit their attention to a single class of word (for example, slang, engineering terms, abbreviations), to a single kind of information (synonyms, usage, word origins), or to a specific subject (African American culture, biography, history). (See Chapters 50–53 for lists of subject dictionaries in various academic disciplines.)

Most dictionaries provide not only the principal forms of regular and irregular verbs but also the plural forms of irregular nouns and the *-er* and *-est* forms of adjectives and adverbs. An adjective or adverb without *-er* and *-est* forms in the dictionary requires the addition of *more* and *most* to show comparison (see pp. 324–25).

Etymology

Dictionaries provide the **etymology** of a word (its history) to indicate its origin and the evolution of its meanings and forms. The dictionary can compress much information about a word into a small space through symbols, abbreviations, and different type fonts. An explanation of these systems appears in the dictionary's opening pages. *Merriam-Webster's* traces *reckon* back most recently to Middle English (ME) and then further back to Old English (OE). The notation "(13c)" before the first definition indicates that the first recorded use of *reckon* to mean "count" occurred in the thirteenth century. When seeking the etymology of a word, be sure to read the entire history, not just the most recent event.

Meanings

Dictionaries divide the general meaning of a word into particular meanings on the basis of how the word is or has been actually used. They arrange a word's meanings differently, either in order of their appearance in the language, earliest first, or in order of their frequency of use, most common first. (*Merriam-Webster's* follows the former practice.) To learn your dictionary's arrangement, consult its opening pages. Then read through a word's entire entry before settling on the meaning that fits the context of what you're reading or writing.

The *Merriam-Webster's* entry for *reckon* ends with two uses of the word in idiomatic expressions (*reckon with* and *reckon without*). These phrases are defined because, as with all idioms, their meanings cannot be inferred simply from the words they consist of (see p. 525).

Labels

Dictionaries apply labels to words or to particular meanings that have a special status or use.

Style labels restrict a word or one of its meanings to a particular level of usage:

- *Slang:* words or meanings inappropriate in writing except for a special effect, such as *crumb* for "a worthless or despicable person."
- ***Informal* or *colloquial:*** words or meanings appropriate for informal writing but not formal writing, such as *great* to mean "very good," as in *a great movie.*

- *Nonstandard* or *substandard:* words or meanings inappropriate for standard American English, such as *ain't.*
- *Vulgar* or *vulgar slang:* words or meanings considered offensive in speech and writing, such as profanity.
- *Poetic* or *literary:* words or meanings used only in poetry or the most formal writing, such as *eve* for *evening* and *o'er* for *over.*

Subject labels tell us that a word or one of its meanings has a special use in a discipline or profession. In its entry for *relaxation,* for instance, *American Heritage* presents specialized meanings with the subject labels *physiology, physics,* and *mathematics.*

Region labels indicate that a particular spelling, pronunciation, or meaning of a word is not national but limited to an area. A regional difference may be indicated by the label *dialect. Merriam-Webster's* labels as dialect (*dial*) the uses of *reckon* to mean "suppose" or "think" (as in *I reckon I'll do that*). More specific region labels may designate areas of the United States or other countries.

Time labels indicate words or their meanings that the language, in evolving, has discarded. *Obsolete* designates words or meanings that are no longer used; *archaic* designates words or meanings that are out of date but are used occasionally.

See pages 512–19 for further discussion of levels of usage and their appropriateness in your writing.

Synonyms

Synonyms are words whose meanings are approximately the same, such as *small* and *little. Merriam-Webster's* defines *reckon* with some words in small capital letters (COUNT, ESTIMATE, CONSIDER, and so on). These are both synonyms and cross-references, in that each word may be looked up in its alphabetical place. Some dictionaries devote separate paragraphs to words with many synonyms.

Illustrative quotations

Dictionaries are made by collecting quotations showing actual uses of words in all kinds of speech and writing. Some of these quotations, or others that the dictionary makers invent, may appear in the dictionary's entries as illustrations of how a word may be used. Five such quotations illustrate uses of *reckon* in the *Merriam-Webster's* entry (in these quotations, ~ stands for the word being illustrated).

EXERCISE 40.1 Using a dictionary

Consult your dictionary on five of the following words. First find out whether your dictionary lists the oldest or the most common meanings first in its entries. Then, for each word, write down (*a*) the division into syllables, (*b*) the pronunciation, (*c*) the grammatical functions and forms, (*d*) the etymology, (*e*) each meaning, and (*f*) any special uses indicated by labels. Finally, use the word in at least two sentences of your own. (You can do this exercise online at *ablongman.com/littlebrown.*)

1. depreciation
2. secretary
3. grammar
4. manifest
5. assassin
6. astrology
7. potlatch
8. plain (*adj.*)
9. ceremony
10. toxic
11. steal
12. obelisk

CHAPTER 41

Spelling and the Hyphen

English spelling is difficult, even for some very experienced and competent writers. You can train yourself to spell better, and this chapter will help you. But you can also improve instantly by acquiring three habits:

- **Carefully proofread all of your writing.**
- **Be suspicious of your spellings.**
- **Check a dictionary *every time* you doubt a spelling.**

Note A spelling checker can help you find and track spelling errors in your papers. But its usefulness is limited, mainly because it can't spot the common error of confusing words with similar spellings, such as *now/not, to/too, their/they're/there,* and *principal/principle.* See pages 62–63 for more on spelling checkers.

41a Recognizing typical spelling problems

Spelling well involves recognizing situations that commonly lead to misspelling: pronunciation can mislead you in several ways; different forms of the same word may have different spellings; and some words have more than one acceptable spelling.

http://www.ablongman.com/littlebrown

Visit the companion Web site for more help and an additional exercise on spelling and the hyphen.

1 Being wary of pronunciation

In English, unlike some other languages, pronunciation of words is an unreliable guide to their spelling. The same letter or combination of letters may have different sounds in different words. (Say aloud these different ways of pronouncing the letters *ough: tough, dough, cough, through, bough.*) In addition, some words contain letters that are not pronounced clearly or at all, such as the *ed* in *asked,* the silent *e* in *swipe,* or the unpronounced *gh* in *tight.*

Pronunciation is a particularly unreliable guide in spelling **homonyms,** words pronounced the same though they have different spellings and meanings: *great/grate, to/too/two.* Some commonly confused homonyms and near-homonyms, such as *accept/except,* are listed below. (See p. 553 for tips on how to use spelling lists.)

Words commonly confused

accept (to receive)
except (other than)

affect (to have an influence on)
effect (result)

all ready (prepared)
already (by this time)

allude (to refer to indirectly)
elude (to avoid)

allusion (indirect reference)
illusion (erroneous belief or perception)

ascent (a movement up)
assent (agreement)

bare (unclothed)
bear (to carry, or an animal)

board (a plane of wood)
bored (uninterested)

born (brought into life)
borne (carried)

brake (stop)
break (smash)

buy (purchase)
by (next to)

capital (the seat of a government)
capitol (the building where a legislature meets)

cite (to quote an authority)
sight (the ability to see)
site (a place)

desert (to abandon)
dessert (after-dinner course)

discreet (reserved, respectful)
discrete (individual or distinct)

elicit (to bring out)
illicit (illegal)

eminent (well known)
imminent (soon to happen)

fair (average, or lovely)
fare (a fee for transportation)

forth (forward)
fourth (after *third*)

gorilla (a large primate)
guerrilla (a kind of soldier)

hear (to perceive by ear)
here (in this place)

heard (past tense of *hear*)
herd (a group of animals)

hole (an opening)
whole (complete)

its (possessive of *it*)
it's (contraction of *it is* or *it has*)

lead (heavy metal)
led (past tense of *lead*)

lessen (to make less)
lesson (something learned)

meat (flesh)
meet (encounter)

(continued)

Words commonly confused
(continued)

no (the opposite of *yes*)
know (to be certain)

passed (past tense of *pass*)
past (after, or a time gone by)

patience (forbearance)
patients (persons under medical care)

peace (the absence of war)
piece (a portion of something)

persecute (to oppress, to harass)
prosecute (to pursue, to take legal action against)

plain (clear)
plane (a carpenter's tool, or an airborne vehicle)

presence (the state of being at hand)
presents (gifts)

principal (most important, or the head of a school)
principle (a basic truth or law)

rain (precipitation)
reign (to rule)
rein (a strap for controlling an animal)

raise (to build up)
raze (to tear down)

right (correct)
rite (a religious ceremony)
write (to make letters)

road (a surface for driving)
rode (past tense of *ride*)

scene (where an action occurs)
seen (past participle of *see*)

seam (a junction)
seem (appear)

stationary (unmoving)
stationery (writing paper)

straight (unbending)
strait (a water passageway)

their (possessive of *they*)
there (opposite of *here*)
they're (contraction of *they are*)

to (toward)
too (also)
two (following *one*)

waist (the middle of the body)
waste (discarded material)

weak (not strong)
week (Sunday through Saturday)

weather (climate)
whether (*if*, or introducing a choice)

which (one of a group)
witch (a sorcerer)

who's (contraction of *who is* or *who has*)
whose (possessive of *who*)

your (possessive of *you*)
you're (contraction of *you are*)

2 Distinguishing between different forms of the same word

Spelling problems may occur when forms of the same word have different spellings, as in the following examples.

Verbs and nouns

Verb	Noun	Verb	Noun
advise	advice	enter	entrance
describe	description	marry	marriage
speak	speech	omit	omission

Nouns and adjectives

Noun	Adjective	Noun	Adjective
comedy	comic	height	high
courtesy	courteous	Britain	British
generosity	generous		

Irregular verbs

begin, began, begun
break, broke, broken
know, knew, known
ring, rang, rung

Irregular nouns

child, children
goose, geese
mouse, mice
shelf, shelves
tooth, teeth
woman, women

Other differences

four, forty
thief, theft

3 Using preferred spellings CULTURE LANGUAGE

Many words have variant spellings as well as preferred spellings. Often the variant spellings listed in an American dictionary are British spellings.

American	British
color, humor	colour, humour
theater, center	theatre, centre
canceled, traveled	cancelled, travelled
judgment	judgement
realize	realise

41b Following spelling rules

Misspelling is often a matter of misspelling a syllable rather than the whole word. The following general rules focus on troublesome syllables, with notes for the occasional exceptions.

1 Distinguishing between *ie* and *ei*

Words like *believe* and *receive* sound alike in the second syllable, but the syllable is spelled differently. Use the familiar jingle to distinguish between *ie* and *ei:*

> *I* before *e*, except after *c*, or when pronounced "ay" as in *neighbor* and *weigh*.

i before *e*	believe	bier	hygiene
	grief	thief	friend

ei after *c*	ceiling	conceive	perceive
	receive	deceit	conceit
ei sounded	neighbor	weight	eight
as "ay"	sleigh	freight	vein

Exceptions In some words an *ei* combination neither follows *c* nor is pronounced "ay." These words include *either, neither, foreign, forfeit, height, leisure, weird, seize,* and *seizure.* This sentence might help you remember some of them: *The weird foreigner neither seizes leisure nor forfeits height.*

EXERCISE 41.1 Distinguishing between *ie* and *ei*

Insert *ie* or *ei* in the words below. Check doubtful spellings in a dictionary. (You can do this exercise online at *ablongman.com/littlebrown.*)

1. br__f	5. for__gn	9. l__surely	13. h__ght
2. dec__ve	6. pr__st	10. ach__ve	14. fr__ght
3. rec__pt	7. gr__vance	11. pat__nce	15. f__nt
4. s__ze	8. f__nd	12. p__rce	16. s__ve

2 Keeping or dropping a final *e*

Many words end with an unpronounced or silent *e: move, brave, late, rinse.* Drop the final *e* when adding an ending that begins with a vowel:

advise + able = advisable
force + ible = forcible
surprise + ing = surprising
guide + ance = guidance

Keep the final, silent *e* when adding an ending that begins with a consonant:

battle + ment = battlement
accurate + ly = accurately
care + ful = careful
like + ness = likeness

Exceptions The silent *e* is sometimes retained before an ending beginning with a vowel. It is kept when *dye* becomes *dyeing,* to avoid confusion with *dying.* It is kept to prevent mispronunciation of words like *shoeing* (not *shoing*) and *mileage* (not *milage*). And the final *e* is often retained after a soft *c* or *g,* to keep the sound of the consonant soft rather than hard:

courageous	changeable	noticeable
outrageous	manageable	embraceable

The silent *e* is also sometimes *dropped* before an ending beginning with a consonant, when the *e* is preceded by another vowel:

argue + ment = argument
due + ly = duly
true + ly = truly

EXERCISE 41.2 Keeping or dropping a final *e*

Combine the following words and endings, keeping or dropping a final *e* as necessary to make correctly spelled words. Check doubtful spellings in a dictionary. (You can do this exercise online at *ablongman.com/littlebrown.*)

1. malice + ious
2. love + able
3. service + able
4. retire + ment
5. sue + ing
6. virtue + ous
7. note + able
8. battle + ing
9. suspense + ion

3 Keeping or dropping a final *y*

Words ending in *y* often change their spelling when an ending is added to them. Change the final *y* to an *i* when it follows a consonant:

beauty, beauties
folly, follies
worry, worried
merry, merrier
supply, supplies
deputy, deputize

But keep the *y* when it follows a vowel, when the ending is *-ing,* or when it ends a proper name:

day, days
obey, obeyed
cry, crying
study, studying
May, Mays
Minsky, Minskys

EXERCISE 41.3 Keeping or dropping a final *y*

Combine the following words and endings, changing or keeping a final *y* as necessary to make correctly spelled words. Check doubtful spellings in a dictionary. (You can do this exercise online at *ablongman.com/littlebrown.*)

1. imply + s
2. messy + er
3. apply + ing
4. delay + ing
5. defy + ance
6. say + s
7. solidify + s
8. Murphy + s
9. supply + ed

4 Doubling consonants

Whether to double a word's final consonant depends first on the number of syllables in the word. In one-syllable words, double the final consonant when a single vowel precedes the final consonant. Otherwise, don't double the consonant.

slap, slapping
tip, tipping
pair, paired
park, parking

In words of more than one syllable, double the final consonant when a single vowel precedes the final consonant *and* the consonant ends a stressed syllable once the ending is added. Otherwise, don't double the consonant.

refer, referring
begin, beginning
occur, occurrence
refer, reference
relent, relented
despair, despairing

EXERCISE 41.4 Doubling consonants

Combine the following words and endings, doubling final consonants as necessary to make correctly spelled words. Check doubtful spellings in a dictionary. (You can do this exercise online at *ablongman.com/littlebrown.*)

1. repair + ing
2. admit + ance
3. benefit + ed
4. shop + ed
5. conceal + ed
6. allot + ed
7. drip + ing
8. declaim + ed
9. parallel + ing

5 Attaching prefixes

Adding a prefix such as *dis, mis,* and *un* does not change the spelling of a word. When adding a prefix, do not drop a letter from or add a letter to the original word:

uneasy	anti-intellectual	defuse	misstate
unnecessary	disappoint	de-emphasize	misspell
antifreeze	dissatisfied	misinform	

(See also p. 557 for when to use hyphens with prefixes: *prehistory* versus *ex-student.*)

6 Forming plurals

Nouns

Most nouns form plurals by adding *s* to the singular form:

boy, boys	table, tables
carnival, carnivals	Murphy, Murphys

Some nouns ending in *f* or *fe* form the plural by changing the ending to *ve* before adding *s:*

leaf, leaves	wife, wives
life, lives	yourself, yourselves

Singular nouns ending in *s, sh, ch,* or *x* form the plural by adding *es:*

kiss, kisses	church, churches
wish, wishes	Jones, Joneses

(Notice that verbs ending in *s, sh, ch,* or *x* form the third-person singular in the same way. *Taxes* and *lurches* are examples.)

Nouns ending in *o* preceded by a vowel usually form the plural by adding *s:*

ratio, ratios	zoo, zoos

Nouns ending in *o* preceded by a consonant usually form the plural by adding *es:*

hero, heroes	tomato, tomatoes

Exceptions Some very common nouns form irregular plurals:

child, children
mouse, mice
man, men
woman, women

Some English nouns that were originally Italian, Greek, Latin, or French form the plural according to their original language:

analysis, analyses
basis, bases
beau, beaux
crisis, crises
criterion, criteria
datum, data
medium, media
phenomenon, phenomena
piano, pianos
thesis, theses

A few such nouns may form irregular or regular plurals: for instance, *index, indices, indexes; curriculum, curricula, curriculums.* The regular plural is more contemporary.

CULTURE LANGUAGE Noncount nouns do not form plurals, either regularly (with an added *s*) or irregularly. Examples of noncount nouns include *equipment, courage,* and *wealth.* (See p. 329.)

Compound nouns

Form plurals of compound nouns in one of two ways. Add *s* to the last word when the component words are roughly equal in importance, whether or not they are hyphenated:

city-states
painter-sculptors
breakthroughs
bucket seats

Add *s* to a noun combined with other parts of speech:

fathers-in-law
passersby

Note, however, that most modern dictionaries give the plural of *spoonful* as *spoonfuls.*

EXERCISE 41.5 Forming plurals

Make the correct plural of each of the following singular words. Check doubtful spellings in a dictionary. (You can do this exercise online at *ablongman.com/littlebrown.*)

1. pile
2. donkey
3. beach
4. summary
5. mile per hour
6. box
7. switch
8. sister-in-law
9. Bales
10. cupful
11. libretto
12. video
13. thief
14. goose
15. hiss
16. appendix

41c Developing spelling skills

The following techniques can help you improve your spelling. In addition, do not overrely on your computer's spelling checker (see pp. 62–63).

commercial
commitment
committed
committee
competent
competition
complement
compliment
conceive
concentrate
concert
condemn
conquer
conscience
conscious
consistency
consistent
continuous
controlled
controversial
convenience
convenient
coolly
course
courteous
criticism
criticize
crowd
cruelty
curiosity
curious
curriculum

deceive
deception
decide
decision
deductible
definitely
degree
dependent
descend
descendant
describe
description
desirable
despair
desperate
destroy
determine
develop
device
devise
dictionary
difference
dining
disagree
disappear
disappoint
disapprove
disastrous
discipline
discriminate
discussion
disease
disgusted
dissatisfied
distinction
divide
divine
division
doctor
drawer

easily
ecstasy
efficiency
efficient
eighth
either
eligible
embarrass
emphasize
empty
enemy
entirely
entrepreneur
environment
equipped
especially
essential
every
exaggerate
exceed
excellent
exercise
exhaust
exhilarate
existence
expense
experience
experiment
explanation
extremely

familiar
fascinate
favorite
February
fiery
finally
forcibly
foreign
foresee
forty
forward
friend
frightening
fulfill

gauge
generally
ghost
government
grammar
grief
guarantee
guard
guidance

happily
harass
height
heroes
hideous
humorous
hungry
hurriedly
hurrying
hypocrisy
hypocrite

ideally
illogical
imaginary
imagine
imitation
immediately
immigrant
incidentally
incredible
independence
independent

individually
inevitably
influential
initiate
innocuous
inoculate
insistent
integrate
intelligence
interest
interference
interpret
irrelevant
irresistible
irritable
island

jealousy
judgment

kindergarten
knowledge

laboratory
leisure
length
library
license
lieutenant
lightning
likelihood
literally
livelihood
loneliness
loose
lose
luxury
lying

magazine
maintenance
manageable
marriage
mathematics
meant
medicine
miniature
minor
minutes
mirror
mischievous
missile
misspelled
morale
morals
mortgage
mournful
muscle
mysterious

naturally
necessary
neighbor
neither
nickel
niece
ninety
ninth
noticeable
nuclear
nuisance
numerous

obstacle
occasion
occasionally
occur
occurrence
official
omission
omit
omitted
opinion
opponent
opportunity
opposite
ordinary
originally

paid
panicky
paralleled
parliament
particularly
peaceable
peculiar
pedal
perceive
perception
performance
permanent
permissible
persistence
personnel
perspiration
persuade
persuasion
physical
physiology
physique
pitiful
planning
playwright
pleasant
poison
politician
pollute
possession
possibly
practically
practice
prairie
precede
preference
preferred
prejudice
preparation
prevalent
primitive
privilege
probably
procedure
proceed
process
professor
prominent
pronunciation
psychology
purpose
pursue
pursuit

quandary
quantity
quarter
questionnaire
quiet
quizzes

realistically
realize
really
rebel

rebelled
recede
receipt
receive
recognize
recommend
reference
referred
relief
relieve
religious
remembrance
reminisce
renown
repetition
representative
resemblance
resistance
restaurant
rhyme
rhythm
ridiculous
roommate

sacrifice
sacrilegious
safety
satellite
scarcity
schedule
science
secretary
seize
separate
sergeant
several
sheriff
shining
shoulder
siege
significance
similar
sincerely
sophomore
source
speak
specimen
speech
sponsor
strategy
strength
strenuous
stretch
strict
strictly
studying
succeed
successful
sufficient
summary
superintendent
supersede
suppress
surely
surprise
suspicious

teammate
technical
technique
temperature
tendency
than
then
thorough
though
throughout
together
tomatoes
tomorrow
tragedy
transferred
truly
twelfth
tyranny

unanimous
unconscious
undoubtedly
unnecessary
until
usable
usually

vacuum
vegetable
vengeance
vicious
villain
visible

weather
Wednesday
weird
wherever
whether
wholly
woman
women
writing

yacht

41d Using the hyphen to form or divide words

The hyphen (-) is a mark of punctuation used either to form words or to divide them at the ends of lines.

1 Forming compound adjectives

When two or more words serve together as a single modifier before a noun, a hyphen or hyphens form the modifying words clearly into a unit:

She is a well-known actor.
The conclusions are based on out-of-date statistics.
Some Spanish-speaking students work as translators.

When the same compound adjectives follow the noun, hyphens are unnecessary and are usually left out.

The actor is well known.
The statistics were out of date.
Many students are Spanish speaking.

Hyphens are also unnecessary in compound modifiers containing an *-ly* adverb, even when these fall before the noun: *clearly defined terms; swiftly moving train.*

When part of a compound adjective appears only once in two or more parallel compound adjectives, hyphens indicate which words the reader should mentally join with the missing part:

School-aged children should have eight- or nine-o'clock bedtimes.

2 Writing fractions and compound numbers

Hyphens join the numerator and denominator of fractions and the parts of the whole numbers twenty-one to ninety-nine:

three-fourths	twenty-four
one-half	eighty-seven

3 Forming coined compounds

Writers sometimes create (coin) temporary compounds and join the words with hyphens:

Muhammad Ali gave his opponent a come-and-get-me look.

4 Attaching some prefixes and suffixes

Do not use hyphens with prefixes except as follows:

- **With the prefixes** *self-, all-,* **and** *ex-: self-control, all-inclusive, ex-student.*
- **With a prefix before a capitalized word:** *un-American.*
- **With a capital letter before a word:** *T-shirt.*
- **To prevent misreading:** *de-emphasize, anti-intellectual.*

The only suffix that regularly requires a hyphen is *-elect,* as in *president-elect.*

5 Eliminating confusion

If you wrote the sentence *Doonesbury is a comic strip character,* the reader might stumble briefly over your meaning. Is Doonesbury a character in a comic strip or a comic (funny) character who strips? A hyphen would prevent any possible confusion: *Doonesbury is a comic-strip character.*

Adding prefixes to words can sometimes create ambiguity. *Recreation* (*creation* with the prefix *re-*) could mean either "a new creation" or "diverting, pleasurable activity." The use of a hyphen, *re-creation,* limits the word to the first meaning. Without a hyphen the word suggests the second meaning.

6 Dividing words at the ends of lines

You can avoid occasional short lines in your documents by dividing some words between the end of one line and the beginning of the next. On a word processor, you can set the program to divide words automatically at appropriate breaks (in the Tools menu, select Language and then Hyphenation). To divide words manually, follow these guidelines:

- **Divide words only between syllables**—for instance, *win-dows,* not *wi-ndows.* Check a dictionary for correct syllable breaks.
- **Never divide a one-syllable word.**
- **Leave at least two letters on the first line and three on the second line.** If a word cannot be divided to follow this rule (for instance, *a-bus-er*), don't divide it.
- **Break an electronic address only after a slash.** Do not hyphenate, because readers may preceive any added hyphens as part of the address.

EXERCISE 41.6 Using hyphens in compound words

Insert hyphens as needed in the following compounds. Mark all compounds that are correct as given. Consult a dictionary as needed. (You can do this exercise online at *ablongman.com/littlebrown.*)

1. reimburse
2. deescalate
3. forty odd soldiers
4. little known bar
5. seven eighths
6. seventy eight
7. happy go lucky
8. preexisting
9. senator elect
10. postwar
11. two and six person cars
12. ex songwriter
13. V shaped
14. reeducate

PART 9

Research Writing

CHAPTER **42**
Planning a Research Project

CHAPTER **43**
Finding Sources

CHAPTER **44**
Working with Sources

CHAPTER **45**
Avoiding Plagiarism and Documenting Sources

CHAPTER **46**
Writing the Paper

CHAPTER **47**
Using MLA Documentation and Format

CHAPTER **48**
Two Research Papers in MLA Style

CHAPTER 42

Planning a Research Project

Research writing gives you a chance to work like a detective solving a case. The mystery is the answer to a question you care about. The search for the answer leads you to consider what others think about your subject, but you do more than simply report their views. You build on them to develop and support your own opinion, and ultimately you become an expert in your own right.

Your investigation will be more productive and enjoyable if you take some steps described in this chapter: plan your work from the start (below), keep a research journal (next page), find an appropriate subject and research question (p. 562), set goals for your sources (p. 564), and keep a working, annotated bibliography (p. 567).

42a Starting out

Research writing is a *writing* process:

- **You work within a particular situation of subject, purpose, audience, and other factors** (see pp. 2–17).
- **You gather ideas and information about your subject** (pp. 18–28).
- **You focus and arrange your ideas** (pp. 29–46).
- **You draft to explore your meaning** (pp. 47–51).
- **You revise and edit to develop, shape, and polish** (pp. 51–65).

Although the process seems neatly sequential in this list, you know from experience that the stages overlap—that, for instance, you may begin drafting before you've gathered all the information you expect to find, and then while drafting you may discover a source that causes you to rethink your approach. Anticipating the process of research writing can free you to be flexible in your search and open to discoveries.

http://www.ablongman.com/littlebrown ▶

Visit the companion Web site for more help and an electronic exercise on research strategy.

A thoughtful plan and systematic procedures can help you follow through on the diverse activities of research writing. One step is to make a schedule like the one on the next page that apportions the available time to the necessary work. You can estimate that each segment marked off by a horizontal line will occupy *roughly* one-quarter of the total time—for example, a week in a four-week assignment or two weeks in an eight-week assignment. The most unpredictable segments are the first two, so get started early enough to accommodate the unexpected.

Complete by:

______ 1. Setting a schedule and beginning a research journal (here and below)
______ 2. Finding a researchable subject and question (next page)
______ 3. Setting goals for sources (p. 564)
______ 4. Finding print and electronic sources (p. 569), and making a working, annotated bibliography (p. 567)

______ 5. Evaluating and synthesizing sources (pp. 588, 598)
______ 6. Gathering information from sources (p. 600), often using summary, paraphrase, and direct quotation (p. 601)
______ 7. Taking steps to avoid plagiarism (p. 611)

______ 8. Developing a thesis statement and creating a structure (p. 620)
______ 9. Drafting the paper (p. 621), integrating summaries, paraphrases, and direct quotations into your ideas (p. 606)

______ 10. Revising and editing the paper (p. 622)
______ 11. Citing sources in your text (p. 618)
______ 12. Preparing the list of works cited or references (p. 618)
______ 13. Preparing the final manuscript (p. 622)
______ Final paper due

(You can download the schedule from *ablongman.com/littlebrown*. Use a duplicate to plan and time the specific steps of each research project you work on.)

42b Keeping a research journal

While working on a research project, carry a notebook or a computer with you at all times to use as a **research journal,** a place to record your activities and ideas. (See p. 19 on journal keeping.) In the journal's dated entries, you can write about the sources you consult, the leads you want to pursue, any difficulties you encounter, and, most important, your thoughts about sources, leads, difficulties, new directions, relationships, and anything else that strikes you. The very act of writing in the journal can expand and clarify your thinking.

Note The research journal is the place to track and develop your own ideas. To avoid mixing up your thoughts and those of others, keep separate notes on what your sources actually say, using one of the methods discussed on pages 600–01.

42c Finding a researchable subject and question

Before reading this section, review the suggestions given in Chapter 1 for finding and narrowing a writing subject (pp. 7–10). Generally, the same procedure applies to writing any kind of research paper. However, selecting and limiting a subject for a research paper can present special opportunities and problems. And before you proceed with your subject, you'll want to transform it into a question that can guide your search for sources.

1 Choosing an appropriate subject

Seek a research subject that interests you and that you care about. (It may be a subject you've already written about without benefit of research.) Starting with your own views will motivate you, and you will be a participant in a dialog when you begin examining sources.

When you settle on a subject, ask the following questions about it. For each requirement, there are corresponding pitfalls.

- **Are ample sources of information available on the subject?**

  Avoid very recent subjects, such as a newly announced medical discovery or a breaking story in today's newspaper.

- **Does the subject encourage research in the kinds and number of sources required by the assignment?**

  Avoid (*a*) subjects that depend entirely on personal opinion and experience, such as the virtues of your hobby, and (*b*) subjects that require research in only one source, such as a straight factual biography.

- **Will the subject lead you to an objective assessment of sources and to defensible conclusions?**

  Avoid subjects that rest entirely on belief or prejudice, such as when human life begins or why women (or men) are superior. Your readers are unlikely to be swayed from their own beliefs.

- **Does the subject suit the length of paper assigned and the time given for research and writing?**

Avoid broad subjects that have too many sources to survey adequately, such as a major event in history.

2 Posing a research question

Asking a question about your subject can give direction to your research by focusing your thinking on a particular approach. To discover your question, consider what about your subject intrigues or perplexes you, what you'd like to know more about. (See the next page for suggestions on using your own knowledge.)

Try to narrow your research question so that you can answer it in the time and space you have available. The question *How will the Internet affect business?* is very broad, encompassing issues as diverse as electronic commerce, information management, and employee training. In contrast, the question *How will Internet commerce benefit consumers?* or *How, if at all, should Internet commerce be taxed?* is much narrower. Each question also requires more than a simple *yes* or *no* answer, so that answering, even tentatively, demands thought about pros and cons, causes and effects.

As you read and write, your question will probably evolve to reflect your increasing knowledge of the subject, and eventually its answer will become your main idea, or thesis statement (see p. 620).

EXERCISE 42.1 Finding a subject and question

Choose three of the following subjects (or three subjects of your own), and narrow each one to at least one subject and question suitable for beginning work on a research paper. (This exercise can be the first step in a research-writing project that continues through Chapters 42–46.)

1. Bilingual education
2. National security and civil rights
3. Distribution of music by conventional versus electronic means
4. Dance in America
5. The history of women's suffrage
6. Genetically modified foods
7. Immigrants in the United States
8. Space exploration
9. Puritan religion and nineteenth-century American literature
10. The effect of television on professional sports
11. Child abuse
12. African Americans and civil rights
13. Tragedy in Greek drama
14. Computer piracy
15. The European exploration of North America before Columbus
16. Villains in the plays of William Shakespeare
17. Television evangelism
18. Science fiction
19. Treatment or prevention of AIDS in the United States or Africa
20. Water pollution
21. Women writers
22. Language in nineteenth-century English poetry
23. Comic film actors
24. An unsolved crime
25. Alternative fuels
26. Male and female heroes in modern fiction

body, *org* from a nonprofit organization, *com* from a commercial organization such as a corporation. The abbreviation is not a firm guide to the kind of source—*edu* sites, for instance, may include student papers and Web logs as well as works by scholars—but it can indicate the context. (See pp. 582–84 for more on types of online sources.)

Older and newer sources

Check the publication date. For most subjects a combination of older, established sources (such as books) and current sources (such as newspaper articles, interviews, or Web sites) will provide both background and up-to-date information. Only historical subjects or very current subjects require an emphasis on one extreme or another.

Impartial and biased sources

Seek a range of viewpoints. Sources that attempt to be impartial can offer an overview of your subject and trustworthy facts. Sources with clear biases can offer a diversity of opinion. Of course, to discover bias, you may have to read the source carefully (see p. 589); but even a bibliographical listing can be informative.

- **Check the author.** You may have heard of the author as a respected researcher (thus more likely to be objective) or as a leading proponent of a certain view (less likely to be objective).
- **Check the title.** It may reveal something about point of view. (Consider these contrasting titles: "Keep the Internet Tax-Free" and "Taxation of Commerce on the Internet: Issues and Questions.")

Note Sources you find on the Internet must be approached with particular care. See pages 590–97.

Sources with helpful features

Depending on your topic and how far along your research is, you may want to look for sources with features such as illustrations (which can clarify important concepts), bibliographies (which can direct you to other sources), and indexes (which can help you develop keywords for electronic searches; see pp. 571–73).

EXERCISE 42.2 Developing a research strategy

Following the suggestions on page 564, write what you already know about the topic you selected in Exercise 42.1 (pp. 563–64), and then frame some questions for which you'll need to find answers. Also in writing, consider the kinds of sources you'll probably need to consult, using the categories given on the preceding pages.

42e Keeping a working, annotated bibliography

To track where sources are, compile a **working bibliography** as you uncover possibilities. When you have a substantial file—say, ten to thirty sources—you can decide which ones seem most promising and look them up first.

1 Tracking source information

When you turn in your paper, you will be expected to attach a list of the sources you have used. So that readers can check or

Information for a working bibliography

For books

Library call number
Name(s) of author(s), editor(s), translator(s), or others listed
Title and subtitle
Publication data:
- Place of publication
- Publisher's name
- Date of publication

Other important data, such as edition or volume number

For periodical articles

Name(s) of author(s)
Title and subtitle of article
Title of periodical
Publication data:
- Volume number and issue number (if any) in which article appears
- Date of issue
- Page numbers on which article appears

For electronic sources

Name(s) of author(s)
Title and subtitle
Publication data for books and articles (see above)
Date of release, online posting, or latest revision
Medium (online, CD-ROM, etc.)
Format of online source (Web site, Web page, e-mail, etc.)
Date you consulted the source
Complete URL (unless source was obtained through a subscription service and has no usable address)
For source obtained through a subscription service:
- Name of database
- Name of service
- Electronic address of the service home page *or* search terms used to reach the source

For other sources

Name(s) of author(s), creator(s), or others listed, such as a government department, recording artist, or photographer
Title of work
Format, such as unpublished letter, live performance, or photograph
Publication or production data:
- Publication title
- Publisher's or producer's name
- Date of publication, release, or production
- Identifying numbers (if any)

You can download these lists from *ablongman.com/littlebrown.* Copy the appropriate list for each source you're using, and fill in the required information.

follow up on your sources, your list must include all the information needed to find the sources, in a format readers can understand. (See pp. 618–19.) The box on the previous page shows the information you should record for each type of source so that you will not have to retrace your steps later.

Note Whenever possible, record source information in the correct format for the documentation style you will be using. Then you will be less likely to omit needed information or to confuse numbers, dates, and other data when it's time to write your citations. This book describes four styles: MLA (see p. 624), APA (see p. 739), Chicago (see p. 721), and CSE (see p. 767). For others, consult one of the guides listed on pages 721, 739, and 767.

2 Annotating source information

Creating annotations for a working bibliography converts it from a simple list into a tool for assessing sources. When you discover a possible source, record not only its publication information but also the following:

- **What you know about the content of the source.** Periodical databases and book catalogs generally include abstracts, or summaries, of sources that can help with this part of the annotation.
- **How you think the source may be helpful in your research.** Does it offer expert opinion, statistics, an important example, or a range of views? Does it place your subject in a historical, social, or economic context?

Taking the time with your annotations can help you discover gaps that may remain in your sources and will later help you decide which sources to pursue in depth. One student annotated a bibliography entry on his computer with a summary and a note on the source features he thought would be most helpful to him:

Entry for an annotated working bibliography

Publication and access information for source	United States. Dept. of Education. National Center for Education Statistics. Internet Access in US Public Schools and Classrooms. 24 Feb. 2005. 12 Mar. 2005 <http://nces.ed.gov/pubsearch/pubsinfo.asp?pubid=2005015>.
Summary of source	Report on the annual NCES survey of the quantity and quality of technology used in K-12 classrooms.
Ideas on use of source	Includes important statistics on trends—student-to-computer ratios, teacher training, computer availability to students in different socioeconomic brackets.

As you become more familiar with your sources, you can use your initial annotated bibliography to record your evaluations of them and more detailed thoughts on how they fit into your research.

EXERCISE 42.3 Compiling an annotated working bibliography

Prepare an annotated working bibliography of at least ten sources for a research paper on one of the following people or on someone of your own choosing. Begin by limiting the subject to a manageable size, posing a question about a particular characteristic or achievement of the person. Then consult reference works, periodical indexes, the library's book catalog, and the Web. (See pp. 578–82 for more on these resources.) For each source, record complete publication information as well as a summary and a note on the source's potential use.

1. Steven Jobs (a founder of Apple Computer), or another business entrepreneur
2. Ruth Bader Ginsburg, or another Supreme Court justice
3. Emily Dickinson, or another writer
4. Shaquille O'Neal, or another sports figure
5. Isamu Noguchi, or another artist

CHAPTER 43

Finding Sources

This chapter discusses conducting electronic searches (next page) and taking advantage of the range of sources, both print and electronic, that you have access to: reference works (p. 573), books (p. 574), periodicals (p. 575), the Web (p. 579), other online sources (p. 582), government publications (p. 584), images

http://www.ablongman.com/littlebrown

Visit the companion Web site for more help and an electronic exercise on finding sources.

(p. 584), and your own interviews, surveys, and other primary sources (p. 586).

A tip for researchers

Take advantage of two valuable resources offered by many libraries:

- **An orientation,** which introduces the library's resources and explains how to reach and use the Web site and the print holdings.
- **Reference librarians,** whose job it is to help you and others navigate the library's resources. Even very experienced researchers often consult reference librarians.

43a Searching electronically

1 Beginning with your library's Web site

As you conduct research, the World Wide Web will be your gateway to ideas and information. Always start with your library's Web site, not with a public search engine such as *Google*. (*Google Scholar,* a new tool that searches for scholarly articles, is discussed on p. 576.) The library site will lead you to vast resources, including books, periodical articles, and reference works. More important, every source you find on the library site will have passed through filters to ensure its value. A scholarly journal article, for instance, undergoes at least three successive reviews: subject-matter experts first deem it worth publishing in the journal; then a database vendor deems the journal worth including in the database; and finally your school's librarians deem the database worth subscribing to.

Google and other search engines may seem more user-friendly than the library's Web site and may seem to return plenty of sources for you to work with. Many of the sources may indeed be reliable and relevant to your research, but many more will not be. In the end, a library Web search will be more efficient and more effective than a direct Web search. (For help with evaluating sources from any resource, see pp. 579–84.)

Note Start with the library's Web site, but don't stop there. Many books, periodicals, and other excellent sources are available only on library shelves, not online, and most instructors expect research papers to be built to some extent on these resources. When you spot promising print sources while browsing the library's online databases, make records of them and then look them up at the library.

2 Kinds of electronic sources

Your school's library and the Web offer several kinds of electronic resources that are suitable for academic research:

- **The library's catalog of holdings** is a database that lists all the resources that the library owns or subscribes to: books, journals, magazines, newspapers, reference works, and more. The catalog may also include the holdings of other school libraries nearby or in your state.
- **Online databases** include indexes, bibliographies, and other reference works. They are your main route to articles in periodicals, providing publication information, summaries, and often full text. Your library subscribes to the databases and makes them available through its Web site. (You may also discover databases directly on the Web, but, again, the library is a more productive starting place.)
- **Databases on CD-ROM** include the same information as online databases, but they must be read at a library computer terminal. Increasingly, libraries are providing CD-ROM databases through their Web sites or are moving away from CD-ROMs in favor of online databases.
- **Full-text resources** contain the entire contents of articles, book chapters, even whole books. The library's databases provide access to the full text of many listed sources. In addition, the Web sites of many periodicals and organizations, such as government agencies, offer the full text of articles, reports, and other publications.

3 Using keywords

Probably the most important element in an electronic search is appropriate **keywords,** or **descriptors,** that name your subject for databases and Web search engines.

Databases vs. the Web

To develop keywords it helps to understand an important difference in how library databases and the open Web work:

- **A database indexes sources by authors, titles, publication years, and its own subject headings.** The subject headings reflect the database's directory of terms and are assigned by people who have read the sources. You can find these subject headings by using your own keywords until you locate a promising source. The information for the source will list the headings under which the database indexes it and other sources like it. (See p. 578 for an illustration.) You can then use those headings for further searches.

- **A Web search engine seeks your keywords in the titles and texts of sites.** The process is entirely electronic, so the performance of a search engine depends on how well your keywords describe your subject and anticipate the words used in sources. If you describe your subject too broadly or describe it specifically but don't match the vocabulary in relevant sources, your search will turn up few relevant sources and probably many that aren't relevant.

Keyword refinement

Every database and search engine provides a system that you can use to refine your keywords for a productive search. The basic operations appear in the box below, but resources do differ. For instance, some assume that *AND* should link two or more keywords, while others provide options specifying "Must contain all the words," "May contain any of the words," and other equivalents for the operations in the box. You can learn a search engine's system by consulting its Advanced Search page.

Ways to refine keywords

Most databases and many search engines work with **Boolean operators,** terms or symbols that allow you to expand or limit your keywords and thus your search.

- **Use *AND* or + to narrow the search** by including only sources that use all the given words. The keywords *Internet AND tax* request only the sources in the shaded area.

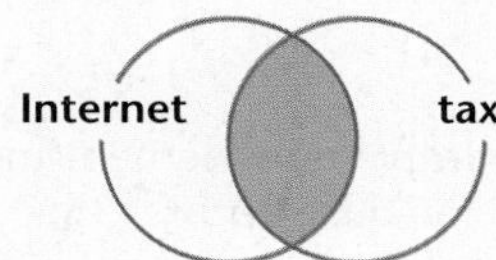

- **Use *NOT* or – ("minus") to narrow the search** by excluding irrelevant words. *Internet AND tax NOT access* excludes sources that use the word *access.*

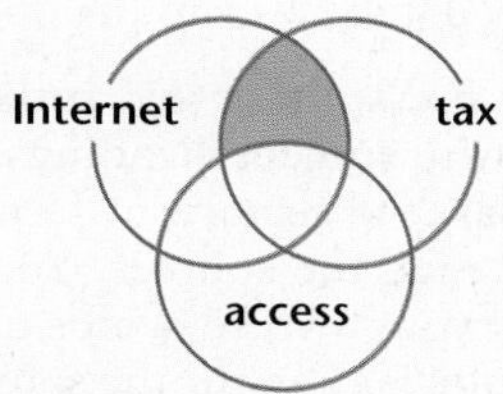

- **Use *OR* to broaden the search** by giving alternate keywords. *Internet OR (electronic commerce) AND tax* allows for sources that use *Internet* or *electronic commerce* (or both) along with *tax.*

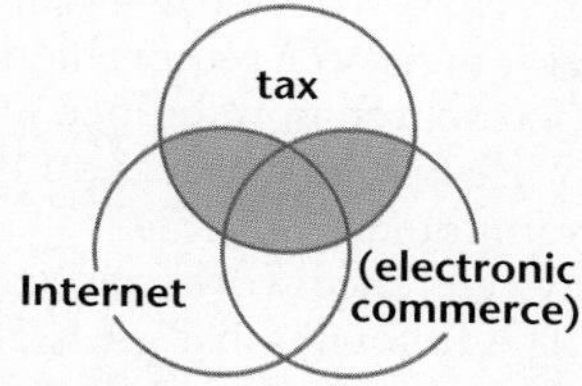

- **Use parentheses or quotation marks to form search phrases.** For instance, *(electronic commerce)* requests the exact phrase, not the separate words.
- **Use *NEAR* to narrow the search** by requiring the keywords to be close to each other—for instance, *Internet NEAR tax.* Depending on the resource you're using, the words could be directly next to each other or many words apart. Some resources use *WITHIN* __ so that you can specify the exact number of words apart—for instance, *Internet WITHIN 10 tax.*
- **Use wild cards to permit different versions of the same word.** In *child**, for instance, the wild card * indicates that sources may include *child, children, childcare, childhood, childish, childlike,* and *childproof.* The example suggests that you have to consider all the variations allowed by a wild card and whether it opens up your search too much. If you seek only two or three from many variations, you may be better off using *OR: child OR children.* (Note that some systems use ?, :, or + for a wild card instead of *.)
- **Be sure to spell your keywords correctly.** Some search tools will look for close matches or approximations, but correct spelling gives you the best chance of finding relevant sources.

Trial and error

You will probably have to use trial and error in developing your keywords, sometimes running dry (turning up few or no sources) and sometimes hitting uncontrollable gushers (turning up hundreds or thousands of mostly irrelevant sources). But the process is not busywork—far from it. Besides leading you eventually to worthwhile sources, it can also teach you a great deal about your subject: how you can or should narrow it, how it is and is not described by others, what others consider interesting or debatable about it, and what the major arguments are.

See pages 581–82 for an example of a student's keyword search of the Web.

43b Finding reference works

Reference works, often available online or on CD-ROM, include encyclopedias, dictionaries, digests, bibliographies, indexes, atlases, almanacs, and handbooks. Your research *must* go beyond these sources, but they can help you decide whether your topic really interests you and whether it meets the requirements for a research paper (p. 562). Preliminary research in reference works can also help you develop keywords for electronic searches and can direct you to more detailed sources on your topic.

You'll find many reference works through your library and directly on the Web. The following list gives general Web references for all disciplines:

Internet Public Library
www.ipl.org
Library of Congress
lcweb.loc.gov
LSU Libraries Webliography
www.lib.lsu.edu/weblio.html
World Wide Web Virtual Library
vlib.org/Overview.html

For Web sites in specific academic disciplines, see pages 700–01 (literature), 718–21 (other humanities), 736–39 (social sciences), and 765–67 (natural and applied sciences). Visit *ablongman.com/littlebrown* for additional print and Web references.

43c Finding books

Your library's catalog is searchable either at a terminal in the library or via the library's Web site. You can search the catalog by author or title, of course, and by your own keywords or the headings

Book catalog full record

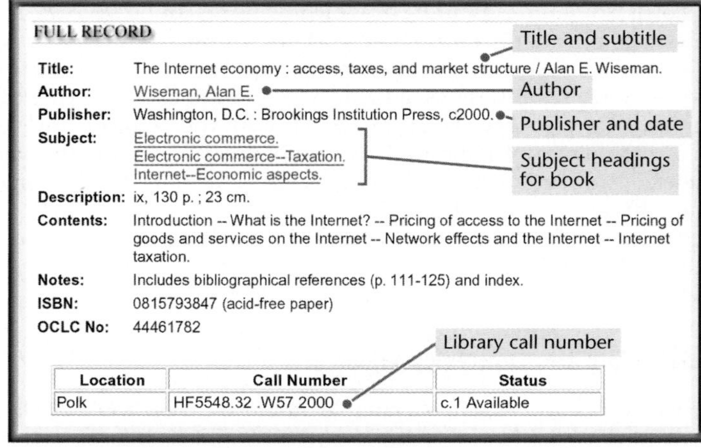
FULL RECORD

Title: The Internet economy : access, taxes, and market structure / Alan E. Wiseman.
Author: Wiseman, Alan E.
Publisher: Washington, D.C. : Brookings Institution Press, c2000.
Subject: Electronic commerce.
Electronic commerce--Taxation.
Internet--Economic aspects.
Description: ix, 130 p. ; 23 cm.
Contents: Introduction -- What is the Internet? -- Pricing of access to the Internet -- Pricing of goods and services on the Internet -- Network effects and the Internet -- Internet taxation.
Notes: Includes bibliographical references (p. 111-125) and index.
ISBN: 0815793847 (acid-free paper)
OCLC No: 44461782

Location	Call Number	Status
Polk	HF5548.32 .W57 2000	c.1 Available

found in *Library of Congress Subject Headings* (*LCSH*). The screen shot on the facing page shows the complete record for a book, including the *LCSH* headings that can be used to find similar sources.

43d Finding periodicals

Periodicals include newspapers, journals, and magazines. Newspapers, the easiest to recognize, are useful for detailed accounts of past and current events. Journals and magazines can be harder to distinguish, but their differences are important.

Journals	Magazines
Examples: *American Anthropologist, Journal of Black Studies, Journal of Chemical Education*	Examples: *The New Yorker, Time, Rolling Stone, People*
Available mainly through academic libraries.	Available in public libraries, on newsstands, and in bookstores.
Articles are intended to advance knowledge in a particular field.	Articles are intended to express opinion, inform, or entertain.
Writers and readers are specialists in the field.	Writers may or may not be specialists in their subjects. Readers are members of the general public or a subgroup with a particular interest.
Articles always include source citations.	Articles rarely include source citations.
Articles are usually long, ten pages or more.	Articles are usually short, fewer than ten pages.
Appearance is bland, with black-only type, little or no decoration, and only illustrations that directly amplify the text, such as graphs.	Appearance varies but is generally lively, with color, decoration (headings, sidebars, and other elements), and illustrations (drawings, photographs).
Issues may appear quarterly or less often.	Issues may appear weekly, biweekly, or monthly.
Issues may be paged separately (like a magazine) or may be paged sequentially throughout an annual volume, so that issue number 3 (the third issue of the year) could open on page 327. (The paging method affects source citations. See pp. 642–44.)	Issues are paged separately, each beginning on page 1.

1 Using periodical databases

How indexes work

Periodical databases index the articles in journals, magazines, and newspapers. Often these databases include abstracts, or summaries, of the articles, and they may offer the full text of the articles as well. Your library subscribes to many periodical databases and to services that offer multiple databases. (See p. 578 for a list.) Most databases and services will be searchable through the library's Web site.

Note The search engine *Google* is developing *Google Scholar*, an engine at *scholar.google.com* that seeks out scholarly articles. Although it could eventually prove a valuable research tool, at this point *Google Scholar* produces results that are far from complete and include more from science and engineering than from the humanities and social sciences.

Selection of databases

To decide which databases to consult, you'll need to consider what you're looking for:

- **How broadly and deeply should you search?** Periodical databases vary widely in what they index. Some, such as *ProQuest*, cover many subjects but don't index the full range of periodicals in each subject. Others, such as *Historical Abstracts*, cover a single subject but then include most of the available periodicals. If your subject ranges across disciplines, then start with a broad database. If your subject focuses on a particular discipline, then start with a narrower database.
- **Which databases most likely include the kinds of resources you need?** The Web sites of many libraries allow you to narrow a database search to a particular kind of periodical (such as newspapers or journals) or to a particular discipline. You can then discover each database's focus by checking the description of the database (sometimes labeled "Help" or "Guide") or the list of indexed resources (sometimes labeled "Publications" or "Index"). The description will also tell you the time period the database covers, so you'll know whether you also need to consult older print indexes at the library.

Database searches

When you first search a database, use your own keywords to locate sources. The procedure is illustrated in the three screen shots on the next two pages. Your goal is to find at least one source that seems just right for your subject, so that you can then see what subject headings the database itself uses for such sources. Using one or more of those headings will focus and speed your search.

The use of abstracts

In screen 3 on the next page, the full article record shows a key feature of many databases' periodical listings: an **abstract** that summarizes the article. By describing research methods, conclusions, and other information, an abstract can tell you whether you want to

1. Initial keyword search of periodical database

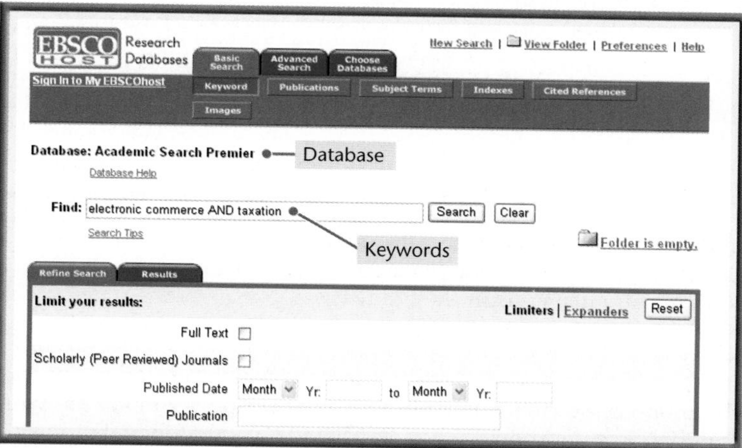

2. Partial keyword search results

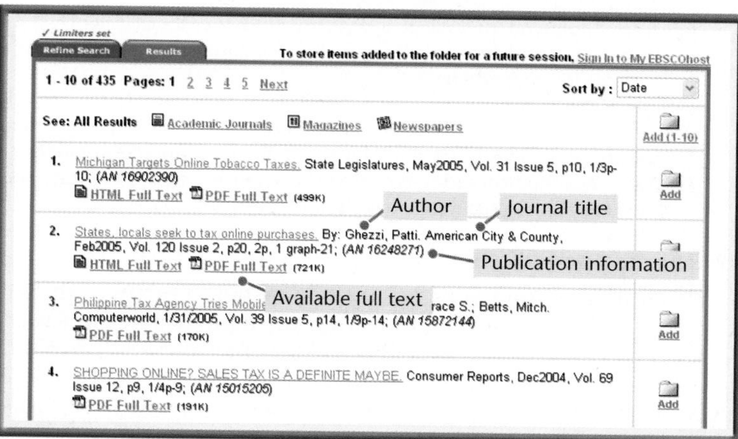

3. Full article record with abstract

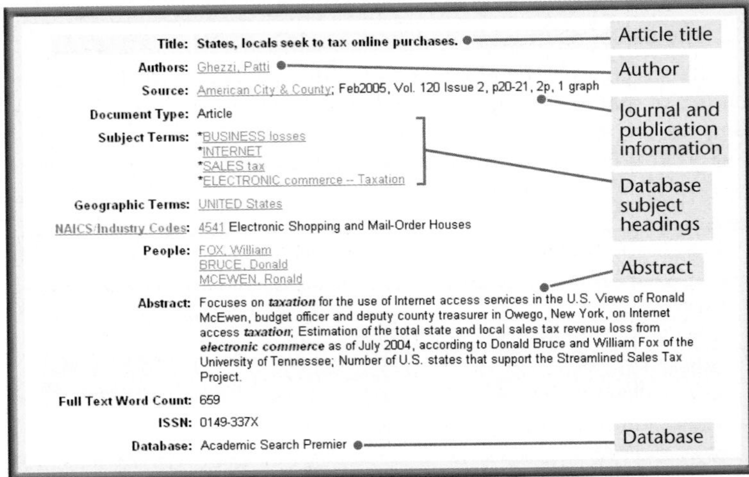

pursue an article and thus save you time. However, the abstract cannot replace the actual article. If you want to use the work as a source, you must consult the full text.

Helpful databases

The list below includes databases to which academic libraries commonly subscribe. Some of these databases cover much the same material, so your library may subscribe to several of them but not all.

EBSCOhost. A periodical index covering magazines and journals in the social sciences, sciences, arts, and humanities. Many articles are available full-text.

InfoTrac. A general periodical index covering the social sciences, sciences, arts, and humanities as well as national news periodicals. It includes full-text articles.

LexisNexis. An index of news, legal, and reference information, with full-text articles. *LexisNexis* includes international, national, and regional newspapers, news magazines, legal publications, and court cases.

ProQuest. A periodical index covering the sciences, social sciences, arts, and humanities, including many full-text articles.

2 Locating periodicals

If an index listing does not include or link directly to the full text of an article, you'll need to consult the periodical itself. Recent issues of periodicals are probably held in the library's periodical area. Back issues are usually stored elsewhere, either in bound volumes or on film that requires a special machine to read. A librarian will show you how to operate the machine.

43e Finding sources on the Web

As an academic researcher, you enter the World Wide Web in two ways: through your library's Web site, and through public search engines such as *Yahoo!* and *Google*. The library entrance, covered in the preceding sections, is your main path to the books and periodicals that, for most subjects, should make up most of your sources. The public entrance, discussed here, can lead to a wealth of information and ideas, but it also has a number of disadvantages:

- **The Web is a wide-open network.** Anyone with the right hardware and software can place information on the Internet, and even a carefully conceived search can turn up sources with widely varying reliability: journal articles, government documents, scholarly data, term papers written by high school students, sales pitches masked as objective reports, wild theories. You must be especially diligent about evaluating Internet sources (see pp. 590–97).
- **The Web changes constantly.** No search engine can keep up with the Web's daily additions and deletions, and a source you find today may be different or gone tomorrow. You should not put off consulting an online source that you think you may want to use.
- **The Web provides limited information on the past.** Sources dating from before the 1980s or even more recently probably will not appear on the Web.
- **The Web is not all-inclusive.** Most books and many periodicals are available only via the library, not directly via the Web.

Clearly, the Web warrants cautious use. It should not be the only resource you work with.

1 Using a search engine

To find sources on the Web, you use a **search engine** that catalogs Web sites in a series of directories and conducts keyword searches. Generally, use a directory when you haven't yet refined your topic or you want a general overview. Use keywords when you have refined your topic and you seek specific information. (See pp. 572–73 on refining keywords.)

Current search engines

The box on the next page lists the currently most popular search engines. To reach any one of them, enter its address in the Address or Location field of your Web browser.

Web search engines

The features of search engines change often, and new ones appear constantly. For the latest on search engines, see the links collected by Search Engine Watch at *searchenginewatch.com/links*.

Directories that review sites

BUBL Link (*bubl.ac.uk*)

Internet Public Library (*ipl.org/div/subject*)

Internet Scout Project (*scout.wisc.edu/archives*)

Librarians' Index to the Internet (*lii.org*)

Most advanced and efficient engines

AlltheWeb (*alltheweb.com*)

One of the fastest and most comprehensive engines, *AlltheWeb* updates its database frequently so that it returns more of the Web's most recent sites. It allows searches for news, pictures, and audio and video files.

Google (*google.com*)

Also fast and comprehensive, *Google* ranks a site based not only on its content but also on the other sites that are linked to it, thus providing a measure of a site's usefulness. *Google* also allows searches for news, discussion groups, and images.

Other engines

AltaVista (*altavista.com*)

Ask (*ask.com*)

Dogpile (*dogpile.com*)

Excite (*excite.com*)

Lycos (*lycos.com*)

MetaCrawler (*metacrawler.com*)

Yahoo! (*yahoo.com*)

Note For a good range of reliable sources, try out more than a single search engine, perhaps as many as four or five. No search engine can catalog the entire Web—indeed, even the most powerful engine may not include half the sites available at any given time, and most engines include only a fifth or less. In addition, most search engines accept paid placements, giving higher billing to sites that pay a fee. These so-called sponsored links are usually marked as such, but they can compromise a search engine's method for arranging sites in response to your keywords.

A sample search engine

The following screen shot from *Google* shows the features common to most search engines.

Google home page

A search engine's Advanced Search option allows you to customize your search (for instance, by selecting a date range, a language, or a number of results to see) and to limit or expand your keywords (for instance, by using *AND, NOT*, and other operators). It may also tell you how the search engine determines the order in which it presents results. (Criteria include the number of times your keywords appear on a site, whether the terms appear in the site's title or address, and, in *Google*'s case, which other sites link to the site.)

Search records

The screen shot above shows two features of your Web browser that allow you to keep track of Web sources and your search:

- ***Favorites* or *Bookmarks* save site addresses as links.** Click one of these terms near the top of the browser screen to add a site you want to return to. A favorite or bookmark remains on file until you delete it.
- ***History* records the sites you visited over a certain period,** such as a single online session or a week's sessions. (After that period, the history is deleted.) If you forgot to bookmark a site, you can click History or Go to locate your search history and recover the site.

2 Examining a sample search

The following sample Web search illustrates how the refinement of keywords can narrow a search to maximize the relevant hits and minimize the irrelevant ones. Kisha Alder, a student researching taxes on Internet commerce, first used the keywords *Internet taxes* on *Google.* But, as shown in the next screen shot, the search produced more than 13 *million* hits, an unusably large number and a sure sign that Alder's keywords needed revision.

1. First *Google* search results

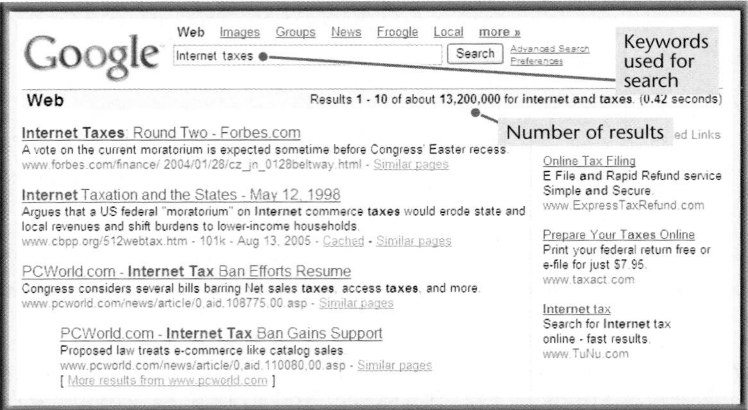

After several tries, Alder arrived at *"sales tax" Internet states reform* to describe her subject more precisely. Narrowed in this way, Alder's search still produced 5,000 hits, but this large number included many potential sources on the first few screens, as shown below.

2. *Google* results with refined keywords

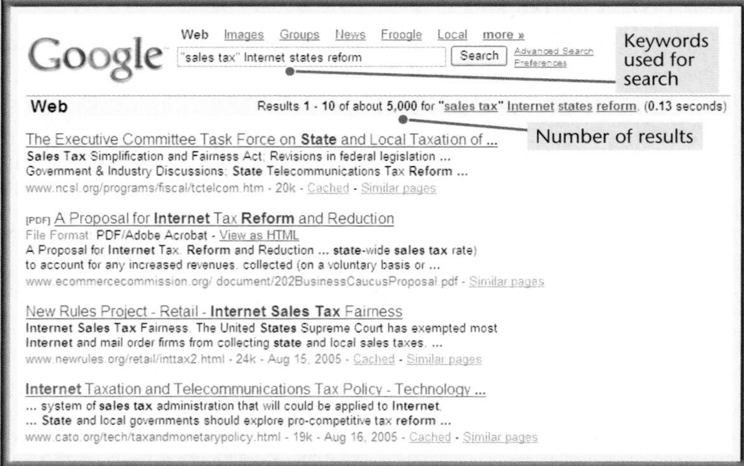

43f Finding other online sources

Several online sources can put you directly in touch with experts and others whose ideas and information may inform your research.

Because these sources, like Web sites, are unfiltered, you must always evaluate them carefully. (See pp. 595–97.)

1 Using electronic mail

As a research tool, e-mail allows you to communicate with others who are interested in your topic. You may, for instance, carry on an e-mail conversation with a teacher at your school or interview an expert in another state to follow up on a scholarly article he or she published. (See pp. 780–83 for more on using e-mail.)

2 Using discussion lists

A **discussion list** (sometimes called a **listserv** or just a **list**) uses e-mail to connect individuals who are interested in a common subject, often with a scholarly or technical focus. By sending a question to an appropriate list, you may be able to reach scores of people who know something about your topic. For an index of discussion lists, see *tile.net/lists*.

When conducting research on a discussion list, follow the guidelines for e-mail etiquette (pp. 782–83) as well as these:

- ***Lurk* for a while**—read without posting messages. Make sure the discussion is relevant to your topic, and get a sense of how the group interacts.
- **Don't ask for information you can find elsewhere.** Most list members are glad to help with legitimate questions but resent messages that rehash familiar debates or that ask them to do someone else's work.
- **Evaluate messages carefully.** Many list subscribers are passionate experts with fair-minded approaches to their topics, but almost anyone with an Internet connection can post a message to a list. See pages 590–97 on evaluating online sources.

3 Using Web forums and newsgroups

Web forums and newsgroups are more open and less scholarly than discussion lists, so their messages require even more diligent evaluation. **Web forums** allow participants to join a conversation simply by selecting a link on a Web page. For a directory of forums, see *delphiforums.com*. **Newsgroups** are organized under subject headings such as *soc* for social issues and *biz* for business. For a directory of newsgroups, see *groups.google.com*.

4 Using Web logs

Web logs, or **blogs,** are personal sites on which an author posts time-stamped comments, generally centering on a common theme,

Many images you find will be available for free, but some sources do charge a fee for use. Before paying for an image, check with a librarian to see if it is available elsewhere for free.

Note You must cite every image source fully in your paper, just as you cite text sources, with author, title, and publication information. In addition, some sources will require that you seek permission from the copyright holder, either the source itself or a third party such as a photographer. Permission is especially likely to be required if you are submitting your paper on the public Web. See page 618 for more about online publication.

43i Generating your own sources

Academic writing will often require you to conduct primary research for information of your own. For instance, you may need to analyze a poem, conduct an experiment, or interview an expert.

An interview can be especially helpful for a research project because it allows you to ask questions precisely geared to your topic. You can conduct an interview in person, over the telephone, or online using electronic mail (p. 583) or a form of synchronous communication (p. 584). A personal interview is preferable if you can arrange it, because you can see the person's expressions and gestures as well as hear his or her tone and words.

Here are a few guidelines for interviews:

- **Call or write for an appointment.** Tell the person exactly why you are calling, what you want to discuss, and how long you expect the interview to take. Be true to your word on all points.
- **Prepare a list of open-ended questions to ask**—perhaps ten or twelve for a one-hour interview. Plan on doing some research for these questions to discover background on the issues and your subject's published views on the issues.
- **Give your subject time to consider your questions.** Don't rush into silences with more questions.
- **Pay attention to your subject's answers** so that you can ask appropriate follow-up questions and pick up on unexpected but worthwhile points.
- **Take care in interpreting answers,** especially if you are online and thus can't depend on facial expressions, gestures, and tone of voice to convey the subject's attitudes.
- **Keep thorough notes.** Take notes during an in-person or telephone interview, or tape-record the interview if you have the equipment and your subject agrees. For online interviews, save the discussion in a file of its own.

- **Verify quotations.** Before you quote your subject in your paper, check with him or her to ensure that the quotations are accurate.
- **Send a thank-you note immediately after the interview.** Promise your subject a copy of your finished paper, and send the paper promptly.

EXERCISE 43.1 Using the library

To become familiar with the research sources available through your library, visit both the library and its Web site for answers to the following questions. Ask a librarian for help whenever necessary. (You can do this exercise online at *ablongman.com/littlebrown.*)

1. Which resources does the library include on its Web site? Which resources require a visit to the library?
2. Where are reference books stored in the library? How are they cataloged and arranged? Which ones are available through the Web site or on CD-ROM? Where and in what format(s) are (*a*) *Contemporary Authors,* (*b*) *Encyclopaedia Britannica,* and (*c*) *MLA International Bibliography of Books and Articles on the Modern Languages and Literatures*?
3. Where is the catalog of the library's periodicals? Where and in what format(s) does the library have current and back issues of the following periodicals: (*a*) the *New York Times,* (*b*) *Time* magazine, and (*c*) *Journal of Social Psychology*?
4. What tools does the library's Web site offer for finding periodical databases that are appropriate for a particular research subject?
5. Research the focus and indexed publications of two periodical databases, such as *InfoTrac, JSTOR, LexisNexis, PAIS,* or *ProQuest.* What disciplines does each database seem most suited for?
6. Does the book catalog cover all of the library's book holdings? If not, which books are not included, and where are they cataloged?
7. What are the library call numbers of the following books: (*a*) *The Power Broker,* by Robert Caro; (*b*) *Heart of Darkness,* by Joseph Conrad; and (*c*) *The Hero with a Thousand Faces,* by Joseph Campbell?

EXERCISE 43.2 Finding library sources

Locate at least six promising articles and books for the subject you began working on in the previous chapter (Exercise 42.1, p. 563, and Exercise 42.2, p. 566). Consider the sources "promising" if they seem directly to address your central research question. Following the guidelines on pages 567–69, make an annotated working bibliography of the sources. Be sure to include all the information you will need to acknowledge the sources in your final paper.

EXERCISE 43.3 Finding Web sources

Use at least two Web search engines to locate six or seven promising sources for your research project. Begin by developing a list of keywords that can be used to query one of the search engines (see p. 580). Check the Advanced Search option of the engine if you need to narrow your search. Then try your refined keywords on the other search engine as well. How do the results differ? What keyword strategies worked best for finding relevant information? Add promising sources to your annotated working bibliography.

CHAPTER 44

Working with Sources

Research writing is much more than finding sources and reporting their contents. The challenge and interest come from *interacting* with sources, reading them critically to discover their meanings, judge their relevance and reliability, and create relationships among them. This chapter shows you how to use the sources you find to extend and support your own ideas, to make your subject your own.

CULTURE LANGUAGE Making a subject your own requires thinking critically about sources and developing independent ideas. These goals may at first be uncomfortable if your native culture emphasizes understanding and respecting established authority more than questioning and enlarging it. The information here will help you work with sources so that you can become an expert in your own right and convincingly convey your expertise to others.

44a Evaluating sources

Before you gather information and ideas from sources, scan them to evaluate what they have to offer and how you might use them.

http://www.ablongman.com/littlebrown

Visit the companion Web site for more help and electronic exercises on working with sources.

1 Judging relevance and reliability

Not all the sources you find will prove worthwhile: some may be irrelevant to your subject, and others may be unreliable. Gauging the relevance and reliability of sources is the essential task of evaluating them. If you haven't already done so, read this book's chapter on critical thinking and reading (pp. 151–79). It provides a foundation for answering the questions in the box below.

Questions for evaluating sources

For online sources, supplement these guidelines with those on pages 590 and 595.

Relevance

- **Does the source devote some attention to your subject?** Check whether the source focuses on your subject or covers it marginally, and compare the source's coverage to that in other sources.
- **Is the source appropriately specialized for your needs?** Check the source's treatment of a topic you know something about, to ensure that it is neither too superficial nor too technical.
- **Is the source up to date enough for your subject?** Check the publication date. If your subject is current, your sources should be, too.

Reliability

- **Where does the source come from?** It matters whether you found the source through your library or directly on the Internet. (If the latter, see pp. 590 and 595.) Check whether a library source is popular or scholarly. Scholarly sources, such as refereed journals and university press books, are generally deeper and more reliable.
- **Is the author an expert in the field?** The authors of scholarly publications tend to be experts. To verify expertise, check an author's credentials in a biography (if the source includes one), in a biographical reference, or by a keyword search of the Web.
- **What is the author's bias?** Every author has a point of view that influences the selection and interpretation of evidence. How do the author's ideas relate to those in other sources? What areas does the author emphasize, ignore, or dismiss? When you're aware of sources' biases, you can attempt to balance them.
- **Is the source fair and reasonable?** Even a strongly biased work should present sound reasoning, adequate evidence, and a fair picture of opposing views—all in an objective, calm tone. The absence of any of these qualities should raise a warning flag.
- **Is the source well written?** A logical organization and clear, error-free sentences indicate a careful author.

You can download these questions from *ablongman.com/littlebrown* and use a copy of the file for each source you are evaluating, providing written answers between the questions.

Note In evaluating sources, you need to consider how they come to you. The sources you find through the library, both print and online, have been previewed for you by their publishers and by your school. They still require your critical reading, but you can have some confidence in the information they contain. With online sources you reach directly, however, you can't assume similar previewing, so your critical reading must be especially rigorous. Special tips for evaluating Web sites and other online sources appear below and on the following pages.

2 Evaluating a Web site

To a great extent, the same critical reading that helps you evaluate library sources will help you evaluate Web sites. But most Web sites have not undergone prior screening by editors and librarians. On your own, you must distinguish scholarship from corporate promotion, valid data from invented statistics, well-founded opinion from clever propaganda.

The strategy summarized in the box below can help you make such distinctions. We'll apply the strategy to the Web site shown on page 592, *Global Warming Information Center,* which turned up in a search for views and data on global warming.

Questions for evaluating Web sites

Supplement these questions with those on the previous page.

- **What type of site are you viewing?** What does the type lead you to expect about the site's purpose and content?
- **Who is the author or sponsor?** How credible is the person or group responsible for the site?
- **What is the purpose of the site?** What does the site's author or sponsor intend to achieve?
- **What does context tell you?** What do you already know about the site's subject that can inform your evaluation? What kinds of support or other information do the site's links provide?
- **What does presentation tell you?** Is the site's design well thought out and effective? Is the writing clear and error-free?
- **How worthwhile is the content?** Are the site's claims well supported by evidence? Is the evidence from reliable sources?

You can download these questions from *ablongman.com/littlebrown.* Use a copy of the file for each source you are evaluating, providing written answers between the questions.

Note To evaluate a Web document, you'll often need to travel to the site's home page to discover the author or sponsoring organization, date of publication, and other relevant information. The page you're reading may include a link to the home page. If it doesn't, you can find it by editing the URL in the Address or Location field of your browser. Working backward, delete the end of the URL up to the last slash and hit Enter. Repeat this step until you reach the home page. There you may also find a menu option, often labeled "About," that will lead you to a description of the site's author or sponsor.

- **Determine the type of site.**

When you search the Web, you're likely to encounter various types of sites. Although they overlap—a primarily informational site may include scholarship as well—the types can usually be identified by their content and purposes. Here are the main types:

- **Sites focusing on scholarship:** These sites have a knowledge-building interest and include research reports with supporting data and extensive documentation of scholarly sources. The URLs of the sites generally end in *edu* (originating from an educational institution), *org* (a nonprofit organization), or *gov* (a government department or agency). Such sites are more likely to be reliable than the others described below.
- **Sites with an informational purpose:** Individuals, nonprofit organizations, schools, corporations, and government bodies all produce sites intended to centralize information on subjects as diverse as astronomy, hip-hop music, and zoo design. The sites' URLs may end in *edu, org, gov,* or *com* (originating from a commercial organization). Such sites generally do not have the knowledge-building focus of scholarly sites and may omit supporting data and documentation, but they can provide useful information and often include links to scholarly sources.
- **Sites focusing on advocacy:** Many sites advocate certain policies or actions. Their URLs usually end in *org,* but they may end in *edu* or *com*. Some advocacy sites include serious, well-documented research to support their positions, but others select or distort evidence.
- **Sites with a commercial purpose:** Corporations and other businesses maintain Web sites to explain or promote themselves or to sell goods and services. The URLs of commercial sites end in *com*. The information on such a site furthers the sponsor's profit-making purpose, but it can include reliable data.
- **Personal sites:** The sites maintained by individuals range from diaries of a family's travels to opinions on political issues to reports on evolving scholarship. The sites' URLs usually end in *com* or *edu*. Personal sites are only as reliable as their authors, but some do provide valuable eyewitness accounts, links to worthy sources, and other usable information. A particular kind of personal site, the Web log, is discussed on pages 595–97.

The home page of the *Global Warming Information Center* gives some information that can be used to tell what type of site it is:

1. **Home page of the *Global Warming Information Center***

- **Identify the author or sponsor.**

A reputable site will list the author or group responsible for the site and will provide information or a link for contacting the author or group. If none of this information is provided, you should not use the source. If you have only the author or group name, you may be able to discover more in a biographical dictionary or through a keyword search. You should also look for mentions of the author or group in your other sources.

As the screen shot shows, the Web site *Global Warming Information Center* names its sponsor right up front: the John P. McGovern M.D. Center for Environmental and Regulatory Affairs. The bottom of this home page gives links to information about the McGovern Center and its parent organization, the National Center for Public Policy Research. Their names imply that both groups are involved in research, so the site does indeed seem to be informational or possibly even scholarly.

- **Gauge purpose.**

A Web site's purpose determines what ideas and information it offers. Inferring that purpose tells you how to interpret what you see on the site. If a site is intended to sell a product or an opinion, it will likely emphasize favorable ideas and information while ignoring or even distorting what is unfavorable. In contrast, if a site is intended to build knowledge—for instance, a scholarly project or journal—it will likely acknowledge diverse views and evidence.

Determining the purpose of a site often requires looking beneath the surface of words and images and beyond the first page. The elements of the *Global Warming* page—the title, the green color, the photo of a child carrying a globe through a field of grass—suggest an environmentalist purpose of informing readers about the theory and consequences of rising earth temperatures caused by pollution. The site's purpose is actually different, though. The home-page links lead to statements about the aims of the McGovern Center and its parent, the National Center. The McGovern Center states that it was launched in the 1900s "to counter misinformation being spread to the public and policymakers by the environmental left." The National Center states its purpose more broadly:

> The National Center for Public Policy Research is a communications and research foundation supportive of a strong national defense and dedicated to providing free market solutions to today's public policy problems. We believe that the principles of a free market, individual liberty, and personal responsibility provide the greatest hope for meeting the challenges facing America in the 21st century.

These two statements imply that the purpose of the McGovern Center's *Global Warming* site is to inform readers about the evidence against global warming in the interest of reducing or overturning environmental regulations.

■ Consider context.

Your evaluation of a Web site should be informed by considerations outside the site itself. Chief among these is your own knowledge: What do you already know about the site's subject and the prevailing views of it? In addition, you can follow some of the site's links to see how they support, or don't support, the site's credibility. For instance, links to scholarly sources lend authority to a site—but *only if* the scholarly sources actually relate to and back up the site's claims.

The *Global Warming* site has a clear anti-regulatory bias, but this view is a significant one in the debates over global warming. That is, the bias does not necessarily disqualify the site as a source on global warming. The question is how reliable its information is: does it come from trustworthy, less-biased sources? All the site's links lead to publications of the McGovern Center or the National Center, so the question can be answered only by looking more deeply at these publications.

■ Look at presentation.

Considering both the look of a site and the way it's written can illuminate its intentions and reliability. Are the site's elements all functional and well integrated, or is the site cluttered with irrelevant material and graphics? Does the site seem carefully constructed and well maintained, or is it sloppy and outdated? Does the design reflect the apparent purpose of the site, or does it undercut or conceal that purpose in some way? Is the text clearly written, or is it difficult to understand?

At first glance, as noted earlier, the *Global Warming* site casts a pro-environmentalist image that turns out not to coincide with its purpose. Otherwise, the site is cleanly designed, with minimal elements laid out clearly. The text on other pages is straightforward and readable. Apparently, the sponsor takes its purpose seriously and has thought out its presentation.

- **Analyze content.**

With information about a site's author, purpose, and context, you're in a position to evaluate its content. Are the ideas and information slanted and, if so, in what direction? Are the views and data authoritative, or do you need to balance them—or even reject them? These questions require close reading of the text and its sources.

The *Global Warming* site links to a wealth of reports and prominently features "Questions and Answers on Global Warming." The following screen shots show two of the items from this page and the footnotes citing sources for the answers.

---

2. Content and documentation from the site

Questions and Answers on Global Warming

1. Is global warming occurring? Have the forecasts of global warming been confirmed by actual measurements?

There is no serious evidence that man-made global warming is taking place. The computer models used in U.N. studies say the first area to heat under the "greenhouse gas effect" should be the lower atmosphere - known as the troposphere.1 Highly accurate, carefully checked satellite data have shown absolutely no such tropospheric warming. There has been surface warming of about half a degree Celsius, but this is far below the customary natural swings in surface temperatures.2

2. Are carbon dioxide emissions from burning fossil fuels the primary cause of climate change? Can the Earth's temperature be expected to rise between 2.5 and 10.4 degrees Fahrenheit in this century as has been reported?

There are many indications that carbon dioxide does not play a significant role in global warming. Richard Lindzen, Ph.D., professor at the Massachusetts Institute of Technology and one of the 11 scientists who prepared a 2001 National Academy of Sciences (NAS) report on climate change, estimates that a doubling of carbon dioxide in the atmosphere would produce a temperature increase of only one degree Celsius.3 In fact, clouds and water vapor appear to be far more important factors related to global temperature. According to Dr. Lindzen and NASA scientists, clouds and water vapor may play a significant role in regulating the Earth's temperature to keep it more constant.4

Assertions about the validity and causes of global warming, citing data and expert opinion as evidence

Footnotes

1 James K. Glassman and Sallie Baliunas, *The Weekly Standard*, June 25, 2001.
2 *Ibid*.
3 Richard Lindzen, professor of meteorology, Massachusetts Institute of Technology and member of the National Academy of Sciences, "Scientists' Report Doesn't Support The Kyoto Treaty," *The Wall Street Journal*, June 11, 2001.
4 Glassman and Baliunas.

Footnotes citing an article in the conservative magazine *The Weekly Standard* and a newspaper report, not scholarly publications that explain methods of gathering and interpreting the data used as evidence

The source mix shown in the preceding screen shot is similar in the other publications found through the *Global Warming* site. Scholars do disagree over whether the earth's temperatures are rising significantly, whether human-made pollution is an important cause, how serious the consequences may be, and how to solve the problem. Because the *Global Warming* site does not offer or refer to the scholarly research, its claims and evidence must be viewed suspiciously and probably rejected for use in a research paper. A usable source need not be less biased, but it must be more substantial.

3 Evaluating other online sources

Web logs and the postings to online discussions require the same critical scrutiny as Web sites do. Web logs can be sources of in-depth information and informed opinion, but they can also be virtually useless. Web forums and newsgroups are similarly suspect. Even if a reliable blog or discussion-group message provides very current information or eyewitness testimony, it will not have the authority of a scholarly publication. An e-mail discussion list may be more trustworthy if its subscribers are professionals in the field, but you will still find wrong or misleading data and skewed opinions.

Use the following strategy for evaluating blogs and messages in online discussions.

Questions for evaluating Web logs and online discussions

Supplement these questions with those on page 589.

- **Who is the author?** How credible is the person writing?
- **What is the author's purpose?** What can you tell about why the author is writing?
- **What does the context reveal?** What do others' responses on a blog or the other messages in a discussion thread indicate about the source's balance and reliability?
- **How worthwhile is the content?** Are the author's claims supported by evidence? Is the evidence from reliable sources?
- **How does the blog or message compare with other sources?** Do the author's claims seem accurate and fair given what you've seen in sources you know to be reliable?

You can download these questions from *ablongman.com/littlebrown.* Use a copy of the file for each source you are evaluating, providing written answers between the questions.

single topic. Write a brief summary of each message (see pp. 141–43 on summarizing). Then analyze and synthesize the messages to develop a one- or two-paragraph evaluation of the discussion. Which messages seem reliable? Which don't? Why?

44b Synthesizing sources

When you begin to locate the differences and similarities among sources, you move into the most significant part of research writing: forging relationships for your own purpose. This **synthesis** is an essential step in reading sources critically, and it continues through the drafting and revision of a research paper. As you infer connections—say, between one writer's opinions and another's or between two works by the same author—you create new knowledge.

Your synthesis of sources will grow more detailed and sophisticated as you proceed through the research-writing process. Unless you are analyzing primary sources such as the works of a poet, at first read your sources quickly and selectively to obtain an overview of your subject and a sense of how the sources approach it. Don't get bogged down in gathering detailed information, but *do* record your ideas about sources in your research journal (p. 561) or your annotated bibliography (p. 568).

■ Respond to sources.

Write down what your sources make you think. Do you agree or disagree with the author? Do you find his or her views narrow, or do they open up new approaches for you? Is there anything in the source that you need to research further before you can understand it? Does the source prompt questions that you should keep in mind while reading other sources?

■ Connect sources.

When you notice a link between sources, jot it down. Do two sources differ in their theories or their interpretations of facts? Does one source illuminate another—perhaps commenting or clarifying or supplying additional data? Do two or more sources report studies that support a theory you've read about or an idea of your own?

■ Heed your own insights.

Apart from ideas prompted by your sources, you are sure to come up with independent thoughts: a conviction, a point of confusion that suddenly becomes clear, a question you haven't seen anyone else ask. These insights may occur at unexpected times, so it's good practice to keep a notebook or computer handy to record them.

Use sources to support your own ideas.

As your research proceeds, the responses, connections, and insights you form through synthesis will lead you to answer your starting research question with a statement of your thesis (see p. 620). They will also lead you to the main ideas supporting your thesis—conclusions you have drawn from your synthesis of sources, forming the main divisions of your paper. When drafting the paper, make sure each paragraph focuses on an idea of your own, with the support for the idea coming from your sources. In this way, your paper will synthesize others' work into something wholly your own.

EXERCISE 44.5 Synthesizing sources

The three passages below address the same issue, the legalization of drugs. What similarities do you see in the authors' ideas? What differences? Write a paragraph of your own in which you use these authors' views as a point of departure for your own view about drug legalization. (You can do this exercise online at *ablongman.com/littlebrown*.)

Perhaps the most unfortunate victims of drug prohibition laws have been the residents of America's ghettos. These laws have proved largely futile in deterring ghetto-dwellers from becoming drug abusers, but they do account for much of what ghetto residents identify as the drug problem. Aggressive, gun-toting drug dealers often upset law-abiding residents far more than do addicts nodding out in doorways. Meanwhile other residents perceive the drug dealers as heroes and successful role models. They're symbols of success to children who see no other options. At the same time the increasingly harsh criminal penalties imposed on adult drug dealers have led drug traffickers to recruit juveniles. Where once children started dealing drugs only after they had been using them for a few years, today the sequence is often reversed. Many children start using drugs only after working for older drug dealers for a while. Legalization of drugs, like legalization of alcohol in the 1930s, would drive the drug-dealing business off the streets and out of apartment buildings and into government-regulated, tax-paying stores. It also would force many of the gun-toting dealers out of the business and convert others into legitimate businessmen.

—Ethan A. Nadelmann, "Shooting Up"

Statistics argue against legalization. The University of Michigan conducts an annual survey of twelfth graders, asking the students about their drug consumption. In 1980, 56.4 percent of those polled said they had used marijuana in the past twelve months, whereas in 2004 only 45.7 percent had done so. Cocaine use was also reduced in the same period (22.6 percent to 15.4 percent). At the same time, twelve-month use of legally available drugs—alcohol and nicotine-containing cigarettes—remained constant at about 75 percent and 55 percent, respectively. The numbers of illegal drug users haven't declined nearly enough: those teenaged marijuana and cocaine users are still vulnerable to addiction and even death, and they threaten to infect their impressionable peers.

But clearly the prohibition of illegal drugs has helped, while the legal status of alcohol and cigarettes has not made them less popular.

—Sylvia Runkle, "The Case Against Legalization"

I have to laugh at the debate over what to do about the drug problem. Everyone is running around offering solutions—from making drug use a more serious criminal offense to legalizing it. But there isn't a real solution. I know that. I used and abused drugs, and people, and society, for two decades. Nothing worked to get me to stop all that behavior except just plain being sick and tired. Nothing. Not threats, not ten-plus years in prison, not anything that was said to me. I used until I got through. Period. And that's when you'll win the war. When all the dope fiends are done. Not a minute before.

—Michael W. Posey, "I Did Drugs Until They Wore Me Out. Then I Stopped."

EXERCISE 44.6 Evaluating and synthesizing sources

Look up the sources in the working bibliography you made in Exercises 43.2 and 43.3 (pp. 587–88). Evaluate the sources for their relevance and reliability. If the sources seem unreliable or don't seem to give you what you need, expand your working bibliography and evaluate the new sources. In your research journal or annotated bibliography, write down your responses to sources, the connections you perceive among sources, and other original ideas that occur to you.

44c Gathering information from sources

You can accomplish a great deal of synthesis while gathering information from your sources. This information gathering is not a mechanical process. Rather, as you read you assess and organize the information in your sources.

Researchers vary in their methods for working with sources, but all methods share the same goals:

- **Keep accurate records of what sources say.** Accuracy helps prevent misrepresentation and plagiarism.
- **Keep accurate records of how to find sources.** These records are essential for retracing steps and for citing sources in the final paper. (See pp. 567–69 on keeping a working bibliography.)
- **Interact with sources.** Reading sources critically leads to an understanding of them, the relationships among them, and their support for one's own ideas.

To achieve these goals, you can take handwritten notes, type notes into your computer, annotate photocopies or printouts of sources, or annotate downloaded documents. On any given project, you may use all the methods. Each has advantages and disadvantages.

- **Handwritten notes:** Taking notes by hand is especially useful if you come across a source with no computer or photocopier handy. But handwritten notes can be risky. It's easy to introduce errors as you work from source to note card. And it's possible to copy source language and then later mistake and use it as your own, thus plagiarizing the source. Always take care to make accurate notes and to place big quotation marks around any passage you quote.
- **Notes on computer:** Taking notes on a computer can streamline the path of source to note to paper, because you can import the notes into your draft as you write. However, computer notes have the same disadvantages as handwritten notes: the risk of introducing errors and the risk of plagiarizing. As with handwritten notes, strive for accuracy, and use quotation marks for quotations.
- **Photocopies and printouts:** Photocopying from print sources or printing out online sources each has the distinct advantages of convenience and reduction in the risks of error and plagiarism during information gathering. But each method has disadvantages, too. The busywork of copying or printing can distract you from the crucial work of interacting with sources. And you have to make a special effort to annotate copies and printouts with the publication information for sources. If you don't have this information for your final paper, you can't use the source.
- **Downloads:** Researching online, you can usually download full-text articles, Web pages, discussion-group messages, and other materials onto your computer. While drafting, you can import source information from one file into another. Like photocopies and printouts, though, downloads can distract you from interacting with sources and can easily become separated from the publication information you must have in order to use the sources. Even more important, directly importing source material creates a high risk of plagiarism. You must keep clear boundaries between your own ideas and words and those of others.

44d Using summary, paraphrase, and quotation

As you take notes from sources or work source material into your draft, you can summarize, paraphrase, quote, or combine methods. The choice should depend on why you are using a source.

Note **Summaries, paraphrases, and quotations all require source citations. A summary or paraphrase without a source citation or a quotation without quotation marks and a source citation is plagiarism.** (See pp. 611–18 for more on plagiarism.)

1 Summarizing

When you **summarize,** you condense an extended idea or argument into a sentence or more in your own words. A full discussion of summary appears on pages 141–43, and you should read that section if you have not already done so.

Summary is most useful when you want to record the gist of an author's idea without the background or supporting evidence. Following is a passage from a government report on the so-called digital divide between US residents with and without access to the Internet. Then a sample computer note shows a summary of the passage.

Original quotation

The following examples highlight the breadth of the digital divide today:

- Those with a college degree are more than *eight times* as likely to have a computer at home, and nearly *sixteen times* as likely to have home Internet access, as those with an elementary school education.
- A high-income household in an urban area is more than *twenty times* as likely as a rural, low-income household to have Internet access.
- A child in a low-income white family is *three times* as likely to have Internet access as a child in a comparable black family, and *four times* as likely to have access as children in a comparable Hispanic household.

—US Department of Commerce, *Falling Through the Net: Toward Digital Inclusion*, p. 7

Summary of source

Digital divide

Dept. of Commerce 7

US residents who are urban, white, college educated, and affluent are much more likely to be connected to the Internet than those who are rural, black or Hispanic, not educated past elementary school, and poor.

2 Paraphrasing

When you **paraphrase,** you follow much more closely the author's original presentation, but you still restate it in your own words and sentence structures. Paraphrase is most useful when you want to present or examine an author's line of reasoning but don't feel the original words merit direct quotation. Here is a paraphrase of the above quotation from the Department of Commerce report.

Paraphrase of source

Digital divide

Dept. of Commerce 7

Likelihood of being connected to the Internet among US groups:

Home connection, elementary education vs. college education: 1/16 as likely.

Any access, rural setting and low-income household vs. urban setting and affluent household: 1/20 as likely.

Any access, low-income black child vs. low-income white child: 1/3 as likely.

Any access, low-income Hispanic child vs. low-income white child: 1/4 as likely.

Notice that the paraphrase follows the original but uses different words and different sentence structures. In contrast, an unsuccessful paraphrase—one that plagiarizes—copies the author's words or sentence structures or both *without quotation marks.* (See p. 616.)

Paraphrasing a source

- **Read the relevant material several times to be sure you understand it.**
- **Restate the source's ideas in your own words and sentence structures.** You need not put down in new words the whole passage or all the details. Select what is relevant to your topic, and restate only that. If complete sentences seem too detailed or cumbersome, use phrases, as in the example on the preceding page.
- **Be careful not to distort meaning.** Don't change the source's emphasis or omit connecting words, qualifiers, and other material whose absence will confuse you later or cause you to misrepresent the source.

CULTURE LANGUAGE If English is not your native language and you have difficulty paraphrasing the ideas in sources, try this. Before attempting a paraphrase, read the original passage several times. Then, instead of "translating" line by line, try to state the gist of the passage without looking at it. Check your effort against the original to be sure you have captured the source author's meaning and emphasis without using his or her words and sentence structures. If you need a synonym for a word, look it up in a dictionary.

3 Direct quotation

Your notes from sources may include many quotations, especially if you rely on photocopies, printouts, or downloads. Whether

EXERCISE 44.9 Gathering information from sources

Continuing from Exercise 44.6 (p. 600), as the next step in preparing a research paper, gather and organize the information from your sources. Mark every note, photocopy, printout, and download with the source's publication information and a heading related to your paper. Annotate relevant passages of photocopies, printouts, and downloads. For handwritten or computer notes, use direct quotation, summary, or paraphrase as seems appropriate, being careful to avoid inaccuracy and plagiarism. (If you need help recognizing plagiarism, see Chapter 45.)

44e Integrating sources into your text

The evidence of others' information and opinions should back up, not dominate, your own ideas. To synthesize evidence, you need to smooth the transitions between your ideas and words and those of your sources, and you need to give the reader a context for interpreting the borrowed material.

Note The examples in this section use the MLA syle of source documentation and also present-tense verbs (such as *disagrees* and *claims*). See pages 609–10 for specific variations in documentation style and verb tense within the academic disciplines. Several other conventions governing quotations are discussed elsewhere in this book:

- **Using commas to punctuate signal phrases** (pp. 446–48).
- **Placing other punctuation marks with quotation marks** (pp. 476–77).
- **Using brackets and the ellipsis mark to indicate changes in quotations** (pp. 485–88).
- **Punctuating and placing parenthetical citations** (pp. 630–32).
- **Formatting long prose quotations and poetry quotations** in MLA style (pp. 665–66) or APA style (pp. 757–58).

1 Introducing borrowed material

Readers will be distracted from your point if borrowed material does not fit into your sentence. In the passage below, the writer has not meshed the structures of her own and her source's sentences:

Awkward One editor disagrees with this view and "a good reporter does not fail to separate opinions from facts" (Lyman 52).

In the following revision the writer adds words to integrate the quotation into her sentence:

Revised — One editor disagrees with this view, maintaining that "a good reporter does not fail to separate opinions from facts" (Lyman 52).

To mesh your own and your source's words, you may sometimes need to make a substitution or addition to the quotation, signaling your change with brackets:

Words added — "The tabloids [of England] are a journalistic case study in bad reporting," claims Lyman (52).

Verb form changed — A bad reporter, Lyman implies, is one who "[fails] to separate opinions from facts" (52). [The bracketed verb replaces *fail* in the original.]

Capitalization changed — "[T]o separate opinions from facts" is the work of a good reporter (Lyman 52). [In the original, *to* is not capitalized.]

Noun supplied for pronoun — The reliability of a news organization "depends on [reporters'] trustworthiness," says Lyman (52). [The bracketed noun replaces *their* in the original.]

2 Interpreting borrowed material

Even when it does not conflict with your own sentence structure, borrowed material will be ineffective if you merely dump it in readers' laps without explaining how you intend it to be understood. Reading the following passage, we must figure out for ourselves that the writer's sentence and the quotation state opposite points of view:

Dumped — Many news editors and reporters maintain that it is impossible to keep personal opinions from influencing the selection and presentation of facts. "True, news reporters, like everyone else, form impressions of what they see and hear. However, a good reporter does not fail to separate opinions from facts" (Lyman 52).

In the revision, the underlined additions tell us how to interpret the quotation:

Revised — Many news editors and reporters maintain that it is impossible to keep personal opinions from influencing the selection and presentation of facts. Yet not all authorities agree with this view. One editor grants that "news reporters, like everyone else, form impressions of what they see and hear." But, he insists, "a good reporter does not fail to separate opinions from facts" (Lyman 52).

Signal phrases

The words *One editor grants* and *he insists* in the revised passage above are **signal phrases:** they tell readers who the source is and what to expect in the quotations that follow. Signal phrases usually contain (1) the source author's name (or a substitute for it, such as *One editor* and *he*) and (2) a verb that indicates the source author's attitude or approach to what he or she says.

Some verbs for signal phrases appear in the list below. These verbs are in the present tense, typical of writing in the humanities. But in the social and natural sciences, the present perfect or past tense is more common. See page 610.

Author is neutral	Author infers or suggests	Author argues	Author is uneasy or disparaging
comments	analyzes	claims	belittles
describes	asks	contends	bemoans
explains	assesses	defends	complains
illustrates	concludes	holds	condemns
notes	considers	insists	deplores
observes	finds	maintains	deprecates
points out	predicts		derides
records	proposes	**Author agrees**	disagrees
relates	reveals		laments
reports	shows	admits	warns
says	speculates	agrees	
sees	suggests	concedes	
thinks	supposes	grants	
writes			

Vary your signal phrases to suit your interpretation of borrowed material and also to keep readers' interest. A signal phrase may precede, interrupt, or follow the borrowed material:

Precedes — Lyman insists that "a good reporter does not fail to separate opinions from facts" (52).

Interrupts — "However," Lyman insists, "a good reporter does not fail to separate opinions from facts" (52).

Follows — "[A] good reporter does not fail to separate opinions from facts," Lyman insists (52).

Background information

You can add information to a quotation to integrate it into your text and inform readers why you are using it. In most cases, provide the author's name in the text, especially if the author is an expert or if readers will recognize the name:

Author named — Harold Lyman grants that "news reporters, like everyone else, form impressions of what they see and hear." But, Lyman insists, "a good reporter does not fail to separate opinions from facts" (52).

If the source title contributes information about the author or the context of the quotation, you can provide it in the text:

Title given — Harold Lyman, in his book *The Conscience of the Journalist*, grants that "news reporters, like everyone else, form impressions of what they see and hear." But, Lyman insists, "a good reporter does not fail to separate opinions from facts" (52).

If the quoted author's background and experience reinforce or clarify the quotation, you can provide these credentials in the text:

Credentials given — Harold Lyman, a newspaper editor for more than forty years, grants that "news reporters, like everyone else, form impressions of what they see and hear." But, Lyman insists, "a good reporter does not fail to separate opinions from facts" (52).

You need not name the author, source, or credentials in your text when you are simply establishing facts or weaving together facts and opinions from varied sources. In the following passage, the information is more important than the source, so the name of the source is confined to a parenthetical acknowledgment:

> To end the abuses of the British, many colonists were urging three actions: forming a united front, seceding from Britain, and taking control of their own international relations (Wills 325–36).

3 Following discipline styles for integrating sources

The preceding guidelines for introducing and interpreting borrowed material apply generally across academic disciplines, but there are differences in verb tense and documentation style.

English and some other humanities

Writers in English, foreign languages, and related disciplines use MLA style for documenting sources and generally use the present tense of verbs in signal phrases. In discussing sources other than works of literature, the present perfect tense is also sometimes appropriate:

> Lyman insists . . . [present].
> Lyman has insisted . . . [present perfect].

In discussing works of literature, use only the present tense to describe both the work of the author and the action in the work:

> Kate Chopin builds irony into every turn of "The Story of an Hour." For example, Mrs. Mallard, the central character, finds joy in the death of her husband, whom she loves, because she anticipates "the long procession of years that would belong to her absolutely" (23).

Avoid shifting tenses in writing about literature. You can, for instance, shorten quotations to avoid their past-tense verbs.

Shift — Her freedom elevates her, so that "she carried herself unwittingly like a goddess of victory" (24).

Revision (quotation) According to one critic of the penal system, the psychology of "the kept" may say less about prisons than the psychology of "the keepers" (Mitford 9).

2 Using a paraphrase or summary: Your own words and sentence structure and a source citation

The example below changes the sentence structure of the original Mitford quotation opposite, but it still uses Mitford's words (underlined) without quotation marks and without a source citation:

Plagiarism In understanding prisons, we should know more about the character and mentality of the keepers than of the kept.

To avoid plagiarism, the writer can use quotation marks and cite the source (see opposite) or *use his or her own words* and still *cite the source* (because the idea is Mitford's, not the writer's):

Revision (paraphrase) Mitford holds that we may be able to learn more about prisons from the psychology of the prison officials than from that of the prisoners (9).

Revision (paraphrase) We may understand prisons better if we focus on the personalities and attitudes of the prison workers rather than those of the inmates (Mitford 9).

In the next example, the writer cites Mitford and does not use her words but still plagiarizes her sentence structure:

Plagiarism One critic of the penal system maintains that the psychology of prison officials may be more informative about prisons than the psychology of prisoners (Mitford 9).

Revision (paraphrase) One critic of the penal system maintains that we may be able to learn less from the psychology of prisoners than from the psychology of prison officials (Mitford 9).

EXERCISE 45.1 Recognizing plagiarism

The following numbered items show various attempts to quote or paraphrase the passage below. Carefully compare each attempt with the original passage. Which attempts are plagiarized, inaccurate, or both, and which are acceptable? Why? (You can do this exercise online at *ablongman.com/littlebrown.*)

I would agree with the sociologists that psychiatric labeling is dangerous. Society can inflict terrible wounds by discrimination, and by confusing health with disease and disease with badness.

—George E. Vaillant, *Adaptation to Life,* p. 361

1. According to George Vaillant, society often inflicts wounds by using psychiatric labeling, confusing health, disease, and badness (361).
2. According to George Vaillant, "psychiatric labeling [such as 'homosexual' or 'schizophrenic'] is dangerous. Society can inflict

terrible wounds by . . . confusing health with disease and disease with badness" (361).

3. According to George Vaillant, when psychiatric labeling discriminates between health and disease or between disease and badness, it can inflict wounds on those labeled (361).
4. Psychiatric labels can badly hurt those labeled, says George Vaillant, because they fail to distinguish among health, illness, and immorality (361).
5. Labels such as "homosexual" and "schizophrenic" can be hurtful when they fail to distinguish among health, illness, and immorality.
6. "I would agree with the sociologists that society can inflict terrible wounds by discrimination, and by confusing health with disease and disease with badness" (Vaillant 361).

45d Acknowledging online sources

Online sources are so accessible and so easy to download into your own documents that it may seem they are freely available, exempting you from the obligation to acknowledge them. They are not. Acknowledging online sources is somewhat trickier than acknowledging print sources, but no less essential. Further, if you are publishing your work on the Web, you need to take account of sources' copyright restrictions as well.

1 Citing online sources in an unpublished project

When you use material from an online source in a print or online document to be distributed just to your class, your obligation to cite sources does not change: you must acknowledge someone else's independent material in whatever form you find it. With online sources, that obligation can present additional challenges:

- **Record complete publication information each time you consult an online source.** Online sources may change from one day to the next or even disappear entirely. See page 568 for the information to record, such as the electronic address and the publication date. Without the proper information, you *may not* use the source.
- **Acknowledge linked sites.** If you use not only a Web site but also one or more of its linked sites, you must acknowledge the linked sites as well. The fact that one person has used a second person's work does not release you from the responsibility to cite the second work.
- **Seek the author's permission before using an e-mail message, discussion-group posting, or Web log contribution.** Obtaining permission advises the author that his or her ideas are about to

2 Revising and editing

For a complex project like a research paper, you'll certainly want to revise in at least two stages—first for thesis, structure, and other whole-paper issues, and then for clarity, grammar, and other sentence-level issues. Chapter 3 supports this two-stage approach with checklists for revision (p. 54) and editing (pp. 60–61). The box below provides additional steps to take when revising a research paper.

Checklist for revising a research paper

Assignment

How does the draft satisfy all of the criteria stated in your teacher's assignment?

Thesis statement

How well does your thesis statement describe your subject and your perspective as they emerged during drafting?

Structure

(Outlining your draft can help you see structure at a glance. See p. 52.)

How consistently does borrowed material illuminate and support—not lead and dominate—your own ideas? How well is the importance of ideas reflected in the emphasis they receive? Will the arrangement of ideas be clear to readers?

Evidence

Where might evidence seem weak or irrelevant to readers?

Reasonableness and clarity

How reasonable will readers find your argument? (See pp. 203–07.) Where do you need to define terms or concepts that readers may not know or may dispute?

You can download this checklist from *ablongman.com/littlebrown*. Copy the checklist for each research paper, answering the questions in writing.

3 Formatting

The final draft of your paper should conform to the document format recommended by your instructor or by the style guide of the discipline in which you are writing. This book details two common formats: Modern Language Association (pp. 664–66) and American Psychological Association (pp. 755–58).

In any discipline you can use a word processor to present your ideas effectively and attractively with readable typefonts, headings, illustrations, and other elements. See pages 118–27 for ideas.

Before you submit your paper, proofread it carefully for typographical errors, misspellings, and other errors. (See p. 65 for proofreading tips.) Unless the errors are very numerous (more than several on a page), you can correct them by whiting out or crossing out (neatly) and inserting the correction (neatly) in ink. Don't let the pressure of a deadline prevent you from proofreading, for even minor errors can impair clarity or annoy readers and thus negate some of the hard work you have put into your project.

EXERCISE 46.3 Drafting your paper

Draft the research paper you have been developing in Chapters 42–45. Before beginning the draft, study your research journal and your source information. While drafting, follow your thesis statement and outline as closely as you need to, but stay open to new ideas, associations, and arrangements.

EXERCISE 46.4 Revising and editing your paper

Using the revision and editing checklists on pages 54 and 60–61 and the checklist and pointers here, revise and edit your research paper. Work to improve not only the presentation of ideas but also, if necessary, the ideas themselves. Make sure you have provided an in-text citation for every summary, paraphrase, and direct quotation of a source and that your list of sources is complete.

EXERCISE 46.5 Preparing and proofreading your final draft

Prepare the final draft of your research paper, following your teacher's requirements for document format. If your teacher does not specify a format, follow the MLA guidelines on pages 664–66. Proofread and correct the paper before submitting it.

13. The Bible

When you cite passages of the Bible in parentheses, abbreviate the title of any book longer than four letters—for instance, Gen. (Genesis), 1 Sam. (1 Samuel), Ps. (Psalms), Prov. (Proverbs), Matt. (Matthew), Rom. (Romans). Then give the chapter and verse(s) in Arabic numerals.

> According to the Bible, at Babel God "did . . . confound the language of all the earth" (Gen. 11.9).

14. An electronic source

Cite an electronic source as you would any other source: usually by author's name or, if there is no author, by title.

> Business forecasts for the fourth quarter tended to be optimistic (White 4).

This example cites a source with page numbers. For a source with paragraph or screen numbers or no numbering, see models 5 and 6 (pp. 626–27).

15. Two or more works in the same citation

If you use a single parenthetical citation to refer to more than one work, separate the references with a semicolon.

> Two recent articles point out that a computer badly used can be less efficient than no computer at all (Gough and Hall 201; Richards 162).

Since long citations in the text can distract the reader, you may choose to cite several or more works in an endnote or footnote rather than in the text. See page 632.

2 Positioning and punctuating parenthetical citations

The following guidelines will help you place and punctuate text citations to distinguish between your and your sources' ideas and to make your own text readable. See also pages 606–10 on editing quotations and using signal phrases to integrate source material into your sentences.

Where to place citations

Position text citations to accomplish two goals:

- **Make it clear exactly where your borrowing begins and ends.**
- **Keep the citation as unobtrusive as possible.**

You can accomplish both goals by placing the parenthetical citation at the end of the sentence element containing the borrowed material. This sentence element may be a phrase or a clause, and it may begin, interrupt, or conclude the sentence. Usually, as in the following examples, the element ends with a punctuation mark.

The inflation rate might climb as high as 30 percent (Kim 164), an increase that could threaten the small nation's stability.

The inflation rate, which might climb as high as 30 percent (Kim 164), could threaten the small nation's stability.

The small nation's stability could be threatened by its inflation rate, which, one source predicts, might climb as high as 30 percent (Kim 164).

In the last example the addition of one source predicts clarifies that Kim is responsible only for the inflation-rate prediction, not for the statement about stability.

When your paraphrase or summary of a source runs longer than a sentence, clarify the boundaries by using the author's name in the first sentence and placing the parenthetical citation at the end of the last sentence.

Juliette Kim studied the effects of acutely high inflation in several South American and African countries since World War II. She discovered that a major change in government accompanied or followed the inflationary period in 56 percent of cases (22-23).

When you cite two or more sources in the same paragraph, position authors' names and parenthetical citations so that readers can see who said what. In the following example, the beginnings and ends of sentences clearly mark the different sources:

For some time, schools have been using computers extensively for drill-and-practice exercises, in which students repeat specific skills such as spelling words, using the multiplication facts, or, at a higher level, doing chemistry problems. But many education experts criticize such exercises for boring students and failing to engage their critical thinking and creativity. Jane M. Healy, a noted educational psychologist and teacher, takes issue with "interactive" software for children as well as drill-and-practice software, arguing that "some of the most popular 'educational' software . . . may be damaging to independent thinking, attention, and motivation" (20). Another education expert, Harold Wenglinsky of the Educational Testing Service, found in a well-regarded 1998 study that fourth and eighth graders who used computers frequently, including for drill and practice, actually did worse on tests than their peers who used computers less often (Does It Compute? 21). In a later article, Wenglinsky concludes that "the quantity of use matters far less than the quality of use." In schools, he says, high-quality computer work, involving critical thinking, is still rare ("In Search" 17).

How to punctuate citations

Generally place a parenthetical citation *before* any punctuation required by your sentence. If the borrowed material is a quotation,

- **Arrange your sources in alphabetical order** by the last name of the author. If an author is not given in the source, alphabetize the source by the first main word of the title (excluding *A*, *An*, or *The*).
- **Type the entire list double-spaced,** both within and between entries.
- **Indent the second and subsequent lines of each entry one-half inch or five spaces from the left.** Your word processor can format this so-called hanging indent automatically. First highlight the material to be indented. Then, on the Format menu, click Paragraph and then either Hanging Indent (in *WordPerfect*) or Special: Hanging (in *Microsoft Word*).

For complete lists of works cited, see the papers by Kisha Alder (p. 675) and Vanessa Haley (p. 682).

The box on these two pages directs you to the MLA formats for works-cited entries. Use your best judgment in adapting the models to your particular sources. If you can't find a model that exactly matches a source you used, locate and follow the closest possible match. You will certainly need to combine formats—for instance, drawing on model 2 ("A book with two or three authors") and model 26 ("An article in a daily newspaper") for a newspaper article with two authors.

MLA works-cited models

1 Listing books

The next page shows the basic format for a book and the location of the required information in a book. When other information is required, it usually falls either between the author's name and the title or between the title and the publication information, as in the following models.

5. A book with an editor

Holland, Merlin, and Rupert Hart-Davis, eds. The Complete Letters of Oscar Wilde. New York: Holt, 2000.

Handle editors' names like authors' names (models 1–3), but add a comma and the abbreviation ed. (one editor) or eds. (two or more editors) after the last editor's name.

6. A book with an author and an editor

Mumford, Lewis. The City in History. Ed. Donald L. Miller. New York: Pantheon, 1986.

When citing the work of the author, give his or her name first, and give the editor's name after the title, preceded by Ed. (singular only, meaning "Edited by"). When citing the work of the editor, use model 5 for a book with an editor, adding By and the author's name after the title: Miller, Donald L., ed. The City in History. By Lewis Mumford.

7. A translation

Alighieri, Dante. The Inferno. Trans. John Ciardi. New York: NAL, 1971.

When citing the work of the author, give his or her name first, and give the translator's name after the title, preceded by Trans. ("Translated by"). When citing the work of the translator, give his or her name first, followed by a comma and trans.; then follow the title with By and the author's name: Ciardi, John, trans. The Inferno. By Dante Alighieri.

When a book you cite by author has a translator *and* an editor, give the translator's and editor's names in the order used on the book's title page.

8. A book with a corporate author

Lorenz Research, Inc. Research in Social Studies Teaching. Baltimore: Arrow, 2000.

Corporate authors include associations, committees, institutions, government bodies, companies, and other groups. List the name of the group as author when a source gives only that name and not an individual's.

9. An anonymous book

The Dorling Kindersley World Reference Atlas. London: Dorling, 2005.

List a book that names no author—neither an individual nor a group—by its full title. Alphabetize the book by the title's first main word (here Dorling), excluding *A, An,* or *The.*

10. The Bible

The Bible. King James Version.

The New English Bible. London: Oxford UP and Cambridge UP, 1970.

When citing a standard version of the Bible (first example), do not underline the title or the name of the version, and you need not provide publication information. For an edition of the Bible (second example), underline the title and give full publication information.

11. A later edition

Bolinger, Dwight L. Aspects of Language. 3rd ed. New York: Harcourt, 1981.

For any edition after the first, place the edition number after the title. (If an editor's name follows the title, place the edition number after the name. See model 18.) Use the appropriate designation for editions that are named or dated rather than numbered—for instance, Rev. ed. for "Revised edition."

12. A republished book

James, Henry. The Golden Bowl. 1904. London: Penguin, 1966.

Republished books include paperbound editions of books originally released in hard bindings and books reissued under new titles. Place the original date of publication (but not the place of publication or the publisher's name) after the title, and then provide the full publication information for the source you are using. If the book was originally published under a different title, add this title after Rpt. of ("Reprint of") at the end of the entry and move the original publication date to follow the title—for example, Rpt. of Thomas Hardy: A Life. 1941.

13. A book with a title in its title

Eco, Umberto. Postscript to The Name of the Rose. Trans. William Weaver. New York: Harcourt, 1983.

When a book's title contains another book title (as here: *The Name of the Rose*), do not underline the second title. When a book's title contains a quotation or the title of a work normally placed in quotation marks, keep the quotation marks and underline both titles: Critical Response to Henry James's "The Beast in the Jungle." (Note that the underlining extends under the closing quotation mark.)

14. A work in more than one volume

Lincoln, Abraham. The Collected Works of Abraham Lincoln. Ed. Roy P. Basler. 8 vols. New Brunswick: Rutgers UP, 1953.

Lincoln, Abraham. The Collected Works of Abraham Lincoln. Ed. Roy P. Basler. Vol. 5. New Brunswick: Rutgers UP, 1953. 8 vols.

If you use two or more volumes of a multivolume work, give the work's total number of volumes before the publication information (8 vols. in the first example). Your text citation will indicate which volume you are citing (see p. 627). If you use only one volume, give that volume number before the publication information (Vol. 5 in the second example). You may add the total number of volumes to the end of the entry (8 vols. in the second example).

If you cite a multivolume work published over a period of years, give the inclusive years as the publication date: for instance, Cambridge: Harvard UP, 1978-90.

15. A work in a series

Bergman, Ingmar. The Seventh Seal. Mod. Film Scripts Ser. 12. New York: Simon, 1995.

Place the name of the series (not quoted or underlined) just before the publication information. Abbreviate common words such as *modern* and *series*. Add any series number after the series title.

16. Published proceedings of a conference

Watching Our Language: A Conference Sponsored by the Program in Architecture and Design Criticism. 6-8 May 2005. New York: Parsons School of Design, 2005.

Whether in or after the title of the conference, supply information about who sponsored the conference, when it was held, and who published the proceedings. Treat a particular presentation at the conference like a selection from an anthology (model 18).

17. An anthology

Kennedy, X. J., and Dana Gioia, eds. Literature: An Introduction to Fiction, Poetry, and Drama. 9th ed. New York: Longman, 2005.

Cite an entire anthology only when citing the work of the editor or editors or when your instructor permits cross-referencing like that shown in model 19. Give the name of the editor or editors (followed by ed. or eds.) and then the title of the anthology.

18. A selection from an anthology

Mason, Bobbie Ann. "Shiloh." Literature: An Introduction to Fiction, Poetry, and Drama. Ed. X. J. Kennedy and Dana Gioia. 9th ed. New York: Longman, 2005. 643-54.

The essentials of this listing are these: author of selection; title of selection (in quotation marks); title of anthology (underlined); editors' names preceded by Ed. (meaning "Edited by"); publication information for the anthology; and inclusive page numbers for the selection (without the abbreviation "pp."). In addition, this source requires an edition number for the anthology. If you wish, you may also supply the original date of publication for the work you are citing, after its title. See model 12 on page 639.

If the work you cite comes from a collection of works by one author and with no editor, use the following form:

Auden, W. H. "Family Ghosts." The Collected Poetry of W. H. Auden. New York: Random, 1945. 132-33.

If the work you cite is a scholarly article that was previously printed elsewhere, provide the complete information for the earlier publication of the piece, followed by Rpt. in ("Reprinted in") and the information for the source in which you found the piece:

Molloy, Francis C. "The Suburban Vision in John O'Hara's Short Stories." Critique: Studies in Modern Fiction 25.2 (1984): 101-13. Rpt. in Short Story Criticism: Excerpts from Criticism of the Works of Short Fiction Writers. Ed. David Segal. Vol. 15. Detroit: Gale, 1989. 287-92.

San Juan, E. "Theme Versus Imitation: D. H. Lawrence's 'The Rocking-Horse Winner.'" D. H. Lawrence Review 3 (1970): 136-40. Rpt. in From Fiction to Film: D. H. Lawrence's "The Rocking-Horse Winner." Ed. Gerald R. Barrett and Thomas L. Erskine. Dickenson Literature and Film Ser. Encino: Dickenson, 1974. 70-74.

19. Two or more selections from the same anthology

Chopin, Kate. "The Storm." Kennedy and Gioia 127-31.

Kennedy, X. J., and Dana Gioia, eds. Literature: An Introduction to Fiction, Poetry, and Drama. 9th ed. New York: Longman, 2005.

O'Connor, Flannery. "Revelation." Kennedy and Gioia 443-58.

When you are citing more than one selection from the same source, your instructor may allow you to avoid repetition by giving the source in full (as in the Kennedy and Gioia entry) and then simply cross-referencing it in entries for the works you used. Thus, instead of full information for the Chopin and O'Connor works, give Kennedy and Gioia and the appropriate pages in that book. Note that each entry appears in its proper alphabetical place among other works cited.

20. An introduction, preface, foreword, or afterword

Donaldson, Norman. Introduction. The Claverings. By Anthony Trollope. New York: Dover, 1977. vii-xv.

An introduction, foreword, or afterword is often written by someone other than the book's author. When citing such a piece, give its name without quotation marks or underlining. (If the piece has a title of its own, provide it, in quotation marks, between the name of the author and the name of the piece.) Follow the title of the book with its author's name preceded by By. Give the inclusive page numbers of the part you cite. (In the preceding example, the small Roman numerals refer to the front matter of the book, before page 1.)

When the author of a preface or introduction is the same as the author of the book, give only the last name after the title:

Gould, Stephen Jay. Prologue. The Flamingo's Smile: Reflections in Natural History. By Gould. New York: Norton, 1985. 13-20.

21. An article in a reference work

Mark, Herman F. "Polymers." The New Encyclopaedia Britannica: Macropaedia. 15th ed. 1991.

"Reckon." Merriam-Webster's Collegiate Dictionary. 11th ed. 2003.

List an article in a reference work by its title (second example) unless the article is signed (first example). For works with entries arranged alphabetically, you need not include volume or page numbers. For well-known works like those listed on the previous page, you may also omit the editors' names and all publication information except any edition number and the year of publication. For works that are not well known, give full publication information:

"Hungarians in America." The Ethnic Almanac. Ed. Stephanie Bernardo. New York: Doubleday, 2001. 109-11.

See also pages 654 and 658, respectively, for encyclopedias appearing online or on a CD-ROM.

2 Listing periodicals: Journals, magazines, and newspapers

The facing page shows the basic format for an article in a periodical (a journal) and the location of the required information in a journal. See page 645 for parallel information on a newspaper article.

Note The treatment of volume and issue numbers and publication dates varies depending on the kind of periodical being cited, as the models indicate. For the distinction between journals and magazines, see page 575.

22. An article in a journal with continuous pagination throughout the annual volume

Lever, Janet. "Sex Differences in the Games Children Play." Social Problems 23 (1996): 478-87.

Information for a journal article

① Selwyn, Neil. ② "The Social Processes of Learning to Use Computers." ③ Social Science Computer Review ④ 23.1 ⑤ (2005): ⑥ 122-35.

Journal cover

SPRING 2005 VOLUME 23 NUMBER 1

SOCIAL SCIENCE COMPUTER REVIEW

④ **Volume and/or issue number,** in Arabic numerals.

⑤ **Year of publication,** in parentheses and followed by a colon.

③ **Title of periodical,** underlined. Omit any *A, An,* or *The* from the beginning of the title. Do not end with a period.

② **Title of article,** in quotation marks. Give the full title and any subtitle, separating them with a colon. End the title with a period inside the final quotation mark.

First page of article

The Social Processes of Learning to Use Computers

NEIL SELWYN

Cardiff School of Social Sciences

① **Author.** Give the full name—last name first, a comma, first name, and any middle name or initial. Omit *Dr., PhD,* or any other title. End the name with a period.

The ability to use a computer is assumed to be a cornerstone of effective citi[...] Age, with a range of initiatives and educational provisions being introduc[...] become competent with information technology (IT). Despite such provision, levels of computer use and competence have been found to vary widely throughout the general population, and we know little of how different ways of learning to use computers contribute to people's eventual use of IT. Based on data from in-depth interviews with 100 adults in the United Kingdom, this article examines the range and social stratification of formal and informal learning about computers that is taking place, suggesting that formal computer instruction orientated toward the general public may inadvertently widen the digital knowledge gap. In particular, the data highlight the importance of informal learning about IT and of encouraging such learning, especially in the home.

AUTHOR'S NOTE: This article is based on a project funded by the Economic and Social Research Council (R000239518). I would like to thank the other members of the Adults Learning@Home project (Stephen Gorard and John Furlong) as well as the individuals who took part in the in-depth interviews. Correspondence concerning this article may be addressed to Neil Selwyn, School of Social Sciences, Cardiff University, Glamorgan Building, King Edward VII Avenue, Cardiff CF10 3WT, UK; e-mail: selwynnc@cardiff.ac.uk.

122

⑥ **Inclusive page numbers of article,** without "pp." Go to the end of the article for the last page number. Provide only as many digits in the last number as needed for clarity, usually two.

Some journals number the pages of issues consecutively throughout a year, so that each issue after the first in a year begins numbering where the previous issue left off—say, at page 132 or 416. For this kind of journal, give the volume number after the title (23 in the example above) and place the year of publication in parentheses. The page numbers will be enough to guide readers to the issue you used.

23. An article in a journal that pages issues separately or that numbers only issues, not volumes

Selwyn, Neil. "The Social Processes of Learning to Use Computers." Social Science Computer Review 23.1 (2005): 122-35.

Some journals page each issue separately (starting each issue at page 1). For these journals, give the volume number, a period, and the issue number (23.1 in the Selwyn entry above and on the previous page). When citing an article in a journal that numbers only issues, not annual volumes, treat the issue number as if it were a volume number, as in model 22.

24. An article in a monthly or bimonthly magazine

Garber, Marjorie. "Our Genius Problem." Atlantic Monthly Sept. 2002: 46-53.

Follow the magazine title with the month and the year of publication. (Abbreviate all months except May, June, and July.) Don't place the date in parentheses, and don't provide a volume or issue number.

25. An article in a weekly or biweekly magazine

Talbot, Margaret. "The Bad Mother." New Yorker 5 Aug. 2004: 40-46.

Follow the magazine title with the day, the month, and the year of publication. (Abbreviate all months except May, June, and July.) Don't place the date in parentheses, and don't provide a volume or issue number.

26. An article in a daily newspaper

Zeller, Tom, Jr. "To Go Global, Do You Ignore Censorship?" New York Times 24 Oct. 2005, natl. ed.: C3+.

See the facing page for an analysis of this entry and the location of the required information in the newspaper.

27. An anonymous article

"The Right to Die." Time 11 Oct. 1996: 101.

Information for a newspaper article

① ② ③ ④

Zeller, Tom, Jr. "To Go Global, Do You Ignore Censorship?" New York Times 24 Oct.

⑤ ⑥

2005, natl. ed.: C3+.

① **Author.** Give the full name—last name first, a comma, first name, and any middle name or initial. Omit *Dr., PhD,* or any other title. End with a period.

⑥ **Page number of article,** without "pp." Include a section designation before the number when the newspaper does the same, as here. Otherwise, give the section between the edition and the colon. Add a plus sign to the page number when the article continues on a later page.

First page of article

THE NEW YORK TIMES, MONDAY, OCTOBER 24, 2005 YT C3

LINK BY LINK

Tom Zeller Jr.

To Go Global, Do You Ignore Censorship?

IT'S bad enough when newspaper editorials, Western human rights groups and ordinary American customers condemn your company for bowing to the Chinese dictatorship and contributing to oppression. But when the outrage begins rising, at great personal risk, from dissident voices trapped inside that dictatorship, well, that has to hurt.

Or not.

Yahoo has suffered a good deal of opprobrium after it was revealed last month that, when government officials came calling, the company's Hong Kong division simply surrendered information on a Chinese citizen who had presumably sought refuge, anonymity and a bit of freedom in the bosom of a Yahoo e-mail address: huoyan1989@yahoo.com.cn.

Internet boom — its online population of 100 million is now second to that of ... two dozen asset management signatories, calling on Internet businesses to ensure that their products "are not being used to commit human rights

② **Title of article,** in quotation marks. Give the full title and any subtitle, separating them with a colon. Unless the title has its own end punctuation (as this one does), end it with a period inside the final quotation mark.

③ **Name of newspaper,** underlined. Give the title as it appears on the first page, omitting *A, An,* or *The.*

First page of newspaper

"All the News That's Fit to Print"

The New York Times

National Edition

Northern California: Patchy clouds at the coast and in the Sierra Nevada. An isolated shower is possible in the mountains. Highs mainly in the 60's and 70's. Weather map is on Page D7.

VOL. CLV . . . . No. 53,377 Copyright © 2005 The New York Times MONDAY, OCTOBER 24, 2005 ONE DOLLAR

④ **Date of publication.** Give the day of the month first, then month, then year. Abbreviate all months except May, June, and July. End the date with a comma if listing the newspaper edition and/or the section designation. Otherwise, end with a colon.

⑤ **Edition.** If the newspaper lists an edition at the top of the first page, include it after the date. End with a comma if listing the section designation. Otherwise, end with a colon.

For an article with no named author, begin the entry with the title of the article. In the list of works cited, alphabetize an anonymous source by the first main word of the title (Right in this model).

28. An editorial or letter to the editor

"Dualing Power Centers." Editorial. New York Times 14 Jan. 2005, natl. ed.: A16.

A personal site:

Lederman, Leon. Topics in Modern Physics—Lederman. 28 Aug. 2005. 12 Dec. 2005 <http://www-ed.fnal.gov/samplers/hsphys/people/lederman.html>.

Cite a personal site with this information: ① Author's name, if any. ② Title, if any, underlined. If the site has no title, describe it with a label such as Home page, without quotation marks or underlining. ③ Date of last revision. ④ Date of your access. ⑤ URL.

A business site:

Prius. 2006. Toyota Motor Corp. 2 Feb. 2006 <http://www.toyota.com/prius>.

For the site of a corporation or other business, give the following: ① Site title, underlined. ② Date of site. ③ Name of sponsoring business. ④ Date of your access. ⑤ URL.

34. A poem, essay, or other short work from an online site

Wheatley, Phillis. "On Virtue." Poems on Various Subjects, Religious and Moral. London: A. Bell, 1773. American Verse Project. 16 May 2001. U of Michigan Humanities Text Initiative. 21 July 2005 <http://name.umdl.umich.edu/BAP5379>.

See the facing page for an analysis of the preceding entry and the location of the required information on the Web site.

35. An online book

An entire book:

Austen, Jane. Emma. 1816. Ed. R. W. Chapman. Oxford: Clarendon, 1926. Oxford Text Archive. 1994. Oxford U. 15 Dec. 2005 <http://ota.ahds.ac.uk/Austen/Emma.1519>.

For a book published online, give the following information: ① Author and title. ② Date of original publication of the book, if not given in item 4. ③ Name of any editor or translator. ④ Any publication information for the original print version of the book, following one of models 1–17. ⑤ Title of the site, underlined. ⑥ Date of electronic publication. ⑦ Name of any sponsoring organization or institution. ⑧ Date of your access. ⑨ URL for the book. If the site has an editor, add the name after the site's title, as in the Conrad entry on page 652.

Information for a short work from an online site

Wheatley, Phillis.① "On Virtue."② Poems on Various Subjects, Religious and Moral. London: A. Bell, 1773.③ American Verse Project.④ 16 May 2001.⑤ U of Michigan Humanities Text Initiative.⑥ 21 July 2005⑦ <http://name.umdl.umich.edu/BAP5379>.⑧

Home page of site

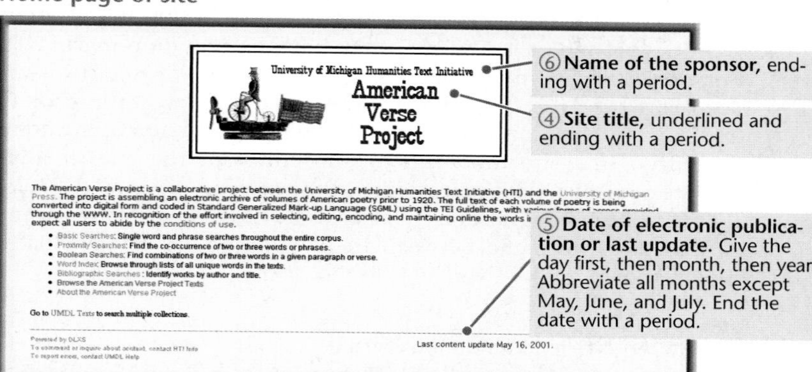

⑥ **Name of the sponsor,** ending with a period.

④ **Site title,** underlined and ending with a period.

⑤ **Date of electronic publication or last update.** Give the day first, then month, then year. Abbreviate all months except May, June, and July. End the date with a period.

Source record for poem

Print Source: *Poems on various subjects, religious and moral*
Phillis Wheatley
A. Bell
London
1773

URL: http://name.umdl.umich.edu/BAP5379

③ **Publication information for any print version.** If the site gives information for a print version of the source, as here, provide it after the source title, following an appropriate model on pp. 636–46.

Poem

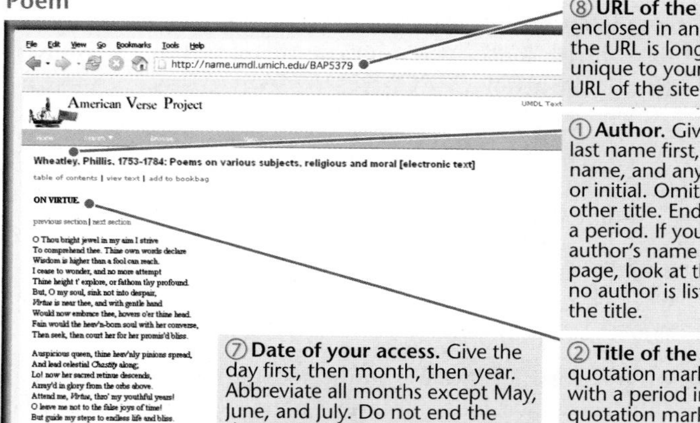

⑧ **URL of the short work,** enclosed in angle brackets. If the URL is long, temporary, or unique to your search, use the URL of the site's home page.

① **Author.** Give the full name—last name first, a comma, first name, and any middle name or initial. Omit *Dr., PhD,* or any other title. End the name with a period. If you don't see the author's name at the top of the page, look at the bottom. If no author is listed, begin with the title.

② **Title of the short work,** in quotation marks. End the title with a period inside the final quotation mark.

⑦ **Date of your access.** Give the day first, then month, then year. Abbreviate all months except May, June, and July. Do not end the date with a period. (Since this date does not appear on the site, record it separately.)

A part of a book:

Conrad, Joseph. "A Familiar Preface." Modern Essays. Ed. Christopher Morley. New York: Harcourt, 1921. Bartleby.com: Great Books Online. Ed. Steven van Leeuwan. Nov. 2000. 16 Feb. 2006 <http://www.bartleby.com/237/8.html>.

For a part of a book published online, provide this information: ① Author of the part. ② Title of the part, in quotation marks. (Do not use quotation marks for Introduction, Foreword, or another standard part.) ③ Title of the book (underlined), editor of the book (if any), and publication information for the print version of the book. ④ Title of the site (underlined) and editor of the site (if any). ⑤ Date of electronic publication. ⑥ Date of your access. ⑦ URL for the part of the book. If the site as a whole has a sponsoring organization, give the name between items 5 and 6, as in the Austen model above.

36. An article in an online journal

Palfrey, Andrew. "Choice of Mates in Identical Twins." Modern Psychology 4.1 (2003): 26-40. 25 Feb. 2006 <http://www.liasu.edu/modpsy/palfrey4(1).htm>.

Give the following information for an online scholarly article that you reach directly: ① Author, article title, journal title, volume and any issue numbers, and publication date, as in model 22 or 23 on pages 642–44. ② Page numbers in the journal or total number of pages, paragraphs, or sections, if any of these are given. Omit reference numbers if the source does not use them. ③ Date of your access. ④ URL for the article.

For a journal article reached through a subscription service, see model 31 (pp. 648–49).

37. An online abstract

Palfrey, Andrew. "Choice of Mates in Identical Twins." Modern Psychology 4.1 (2003): 26-40. Abstract. 25 Feb. 2006 <http://www.liasu.edu/modpsy/abstractpalfrey4(1).htm>.

Treat an online abstract like an online journal article (model 36), but add "Abstract" (without quotation marks or underlining) between the publication information and the date of your access.

38. An article in an online newspaper or on a newswire

Still, Lucia. "On the Battlefields of Business, Millions of Casualties." New York Times on the Web 3 Mar. 2005. 17 Aug. 2005 <http://www.nytimes.com/specials/downsize/05down1.html>.

Provide the following information for an online newspaper article that you reach directly: ① Author, article title, newspaper title, and publication date as in model 26 (p. 644). Give section, page, or paragraph numbers if the newspaper does. ② Date of your access. ③ URL for the article.

Treat a newswire article similarly, substituting the title of the online wire service for the newspaper title (this article has no named author):

"Film, Fashion Asked to Stop Glamorizing Smoking." Reuters 18 Feb. 2003. 28 Feb. 2003 <http://www.reuters.com/newsArticle.jhtml?type=industryNewsID2246811>.

See model 31 (pp. 648–49) when citing a newspaper or newswire article that you reached through a subscription service.

39. An article in an online magazine

Lewis, Ricki. "The Return of Thalidomide." Scientist 22 Jan. 2001: 5. 24 Jan. 2006 <http://www.the-scientist.com/yr2001/jan/lewis_pl_010122.html>.

Provide the following information for an online magazine article that you reach directly: ① Author's name, article title, magazine title, and publication date, as in model 24 or 25 on page 644. ② Any page, paragraph, or other reference numbers. ③ Date of your access. ④ URL for the article.

See model 31 (pp. 648–49) when citing a magazine article that you reached through a subscription service.

40. An online review

Detwiler, Donald S., and Chu Shao-Kang. Rev. of Important Documents of the Republic of China, ed. Tan Quon Chin. Journal of Military History 56.4 (1992): 669-84. 16 Sept. 2005 <http://www.jstor.org/fcgi-bin/jstor/viewitem.fcg/08993718/96p0008x>.

Cite an online review as follows: ① Author, any review title, Rev. of and the title of the reviewed book, author or editor of the reviewed

47. The home page for a course or department

Anderson, Daniel. Business Communication. Course home page. Jan.-June 2003. Dept. of English, U of North Carolina. 16 Feb. 2003 <http://sites.unc.edu/daniel/eng32/index.html>.

For the home page of a course, provide this information: ① Instructor's name. ② Course title, without quotation marks or underlining. ③ The description Course home page. ④ Inclusive dates of the course. ⑤ Names of the department and the school, separated by a comma. ⑥ Date of your access. ⑦ URL for the home page.

For a department home page, give the department name first, followed by Dept. home page, the name of the school, your access date, and the URL:

Computer Engineering. Dept. home page. Santa Clara U School of Engineering. 12 Oct. 2005 <http://www.cse.scu.edu>.

48. An entry on a Web log

Daswani, Susheel. "Hollywood vs. Silicon Valley." Berkeley Intellectual Property Weblog. 16 Mar. 2005. 22 Aug. 2005 <http://www.biplog.com/archive/cat_hollywood.html>.

To cite an entry on a Web log, give the following: ① Author's name. (See p. 596 for tips on finding the full names of authors who use only screen names.) ② Title of the entry, in quotation marks. ③ Title of the Web log, underlined. ④ Date of the entry. ⑤ Date of your access. ⑥ URL for the entry.

49. Electronic mail

Millon, Michele. "Re: Grief Therapy." E-mail to the author. 4 May 2005.

For e-mail, give the following: ① Writer's name. ② Title, if any, from the e-mail's subject heading, in quotation marks. ③ Description of the transmission, including to whom it was sent. ④ Date of posting.

50. A posting to an e-mail discussion list

Tourville, Michael. "European Currency Reform." Online posting. 6 Jan. 2006. International Finance Discussion List. 12 Jan. 2006 <http://www.weg.isu.edu/finance-dl/archive/46732>.

Whenever possible, cite an archived version of a posting to an e-mail discussion list so that readers can find it without difficulty. Give this information for the posting: ① Author's name. (See p. 596 for tips on finding the full names of authors who use only screen names.) ② Title, if any, from the e-mail's subject heading, in quotation marks. ③ Online posting. ④ Date of posting. ⑤ Name of the discussion list, without quotation marks or underlining. ⑥ Date of your access. ⑦ URL, if known, or e-mail address for the list's moderator or supervisor.

51. A posting to a newsgroup or Web forum

A newsgroup:

Cramer, Sherry. "Recent Investment Practices in US Business." Online posting. 26 Mar. 2005. Young Entrepreneurs. 3 Apr. 2005 <http://finance.groups.yahoo.com/group/youngentrepreneurs3>.

For a posting to a newsgroup, give the following: ① Author's name. (See p. 596 for tips on finding the full names of authors who use only screen names.) ② Title from the subject heading, in quotation marks. ③ Online posting. ④ Date of posting. ⑤ Name of the newsgroup, without quotation marks or underlining. ⑥ Date of your access. ⑦ URL for the group. If you read the posting on a news server instead of on the Web, omit the group name before your access date and give the group name in the URL, preceded by news: <news:biz.startups.youngentrepreneurs.2700>.

A Web forum:

Razi, N. M. "Hypothyroidism." Online posting. 6 July 2005. Homeopathy Forum. 28 Jan. 2006 <http://www.hpathy.com/homeopathy/forums/forum_topics.asp?FID=328>.

For a posting to a Web forum, provide this information: ① Author's name. (See p. 596 for tips on finding the full names of authors who use only screen names.) ② Title, if any, in quotation marks. ③ Online posting. ④ Date of posting. ⑤ Name of the forum, without quotation marks or underlining. ⑥ Date of your access. ⑦ URL for the forum.

52. A synchronous communication

Bruckman, Amy. MediaMOO Symposium: Virtual Worlds for Business? 20 Jan. 2006. MediaMOO. 26 Feb. 2006 <http://www.co.gatech.edu/fac/Amy.Bruckman/MediaMOO/cscw-symposium-06.html>.

Whenever possible, cite an archived version of a synchronous communication so that readers can find it without difficulty. Provide this information: ① Speaker's name. ② Description of the event, without quotation marks or underlining. ③ Date of the event. ④ Forum, without quotation marks or underlining. ⑤ Date of your access. ⑥ URL for the archive.

53. A source on a periodical CD-ROM database

Hakim, Danny. "Iacocca, Away from the Grind, Still Has a Lot to Say." New York Times 19 July 2005, natl. ed.: C1+. New York Times Ondisc. CD-ROM. UMI-ProQuest. Sept. 2005.

Databases on CD-ROM are issued periodically—for instance, every six months or every year. The journals, newspapers, and other publications included in such a database are generally available in print as well, so your works-cited entry should give the information for both formats: ① Information for the print version, following models on pages 642–46. ② Title of the CD-ROM, underlined. ③ Medium, CD-ROM. ④ Name of the vendor (or distributor) of the CD-ROM. ⑤ Date of electronic publication.

54. A source on a nonperiodical CD-ROM

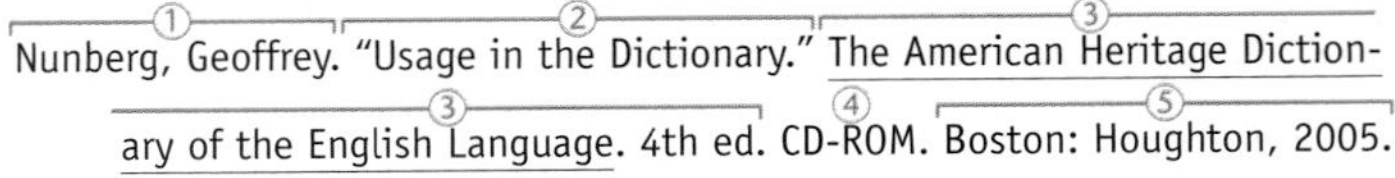
Nunberg, Geoffrey. "Usage in the Dictionary." The American Heritage Dictionary of the English Language. 4th ed. CD-ROM. Boston: Houghton, 2005.

Single-issue CD-ROMs may be encyclopedias, dictionaries, books, and other resources that are published just once, like printed books. Use this format: ① Author's name, if any. ② Title of the source. Use quotation marks for short works, such as an article. Underline the title if it is a book. ③ Title of the entire CD-ROM, underlined. This CD-ROM also includes an edition number. ④ Medium, CD-ROM. ⑤ CD-ROM's place of publication, publisher, and date of publication.

See also pages 642 and 654, respectively, for models of print and online reference works.

55. Computer software

Project Scheduler 9000. Vers. 5.1. Orlando: Scitor, 2006.

For software, provide the following: ① Title, underlined. ② Version number. ③ Publication information, including place of publication, publisher, and date. If the software has a listed author, give his or her name first in the entry. If you consulted or obtained the software online, replace the publication information with the date of your access and the URL, as in earlier examples.

4 Listing other print and nonprint sources

56. A government publication

Board of Governors. US Federal Reserve System. Federal Reserve Bulletin Aug. 2005: 20-21.

Hawaii. Dept. of Education. Kauai District Schools, Profile 2004-05. Honolulu: Hawaii Dept. of Education, 2005.

Stiller, Ann. Historic Preservation and Tax Incentives. US Dept. of Interior. Washington: GPO, 2002.

United States. Cong. House. Committee on Ways and Means. Medicare Payment for Outpatient Occupational Therapy Services. 108th Cong., 1st sess. Washington: GPO, 2003.

If an author is not listed for a government publication, give the appropriate agency as author, as in the first, second, and last examples. Provide information in the order illustrated, separating elements with a period: the name of the government, the name of the agency (which may be abbreviated), and the title and publication information. For a congressional publication (last example), give the house and committee involved before the title, and give the number and session of Congress after the title. In the last two examples, GPO stands for the US Government Printing Office.

57. A pamphlet

Medical Answers About AIDS. New York: Gay Men's Health Crisis, 2006.

Most pamphlets can be treated as books. In the example above, the pamphlet has no listed author, so the title comes first. If the pamphlet has an author, list his or her name first, followed by the title and publication information as given here.

58. An unpublished dissertation or thesis

Wilson, Stuart M. "John Stuart Mill as a Literary Critic." Diss. U of Michigan, 1990.

The title is quoted rather than underlined. Diss. stands for "Dissertation." U of Michigan is the institution that granted the author's degree.

59. An image (artwork, advertisement, graph, etc.)

A work of art:

Hockney, David. Place Furstenberg, Paris. 1985. College Art Gallery, New Paltz, New York. David Hockney: A Retrospective. Ed. Maurice Tuchman and Stephanie Barron. Los Angeles: Los Angeles County Museum of Art, 1988. 247.

For a work of art, name the artist and give the title (underlined), the date of creation, and the name and location of the owner. For a work you see only in a reproduction, provide the complete publication information, too, as in the Hockney model. Omit such information only if you examined the actual work.

A photograph:

Heinz, Thomas A. Fallingwater: Exterior Detail. Frank Lloyd Wright: Architect. Ed. Terence Riley. New York: Museum of Modern Art, 2000. 236.

Treat a photograph you find in a collection or book like a work of art, with photographer's name (if known), photograph title (underlined), and date. Add the owner's name (as in the Hockney entry above) if the photograph is an artwork and not an illustration. Give the publication information unless you examined an actual print of the photograph.

For a personal photograph by you or someone else, describe the subject (without quotation marks or underlining), say who took the photograph, and add the date:

Children in Central Park. Personal photograph by the author. 16 Mar. 2006.

An advertisement:

Jetta by Volkswagen. Advertisement. New Yorker 25 July 2005: 31.

Cite an advertisement with the name of the product or company advertised, the description Advertisement, and the publication information.

A cartoon or comic strip:

Trudeau, Garry. "Doonesbury." Comic strip. San Francisco Chronicle 28 Aug. 2005: E6.

Cite a cartoon or comic strip with the artist's name, the title (in quotation marks), the description Cartoon or Comic strip, and the publication information.

A map, chart, graph, or diagram:

Women in the Armed Forces. Map. Women in the World: An International Atlas. By Joni Seager and Ann Olson. New York: Touchstone, 2006. 44-45.

List the image by its title (underlined) unless its creator is credited on the source. Provide a description (Map, Chart, and so on) and then the publication information.

60. A television or radio program

"I'm Sorry, I'm Lost." By Alan Ball. Dir. Jill Soloway. Six Feet Under. HBO. 2 July 2005.

Start with the title unless you are citing the work of a person or persons. The example here includes an episode title (in quotation marks), the writer's and director's names, the program title (underlined), the name of the network, and the date. If the program aired on a local TV station, identify the station between the network and the date—for example, WGBH, Boston.

61. A sound recording

Brahms, Johannes. Piano Concerto no. 2 in B-flat, op. 83. Perf. Artur Rubinstein. Cond. Eugene Ormandy. Philadelphia Orch. LP. RCA, 1972.

Springsteen, Bruce. "Empty Sky." The Rising. Columbia, 2002.

Begin with the name of the individual whose work you are citing. If you're citing a song or song lyrics, give the title in quotation marks. Then provide the title of the recording, not underlined if it identifies a composition by form, number, and key (first example). After the title, provide the names of any other artists it seems appropriate to mention, the manufacturer of the recording, and the date of release. If the medium is other than compact disk, provide it immediately before the manufacturer's name—for instance, LP (as in the first example) or Audiocassette.

62. A film, DVD, or video recording

The Lord of the Rings: The Return of the King. Dir. Peter Jackson. New Line, 2003.

Start with the title of the work you are citing, unless you are citing the contribution of a particular individual (see the next example). Give additional information (director, writer, lead performers, and so on) as you judge appropriate. For a film, end with the distributor and date.

For a DVD or videocassette, include the original release date (if any) and the medium (DVD, Videocassette) before the distributor's name:

George Balanchine, chor. Serenade. Perf. San Francisco Ballet. Dir. Hilary Bean. 1991. Videocassette. PBS Video, 1997.

63. A musical composition

Fauré, Gabriel. Sonata for Violin and Piano no. 1 in A Major, op. 15.

Don't underline musical compositions, such as the one above, that are identified only by form, number, and key. Do underline titled operas, ballets, and compositions (Carmen, Sleeping Beauty, The 1812 Overture). Use quotation marks for songs.

64. A performance

Barenboim, Daniel, cond. Chicago Symphony Orch. Symphony Center, Chicago. 22 Jan. 2006.

The English Only Restaurant. By Silvio Martinez Palau. Dir. Susana Tubert. Puerto Rican Traveling Theater, New York. 27 July 2005.

As with films and television programs, place the title first unless you are citing the work of an individual (first example). Provide additional information about participants after the title, as well as the theater, city, and date. Note that the orchestra name in the first example is neither quoted nor underlined.

65. A letter

Buttolph, Mrs. Laura E. Letter to Rev. and Mrs. C. C. Jones. 20 June 1857. In The Children of Pride: A True Story of Georgia and the Civil War. Ed. Robert Manson Myers. New Haven: Yale UP, 1972. 334-35.

List a published letter under the writer's name. Specify that the source is a letter and to whom it was addressed, and give the date on which it was written. Treat the remaining information like that for a selection from an anthology (model 18, p. 640). (See also p. 645 for the format of a letter to the editor of a periodical.)

For a letter in the collection of a library or archive, specify the writer, recipient, and date, as above, and give the name and location of the archive as well:

James, Jonathan E. Letter to his sister. 16 Apr. 1970. Jonathan E. James Papers. South Dakota State Archive, Pierre.

For a letter you receive, give the name of the writer, note the fact that the letter was sent to you, and provide the date of the letter:

Packer, Ann E. Letter to the author. 15 June 2005.

Use the form above for personal e-mail as well, substituting E-mail for Letter: E-mail to the author (see p. 656).

66. A lecture or address

Carlone, Dennis. "Architecture for the City of the Twenty-First Century." Symposium on the City. Urban Issues Group. Cambridge City Hall, Cambridge. 22 May 2005.

Give the speaker's name, the title (in quotation marks), the title of the meeting, the name of the sponsoring organization, the location of the lecture, and the date. If the lecture has no title, use Lecture, Address, or another description instead.

Although the *MLA Handbook* does not provide a specific style for classroom lectures in your courses, you can adapt the preceding format for this purpose:

Chang, Julia. Class lecture on the realist novel. Homans College. 20 Jan. 2006.

67. An interview

Graaf, Vera. Personal interview. 19 Dec. 2005.

Rumsfeld, Donald. Interview. Frontline. PBS. WGBH, Boston. 10 Oct. 2005.

Begin with the name of the person interviewed. For an interview you conducted, specify Personal interview or the medium (such as Telephone interview or E-mail interview), and then give the date. For an interview you read, heard, or saw, provide the title if any or Interview if there is no title, along with other bibliographic information and the date.

EXERCISE 47.1 Writing works-cited entries

Prepare works-cited entries from the following information. Follow the models of the *MLA Handbook* given in this chapter unless your teacher specifies a different style. For titles, use underlining (as here) unless your instructor requests italics. Arrange the finished entries in alphabetical order, not numbered. (You can do this exercise online at *ablongman.com/littlebrown.*)

1. A journal article titled "Networking the Classroom" by Christopher Conte. The article appears in volume 5 of CQ Researcher, a journal that pages issues continuously throughout each annual volume. Volume 5 is dated 2004. The article runs from page 923 to page 943.
2. A magazine article on a database that is also available in print. The author is Larry Irving. The title is "The Still Yawning Divide." The article appears in the March 12, 2005, issue of Newsweek, a weekly magazine, and starts on page 64. You consulted the article on November 14, 2005, through the database Expanded Academic ASAP from the service InfoTrac (http://www.galegroup.com). You reached the database through Southeast State University's Polk Library.
3. A government document you consulted on November 12, 2005, over the Internet. The author is the National Center for Education

Statistics, an agency within the United States Department of Education. The title of the document is Internet Access in Public Schools. It was published February 24, 2005, and can be accessed at http://www.ed.gov/nces/edstats.

4. A book called Failure to Connect: How Computers Affect Our Children's Minds—For Better and Worse, written by Jane M. Healy and published in 2000 by Simon & Schuster in New York.
5. An article in the October 9, 2004, issue of the magazine The Nation titled "The Threat to the Net." The article is by Jeff Chester and appears on pages 6 to 7 of the magazine. You found it through Polk Library at Southeast State University on November 14, 2005, using the database Expanded Academic ASAP from the service InfoTrac. The home page URL for the database is http://www.galegroup.com.
6. A pamphlet titled Bridging the Digital Divide, with no named author. It was published in 2005 by the ALA in Chicago.
7. An article titled "MyPyramid.gov: Achieving E-Health for All?" on the Web site Digital Divide Network at http://www.digitaldivide.net/articles. The Web site is sponsored by the Benton Foundation. The article is by Andy Carvin and is dated February 22, 2005. You found it on November 10, 2005.
8. An e-mail interview you conducted with Mary McArthur on October 31, 2005.

47c Using MLA document format

The document format recommended by the *MLA Handbook* is fairly simple, with just a few elements. See also pages 118–27 for guidelines on type fonts, headings, lists, illustrations, and other features that are not specified in MLA style.

The samples below and on the next page show the formats for the first page and a later page of a paper. For the format of the list of works cited, see pages 633–34.

First page of MLA paper

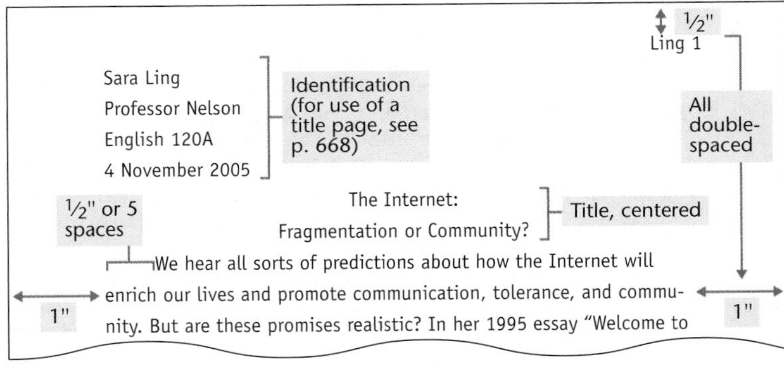

Later page of MLA paper

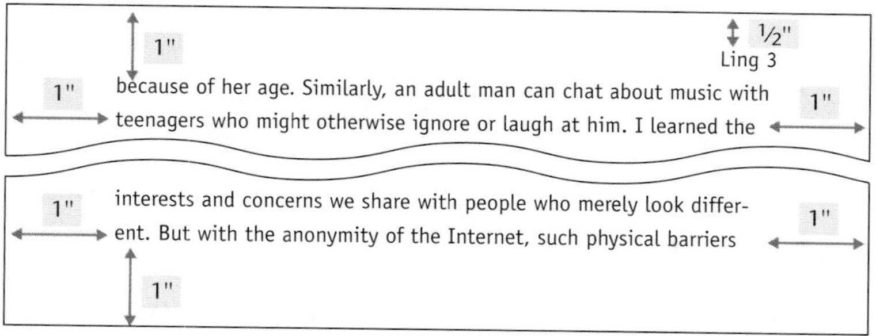

Margins Use minimum one-inch margins on all sides of every page.

Spacing and indentions Double-space throughout. Indent paragraphs one-half inch or five spaces. (See below for indention of poetry and long prose quotations.)

Paging Begin numbering on the first page, and number consecutively through the end (including the list of works cited). Type Arabic numerals (1, 2, 3) in the upper right about one-half inch from the top. Place your last name before the page number in case the pages later become separated.

Identification and title The *MLA Handbook* does not require a title page for a paper. If your instructor asks you to supply a title page, see page 668. Otherwise, follow the sample on the previous page, providing your name, the date, and other information requested by your instructor. Place this identification an inch from the top of the page, aligned with the left margin and double-spaced.

Double-space again, and center the title. Do not highlight the title with underlining, boldface, larger type, or quotation marks. Capitalize the words in the title according to guidelines on page 493. Double-space the lines of the title and between the title and the text.

Poetry and long prose quotations Treat a single line of poetry like any other quotation, running it into your text and enclosing it in quotation marks. You may run in two or three lines of poetry as well, separating the lines with a slash surrounded by space.

> An example of Robert Frost's incisiveness is in two lines from "Death of the Hired Man": "Home is the place where, when you have to go there / They have to take you in" (119-20).

Always set off from your text a poetry quotation of more than three lines. Use double spacing above and below the quotation and for the quotation itself. Indent the quotation one inch or ten spaces from the left margin. *Do not add quotation marks.*

> Emily Dickinson stripped ideas to their essence, as in this description of "A narrow Fellow in the Grass," a snake:
>
> > I more than once at Noon
> > Have passed, I thought, a Whip lash
> > Unbraiding in the Sun
> > When stopping to secure it
> > It wrinkled, and was gone – (12-16)

Also set off a prose quotation of more than four typed lines. (See pp. 603–04 on when to use such long quotations.) Double-space and indent as with the poetry example above. *Do not add quotation marks.*

> In the influential Talley's Corner from 1967, Elliot Liebow observes that "unskilled" construction work requires more skill than is generally assumed:
>
> > A healthy, sturdy, active man of good intelligence requires from two to four weeks to break in on a construction job. . . . It frequently happens that his foreman or the craftsman he services is not willing to wait that long for him to get into condition or to learn at a glance the difference in size between a rough 2 x 8 and a finished 2 x 10. (62)

Do not use a paragraph indention for a quotation of a single complete paragraph or a part of a paragraph. Use paragraph indentions of one-quarter inch or three spaces only for a quotation of two or more complete paragraphs.

CHAPTER 48

Two Research Papers in MLA Style

The following pages show the research papers of Kisha Alder and Vanessa Haley. (Alder's paper begins on p. 668, Haley's on p. 677.) Both students followed the style of the *MLA Handbook* for documenting sources and formatting their papers. Accompanying both students' papers are comments on format, source citations, and other matters.

Note Because Kisha Alder's paper addresses a current Internet controversy, many of its sources come from the Internet and do not use page or other reference numbers. Thus the in-text citations of these sources do not give reference numbers. In a paper relying solely on printed journals, books, and other traditional sources, most if not all in-text citations would include page numbers.

Format of a title page and outline

A title page is not required by MLA style but may be required by your teacher. If so, or if you are required to submit an outline with your paper, prepare a title page as shown on the next page. If your teacher does not require a title page, follow MLA style as shown on page 664 and in Vanessa Haley's paper on page 677: place your name, the identifying information, and the date on the first page of the paper.

Some teachers ask students to submit an outline of the final paper. For advice on constructing a formal sentence or topic outline, see pages 38–41. Kisha Alder's formal sentence outline follows her title page on page 669.

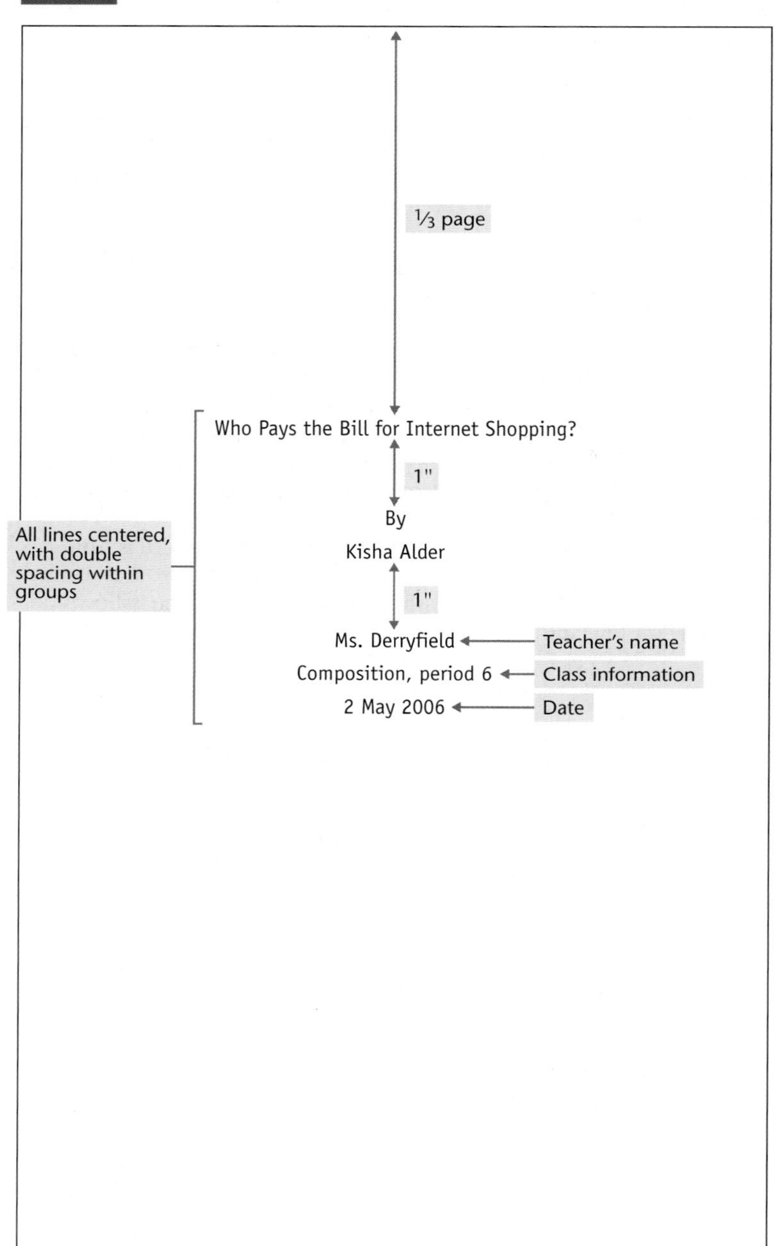
1⁄3 page
Who Pays the Bill for Internet Shopping?
1"
By
Kisha Alder
1"
Ms. Derryfield
Teacher's name
Composition, period 6
Class information
2 May 2006
Date
All lines centered, with double spacing within groups

Outline

Thesis statement: To improve equity between online and traditional stores and between consumers with and without Internet access, tax laws should be revised to allow collection of sales taxes on Internet purchases.

I. Internet taxation is now determined at the federal level.
   A. The Supreme Court has freed vendors from collecting taxes in states where they do not have stores.
   B. A 1998 law, extended in 2004, placed a moratorium on Internet taxes.

II. A tax-free Internet is unfair to brick-and-mortar stores.
   A. Sales taxes can make brick-and-mortar purchases significantly more expensive than online purchases.
   B. Sales taxes exceed online merchants' shipping charges.

III. A tax-free Internet is unfair to consumers who lack Internet access.
   A. A government report shows a huge "digital divide" among US residents.
      1. The affluent have much better Internet access than the poor.
      2. College-educated whites have much better Internet access than elementary-educated nonwhites.
   B. The digital divide means the poor pay sales taxes that the affluent avoid by shopping online.

IV. The three main arguments against Internet taxation do not rebut the issue of fairness.
   A. Taxes on Internet commerce would not, as claimed, undermine the freedom of the Internet.
   B. Internet commerce does not, as claimed, deserve protection not given to traditional commerce.
   C. The very real complexities of Internet taxation do not, as claimed, justify a permanent ban on taxation.

Alder 1

Title centered

Double-space throughout

Introduction: gives background to establish the issue

Citation form: shortened title for anonymous source; online source has no page number

Thesis statement

Background on Internet taxation (next two paragraphs)

Citation form: law case; case name underlined in the text citation

Citation form: source with two authors

Quotation over four lines set off without quotation marks (see p. 666)

Who Pays the Bill for Internet Shopping?

Going to the mall may soon go out of style. These days more and more people are shopping from home over the Internet. In 2002 electronic commerce (e-commerce) took in approximately $40 billion from shoppers; by 2007 that amount is expected to be $105 billion or more ("Sales Tax"). These numbers are good news for the online stores and for online shoppers, who can anticipate increasing variety in e-commerce offerings. But because taxes are not collected on Internet sales as they are on purchases in almost all states, online stores compete unfairly with traditional "brick-and-mortar" stores, and shoppers with Internet access have an unfair advantage over shoppers with no such access. To improve equity between online and traditional stores and between consumers with and without Internet access, tax laws should be revised to allow collection of sales taxes on Internet purchases.

Internet commerce is regulated by the same tax laws that govern other commerce. However, in 1992 the Supreme Court ruled that vendors do not have to collect taxes on behalf of states where they do not have a physical presence, because such collection would place an unconstitutional burden on interstate commerce (Quill Corp. v. North Dakota 5-8). Buyers are supposed to send the correct taxes to their state governments voluntarily, but they rarely do and states currently have no way to collect (Zimmerman and Hoover 45). In a decision addressing mail-order sales but considered applicable to Internet sales, the Court's majority urged Congress to reexamine the tax laws governing interstate commerce:

> The underlying issue is not only one that Congress may be better qualified to resolve, but also one

Alder 2

> that Congress has the ultimate power to resolve. . . . Accordingly, Congress is now free to decide whether, when, and to what extent the States may burden interstate mail-order concerns with a duty to collect use taxes. (Quill Corp. v. North Dakota 18-19)

Ellipsis mark signals omission from quotation

Citation form: after displayed quotation, citation follows sentence period and one space

Because of this decision, Congress has been wrestling with whether and how to tax Internet commerce.

Congress did take some action in 1998, when e-commerce was blossoming, by placing a temporary moratorium on new Internet taxes and by creating the Advisory Commission on Electronic Commerce to study the taxation issue and recommend solutions. A majority of the commission recommended extending the moratorium for another five years, through 2006, so that the taxation issue could be studied further and the state and local taxing authorities could simplify their complex and overlapping tax systems (US Advisory Commission). Congress agreed and voted in 2002 and again in 2004 to extend the moratorium, which now runs through 2007. Meanwhile, the debate over taxing e-commerce continues to heat up. On one side are state and local governments that are attempting to regain lost revenue with a uniform tax rate that would apply to Internet purchases. On the other side are those who would transform the moratorium on Internet sales taxes into a permanent ban ("Congress").

Common knowledge of congressional votes does not require source citations

Source: corporate author. Citation form: corporate author only, because online source has no page or other reference numbers

Citation form: shortened title for anonymous source; no page number for one-page source

As long as the moratorium is in effect, Internet shopping is essentially tax-free. Yet in almost all states, traditional shopping is subject to sales tax. Brick-and-mortar stores that are required by law to charge and collect sales taxes are at a distinct disadvantage compared to the online stores with no such burden. The local bookstore, music store, and drugstore must charge sales tax; their competitors

Contrast between online and traditional commerce (next two paragraphs)

Alder 5

Citation form: author not named in the text

Citation form (here and end of paragraph): corporate author named in the text

Summary reduces six pages in the source to a list of four points

Position of citation indicates that all preceding information comes from the Deloitte source

(Granfield 57). As outlined by more neutral observers—members of the respected accounting firm of Deloitte Touche Tohmatsu—the main complexities are very real: the existence of more than 3000 state and local taxing authorities in the United States, each with its own regulations and rates; the need to bring these jurisdictions into agreement on how to rationalize and simplify their systems; the concern that any federally imposed solution might violate states' rights; and finally the uncertainty about whether an online vendor conducts taxable business where its office, its server, its customer, or all three are located (67-72).

Citation form: author's name only, because online source has no page or other reference numbers

Citation form: indirect source (Kranz quoted by Krebs)

The complexities do seem nightmarish, as tax opponents claim, but change is underway. In October 2005 nineteen states launched a voluntary program, the Streamlined Sales Tax Project, to tax Internet transactions using a uniform tax system. Online merchants who participate receive free collection and remittance software and services (Krebs). Stephen Kranz of the Council on State Taxation says that "states, local governments, and businesses interested in reducing the complexity of sales taxes have created a plan that might work nationwide" (qtd. in Krebs). The states hope that the success of the pilot will lead Congress to pass into law a mandatory national sales tax program.

Conclusion: summary and a call for action

The Internet has introduced many improvements in our lives, including the ability to make purchases with the click of a mouse. But at the same time the tax-free status of Internet commerce has allowed it to compete unfairly with traditional businesses and given an unfair financial advantage to those who most likely already have plenty of advantages. Congress and Internet businesses must recognize these inequities and must work with state and local taxing authorities to remedy them.

Alder 6

Works Cited

Angeles, Lemuel. "Internet Freedom." Online posting. 8 Oct. 2005. ZDNet Talkback. 18 Nov. 2005 <http://www.zdnet.com/tklbck/comment/22/0,7056.html>.

Deloitte Touche Tohmatsu. Establishing a Framework to Evaluate E-Commerce Tax Options. Berkeley: U of California P, 2004.

"Congress Votes to Ban States from Taxing Internet" New York Times 20 Nov. 2004, late ed.: C4. LexisNexis Academic. LexisNexis. Southeast State U, Polk Lib. 14 Nov 2005 <http://www.lexisnexis.com>.

Granfield, Anne. "Taxing the Internet." Forbes 17 Dec. 2004: 56-58.

James, Nora. E-mail interview. 26 Nov. 2005.

Krebs, Brian. "States Move Forward on Internet Sales Tax." washingtonpost.com 1 July 2005. 18 Nov. 2005 <http://www. washingtonpost.com/wp-dyn/content/article/2005/07/01>.

Quill Corp. v. North Dakota. 504 US 298. 1992.

"Sales Tax on Internet Buys Could Help Fill Budget Gaps." Associated Press State and Local Wire. 26 Aug. 2005. LexisNexis Academic. LexisNexis. Southeast State U, Polk Lib. 18 Nov. 2005 <http://www.lexisnexis.com>.

United States. Advisory Commission on Electronic Commerce. Report to Congress. Apr. 2000. 25 Nov. 2005 <http://www.ecommercecommission.org/report.htm>.

---. Dept. of Commerce. National Telecommunications and Information Admin. A Nation Online: Entering the Broadband Age. Sept. 2004. 22 Nov. 2005 <http://www.ntia.doc.gov/reports/anol/index/html>.

Wiseman, Alan E. The Internet Economy: Access, Taxes, and Market Structure. Washington: Brookings, 2005.

New page

Heading centered

Sources are alphabetized by authors' last names

Second and subsequent lines of each source are indented one-half inch

An anonymous article listed and alphabetized by title; source obtained through a library subscription service

A magazine article

An e-mail interview

An online newspaper article

A law case: name not underlined in list of works cited

A government publication with no named author, so government body given as author

Second source by author of two or more cited works: three hyphens replace author's name (*United States*)

A book

Alder 7

A page on a Web site

Wyden, Ron. "Statement on the Internet Tax Non-Discrimination Act." Ron Wyden Online. 7 Jan. 2003. 16 Nov. 2005 <http://wyden.senate.gov/media/speeches/2003/01072003_internettax_statement.html>.

An article from a journal that pages each issue separately. A source with two authors

Zimmerman, Malai, and Kent Hoover. "Use of Third Parties to Collect State and Local Taxes on Internet Sales." Pacific Business Journal 26.2 (2004): 45-48.

Haley 1

Vanessa Haley

Mr. Moisan

English 101

6 Feb. 2006

Format of heading and title when no title page is required (see also p. 664)

Annie Dillard's Healing Vision

It is almost a commonplace these days that human arrogance is destroying the environment. Environmentalists, naturalists, and now the man or woman on the street seem to agree: the long-held belief that human beings are separate from nature, destined to rise above its laws and conquer it, has been ruinous.

Introduction of environmental theme

Unfortunately, the defenders of nature tend to respond to this ruinous belief with harmful myths of their own: nature is pure and harmonious; humanity is corrupt and dangerous. Much writing about nature lacks a recognition that human beings and their civilization are as much a part of nature as trees and whales are, neither better nor worse. Yet without such a recognition, how can humans overcome the damaging sense of separation between themselves and the earth? How can humans develop realistic solutions to environmental problems that will work for humanity and the rest of nature?

Focus on issue to be resolved

One nature writer who seems to recognize the naturalness of humanity is Annie Dillard. In her best-known work, the Pulitzer Prize-winning Pilgrim at Tinker Creek, she is a solitary person encountering the natural world, and some critics fault her for turning her back on society. But in those encounters with nature, Dillard probes a spiritual as well as a physical identity between human beings and nature that could help to heal the rift between them.

Introduction of Dillard to resolve issue

Thesis statement

Dillard is not renowned for her sense of involvement with human society. Like Henry David Thoreau, with whom she is often compared, she retreats from rather than confronts human society. The critic Gary McIlroy points out that although

Acknowledgment of opposing critical view

Haley 2

Thoreau discusses society a great deal in Walden, he makes no attempt "to find a middle ground between it and his experiment in the woods" (113). Dillard has been similarly criticized. For instance, the writer Eudora Welty comments that

> Annie Dillard is the only person in her book, substantially the only one in her world; I recall no outside human speech coming to break the long soliloquy of the author. Speaking of the universe very often, she is yet self-surrounded and, beyond that, book-surrounded. Her own book might have taken in more of human life without losing a bit of the wonder she was after. (37)

First response to opposing view

It is true, as Welty says, that in Pilgrim Dillard seems detached from human society. However, she actually was always close to it at Tinker Creek. In a later book, Teaching a Stone to Talk, she says of the neighborhood, "This is, mind you, suburbia. It is a five-minute walk in three directions to rows of houses. . . . There's a 55 mph highway at one end of the pond, and a nesting pair of wood ducks at the other" (qtd. in Suh).

Second response to opposing view

Rather than hiding from humanity, Dillard seems to be trying to understand it through nature. In Pilgrim she reports buying a goldfish, which she names Ellery Channing. She recalls once seeing through a microscope "red blood cells whip, one by one, through the capillaries" of yet another goldfish (124). Now watching Ellery Channing, she sees the blood in his body as a bond between fish and human being: "Those red blood cells are coursing in Ellery's tail now, too, in just that way, and through his mouth and eyes as well, and through mine" (125). Gary McIlroy observes that this blood, "a symbol of the sanctity of life, is a common bond between Dillard and the fish, between animal and human life in general, and between Dillard and other people" (115).

Secondary source's analysis of Dillard

Haley 3

For Dillard, the terror and unpredictability of death unify all life. The most sinister image in Pilgrim—one that haunts Dillard—is that of the frog and the water bug. Dillard reports walking along an embankment scaring frogs into the water when one frog refused to budge. As Dillard leaned over to investigate, the frog "slowly crumpled and began to sag. The spirit vanished from his eyes as if snuffed. His skin emptied and dropped; his very skull seemed to collapse and settle like a kicked tent" (6). The frog was the victim of a water bug that injects poisons to "dissolve the victim's muscles and bones and organs" (6). Such events lead Dillard to wonder about a creator who would make all life "power and beauty, grace tangled in a rapture with violence" (8). Human beings no less than frogs and water bugs are implicated in this tangle.

Dillard is equally as disturbed by birth as by death. In a chapter of Pilgrim called "Fecundity," she focuses on the undeniable reproductive urge of entire species. Her attitude is far from sentimental:

> I don't know what it is about fecundity that so appalls. I suppose it is the teeming evidence that birth and growth, which we value, are ubiquitous and blind, that life itself is so astonishingly cheap, that nature is as careless as it is bountiful, and that with extravagance goes a crushing waste that will one day include our own cheap lives. (160)

The cheapness and brutality of life are problems Dillard wrestles with, wondering which is "amiss": the world, a "monster," or human beings, with their "excessive emotions" (177-78). No matter how hard she tries to leave human society, Dillard has no choice but to "bring human values to the creek" (179). The violent, seemingly pointless birth and death of all life are, spiritually,

Combination of quotation and Haley's own analysis (next four paragraphs) interprets and synthesizes Dillard's ideas

Mixture of summary and quotation provides context and keeps quotations trim

Discussion of physical identity of all creatures: death and birth

Comment on quotation advises reader what to look for

Quotations, including some long ones set off from the text, convey Dillard's voice as well as her ideas

Discussion of spiritual identity of all creatures

Haley 4

> two branches of the same creek, the creek that waters the world. . . . We could have planned things more mercifully, perhaps, but our plan would never get off the drawing board until we agreed to the very compromising terms that are the only ones that being offers. (180)

Haley's interpretation of Dillard's ideas

For Dillard, accepting the monstrousness as well as the beauty of "being" is the price all living things pay for freedom.

Resolution of Dillard's concerns

In "The Waters of Separation," the final chapter of Pilgrim, Dillard writes about a winged maple key, or seed. At this point in the book, the critic Sandra Humble Johnson notes, Dillard "has been humbled and emptied; she can no longer apply effort to her search for meaning in a parasitic world" (4). It is the winter solstice—the shortest day of the year. And then Dillard spies the maple key descending to earth and germination. "It rose, just before it would have touched a thistle, and hovered pirouetting in one spot, then twirled on and finally came to rest" (267). The key moved, says Dillard, "like a creature muscled and vigorous, or a creature spread thin to that other wind, the wind of the spirit . . . , a generous, unending breath" (268). Dillard vows to see the maple key in all of the earth and in herself. "If I am a maple key falling, at least I can twirl" (268).

Conclusion: ties together divergent critical views, environmental theme, and Dillard's work

According to the critic John Becker, "Annie Dillard does not walk out on ordinary life in order to bear witness against it"; instead, she uses the distance from other people "to make meaning out of the grotesque disjointedness of man and nature" (408). Gary McIlroy says, nonetheless, that Dillard "does not succeed in encompassing within her vision any but the most fragmentary consequences for society at large" (116). Possibly both are correct. In Pilgrim at Tinker Creek, Annie Dillard suggests a vision of identity among all living things

Haley 5

that could inform modern humanity's efforts to thrive in harmony with its environment, but she does not make the leap to practicalities. Life, she says, "is a faint tracing on the surface of a mystery. . . . We must somehow take a wider view, look at the whole landscape, really see it, and describe what's going on here" (9). The description, and acting on it, may take generations. As we proceed, however, we may be guided by Dillard's efforts to mend the disjointedness, to see that human beings and maple keys alike twirl equally.

Haley 6

Works Cited

Becker, John E. "Science and the Sacred: From Walden to Tinker Creek." Thought: A Review of Culture and Idea 62 (1989): 400-13.

Dillard, Annie. Pilgrim at Tinker Creek. New York: Harper, 1974.

Johnson, Sandra Humble. The Space Between: Literary Epiphany in the Work of Annie Dillard. Kent: Kent State UP, 1992.

McIlroy, Gary. "Pilgrim at Tinker Creek and the Social Legacy of Walden." South Atlantic Quarterly 85.2 (1996): 111-16.

Suh, Grace. "Ideas Are Tough, Irony Is Easy." Yale Herald Online 4 Oct. 2005. 22 Jan. 2006 <http://yaleherald.com/archive/xxii/10.4.05/ae/dillard.html>.

Welty, Eudora. Rev. of Pilgrim at Tinker Creek, by Annie Dillard. New York Times Book Review 24 Mar. 1974: 36-37. ProQuest Historical Newspapers. ProQuest. Santa Clara U, Orradre Lib. 20 Jan. 2006 <http://proquest.umi.com>.

PART 10

Writing in the Academic Disciplines

CHAPTER 49
Working with the Goals and Requirements of the Disciplines

CHAPTER 50
Reading and Writing About Literature

CHAPTER 51
Writing in Other Humanities

CHAPTER 52
Writing in the Social Sciences

CHAPTER 53
Writing in the Natural and Applied Sciences

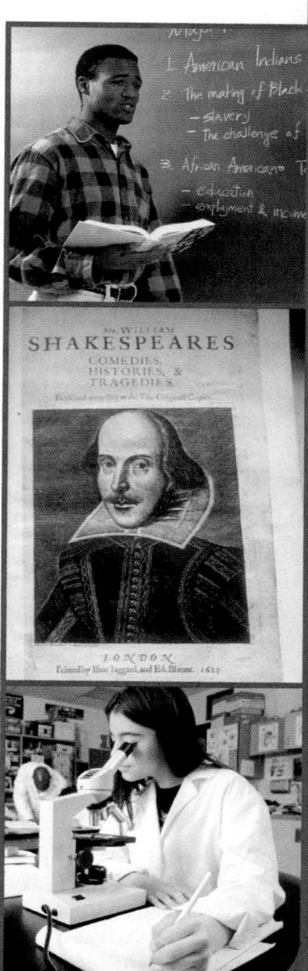

CHAPTER 49

Working with the Goals and Requirements of the Disciplines

Chapter 6 outlines the general concerns of subject, purpose, and audience that figure in most academic writing situations. The disciplines have more in common as well: methods of gathering evidence, kinds of assignments, scholarly tools, language conventions, and styles for source citations and document formats. This chapter introduces these common goals and requirements. The following chapters then distinguish the disciplines along the same lines, focusing on literature (Chapter 50), other humanities (51), the social sciences (52), and the natural and applied sciences (53).

49a Using methods and evidence

The **methodology** of a discipline is the way its practitioners study their subjects—that is, how they proceed when investigating the answers to questions. Methodology relates to the way practitioners analyze evidence and ideas. For instance, a literary critic and a social historian would probably approach Shakespeare's *Hamlet* quite differently: the literary critic might study the play for a theme among its poetic images; the historian might examine the play's relation to Shakespeare's context—England at the turn of the seventeenth century.

Whatever their approach, academic writers do not compose entirely out of their personal experience. Rather, they combine the evidence of their experience with that appropriate to the discipline, drawing well-supported conclusions about their subjects. The evidence of the discipline comes from research like that described in Chapters 42–44—from primary or secondary sources.

http://www.ablongman.com/littlebrown ▶

Visit the companion Web site for more help with writing in the academic disciplines.

Guidelines for academic writers

- **Become familiar with the methodology and the kinds of evidence for the discipline in which you are writing.**
- **Analyze the special demands of each assignment.** The questions you set out to answer, the assertions you wish to support, will govern how you choose your sources and evidence.
- **Become familiar with the discipline's specialized tools and language.**
- **Use the discipline's style for source citations and document format.**

- **Primary sources** are firsthand or original accounts, such as historical documents, works of art, and reports on experiments that the writer has conducted. When you use primary sources, you conduct original research, generating your own evidence. You might use your analysis of a painting as evidence for an interpretation of the painting. Or you might use data from your own survey of students to support your conclusions about students' attitudes.
- **Secondary sources** are books and articles written *about* primary sources. Much academic writing requires that you use such sources to spark, extend, or support your own ideas, as when you review the published opinions on your subject before contributing conclusions from your original research.

49b Understanding writing assignments

For most academic writing, your primary purpose will be either to explain something to your readers or to persuade them to accept your conclusions. To achieve your purpose, you will adapt your writing process to the writing situation, particularly to your readers' likely expectations for evidence and how you use it. Most assignments will contain key words that imply some of these expectations—words such as *compare, define, analyze,* and *illustrate* that express customary ways of thinking about and organizing a vast range of subjects. Pages 92–102 and 147 explore these so-called rhetorical strategies. You should be aware of them and alert to the wording in assignments that directs you to use them.

49c Using tools and language

When you write in an academic discipline, you use the scholarly tools of that discipline, particularly its periodical indexes. In

Literary authors are concerned with presenting human experience concretely, with *showing* rather than *telling.* Consider the following proverb and an unmemorable paraphrase of it:

> A rolling stone gathers no moss.
>
> If a rock is always moving around, vegetation won't have a chance to grow on it.

In the original proverb, the meaning of the concrete words *rolling, stone, gathers,* and *moss* are not literal but **figurative**—that is, the words mean something other than what they literally say. The proverb is not about stones or moss but about the way some people live their lives: rushing through, they don't take the time to reflect and develop.

The power of the proverb comes from its figurative representation of experience and also from its contrasts. Each noun (*stone, moss*) has one syllable, whereas each word of motion (*rolling, gathers*) has two syllables, with the accent on the first of the two. The six words offer a small but complete world: hard (*stone*) and soft (*moss*), inorganic and organic, rest and motion. Such relationships unify the proverb into a pleasing whole that stays in our minds.

1 Reading a work of literature

Reading literature critically involves interacting with a text. The techniques complement those for critically reading any text, so if you haven't read Chapter 8 on such reading, you should do so. Responding critically is a matter not of making negative judgments but of analyzing the parts, interpreting their meanings, seeing how the parts relate, and evaluating significance or quality.

Reading and responding

You can preview a literary text somewhat as you can preview any other text. You may gauge the length of the text and the difficulty of the language to determine whether you can read it in one sitting, and you may read a biographical note to learn about the author. In a literary text, however, you won't find aids such as section headings or summaries that can make previewing other texts especially informative. You have to dive into the words themselves.

Do write while reading. Writing your thoughts down as you read keeps you actively engaged in the text, clarifies your thoughts, and records your immediate insights for later use in writing assignments or class discussions. If you own the book you are reading, annotate the pages themselves:

- **Underline or highlight passages** as you read and during class discussions.

- **Annotate the margins,** using the top margins to note key scenes or events and using the side margins to note passages you like, don't like, or find puzzling.

If you don't own the book, make these annotations on sticky notes, separate sheets of paper, or your computer. Whatever method you use, keep separate records of key information—moments of character development, shifts in time or setting, or recurring allusions, images, or themes.

An effective way to interact with a text is to keep a **reading journal.** A journal is not a diary in which you record your doings; instead, it is a place to develop and store your reflections on what you read, such as an answer to a question you may have posed in the margin of the text. You could make an entry in the form of a letter to the author or from one character to another. In many literature courses, students collaborate to develop their understanding of a literary work. In such a case, you may want to use your journal to reflect on what other students have said—for instance, why your opinion differs so much from someone else's.

You can keep a reading journal in a notebook or on your computer. Some readers prefer a two-column format like that illustrated on pages 696–97, with summaries, paraphrases, and quotations from the text on the left and with their own responses to these passages on the right. Or you may prefer a less structured format like that of the journal entry on page 692.

Reading a sample story

Following is a very short story by Kate Chopin (1851–1904). (The last name is pronounced in the French way, something like "show pan.") After the story are a student's annotations and journal entry on the story.

Kate Chopin

The Story of an Hour

Knowing that Mrs. Mallard was afflicted with a heart trouble, great care was taken to break to her as gently as possible the news of her husband's death.

It was her sister Josephine who told her, in broken sentences, veiled hints that revealed in half concealing. Her husband's friend Richards was there, too, near her. It was he who had been in the newspaper office when intelligence of the railroad disaster was received, with Brently Mallard's name leading the list of "killed." He had only taken the time to assure himself of its truth by a second telegram, and had hastened to forestall any less careful, less tender friend in bearing the sad message.

She did not hear the story as many women have heard the same, with a paralyzed inability to accept its significance. She wept at once with sudden, wild abandonment, in her sister's arms. When the storm of grief had spent itself she went away to her room alone. She would have no one follow her.

There stood, facing the open window, a comfortable, roomy armchair. Into this she sank, pressed down by a physical exhaustion that haunted her body and seemed to reach into her soul.

She could see in the open square before her house the tops of trees that were all aquiver with the new spring life. The delicious breath of rain was in the air. In the street below a peddler was crying his wares. The notes of a distant song which some one was singing reached her faintly, and countless sparrows were twittering in the eaves.

There were patches of blue sky showing here and there through the clouds that had met and piled one above the other in the west facing her window.

She sat with her head thrown back upon the cushion of the chair quite motionless, except when a sob came up into her throat and shook her, as a child who has cried itself to sleep continues to sob in its dreams.

She was young, with a fair, calm face, whose lines bespoke repression and even a certain strength. But now there was a dull stare in her eyes, whose gaze was fixed away off yonder on one of those patches of blue sky. It was not a glance of reflection, but rather indicated a suspension of intelligent thought.

There was something coming to her and she was waiting for it, fearfully. What was it? She did not know; it was too subtle and elusive to name. But she felt it creeping out of the sky, reaching toward her through the sounds, the scents, the color that filled the air.

Now her bosom rose and fell tumultuously. She was beginning to recognize this thing that was approaching to possess her, and she was striving to beat it back with her will—as powerless as her two white slender hands would have been.

When she abandoned herself a little whispered word escaped her slightly parted lips. She said it over and over under her breath: "Free, free, free!" The vacant stare and the look of terror that had followed it went from her eyes. They stayed keen and bright. Her pulses beat fast, and the coursing blood warmed and relaxed every inch of her body.

She did not stop to ask if it were not a monstrous joy that held her. A clear and exalted perception enabled her to dismiss the suggestion as trivial.

She knew that she would weep again when she saw the kind, tender hands folded in death; the face that had never looked save with love upon her, fixed and gray and dead. But she saw beyond that bitter moment a long procession of years to come that would belong to her absolutely. And she opened and spread her arms out to them in welcome.

There would be no one to live for her during those coming years; she would live for herself. There would be no powerful will bending her in the blind persistence with which men and women believe they have a right to impose a private will upon a fellow creature. A kind intention or a cruel intention made the act seem no less a crime as she looked upon it in that brief moment of illumination.

And yet she had loved him—sometimes. Often she had not. What did it matter! What could love, the unsolved mystery, count for in face of this possession of self-assertion which she suddenly recognized as the strongest impulse of her being.

"Free! Body and soul free!" she kept whispering.

Josephine was kneeling before the closed door with her lips to the keyhole, imploring for admission. "Louise, open the door! I beg; open the door—you will make yourself ill. What are you doing, Louise? For heaven's sake open the door."

"Go away. I am not making myself ill." No; she was drinking in the very elixir of life through that open window.

Her fancy was running riot along those days ahead of her. Spring days, and summer days, and all sorts of days that would be her own. She breathed a quick prayer that life might be long. It was only yesterday she had thought with a shudder that life might be long.

She arose at length and opened the door to her sister's importunities. There was a feverish triumph in her eyes, and she carried herself unwittingly like a goddess of Victory. She clasped her sister's waist and together they descended the stairs. Richards stood waiting for them at the bottom.

Some one was opening the front door with a latchkey. It was Brently Mallard who entered, a little travel-stained, composedly carrying his grip-sack and umbrella. He had been far from the scene of accident, and did not even know there had been one. He stood amazed at Josephine's piercing cry; at Richards' quick motion to screen him from the view of his wife.

But Richards was too late.

When the doctors came they said she had died of heart disease—of joy that kills.

Following a student's work

In this chapter we'll follow the analysis and writing of a student, Janet Vong, to see one approach to Chopin's story. Vong first annotated the story while reading it. Here are the opening five paragraphs with her notes:

Knowing that Mrs. Mallard was afflicted with a heart trouble, great care was taken to break to her as gently as possible the news of her husband's death. *"heart disease" at end of story*

no dialog—why? It was her sister Josephine who told her, in broken sentences, veiled hints that revealed in half concealing. Her husband's friend Richards was there, too, near her. *third-person narrator* It was he who had been in the newspaper office when intelligence of the railroad disaster was received, with Brently Mallard's name leading the list of "killed." He had only taken the time to assure himself of its truth by a second telegram, and had hastened to forestall any less careful, less tender friend in bearing the sad message. *Too hasty, it turns out*

Would men have heard differently? Is au. sexist?

She did not hear the story as many women have heard the same, with a paralyzed inability to accept its significance. She wept at once with sudden, wild abandonment, in her sister's arms. When the storm of grief had spent itself she went away to her room alone. She would have no one follow her.

←old-fashione[d] style

There stood, facing the open window, a comfortable, roomy armchair. Into this she sank, pressed down by a physical exhaustion that haunted her body and seemed to reach into her soul.

Notices spring odd in a story of death

symbol

She could see in the open square before her house the tops of trees that were all aquiver with the new spring life. The delicious breath of rain was in the air. In the street below a peddler was crying his wares. The notes of a distant song which some one was singing reached her faintly, and countless sparrows were twittering in the eaves.

Writing in her journal, Vong posed questions about the story—critical points, curiosities about characters, possible implications:

Title nothing special. What might be a better title?
Could a woman who loved her husband be so heartless? Is she heartless? Did she love him?
What are (were) Louise's feelings about her husband?
Did she want too much? What did she want?
Could this story happen today? Feminist interpretation?
Sister (Josephine)—a busybody?
Tricky ending—but maybe it could be true.
"And yet she had loved him—sometimes. Often she had not." Why does one love someone "sometimes"?
Irony: plot has reversal. Are characters ironic too?

Vong's journal entry illustrates brainstorming—the discovery technique of listing ideas (or questions) however they occur, without editing (see pp. 23–24). Another productive journal technique is focused freewriting—concentrating on a single issue (such as one of Vong's questions) and writing nonstop for a set amount of time, again without editing (p. 22). A double-column journal can be useful for analyzing an author's style (p. 696).

2 Taking a critical approach to literature

Like any discipline, the study of literature involves particular frameworks of analysis—particular ways of seeing literary works that help determine what parts the critical reader identifies and how he or she interprets them.

- **Historical or cultural criticism** focuses on the context in which a literary work was created and how that context affected the work. It may take the form of **biographical criticism**, which relates the author's life and ideas to a work of literature; **social or Marxist criticism,** which emphasizes issues of economics and class structure surrounding a work; or **postcolonial criticism,** focusing on works produced in former European colonies, which considers the aftereffects of European colonial rule.

- **Feminist or gender criticism** focuses on the representation of gender in literature, often in the literary canon—the body of work represented in standard anthologies, discussed in the schools, and examined in the scholarly journals. Feminist critics are especially concerned with the writings of women and with the responses of women to the depiction of both sexes in literature.
- **Archetypal criticism** uses psychological ideas about "collective memory" to explain characters and situations that appear in many literary works over time—for instance, heros and villains, star-crossed lovers, journeys, and quests.
- **Reader-response criticism** focuses on the reactions of an audience to a work of literature, asking why readers respond as they do to a text. In this view the meaning of the text lies not just on the page but in how the reader constructs the text.
- **Deconstructive criticism** regards a work of literature skeptically, resisting the obvious meanings and focusing on the ambiguities in the work, especially the internal contradictions. Perceiving that the relationship of words and their meanings is both arbitrary and forever changing—even within the same work—deconstructive critics emphasize multiple meanings and what a text does not say.
- **Formalist criticism** focuses primarily on a literary work as a constructed text, as an independent unity understood in itself rather than as an artifact of a particular context or reader response. Beginning with a personal response, the formalist critic tries to account for the response by examining the form of the work (hence *formalist*) and the relations among its elements.

This chapter emphasizes formalist criticism because it engages you immediately in the work of literature itself, without requiring extensive historical or cultural background, and because it introduces the conventional elements of literature that all critical approaches discuss, even though they view the elements differently.

3 Analyzing the elements of literature

The box on the next two pages lists the elements of literary works—plot, characters, setting, and so on—and offers questions about each one that can help you think constructively and imaginatively about what you read. After the box, we'll see how these elements both contribute to and grow out of an author's style.

Questions for a literary analysis

See also the related tips for analyzing a writer's style (p. 696). And see later boxes for specific questions on fiction (p. 708), poetry (p. 709), and drama (p. 712).

Plot

The relationships and patterns of events.

What actions happen?
What conflicts occur?
How do the events connect to each other and to the whole?

Characters

The people the author creates, including the narrator of a story or the speaker of a poem.

Who are the principal people in the work?
How do they interact?
What do their actions, words, and thoughts reveal about their personalities and the personalities of others?
Do the characters stay the same, or do they change? Why?

Point of view

The perspective or attitude of the speaker in a poem or the voice who tells a story. The point of view may be **first person** (a participant, using *I*) or **third person** (an outsider, using *he, she, it, they*). A first-person narrator may be a major or a minor character in the narrative and may be **reliable** or **unreliable** (unable to report events wholly or accurately). A third-person narrator may be **omniscient** (knows what goes on in all characters' minds), **limited** (knows what goes on in the mind of only one or two characters), or **objective** (knows only what is external to the characters).

Who is the narrator (or the speaker of a poem)?
What point of view is used in the work?
How does the narrator's point of view affect the narrative?
If there are shifts in point of view or multiple narrators, how do they affect the narrative?

Tone

The narrator's or speaker's attitude, perceived through the words (for instance, joyful, bitter, or confident).

What tone (or tones) do you hear? If there is a change, how do you account for it?
Is there an ironic contrast between the narrator's tone (for instance, confidence) and what you take to be the author's attitude (for instance, pity for human overconfidence)?

Imagery

Word pictures or details involving the senses: sight, sound, touch, smell, taste.

What images does the writer use? What senses do they draw on?
What patterns are evident in the images (for instance, religious or commercial images)?
What is the significance of the imagery?

Symbolism

Concrete images standing for larger and more abstract ideas. For instance, the American flag may symbolize freedom, a tweeting bird may symbolize happiness, or a dead flower may symbolize mortality.

What symbols does the author use? What does each one seem to signify?
How does the symbolism relate to the other elements of the work, such as character or theme?

Allusions

References to sources and events outside the work.

Does the author allude or refer to sources or events, such as a story in the Bible, a Greek myth, a war, a popular song, or an infamous crime?
What effect do these allusions have on the work?

Setting

The place and time of the action.

What does the locale contribute to the work?
Are scene shifts significant?
Does the setting have symbolic value?

Form

The shape or structure of the work.

What *is* the form? (For example, a poem might divide sharply in the middle, moving from happiness to sorrow. A story might compress some scenes and draw out others.)
What parts of the work does the form emphasize, and why?
How does each part of the work contribute to the whole?

Themes

The main ideas—conceptions of human experience suggested by the work as a whole. A theme is neither a plot (what happens) nor a subject (such as mourning or marriage). Rather it is what the author says with that plot about that subject.

Can you state each theme in a sentence? Avoid mentioning specific characters or actions; instead, write an observation applicable to humanity in general. For instance, you might state the following about Kate Chopin's "The Story of an Hour": *Happiness depends partly on freedom.*
Do certain words, passages of dialog or description, or situations seem to represent the themes most clearly?
How do the work's elements combine to develop the themes?

4 Analyzing a writer's style

The style of a literary work involves many of the elements listed in the preceding box, such as point of view, tone, imagery, and form. Through word choices, figures of speech, and sentence structures, the author tries to bring readers to share his or her view of the work's characters and plot. To analyze style, consider these questions:

- **How do the author's word choices (diction) affect the work?** Are the words simple, complex, or somewhere in between? What tone does the language create, such as humor, seriousness, anxiety, or sadness? What does any slang, dialect, or colloquial language contribute to the work? What do images, including figurative language, contribute?
- **How do sentence length and complexity affect the work?** Are sentences notably short and simple or notably long and complicated? How does their structure influence the tone?
- **Do some words, images, or symbols recur in the work?** What purpose does this repetition serve?
- **Do elements shift in the work?** What is the significance of any change in point of view, imagery, or tone?

If analyzing a writer's style seems difficult, begin by heeding your emotions as you read the work. Do you feel amused? worried? excited? sad? Where does your sympathy lie? Noting your responses is an important step to understanding what features of the work trigger those responses.

Many writers generate ideas about style with a **double-column journal:** quotations from the work or notes about it on the left and reflections on those points on the right. The following example comes from Janet Vong's analysis of Chopin's "The Story of an Hour":

Text	**Responses**
The husband's death is described in the first two pars.: "Brently Mallard's death leading the list of 'killed.'"	In retrospect, the quotation marks around "killed" foreshadow that the news is false.
"She did not hear the story as many women have heard the same. . . . She wept at once with sudden, wild abandonment. . . . When the storm of grief had spent itself . . ." (par. 3)	Mrs. M seems different (at first) in the face of her grief. Just a few strong words depict a raw surge of emotion.
Big shift in tone in par. 5, from "afflicted," "disaster," "paralyzed," "storm," "pressed," to spring imagery: "aquiver," "delicious," "twittering," "patches of blue sky."	More foreshadowing: Mrs. M's mood is going to change. The point of view is shifting here, too, from objective 3rd person to limited 3rd person: we're beginning to see through Mrs. M's eyes.

Pars. 9-19: "'Free, free, free!'" "coursing blood," "live for herself," "illumination," "'Free! Body and soul free!'" "elixir of life," "fancy was running riot."

Over and over, Mrs. M discovers and savors her new freedom. Half the story is devoted to this mood.

Mrs. M's efforts to repress her joy ("striving to beat it back with her will," par. 10). Thoughts of Mr. M's kindness ("kind, tender, hands . . . never looked save with love upon her," par. 13). Source of her unhappiness (Mr. M's "powerful will bending her in . . . blind persistence," par. 14).

Mrs. M seems a bit monstrous (suggested by "monstrous joy," par. 12) but is made sympathetic by these passages that humanize and explain her.

"She arose at length. . . ," "Some one was opening the door. . . ," "they said she had died of heart disease—of joy that kills" (last 4 pars.).

Back to objective 3rd person: a bird's-eye view for the ironic ending.

5 Finding meaning and evidence in literature

One significant attribute of a literary work is its *meaning,* or what we can interpret to be its meaning. Readers may well disagree over the persuasiveness of someone's argument, but they will rarely disagree over its meaning. With literature, however, disagreements over meaning occur all the time because (as we have seen) literature *shows* rather than *tells:* it gives us concrete images of imagined human experiences, but it usually does not say how we ought to understand the images.

Further, readers bring to their reading not only different critical views, as noted earlier, but also different personal experiences. A woman who has recently lost her husband may interpret "The Story of an Hour" differently from most other readers. Or a story that bores a reader at age fifteen may deeply move him at twenty-five. The words on the page remain the same, but their meaning changes.

In writing about literature, then, we can offer only our *interpretation* of meaning rather than *the* meaning. Still, most people agree that there are limits to interpretation: it must be both supported by evidence from the text and not contradicted by the text. For instance, the student who says that in "The Story of an Hour" Mrs. Mallard does not die but merely falls into a deathlike trance goes beyond the permissible limits because the story offers no evidence for such an interpretation.

The *evidence* for a literary analysis always comes from at least one primary source (the work or works being discussed) and may come from secondary sources (critical and historical works). (See

p. 685 for more on primary and secondary sources.) For example, if you were writing about Chopin's "The Story of an Hour," the primary material would be the story itself, and the secondary material (if you used it) might be critical studies of Chopin.

The bulk of your evidence in writing about literature will usually be quotations from the work, although you will occasionally summarize or paraphrase as well (see pp. 602–03). When using quotations, they must support, not replace, your own insights, advancing your argument and proving your point. Keep in mind the criteria in the box on page 703.

Your teacher will probably tell you if you are expected to consult secondary sources for an assignment. They can help you understand a writer's work, but your primary concern should always be the work itself, not what critics A, B, and C say about it. In general, then, quote or summarize secondary material sparingly. And always cite your sources.

6 Seeing arguments in literature

Like nonfiction, literary texts often make arguments, sometimes overtly but more often subtly. As a reader, you can often discern the argument through its elements—the tone of the speaker or narrator, the comments of a trusted character, the workings of the plot, or the description of the setting. Following is the opening of *Hard Times* (1849), a novel by Charles Dickens. As you read, speculate about what argument the novel makes.

> "Now, what I want is, Facts. Teach these boys and girls nothing but Facts. Facts alone are wanted in life. Plant nothing else, and root out everything else. You can only form the minds of reasoning animals upon Facts; nothing else will ever be of any service to them. This is the principle on which I bring up my own children, and this is the principle on which I bring up these children. Stick to Facts, sir!"
>
> The scene was a plain, bare, monotonous vault of a schoolroom, and the speaker's square forefinger emphasized his observations by underscoring every sentence with a line on the schoolmaster's sleeve. The emphasis was helped by the speaker's square wall of a forehead, which had his eyebrows for its base, while his eyes found commodious cellarage in two dark caves, overshadowed by the wall. The emphasis was helped by the speaker's mouth, which was wide, thin, and hard set. The emphasis was helped by the speaker's voice, which was inflexible, dry, and dictatorial. The emphasis was helped by the speaker's hair, which bristled on the skirts of his bald head, a plantation of firs to keep the wind from its shining surface, all covered with knobs, like the crust of a plum pie, as if the head had scarcely warehouse-room for the hard facts stored inside. The speaker's obstinate carriage, square coat, square legs, square shoulders—nay, his

very neckcloth, trained to take him by the throat with an unaccommodating grasp, like a stubborn fact, as it was—all helped the emphasis.

"In this life, we want nothing but Facts, sir; nothing but Facts!"

In this passage the argument of the quoted speaker (whose name is Mr. Gradgrind) is clear: teachers should teach facts and nothing else. However, the description of Gradgrind in the second paragraph makes him so unappealing that you are unlikely to sympathize with him. For example, the repetition of *emphasis* and *square* makes Gradgrind both boringly didactic and ridiculous, a caricature of a teacher. You can expect that the narrator might advance an argument different from Gradgrind's, perhaps that education requires something besides facts.

To read Chopin's "The Story of an Hour" as an argument, you might focus on this sentence:

> There would be no powerful will bending her in the blind persistence with which men and women believe they have a right to impose a private will upon a fellow creature.

In this statement about individuality and personal freedom, the author argues for a measure of freedom and self-determination for all people.

50b Understanding writing assignments in literature

A literature teacher may ask you to write one or more of the following types of papers. The first three are the most common.

- **A literary analysis paper:** Give your ideas about a work of literature—your interpretation of its meaning, context, or representations based on specific words, characters, and events.
- **A style analysis paper:** Examine how an author uses words and constructs sentences to achieve certain effects in the work.
- **A literary research paper:** Combine analysis of a literary work with research about the work and perhaps its author. A literary research paper draws on both primary and secondary sources. For example, you might respond to what scholars have written about the symbolism in a play by Tennessee Williams, or you might research medieval England as a way to understand the context of Chaucer's *Canterbury Tales*.
- **A personal response or reaction paper:** Give your thoughts and feelings about a work of literature. For example, you might compare a novel's description of a city with your experience of the same city.

- **A book review:** Give a summary of a book and a judgment about the book's value. In a review of a novel, for example, you might discuss whether the plot is interesting, the characters are believable, and the writing style is enjoyable. You might also compare the work to other works by the author.
- **A theater review:** Give your reactions to and opinions about a theatrical performance. You might summarize the plot of the play, describe the characters, identify the prominent themes, evaluate the other elements (writing, performances, direction, stage setting), and make a recommendation to potential viewers.

50c Using the tools and language of literary analysis

1 Writing tools

The fundamental tool for writing about literature is reading critically. Asking analytical questions such as those on pages 694–95 can help you focus your ideas. In addition, keeping a reading journal can help you develop your thoughts. Keep careful, well-organized notes on any research materials. Finally, discuss the work with others who have read it. They may offer reactions and insights that will help you shape your own ideas.

2 Language considerations

Use the present tense of verbs to describe both the action in a literary work (*Brently Mallard suddenly appears*) and the writing of an author (*Chopin briefly describes the view* or *In his essay he comments that* . . .). Use the past tense to describe events that actually occurred in the past (*Chopin was born in 1851*).

Some teachers discourage students from using personal pronouns in writing about literature. *You* and *we* can seem chummy or condescending: *You can see this attitude clearly* . . . ; *We understand the character's motives to be*. . . . Both pronouns can be avoided by direct statements: *This attitude appears clearly* . . . ; *The character's motives are*. . . . The pronoun *I* can sound egotistical and can narrow the appeal of your argument. The sentence *I don't think the central irony resides in Richards's actions* focuses the attention on the writer and can be dismissed as merely one person's opinion. In contrast, *The central irony does not reside in Richards's actions* removes the writer and focuses readers on the claim.

3 Research sources

In addition to the following resources on literature, you may also want to consult some on other humanities (pp. 718–21).

Specialized encyclopedias, dictionaries, and bibliographies

Bibliographical Guide to the Study of the Literature of the USA
Cambridge Bibliography of English Literature
Cambridge Encyclopedia of Language
Cambridge Guide to Literature in English
Dictionary of Literary Biography
Handbook to Literature
Literary Criticism Index
McGraw-Hill Encyclopedia of World Drama
MLA International Bibliography of Books and Articles on the Modern Languages and Literatures
New Princeton Encyclopedia of Poetry and Poetics
Oxford Companion to American Literature
Oxford Companion to the Theatre
Schomburg Center Guide to Black Literature from the Eighteenth Century to the Present

Indexes

Abstracts of Folklore Studies
Dissertation Abstracts International (doctoral dissertations)
Humanities Index
Literary Criticism Index
MLA International Bibliography of Books and Articles on the Modern Languages and Literatures

Book reviews

Book Review Digest
Book Review Index
Index to Book Reviews in the Humanities

Web sources

For updates of these sources and URLs, visit *ablongman.com/littlebrown*.

Alex Catalog of Electronic Texts (*infomotions.com/alex*)
EServer (*eserver.org*)
Internet Public Library: Online Literary Criticism (*ipl.org/div/litcrit*)
Key Sites on American Literature (*usinfo.state.gov/products/pubs/oal/amlitweb.htm*)
Literary Index (*www.galenet.com/servlet/LitIndex*)
Literary Resources on the Net (*andromeda.rutgers.edu/~jlynch/Lit*)
Online Books Page (*online books.library.upenn.edu*)
Voice of the Shuttle: Drama, Theater, and Performance Art Studies (*vos.ucsb.edu/browse.asp?id=782*)
Voice of the Shuttle: Literature (*in English*) (*vos.ucsb.edu/browse.asp?id=3*)
Voice of the Shuttle: Literatures (*Other than English*) (*vos.ucsb.edu/browse.asp?id=2719*)

50d Citing sources and formatting documents in writing about literature

Unless your teacher specifies otherwise, use the documentation style of the Modern Language Association (MLA), detailed in Chapter 47. In this style, parenthetical citations in the text of the paper refer to a list of works cited at the end. Sample papers illustrating this style appear in Chapter 48 as well as in this chapter.

Use MLA format for headings, margins, and other elements, as detailed on pages 664–66.

50e Drafting and revising a literary analysis

The process for writing a literary analysis is similar to that for any other kind of essay: once you've done the reading and thought about it, you need to focus your ideas, gather evidence, draft, and revise.

1 Conceiving a thesis

After reading, rereading, and making notes, you probably will be able to formulate a tentative thesis statement—an assertion of your main point, your argument. (For more on thesis statements, see pp. 29–34.) Clear the air by glancing over your notes and by jotting down a few especially promising ideas—brief statements of what you think your key points may be and their main support. If necessary, go back to the work to expand your notes. Here are some approaches to conceiving a thesis:

- **Seek patterns in the work.** What do recurring elements—sounds, words, images, symbols, events—contribute to the themes?
- **Study the structure of the work.** What does the author's arrangement of the parts contribute to meaning? In a novel you might consider the order of scenes and their relative emphasis. In poetry you might consider patterns of general and specific or comparison and contrast.
- **Examine a part of the work.** Does a particular character, image, symbol, event, or other element seem especially significant to overall meaning?

Considering Kate Chopin's "The Story of an Hour," Janet Vong at first explored the idea that Mrs. Mallard, the main character, was unrealistic and thus unconvincing. (See Vong's journal entry on p. 692.) But the more Vong examined the story and her notes, the more she was impressed by a pattern of ironies, or reversals, that actually helped to make Mrs. Mallard believable. In her journal Vong explored the idea that the many small reversals paved the way for Mrs. Mallard's own reversal from grief to joy:

title? "Ironies in an Hour" (?) "An Hour of Irony" (?) "Kate Chopin's Irony" (?)
thesis: irony at end is prepared for
chief irony: Mrs. M. dies just as she is beginning to enjoy life
smaller ironies:

1. "sad message" brings her joy
2. Richards is "too late" at end
3. Richards is too early at start
4. "joy that kills"
5. death brings joy and life

From these notes Vong developed her thesis statement:

> The irony of the ending is believable partly because it is consistent with earlier ironies in the story.

This thesis statement asserts a specific idea that can be developed, debated, and convincingly argued with evidence from Chopin's story. A good thesis statement will neither assert a fact (*Mrs. Mallard dies soon after hearing that her husband has died*) nor overgeneralize (*The story is an insult to women*).

2 Gathering evidence

In writing about literature, you support your ideas about a work mainly with evidence gathered from the work itself: most often quotations and sometimes paraphrases. You may also draw on plot summary, and for literary research papers you will draw on secondary sources.

The box below offers guidelines for using quotations in literary analysis.

Guidelines for using quotations in literary analysis

- **Use quotations to support your assertions, not to replace them or pad the paper.** Whenever possible, embed quotations into your paragraphs to show that they are subordinate to your ideas. Quote at length only when necessary to your argument.
- **Specify how each quotation relates to your idea.** Introduce the quotation—for example, *At the outset Chopin conveys the sort of person Richards is: ". . ."* Sometimes, comment after the quotation. (See pages 607–10 for more on integrating quotations into your writing.)
- **Keep quotations as brief as possible.** Use only the words necessary to make your point: *She looks forward to "summer days" (13), but she will not see even the end of this spring day.*
- **Reproduce spelling, punctuation, capitalization, and all other features exactly as they appear in the source.** See page 485 for the use of brackets when you need to add something to a quotation, and see page 486 for the use of an ellipsis mark when you need to omit something from a quotation.
- **Document your sources.** See page 618.

While quotations from a literary work convey the author's style and tone, paraphrases from the work can inject variety and help to establish your own writer's voice. Because a paraphrase restates the original in your own words, it can also be easier than a quotation to mesh into your idea. For more on writing paraphrases, see pages 602–03.

Summary of a work's plot also has its uses in literary analysis—to a point. Summary is *not* analysis, so it should always have a clear purpose and be as brief as possible. You may want to summarize an entire work if you think readers are unfamiliar with it, or you may want to use plot elements as evidence, the way Janet Vong uses the ironic ending of Chopin's "The Story of an Hour" in her final paper on pages 706–07.

In literary research papers, your evidence will come not only from the work itself but also from secondary sources such as scholarly works and critical appraisals. The thesis and principal ideas of the paper must still be your own, but you may supplement your reading of the work with the views of respected scholars or critics. Sometimes you may choose to build your own argument in part by disputing others' views. However you draw on secondary sources, remember that they must be clearly identified and documented, even when you use your own words.

Note You can find student essays on the Web that may lead you to other sources or may suggest ideas you hadn't considered. If you want to use another student's paper as a secondary source, you must evaluate it with special care because it will not have passed through a reviewing process, as an article in a scholarly journal does. (See pp. 590–97 on evaluating online sources.) You must also, of course, clearly identify and document the source: borrowing other students' ideas or words without credit is plagiarism. (See pp. 611–18.)

3 Writing a draft

Drafting your essay is your opportunity to develop your thesis or to discover it if you haven't already. The following draft by Janet Vong is rough: the introduction is abrupt, the thesis is not clearly stated, and the pace is rushed. But drafting did lead Vong to develop and support her ideas. The numbers in parentheses refer to the pages from which she drew the quotations. (See pp. 624–30 on this form of documentation.) Ask your teacher whether you should always give such citations, especially for a short poem or story like Chopin's.

Ironies in an Hour

After we know how the story turns out, if we reread it we find irony at the very start, as is true of many other stories. Mrs. Mallard's friends assume, mistakenly, that Mrs. Mallard was deeply in love with her husband, Brently Mallard. They take great care to tell her gently of his death. The friends mean well, and in fact they do well. They bring her an hour of life, an hour of freedom. They think their news is sad. Mrs. Mallard at first expresses grief when she hears the news, but soon she finds joy in it. So Richards's "sad message" (23), though sad in Richards's eyes, is in fact a happy message.

Among the ironic details is the statement that when Mallard enters the house, Richards tries to conceal him from Mrs. Mallard, but Richards is "too late" (24). This is ironic because earlier Richards has "hastened" (23) to bring his sad message; if he had been too late at the start, Brently Mallard would have arrived at home first, and Mrs. Mallard's life would not end an hour later but would simply go on as before. Yet another irony at the end of the story is the diagnosis of the doctors. The doctors say she died of "heart disease—of joy that kills" (24). In one sense the doctors are right: Mrs. Mallard has experienced a great joy. But of course the doctors totally misunderstand the joy that kills her.

The central irony resides not in the well-intentioned but ironic actions of Richards, or in the unconsciously ironic words of the doctors, but in her own life. She "sometimes" (24) loved her husband, but in a way she has been dead. Now, his apparent death brings her new life. This new life comes to her at the season of the year when "the tops of trees . . . were all aquiver with the new spring life" (23). But, ironically, her new life will last only an hour. She looks forward to "summer days" (24), but she will not see even the end of this spring day. Her years of marriage were ironic. They brought her a sort of living death instead of joy. Her new life is ironic, too. It grows out of her moment of grief for her supposedly dead husband, and her vision of a new life is cut short.

4 Revising and editing

As in other writing, use at least two drafts to revise and edit, so that you can attend separately to the big structural issues and the smaller surface problems. See pages 54 and 60–61 for general revision and editing checklists. The additional checklist below can help you with a literary analysis.

Checklist for revising a literary analysis

- **Title:** Does the title of your essay suggest your approach to the work? Will it interest or intrigue the reader?
- **Introduction:** Does the introductory paragraph name the author and the title so that readers know exactly what work you are discussing? (Avoid opening sentences such as "In this story. . . .") Does the introduction state and develop your thesis a bit so that readers know where they will be going? Does it attempt to draw in the reader?

(continued)

Checklist for revising a literary analysis
(continued)

- **Organization:** How effective is the organization? The essay should not dwindle or become anticlimactic; rather, it should build up.
- **Quotations:** What evidence does each quotation provide? Do quotations let readers hear the author's voice? Do they support, not replace, your own ideas? Are they embedded in your paragraphs?
- **Analysis vs. summary:** Is the essay chiefly devoted to analysis, not to summary? Summarize the plot only briefly and only to further your own ideas. A summary is not an essay.
- **Verb tenses:** Have you used the present tense of verbs to describe both the author's work and the action in the work (for example, *Chopin shows* or *Mrs. Mallard dies*)?
- **Evaluation:** How well will readers understand your evaluation of the work and what it is based on? Your evaluation may be implied (as in Janet Vong's essay on "The Story of an Hour"), or it may be explicit. In either case, give the reasons why you have judged the work as you have.
- **Are all your sources documented in MLA style?**

Janet Vong's final draft appears below with annotations that highlight some of its features.

An essay on fiction (no secondary sources)

Author's name and identification in MLA format (p. 665)

Janet Vong

Mr. Romano

English III, period 4

20 February 2006

Paper title incorporating author and title of analyzed work

Ironies of Life in Kate Chopin's "The Story of an Hour"

Introduction naming author/title and stating thesis

Kate Chopin's "The Story of an Hour" has an ironic ending: Mrs. Mallard dies just when she is beginning to live. On first reading, the ending seems almost too ironic for belief. On rereading the story, however, one sees that the ending is believable partly because it is consistent with other ironies in the story.

Detailing of story's ironies, using quotations and some summary to emphasize the reversals

The story's ironies appear at the very start. Because Mrs. Mallard's friends and her sister assume, mistakenly, that she was deeply in love with her husband, Brently Mallard, they take great care to tell her gently of his death. They mean well, and in fact they do well, bringing her an hour of life, an hour of joyous freedom, but it is ironic that they think their news is sad. True, Mrs. Mallard at first expresses grief when she hears the news, but soon (unknown to the others) she finds joy. So

Richards's "sad message" (23), though sad in Richards's eyes, is in fact a happy message.

Among the small but significant ironic details is the statement near the end of the story that when Mallard enters the house, Richards tries to conceal him from Mrs. Mallard, but Richards is "too late" (24). Almost at the start of the story, in the second paragraph, Richards has "hastened" (23) to bring his sad news. But if Richards had arrived too late at the start, Brently Mallard would have arrived at home first, and Mrs. Mallard's life would not end an hour later but would simply go on as before. Yet another irony at the end of the story is the diagnosis of the doctors. They say she died of "heart disease—of joy that kills" (24). In one sense they are right: Mrs. Mallard has for the last hour experienced a great joy. But of course the doctors totally misunderstand the joy that kills her. It is not joy at seeing her husband alive, but her realization that the great joy she experienced during the last hour is over.

Parenthetical citations in MLA style referring to the work cited at the end of the paper (see p. 624)

All of these ironic details add richness to the story, but the central irony resides not in the well-intentioned but ironic actions of Richards, or in the unconsciously ironic words of the doctors, but in Mrs. Mallard's own life. She "sometimes" (24) loved her husband, but in a way she has been dead, a body subjected to her husband's will. Now, his apparent death brings her new life. Appropriately, this new life comes to her at the season of the year when "the tops of trees . . . were all aquiver with the new spring life" (23). But, ironically, her new life will last only an hour. She is "Free, free, free" (24)—but only until her husband walks through the doorway. She looks forward to "summer days" (24), but she will not see even the end of this spring day. If her years of marriage were ironic, bringing her a sort of living death instead of joy, her new life is ironic, too, not only because it grows out of her moment of grief for her supposedly dead husband, but also because her vision of "a long procession of years" (24) is cut short within an hour on a spring day.

[New page.]

Work Cited

Chopin, Kate. "The Story of an Hour." An Introduction to Literature: Fiction, Poetry, and Drama. Ed. Sylvan Barnet, William Burto, and William E. Cain. 13th ed. New York: Longman, 2004. 23-24.

New page for work cited in MLA style (p. 633)

50f Writing about fiction, poetry, and drama

A work of literature falls into a category, or **genre**—such as fiction, poetry, or drama—depending on how it is structured. The

An essay on poetry with secondary sources

The following sample paper on a short poem by Gwendolyn Brooks illustrates a literary analysis that draws not only on the poem itself but also on secondary sources—that is, critical works *about* the poem. In the opening paragraph, for instance, the writer uses brief quotations from two secondary sources to establish the problem, the topic that he will address. These quotations, like the two later quotations from secondary material, are used to make points, not to pad the essay.

Note In the paper, the parenthetical citations for Brooks's poem give line numbers of the poem, whereas the citations for the secondary sources give page numbers of the sources. See pages 624 and 629, respectively, for these two forms of citation.

Gwendolyn Brooks

The Bean Eaters

They eat beans mostly, this old yellow pair.
Dinner is a casual affair.
Plain chipware on a plain and creaking wood,
Tin flatware.

Two who are Mostly Good.
Two who have lived their day,
But keep on putting on their clothes
And putting things away.

And remembering . . .
Remembering, with twinklings and twinges,
As they lean over the beans in their rented back room that
is full of beads and receipts and dolls and cloths,
tobacco crumbs, vases and fringes.

Kenneth Scheff

Ms. Moran

English II, period 5

7 February 2006

Marking Time Versus Enduring in

Gwendolyn Brooks's "The Bean Eaters"

Gwendolyn Brooks's poem "The Bean Eaters" runs only eleven lines. It is written in plain language about very plain people. Yet its meaning is ambiguous. One critic, George E. Kent, says the old couple who eat beans "have had their day and exist now as time-markers" (141). However, another reader, D. H. Melhem, perceives not so much time marking as "endurance" in the old couple (123). Is this poem a despairing picture of old age or a more positive portrait?

"The Bean Eaters" describes an "old yellow pair" who "eat beans mostly" (line 1) off "Plain chipware" (3) with "Tin flatware" (4) in "their rented back room" (11). Clearly, they are poor. They live alone, not with friends or relatives—children or grandchildren are not mentioned—but with memories and a few possessions (9-11). They are "Mostly Good" (5), words Brooks capitalizes at the end of a line, perhaps to stress the old people's adherence to traditional values as well as their lack of saintliness. They are unexceptional.

The isolated routine of the couple's life is something Brooks draws attention to with a separate stanza:

> Two who are Mostly Good.
> Two who have lived their day,
> But keep on putting on their clothes
> And putting things away. (5-8)

Brooks emphasizes how isolated the couple is by repeating "Two who." Then she emphasizes how routine their life is by repeating "putting."

A pessimistic reading of this poem seems justified. The critic Harry B. Shaw reads the lines just quoted as perhaps despairing: "they are putting things away as if winding down an operation and readying for withdrawal from activity" (80). However, Shaw observes, the word "But" also indicates that the couple resist slipping away, that they intend to hold on (80). This dual meaning is at the heart of Brooks's poem: the old people live a meager existence, yes, but their will, their self-control, and their connection with another person—their essential humanity—are unharmed.

The truly positive nature of the poem is revealed in the last stanza. In Brooks's words, the old couple remembers with some "twinges" perhaps, but also with "twinklings" (10), a cheerful image. As Melhem says, these people are "strong in mutual affection and shared memories" (123). And the final line, which is much longer than all the rest and which catalogs the evidence of the couple's long life together, is almost musically affirmative: "As they lean over the beans in their rented back room that is full of beads and receipts and dolls and cloths, tobacco crumbs, vases and fringes" (11).

What these people have is not much, but it is something.

[New page.]

Works Cited

Brooks, Gwendolyn. "The Bean Eaters." An Introduction to Literature: Fiction, Poetry, and Drama. Ed. Sylvan Barnet, William Burto, and William E. Cain. 13th ed. New York: Longman, 2004. 807.

Kent, George E. A Life of Gwendolyn Brooks. Lexington: UP of Kentucky, 1990.

Melhem, D. H. Gwendolyn Brooks: Poetry and the Heroic Voice. Lexington: UP of Kentucky, 1987.

Shaw, Harry B. Gwendolyn Brooks. Twayne's United States Authors Ser. 395. Boston: Twayne, 1980.

3 Writing about drama

Because plays—even some one-act plays—are relatively long, analytic essays on drama usually focus on only one aspect of the play, such as the structure of the play, the function of a single scene, or a character's responsibility for his or her fate. The essay's introduction indicates what the topic is and why it is of some importance, and the introduction may also state the thesis. The conclusion often extends the analysis, showing how a study of the apparently small topic helps to illuminate the play as a whole.

The "Questions for a literary analysis" on pages 694–95 will help you think about any work of literature, including a play, and find a topic to write on. The questions below provide additional prompts for thinking about drama.

Questions for analyzing drama

- **How does the plot (the sequence of happenings) unfold?** Does it seem plausible? If not, is the implausibility a fault? If there is more than one plot, are the plots parallel, or are they related by way of contrast? How do particular scenes advance the plot and ultimately contribute to the play's themes?
- **Are certain happenings recurrent?** If so, how are they significant?
- **What kinds of conflict are in the play**—for instance, between two groups, two individuals, or two aspects of a single individual? How are the conflicts resolved? Is the resolution satisfying to you?
- **How does the author develop the characters?** How trustworthy are the characters when they describe themselves or others? What purpose does each character serve? Do some characters serve as **foils,** or contrasts, for other characters, thus helping to define the other characters? Do the characters change as the play proceeds? Are the characters' motivations convincing? How do minor characters contribute to the play's meaning?
- **What do the author's stage directions add to your understanding of the play?** If there are few stage directions, what do the speeches imply about the characters' manner, tone, and gestures?
- **What do you make of the setting, or location?** Does it help to reveal character or theme? Do changes in setting parallel changes in plot or character development? How do various settings contribute to the themes of the play?
- **Do certain costumes** (dark suits, flowery shawls, stiff collars) **or properties** (books, pictures, candlesticks) **strike you as symbolic?**
- **What is the author's relationship to the audience?** Do characters speak directly to the audience in asides or soliloquies? If so, what is their effect?

An essay on drama (no secondary sources)

The following essay on William Shakespeare's *Macbeth* focuses on the title character, examining the extent to which he is and is not a tragic hero. Although the writer bases the essay on his personal response to the play, he does not simply state a preference, as if saying he likes vanilla more than chocolate; instead, he argues a case and offers evidence from the play to support his claims.

The writer delays stating his thesis fully until the final paragraph: Macbeth is a hero even though he is a villain. But this thesis is nonetheless evident throughout the essay, from the title through the opening three paragraphs (which establish a context and the case the writer will oppose) through each of the five body paragraphs (which offer five kinds of evidence for the thesis).

Note The parenthetical citations in this essay include act, scene, and line numbers—MLA style for citations of verse plays (see p. 629).

Michael Spinter

Mrs. Nelson

English III, period 4

6 May 2006

Macbeth as Hero

When we think of a tragic hero, we probably think of a fundamentally sympathetic person who is entangled in terrifying circumstances and who ultimately dies, leaving us with a sense that the world has suffered a loss. For instance, Hamlet must avenge his father's murder, and in doing so he performs certain actions that verge on the wrongful, such as behaving cruelly to his beloved Ophelia and his mother and killing Rosencrantz and Guildenstern; but we believe that Hamlet is fundamentally a decent man and that Denmark is the poorer for his death.

Macbeth, however, is different. He kills King Duncan and Duncan's grooms, kills Banquo, attempts to kill Banquo's son, and finally kills Lady Macduff and her children as well as her servants. True, the only people whom he kills with his own hands are Duncan and the grooms—the other victims are destroyed by hired murderers—but clearly Macbeth is responsible for all of the deaths. He could seem an utterly unscrupulous, sneaking butcher rather than a tragic hero for whom a reader can feel sympathy.

Certainly most of the other characters in the play feel no sympathy for Macbeth. Macduff calls him a "hell-kite," or a hellish bird of prey (4.3.217), a "tyrant" (5.7.14), a "hell-hound" (5.8.3), and a "coward" (5.8.23). To Malcolm he is a "tyrant" (4.3.12), "devilish Macbeth" (4.3.117), and a "butcher" (5.8.69). Readers and spectators can hardly deny the truth of these characterizations. And yet Macbeth does not seem merely villainous. It would be going too far to say that we always sympathize with him, but we are deeply interested in him and do not dismiss him in disgust as an out-and-out monster. How can we account for his hold on our feelings? At least five factors play their parts.

Macbeth appeals to us because he is an impressive military figure. In the first extended description of Macbeth, the Captain speaks of "brave Macbeth—well he deserves that name" (1.2.16). The Captain tells how Macbeth valiantly fought on behalf of his king, and King Duncan exclaims, "O valiant cousin! Worthy gentleman!" (1.2.2). True, Macbeth sometimes cringes, such as when he denies responsibility for Banquo's death: "Thou canst not say I did it" (3.4.51). But throughout most of the play, we see him as a bold and courageous soldier.

Of course, Macbeth's ability as a soldier is not enough by itself to explain his hold on us. He is at the same time a victim—a victim of his wife's ambition and a victim of the witches. Yes, he ought to see through his wife's schemes, and he ought to resist the witches, just as Banquo resists them, but surely Macbeth is partly tricked into crime. He is responsible, but we can imagine ourselves falling as he does, and his status as a victim arouses our sympathy.

Also contributing to our sense of the character's humanity is the conscience Macbeth retains despite his terrible deeds. For instance, after he murders Duncan he cannot sleep at night. When he tells Lady Macbeth that he has heard a voice saying, "Macbeth does murder sleep" (2.2.35), she ridicules him, but the voice is prophetic: he is doomed to sleepless nights. We in the audience are glad that Macbeth is tormented by his deed, since it shows that he knows he has done wrong and that he still has some decent human feelings.

Macbeth also eventually loses all of his allies, even his wife, and he then claims our sympathy as a lonely, guilt-haunted figure. On this point, scene 2 of act 3 is especially significant. When Lady Macbeth asks Macbeth why he keeps to himself (line 8), he confides something of the mental stress that he is undergoing. But when she asks, "What's to be done?" (44), he cannot bring himself to tell her that he is plotting the deaths of Banquo and Fleance. Instead of further involving his wife, the only person with whom he might still have a human connection, Macbeth says, "Be innocent of the knowledge, dearest chuck . . ." (45). The word chuck, an affectionate form of chick, shows warmth and intimacy that are touching, but his refusal or his inability to confide in his wife and former partner in crime shows how fully isolated he is from all human contact. We cannot help feeling sorry for him.

Finally, Macbeth holds our interest, instead of disgusting us, because he speaks eloquently. The greatness of his language compels us to listen to him with rapt attention. Some speeches are very familiar, such as "My way of life / Is fall'n into the sear, the yellow leaf . . ." (5.3.23-24) and "Tomorrow and tomorrow and tomorrow / Creeps in this petty pace from day to day . . ." (5.5.19-20). But almost every speech Macbeth utters is equally memorable for its grace and passion—from his first, "So foul and fair a day I have not seen" (1.3.38), to his last:

Before my body
I throw my warlike shield. Lay on, Macduff:
And damned be him that first cries, "Hold, enough!" (5.8.32-34)

If we stand back and judge Macbeth only by what he does, we of course say that he is a foul murderer. But if we read the play attentively, or witness a performance, and give due weight to Macbeth's bravery, his role as a victim, his tormented conscience, his isolation, and especially his moving language, we do not simply judge him. Rather, we see that, villain though he is, he is not merely awful but also awesome.

[New page.]

Work Cited

Shakespeare, William. The Tragedy of Macbeth. Ed. Sylvan Barnet. Rev. ed. New York: NAL, 1987.

In history the tools are those of any thorough and efficient researcher, as discussed in Chapters 42–44: a system for finding and tracking sources; a methodical examination of sources, including evaluating and synthesizing them; a system for gathering source information; and a separate system, such as a research journal, for tracking one's own evolving thoughts.

2 Language considerations

Historians strive for precision and logic. They do not guess about what happened or speculate about "what if." They avoid trying to influence readers' opinions with words having strongly negative or positive connotations, such as *stupid* or *brilliant*. Instead, historians show the evidence and draw conclusions from that. Generally, they avoid using *I* because it tends to draw attention away from the evidence and toward the writer.

Writing about history demands some attention to the tenses of verbs to maintain consistency. Generally, historians use the past tense to refer to events that occurred in the past. They reserve the present tense only for statements about the present or statements of general truths. For example:

> Franklin Delano Roosevelt died in 1945. Many of Roosevelt's economic reforms persist in programs such as Social Security, unemployment compensation, and farm subsidies.

3 Research sources

The following lists give resources in the humanities. (Resources for literature appear on pp. 700–01.)

■ Specialized encyclopedias, dictionaries, and bibliographies

The arts

Architecture: From Prehistory to Post-Modernism
Dance Encyclopedia
Dictionary of Art
Encyclopedia of Pop, Rock, and Soul
Encyclopedia of World Art
Film Research: A Critical Bibliography
Film Review Annual
Guide to the Literature of Art History
International Cyclopedia of Music and Musicians
International Encyclopedia of Communications
International Television and Video Almanac
MLA International Bibliography of Books and Articles on the Modern Languages and Literatures
New Grove Dictionary of Music and Musicians
New Grove Dictionary of Opera
New Harvard Dictionary of Music

Oxford Companion to Twentieth-Century Art
Variety's Film Reviews

History

Afro-American Reference
American Heritage Encyclopedia of American History
American Indian Studies: A Bibliographic Guide
Cambridge Ancient History
Cambridge History of China
Dictionary of American History
Dictionary of American Immigration History
Dictionary of the Middle Ages
Encyclopedia of American History
Encyclopedia of Asian History
Encyclopedia of Latin-American History
Encyclopedia of World History
Guide to American Foreign Relations Since 1700
Harvard Guide to American History
History: Illustrated Search Strategy and Sources
Middle East Bibliography
Modern Encyclopedia of Russian and Soviet History
New Cambridge Modern History
Oxford Classical Dictionary
The Study of the Middle East: Research and Scholarship in the Humanities and Social Sciences

Philosophy and religion

Catholic Encyclopedia
Concise Encyclopedia of Islam
Dictionary of the History of Ideas
Encyclopedia Judaica
Encyclopedia of Asian Philosophy
Encyclopedia of Ethics
Encyclopedia of Philosophy
Encyclopedia of Religion
Interpreter's Dictionary of the Bible
Library Research Guide to Religion and Theology
New Standard Jewish Encyclopedia
Oxford Dictionary of the Christian Church
Research Guide to Philosophy

Indexes

America: History and Life
Art Index
Arts and Humanities Citation Index
Avery Index to Architectural Periodicals
Dissertation Abstracts International (doctoral dissertations)
Film Literature Index
Historical Abstracts
Humanities Index

Musical Literature International
Music Index
Philosopher's Index
Religion Index

Book reviews

Book Review Digest
Book Review Index

Web sources

For updates of these sources and URLs, visit *ablongman.com/littlebrown*.

General
Arts and Humanities Data Service (*ahds.ac.uk*)
BUBL Information Service (*bubl.ac.uk*)
EDSITEment (*edsitement.neh.gov*)
Humbul Humanities Hub (*humbul.ac.uk*)
Internet Public Library (*ipl.org/div/subject/browse/hum00.00.00*)
Librarians' Index to the Internet: Arts and Humanities (*lii.org/search/file/artscraftshum*)
Voice of the Shuttle Humanities (*vos.ucsb.edu*)

Art
Artnet (*artnet.com*)
BUBL Link: The Arts (*bubl.ac.uk/link/linkbrowse.cfm?menuid=9847*)
World Wide Arts Resources (*wwar.com/browse.html*)

Dance
BUBL Link: Dance (*bubl.ac.uk/link/d/dance.htm*)
Google Directory: Dance (*directory.google.com/Top/Arts/Performing_Arts/Dance*)

Film
CinemaSpot (*cinemaspot.com*)
Film Studies on the Internet (*www.ualberta.ca/~slis/guides/films/film.htm*)
Internet Movie Database (*imdb.com*)

History
British History Resources on the Internet (*libraries.rutgers.edu/rul/rr_gateway/research_guides/history.shtml*)
Best of History Web Sites (*besthistorysites.net*)
Librarians' Index to the Internet: History (*lii.org/search/file/history*)
National Women's History Project (*nwhp.org*)

Music
American Music Resource (*amrhome.net*)
MusicMoz (*musicmoz.org*)
Music Theory Online (*societymusictheory.org/mto*)
Web Resources for Research in Music (*www.music.ucc.ie/wrrm*)

Philosophy

Guide to Philosophy on the Internet (*www.earlham.edu/~peters/gpi*)
Philosophy Documentation Center (*pdcnet.org*)
Philosophy Pages (*philosophypages.com*)
Social Science Information Gateway: Philosophy (*sosig.ac.uk/philosophy*)

Religion

Academic Info: Religion Gateway (*academicinfo.net/religindex.html*)
Pluralism Project (*pluralism.org/directory/index.php*)
Religious Studies Web Guide (*www.acs.ucalgary.ca/~lipton*)
Virtual Religion Index (*religion.rutgers.edu/vri*)

Theater

McCoy's Brief Guide to Internet Resources in Theater and Performance Studies (*stetson.edu/departments/csata/thr_guid.html*)
Theater Connections (*uncc.edu/jvanoate/theater*)
TheatreHistory.com (*theatrehistory.com*)

51d Citing sources in Chicago style

Writers in the humanities generally rely on one of the following guides for source-citation style:

The Chicago Manual of Style, 15th ed., 2003
Joseph Gibaldi, *MLA Handbook for Writers of Research Papers,* 6th ed., 2003
Kate L. Turabian, *A Manual for Writers of Term Papers, Theses, and Dissertations,* 6th ed., rev. John Grossman and Alice Bennett, 1996

The recommendations of the *MLA Handbook* are discussed and illustrated in Chapter 47. Unless your teacher specifies otherwise, use these recommendations for papers in English and foreign languages. In history, art history, and many other disciplines, however, writers rely on *The Chicago Manual of Style* or the student reference adapted from it, *A Manual for Writers.*

Both books detail two documentation styles. One, used mainly by scientists and social scientists, closely resembles the style of the American Psychological Association, covered in Chapter 52. The other style, used more in the humanities, calls for footnotes or endnotes and an optional bibliography. This style is described below.

1 Using Chicago notes and a list of works cited

In the Chicago note style, a raised numeral in the text refers the reader to source information in endnotes or footnotes. In these notes, the first citation of each source contains all the information readers need to find the source. Thus your teacher may consider a

Note	Works-cited entry
Indent the first line five spaces.	Indent the second and subsequent lines five spaces.
Give the author's name in normal order.	Begin with the author's last name.
Use commas between elements such as author's name and title.	Use periods between elements.
Enclose publication information in parentheses, with no preceding punctuation	Precede the publication information with a period, and don't use parentheses.
Include the specific page number(s) you borrowed from, omitting "p." or "pp."	Omit page numbers except for parts of books or articles in periodicals.

You can instruct your computer to position footnotes at the bottoms of appropriate pages. It will also automatically number notes and renumber them if you add or delete one or more.

2 Following Chicago models

The Chicago models for common sources are indexed on the next page. The models show notes and works-cited entries together for easy reference. Be sure to use the numbered note form for notes and the unnumbered works-cited form for works-cited entries.

Books

1. A book with one, two, or three authors

1. Carol Gilligan, *In a Different Voice: Psychological Theory and Women's Development* (Cambridge: Harvard University Press, 1982), 27.

Gilligan, Carol. *In a Different Voice: Psychological Theory and Women's Development*. Cambridge: Harvard University Press, 1982.

1. Dennis L. Wilcox, Phillip H. Ault, and Warren K. Agee, *Public Relations: Strategies and Tactics,* 6th ed. (New York: Irwin, 2005), 182.

Wilcox, Dennis L., Phillip H. Ault, and Warren K. Agee. *Public Relations: Strategies and Tactics*. 6th ed. New York: Irwin, 2005.

2. A book with more than three authors

2. Geraldo Lopez and others, *China and the West* (Boston: Little, Brown, 2004), 461.

Lopez, Geraldo, Judith P. Salt, Anne Ming, and Henry Reisen. *China and the West.* Boston: Little, Brown, 2004.

3. A book with an editor

3. Hendrick Ruitenbeek, ed., *Freud as We Knew Him* (Detroit: Wayne State University Press, 1973), 64.

Chicago note and works-cited models

Ruitenbeek, Hendrick, ed. *Freud as We Knew Him*. Detroit: Wayne State University Press, 1973.

4. A book with an author and an editor

4. Lewis Mumford, *The City in History,* ed. Donald L. Miller (New York: Pantheon, 1986), 216-17.

Mumford, Lewis. *The City in History*. Edited by Donald L. Miller. New York: Pantheon, 1986.

5. A translation

5. Dante Alighieri, *The Inferno,* trans. John Ciardi (New York: New American Library, 1971), 51.

Alighieri, Dante. *The Inferno*. Translated by John Ciardi. New York: New American Library, 1971.

6. An anonymous work

6. *The Dorling Kindersley World Reference Atlas* (London: Dorling Kindersley, 2005), 150-51.

The Dorling Kindersley World Reference Atlas. London: Dorling Kindersley, 2005.

7. A later edition

7. Dwight L. Bolinger, *Aspects of Language,* 3rd ed. (New York: Harcourt Brace Jovanovich, 1981), 20.

Bolinger, Dwight L. *Aspects of Language*. 3rd ed. New York: Harcourt Brace Jovanovich, 1981.

8. A work in more than one volume

Citation of one volume without a title:

8. Abraham Lincoln, *The Collected Works of Abraham Lincoln,* ed. Roy P. Basler (New Brunswick: Rutgers University Press, 1953), 5:426-28.

Lincoln, Abraham. *The Collected Works of Abraham Lincoln*. Edited by Roy P. Basler. Vol. 5. New Brunswick: Rutgers University Press, 1953.

Citation of one volume with a title:

8. Linda B. Welkin, *The Age of Balanchine,* vol. 3 of *The History of Ballet* (New York: Columbia University Press, 1999), 56.

Welkin, Linda B. *The Age of Balanchine*. Vol. 3 of *The History of Ballet*. New York: Columbia University Press, 1999.

9. A selection from an anthology

9. Rosetta Brooks, "Streetwise," in *The New Urban Landscape,* ed. Richard Martin (New York: Rizzoli, 2005), 38-39.

Brooks, Rosetta. "Streetwise." In *The New Urban Landscape,* ed. Richard Martin, 37-60. New York: Rizzoli, 2005.

10. A work in a series

10. Ingmar Bergman, *The Seventh Seal,* Modern Film Scripts, no. 12 (New York: Simon and Schuster, 1995), 27.

Bergman, Ingmar. *The Seventh Seal*. Modern Film Scripts, no. 12. New York: Simon and Schuster, 1995.

11. An article in a reference work

11. *Merriam-Webster's Collegiate Dictionary,* 11th ed., s.v. "reckon."

Merriam-Webster's Collegiate Dictionary, 11th ed. S.v. "reckon."

As in the example, use the abbreviation s.v. (Latin *sub verbo,* "under the word") for reference works that are alphabetically arranged. Well-known works like the one listed here do not need publication information except for edition number. Chicago style generally recommends notes only, not works-cited entries, for reference works; a works-cited model is given here in case your instructor requires such entries.

■ Periodicals: Journals, magazines, newspapers

12. An article in a journal

12. Janet Lever, "Sex Differences in the Games Children Play," *Social Problems* 23 (1996): 482.

Lever, Janet. "Sex Differences in the Games Children Play." *Social Problems* 23 (1996): 478-87.

Provide the issue number if the journal numbers issues. The issue number is required for any journal that pages each issue separately or that numbers only issues, not volumes:

12. June Dacey, "Management Participation in Corporate Buy-Outs," *Management Perspectives* 7, no. 4 (1998): 22.

Dacey, June. "Management Participation in Corporate Buy-Outs." *Management Perspectives* 7, no. 4 (1998): 20-31.

13. An article in a magazine

13. Mark Stevens, "Low and Behold," *New Republic,* December 24, 2005, 28.

Stevens, Mark. "Low and Behold." *New Republic,* December 24, 2005, 27-33.

Chicago works-cited style does not require inclusive page numbers for magazine articles, so 27-33 could be omitted from the preceding example.

14. An article in a newspaper

14. Gina Kolata, "Kill All the Bacteria!" *New York Times,* January 7, 2006, national edition, B1.

Kolata, Gina. "Kill All the Bacteria!" *New York Times,* January 7, 2006, national edition, B1, B6.

Chicago style does not require page numbers for newspaper citations, whether in notes or in works-cited entries. Thus B1 and B1, B6 could be omitted from the above examples.

15. A review

15. John Gregory Dunne, "The Secret of Danny Santiago," review of *Famous All over Town,* by Danny Santiago, *New York Review of Books,* August 16, 1994, 25.

Dunne, John Gregory. "The Secret of Danny Santiago." Review of *Famous All over Town,* by Danny Santiago. *New York Review of Books,* August 16, 1994, 17-27.

Electronic sources

The Chicago Manual's models for documenting electronic sources derive mainly from those for print sources, with the addition of an electronic address (URL) or other indication of the medium along with any other information that may help readers locate the source. Chicago requires the date of your access to an online source only if the source could change significantly (for instance, a report on medical research). However, your teacher may require access dates for a broader range of online sources, so they are included in the following models (in parentheses at the end).

Note Chicago style allows many ways to break URLs between the end of one line and the beginning of the next: after slashes, before most punctuation marks (periods, commas, question marks, and so on), and before or after equal signs and ampersands (&). *Do not* break after a hyphen or add any hyphens.

16. A work on CD-ROM or DVD-ROM

16. *The American Heritage Dictionary of the English Language,* 4th ed., CD-ROM (Boston: Houghton Mifflin, 2000).

The American Heritage Dictionary of the English Language. 4th ed. CD-ROM. Boston: Houghton Mifflin, 2000.

17. A work from an online database

17. Irina Netchaeva, "E-Government and E-Democracy," *International Journal for Communication Studies* 64 (2002): 470-71, http://www.epnet.com (accessed December 20, 2005).

Netchaeva, Irina. "E-Government and E-Democracy." *International Journal for Communication Studies* 64 (2002): 467-78. http://www.epnet.com (accessed December 20, 2005).

For news and journal databases, including those to which your library subscribes, you may omit the name of the database. Give its main URL (as in the examples) unless the work has a usable URL of its own. (See p. 649 for more on database URLs.)

18. An online book

18. Jane Austen, *Emma*, ed. R. W. Chapman (1816; Oxford: Clarendon, 1926; Oxford Text Archive, 2004), chap. 1, http://ota.ahds.ac.uk/Austen/Emma.1519 (accessed December 15, 2005).

Austen, Jane. *Emma*. Edited by R. W. Chapman. 1816. Oxford: Clarendon, 1926. Oxford Text Archive, 2004. http://ota.ahds.ac.uk/Austen/Emma.1519 (accessed December 15, 2005).

19. An article in an online journal

19. Andrew Palfrey, "Choice of Mates in Identical Twins," *Modern Psychology* 4, no. 1 (2003): 28, http://www.liasu/edu/modpsy/palfrey4(1).htm (accessed February 25, 2006).

Palfrey, Andrew. "Choice of Mates in Identical Twins." *Modern Psychology* 4, no. 1 (2003): 26-40. http://www.liasu/edu/modpsy/palfrey4(1).htm (accessed February 25, 2006).

20. An article in an online magazine

20. Ricki Lewis, "The Return of Thalidomide," *Scientist,* January 22, 2001, http://www.the-scientist.com/yr2001/jan/lewis_pl_010122.html (accessed January 24, 2006).

Lewis, Ricki. "The Return of Thalidomide." *Scientist,* January 22, 2001. http://www.the-scientist.com/yr2001/jan/lewis_pl_010122.html (accessed January 24, 2006).

21. An article in an online newspaper

21. Lucia Still, "On the Battlefields of Business, Millions of Casualties," *New York Times on the Web,* March 3, 2005, http://www.nytimes.com/specials/downsize/03down1.html (accessed August 17, 2005).

Still, Lucia. "On the Battlefields of Business, Millions of Casualties." *New York Times on the Web,* March 3, 2005. http://www.nytimes.com/specials/downsize/03down1.html (accessed August 17, 2005).

22. An article in an online reference work

22. *Encyclopaedia Britannica Online,* s.v. "Wu-ti," http://www.eb.com:80 (accessed December 23, 2005).

Encyclopaedia Britannica Online. S.v. "Wu-ti." http://www.eb.com:80 (accessed December 23, 2005).

23. An online audio or visual source

A work of art:

23. Jackson Pollock, *Shimmering Substance,* oil on canvas, 1946, Museum of Modern Art, New York, WebMuseum, http://www.ibiblio.org/wm/paint/auth/Pollock/pollock.shimmering.jpg (accessed March 12, 2006).

Pollock, Jackson. *Shimmering Substance.* Oil on canvas, 1946. Museum of Modern Art, New York. WebMuseum. http://www.ibiblio.org/wm/paint/auth/Pollock/pollock.shimmering.jpg (accessed March 12, 2006).

A sound recording:

23. Ronald W. Reagan, State of the Union Address, January 26, 1982, Vincent Voice Library, Digital and Multimedia Center, University of Michigan, http://www.lib.msu.edu/vincent/presidents/reagan.html (accessed May 6, 2005).

Reagan, Ronald W. State of the Union Address. January 26, 1982. Vincent Voice Library. Digital and Multimedia Center, University of Michigan. http://www.lib.msu.edu/vincent/presidents/reagan.html (accessed May 6, 2005).

A film or film clip:

23. Leslie J. Stewart, *96 Ranch Rodeo and Barbecue* (1951), 16mm, from Library of Congress, *Buckaroos in Paradise: Ranching Culture in Northern Nevada, 1945-1982,* MPEG, http://lcweb2.loc.gov/ammem/afc96ran_v034 (accessed January 7, 2006).

Stewart, Leslie J. *96 Ranch Rodeo and Barbecue*. 1951, 16 mm. From Library of Congress, *Buckaroos in Paradise: Ranching Culture in Northern Nevada, 1945-1982.* MPEG. http://lcweb2.loc.gov/ammem/afc96ran_v034 (accessed January 7, 2006).

24. An entry on a Web log or posting to a discussion group

24. Susheel Daswani, "Hollywood vs. Silicon Valley," Berkeley Intellectual Property Weblog, March 16, 2005, http://www.biplog.com/archive/cat_hollywood.html (accessed August 22, 2005).

Daswani, Susheel. "Hollywood vs. Silicon Valley." Berkeley Intellectual Property Weblog. March 16, 2005. http://www.biplog.com/archive/cat_hollywood.html (accessed August 22, 2005).

24. Michael Tourville, "European Currency Reform," e-mail to International Finance Discussion List, January 6, 2006, http://www.weg.isu.edu/finance-dl/archive/46732 (accessed January 12, 2006).

Tourville, Michael. "European Currency Reform." E-mail to International Finance Discussion List. January 6, 2006. http://www.weg.isu.edu/finance-dl/archive/46732 (accessed January 12, 2006).

25. Electronic mail

25. Michele Millon, "Re: Grief Therapy," e-mail message to author, May 4, 2005.

Millon, Michele. "Re: Grief Therapy." E-mail message to author. May 4, 2005.

Other sources

26. A government publication

26. House Committee on Ways and Means, *Medicare Payment for Outpatient Physical and Occupational Therapy Services,* 108th Cong., 1st sess., 2003, H. Doc. 409, 12-13.

U.S. Congress. House. Committee on Ways and Means. *Medicare Payment for Outpatient Physical and Occupational Therapy Services*. 108th Cong., 1st sess., 2003. H. Doc. 409.

26. Hawaii Department of Education, *Kauai District Schools, Profile 2004-05* (Honolulu, 2005), 27.

Hawaii. Department of Education. *Kauai District Schools, Profile 2004-05.* Honolulu, 2005.

27. A published letter

27. Mrs. Laura E. Buttolph to Rev. and Mrs. C. C. Jones, June 20, 1857, in *The Children of Pride: A True Story of Georgia and the Civil War,* ed. Robert Manson Myers (New Haven, CT: Yale University Press, 1972), 334.

Buttolph, Laura E. Mrs. Laura E. Buttolph to Rev. and Mrs. C. C. Jones, June 20, 1857. In *The Children of Pride: A True Story of Georgia and the Civil War,* edited by Robert Manson Myers. New Haven, CT: Yale University Press, 1972.

28. A published or broadcast interview

28. Donald Rumsfeld, interview by William Lindon, *Frontline,* PBS, October 13, 2005.

Rumsfeld, Donald. Interview by William Lindon. *Frontline*. PBS, October 13, 2005.

29. A personal letter or interview

29. Ann E. Packer, letter to author, June 15, 2005.

Packer, Ann E. Letter to author. June 15, 2005.

29. Vera Graaf, interview by author, December 19, 2005.

Graaf, Vera. Interview by author. December 19, 2005.

30. A work of art

30. John Singer Sargent, *In Switzerland,* watercolor, 1908, Metropolitan Museum of Art, New York.

Sargent, John Singer. *In Switzerland*. Watercolor, 1908. Metropolitan Museum of Art, New York.

31. A film, DVD, or video recording

31. George Balanchine, *Serenade,* DVD, San Francisco Ballet (New York: PBS Video, 2003).

Balanchine, George. *Serenade*. DVD. San Francisco Ballet. New York: PBS Video, 2003.

32. A sound recording

32. Johannes Brahms, Piano Concerto no. 2 in B-flat, Artur Rubinstein, Philadelphia Orchestra, Eugene Ormandy, compact disc, RCA BRC4-6731.

Brahms, Johannes. Piano Concerto no. 2 in B-flat. Artur Rubinstein. Philadelphia Orchestra. Eugene Ormandy. Compact disc. RCA BRC4-6731.

Shortened notes

To streamline documentation, Chicago style recommends shortened notes for sources that are fully cited elsewhere, either in a complete list of works cited or in previous notes. Ask your instructor whether your paper should include a list of works cited and, if so, whether you may use shortened notes for first references to sources as well as for subsequent references.

A shortened note contains the author's last name, the work's title (minus any initial *A*, *An*, or *The*), and the page number. Reduce long titles to four or fewer key words.

Complete note

8. Janet Lever, "Sex Differences in the Games Children Play," *Social Problems* 23 (1996): 482.

Complete works-cited entry

Lever, Janet. "Sex Differences in the Games Children Play." *Social Problems* 23 (1996): 478-87.

Shortened note

12. Lever, "Sex Differences," 483.

You may use the Latin abbreviation ibid. (meaning "in the same place") to refer to the same source cited in the preceding note. Give a page number if it differs from that in the preceding note.

12. Lever, "Sex Differences," 483.

13. Gilligan, *In a Different Voice,* 92.

14. Ibid., 93.

15. Lever, "Sex Differences," 483.

Chicago style allows for in-text parenthetical citations when you cite one or more works repeatedly. In the following example, the raised number 2 refers to the source information in a note; the number in parentheses is a page number in the same source.

British rule, observes Stuart Cary Welch, "seemed as permanent as Mount Everest."[2] Most Indians submitted, willingly or not, to British influence in every facet of life (42).

CHAPTER 52

Writing in the Social Sciences

The social sciences—including anthropology, economics, education, management, political science, psychology, and sociology—focus on the study of human behavior. As the name implies, the social sciences examine the way human beings relate to themselves, to their environment, and to one another.

52a Using the methods and evidence of the social sciences

Researchers in the social sciences systematically pose a question, formulate a **hypothesis** (a generalization that can be tested), collect data, analyze those data, and draw conclusions to support, refine, or disprove their hypothesis. This is the scientific method developed in the natural sciences (see p. 762).

Social scientists gather data in several ways:

- **They make firsthand observations of human behavior,** recording the observations in writing or on audio- or videotape.
- **They interview subjects about their attitudes and behavior,** recording responses in writing or on tape. (See pp. 586–87 for guidelines on conducting an interview.)
- **They conduct broader surveys using questionnaires,** asking people about their attitudes and behavior. (See the box on the next page.)
- **They conduct controlled experiments,** structuring an environment in which to encourage and measure a specific behavior.

In their writing, social scientists explain their own research or analyze and evaluate others' research.

To avoid confusing your reflections on the evidence with the evidence itself, keep records of actual data—notes from interviews, observations, surveys, and experiments—separately from the journal.

2 Language considerations

Each social science discipline has specialized terminology for concepts basic to the discipline. In sociology, for example, the words *mechanism, identity,* and *deviance* have specific meanings different from those of everyday usage. And *identity* means something different in sociology, where it applies to groups of people, than in psychology, where it applies to the individual. Social scientists also use precise terms to describe or interpret research. For instance, they say *The subject expressed a feeling of* rather than *The subject felt* because human feelings are not knowable for certain; or they say *These studies indicate* rather than *These studies prove* because conclusions are only tentative.

Just as social scientists strive for objectivity in their research, so they strive to demonstrate their objectivity through language in their writing. They avoid expressions such as *I think* in order to focus attention on what the evidence shows, not the researcher's opinions. (However, many social scientists prefer *I* to *the researcher* when they refer to their own actions, as in *I then interviewed the subjects.* Ask your instructor for his or her preferences.) Social scientists also avoid direct or indirect expression of their personal biases or emotions, either in discussions of other researchers' work or in descriptions of research subjects. Thus one social scientist does not call another's work *sloppy* or *immaculate* and does not refer to his or her own subjects as *drunks* or *innocent victims.* Instead, the writer uses neutral language and ties conclusions strictly to the data.

3 Research sources

Specialized encyclopedias, dictionaries, and bibliographies

General

International Bibliography of the Social Sciences
International Encyclopedia of the Social and Behavioral Sciences
The Social Science Encyclopedia

Business and economics

Accountant's Handbook
Dictionary of Business and Economics
Encyclopedia of Advertising
Encyclopedia of Banking and Finance
Encyclopedia of Business Information Sources
Encyclopedia of Management
Handbook of Modern Marketing

McGraw-Hill Encyclopedia of Economics
The MIT Dictionary of Modern Economics
The New Palgrave Dictionary of Economics and the Law

Education
Bibliographic Guide to Education
Encyclopedia of American Education
Encyclopedia of Education
Encyclopedia of Educational Research
The Philosophy of Education: An Encyclopedia

Political science and law
Black's Law Dictionary
Guide to American Law
Index to Legal Periodicals and Books
Information Sources of Political Sciences
Political Science: A Guide to Reference and Information Sources

Psychology, sociology, and anthropology
African American Encyclopedia
Afro-American Reference
Asian American Studies
Bibliographic Guide to Psychology
Encyclopedia of Anthropology
Encyclopedia of Crime and Justice
Encyclopedia of Psychology
Encyclopedia of Sociology
Guide to Research on North American Indians
Library Use: A Handbook for Psychology
Macmillan Dictionary of Anthropology
A Native American Encyclopedia: History, Culture, and Peoples
Race and Ethnic Relations: A Bibliography
Sociology: A Guide to Reference and Information Sources
Sourcebook of Hispanic Culture in the United States

Indexes

ABC: Pol Sci
ABI/INFORM (business)
Abstracts in Anthropology
Business Periodicals Index
Business Publications Index and Abstracts
Business Source Premier
Criminal Justice Periodicals Index
Dissertation Abstracts International (doctoral dissertations)
EconLit
Education Index
ERIC, *Current Index to Journals in Education*
Human Resources Abstracts
Index to Legal Periodicals
International Political Science Abstracts

Journal of Economic Literature
PAIS International in Print (government publications and political science journals)
PsychInfo
PsychLIT
Psychological Abstracts
Social Sciences Index
Sociofile
Sociological Abstracts
Urban Affairs Abstracts
Wilson Business Abstracts

Book reviews

Index to Book Reviews in the Social Sciences

Web sources

For updates of these sources and URLs, visit *ablongman.com/littlebrown*.

General

Data on the Net (*odwin.ucsd.edu/idata*)
Social Science Information Gateway (*sosig.ac.uk*)
WWW Virtual Library: Social and Behavorial Sciences (*vlib.org/SocialSciences*)

Anthropology

American Anthropological Association (*aaanet.org*)
American Folklife Center (*loc.gov/folklife*)
Anthro.Net (*anthro.net*)
Anthropology Resources on the Internet (*anthropologie.net*)

Business and economics

Biz/ed (*bized.ac.uk*)
Academic Info: Business Administration (*academicinfo.net/bus.html*)
Resources for Economists on the Internet (*rfe.org*)
Virtual International Business and Economic Sources (*library.uncc.edu/display/?dept=reference&format=open&page=68*)

Education

Education Reference Desk (*eduref.org*)
Gateway to Educational Materials (*thegateway.org*)
Learner.org (*learner.org*)
Social Science Information Gateway: Education (*sosig.ac.uk/roads/subject-listing/World/educ.html*)
US Department of Education (*ed.gov*)

Ethnic and gender studies

Diversity and Ethnic Studies (*public.iastate.edu/~savega/divweb2.htm*)
Diversity Database (*inform.umd.edu/EdRes/Topic/Diversity*)
Voice of the Shuttle: Gender Studies (*vos.ucsb.edu/browse.asp?id=2711*)
Gender Inn (*www.uni-koeln.de/phil-fak/englisch/datenbank/e_index.htm*)

Political science and law

Legal Information Institute (*www.law.cornell.edu*)
Librarians' Index to the Internet: Law (*lii.org/search/file/law*)
Oyez: US Supreme Court Multimedia (*www.oyez.org*)
Political Science Resources (*psr.keele.ac.uk*)
Thomas Legislative Information on the Internet (*thomas.loc.gov*)
Ultimate Political Science Links (*www.rvc.cc.il.us/faclink/pruckman/PSLinks.htm*)

Psychology

Encyclopedia of Psychology (*www.psychology.org*)
PsychCrawler (*www.psychcrawler.com*)
Psychology: Online Resource Central (*psych-central.com*)
Psych Web (*psywww.com*)

Sociology

Social Science Information Gateway: Sociology (*sosig.ac.uk/roads/subject-listing/World/sociol.html*)
SocioSite (*www2.fmg.uva.nl/sociosite*)
SocioWeb (*socioweb.com*)
WWW Virtual Library: Sociology (*socserv2.socsci.mcmaster.ca/w3virtsoclib*)

52d Citing sources in APA style

Some of the social sciences publish style guides that advise practitioners how to organize, document, and type papers. The following is a partial list:

American Anthropological Association, *AAA Style Guide*, 2002, *http://www.aaanet.org/pubs/style_guide.htm*
American Political Science Association, *Style Manual for Political Science*, 2001
American Psychological Association, *Publication Manual of the American Psychological Association*, 5th ed., 2001
American Sociological Association, *ASA Style Guide*, 2nd ed., 1997
Linguistic Society of America, "LSA Style Sheet," published every December in *LSA Bulletin*
A Uniform System of Citation (law), 17th ed., 2001

By far the most widely used style is that of the American Psychological Association (APA), so we detail it here. Always ask your instructor in any discipline what style you should use.

Note If you use APA style frequently and write on a computer, you may want to obtain *APA-Style Helper*, a student's companion to the *Publication Manual of the American Psychological Association* that formats source citations in APA style. It can be downloaded (for a fee) from the APA Web site at *apa.org/software*. Other bibliography programs can also help with APA style. See page 619.

1 Using APA parenthetical text citations

In the APA documentation style, parenthetical citations within the text refer the reader to a list of sources at the end of the text. A parenthetical citation contains the author's last name, the date of publication, and sometimes the page number from which material is borrowed.

1. Author not named in your text

One critic of Milgram's experiments insisted that the subjects "should have been fully informed of the possible effects on them" (Baumrind, 1988, p. 34).

When you do not name the author in your text, place in parentheses the author's last name and the date of the source. Separate the elements with commas. Position the reference so that it is clear what material is being documented *and* so that the reference fits as smoothly as possible into your sentence structure. (See pp. 630–32 for guidelines.) The following would also be correct:

In the view of one critic of Milgram's experiments (Baumrind, 1988), the subjects "should have been fully informed of the possible effects on them" (p. 34).

Unless none is available, the APA requires a page or other identifying number for a direct quotation (as in the preceding examples) and recommends an identifying number for a paraphrase. Use an appropriate abbreviation or symbol before the number—for instance, p. for *page* and ¶ for *paragraph* (or para. if you do not have the symbol). The identifying number may fall with the author and date (first example) or by itself in a separate pair of parentheses (second example). See also model 11, page 743.

2. Author named in your text

Baumrind (1988) insisted that the subjects in Milgram's study "should have been fully informed of the possible effects on them" (p. 34).

APA parenthetical text citations

When you use the author's name in the text, do not repeat it in the reference. Place the source date in parentheses after the author's name. Place any page or paragraph reference either after the borrowed material (as in the example) or with the date: (1988, p. 34). If you cite the same source again in the paragraph, you need not repeat the reference as long as it is clear that you are using the same source and the page number (if any) is the same. Here is a later sentence from the paragraph containing the preceding example:

> Baumrind also criticized the experimenters' rationale.

3. A work with two authors

> Pepinsky and DeStefano (1997) demonstrated that a teacher's language often reveals hidden biases.

> One study (Pepinsky & DeStefano, 1997) demonstrated the hidden biases often revealed in a teacher's language.

When given in the text, two authors' names are connected by and. In a parenthetical citation, they are connected by an ampersand, &.

4. A work with three to five authors

> Pepinsky, Dunn, Rentl, and Corson (1999) further demonstrated the biases evident in gestures.

In the first citation of a work with three to five authors, name all the authors, as in the example above.

In the second and subsequent references to a work with three to five authors, generally give only the first author's name, followed by et al. (Latin abbreviation for "and others"):

> In the work of Pepinsky et al. (1999), the loaded gestures included head shakes and eye contact.

However, two or more sources published in the same year could shorten to the same form—for instance, two references shortening to Pepinsky et al., 1999. In that case, cite the last names of as many authors as you need to distinguish the sources, and then give et al.: for instance, (Pepinsky, Dunn, et al., 1999) and (Pepinsky, Bradley, et al., 1999).

5. A work with six or more authors

> One study (Rutter et al., 2003) attempted to explain these geographical differences in adolescent experience.

For six or more authors, even in the first citation of the work, give only the first author's name, followed by et al. If two or more sources published in the same year shorten to the same form, give additional names as explained with model 4.

6. A work with a group author

An earlier prediction was even more somber (Lorenz Research, 2003).

For a work that lists an institution, agency, corporation, or other group as author, treat the name of the group as if it were an individual's name. If the name is long and has a familiar abbreviation, you may use the abbreviation in the second and subsequent citations. For example, you might abbreviate American Psychological Association as APA.

7. A work with no author or an anonymous work

One article ("Right to Die," 1996) noted that a death-row inmate may crave notoriety.

For a work with no named author, use the first two or three words of the title in place of an author's name, excluding an initial *The, A,* or *An.* Italicize book and journal titles, place quotation marks around article titles, and capitalize the significant words in all titles cited in the text. (In the reference list, however, do not use quotation marks for article titles, and capitalize only the first word in all but periodical titles. See pp. 743 and 744.)

For a work that lists "Anonymous" as the author, use this word in the citation: (Anonymous, 1999).

8. One of two or more works by the same author(s)

At about age seven, most children begin to use appropriate gestures to reinforce their stories (Gardner, 1973a).

When you cite one of two or more works by the same author(s), the date will tell readers which source you mean—as long as your reference list includes only one source published by the author(s) in that year. If your reference list includes two or more works published by the same author(s) *in the same year,* the works should be lettered in the reference list (see p. 747). Then your parenthetical citation should include the appropriate letter: 1973a in the preceding example.

9. Two or more works by different authors

Two studies (Herskowitz, 1994; Marconi & Hamblen, 1999) found that periodic safety instruction can dramatically reduce employees' accidents.

List the sources in alphabetical order by their authors' names. Insert a semicolon between sources.

10. An indirect source

Supporting data appeared in a study by Wong (cited in Marconi, 2004).

The phrase cited in indicates that the reference to Wong's study was found in Marconi. Only Marconi then appears in the list of references.

11. An electronic source

Ferguson and Hawkins (2002) did not anticipate the "evident hostility" of participants (¶ 6).

Electronic sources can be cited like printed sources, usually with the author's last name and the publication date. When quoting or paraphrasing electronic sources that number paragraphs instead of pages, provide the paragraph number preceded by the symbol ¶ if you have it, or by para. Even if the source does not number its paragraphs, you can still direct readers to a specific location by listing the heading under which the quotation appears and then (counting paragraphs yourself) the number of the paragraph in which the quotation appears—for example, (Morrison & Lee, 2004, Method section, ¶ 4). When the source does not number pages or paragraphs or provide frequent headings, omit any reference number.

2 Using an APA reference list

In APA style, the in-text parenthetical citations refer to the list of sources at the end of the text. This list, titled References, includes full publication information on every source cited in the paper. The list falls at the end of the paper, numbered in sequence with the preceding pages.

The following sample shows the format of the first page of the APA reference list:

APA reference list

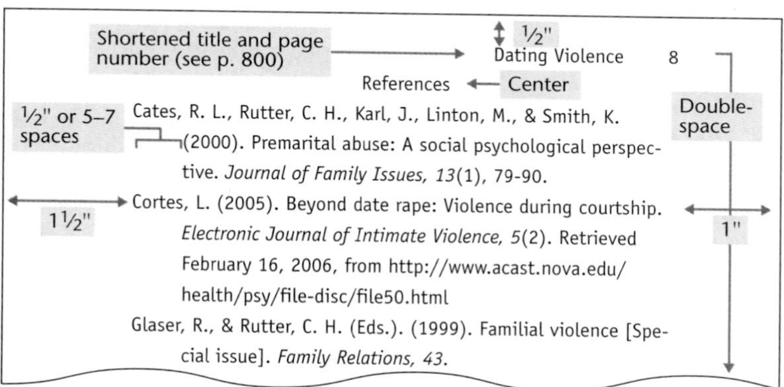

Arrangement Arrange sources alphabetically by the author's last name. If there is no author, alphabetize by the first main word of the title.

Spacing Double-space everything in the references, as shown in the sample, unless your instructor requests single spacing. (If you do single-space the entries themselves, always double-space *between* them.)

Indention As illustrated in the sample, begin each entry at the left margin, and indent the second and subsequent lines five to seven spaces or one-half inch. See page 634 for instructions on creating this so-called hanging indent on your word processor.

Punctuation Separate the parts of the reference (author, date, title, and publication information) with a period and one space. Do not use a final period in references to electronic sources, which conclude with an electronic address (see pp. 750–52).

Authors For works with up to six authors, list all authors with last name first, separating names and parts of names with commas. Use initials for first and middle names even when names are listed fully on the source itself. Use an ampersand (&) before the last author's name. See model 3, page 746, for the treatment of seven or more authors.

Publication date Place the publication date in parentheses after the author's or authors' names, followed by a period. Generally, this date is the year only, though for some sources (such as magazine and newspaper articles) it includes month and sometimes day as well.

Titles In titles of books and articles, capitalize only the first word of the title, the first word of the subtitle, and proper nouns; all other words begin with small letters. In titles of journals, capitalize all significant words (see p. 493 for guidelines). Italicize the titles of books and journals. Do not italicize or use quotation marks around the titles of articles.

City of publication For sources that are not periodicals (such as books or government publications), give the city of publication. The following US cities do not require state names as well: Baltimore, Boston, Chicago, Los Angeles, New York, Philadelphia, and San Francisco. Follow their names with a colon. For most other cities, add a comma after the city name, give the two-letter postal abbreviation of the state, and then add a colon. (You may omit the state if the publisher is a university whose name includes the state name, such as University of Arizona.)

Publisher's name Also for nonperiodical sources, give the publisher's name after the place of publication and a colon. Use shortened names for many publishers (such as Morrow for William Morrow), and omit *Co.*, *Inc.*, and *Publishers.* However, give full names for associations, corporations, and university presses (such as Harvard University Press), and do not omit *Books* or *Press* from a publisher's name.

Page numbers Use the abbreviation p. or pp. before page numbers in books and in newspapers. Do *not* use the abbreviation for journals and magazines. For inclusive page numbers, include all figures: 667–668.

If the following pages don't provide a model for a kind of source you used, try to find one that comes close, and provide ample information so that readers can trace the source. Often, you will have to combine models to cite a source accurately—for instance, combining

APA reference-list models

Books

Periodicals

Electronic sources

Other sources

The first entry cites a single volume (5) in the eight-volume set. The second cites all eight volumes. Use the abbreviation Vol. or Vols. in parentheses, and follow the closing parenthesis with a period. In the absence of an editor's name, the description of volumes would follow the title directly: *The collected works of Abraham Lincoln* (Vol. 5).

11. An article or chapter in an edited book

Paykel, E. S. (1999). Life stress and psychiatric disorder: Applications of the clinical approach. In B. S. Dohrenwend & B. P. Dohrenwend (Eds.), *Stressful life events: Their nature and effects* (pp. 239-264). New York: Wiley.

Give the publication date of the collection (1999 above) as the publication date of the article or chapter. After the article or chapter title and a period, say In and then provide the editors' names (in normal order), (Eds.) and a comma, the title of the collection, and the page numbers of the article in parentheses.

Periodicals: Journals, magazines, newspapers

12. An article in a journal with continuous pagination throughout the annual volume

Emery, R. E. (2005). Marital turmoil: Interpersonal conflict and the children of discord and divorce. *Psychological Bulletin, 92,* 310-330.

See page 644 for an explanation of journal pagination. Note that you do not place the article title in quotation marks and that you capitalize only the first words of the title and subtitle. In contrast, you italicize the journal title and capitalize all significant words. Separate the volume number from the title with a comma, and italicize the number. Do not add "pp." before the page numbers.

13. An article in a journal that pages issues separately

Dacey, J. (1998). Management participation in corporate buy-outs. *Management Perspectives, 7*(4), 20-31.

Consult page 644 for an explanation of journal pagination. In this case, place the issue number in parentheses after the volume number without intervening space. Do *not* italicize the issue number.

14. An abstract of a journal article

Emery, R. E. (2005). Marital turmoil: Interpersonal conflict and the children of discord and divorce. *Psychological Bulletin, 92,* 310-330. Abstract obtained from *Psychological Abstracts*, 2005, *69*, Item 1320.

When you cite the abstract of an article, rather than the article itself, give full publication information for the article, followed by

Abstract obtained from and the information for the collection of abstracts, including title, date, volume number, and either page number or other reference number (Item 1320 in the example).

15. An article in a magazine

Williams, N. (2005, October 24). Beethoven's late quartets. *The New York Review of Books*, 16-18.

If a magazine has volume and issue numbers, give them as in models 12 and 13. Also give the full date of the issue: year, followed by a comma, month, and day (if any). Give all page numbers even when the article appears on discontinuous pages, without "pp."

16. An article in a newspaper

Kolata, G. (2006, January 7). Kill all the bacteria! *The New York Times*, pp. B1, B6.

Give month *and* day along with year of publication. Use *The* in the newspaper name if the paper itself does. Precede the page number(s) with p. or pp.

17. An unsigned article

The right to die. (1996, October 11). *Time, 121*, 101.

List and alphabetize the article under its title, as you would a book with no author (model 7, p. 747).

18. A review

Dinnage, R. (1987, November 29). Against the master and his men [Review of the book *A mind of her own: The life of Karen Horney*]. *The New York Times Book Review*, 10-11.

If the review is not titled, use the bracketed information as the title, keeping the brackets.

■ Electronic sources

In general, the APA's electronic-source references begin as those for print references do: author(s), date, title. Then you add information on when and where you retrieved the source—for example, an online source might end Retrieved January 8, 2006, from http://www.isu.edu/finance-dl/46732 (in APA style, no period follows a URL at the end of the reference).

Using the following models for electronic sources, you may have to improvise to match your source to a model. Try to locate all the information required by a model, referring to the sample sources on pages 567–69 for help. However, if you search for and still cannot find some information, then give what you can find. If a source has no publication date, use n.d. (for *no date*) in place of a publication date (see model 28, p. 751).

Note When you need to divide a URL from one line to the next, APA style calls for breaking *only* after a slash or before a period. Do not hyphenate a URL.

19. A journal article that is published online and in print

Palfrey, A. (2003). Choice of mates in identical twins [Electronic version]. *Modern Psychology, 4*(1), 26-40.

If you consulted the online version of a journal article that appears the same way both online and in print, follow model 12 or 13 (p. 748) for a print journal article, and insert [Electronic version] between the article title and the following period.

If you believe that the online version you consulted differs in some way from the print version, omit the bracketed insert and provide a retrieval statement with the date of your access and the complete URL for the article:

Grady, G. F. (2003). The here and now of hepatitis B immunization. *Today's Medicine, 13*, 145-151. Retrieved December 27, 2005, from http://www.fmrt.org/todaysmedicine/Grady050203.html

20. An article in an online journal

Wissink, J. A. (2004). Techniques of smoking cessation among teens and adults. *Adolescent Medicine, 2*. Retrieved August 16, 2005, from http://www.easu.edu/AdolescentMedicine/2-Wissink.html

If the article has an identifying number, give it after the volume number and a comma.

21. A journal article retrieved from an electronic database

Wilkins, J. M. (1999). The myths of the only child. *Psychology Update, 11*(1), 16-23. Retrieved December 20, 2005, from ProQuest Direct database.

Many reference works and periodicals are available full-text from electronic databases to which your library subscribes, such as ProQuest Direct or LexisNexis. Your reference need not specify how you reached the database—for instance, through a Web site or on a CD-ROM. However, it should provide the appropriate information for the source itself—in the example here, for a journal article—and it should conclude with a retrieval statement giving the date of your access and the name of the database.

22. An abstract retrieved from an electronic database

Wilkins, J. M. (1999). The myths of the only child. *Psychology Update, 11*(1), 16-23. Abstract retrieved December 20, 2005, from ProQuest Direct database.

23. An article in an online newspaper

Pear, R. (2006, January 23). Gains reported for children of welfare to work families. *The New York Times on the Web*. Retrieved January 23, 2006, from http://www.nytimes.com/2006/01/23/national/23/WELF.html

24. An entire Web site (text citation)

The APA's Web site provides answers to frequently asked questions about style (http://www.apa.org).

Cite an entire Web site (rather than a specific page or document) by giving the URL in your text.

25. An independent document on the Web

Anderson, D. (2005, May 1). *Social constructionism and MOOs*. Retrieved August 6, 2005, from http://sites.unc.edu/~daniel/social_constructionism

Treat the title of an independent Web document like the title of a book. If the document has no named author, begin with the title and place the publication date after the title.

26. A document from the Web site of a university or government agency

McConnell, L. M., Koenig, B. A., Greeley, H. T., & Raffin, T. A. (2004, August 17). *Genetic testing and Alzheimer's disease: Has the time come?* Retrieved September 1, 2005, from Stanford University, Project in Genomics, Ethics, and Society Web site: http://scbe.stanford.edu/pges

Provide the name of the host organization and any sponsoring program as part of the retrieval statement.

27. An online government report

U.S. Department of Commerce, National Telecommunications and Information Administration. (2005, February). *A nation online: Entering the broadband age*. Retrieved January 22, 2006, from http://www.ntia.doc.gov/reports/anol/index.html

28. A multipage online document

Elston, C. (n.d.). *Multiple intelligences*. Retrieved June 6, 2005, from http://education.com/teachspace/intelligences

APA title page

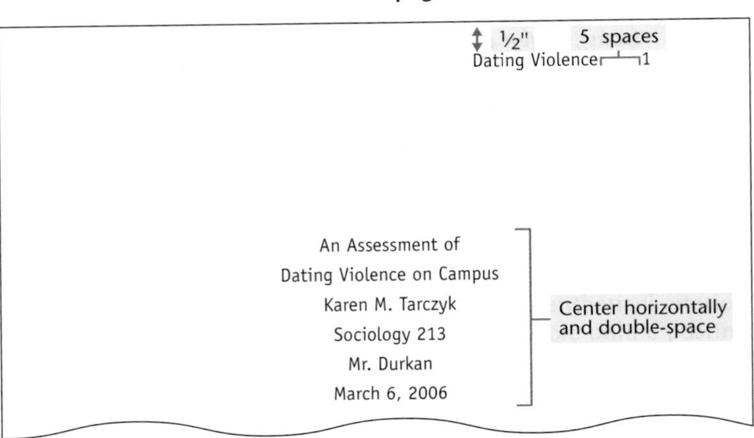

APA abstract

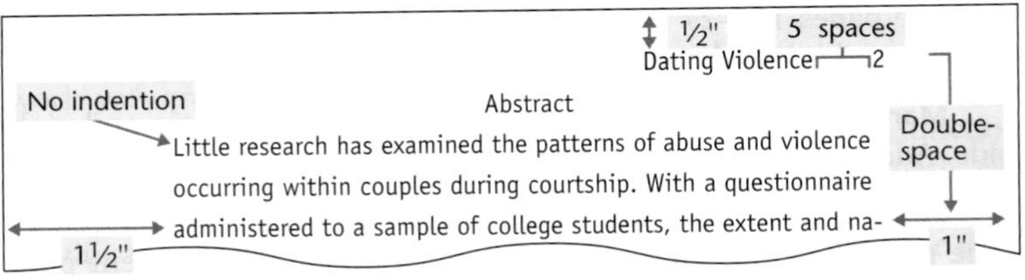

First page of APA body

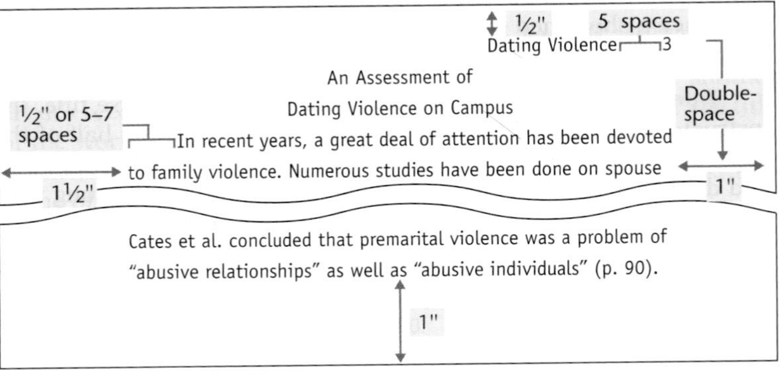

Body Begin with a restatement of the paper's title and then an introduction (not labeled). The introduction concisely presents the problem you researched, your research method, the relevant background (such as related studies), and the purpose of your research.

The next section, labeled Method, provides a detailed discussion of how you conducted your research, including a description of the research subjects, any materials or tools you used (such as questionnaires), and the procedure you followed. In the illustration below, the label Method is a first-level heading and the label *Sample* is a second-level heading.

Later page of APA body

Dating Violence 4

All the studies indicate a problem that is being neglected. My objective was to gather data on the extent and nature of premarital violence and to discuss possible interpretations.

Method

Sample

Double-space

I conducted a survey of 200 students (134 females, 66 males) at a large state university in the northeastern United States. The sample consisted of students enrolled in an introductory sociology

Format headings (including a third level, if needed) as follows:

First-Level Heading

Second-Level Heading

Third-level heading. Run this heading into the text paragraph with a standard paragraph indention.

The Results section (labeled with a first-level heading) summarizes the data you collected, explains how you analyzed them, and presents them in detail, often in tables, graphs, or charts.

The Discussion section (labeled with a first-level heading) interprets the data and presents your conclusions. (When the discussion is brief, you may combine it with the previous section under the heading Results and Discussion.)

The References section, beginning a new page, includes all your sources. See pages 743–45 for an explanation and sample.

Long quotations Run into your text all quotations of forty words or less, and enclose them in quotation marks. For quotations of more than forty words, set them off from your text by indenting all lines one-half inch or five spaces, double-spacing above and below. For student papers, the APA allows single-spacing of displayed quotations:

Echoing the opinions of other Europeans at the time, Freud (1961) had a poor view of Americans:

> The Americans are really too bad. . . . Competition is much more pungent with them, not succeeding means civil death to every one, and they have no private resources apart from their profession, no hobby, games, love or other interests of a cultured person. And success means money. (p. 86)

Do not use quotation marks around a quotation displayed in this way.

Illustrations Present data in tables, graphs, or charts, as appropriate. (See the sample on p. 760 for a clear table format to follow.) Begin each illustration on a separate page. Number each kind of illustration consecutively and separately from the other (Table 1, Table 2, etc., and Figure 1, Figure 2, etc.). Refer to all illustrations in your text—for instance, (see Figure 3). Generally, place illustrations immediately after the text references to them. (See pp. 122–27 for more on illustrations.)

52f Examining a sample social science paper

On the following pages are excerpts from a sociology paper. The student followed the organization described on the preceding pages both in establishing the background for her study and in explaining her own research. She also followed the APA style of source citation and document format, although page borders and running heads are omitted here and only the required page breaks are indicated.

Excerpts from a research report

[Title page. See also pp. 755 and 756]

An Assessment of

Dating Violence on Campus

Karen M. Tarczyk

Sociology 213

Mr. Durkan

March 6, 2006

[New page.]

Abstract

Little research has examined the patterns of abuse and violence occurring within couples during courtship. With a questionnaire administered to a sample of college students, the extent and nature of such abuse and violence were investigated. The results, some interpretations, and implications for further research are discussed.

[New page.]

An Assessment of Dating
Violence on Campus

In recent years, a great deal of attention has been devoted to family violence. Numerous studies have been done on spouse and child abuse. However, violent behavior occurs in dating relationships as well, yet the problem of dating violence has been relatively ignored by sociological research. It should be examined further since the premarital relationship is one context in which individuals learn and adopt behaviors that surface later in marriage.

The sociologist James Makepeace (1989) contended that courtship violence is a "potential mediating link" between violence in one's family of orientation and violence in one's later family of procreation (p. 103). Studying dating behaviors at Bemidji State University in Minnesota, Makepeace reported that one-fifth of the respondents had had at least one encounter with dating violence. He then extended these percentages to students nationwide, suggesting the existence of a major hidden social problem.

More recent research supports Makepeace's. Cates, Rutter, Karl, Linton, and Smith (2000) found that 22.3% of respondents at Oregon State University had been either the victim or the perpetrator of premarital violence. Another study (Cortes, 2005) found that so-called date rape, while much more publicized and discussed, was reported by many fewer woman respondents (2%) than was other violence during courtship (21%).

[The introduction continues.]

All these studies indicate a problem that is being neglected. My objective was to gather data on the extent and nature of premarital violence and to discuss possible interpretations.

Method

Sample

I conducted a survey of 200 students (134 females, 66 males) at a large state university in the northeastern United States. The sample consisted of students enrolled in an introductory sociology course.

[The explanation of method continues.]

The Questionnaire

A questionnaire exploring the personal dynamics of relationships was distributed during regularly scheduled class. Questions were answered anonymously in a 30-minute time period. The survey consisted of three sections.

[The explanation of method continues.]

Section 3 required participants to provide information about their current dating relationships. Levels of stress and frustration, communication between partners, and patterns of decision making were examined. These variables were expected to influence the amount of violence in a relationship. The next part of the survey was adopted from Murray Strauss's Conflict Tactics Scales (1992). These scales contain 19 items designed to measure conflict and the means of conflict resolution, including reasoning, verbal aggression, and actual violence.

Results

The questionnaire revealed significant levels of verbal aggression and threatened and actual violence among dating couples. A high number of students, 50% (62 of 123 subjects), reported that they had been the victim of verbal abuse. In addition, almost 14% (17 of 123) of respondents admitted being threatened with some type of violence, and more than 14% (18 of 123) reported being pushed, grabbed, or shoved. (See Table 1.)

[The explanation of results continues.]

[Table on a page by itself.]

Table 1

Incidence of Courtship Violence

Type of violence	Number of students reporting	Percentage of sample
Insulted or swore	62	50.4
Threatened to hit or throw something	17	13.8
Threw something	8	6.5
Pushed, grabbed, or shoved	18	14.6
Slapped	8	6.5
Kicked, bit, or hit with fist	7	5.7
Hit or tried to hit with something	2	1.6
Threatened with a knife or gun	1	0.8
Used a knife or gun	1	0.8

Discussion

Violence within premarital relationships has been relatively ignored. The results of the present study indicate that abuse and force do occur in dating relationships. Although the percentages are small, so was the sample. Extending them to the entire campus population would mean significant numbers. For example, if the nearly 6% incidence of being kicked, bitten, or hit with a fist is typical, then 300 students of a 5,000-member student body might have experienced this type of violence.

[The discussion continues.]

If the courtship period is characterized by abuse and violence, what accounts for it? The other sections of the survey examined some variables that appear to influence the relationship. Level of stress and frustration, both within the relationship and in the respondent's life, was one such variable. The communication level between partners, both the frequency of discussion and the frequency of agreement, was another.

[The discussion continues.]

The method of analyzing the data in this study, utilizing frequency distributions, provided a clear overview. However, more tests of significance and correlation and a closer look at the social and individual variables affecting the relationship are warranted. The courtship period may set the stage for patterns of married life. It merits more attention.

[New page.]

References

Cates, R. L., Rutter, C. H., Karl, J., Linton, M., & Smith, K. (2000). Premarital abuse: A social psychological perspective. *Journal of Family Issues, 13*(1), 79-90.

Cortes, L. (2005). Beyond date rape: Violence during courtship. *Electronic Journal of Intimate Violence, 5*(2). Retrieved February 16, 2006, from http://www.acast.nova.edu/health/psy/file-disc/file50.html

Glaser, R., & Rutter, C. H. (Eds.). (1999). Familial violence [Special issue]. *Family Relations, 43.*

Makepeace, J. M. (1989). Courtship violence among college students. *Family Relations, 28*, 97-103.

Strauss, M. L. (1992). *Conflict Tactics Scales.* New York: Sociological Tests.

In addition, laboratory or research reports may include a list of references (if other sources were consulted). They almost always include tables and figures (graphs and charts) containing the data from the research (see p. 776).

53c Using the tools and language of the sciences

Tools and language concerns vary from discipline to discipline in the sciences. Consult your instructor for specifics about the field in which you are writing. You can also discover much about a discipline's tools and language from the research sources listed on the next three pages.

1 Writing tools

In the sciences a **lab notebook** or **scientific journal** is almost indispensable for accurately recording the empirical data from observations and experiments. Use such a notebook or journal for these purposes:

- **Record observations** from reading, from class, or from the lab.
- **Ask questions and refine hypotheses.**
- **Record procedures.**
- **Record results.**
- **Keep an ongoing record of ideas and findings** and how they change as data accumulate.
- **Sequence and organize your material** as you compile your findings and write your report.

Make sure that your records of data are clearly separate from your reflections on the data so that you don't mistakenly confuse the two in drawing your conclusions.

2 Language considerations

Science writers prefer to use objective language that removes the writer as a character in the situation and events being explained, except as the impersonal agent of change, the experimenter. Although usage is changing, scientists still rarely use *I* in their reports and evaluations, and they often resort to the passive voice of verbs, as in *The mixture was then subjected to centrifugal force.* This conscious objectivity focuses attention (including the writer's) on the empirical data and what they show. It discourages the writer from, say, ascribing motives and will to animals and plants. For instance, instead of asserting that the sea tortoise *evolved* its hard shell *to protect* its body, a scientist would write only what could be observed: that the hard shell *covers and thus protects* the tortoise's body.

Science writers typically change verb tenses to distinguish between established information and their own research. For established information, such as that found in journals and other reliable sources, use the present tense: *Baroreceptors monitor blood pressure.* For your own and others' research, use the past tense: *The bacteria died within three hours. Marti reported some success.*

Each discipline in the natural and applied sciences has a specialized vocabulary that permits precise, accurate, and efficient communication. Some of these terms, such as *pressure* in physics, have different meanings in the common language and must be handled carefully in science writing. Others, such as *enthalpy* in chemistry, have no meanings in the common language and must simply be learned and used correctly.

3 Research sources

The following lists give resources in the sciences.

Specialized encyclopedias, dictionaries, and bibliographies

American Medical Association Encyclopedia of Medicine
Bibliographic Guide to the History of Computing, Computers, and the Information Processing Industry
Concise Oxford Dictionary of Mathematics
Dorland's Illustrated Medical Dictionary
Encyclopedia of Bioethics
Encyclopedia of Chemistry
Encyclopedia of Computer Science and Technology
Encyclopedia of Ecology
Encyclopedia of Electronics
Encyclopedia of Oceanography
Encyclopedia of Physics
Encyclopedic Dictionary of Mathematics
Grzimek's Animal Life Encyclopedia
Information Sources in the Life Sciences
Introduction to Reference Sources in Health Sciences
McGraw-Hill Encyclopedia of Engineering
McGraw-Hill Encyclopedia of the Geological Sciences
McGraw-Hill Encyclopedia of Science and Technology
Science and Technology in World History
Space Almanac
Van Nostrand's Scientific Encyclopedia
World Resources (environment)

Indexes

ACM Guide to Computing Literature
Applied Science and Technology Index
Bibliography and Index of Geology
Biological Abstracts
Biological and Agricultural Index

Chemical Abstracts
Compendex Engineering Index
Computer Abstracts
Computer Literature Index
Cumulative Index to Nursing and Allied Health Literature
Dissertation Abstracts International
Ecology Abstracts
Engineering Index
Environment Abstracts
General Science Index
Index Medicus
MathSciNet: Mathematical Reviews
Physics Abstracts
Science Citation Index

Book reviews

Technical Book Review Index

Web sources

For updates of these sources and URLs, visit *ablongman.com/littlebrown*.

General

BUBL Link: Natural Sciences and Mathematics (*bubl.ac.uk/link/linkbrowse.cfm?menuid=6402*)
Google Directory: Science (*directory.google.com/Top/Science*)
Librarians' Index to the Internet: Science (*lii.org/search/file/scitech*)
The National Academies: Science, Engineering, and Medicine (*nas.edu*)
WWW Virtual Library: Natural Sciences and Mathematics (*vlib.org/Science.html*)

Biology

BioMedNet (*bmn.com*)
Biology Online (*biology-online.org*)
Biology.Arizona.Edu (*biology.arizona.edu*)
National Biological Information Infrastructure (*www.nbii.gov*)

Chemistry

Chemistry.org (*chemistry.org/portal/a/c/s/1/home.html*)
WWW Virtual Library: Links for Chemists (*liv.ac.uk/Chemistry/Links/links.html*)

Computer science

IEEE Computer Society (*computer.org*)
University of Texas Virtual Computer Library (*utexas.edu/computer/vcl*)
WWW Virtual Library: Computing and Computer Science (*vlib.org/Computing*)

Engineering

American Society of Civil Engineers (*pubs.asce.org*)
Internet Guide to Engineering, Mathematics, and Computing (*eevl.ac.uk*)
National Academy of Engineering (*nae.edu*)

Environmental science

Center for International Earth Science Information Network (*ciesin.org*)
EE-Link: Environmental Education on the Internet (*eelink.net*)
EnviroLink (*envirolink.org*)
Environment Directory (*webdirectory.com*)

Geology

American Geological Institute (*www.agiweb.org*)
Digital Library for Earth System Education (*dlese.org*)
Geosource (*www.library.uu.nl/geosource*)
US Geological Survey Library (*library.usgs.gov*)

Health sciences

American Medical Association (*ama-assn.org*)
Centers for Disease Control and Prevention (*www.cdc.gov*)
Hardin MD (*www.lib.uiowa.edu/hardin/md*)
World Health Organization (*who.int/en*)

Mathematics

Math on the Web (*www.ams.org/mathweb*)
Internet Mathematics Library (*mathforum.org/library*)
Mathematical Atlas (*math-atlas.org*)

Physics and astronomy

American Institute of Physics (*aip.org*)
Astronomy Links (*astronomylinks.com*)
PhysicsWeb (*physicsweb.org*)
Science@NASA (*science.hq.nasa.gov/index.html*)

53d Citing sources in CSE style

Within the natural and applied sciences, practitioners use one of two styles of documentation, varying slightly from discipline to discipline. Following are some of the style guides most often consulted:

American Chemical Society, *ACS Style Guide: A Manual for Authors and Editors,* 2nd ed., 1997
American Institute of Physics, *Style Manual for Guidance in the Preparation of Papers,* 4th ed., 1997
American Medical Association Manual of Style, 9th ed., 1998
Council of Biology Editors, *Scientific Style and Format: The CBE Manual for Authors, Editors, and Publishers,* 6th ed., 1994

The most thorough and widely used of these guides is the last one, *Scientific Style and Format*. Its sponsoring organization, the Council of Science Editors, was until 2000 called the Council of Biology Editors, so the style is abbreviated either CSE (as in this book) or CBE.

Scientific Style and Format details both styles of scientific documentation: one using author and date and one using numbers. Both types of text citation refer to a list of references at the end of the paper (see the next page). Ask your teacher which style you should use.

1 Using CSE name-year text citations

In the CSE name-year style, parenthetical text citations provide the last name of the author being cited and the source's year of publication. At the end of the paper, a list of references, arranged alphabetically by authors' last names, provides complete information on each source.

The CSE name-year style closely resembles the APA name-year style detailed on pages 740–43. You can follow the APA examples for in-text citations, making several notable changes for CSE:

- **Do not use a comma to separate the author's name and the date:** (Baumrind 1968, p. 34).
- **Separate two authors' names with and (not "&"):** (Pepinsky and DeStefano 1997).
- **Use and others (not "et al.") for three or more authors:** (Rutter and others 1996).
- **List unnamed or anonymous authors as Anonymous,** both in the citation and in the list of references: (Anonymous 1976).

2 Using CSE numbered text citations

In the CSE number style, raised numbers in the text refer to a numbered list of references at the end of the paper.

Two standard references[1,2] use this term.

These forms of immunity have been extensively researched.[3]

Hepburn and Tatin[2] do not discuss this project.

Assignment of numbers The number for each source is based on the order in which you cite the source in the text: the first cited source is 1, the second is 2, and so on.

Reuse of numbers When you cite a source you have already cited and numbered, use the original number again (see the last example above, which reuses the number 2 from the first example).

This reuse is the key difference between the CSE numbered citations and numbered references to footnotes or endnotes. In the CSE style, each source has only one number, determined by the order in which the source is cited. With notes, in contrast, the numbering proceeds in sequence, so that each source has as many numbers as it has citations in the text.

Citation of two or more sources When you cite two or more sources at once, arrange their numbers in sequence and separate them with a comma and no space, as in the first example on the previous page.

3 Using a CSE reference list

For both the name-year and the number styles of in-text citation, provide a list, titled References, of all sources you have cited. Format the page as shown for APA references on page 743, except that CSE entries are single-spaced.

The following examples show the differences and similarities between the name-year and number styles:

Name-year style

Hepburn PX, Tatin JM. 2005. Human physiology. New York: Columbia Univ Pr. 1026 p.

Number style

2. Hepburn PX, Tatin JM. Human physiology. New York: Columbia Univ Pr; 2005. 1026 p.

Spacing In both styles, single-space each entry and double-space between entries.

Arrangement In the name-year style, arrange entries alphabetically by authors' last names. In the number style, arrange entries in numerical order—that is, in order of their citation in the text.

Format In both styles, begin the first line of each entry at the left margin and indent subsequent lines.

Authors In both styles, list each author's name with the last name first, followed by initials for first and middle names. Do not use a comma between an author's last name and initials, and do not use periods or spaces with the initials. Do use a comma to separate authors' names.

Placement of dates In the name-year style, the date follows the author's or authors' names. In the number style, the date follows the publication information (for a book) or the periodical title (for a journal, magazine, or newspaper).

Journal titles In both styles, do not underline or italicize journal titles. For titles of two or more words, abbreviate words of six or more letters (without periods) and omit most prepositions, articles, and conjunctions. Capitalize each word. For example, *Journal of Chemical and Biochemical Studies* becomes J Chem Biochem Stud.

Book and article titles In both styles, do not underline, italicize, or use quotation marks around a book or an article title. Capitalize only the first word and any proper nouns.

Publication information for journal articles The name-year and number styles differ in the placement of the publication date (see opposite). However, both styles end with the journal's volume number, any issue number in parentheses, a colon, and the inclusive page numbers of the article, run together without space: 28:329-30 or 62(2):26-40.

The following box indexes the CSE models. The examples include both a name-year reference and a number reference for each type of source.

CSE reference-list models

Books

1. A book with one author

Gould SJ. 1987. Time's arrow, time's cycle. Cambridge: Harvard Univ Pr. 222 p.

1. Gould SJ. Time's arrow, time's cycle. Cambridge: Harvard Univ Pr; 1987. 222 p.

2. A book with two to ten authors

Hepburn PX, Tatin JM. 2005. Human physiology. New York: Columbia Univ Pr. 1026 p.

2. Hepburn PX, Tatin JM. Human physiology. New York: Columbia Univ Pr; 2005. 1026 p.

3. A book with more than ten authors

Evans RW, Bowditch L, Dana KL, Drummond A, Wildovitch WP, Young SL, Mills P, Mills RR, Livak SR, Lisi OL, and others. 2004. Organ transplants: ethical issues. Ann Arbor: Univ of Michigan Pr. 498 p.

3. Evans RW, Bowditch L, Dana KL, Drummond A, Wildovitch WP, Young SL, Mills P, Mills RR, Livak SR, Lisi OL, and others. Organ transplants: ethical issues. Ann Arbor: Univ of Michigan Pr; 2004. 498 p.

4. A book with an editor

Jonson P, editor. 2006. Anatomy yearbook 2005. Los Angeles: Anatco. 628 p.

4. Jonson P, editor. Anatomy yearbook 2005. Los Angeles: Anatco; 2006. 628 p.

5. A selection from a book

Krigel R, Laubenstein L, Muggia F. 2005. Kaposi's sarcoma. In: Ebbeson P, Biggar RS, Melbye M, editors. AIDS: a basic guide for clinicians. 2nd ed. Philadelphia: WB Saunders. p 100-26.

5. Krigel R, Laubenstein L, Muggia F. Kaposi's sarcoma. In: Ebbeson P, Biggar RS, Melbye M, editors. AIDS: a basic guide for clinicians. 2nd ed. Philadelphia: WB Saunders; 2005. p 100-26.

6. An anonymous work

[Anonymous]. 2006. Health care for multiple sclerosis. New York: US Health Care. 86 p.

6. [Anonymous]. Health care for multiple sclerosis. New York: US Health Care; 2006. 86 p.

7. Two or more cited works by the same author published in the same year

Gardner H. 1973a. The arts and human development. New York: J Wiley. 406 p.

Gardner H. 1973b. The quest for mind: Piaget, Lévi-Strauss, and the structuralist movement. New York: AA Knopf. 492 p.

(The number style does not require such forms.)

Periodicals: Journals, magazines, newspapers

8. An article in a journal with continuous pagination throughout the annual volume

Ancino R, Carter KV, Elwin DJ. 2004. Factors contributing to viral immunity: a review of the research. Dev Biol 30:156-9.

8. Ancino R, Carter KV, Elwin DJ. Factors contributing to viral immunity: a review of the research. Dev Biol 2004;30:156-9.

17. Millon M. Grief therapy [Internet]. Message to: Naomi Sakai. 2005 May 4, 3:16 pm [cited 2005 May 4]. [about 2 screens].

18. A posting to a discussion list

Stalinsky Q. 2005 Aug 16. The hormone-replacement study. In: Women Physicians Congress [Internet]. [Chicago: American Medical Association]; 9:26 am [cited 2005 Aug 17]. [about 8 paragraphs]. Available from: ama-wpc@ama-assn.org

18. Stalinsky Q. The hormone-replacement study. In: Women Physicians Congress [Internet]. [Chicago: American Medical Association]; 2005 Aug 16, 9:26 am [cited 2005 Aug 17]. [about 8 paragraphs]. Available from: ama-wpc@ama-assn.org

19. Computer software

Project scheduler 9000 [computer program]. 2006. Version 5.1. Orlando (FL): Scitor. CD-ROM. System requirements: IBM PC or compatible; Windows 98 or higher; 32 MB RAM; minimum 50 MB free disk space.

19. Project scheduler 9000 [computer program]. Version 5.1. Orlando (FL): Scitor; 2006. CD-ROM. System requirements: IBM PC or compatible; Windows 98 or higher; 32 MB RAM; minimum 50 MB free disk space.

Other sources

20. A government publication

Committee on Science and Technology, House (US). 2003. Hearing on procurement and allocation of human organs for transplantation. 108th Cong., 1st Sess. House Doc. nr 409.

20. Committee on Science and Technology, House (US). Hearing on procurement and allocation of human organs for transplantation. 108th Cong., 1st Sess. House Doc. nr 409; 2003.

21. A nongovernment report

Warnock M. 2004. Report of the Committee on Fertilization and Embryology. Baylor University, Department of Embryology. Waco (TX): Baylor Univ. Report nr BU/DE.4261.

21. Warnock M. Report of the Committee on Fertilization and Embryology. Baylor University, Department of Embryology. Waco (TX): Baylor Univ; 2004. Report nr BU/DE.4261.

22. A sound recording, video recording, DVD, or film

Teaching Media. 2005. Cell mitosis [DVD]. White Plains (NY): Teaching Media. 40 min, sound, color.

22. Cell mitosis [DVD]. White Plains (NY): Teaching Media; 2005. 40 min, sound, color.

53e Examining a sample science paper

The following biology paper illustrates the CSE number style for documenting sources. On page 777 passages from the paper and a reformatted list of references show the name-year style. Except for the citations and the references, the paper is formatted in APA style because CSE does not specify a format.

A laboratory report: CSE number style

[Title page.]

Exercise and Blood Pressure

Liz Garson

Biology 161

Ms. Traversa

December 13, 2005

[New page.]

Abstract

The transient elevation of blood pressure following exercise was demonstrated by pressure measurements of twenty human subjects before and after exercise.

[New page.]

Exercise and Blood Pressure

Introduction

The purpose of this experiment was to verify the changes in blood pressure that accompany exercise, as commonly reported.[1,2] A certain blood pressure is necessary for the blood to supply nutrients to the body tissues. Baroreceptors near the heart monitor pressure by determining the degree to which blood stretches the wall of the blood vessel.

[The introduction continues.]

During exercise, the metabolic needs of the muscles override the influence of the baroreceptors and result in an increase in blood pressure. This increase in blood pressure is observed uniformly (irrespective of sex or race), although men demonstrate a higher absolute systolic pressure than do women.[3] During strenuous exercise, blood pressure can rise to 40 percent above baseline.[1]

Method

The subjects for this experiment were twenty volunteers from laboratory classes, ten men and ten women. All pressure measurements were performed using a standard sphygmomanometer, which was tested for accuracy. To ensure consistency, the same sphygmomanometer was used to take all readings. In addition, all measurements were taken by the same person to avoid discrepancies in method or interpretation.

The first pressure reading was taken prior to exercise as the subject sat in a chair. This pressure was considered the baseline for each subject. All subsequent readings were interpreted relative to this baseline.

In the experiment, the subjects ran up and down stairs for fifteen minutes. Immediately after exercising, the subjects returned to the laboratory to have their pressure measured. Thirty minutes later, the pressure was measured for the final time.

Results

Table 1 contains the blood pressure measurements for the male and female subjects. With the exception of subjects 3 and 14, all subjects demonstrated the expected post-exercise increase in blood pressure, with a decline to baseline or near baseline thirty minutes after exercise. The data for subjects 3 and 14 were invalid because the subjects did not perform the experiment as directed.

[Table on a page by itself.]

Table 1. Blood pressure measurements for all subjects (mmHg)

Subject	Baseline[a]	Post-exercise	30-minute reading
Male			
1	110/75	135/80	115/75
2	125/80	140/90	135/85
3	125/70	125/70	125/70
4	130/85	170/100	140/90
5	120/80	125/95	120/80
6	115/70	135/80	125/75
7	125/70	150/80	130/70
8	130/80	145/85	130/80
9	140/75	180/85	155/80
10	110/85	135/95	115/80
Female			
11	110/60	140/85	115/60
12	130/75	180/85	130/75
13	125/80	140/90	130/80
14	90/60	90/60	90/60
15	115/65	145/70	125/65
16	100/50	130/65	110/50
17	120/80	140/80	130/80
18	110/70	135/80	120/75
19	120/80	140/90	130/80
20	110/80	145/90	120/80

[a]Normal blood pressure at rest: males, 110-130/60-90; females, 110-120/50-80.

Discussion

As expected, most of the subjects demonstrated an increase in blood pressure immediately after exercise and a decline to near baseline levels thirty minutes after exercise. The usual pressure increase was 20-40 mmHg for the systolic pressure and 5-10 mmHg for the diastolic pressure.

In the two cases in which blood pressure did not elevate with exercise (subjects 3 and 14), the subjects simply left the laboratory and returned fifteen minutes later without having exercised. The experimental design was flawed in not assigning someone to observe the subjects as they exercised.

[New page.]

References

1. Guyton AC. Textbook of medical physiology. Philadelphia: WB Saunders; 2004. 998 p.
2. Rowell LB. Blood pressure regulation during exercise. Ann Med 1999;28:329-33.
3. Gleim GW, Stachenfeld NS. Gender differences in the systolic blood pressure response to exercise. Am Heart J 2001;121:524-30.

A laboratory report: CSE name-year style

These excerpts from the preceding paper show documentation in CSE name-year style:

The purpose of this experiment was to verify the changes in blood pressure that accompany exercise, as commonly reported (Guyton 2004; Rowell 1999).

This increase in blood pressure is observed uniformly (irrespective of sex or race), although men demonstrate a higher absolute systolic pressure than do women (Gleim and Stachenfeld 2001). During strenuous exercise, blood pressure can rise to 40 percent above baseline (Guyton 2004).

References

Gleim GW, Stachenfeld NS. 2001. Gender differences in the systolic blood pressure response to exercise. Am Heart J 121:524-30.

Guyton AC. 2004. Textbook of medical physiology. Philadelphia: WB Saunders. 998 p.

Rowell LB. 1999. Blood pressure regulation during exercise. Ann Med 28:329-33.

the original message. The *Subject* line will automatically contain the original subject heading preceded by *Re:* (from Latin, meaning "In reference to"), so change the heading if you change or expand the subject. Many e-mail programs can be set to reprint the entire original message, allowing you to insert your responses where appropriate or to respond to part of the message and delete the rest. If you add more recipients to your response, make sure not to pass on previous private messages by mistake.

E-mail response

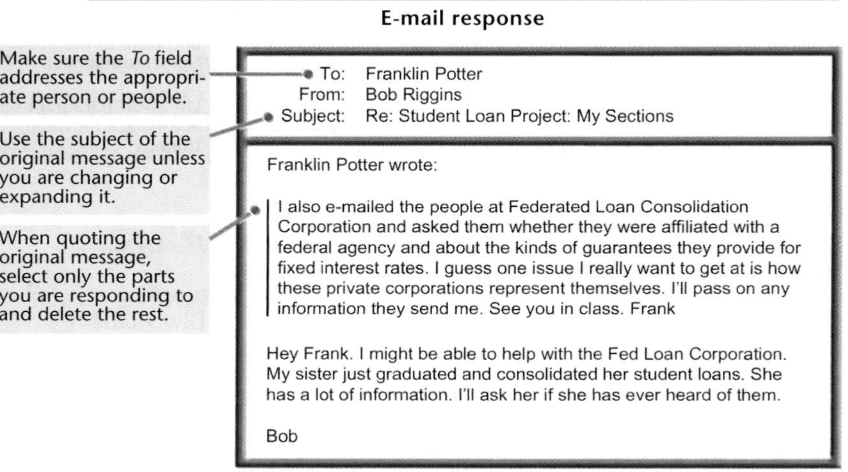

3 Observing netiquette

To communicate effectively online, you'll need to abide by some rules of behavior and simple courtesies. You won't always see others observing this **netiquette,** or Internet etiquette, but you will see that those who do observe it receive the more thoughtful and considerate replies.

Addressing messages

- **Avoid spamming.** With a few keystrokes, you can broadcast a message to many recipients at once—all the students in a class, say, or all the members of an athletic team. Occasionally, you may indeed have a worthwhile idea or important information that everyone on the list will want to know. But flooding whole lists with irrelevant messages—called **spamming**—is rude and irritating.
- **Avoid sending frivolous messages to all the members of a group.** Instead of dashing off "I agree" and distributing the two-word message widely, put some time into composing a thoughtful response and send it only to those who will be interested.

Composing messages

- **Remember that the messages you receive represent individuals.** Don't say or do anything that you wouldn't say or do face to face.
- **Use names.** In the body of your message, address your reader(s) by name if possible and sign off with your own name and information on how to contact you. Your own name is especially important if your e-mail address does not spell it out.
- **Pay careful attention to tone.** Refrain from **flaming,** or attacking, correspondents. Don't use all capital letters, which SHOUT. And use irony or sarcasm only cautiously: in the absence of facial expressions, they can lead to misunderstandings. To indicate irony and emotions, you can use **emoticons,** such as the smiley :-). These sideways faces can easily be overused, though, and should not substitute for thoughtfully worded opinions.
- **Avoid saying anything in e-mail that you would not say in a printed document such as a letter or memo.** E-mail can usually be retrieved from the server, and in business and academic settings it may well be retrieved in disputes over contracts, grades, and other matters.

Reading and responding to messages

- **Be a forgiving reader.** Avoid nitpicking over spelling or other surface errors. And because attitudes are sometimes difficult to convey, give authors an initial benefit of the doubt: a writer who at first seems hostile may simply have tried too hard to be concise; a writer who at first seems unserious may simply have failed at injecting humor into a worthwhile message.
- **Forward messages only with permission.** You may want to send a message you've received to someone else, but do so only if you know that the author of the message won't mind.
- **Avoid participating in flame "wars,"** overheated dialogs that contribute little or no information or understanding. If a war breaks out in a discussion, ignore it: don't rush to defend someone who is being attacked, and don't respond even if you are under attack yourself.

54b Collaborating online

Writing often involves collaborating with others as much as it does working in solitude. Indeed, many businesses and teachers expect writers to collaborate on generating ideas and producing and revising drafts. Computers have vastly expanded the options for collaboration, ranging from simple e-mail exchanges to video conferencing and virtual environments.

In this section we look at strategies for online collaboration in your classes. Your teachers or your school's technology advisers will

occurring in the same space. If you have trouble tracking all the messages, concentrate on the ones that relate to your interest.

- **Write as quickly and fluidly as possible.** Don't worry about producing perfect prose.

2 Working on drafts

In writing and other classes, you and your fellow students may be invited to exchange and respond to one another's projects by e-mail or over the Web. To guide your reading of others' work, use the revision checklist on page 54 and the collaboration tips on pages 68–71. Focus on the deep issues in others' drafts, especially early drafts: thesis, purpose, audience, organization, and support for the thesis. Hold comments on style, grammar, punctuation, and other surface matters until you're reviewing late drafts, if indeed you are expected to comment on them at all.

Exchanging drafts online generally requires a file-naming system that identifies each project's writer, title, and version. Your instructor may establish such a system, or you and your classmates can develop one.

54c Creating effective Web compositions

Creating a Web page or site is sometimes as simple as saving a document in a different format, but more often it means thinking in a new way.

The diagrams on the facing page show a key difference between traditional printed documents and Web sites. Most traditional documents are meant to be read in sequence from start to finish. In contrast, most Web sites are so-called hypertexts: they are intended to be examined in whatever order readers choose as they follow links to pages within the site and to other sites.

When you create a composition for the Web, it will likely fall into one of two categories discussed in this section: pages such as class papers that resemble printed documents in being linear and text-heavy and that call for familiar ways of writing and reading; or "native" hypertext documents that you build from scratch, which call for screen-oriented writing and reading.

These general guidelines will help you create effective Web sites:

- **Plan the site carefully.** A hypertext can disorient readers as they scroll up and down and pursue various links. Page length, links, menus, and other cues should work to keep readers oriented.
- **Anticipate what readers may see on their screens.** Each reader's screen frames and organizes the experience of a Web

Traditional print document

ReadingWorks
Literacy Introduction
2
Resources for Tutors
3
Resources for Students
4
Exercises

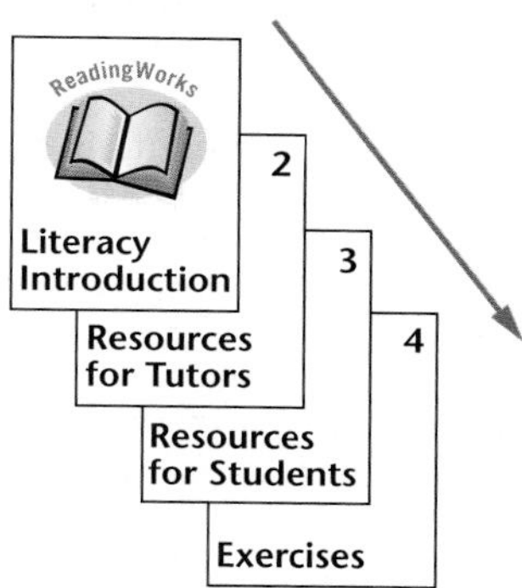

Web site

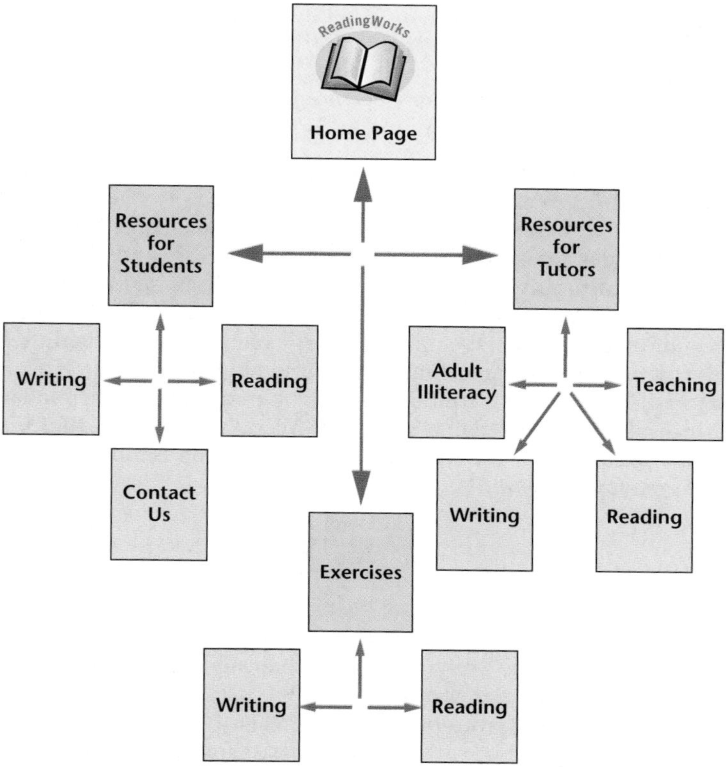

ReadingWorks
Home Page
Resources for Students
Resources for Tutors
Writing
Reading
Contact Us
Adult Illiteracy
Teaching
Writing
Reading
Exercises
Writing
Reading

composition. Screen space is limited, and it varies from one computer to another. Text and visual elements should be managed for maximum clarity and effectiveness on a variety of screens.

- **Integrate visual and sound elements into the text.** Web compositions can include not only tables, charts, and photographs (which printed documents may also have) but also video (such as animation or film clips) and audio (such as music or excerpts from speeches). However, any visual or sound elements should not merely embellish the text but contribute substantially to it. In addition, you should find out whether your readers' equipment will likely be able to handle multimedia elements and whether readers themselves may have disabilities that prevent their seeing or hearing such elements (see the note below).
- **Acknowledge your sources.** It's easy to incorporate material from other sources into a Web site, but you have the same obligation to cite your sources as you do in a printed document (see pp. 611–16). Further, your Web site is a form of publication, like a magazine or a book. Unless the material you are using explicitly allows copying without permission, you may need to seek the copyright holder's permission, just as print publishers do. (See pp. 617–18 for more on copyright.)

Note If you anticipate that some of your readers may have visual, hearing, or reading disabilities, you'll need to consider their needs while designing Web sites. Some of these considerations are covered under document design on pages 127–28, and others are fundamental to any effective Web design, as discussed in this section. In addition, avoid any content that relies exclusively on images or sound, instead supplementing such elements with text descriptions. At the same time, try to provide key concepts both as text and as images and sound. For more on Web design for readers with disabilities, visit the World Wide Web Consortium at *w3.org/tr/wai-webcontent* or the American Council for the Blind at *acb.org/accessible-formats.html*.

1 Using HTML

Most Web pages are created using hypertext markup language, or HTML, and an HTML editor. The HTML editing program inserts command codes into your document that achieve the effects you want when the material appears on the Web.

From the user's point of view, most HTML editors work much as word processors do, with similar options for sizing, formatting, and highlighting copy and with a display that shows what you will see in the final version. Indeed, you can compose a Web page without bothering at all about the behind-the-scenes HTML coding. As you gain experience with Web building, however, you may want to create more sophisticated pages by editing the codes themselves.

There are many HTML editors on the market. The Web site for this book (*ablongman.com/littlebrown*) provides links to free or low-cost editors.

2 Creating online papers

If a teacher asks you to post a paper to a Web site, you can compose it on your word processor and then use the Save As HTML function available on most programs to translate it into a Web page. After translating the paper, your word processor should allow you to modify some of the elements on the page, or you can open the translated document in an HTML editor. The illustration below shows the opening screen of a student's project for a composition class.

Paper submitted on the Web

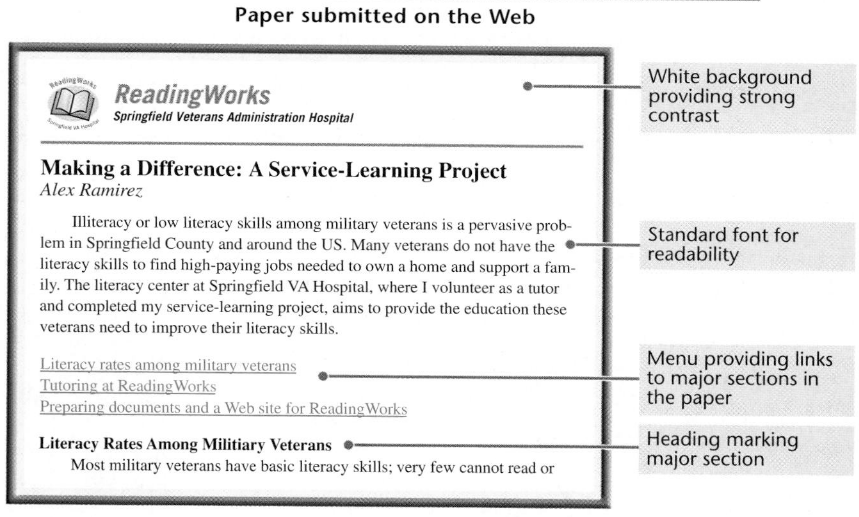

3 Creating original sites

When you create an original Web site, you need to be aware that Web readers generally alternate between skimming pages for highlights and focusing intently on sections of text. To facilitate this kind of reading, you'll want to consider the guidelines on pages 786–88 for handling text and also your site's structure and content, flow, ease of navigation, and use of images, video, and sound.

Structure and content

Organize your site so that it efficiently arranges your content and also orients readers:

- **Sketch possible site plans before getting started.** (See p. 787 for an example.) Your aim is to develop a sense of the major components of your project and to create a logical space for each component.
- **Consider how menus on the site's pages can provide overviews of the organization as well as direct access to the pages.** The Web page below includes a menu on the left side of the page.
- **Treat the first few sentences of any page as a get-acquainted space for you and your readers.** On the page below, the text hooks readers with questions and orients them with general information.
- **Distill your text so that it includes only essential information.** Concise prose is essential in any writing situation, of course. But Web readers expect to scan text quickly and, in any event, have difficulty following long text passages on a computer screen.

Original Web site

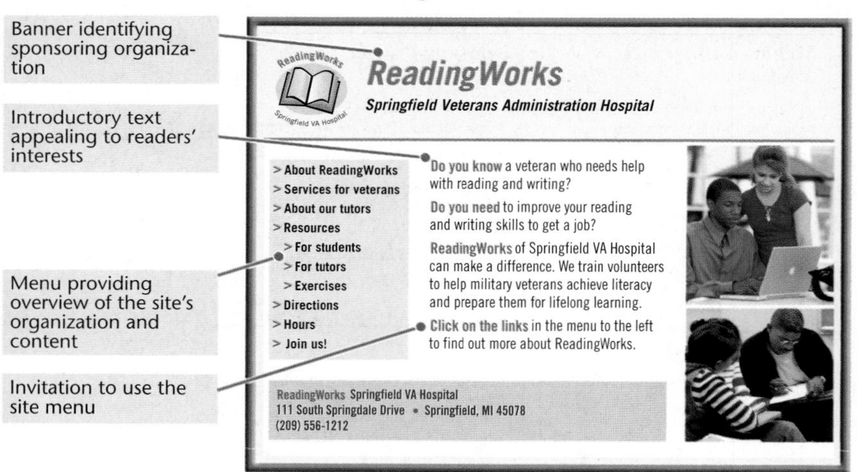

Flow

Beginning Web authors sometimes start at the top of the page and then add element upon element until information proceeds down the screen much as it would in a printed document. However, by thinking about how information will flow on a page, you can take better advantage of the Web's visual nature:

- **Standardize elements of your design to create expectations in readers and to fulfill those expectations.** For instance, develop a uniform style for the main headings of pages, for headings within pages, and for menus.
- **Make scanning easy for readers.** Focus readers on crucial text by adding space around it. Add headings to break up text and to highlight content. Use lists to reinforce the parallel importance of items. (See pp. 118–22 for more on all these design elements.)

Easy navigation

A Web site of more than a few pages requires a menu on every page so that readers can navigate the site. Like the table of contents in a book, a menu lists the features of the site, giving its plan at a glance. By clicking on any item in the list, readers can go directly to a page that interests them.

You can embed a menu at the top, side, or bottom of a page. Menus at the top or side are best on short pages because they will not scroll off the screen as readers move down the page. On longer pages, menus at the bottom prevent readers from dead-ending—that is, reaching a point where they can't easily move forward or backward. You can also use a combination of menus.

In designing a menu, keep it simple: many different type fonts and colors will overwhelm readers instead of orienting them. And make the menus look the same from one page to the next so that readers recognize them easily.

Images, video, and sound

Exploring the Web, you'll see that site designers have taken advantage of the Web's ability to handle multimedia elements—images, video, and sound. Most Web readers expect at least some enhancement of text.

Note See pages 617–18 on observing copyright restrictions with images, video, and sound.

Images

Several guidelines can help you use images effectively in your Web compositions:

- **Use visual elements for a purpose.** They should supplement or replace text, highlight important features, and direct the flow of information. Don't use them for their own sake, as mere decoration.
- **Make the size of your files a central concern** so that readers don't have to wait forever for your site to download. If you are using lines or other icons, choose a limited number. If you are using photographs or other images, try to keep the file size below thirty kilobytes (30k).

Sincerely are common closes. For less formal letters, you may choose to use *Regards, Best wishes,* or the like. Only the first word of the close is capitalized, and the close is followed by a comma.

Signature The signature of a business letter falls below the close and has two parts. One is your name typed on the fourth line below the close. The other is your handwritten signature, which fills the space between the close and your typed name. The signature should consist only of your name, as you sign checks and other documents.

Other information Below the signature at the left margin, you may want to include additional information such as *Enc. 3* (indicating that there are three enclosures with the letter) or *cc: Margaret Newton* (indicating that a copy is being sent to the person named).

The envelope

The envelope should accommodate the letter once it is folded horizontally in thirds. The following are the common Postal Service abbreviations for addresses:

Street names

Avenue	AVE	Expressway	EXPY	Road	RD
Boulevard	BLVD	Freeway	FWY	Square	SQ
Circle	CIR	Lane	LN	Street	ST
Court	CT	Parkway	PKY	Turnpike	TPKE

Compass points

North	N	West	W	Southwest	SW
East	E	Northeast	NE	Northwest	NW

State names

Alabama	AL	Kentucky	KY	North Dakota	ND
Alaska	AK	Louisiana	LA	Ohio	OH
Arizona	AZ	Maine	ME	Oklahoma	OK
Arkansas	AR	Maryland	MD	Oregon	OR
California	CA	Massachusetts	MA	Pennsylvania	PA
Colorado	CO	Michigan	MI	Puerto Rico	PR
Connecticut	CT	Minnesota	MN	Rhode Island	RI
Delaware	DE	Mississippi	MS	South Carolina	SC
District of Columbia	DC	Missouri	MO	South Dakota	SD
Florida	FL	Montana	MT	Tennessee	TN
Georgia	GA	Nebraska	NE	Texas	TX
Hawaii	HI	Nevada	NV	Utah	UT
Idaho	ID	New Hampshire	NH	Vermont	VT
Illinois	IL	New Jersey	NJ	Virginia	VA
Indiana	IN	New Mexico	NM	Washington	WA
Iowa	IA	New York	NY	West Virginia	WV
Kansas	KS	North Carolina	NC	Wisconsin	WI
				Wyoming	WY

Envelope for a business letter

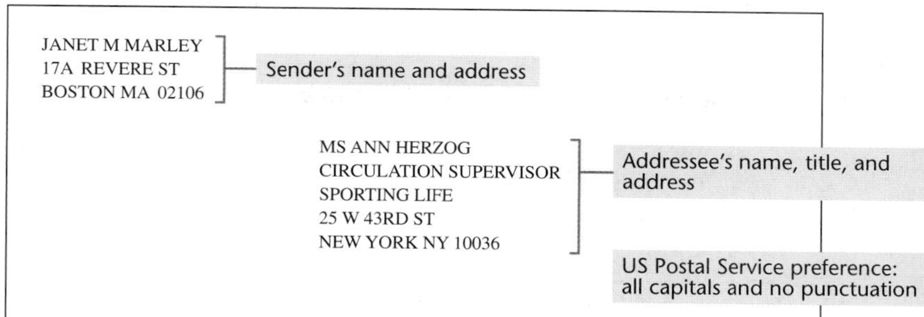

2 Writing requests and complaints

Letters requesting something—for instance, a pamphlet, information about a product, a T-shirt advertised in a magazine—must be specific and accurate about the item you are requesting. The letter should describe the item completely and, if applicable, include a copy or description of the advertisement or other source that prompted your request.

Letters complaining about a product or a service (such as a wrong billing from a wireless company) should be written in a reasonable but firm tone. (See the sample letter on p. 794.) Assume that the addressee is willing to resolve the problem when he or she has the relevant information. In the first sentence of the letter, say what you are writing about. Then provide as much background as needed, including any relevant details from past correspondence (as in the sample letter). Describe exactly what you see as the problem, sticking to facts and avoiding discourse on the company's social responsibility or your low opinion of its management. In the clearest and fewest possible words and sentences, proceed directly from one point to the next without repeating yourself. Always include your opinion of how the problem can be solved. Many companies are required by law to establish a specific procedure for complaints about products and services. If you know of such a procedure, be sure to follow it.

3 Writing business memos

Unlike business letters, which address people in other organizations, business memorandums (memos, for short) address people within the same organization. A memo can be quite long, but more often it deals briefly with a specific topic, such as an answer to a question, a progress report, or an evaluation. Both the content and the format of a memo aim to get to the point and dispose of it quickly.

- **Content**
- **State your reason for writing in the first sentence.** You might outline a problem, make a request, refer to a request that prompted the memo, or briefly summarize new findings. Do not, however, waste words with expressions like *The purpose of this memo is. . . .*

Business memo

Heading: company's name, addressee's name, writer's name and initials, date, and subject description

Bigelow Wax Company

TO: Aileen Rosen, Director of Sales
FROM: Patricia Phillips, Territory 12 PP
DATE: March 17, 2006
SUBJECT: 2005 sales of Quick Wax in Territory 12

Body: single-spaced with double spacing between paragraphs; paragraphs not indented

Since it was introduced in January 2005, Quick Wax has been unsuccessful in Territory 12 and has not affected the sales of our Easy Shine. Discussions with customers and my own analysis of Quick Wax suggest three reasons for its failure to compete with our product.

1. Quick Wax has not received the promotion necessary for a new product. Advertising—primarily on radio—has been sporadic and has not developed a clear, consistent image for the product. In addition, the Quick Wax sales representative in Territory 12 is new and inexperienced; he is not known to customers, and his sales pitch (which I once overheard) is weak. As far as I can tell, his efforts are not supported by phone calls or mailings from his home office.

2. When Quick Wax does make it to the store shelves, buyers do not choose it over our product. Though priced competitively with our product, Quick Wax is poorly packaged. The container seems smaller than ours, though in fact it holds the same eight ounces. The lettering on the Quick Wax package (red on blue) is difficult to read, in contrast to the white-on-green lettering on the Easy Shine package.

3. Our special purchase offers and my increased efforts to serve existing customers have had the intended effect of keeping customers satisfied with our product and reducing their inclination to stock something new.

People receiving copies

Copies: L. Mendes, Director of Marketing
J. MacGregor, Customer Service Manager

- **Devote the first paragraph to a succinct presentation of your solution, recommendation, answer, or evaluation.** The first paragraph should be short, and by its end your reader should know precisely what to expect from the rest of the memo: the details and reasoning that support your conclusion.
- **Deliver the support in the body of the memo.** The paragraphs may be numbered or bulleted so that the main divisions of your message are easy to see. In a long memo, you may need headings (see pp. 121–22).
- **Suit your style and tone to your audience.** For instance, you'll want to address your boss or a large group of readers more formally than you would a coworker who is also a friend.
- **Write concisely.** Keep your sentences short and your language simple, using technical terms only when your readers will understand them. Say only what readers need to know.

4 Communicating electronically

Electronic communication—mainly e-mail and faxes—adds a few twists to business writing. E-mail plays such a prominent role in communication of all sorts that we discuss it extensively as part of writing online (see pp. 780–83). Generally, the standards for business e-mail are the same as for other business correspondence.

Faxes follow closely the formats of print documents, but there are some unique concerns:

- **Consider legibility.** Small type, photographs, horizontal lines, and other elements that look fine on your copy may not be legible to the addressee.
- **Include a cover sheet.** Most faxes require a cover sheet with the addressee's name, company, and fax number; the date, time, and subject; your own name and fax and telephone numbers; and the total number of pages (including the cover sheet) in the fax.
- **Advise your addressee to expect a fax.** The advice is essential if the fax is confidential because the machine is often shared.
- **Consider urgency.** Transmission by fax can imply that the correspondence is urgent. If yours isn't, you may want to use the mail instead.

55b Writing a job application

In applying for an internship or a job or when requesting a job interview, send both a résumé and a cover letter. If you need to submit your application electronically, see pages 801 and 803.

1 Writing the cover letter

The cover letter should be formatted in block style (p. 794) or modified block style (below). Use the sample below and these guidelines in composing the letter:

- **Interpret your résumé for the particular job.** Don't detail your entire résumé, reciting your job history. Instead, highlight and reshape only the relevant parts.

Job-application letter (modified block style)

Return-address heading: falls to the right of center in modified block format

3712 Swiss Avenue
Dallas, TX 75204
March 2, 2006

Raymond Chipault
Human Resources Manager
Dallas News
Communications Center
Dallas, TX 75222

Dear Mr. Chipault:

In response to your posting in the English Department of Southern Methodist University, I am applying for the summer job of part-time editorial assistant for the *Dallas News*.

I am now enrolled at Southern Methodist University as a sophomore, with a dual major in English literature and journalism. My courses so far have included news reporting, copy editing, and electronic publishing. I worked a summer as a copy aide for my hometown newspaper, and for two years I have edited and written sports stories and features for the university newspaper. My feature articles cover subjects as diverse as campus elections, parking regulations, visiting professors, and speech codes.

As the enclosed résumé and writing samples indicate, my education and knowledge of newspaper work prepare me for the opening you have.

I am available for an interview at your convenience and would be happy to show more samples of my writing. Please e-mail me at ianirv@mail.smu.edu or call me at 214-744-3816.

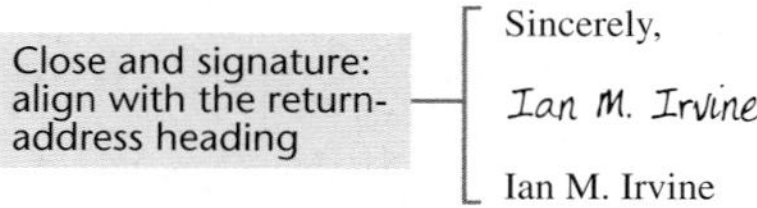

Enc.

- **Announce at the outset what job you seek and how you heard about it.**
- **Include any special reason you have for applying,** such as a specific career goal.
- **Summarize your qualifications for this particular job,** including relevant facts about education and employment and emphasizing notable accomplishments. Mention that additional information appears in an accompanying résumé.
- **Describe your availability.** At the end of the letter, mention that you are free for an interview at the convenience of the addressee, or specify when you will be available (for instance, when your current job or classes leave you free).

2 Writing and formatting the résumé

The résumé that accompanies your letter of application should provide information in table format that allows a potential employer to evaluate your qualifications. The résumé should include your name and address, a career objective, your education and employment history, special skills or awards, and information about how to obtain your references. All the information should fit on one uncrowded page, unless your education and experience are extensive. See the sample on the next page for writing and formatting guidelines for a résumé that you submit in print.

Some employers may ask for an electronic version of your résumé so that they can add it to a computerized database of applicants. The employers may scan your printed résumé to convert it to an electronic file, which they can then store in an appropriate database. Or they may ask you to provide the résumé electronically, either attaching it to or embedding it in an e-mail message. If an employer requests a scannable or electronic résumé, follow the guidelines below and consult the sample on page 803.

- **Keep the design simple for accurate scanning or electronic transmittal.** Avoid images, unusual type, more than one column, vertical or horizontal lines, italics, or underlining.
- **Use concise, specific words to describe your skills and experience.** The employer's computer may use keywords (often nouns) to identify the résumés of suitable job candidates, and you want to ensure that your résumé includes the appropriate keywords. Name your specific skills—for example, the computer programs you can operate—and write concretely with words like *manager* (not *person with responsibility for*) and *reporter* (not *staff member who reports*). Look for likely keywords in the employer's description of the job you seek.

- **Do your research.** The standard formats of reports and proposals require you to be well informed, so be alert to where you have enough information or where you don't.
- **Focus on the purpose of each section.** Stick to the point of each section, saying only what you need to say, even if you have additional information. Each section should accomplish its purpose and contribute to the whole.
- **Follow an appropriate format.** In many businesses, reports and proposals have specific formatting requirements. If you are unsure about the requirements, ask your supervisor.

Report

Descriptive title conveying report's contents

Standard format: summary, statement of the problem, solutions, and (not shown) recommendations

Major sections delineated by headings

Formal tone, appropriate to a business-writing situation

Single spacing with double spacing between paragraphs and around the list

Bulleted list emphasizing alternative solutions

Canada Geese at ABC Institute: An Environmental Problem

Summary

The flock of Canada geese on and around ABC Institute's grounds has grown dramatically in recent years to become a nuisance and an environmental problem. This report reviews the problem, considers possible solutions, and proposes that ABC Institute and the US Fish and Wildlife Service cooperate to reduce the flock by humane means.

The Problem

Canada geese began living at Taylor Lake next to ABC Institute when they were relocated there in 1985 by the state game department. As a nonmigratory flock, the geese are present year-round, with the highest population each year occurring in early spring. In recent years the flock has grown dramatically. The Audubon Society's annual Christmas bird census shows a thirty-fold increase from the 37 geese counted in 1986 to the 1125 counted in 2005.

The principal environmental problem caused by the geese is pollution of grass and water by defecation. Geese droppings cover the ABC Institute's grounds as well as the park's picnicking areas. The runoff from these droppings into Taylor Lake has substantially affected the quality of the lake's water, so that local authorities have twice (2004 and 2005) issued warnings against swimming.

Possible Solutions

The goose overpopulation and resulting environmental problems have several possible solutions:

- Harass the geese with dogs and audiovisual effects (light and noise) so that the geese choose to leave. This solution is inhumane to the geese and unpleasant for human neighbors.
- Feed the geese a chemical that will weaken the shells of their eggs and thus reduce growth of the flock. This solution is inhumane to the geese and also impractical, because geese are long-lived.
- Kill adult geese. This solution is, obviously, inhumane to the geese.
- Thin the goose population by trapping and removing many geese (perhaps 600) to areas less populated by humans, such as wildlife preserves.

Though costly (see figures below), the last solution is the most humane. It would be harmless to the geese, provided that sizable netted enclosures are used for traps. [Discussion of solution and "Recommendations" follow.]

Internal proposal

Springfield Veterans Administration Hospital

To: Jefferson Green, Director, Finance and Operations
From: Kate Goodman, Director, ReadingWorks *KG*
Date: October 17, 2005
Subject: Budget proposal for ReadingWorks Awards Dinner

Memo format for internal proposal (p. 798)

OVERVIEW

ReadingWorks requests funding for an awards dinner.

"Overview": statement of proposal

NEED

ReadingWorks, the literacy center operated by Springfield VA Hospital, has for 6 years served between 50 and 70 patients/students a year with a small paid staff and a corps of dedicated volunteers. In the past year the center's paid staff and 20 volunteers provided more than 1260 hours of literacy tutoring to 67 students, an increase of 14 students over last year. I want to recognize the efforts and accomplishments of our students and tutors by holding an awards dinner for them and their families.

"Need": justification for the request

Formal tone appropriate for a proposal

PLAN

I propose the following event for Friday, May 25, 7:30 to 10:30 PM: dinner and nonalcoholic beverages for approximately 135 students, tutors, and their guests; entertainment; and certificates for approximately 20 students and tutors. I request the use of Suite 42 because it can accommodate as many as 200 people as well as caterers and a DJ. Hospital staff will need to have the room ready by 6:00 PM on May 25.

"Plan": explanation of request

BUDGET

Dinner and beverages for about 135 attendees	$2700
Music for two hours	200
Certificates	50
TOTAL	$2950

Bids from local businesses are attached.

"Budget" and "Personnel": details on the proposal's requirements

PERSONNEL

Five hospital employees will be needed to set up, take down, and clean Suite 42 before and after the dinner.

Single spacing with double spacing between sections

55d Writing for community work

At some point in your life, you're likely to volunteer for a community organization such as a soup kitchen, a daycare center, a literacy program, or a tutoring center for immigrants learning English. Some high school and college courses involve service learning, in which you do such volunteer work, write about the experience for your course, and write *for* the organization you're helping.

The writing you do for a community group may range from flyers to newsletters to grant proposals. Two guidelines in particular will help you prepare effective projects:

- **Craft each document for its purpose and audience.** You are trying to achieve a specific aim with your readers, and the approach and tone you use will influence their responses. If, for example, you are writing letters to local businesses to raise funds for a homeless shelter, bring to mind the person or people who will read your letter. How can you best persuade those readers to donate money?

Flyer

Large type and color focusing a distant reader's attention on important information: what's happening, when, where, and who is invited

FIRST ANNUAL AWARDS DINNER

White space drawing viewers' eyes to main message and creating flow among elements

WHEN

Friday night
May 25
7:30 to 10:30

Color highlighting only key information

WHERE

Suite 42
Springfield VA Hospital

For information contact ReadingWorks 209-556-1212

WHO

Students, tutors, and their families are invited to join us for an evening of food and music as we celebrate their efforts and accomplishments.

Less important information set in smaller type

ReadingWorks of Springfield Veterans Administration Hospital
111 South Springdale Drive
Springfield, MI 45078

- **Expect to work with others.** Much public writing is the work of more than one person. Even if you draft the document on your own, others will review the content, tone, and design. Such collaboration is rewarding, but it sometimes requires patience and goodwill. See pages 68–71 and 783–86 for advice on collaborating.

The illustrations here and on the next page show a flyer, a newsletter, and a brochure prepared for ReadingWorks, a literacy program. See also pages 794–99 and 802–05 on business letters, memos, and proposals, as well as pages 815–16 on *PowerPoint* presentations.

Newsletter

ReadingWorks

Springfield Veterans Administration Hospital SUMMER 2005

From the director

Can you help? With more and more learners in the ReadingWorks program, we need more and more tutors. You may know people who would be interested in participating in the program, if only they knew about it.

Those of you who have been tutoring VA patients in reading and writing know both the great need you fulfill and the great benefits you bring to the students. New tutors need no special skills—we'll provide the training—only patience and an interest in helping others.

We've scheduled an orientation meeting for Friday, September 12, at 6:30 PM. Please come and bring a friend who is willing to contribute a couple of hours a week to our work.

Thanks,
Kate Goodman

IN THIS ISSUE

FIRST ANNUAL AWARDS DINNER

A festive night for students and tutors

The first annual ReadingWorks Awards Dinner on May 25th was a great success. Springfield's own Golden Fork provided tasty food and Amber Allen supplied lively music. The students decorated Suite 42 on the theme of books and reading. In all, 127 people attended.

The highlight of the night was the awards ceremony. Nine students, recommended by their tutors, received certificates recognizing their efforts and special accomplishments in learning to read and write:

Ramon Berva
Edward Byar
David Dunbar
Tony Garnier
Chris Guigni
Akili Haynes
Josh Livingston
Alex Obeld
B. J. Resnansky

In addition, nine tutors received certificates commemorating five years of service to ReadingWorks:

Anita Crumpton
Felix Cruz-Rivera
Bette Elgen
Kayleah Bortoluzzi
Harriotte Henderson
Ben Obiso
Meggie Puente
Max Smith
Sara Villante

Congratulations to all!

PTSD: New Guidelines

Most of us are working with veterans who have been diagnosed with post-traumatic stress disorder. Because this disorder is often complicated by alcoholism, depression, anxiety, and other problems, the National Center for PTSD has issued some guidelines for helping PTSD patients in ways that reduce their stress.

- The hospital must know your tutoring schedule, and you need to sign in and out before and after each tutoring session.
- To protect patients' privacy, meet them only in designated visiting and tutoring areas, never in their rooms.
- Treat patients with dignity and respect, even when (as sometimes happens) they grow frustrated and angry. Seek help from a nurse or orderly if you need it.

Multicolumn format allowing room for headings, articles, and other elements on a single page

Two-column heading emphasizing the main article

Elements helping readers skim for highlights: spacing, varied font sizes, lines, and a bulleted list

Color focusing readers' attention on banner, headlines, and table of contents

Lively but uncluttered overall appearance

Box in the first column highlighting table of contents

Checklist for an oral presentation

- **Purpose:** What do you want your audience to know or do as a result of your presentation? How can you achieve your purpose in the time and setting you've been given? (See the previous page and below.)
- **Audience:** What do you know about the characteristics and opinions of your audience? How can this information help you adapt your presentation to your audience's interests, needs, and opinions? (See below.)
- **Organization and content:** How are your ideas arranged? Where might listeners have difficulty following you? What functions do your introduction and conclusion perform? How relevant and interesting is your supporting material for your topic and your audience? (See opposite.)
- **Method of delivery:** What method of delivery do you plan: extemporaneous? reading from a text? memorized? a mixture? How does your method suit the purpose, setting, and occasion of your presentation? (See pp. 812–14.)
- **Vocal and physical delivery:** In rehearsing your presentation, what do you perceive as your strengths and weaknesses? Is your voice suitably loud for the setting? Are you speaking clearly? Are you able to move your eyes around the room so that you'll be making eye contact during the presentation? Is your posture straight but not stiff? Do your gestures reinforce your ideas? Do you use visual aids appropriately? (See pp. 814–15.)
- **Confidence and credibility:** What techniques will you use to overcome the inevitable anxiety about speaking? How will you project your confidence and competence? (See pp. 816–17.)

In school and work settings, oral presentations may include anything from a five-minute report before a few peers to an hour-long address before a hundred people. Whatever the situation, you're likely to be speaking for the same reasons that you write in school or at work: to explain something to listeners or to persuade listeners to accept your opinion or take an action. See pages 15–16 for more on these purposes.

Adapting to your audience is a critical task in public speaking as well as in writing. You'll want to consider the questions about audience on page 12. But a listening audience requires additional considerations as well:

- **Why is your audience assembled?** Listeners who attend because they want to hear you and your ideas may be easier to interest and motivate then listeners who are required to attend.
- **How large is your audience?** With a small group you can be informal. If you are speaking to a hundred or more people, you

may need a public address system, a lectern, special lighting, and audiovisual equipment.

- **Where will you speak?** Your approach should match the setting—more casual for a small classroom, more formal for an auditorium.
- **How long are you scheduled to speak?** Whatever the time limit, stick to it. Audiences lose patience with someone who speaks longer than expected.

When speaking, unlike when writing, you can see and hear your audience's responses during your presentation. If you sense that an audience is bored, try to spice up your presentation. If an audience is restless, consult your watch to make sure you have not gone over your time. If you sense resistance, try to make midspeech adjustments to respond to that resistance.

56c Organizing the presentation

An effective oral presentation, like an effective essay, has a recognizable shape. The advice in Chapter 2 for organizing and outlining an essay serves the speechmaker as well as the writer (see pp. 35–46). Here are additional considerations for the introduction, conclusion, and supporting material.

1 The Introduction

First impressions count. A strong beginning establishes an important relationship among three elements in an oral presentation: you, your topic, and your audience. More specifically, the beginning of an oral presentation should try to accomplish three goals:

- **Gain the audience's attention and interest.** Begin with a question, an unusual example or statistic, or a short, relevant story.
- **Put yourself in the speech.** If you demonstrate your expertise, experience, or concern, your audience will be more interested in what you say and more trusting of you.
- **Introduce and preview your topic and purpose.** By the time your introduction is over, listeners should know what your topic is and the direction in which you wish to take them as you develop your ideas.

In addition to these guidelines for beginning a speech, there are some important pitfalls to avoid:

- **Don't try to cram too much into your introduction.** Focus on engaging the audience and quickly previewing your talk.

- **Don't begin with an apology.** A statement such as *I wish I'd been given more time to get ready for this presentation* will only undermine your listeners' confidence in you.
- **Don't begin with *My speech is about. . . .*** The statement is dull, and it does little to clarify purpose.

2 Supporting material

Just as you do when writing, you can and should use facts, statistics, examples, and expert opinions to support spoken arguments (see pp. 185–86). In addition, as a speaker you can draw on other kinds of supporting material:

- **Use vivid description.** Paint a mental image of a scene, a concept, an event, or a person.
- **Use well-chosen quotations.** They can add an emotional or humorous moment to your speech.
- **Use true or fictional stories.** A memorable narrative can rivet the audience's attention and illustrate your point.
- **Use analogies.** Comparisons between essentially unlike things, such as a politician and a tightrope walker, link concepts memorably. (For more on analogy, see pp. 99–100.)

Use a variety of supporting material in your speech. A presentation that is nothing but statistics can bore an audience. Nonstop storytelling may interest listeners but fail to achieve your purpose.

3 The conclusion

Last impressions count as much as first impressions. You may hope that listeners will remember every detail of your speech, but they are more likely to leave with a general impression and a few ideas about you and your message. You want your conclusion to be clear, of course, but you also want it to be memorable. Remind listeners of how your topic and main idea connect to their needs and interests.

56d Delivering the presentation

Writing and speaking differ most obviously in the form of delivery: the writer is represented in print; the speaker is represented in person. This section describes the methods and techniques of oral presentation as well as some ways of coping with stage fright.

1 Methods of delivery

An oral presentation may be delivered impromptu, extemporaneously, from a text, or from memory. No one technique is best for all speeches; indeed, a single speech may include two or more forms or even all four—perhaps a memorized introduction, an extemporaneous body in which quotations are read from a text, and impromptu responses to audience questions during or after the speech.

Speaking impromptu

Impromptu means "without preparation": an impromptu presentation is one you deliver off-the-cuff, with no planning or practice. You may be called on in a class to express your opinion or to summarize something you've written. You may speak up at a neighborhood meeting. An audience member may ask you a question at the end of an oral presentation. The only way to prepare for such incidents is to be well prepared in general—to be caught up on course reading, for instance, or to know the facts in a debate.

Speaking extemporaneously

Extemporaneous speaking—that done with some preparation, but without reading from a text—is the most common form of presentation, typical of class lectures and business briefings. With extemporaneous speaking, you have time to prepare and practice in advance. Then, instead of following a script of every word, you speak from notes that guide you through the presentation.

Speaking from a text

Delivering a presentation from a text involves writing the text out in advance and then reading aloud from it. With a text in front of you, you're unlikely to lose your way. However, a reading speaker can be dull for an audience. Try to avoid this form of delivery for an entire presentation.

If you do use a text, write it so that it sounds spoken (less formal) rather than written (more formal): for instance, the sentence *Although costs rose, profits remained steady* would sound fine in writing but stiff and awkward in speech because in conversation we rarely use such a structure. In addition, rehearse thoroughly so that you can read with expression and can look up frequently to make eye contact with listeners (see the next page).

Speaking from memory

A memorized presentation has a distinct advantage: complete freedom from notes or a text. That means you can look at your audience every minute and can move away from a lectern and even into the audience. However, you may be like most speakers in seeming less relaxed, not more relaxed, when presenting from memory: your mind is too busy retrieving the next words to attend to the responses of the audience. Further, you risk forgetting your place or a whole passage.

For these reasons, many experts discourage memorization. At least reserve the method for the introduction, perhaps, or some other part with which you want to make a strong impression. Rehearse not only to memorize the words but, beyond that, to deliver the words fresh, as if for the first time.

2 Vocal delivery

The sound of your voice will influence how your listeners receive you. When rehearsing, consider volume, speed, and articulation.

- **Speak loudly.** In a meeting with five other people, you can speak in a normal volume. As your audience grows in size, so should your volume. Most speakers can project to as many as a hundred people, but a larger audience may require a microphone.
- **Speak slowly enough to be understandable.**
- **Speak clearly and correctly.** To avoid mumbling or slurring words, practice articulating. Sometimes it helps to open your mouth a little wider than usual.

3 Physical delivery

You are more than your spoken words when you make an oral presentation. Your face and body also play a role in how your speech is received.

- **Make eye contact with listeners.** Move your gaze around the entire room, settle on someone, and establish direct eye contact; then move on to someone else.
- **Stand up.** Always stand for a presentation, unless it takes place in a small room where standing would be inappropriate. You can see more audience members when you stand, and they in turn can hear your voice and see your gestures more clearly.
- **Stand straight, and move around.** Turn your body toward one side of the room and then the other, step out from behind any lectern or desk, and gesture appropriately, as you would in conversation.

4 Visual aids

You can supplement an oral presentation with visual aids such as posters, models, slides, videos, or presentation software such as *PowerPoint*. Visual aids can emphasize key points, organize related concepts, and illustrate complex procedures. They can gain the attention of listeners and improve their understanding and memory.

The following guidelines can help you create effective and appropriate visual aids:

- **Use visual aids to underscore your points.** Short lists of key ideas, illustrations such as graphs or photographs, or objects such as models can make your presentation more interesting and memorable. But use visual aids judiciously: a constant flow of illustrations or objects will bury your message.
- **Match visual aids and setting.** An audience of five people may be able to see a photograph and share a chart; an audience of a hundred will need projected images.
- **Coordinate visual aids with your message.** Time each visual aid to reinforce a point you're making. Tell listeners what they're looking at—what they should be getting from the aid. Give them enough viewing time so they don't mind turning their attention back to you.
- **Show visual aids only while they're needed.** To regain your audience's attention, remove or turn off any aid as soon as you have finished with it.

Many speakers use *PowerPoint* or other software to project visual aids. (See the sample slides on the next page.) Screens of brief points supported by data, images, or video can help listeners follow your main points. To use *PowerPoint* or other software effectively, follow the guidelines above and also the following:

- **Don't put your whole presentation on screen.** Select key points, and distill them to as few words as possible. Think of the slides as quick, easy-to-remember summaries.
- **Use a simple design.** Avoid turning your presentation into a show about the software's many capabilities.
- **Use a consistent design.** For optimal flow through the presentation, each slide should be formatted similarly.
- **Add only relevant illustrations.** Avoid loading the presentation with mere decoration.

5 Practice

Practicing an oral presentation is the speechmaker's equivalent of editing and proofreading a written text. You won't gain much by practicing silently in your head; instead, you need to rehearse out loud, with the notes you will be using. For your initial rehearsals, you can gauge your performance by making an audio- or videotape of yourself or by practicing in front of a mirror. A recording will let you hear mumbling, too-rapid delivery, grammatical errors, mispronounced words, and unclear concepts. A mirror or video will reveal your stance, your gestures, and your eye contact. Any of these practice techniques will tell you if your presentation is running too long or too short.

PowerPoint slides

First slide, introducing the project and presentation

Simple, consistent slide design focusing viewers' attention on information, not *PowerPoint* features

Making a Difference?

A Service-Learning Project at ReadingWorks

Springfield Veterans Administration Hospital

Jessica Cho
Nathan Hall
Alex Ramirez

FALL 2005

ReadingWorks
Springfield VA Hospital

Later slide, using brief, bulleted points to be explained by the speaker

Photographs reinforcing the project's activities

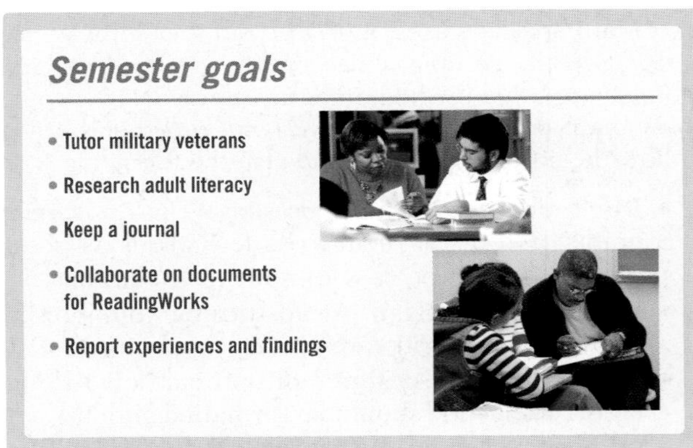

If you plan to use visual aids, you'll need to practice with them, too, preferably in the room where you'll make the presentation and certainly with the help of anyone who will be assisting you. Your goal is to eliminate hitches (upside-down slides, missing charts) and to weave the visuals seamlessly into your presentation.

6 Stage fright

Many people report that speaking in front of an audience is their number-one fear. Even many experienced and polished speakers have some anxiety about delivering an oral presentation, but they use this nervous energy to their advantage, letting it propel them into working hard on each presentation, and rehearsing until they're satisfied with their delivery. They know that the symptoms of anxiety are usually imperceptible to listeners, who cannot see or hear a racing heart, upset stomach, cold hands, and worried thoughts.

Several techniques can help you reduce your level of anxiety:

- **Use simple relaxation exercises.** Deep breathing or tensing and relaxing your stomach muscles can ease some of the physical symptoms of speech anxiety.
- **Think positively.** Instead of worrying about the mistakes you might make, concentrate on how well you've prepared and practiced your presentation and how significant your ideas are.
- **Don't avoid opportunities to speak in public.** Practice and experience build speaking skills and offer the best insurance for success.

CHAPTER 57

Applying to College

As you prepare to apply to college, you will likely take one or more standardized tests designed to assess your high school achievement and predict your success in college. College-admissions tests such as the SAT and ACT may influence your acceptance to college, while Advanced Placement (AP) exams may earn you college credit, advanced standing, or both.

Of course, the admissions staff of a college or university bases its decisions on more than just test scores. It also considers your high school courses, grades, teacher recommendations, and community activities as well as your letter of intent, or essay, on the school's application.

This chapter offers advice for taking the reading and writing sections of the SAT (p. 818) and ACT (p. 828) and the AP exams in English language and composition and literature and composition (p. 830). The chapter concludes with suggestions for writing a college-application essay (p. 833).

Tips for taking timed exams

- **Be prepared.** Familiarize yourself with the format of the test you will be taking by visiting its Web site: *collegeboard.com* for the SAT and AP exams; *act.org* for the ACT. Get a good night's sleep and eat breakfast before the test. Bring a snack and no. 2 pencils (with good erasers) to the test.
- **Read all directions carefully.** Under time pressure, you may be tempted to skip the instructions, but don't. Knowing exactly what the question or prompt is asking allows you to answer more quickly and accurately.
- **Answer easy questions first.** All questions count for the same number of points, so first answer the ones you know for certain. Mark questions you skip or feel unsure about so that you can return to them if you have time.
- **Use the process of elimination.** On multiple-choice questions, rule out answers you know are incorrect and choose the best answer from those remaining.
- **Know how the test is scored so that you know whether to guess.** On the SAT and AP exams, incorrect answers lower your score, so it's best not to take wild guesses. However, if you can eliminate one or two answers, you should guess from those remaining. On the ACT, only correct answers are counted, so you should answer every question even if you have to guess.
- **Budget your time.** Whether you're writing an essay or working through multiple-choice or sentence-completion questions, be aware of how much time you have for each section. Avoid lingering too long over a part of an essay or a single question.

57a Preparing for the SAT and ACT exams

The most widespread college-admissions exams are the SAT and the ACT. Since the tests are similar, this section focuses on the more common SAT. See pages 828–30 for a brief discussion of the ACT.

The general SAT exam, formally called the SAT Reasoning Test, consists of three parts: writing, critical reading, and mathematics. Here we treat the first two of these, but some of the skills we discuss—such as prediction, close attention, and analysis—apply to the math exam as well.

1 Taking the SAT writing section

The writing section of the SAT consists of two sections:

- **Multiple-choice questions,** requiring you to choose revisions of sentences and paragraphs and to identify sentence errors.

- **Short essay,** testing your ability to develop and support a main idea or thesis statement, organize ideas and express them clearly, write persuasively for an audience, and craft clear and correct sentences.

SAT multiple choice

The SAT usually tests the following topics. You can review each one at the handbook pages given in parentheses. (For an overview of areas tested by the ACT, see p. 828.)

- Pronoun case (pp. 269–76) and pronoun reference (pp. 352–58)
- Verb tense (pp. 294–98) and sequence of tenses (pp. 298–300)
- Active and passive verbs (pp. 304–05)
- Subject-verb agreement (pp. 307–14) and pronoun-antecedent agreement (pp. 315–19)
- Use of adjectives, adverbs, and comparisons (pp. 321–26)
- Sentence fragments (pp. 336–43)
- Comma splices and fused sentences (pp. 344–50)
- Consistency (avoiding shifts) in person, number, tense, and mood (pp. 360–62)
- Misplaced and dangling modifiers (pp. 366–74)
- Incomplete sentences and comparisons (pp. 380–82)
- Coordination and subordination (pp. 396–404)
- Parallelism (pp. 407–10)
- Appropriate and exact language (Chapters 37–38)
- Idioms (pp. 525–27)
- Wordiness (pp. 531–36)
- Punctuation (Chapters 27–32)

Besides the tips in the box on the previous page, the following strategies will help you answer multiple-choice writing questions:

- **Read the directions carefully.** The directions tell you what to do, often contain time-saving information, and may vary from question to question.
- **Mark errors as you read.** Underline or circle sentences that don't look right to you.
- **Read the answer options all the way through before choosing or eliminating any answers.**

Improving sentences

Some of the SAT's multiple-choice questions assess your ability to recognize correct and incorrect sentences. You are given a full sentence, part or all of which is underlined. You must analyze the underlined section, determine whether it contains an error, and, if so, identify the correction.

In the following example, notice that the directions state that option A repeats the underlined part of the original sentence. Thus you don't need to read option A unless you are sure that the original sentence is already correct.

> **Directions:** The following sentences test correctness and effectiveness of expression. Part of each sentence or the entire sentence is underlined; beneath each sentence are five ways of phrasing the underlined material. Choice A repeats the original phrasing; the other four choices are different. If you think the original phrasing produces a better sentence than any of the alternatives, select choice A; if not, select one of the other choices.
>
> 1. Experiences in the daily lives of Chinese immigrants, which are vividly described in the works of Maxine Hong Kingston.
>
>   (A) Experiences in the daily lives of Chinese immigrants, which are vividly described in the works of Maxine Hong Kingston.
>
>   (B) Experiences in the daily lives of Chinese immigrants being vividly described in the works of Maxine Hong Kingston.
>
>   (C) The works of Maxine Hong Kingston vividly describe experiences in the daily lives of Chinese immigrants.
>
>   (D) Maxine Hong Kingston, in her vivid work, describing experiences in the daily lives of Chinese immigrants.
>
>   (E) Maxine Hong Kingston, whose work vividly describe experiences in the daily lives of Chinese immigrants.

As you read the original sentence, listen to whether or not it sounds awkward. If it seems wrong, then you can tentatively eliminate A and move on to the other four choices. Reading the example, if you recognize immediately that the original is a sentence fragment, you can then read *for* the choice that is a complete sentence. Option B is not because *being* is not a finite verb (like *are*) that can serve alone as a sentence verb. Option C, however, *is* complete, and you can tentatively select it as the answer. First, though, read through options D and E to be sure they are wrong. (For a review of sentence fragments, see pp. 336–43.)

Identifying sentence errors

Another type of multiple-choice question provides a sentence with four parts underlined. You must identify an error in one of the underlined parts or recognize that the sentence is correct as given. Here is a sample:

> **Directions:** The following sentences test your ability to recognize grammar and usage errors. Each sentence contains either a single error or no error at all. No sentence contains more than one error. The error, if there is one, is underlined and lettered. If the sentence contains an error,

select the one underlined part that must be changed to make the sentence correct. If the sentence is correct, select choice E.

1. The other (A) negotiators and her (B) immediately (C) rejected the proposal presented by (D) the management. No error. (E)

You might spot option B—the pronoun *her*—as incorrect. Before committing to an answer, test it—in this case, by starting the sentence with the pronoun alone: *Her immediately rejected*. (For a review of pronoun case, see pp. 269–76.)

Improving paragraphs

A third kind of multiple-choice question asks you to recognize problems in the unity, coherence, and development of paragraphs and to choose answers that improve the paragraphs. Reading the paragraphs carefully will help you see their problems and anticipate the test questions. The following tips can focus your attention:

- **Look for the topic sentence of each paragraph.**
- **Check that sentences are clear, smooth, and specific.** Sentences that cause you to stumble in your reading are likely to need revision.
- **Check that each sentence logically follows the one before it.** Watch for abrupt transitions or sentences that seem to change the topic.
- **Notice any repetition that makes the paragraph flabby or unwieldy.**

Here is a sample draft essay and the directions for reading it:

> **Directions:** The following passage is an early draft of an essay. Some parts of the passage need to be rewritten. Read the passage and select the best answers for the questions that follow. Some questions are about particular sentences or parts of sentences and ask you to improve sentence structure or word choice. Other questions ask you to consider organization and development. In choosing answers, follow the requirements of standard written English.
>
> (1) Many types of frogs hibernate, essentially sleeping through the winter. (2) They protect themselves from cold by burrowing into the dirt or camping out under piles of leaves. (3) Some frogs are even equipped with mechanisms that allow them to survive being frozen. (4) One type of frog, the wood frog, can survive even when 65% of its total body water turns to ice. (5) These frogs appear to be dead but, it seems miraculous, they are not.
>
> (6) Frozen frogs have extensive ice formation in their body cavities and in the spaces between their cells. (7) The reason that these frogs survive, however, is that no ice forms within their cells. (8) Ice crystals form within cells, they can kill an animal by puncturing certain

specialized parts of the cells. (9) These frogs are protected from the harmful effects of freezing by a chemical reaction. (10) When the first ice crystals begin to form on the skin of a hibernating frog, an internal alarm goes off. (11) This causes the frog's cells to fill with glucose. (12) Precisely the opposite occurs in the spaces between the cells. (13) There special proteins promote the formation of ice crystals. (14) This draws water away from the cells so it does not freeze there.

If you read this essay with attention to its clarity and effectiveness, you might be able to predict the sample test questions discussed below.

1. In context, which word should be inserted at the beginning of sentence 8?

   (A) Because

   (B) Although

   (C) While

   (D) If

   (E) Since

Any of the answers will make the first clause subordinate and thus fix the comma splice in sentence 8, but the correct answer must also make sense in context. In sentence 8, the first clause describes a condition (*Ice crystals form within cells*), and the second describes a result (*they can kill an animal*). The word starting the first clause must then fit this pattern, and only option D (*If*) does so. The other options set up either a contradiction (B, *Although*; C, *While*), or a cause-and-effect relationship (A, *Because*; E, *Since*). *If* also works in the context of sentence 7, which has just stated that ice does *not* form in the frogs' cells. All of the other options seem to contradict that statement.

Here is another question on the essay:

2. Which of the following facts about glucose is most important to add to sentence 11?

   (A) Glucose acts as an antifreeze.

   (B) Glucose can be stored in the liver.

   (C) Glucose is regulated by two hormones, insulin and glucagon.

   (D) Glucose is used by the cells for energy.

   (E) Glucose is a blood sugar found in vertebrates.

The answer to this question must explain why the frogs' cells filling with glucose is *Precisely the opposite* (sentence 12) of proteins' causing ice crystals between cells (sentence 13). Only option A (*Glucose acts as an antifreeze*) provides this explanation. All the others add irrelevant information to the paragraph and disrupt its unity.

SAT short essay

The short-essay section of the SAT tests your ability to write an argument about a topic supplied in a prompt. You will have twenty-five minutes to plan, draft, and review an essay that develops a main point with evidence drawn from your reading, classwork, experience, and observations. The trained graders who score your essay will view it as a rough draft but look for clearly stated ideas, evidence for the ideas, and writing that follows the conventions of standard American English.

The following prompt and assignment are similar to those given on the SAT:

> Life's trials, not its comforts, are what shape and mold us into who we are.
>
> **Assignment:** Do you agree with the statement above, or are there times when you believe it proves false? Plan and write an essay in which you develop your point of view on this issue. Support your position with reasoning and examples taken from your reading, studies, experience, or observation.

Always read the prompt carefully to be sure you understand it. In the sample prompt, for instance, the word *trials* is key. If its meaning in this context is unfamiliar, you can infer from its position in the statement that it is the opposite of *comforts*. Once you're certain of the prompt's meaning, decide on your position—whether you agree or disagree with the statement—and begin developing the evidence for your view.

The following guidelines can help you produce an essay:

- **Use some time for planning.** Before you start writing, take a few minutes to read the prompt, determine your position, and jot down your main ideas and evidence.
- **Write about the topic given in the prompt.** Your essay must address the prompt directly. If it doesn't, you could receive zero points for your essay.
- **State your thesis early and clearly.** Assert your position succinctly in your opening paragraph, even in your opening sentence. For instance: *An easy life free of discomfort and worry may seem a worthy goal, but it is through struggle with life's trials, meeting and overcoming challenges, that we gain strength and self-knowledge.*
- **Choose evidence that supports your thesis.** For the preceding thesis, you might use evidence drawn from literature (in *Gulliver's Travels,* Gulliver often goes out to sea to challenge himself and see how far he can open his mind), the news (hurricane devastation or the war in Iraq), history (the American Revolution or the Civil Rights struggle), or personal experience.

- **Craft sentences carefully.** Although you must write quickly, take the time to demonstrate the logic of your ideas and show the relationships between them. As much as possible, choose appropriate and exact words and use correct grammar and punctuation.
- **Write legibly.** People who are not familiar with your handwriting must be able to read what you write.
- **Allow time for review.** You won't have the leisure for thorough revision, but do allow a few minutes to reread your essay and make minor changes in wording or even in the arrangement of ideas.

(For additional help with writing essay exams, see pp. 145–50.)

2 Taking the SAT critical-reading section

The critical-reading section of the SAT contains two types of questions:

- **Sentence-completion questions,** testing your knowledge of vocabulary and your understanding of how parts of sentences fit together.
- **Passage-based reading questions,** testing your understanding of vocabulary, content, ideas, and writing strategies.

You've practiced the skills you need to answer these questions in your high school work. For more preparation, consult Chapter 8 on critical thinking and reading (pp. 152–64).

Note As a rule, work on sentence-completion questions first because they take less time than passage-based reading questions.

SAT sentence completions

The sentence-completion questions provide sentences with blanks and ask you to choose the best word or words to complete the sentences. In addition to the general test-taking tips in the box on page 818, use the following strategies to answer sentence-completion questions:

- **Use clues in sentence structure.** Often the grammar or punctuation of a sentence provides information about the type of word or words needed in the correct answer.
- **Consider root words, prefixes, suffixes, and familiar sayings or phrases.** They can help you determine the meanings of words.

We'll look at two sample sentence-completion questions. The following directions apply to both:

Directions: Each sentence below has one or two blanks, each blank indicating that something has been omitted. Beneath the sentence are five words or sets of words labeled A through E. Choose the word or set of words that, when inserted in the sentence, *best* fits the meaning of the sentence as a whole.

1. The young reporter was glad to be learning the basics at the local newspaper, but he was becoming bored with ------- news stories and was ------- to cover more exciting action.

   (A) lengthy . . . reluctant
   (B) alluring . . . enthusiastic
   (C) diverse . . . reticent
   (D) numerous . . . fearful
   (E) routine . . . eager

Often you can find the correct answer by eliminating options that definitely aren't correct because they don't work in the context of the sentence. In question 1, you can eliminate B and C because of their first words: a reporter wouldn't be bored with *alluring* or *diverse* stories. And you can eliminate options A, C, and D because of their second words: a reporter who wants to report more exciting stories wouldn't be *reluctant, reticent,* or *fearful.* That leaves E as your response. Fitting its words into the blanks verifies the answer: *The young reporter was glad to be learning the basics at the local newspaper, but he was becoming bored with routine news stories and was eager to cover more exciting action.*

The next question is more difficult:

2. Mrs. Surice felt that Ed's ------- comments during class discussion helped the other students understand the complex ideas presented in the book.

   (A) predictive
   (B) incisive
   (C) derisive
   (D) erratic
   (E) sarcastic

The correct answer will define comments that *helped the other students understand the complex ideas presented in the book.* You might know the correct word right away: *incisive* (B), which means "penetrating, clear." If you don't spot the right word, eliminate the words you know to be wrong: *sarcastic* (E), "scornful"; *derisive* (C), "mocking, ridiculing"; and *erratic* (D), "uneven." Even if you don't know *predictive* (A), you probably know *predict,* which suggests comments that say what comes next, not enlighten.

SAT passage-based reading

Passage-based reading questions test your ability to draw conclusions from reading selections of 100 to 850 words. The passages are drawn from a variety of texts—fiction, general nonfiction, and academic writing—and they include narrative, exposition, and argument. Questions test your understanding of vocabulary and content and often ask you to evaluate some aspect of the text. Sometimes passages are paired, and the questions address both the individual passages and comparisons between them.

In addition to the general test-taking tips in the box on page 818, use the following strategies to work through passage-based reading questions:

- **Read carefully.** The information you need to answer the questions is always in the passage.
- **Don't jump from passage to passage.** Answer as many questions as you can about a passage before moving on. That way, you don't have to refamiliarize yourself with the passage at a later time.
- **Determine the meanings of unfamiliar words** by considering related words, the context of the passage, familiar sayings or phrases, and root words, prefixes, and suffixes.

The following sample includes two questions about a pair of passages.

Directions: The passages below are followed by questions based on their content; questions following a pair of related passages may also be based on the relationship between the paired passages. Answer the questions on the basis of what is stated or implied in the passages and in any introductory material that may be provided.

The legend of King Arthur and the Knights of the Round Table is one of the most enduring in Western literature. Below, two authors consider the factual foundations of the myth.

Passage 1

The Arthur who has become part of the fabric of our lives today is mostly a creation of medieval times, when troubadours and chroniclers made him into a hero of romance, a noble ruler whose knights were patterns of chivalry. The myth has become so real to us that we tend to forget the existence of an actual, historical Arthur. He may not have been a king in the sense that we understand kingship. He may not have been even a particularly good or generous or idealistic man. All we know, in starting out to search for him, is that he must have been a remarkable person, because fame does not come without good reason.

Passage 2

We have no reason to think that Arthur was a territorial ruler, attached to a particular kingdom. It is more likely that he was either a freelance who offered the services of himself and a band of followers to whatever king would pay best, or an overall commander appointed collectively by the kings of the Britons. Britons were capable of taking cooperative action to appoint a commander who could fight their enemies wherever they appeared. Such a role might fit a phrase in the *Historia Britonum,** in which Arthur was said to have fought "along with the kings of the Britons," but he himself was a *dux bellorum* [warrior, or "war duke"].

* Or *History of the Britons,* probably written in the 9th century.

1. The authors of both passages assume that the legendary King Arthur was

   (A) the leader of a heroic group of knights
   (B) an actual historical figure
   (C) a military rather than a political leader
   (D) the invention of poets
   (E) hired by several different kings

Question 1 asks you to look for a similarity between the two passages. You can start by eliminating the choices that don't describe *both* passages: option A, because only passage 1 describes Arthur as a leader of a heroic group of knights; option C, because only passage 2 considers him as a military leader; option D, because neither passage makes him a fictional figure; and option E, because only passage 2 describes him as possibly hired by a group of kings. The answer has to be B: both writers assume Arthur was an actual historical figure.

The following question asks you to draw a conclusion from your reading about one of the passages:

2. In passage 1, "a king in the sense that we understand kingship" most probably refers to

   (A) one member of a group of rulers sharing power in a certain region
   (B) a warlord with a loyal band of followers
   (C) the hero of a romantic folktale
   (D) a military commander for hire
   (E) the political ruler of a specific area

To answer this question, you want to locate the common meanings of *king* and *kingship.* Again eliminate the options that definitely don't work: *member of a group of rulers sharing power* (A), *warlord* (B), and *military commander* (D). (We think of kings as ruling alone and of war making as being only sometimes one of their roles.) Option C, *hero of a romantic folktale,* may seem attractive because passage 1 refers to Arthur as such in medieval times. But the passage goes on to emphasize Arthur's actuality, and in any event we know kings to be real. That leaves option E, *the political ruler of a specific area*, which is indeed a common meaning of *king*.

3 Taking the ACT

The ACT exam is divided into four tests: English, mathematics, reading, and science. A fifth test, a short-essay exam, is optional. In this section we discuss the English, reading, and writing tests.

ACT English test

The ACT English exam includes multiple-choice in two subsections: identifying sentence errors and improving sentences and paragraphs. The following topics will likely be tested on the ACT. To review, consult the handbook chapters and pages in parentheses.

- The writing process (Chapters 1–3)
- Organization (Chapter 2; Chapter 4, pp. 81–85)
- Style, including emphasis, parallelism, variety, appropriate and exact language, idioms, and conciseness (Chapters 23–26 and 37–39)
- Case of nouns and pronouns (pp. 269–76)
- Verbs (pp. 277–305)
- Subject-verb agreement (pp. 307–14)
- Pronoun-antecedent agreement (pp. 315–19)
- Adjectives and adverbs (pp. 321–26)
- Sentence fragments (pp. 336–43)
- Comma splices and fused sentences (pp. 344–50)
- Pronoun reference (pp. 352–58)
- Misplaced and dangling modifiers (pp. 366–74)
- Shifts (pp. 360–62)
- Coordination and subordination (pp. 396–404)
- Punctuation, including the relation between punctuation and meaning (Chapters 27–32)

As you prepare for the ACT, use the test-taking strategies in the box on page 818. You can also review strategies for taking the corresponding parts of the SAT: "Improving sentences" (p. 819), "Identifying sentence errors" (p. 820), and "Improving paragraphs" (p. 821). Be aware that the ACT's question format differs from that of the SAT, so you should consult the sample test questions at *act.org* to familiarize yourself with the ACT format.

Following is a sample sentence from an ACT English test, with a potential error underlined and numbered. The ACT presents such sentences in the context of full paragraphs, and on the actual exam this sentence falls in a six-paragraph passage with fifteen questions.

After the final performance of one last practice landing, the French instructor nodded to the young African-American woman at the controls and jumped to the ground.
(1)

1. (A) NO CHANGE
   (B) one finally ultimate
   (C) one final
   (D) one last final

The underlined section of the sentence is wordy and redundant. Options B and D reduce the wordiness, but they are still redundant (*finally ultimate* and *last final*). Option C is the correct choice.

ACT reading test

The ACT reading test asks you to answer questions about four passages drawn from the social sciences, natural sciences, humanities, and prose fiction. Unlike the SAT, which sometimes asks for comparison of two passages, the ACT always gives only one passage at a time. The multiple-choice questions that follow the four passages test abilities such as determining main ideas, locating and interpreting important details, understanding the sequence of events, making comparisons and generalizations, and analyzing the author's style, voice, and method. The ACT does not test vocabulary, so it contains nothing comparable to the SAT's sentence-completion questions.

To prepare for the ACT reading test, consult the discussion of the SAT passage-based reading section on pages 826–28, the sample test questions and analysis at *act.org,* and also this book's Chapter 8 on critical thinking and reading.

ACT writing test

The ACT writing test is optional. Before you decide to take it, check to see whether it is required by the colleges you are applying to. If you choose to take the writing test, consult the advice on pages 823–24 of this chapter as well as the guidelines for taking any essay exam on pages 145–50.

ACT writing prompts, such as the one below, usually draw on general knowledge. They also provide details to help you frame your response. Here is an example:

> In some high schools, many teachers and parents have encouraged the school to adopt a dress code that sets guidelines for what students can wear in the school building. Some parents and teachers support a dress code because they think it will improve the learning environment in the school. Other teachers and parents do not support a dress code because they think it restricts the individual student's freedom of expression. In your opinion, should high schools adopt dress codes for students?

> In your essay, take a position on this question. You may write about either one of the two points of view given, or you may present a different point of view on this question. Use specific reasons and examples to support your position.

As with the SAT, be sure you understand the prompt and the instructions before you begin to write. Here, you are asked to express an opinion about the dress-code debate and to support the opinion using specific reasons and examples. You should decide quickly what your opinion is and think of a few examples to use in support of your position. Your next step is to state it clearly, and argue for it with evidence drawn from your reading, observations, and experience. You may use reasons given in the prompt as long as you provide details to back them up.

57b Preparing for the AP English exams

Advanced Placement (AP) courses in high school teach the kinds of thinking, reading, and writing activities typical of an introductory college course. Some of these courses prepare students to take the two AP English exams, the literature and composition exam and the language and composition exam. Because high scores on the exams can exempt you from college courses or earn you credits toward a college degree, AP exams are more rigorous and more specific than the general SAT and ACT exams.

Both AP English exams require you to answer multiple-choice questions about passages of prose or poetry and to answer three free-response questions based on passages or prompts. The College Board, sponsor of the AP test, does not permit reproduction of its sample questions. For samples and additional test-taking strategies, visit the AP Web site at *collegeboard.com*.

1 Answering AP multiple-choice questions

The multiple-choice questions on both AP English exams test a variety of reading skills, including your ability to do the following:

- **Read closely and analyze a variety of texts,** including nonfiction prose, fiction, poetry, and drama.
- **Interpret the meaning of a text by analyzing an author's style,** including sentence structure, word choice, tone, and figurative language.
- **Analyze organization and structure,** including the writer's strategies for openings and closings, transitions among ideas, and repetition and variation in sentence structure and paragraphs.
- **Recognize rhetorical strategies,** understanding the relationships among speaker, subject, and audience.

The literature and composition exam uses literary texts from a variety of historical periods, in various genres, and on a wide range of topics. The language and composition exam frequently supplies nonfiction prose (narrative, expository, and argumentative), as well as fiction and poetry.

As with any timed test, be sure to read the text closely and completely before answering any questions. Try to infer the meanings of unfamiliar words from the context of the passage, and prepare yourself for the questions that follow by predicting as you read. Answer easy questions first, use the process of elimination to make the best choices, and mark questions you skip so that you can return to them later if you have time. In addition, use the general test-taking tips in the box on page 818.

2 Answering AP free-response questions

Both of the AP English exams require students to write three essays in two hours. Unlike the SAT and ACT essay prompts, which are fairly open-ended, most or all of the AP essay prompts ask you to read passages and respond to them directly. Even when the third essay question is more open-ended, it is still more academic than the SAT and ACT prompts.

Plan to spend forty minutes on each essay, including the time it takes to read the directions and the prompt or passage. Focus on demonstrating interpretive skill, developing ideas carefully, and writing clearly and persuasively. Use the following strategies to craft your essays:

- **Read the directions and assignment before you start reading the passage or prompt.** Be sure that you do what's required, whether analyzing style, interpreting meaning, arguing a position, explaining a writer's strategies, or something else.
- **Read the passage or prompt carefully,** marking words or phrases for ideas and quotations.
- **Develop your thesis statement.** In a sentence or two, address the assignment directly and identify your main points.
- **Choose evidence that supports your thesis and main points.** Use concrete, specific details to support your ideas, quoting or paraphrasing the passage. Allot roughly equal space to each of your main points.
- **Write legibly.** People who are not familiar with your handwriting must be able to read what you write.
- **Allow time for review.** You won't have the leisure for thorough revision, but do allow a few minutes to reread your essay and make minor changes in wording or even in the arrangement of ideas.

- **Choose an appropriate subject.** Use the essay to tell the college something about you that isn't evident from your transcript, letters of recommendation, or test scores, such as a nonacademic achievement, a challenge you've surmounted, or why you want to attend the college you're applying to. Gather ideas by talking to others, including teachers, who have experience with writing and reading application essays. For more on choosing a subject, see pages 7–9.
- **Use your strengths as a writer.** If you're adept at storytelling, consider an essay that develops from a narrative. If argument comes easily, consider a persuasive essay about a topic you care about. If you're funny, consider a humorous essay. If you aren't sure what your strengths are, look back at writing you've done in school to see what your peers and teachers liked and didn't like.
- **Choose examples carefully.** Use experiences, reading, and other sources to make your ideas concrete and specific: a conversation you had, something you witnessed, a difficult choice, or a moment of enlightenment. For more on developing and shaping ideas, see pages 18–46.
- **Take care with the introduction and conclusion.** Your introduction should draw readers into your essay, focusing them on your subject and what you have to say. Your conclusion should not summarize your essay but instead comment on what you've said in the essay or look to the future. For more on introductions and conclusions, see pages 104–10.
- **Share your completed draft with friends, family, or teachers.** Other readers may see opportunities for developing an example or idea, catch unclear or incorrect sentence constructions, or suggest changes in wording. For more on revising an essay, see pages 51–71.
- **Edit and proofread your essay before you send it.** Readers will look for polished sentences, correct punctuation, and perfect spelling in your essay, so take the time you need to read it carefully before you send it. See the editing and proofreading checklists on pages 60–61 and 65.

The student who wrote the following application essay was responding to a general prompt suggesting that she tell of an experience that had changed her. Notice that she makes the experience specific while holding her focus on the change it caused.

As I waited for my student on my first day as a literacy tutor, I felt young and inexperienced. I was a newly certified tutor, but my eight hours of training now seemed distant and possibly useless. When my student, a Hmong woman named Mai Thao, entered the room, I summoned my courage, smiled, and greeted her, and she smiled back. We got to work, and to my relief the hour went smoothly. Today, with over a year of weekly tutoring sessions behind me, I have gained confidence in my ability as a tutor, but even more I have learned to appreciate the experiences of immigrants and have found direction for my college career.

Tutoring Mai Thao and meeting other clients of the literacy center have opened my eyes to a world far beyond my high school. Like other immigrants, Mai Thao chose to leave her home and come to the United States in the hope of economic opportunity. She works hard at her job, studies English, and educates her children, trying to maintain her cultural identity while also assimilating into US culture. She had little formal education, so as she learns to speak and understand English she is also learning to read and write in any language. Activities that most glide through—shopping for food, making a doctor's appointment, asking for directions, taking a driver's test—have been huge hurdles for her. I don't think I or most people I know could surmount such challenges.

As much as tutoring has opened my mind, so has it confirmed my ability to teach and shown me a path. I have prepared lesson plans, handouts, and props that have helped Mai Thao learn the everyday language she needs to negotiate life in the United States. I've come to love teaching and to appreciate my own education, which until a year ago I had taken for granted. I am eager to attend ______ College, where the programs in foreign languages, teaching, and public policy will prepare me for what I see as a lifetime's commitment to education.

It's often said that globalization is making the world smaller, but I see the world as growing larger: through the media and from immigrants in our communities, we are more aware of people different from ourselves and of their opportunities and challenges. The leaders of the future will have to be open to difference and willing to bridge it. I want to be one of those leaders.

and which, and who *And which* or *and who* is correct only when used to introduce a second clause beginning with the same relative pronoun: *Jill is my cousin who goes to school here and who calls me constantly.* Otherwise, *and* is not needed: *WCAS is my favorite AM radio station, which* [not *and which*] *I listen to every morning.*

ante-, anti- The prefix *ante-* means "before" (*antedate, antebellum*); *anti-* means "against" (*antiwar, antinuclear*). Before a capital letter or *i, anti-* takes a hyphen: *anti-Freudian, anti-isolationist.*

anxious, eager *Anxious* means "nervous" or "worried" and is usually followed by *about. Eager* means "looking forward" and is usually followed by *to. I've been anxious about getting blisters. I'm eager* [not *anxious*] *to get new running shoes.*

anybody, any body; anyone, any one *Anybody* and *anyone* are indefinite pronouns; *any body* is a noun modified by *any; any one* is a pronoun or adjective modified by *any. How can anybody communicate with any body of government? Can anyone help Amy? She has more work than any one person can handle.*

any more, anymore *Any more* means "no more"; *anymore* means "now." Both are used in negative constructions: *He doesn't want any more. She doesn't live here anymore.*

anyplace Colloquial for *anywhere.*

anyways, anywheres Nonstandard for *anyway* and *anywhere.*

apt, liable, likely *Apt* and *likely* are interchangeable. Strictly speaking, though, *apt* means "having a tendency to": *Horace is apt to forget his lunch in the morning. Likely* means "probably going to": *Horace is leaving so early today that he's likely to catch the first bus.*

Liable normally means "in danger of" and should be confined to situations with undesirable consequences: *Horace is liable to trip over that hose.* Strictly, *liable* means "responsible" or "exposed to": *The owner will be liable for Horace's injuries.*

are, is Use *are* with a plural subject (*books are*), *is* with a singular subject (*book is*).

as Substituting for *because, since,* or *while, as* may be vague or ambiguous: *As the researchers asked more questions, their money ran out.* (Does *as* mean "while" or "because"?) *As* should never be used as a substitute for *whether* or *who. I'm not sure whether* [not *as*] *we can make it. That's the man who* [not *as*] *gave me directions.*

as, like See *like, as.*

as, than In comparisons, *as* and *than* precede a subjective-case pronoun when the pronoun is a subject: *I love you more than he* [*loves you*]. *As* and *than* precede an objective-case pronoun when the pronoun is an object: *I love you as much as* [*I love*] *him.* (See also p. 273.)

assure, ensure, insure *Assure* means "to promise": *He assured us that we would miss the traffic. Ensure* and *insure* often are used interchangeably to mean "make certain," but some reserve *insure* for matters of legal and financial protection and use *ensure* for more general meanings:

We left early to ensure that we would miss the traffic. It's expensive to insure yourself against floods.

as to A stuffy substitute for *about: The suspect was questioned about* [not *as to*] *her actions.*

at The use of *at* after *where* is wordy and should be avoided: *Where are you meeting him?* is preferable to *Where are you meeting him at?*

at this point in time Wordy for *now, at this point,* or *at this time.*

averse, adverse See *adverse, averse.*

awful, awfully Strictly speaking, *awful* means "awe-inspiring." As intensifiers meaning "very" or "extremely" (*He tried awfully hard*), *awful* and *awfully* should be avoided in formal speech or writing.

a while, awhile *Awhile* is an adverb; *a while* is an article and a noun. Thus *awhile* can modify a verb but cannot serve as the object of a preposition, and *a while* is just the opposite: *I will be gone awhile* [not *a while*]. *I will be gone for a while* [not *awhile*].

bad, badly In formal speech and writing, *bad* should be used only as an adjective; the adverb is *badly. He felt bad because his tooth ached badly.* In *He felt bad,* the verb *felt* is a linking verb and the adjective *bad* is a subject complement. (See also pp. 324–25.)

being as, being that Colloquial for *because,* the preferable word in formal speech or writing: *Because* [not *Being as*] *the world is round, Columbus never did fall off the edge.*

beside, besides *Beside* is a preposition meaning "next to." *Besides* is a preposition meaning "except" or "in addition to" as well as an adverb meaning "in addition." *Besides, several other people besides you want to sit beside Dr. Christensen.*

better, had better *Had better* (meaning "ought to") is a verb modified by an adverb. The verb is necessary and should not be omitted: *You had better* [not just *better*] *go.*

between, among See *among, between.*

bring, take Use *bring* only for movement from a farther place to a nearer one and *take* for any other movement. *First, take these books to the library for renewal, then take them to Mr. Daniels. Bring them back to me when he's finished.*

bunch In formal speech and writing, *bunch* (as a noun) should be used only to refer to clusters of things growing or fastened together, such as bananas and grapes. Its use to mean a group of items or people is colloquial; *crowd* or *group* is preferable.

burst, bursted; bust, busted *Burst* is a standard verb form meaning "to fly apart suddenly." Its main forms are *burst, burst, burst;* the form *bursted* is nonstandard. The verb *bust* (*busted*) is slang.

but, hardly, scarcely These words are negative in their own right; using *not* with any of them produces a double negative (see p. 326). *We have but* [not *haven't got but*] *an hour before our plane leaves. I could hardly* [not *couldn't hardly*] *make out her face.*

but, however, yet Each of these words is adequate to express contrast. Don't combine them. *He said he had finished, yet* [not *but yet*] *he continued.*

but that, but what These wordy substitutes for *that* and *what* should be avoided: *I don't doubt that* [not *but that*] *you are right.*

calculate, figure, reckon As substitutes for *expect* or *imagine* (*I figure I'll go*), these words are colloquial.

can, may Strictly, *can* indicates capacity or ability, and *may* indicates permission: *If I may talk with you a moment, I believe I can solve your problem. May* also indicates possibility: *You may like what you hear.*

can't help but This idiom is common but redundant. Either *I can't help wishing* or the more formal *I cannot but wish* is preferable to *I can't help but wish.*

case, instance, line Expressions such as *in the case of, in the instance of,* and *along the lines of* are usually unnecessary padding and should be avoided.

censor, censure To *censor* is to edit or remove from public view on moral or some other grounds; to *censure* is to give a formal scolding. *The lieutenant was censured by Major Taylor for censoring the letters her soldiers wrote home from boot camp.*

center around *Center on* is more logical than, and preferable to, *center around.*

climatic, climactic *Climatic* comes from *climate* and refers to weather: *Last winter's temperatures may indicate a climatic change. Climactic* comes from *climax* and refers to a dramatic high point: *During the climactic duel between Hamlet and Laertes, Gertrude drinks poisoned wine.*

complement, compliment To *complement* something is to add to, complete, or reinforce it: *Her yellow blouse complemented her black hair.* To *compliment* something is to make a flattering remark about it: *He complimented her on her hair. Compliment* also functions as a noun: *She thanked him for the compliment.* The adjective *complimentary* can also mean "free": *complimentary tickets.*

compose, comprise *Compose* means "to make up": *The parts compose the whole. Comprise* means "to consist of": *The whole comprises the parts.* Thus, *The band comprises* [not *is comprised of*] *twelve musicians. Twelve musicians compose* [not *comprise*] *the band.*

conscience, conscious *Conscience* is a noun meaning "a sense of right and wrong"; *conscious* is an adjective meaning "aware" or "awake." *Though I was barely conscious, my conscience nagged me.*

contact Often used imprecisely as a verb instead of a more exact word such as *consult, talk with, telephone,* or *write to.*

continual, continuous *Continual* means "constantly recurring": *Most movies on television are continually interrupted by commercials. Continuous* means "unceasing": *Some cable channels present movies continuously without commercials.*

convince, persuade In the strictest sense, to *convince* someone means to change his or her opinion; to *persuade* someone means to move him or her to action. *Convince* is thus properly followed by *of* or *that,* whereas *persuade* is followed by *to: Once he convinced Othello of Desdemona's infidelity, Iago easily persuaded him to kill her.*

could care less The expression is *could not* [*couldn't*] *care less. Could care less* indicates some care, the opposite of what is intended.

could of See *have, of.*

couple of Used colloquially to mean "a few" or "several."

credible, creditable, credulous *Credible* means "believable": *It's a strange story, but it seems credible to me. Creditable* means "deserving of credit" or "worthy": *Steve gave a creditable performance. Credulous* means "gullible": *The credulous Claire believed Tim's lies.* See also *incredible, incredulous.*

criteria The plural of *criterion* (meaning "standard for judgment"): *Our criteria are strict. The most important criterion is a sense of humor.*

data The plural of *datum* (meaning "fact"): *Out of all the data generated by these experiments, not one datum supports our hypothesis.* Usually, a more common term such as *fact, result,* or *figure* is preferred to *datum.* Though *data* is often used with a singular verb, many readers prefer the plural verb and it is always correct: *The data fail* [not *fails*] *to support the hypothesis.*

device, devise *Device* is the noun, and *devise* is the verb: *Can you devise some device for getting his attention?*

different from, different than *Different from* is preferred: *His purpose is different from mine.* But *different than* is widely accepted when a construction using *from* would be wordy: *I'm a different person now than I used to be* is preferable to *I'm a different person now from the person I used to be.*

differ from, differ with To *differ from* is to be unlike: *The twins differ from each other only in their hairstyles.* To *differ with* is to disagree with: *I have to differ with you on that point.*

discreet, discrete *Discreet* (noun form *discretion*) means "tactful": *What's a discreet way of telling Maud to be quiet? Discrete* (noun form *discreteness*) means "separate and distinct": *Within a computer's memory are millions of discrete bits of information.*

disinterested, uninterested *Disinterested* means "impartial": *We chose Pete, as a disinterested third party, to decide who was right. Uninterested* means "bored" or "lacking interest": *Unfortunately, Pete was completely uninterested in the question.*

don't *Don't* is the contraction for *do not,* not for *does not: I don't care, you don't care, and he doesn't* [not *don't*] *care.*

due to *Due* is an adjective or noun; thus *due to* is always acceptable as a subject complement: *His gray hairs were due to age.* Many object to *due to* as a preposition meaning "because of" (*Due to the holiday, class was canceled*). A rule of thumb is that *due to* is always correct after a form of the verb *be* but questionable otherwise.

he, she; he/she Convention has allowed the use of *he* to mean "he or she": *After the infant learns to creep, he progresses to crawling.* However, many writers today consider this usage inaccurate and unfair because it seems to exclude females. The construction *he/she,* one substitute for *he,* is awkward and objectionable to most readers. The better choice is to make the pronoun plural, to rephrase, or, sparingly, to use *he or she.* For instance: *After infants learn to creep, they progress to crawling. After learning to creep, the infant progresses to crawling. After the infant learns to creep, he or she progresses to crawling.* (See also pp. 317–19 and 518.)

herself, himself See *myself, herself, himself, yourself.*

hisself Nonstandard for *himself.*

hopefully *Hopefully* means "with hope": *Freddy waited hopefully for a glimpse of Eliza.* The use of *hopefully* to mean "it is to be hoped," "I hope," or "let's hope" is now very common; but since many readers continue to object strongly to the usage, you should avoid it. *I hope* [not *Hopefully*] *the law will pass.*

idea, ideal An *idea* is a thought or conception. An *ideal* (noun) is a model of perfection or a goal. *Ideal* should not be used in place of *idea: The idea* [not *ideal*] *of the play is that our ideals often sustain us.*

if, whether For clarity, use *whether* rather than *if* when you are expressing an alternative: *If I laugh hard, people can't tell whether I'm crying.*

illicit See *elicit, illicit.*

illusion See *allusion, illusion.*

immigrate, emigrate See *emigrate, immigrate.*

impact Both the noun and the verb *impact* connote forceful or even violent collision. Avoid the increasingly common diluted meanings of *impact:* "an effect" (noun) or "to have an effect on" (verb). The diluted verb (*The budget cuts impacted social science research*) is bureaucratic jargon.

implicit See *explicit, implicit.*

imply, infer Writers or speakers *imply,* meaning "suggest": *Jim's letter implies he's having a good time.* Readers or listeners *infer,* meaning "conclude": *From Jim's letter I infer he's having a good time.*

in, into *In* indicates location or condition: *He was in the garage. She was in a coma. Into* indicates movement or a change in condition: *He went into the garage. She fell into a coma.* Generally avoid the slang sense of *into* meaning "interested in" or "involved in": *I am into Zen.*

in . . . A number of phrases beginning with *in* are needlessly wordy and should be avoided: *in the event that* (for *if*); *in the neighborhood of* (for *approximately* or *about*); *in this day and age* (for *now* or *nowadays*); *in spite of the fact that* (for *although* or *even though*); and *in view of the fact that* (for *because* or *considering that*). Certain other *in* phrases are nothing but padding and can be omitted entirely: *in nature, in number, in reality,* and *in a very real sense.* (See also pp. 533–34.)

incredible, incredulous *Incredible* means "unbelievable"; *incredulous* means "unbelieving": *When Nancy heard Dennis's incredible story, she was frankly incredulous.* See also *credible, creditable, credulous.*

individual, person, party *Individual* should refer to a single human being in contrast to a group or should stress uniqueness: *The US Constitution places strong emphasis on the rights of the individual.* For other meanings *person* is preferable: *What person* [not *individual*] *wouldn't want the security promised in that advertisement? Party* means "group" (*Can you seat a party of four for dinner?*) and should not be used to refer to an individual except in legal documents. See also *people, persons.*

infer See *imply, infer.*

in regards to Nonstandard for *in regard to, as regards,* or *regarding.* See also *regarding.*

inside of, outside of The *of* is unnecessary when *inside* and *outside* are used as prepositions: *Stay inside* [not *inside of*] *the house. The decision is outside* [not *outside of*] *my authority. Inside of* may refer colloquially to time, though in formal English *within* is preferred: *The law was passed within* [not *inside of*] *a year.*

instance See *case, instance, line.*

insure See *assure, ensure, insure.*

irregardless Nonstandard for *regardless.*

is, are See *are, is.*

is because See *reason is because.*

is when, is where These are faulty constructions in sentences that define: *Adolescence is a stage* [not *is when a person is*] *between childhood and adulthood. Socialism is a system in which* [not *is where*] *government owns the means of production.* (See also p. 378.)

its, it's *Its* is the pronoun *it* in the possessive case: *That plant is losing its leaves. It's* is a contraction for *it is* or *it has: It's* [*It is*] *likely to die. It's* [*It has*] *got a fungus.* Many people confuse *it's* and *its* because possessives are most often formed with *-'s;* but the possessive *its,* like *his* and *hers,* never takes an apostrophe.

-ize, -wise The suffix *-ize* changes a noun or adjective into a verb: *revolutionize, immunize.* The suffix *-wise* changes a noun or adjective into an adverb: *clockwise, otherwise, likewise.* Avoid the two suffixes except in established words: *The two nations are ready to settle on* [not *finalize*] *an agreement. I'm highly sensitive* [not *sensitized*] *to that kind of criticism. Financially* [not *Moneywise*], *it's a good time to invest in real estate.*

kind of, sort of, type of In formal speech and writing, avoid using *kind of* or *sort of* to mean "somewhat": *He was rather* [not *kind of*] *tall.*

Kind, sort, and *type* are singular and take singular modifiers and verbs: *This kind of dog is easily trained.* Agreement errors often occur when these singular nouns are combined with the plural adjectives *these* and *those: These kinds* [not *kind*] *of dogs are easily trained. Kind,*

party See *individual, person, party.*

people, persons In formal usage, *people* refers to a general group: *We the people of the United States. . . . Persons* refers to a collection of individuals: *Will the person or persons who saw the accident please notify. . . .* Except when emphasizing individuals, prefer *people* to *persons.* See also *individual, person, party.*

per Except in technical writing, an English equivalent is usually preferable to the Latin *per: $10 an* [not *per*] *hour; sent by* [not *per*] *parcel post; requested in* [not *per* or *as per*] *your letter.*

percent (per cent), percentage Both these terms refer to fractions of one hundred. *Percent* always follows a numeral (*40 percent of the voters*), and the word should be used instead of the symbol (%) in general writing. *Percentage* stands alone (*the percentage of votes*) or follows an adjective (*a high percentage*).

person See *individual, person, party.*

persons See *people, persons.*

persuade See *convince, persuade.*

phenomena The plural of *phenomenon* (meaning "perceivable fact" or "unusual occurrence"): *Many phenomena are not recorded. One phenomenon is attracting attention.*

plenty A colloquial substitute for *very: The reaction occurred very* [not *plenty*] *fast.*

plus *Plus* is standard as a preposition meaning *in addition to: His income plus mine is sufficient.* But *plus* is colloquial as a conjunctive adverb: *Our organization is larger than theirs; moreover* [not *plus*], *we have more money.*

practicable, practical *Practicable* means "capable of being put into practice"; *practical* means "useful" or "sensible": *We figured out a practical new design for our kitchen, but it was too expensive to be practicable.*

precede, proceed The verb *precede* means "come before": *My name precedes yours in the alphabet.* The verb *proceed* means "move on": *We were told to proceed to the waiting room.*

prejudice, prejudiced *Prejudice* is a noun; *prejudiced* is an adjective. Do not drop the *-d* from *prejudiced: I knew that my parents were prejudiced* [not *prejudice*].

pretty Overworked as an adverb meaning "rather" or "somewhat": *He was somewhat* [not *pretty*] *irked at the suggestion.*

previous to, prior to Wordy for *before.*

principal, principle *Principal* is an adjective meaning "foremost" or "major," a noun meaning "chief official," or, in finance, a noun meaning "capital sum." *Principle* is a noun only, meaning "rule" or "axiom." *Her principal reasons for confessing were her principles of right and wrong.*

proceed, precede See *precede, proceed.*

provided, providing *Provided* may serve as a subordinating conjunction meaning "on the condition (that)"; *providing* may not. *The grocer* *will begin providing food for the soup kitchen provided* [not *providing*] *we find a suitable space.*

question of whether, question as to whether Wordy substitutes for *whether.*

raise, rise *Raise* means "lift" or "bring up" and takes a direct object: *The Kirks raise cattle.* Its main forms are *raise, raised, raised. Rise* means "get up" and does not take an object: *They must rise at dawn.* Its main forms are *rise, rose, risen.* (See also p. 283.)

real, really In formal speech and writing, *real* should not be used as an adverb; *really* is the adverb and *real* an adjective. *Popular reaction to the announcement was really* [not *real*] *enthusiastic.*

reason is because Although colloquially common, this expression should be avoided in formal speech and writing. Use a *that* clause after *reason is: The reason he is absent is that* [not *is because*] *he is sick.* Or: *He is absent because he is sick.*

reckon See *calculate, figure, reckon.*

regarding, in regard to, with regard to, relating to, relative to, with respect to, respecting Stuffy substitutes for *on, about,* or *concerning: Mr. McGee spoke about* [not *with regard to*] *the plans for the merger.*

respectful, respective *Respectful* means "full of (or showing) respect": *Be respectful of other people. Respective* means "separate": *The French and the Germans occupied their respective trenches.*

rise, raise See *raise, rise.*

scarcely See *but, hardly, scarcely.*

sensual, sensuous *Sensual* suggests sexuality; *sensuous* means "pleasing to the senses." *Stirred by the sensuous scent of meadow grass and flowers, Cheryl and Paul found their thoughts growing increasingly sensual.*

set, sit *Set* means "put" or "place" and takes a direct object: *He sets the pitcher down.* Its main forms are *set, set, set. Sit* means "be seated" and does not take an object: *She sits on the sofa.* Its main forms are *sit, sat, sat.* (See also p. 283.)

shall, will *Will* is the future-tense helping verb for all persons: *I will go, you will go, they will go.* The main use of *shall* is for first-person questions requesting an opinion or consent: *Shall I order a pizza? Shall we dance?* (Questions that merely inquire about the future use *will: When will I see you again?*) *Shall* can also be used for the first person when a formal effect is desired (*I shall expect you around three*), and it is occasionally used with the second or third person to express the speaker's determination (*You shall do as I say*).

should, would *Should* expresses obligation: *I should fix dinner. You should set the table. Jack should wash the dishes. Would* expresses a wish or hypothetical condition: *I would do it. Wouldn't you?* When the context is formal, however, *should* is sometimes used instead of *would* in the first person: *We should be delighted to accept.*

should of See *have, of.*

since *Since* mainly relates to time: *I've been waiting since noon.* But *since* is also often used to mean "because": *Since you ask, I'll tell you.*

uninterested See *disinterested, uninterested.*

unique *Unique* means "the only one of its kind" and so cannot sensibly be modified with words such as *very* or *most: That was a unique* [not *a very unique* or *the most unique*] *movie.*

until See *till, until, 'til.*

upon, on See *on, upon.*

usage, use *Usage* refers to conventions, most often those of a language: *Is "hadn't ought" proper usage? Usage* is often misused in place of the noun *use: Wise use* [not *usage*] *of insulation can save fuel.*

use, utilize *Utilize* can be used to mean "make good use of": *Many teachers utilize computers for instruction.* But for all other senses of "place in service" or "employ," prefer *use.*

used to See *supposed to, used to.*

wait for, wait on In formal speech and writing, *wait for* means "await" (*I'm waiting for Paul*), and *wait on* means "serve" (*The owner of the store herself waited on us*).

ways Colloquial as a substitute for way: *We have only a little way* [not *ways*] *to go.*

well See *good, well.*

whether, if See *if, whether.*

which, that See *that, which.*

which, who, that See *that, who, which.*

who, whom *Who* is the subject of a sentence or clause (*We don't know who will come*). *Whom* is the object of a verb or preposition (*We do not know whom we invited*). (See also pp. 273–75.)

who's, whose *Who's* is the contraction of *who is* or *who has: Who's* [*Who is*] *at the door? Jim is the only one who's* [*who has*] *passed. Whose* is the possessive form of *who: Whose book is that?*

will, shall See *shall, will.*

wise See *-ize, -wise.*

with regard to, with respect to See *regarding.*

would See *should, would.*

would have Avoid this construction in place of *had* in clauses that begin *if* and state a condition contrary to fact: *If the tree had* [not *would have*] *withstood the fire, it would have been the oldest in the state.* (See also p. 303.)

would of See *have, of.*

you In all but very formal writing, *you* is generally appropriate as long as it means "you, the reader." In all writing, avoid indefinite uses of *you,* such as *In one ancient tribe your first loyalty was to your parents.* (See also pp. 356–57.)

your, you're *Your* is the possessive form of *you: Your dinner is ready. You're* is the contraction of *you are: You're bound to be late.*

yourself See *myself, herself, himself, yourself.*

Glossary of Terms

This glossary defines terms of grammar, rhetoric, literature, and Internet research. Page numbers in parentheses refer you to sections of the text where the term is explained more fully.

absolute phrase A phrase consisting of a noun or pronoun plus the *-ing* or *-ed* form of a verb (a participle): *Our accommodations arranged, we set out on our journey. They will hire a local person, other things being equal.* An absolute phrase modifies a whole clause or sentence (rather than a single word), and it is not joined to the rest of the sentence by a connector. (See pp. 253–54.)

abstract and concrete Two kinds of language. **Abstract** words refer to ideas, qualities, attitudes, and conditions that can't be perceived with the senses: *beauty, guilty, victory.* **Concrete** words refer to objects, persons, places, or conditions that can be perceived with the senses: *Abilene, scratchy, toolbox.* See also *general and specific.* (See pp. 523–24.)

acronym A pronounceable word formed from the initial letter or letters of each word in an organization's title: NATO (North Atlantic Treaty Organization).

active voice See *voice.*

adjectival A term sometimes used to describe any word or word group, other than an adjective, that is used to modify a noun. Common adjectivals include nouns (*wagon train, railroad ties*), phrases (*fool on the hill*), and clauses (*the man that I used to be*).

adjective A word used to modify a noun (*beautiful morning*) or a pronoun (*ordinary one*). (See Chapter 16.) Nouns, some verb forms, phrases, and clauses may also serve as adjectives: *book sale; a used book; sale of old books; the sale, which occurs annually.* (See *clauses, prepositional phrases,* and *verbals and verbal phrases.*)

Adjectives come in several classes:

- A **descriptive adjective** names some quality of the noun: *beautiful morning, dark horse.*
- A **limiting adjective** narrows the scope of a noun. It may be a **possessive** (*my, their*); a **demonstrative adjective** (*this train, these days*); an **interrogative adjective** (*what time? whose body?*); or a number (*two boys*).
- A **proper adjective** is derived from a proper noun: *French language, Machiavellian scheme.*

Adjectives also can be classified according to position:

- An **attributive adjective** appears next to the noun it modifies: *full moon.*
- A **predicate adjective** is connected to its noun by a linking verb: *The moon is full.* See also *complement.*

body In a piece of writing, the large central part where ideas supporting the thesis are presented and developed. See also *conclusion* and *introduction*.

bookmark In Internet use, an electronic address you save for later reference. (See p. 581.)

brainstorming A technique for generating ideas about a subject: concentrating on the subject for a fixed time (say, fifteen minutes), you list every idea and detail that comes to mind. (See pp. 23–24.)

browser A computer program that makes it possible to search the World Wide Web.

cardinal number The type of number that shows amount: *two, sixty, ninety-seven.* Contrast *ordinal number* (such as *second, ninety-seventh*).

case The form of a noun or pronoun that indicates its function in the sentence. Most pronouns have three cases:

- The **subjective case** (*I, she*) for the subject of a verb or for a subject complement.
- The **objective case** (*me, her*) for the object of a verb, verbal, or preposition.
- The **possessive case** to indicate ownership, used either as an adjective (*my, her*) or as a noun (*mine, hers*).

(See p. 270 for a list of the forms of personal and relative pronouns.)

Nouns use the subjective form (*dog, America*) for all cases except the possessive (*dog's, America's*).

cause-and-effect analysis The determination of why something happened or what its consequences were or will be. (See pp. 27 and 100–01.)

character The people or animals in a literary work, including the narrator of a story or the speaker of a poem. Characters are often classified by their importance in a work (major or minor), by the roles they play, and by their type. See also *foil* and p. 708.

- The **protagonist** is the central character of a work. Sometimes the protagonist is a **hero**, embodying noble or courageous values.
- The **antagonist** opposes the central character, or protagonist, of a work. Sometimes the antagonist is an **antihero** or villain, representing ignoble traits.
- A **flat character** shows a single dominant trait.
- A **round character** displays a range of human traits and behaviors.

chiasmus A rhetorical scheme in which two phrases mirror each other in reverse grammatical order: *From one who knows, who comes from two. By day we live, we die by night.*

Chicago style A style of documentation recommended by *The Chicago Manual of Style* and used in history, art, and other humanities. (For discussion and examples, see pp. 721–32.)

chronological organization The arrangement of events as they occurred in time, usually from first to last. (See pp. 42–43, 82.)

citation In research writing, the way of acknowledging material borrowed from sources. Most systems of citation are basically similar: a number or brief parenthetical reference in the text indicates that particular material is borrowed and directs the reader to information on the source at the end of the work. The systems do differ, however. (See pp. 624–63 for MLA style, pp. 721–32 for Chicago style, pp. 739–55 for APA style, and pp. 767–74 for CSE style.)

claim A positive statement or assertion that requires support. Claims are the backbone of any argument. (See pp. 182–85.)

classification The sorting of many elements into groups based on their similarities. (See pp. 27 and 97–98.)

clause A group of related words containing a subject and predicate. A **main (independent) clause** can stand by itself as a sentence. A **subordinate (dependent) clause** serves as a single part of speech and so cannot stand by itself as a sentence.

Main clause	We can go to the movies.
Subordinate clause	We can go if Julie gets back on time.

A subordinate clause may function as an adjective (*The car that hit Fred was speeding*), an adverb (*The car hit Fred when it ran a red light*), or a noun (*Whoever was driving should be arrested*). (See pp. 256–57.)

clichés See *trite expressions.*

climactic organization The arrangement of material in order of increasing drama or interest, leading to a climax. (See pp. 44, 84.)

climax The point in a play or narrative to which all action leads, followed by plot resolution and conclusion. In *Romeo and Juliet,* the climax occurs during the lovers' death scene. See also *denouement.*

clip art Drawings and icons available on word processors, CD-ROMs, and the Web, generally used to embellish documents. (See pp. 126–27.)

clustering A technique for generating ideas about a subject: drawing and writing, you branch outward from a center point (the subject) to pursue the implications of ideas. (See pp. 24–25.)

coherence The quality of an effective essay or paragraph that helps readers see relations among ideas and move easily from one idea to the next. (See pp. 44–45, 79–90.)

collaborative learning In a writing course, students working together in groups to help each other become better writers and readers. (See pp. 68–71, 783–86.)

collective noun See *noun.*

colloquial language The words and expressions of everyday speech. Colloquial language can enliven informal writing but is generally inappropriate in formal academic or business writing. See also *formal and informal.* (See pp. 514–15.)

comma splice A sentence error in which two main clauses are separated by a comma with no coordinating conjunction. (See Chapter 18.)

Comma splice	The book was long, it contained useful data.
Revised	The book was long**;** it contained useful data.
Revised	The book was long**,** and it contained useful data.

contrast See *comparison and contrast.*

coordinate adjectives Two or more adjectives that equally modify the same noun or pronoun: *The camera panned the vast, empty desert.* (See pp. 443–45.)

coordinating conjunction See *conjunction.*

coordination The linking of words, phrases, or clauses that are of equal importance, usually with a coordinating conjunction: *He and I laughed, but she was not amused.* Contrast *subordination.* (See pp. 397–99.)

correlative conjunction (correlative) See *conjunction.*

count noun See *noun.*

courseware A program for online communication and collaboration among the teacher and students in a course. (See p. 783.)

critical thinking, reading, and writing Looking beneath the surface of words and images to discern meaning and relationships and to build knowledge. (See Chapter 8.)

CSE style Either of two styles of documenting sources recommended by the Council of Science Editors (formerly the Council of Biology Editors) and frequently used in the natural and applied sciences and in mathematics. (For discussion and examples, see pp. 767–74.)

cumulative (loose) sentence A sentence in which modifiers follow the subject and verb: *Ducks waddled by, their tails swaying and their quacks rising to heaven.* Contrast *periodic sentence.* (See pp. 389–90.)

dangling modifier A modifier that does not sensibly describe anything in its sentence. (See pp. 372–74.)

Dangling	Having arrived late, the concert had already begun.
Revised	Having arrived late, we found that the concert had already begun.

data In argument, a term used for *evidence.* See *evidence.*

database A collection and organization of information (data). A database may be printed, but the term is most often used for electronic sources.

declension A list of the forms of a noun or pronoun, showing inflections for person (for pronouns), number, and case. See p. 270 for a declension of the personal and relative pronouns.

deductive reasoning Applying a generalization to specific circumstances in order to reach a conclusion. See also *syllogism.* Contrast *inductive reasoning.* (See pp. 204–07.)

definition Specifying the characteristics of something to establish what it is and is not. (See pp. 26, 95–96, 184.)

degree See *comparison.*

demonstrative adjective See *adjective.*

demonstrative pronoun See *pronoun.*

denotation The main or dictionary definition of a word. Contrast *connotation.* (See pp. 521–22.)

denouement A French term ("untying") signifying the resolution of the plot following the climax. In *Romeo and Juliet,* the denouement follows the deaths of the ill-fated lovers and concludes with the survivors resolving to end their family feuds. See also *climax.*

dependent clause See *clause.*

derivational suffix See *suffix.*

description Detailing the sensory qualities of a thing, person, place, or feeling. (See pp. 26 and 94.)

descriptive adjective See *adjective.*

descriptor See *keyword(s).*

determiner A word that marks and precedes a noun: for example, *a, an, the, my, your.* See also *article.* (See pp. 328–32 for the uses of determiners before nouns.)

developing (planning) The stage of the writing process when one finds a subject, explores ideas, gathers information, focuses on a central theme, and organizes material. Compare *drafting* and *revising.* (See Chapters 1–2.)

dialect A variety of a language used by a specific group or in a specific region. A dialect may be distinguished by its pronunciation, vocabulary, and grammar. (See pp. 134–36 and 513–14.)

diction The choice and use of words. (See Chapters 37–39.)

dictionary form See *plain form.*

direct address A construction in which a word or phrase indicates the person or group spoken to: *Have you finished, John? Farmers, unite.*

direct object See *object.*

direct question A sentence asking a question and concluding with a question mark: *Do they know we are watching?* Contrast *indirect question.*

direct quotation (direct discourse) See *quotation.*

discussion list A mailing list of subscribers who use e-mail to converse on a particular subject.

division See *analysis.*

documentation In research writing, supplying citations that legitimate the use of borrowed material and support claims about its origins. Contrast *plagiarism.* (See pp. 618–19.)

document design The control of a document's elements to achieve the flow, spacing, grouping, emphasis, and standardization that are appropriate for the writing situation. (See Chapter 5.)

domain The part of a Web address (or URL) that gives the organization sponsoring the site.

double negative A generally nonstandard form consisting of two negative words used in the same construction so that they effectively cancel each other: *I don't have no money.* Rephrase as *I have no money* or *I don't have any money.* (See p. 326.)

double possessive A possessive using both the ending *-'s* and the preposition *of: That is a favorite expression of Mark's.*

double talk (doublespeak) Language intended to confuse or to be misunderstood. (See p. 516.)

download To transfer data from another computer.

drafting The stage of the writing process when ideas are expressed in connected sentences and paragraphs. Compare *developing (planning)* and *revising*. (See pp. 48–50.)

editing A distinct step in revising a written work, focusing on clarity, tone, and correctness. Compare *revising*. (See pp. 60–62.)

ellipsis The omission of a word or words from a quotation, indicated by the three spaced periods of an **ellipsis mark:** *"that all . . . are created equal."*

elliptical clause A clause omitting a word or words whose meaning is understood from the rest of the clause: *David likes Minneapolis better than* [*he likes*] *Chicago*. (See p. 257.)

emoticon Sideways faces made up of punctuation, used to convey emotion or irony in electronic communication. (See p. 783.)

emotional appeal See *appeals*.

emphasis The manipulation of words, sentences, and paragraphs to stress important ideas. (See Chapter 23.)

epic A long narrative poem written in an elevated style and celebrating important episodes in the life of a hero and the hero's companions. See also *genre*.

essay A nonfiction composition of multiple paragraphs, focused on a single subject and with a central idea or thesis.

essential element A word or word group that is necessary to the meaning of a sentence because it limits the thing it refers to: removing it would leave the meaning unclear or too general. Also called a **restrictive element,** an essential element is not set off by punctuation: *The keys to the car are on the table. That man who called about the apartment said he'd try again tonight*. Contrast *nonessential element*. (See pp. 437–40, 452.)

ethical appeal See *appeals*.

ethos See *appeals*.

etymology The history of a word's meanings and forms.

euphemism A presumably inoffensive word that a writer or speaker substitutes for a word deemed possibly offensive or too blunt—for example, *passed away* for "died." (See pp. 516–17.)

evaluation A judgment of the quality, value, currency, bias, or other aspects of a work. (See pp. 164, 173, 588–97.)

evidence The facts, examples, expert opinions, and other information that support the claims in an argument. (See pp. 184–88, 208–09.)

expletive A sentence that postpones the subject by beginning with *there* or *it* and a form of the verb *be: It is impossible to get a ticket. There should be more seats available*. (See p. 266.)

exposition Writing whose primary purpose is to explain something about a subject.

fallacies Errors in reasoning. Some evade the issue of the argument; others oversimplify the argument. (See pp. 193–99.)

faulty predication A sentence error in which the meanings of subject and predicate conflict, so that the subject is said to be or do something illogical: *The installation of air bags takes up space in a car's steering wheel and dashboard.* (See pp. 378–79.)

figurative language (figures of speech) Expressions that suggest meanings different from their literal meanings in order to achieve special effects. (See pp. 527–29.) See also specific figures: *hyperbole, irony, metaphor, metonymy, paradox, personification, simile, synecdoche, understatement, zeugma.*

finite verb Any verb that makes an assertion or expresses a state of being and can stand as the main verb of a sentence or clause: *The moose eats the leaves.* (See p. 250.) Contrast *verbal,* which is formed from a finite verb but is unable to stand alone as the main verb of a sentence: *I saw the moose eating the leaves.*

first person See *person.*

flame To attack an online correspondent personally, as in a discussion list or newsgroup. (See p. 783.)

foil A character in a literary work who contrasts with another character and thus helps to define that other character. (See p. 708.)

form The way in which an oral, visual, or written communication is organized, structured, or presented. Form is typically differentiated from content: whereas content refers to the ideas in a work, form refers to how ideas are represented. Form operates on many levels, ranging from sentence styles to larger organizational structures, such as genre and argument.

formal and informal Levels of usage achieved through word choice and sentence structure. More informal writing, as in a letter to an acquaintance or a personal essay, resembles some speech in its colloquial language, contractions, and short, fairly simple sentences. More formal writing, as in academic papers and business reports, avoids these attributes of speech and tends to rely on longer and more complicated sentences.

format In a document such as an academic paper or a business letter, the arrangement and spacing of elements on the page. See also *document design.*

fragment See *sentence fragment.*

frame A window on a computer screen. With two or more frames on the same screen, a Web designer can show two or more documents at once.

free verse Poetry characterized by a lack of regular rhyme scheme and meter and by varied line lengths. See also *meter.*

freewriting A technique for generating ideas: in a fixed amount of time (say, fifteen minutes), you write continuously without stopping to reread. (See pp. 22–23.)

function word A word, such as an article, conjunction, or preposition, that serves primarily to clarify the roles of and relations between other

pronouns; *conjugation,* the inflection of verbs; and *comparison,* the inflection of adjectives and adverbs.

inflectional suffix See *suffix.*

informal See *formal and informal.*

intensifier A modifier that adds emphasis to the word(s) it modifies: for example, *very slow, so angry.*

intensive pronoun See *pronoun.*

interjection A word standing by itself or inserted in a construction to exclaim or command attention: *Hey! Ouch! What the heck did you do that for?*

interpretation The determination of meaning or significance—for instance, in a work such as a poem or photograph or in the literature on some issue such as job discrimination. (See pp. 161–62, 172.)

interrogative Functioning as or involving a question.

interrogative adjective See *adjective.*

interrogative pronoun See *pronoun.*

intransitive verb A verb that does not take a direct object: *The woman laughed.* (See p. 240.)

introduction The opening of an essay, a transition for readers between their world and the writer's. The introduction often contains a statement of the writer's thesis. (See pp. 104–08 for suggestions.)

invention The discovery and exploration of ideas, usually occurring most intensively in the early stages of the writing process. (See pp. 18–28 for invention techniques.)

inversion A reversal of usual word order in a sentence, as when a verb precedes its subject or an object precedes its verb: *Down swooped the hawk. Our aims we stated clearly.*

IRC See *synchronous communication.*

irony The use of words to suggest a meaning different from what the words say literally: *What a happy face!* (said to someone scowling miserably); *With that kind of planning, prices are sure to go down* (written with the expectation that prices will rise). Compare *paradox* and *understatement.*

irregular verb A verb that forms its past tense and past participle in some other way than by the addition of *-d* or *-ed* to the plain form: for example, *go, went, gone; give, gave, given.* Contrast *regular verb.* (See pp. 281–82 for a list of irregular verbs.)

jargon In one sense, jargon is the specialized language of any group, such as doctors or baseball players. In another sense, jargon is vague, pretentious, wordy, and ultimately unclear writing such as that found in some academic, business, and government publications. (See p. 537.)

journal A personal record of observations, reactions, ideas, and other thoughts. Besides providing a private place to think in writing, a journal is useful for making notes about reading (pp. 153–54, 155–56, 168, 696–97), discovering ideas for essays (pp. 19–21), and keeping track of research (pp. 561–62, 688–89, 735–36, 764).

journalist's questions A set of questions useful for probing a subject to discover ideas about it. (See pp. 25–26.)

keyword(s) A word or words that define a subject, used for searching databases and the Web. (See pp. 571–73.)

lexical word A word, such as a noun, verb, or modifier, that carries part of the meaning of language. Contrast *function word.*

linear text Text such as a conventional printed document that is intended to be read in sequence. Contrast *hypertext.* (See pp. 786–87.)

linking verb A verb that relates a subject to its complement: *Julie is a Democrat. He looks harmless. The boy became a man.* Common linking verbs are the forms of *be;* the verbs relating to the senses, such as *look* and *smell;* and the verbs *become, appear,* and *seem.* (See p. 242.)

listserv See *discussion list.*

litotes See *understatement.*

logical agreement See *agreement.*

logical fallacies See *fallacies.*

logos See *appeals.*

lurking Reading but not participating in an Internet discussion list, newsgroup, or Web forum. (See p. 583.)

main clause See *clause.*

main verb The part of a verb phrase that carries the principal meaning: *had been walking, could happen, was chilled.* See also *verb phrase.*

mass noun Another term for noncount noun. See *noun.*

mechanics The use of capital letters, underlining or italics, abbreviations, numbers, and divided words. (See Chapters 33–36.)

metaphor A figure of speech that implies a comparison between two unlike things: *The wind stabbed through our clothes.* A **mixed metaphor** is a confusing or ludicrous combination of incompatible figures: *The wind stabbed through our clothes and shook our bones.* Contrast *simile.*

meter The rhythmic patterns of accented syllables in a line of poetry. The patterns are divided up into feet. (See also *prosody.*) Common metrical feet:

- **Iamb**, two syllables with the stress on the second syllable: *away, seduce.* Five iambs in a row make an iambic pentameter line: *if music be the food of love, play on.*
- **Trochee**, two syllables with the stress on the first syllable: *someone, lady.*
- **Spondee**, two syllables with equal stress on both syllables: *hotdog, cowboy, cupcake.*
- **Anapest**, three syllables with the stress on the third syllable: *on the loose, unamused.*
- **Dactyl**, three syllables with the stress on the first syllable: *nobody, tenderly.*

metonymy A figure of speech in which a name refers to a complete entity: *The school sent the students home early because of the snowstorm.* See also *synecdoche.*

point of view The perspective or attitude of the narrator or speaker in a work of literature. See also *person* and p. 694. Common points of view in literature:

- A **first-person narrator** is a character in the story.
- A **third-person narrator** is a voice outside the story.
- A **third-person omniscient narrator** is an all-knowing voice outside the story who can explain any character's thoughts and feelings.
- A **limited omniscient narrator** has detailed knowledge of one or more characters, but not all.
- An **unreliable narrator** provides the reader with false or misleading explanations of characters or events.

positive degree See *comparison.*

possessive See *case.*

predicate The part of a sentence that makes an assertion about the subject. A predicate must contain a finite verb and may contain modifiers, objects of the verb, and complements. The **simple predicate** consists of the verb and its helping verbs: *A wiser person would have made a different decision.* The **complete predicate** includes the simple predicate and any modifiers, objects, and complements: *A wiser person would have made a different decision.* See also *intransitive verb, linking verb,* and *transitive verb.* (See pp. 235–36, 240–43.)

predicate adjective See *complement.*

predicate noun (predicate nominative) See *complement.*

prefix A letter or group of letters (such as *sub, in, dis, pre*) that can be added at the beginning of a root or word to create a new word: *sub* + *marine* = *submarine; dis* + *grace* = *disgrace.* Contrast *suffix.*

premise Generally, a claim or assumption basic to an argument. In a deductive syllogism, one premise applied to another leads logically to a conclusion. See also *inference* and *syllogism.* (See pp. 204–07.)

preposition A word that forms a noun or pronoun (plus any modifiers) into a prepositional phrase: *about love, down the steep stairs.* The common prepositions include these as well as *after, before, by, for, from, in, on, to,* and many others. (See p. 247.)

prepositional phrase A word group consisting of a preposition and its object, plus any modifiers. A prepositional phrase usually functions as an adjective (*The boy in green stood up*) or as an adverb (*He walked to the speaker's platform*). (See pp. 247–48.)

present participle See *participle.*

present perfect tense See *tense.*

present tense See *tense.*

pretentious writing Writing that is more elaborate than the writing situation requires, usually full of fancy phrases and showy words. (See pp. 515–16.)

primary source Firsthand information, such as an eyewitness account of events; a diary, speech, or other historical document; a work of literature or art; a report of a survey or experiment; and one's own interview, observation, or correspondence. Contrast *secondary source.* (See p. 565.)

principal clause A main or independent clause. See *clause.*

principal parts The plain form, past-tense form, and past participle of a verb. See *verb forms.* (See pp. 277–79.)

problem-solution organization The arrangement of material to state and explain a problem and then to propose and explain a solution. (See pp. 43–44, 83–84.)

process analysis The explanation of how something works or how to do something. (See pp. 27, 101–02.)

progressive tense See *tense.*

pronoun A word used in place of a noun. There are eight types of pronouns:

- **Personal pronouns** refer to a specific individual or to individuals: *I, you, he, she, it, we, they.* (See p. 270.)
- **Indefinite pronouns,** such as *everybody* and *some,* do not refer to specific nouns (*Everybody speaks*). (See pp. 311–12.)
- **Relative pronouns**—*who, whoever, which, that*—relate groups of words to nouns or pronouns (*The book that won is a novel*). (See pp. 256, 270.)
- **Interrogative pronouns**—*who, whom, whose, which, what*—introduce questions (*Who will contribute?*).
- **Intensive pronouns**—personal pronouns plus *-self* or *-selves*—emphasize a noun or other pronoun (*He himself asked that question*). (See pp. 270, 847.)
- **Reflexive pronouns** have the same form as intensive pronouns. They indicate that the sentence subject also receives the action of the verb (*They injured themselves*). (See pp. 270, 847.)
- **Demonstrative pronouns** such as *this, that,* and *such* identify or point to nouns (*This is the problem*).
- **Reciprocal pronouns**—*each other* and *one another*—are used as objects of verbs when the subjects are plural (*They loved each other*).

proofreading Reading and correcting a final draft for misspellings, typographical errors, and other mistakes. (See pp. 64–65.)

proper adjective See *adjective.*

proper noun See *noun.*

protagonist See *character.*

purpose For a writer, the chief reason for communicating something about a subject to a particular audience. Purposes are both general (usually explanation or persuasion) and specific (taking into account the subject and desired outcome). (See pp. 15–17.)

quotation Repetition of what someone has written or spoken. In **direct quotation (direct discourse)**, the person's words are duplicated exactly and enclosed in quotation marks: *Polonius told his son, Laertes, "Neither a borrower nor a lender be."* An **indirect quotation (indirect**

sexist language Language expressing narrow ideas about men's and women's roles, positions, capabilities, or value. (See pp. 516–19.)

signal phrase Words that indicate who is being quoted: *"In the future," said Andy Warhol, "everyone will be world-famous for fifteen minutes."* (For punctuating signal phrases, see pp. 446–48. For using signal phrases to integrate quotations, see pp. 607–09.)

simile A figure of speech that compares two unlike things explicitly, using *like* or *as*: *The sky glowered like an angry parent.* Contrast *metaphor.*

simple predicate See *predicate.*

simple sentence See *sentence.*

simple subject See *subject.*

simple tense See *tense.*

singular One. See *number.*

slang Expressions used by the members of a group to create bonds and sometimes exclude others. Most slang is too vague, short-lived, and narrowly understood to be used in any but very informal writing. (See p. 514.)

sonnet A type of poem especially popular in love poetry consisting of fourteen lines and using a regular rhyme scheme. An **English sonnet** contains three four-line stanzas and concludes with a rhyming couplet. An **Italian sonnet** contains two stanzas of eight and six lines, respectively. See also *rhyme scheme* and *stanza.*

source A place where information or ideas may be found: book, article, Web site, work of art, television program, and so on.

spam To send an irrelevant and unsolicited electronic message to many recipients at once, such as all the subscribers to a discussion list.

spatial organization In a description of a person, place, or thing, the arrangement of details as they would be scanned by a viewer—for instance, from top to bottom or near to far. (See pp. 42 and 81–82.)

speaker The voice in a literary work, usually a poem. See also *narrator* and *persona.*

specific See *general and specific.*

split infinitive The often awkward interruption of an infinitive and its marker *to* by an adverb: *Management decided to immediately introduce the new product.* (See pp. 369–70.)

squinting modifier See *misplaced modifier.*

standard American English The dialect of English used and expected by educated writers and readers in colleges and universities, businesses, and professions. (See pp. 132–36, 512–13.)

stanza Two or more lines of poetry set off with extra spacing to mark a related group.

style The distinctive way an author uses language in his or her writing. Style is a culmination of a number of traits, including diction, tone, imagery, and syntax.

subject In grammar, the part of a sentence that names something and about which an assertion is made in the predicate. The **simple subject** consists of the noun alone: *The quick brown fox jumps over the lazy dog.* The **complete subject** includes the simple subject and its modifiers: *The quick brown fox jumps over the lazy dog.* (See pp. 235–36.)

subject complement See *complement.*

subjective See *case.*

subjunctive See *mood.*

subordinate clause See *clause.*

subordinating conjunction See *conjunction.*

subordination The use of grammatical constructions to de-emphasize one element in a sentence by making it dependent on rather than equal to another element: *Although I left six messages for him, the doctor failed to call.* Contrast *coordination.* (See pp. 400–04.)

substantive A word or word group used as a noun.

suffix A **derivational suffix** is a letter or group of letters that can be added to the end of a root word to make a new word, often a different part of speech: *child, childish; shrewd, shrewdly; visual, visualize.* An **inflectional suffix** adapts a word to different grammatical relations: *boy, boys; fast, faster; tack, tacked.*

summary A condensation and restatement of source material in one's own words and sentence structures, useful in reading for comprehending the material (see pp. 141–43) and in research writing for presenting the gist of the original author's idea (p. 602). Summaries appearing in a paper must always be acknowledged in source citations.

superlative See *comparison.*

syllogism A form of deductive reasoning in which two premises stating generalizations or assumptions together lead to a conclusion. *Premise:* Hot stoves can burn me. *Premise:* This stove is hot. *Conclusion:* This stove can burn me. See also *deductive reasoning.* (See pp. 204–07.)

symbolism The use of a concrete thing to suggest something larger and more abstract, as a red rose may symbolize passion or romance. (See p. 695.)

synchronous communication Real-time, simultaneous communication over the Internet, analogous to a telephone conversation. Instant messaging and MOOs are examples. (See p. 584.)

synecdoche A figure of speech in which a part stands for the whole: *She braved the waves and swam to safety.* Contrast *metonymy.*

synonyms Words with approximately but not exactly the same meanings, such as *snicker, giggle,* and *chortle.* (See p. 522.)

syntax In sentences, the grammatical relations among words and the ways those relations are indicated.

synthesis Drawing connections among the elements within a work (such as the images in a poem) or among entire works (entire poems). Synthesis is an essential skill in critical thinking, reading, and writing (see pp. 162–63, 172–73) and in research writing (pp. 598–99).

Web forum A discussion group on the Web, open to everyone and organized around subjects.

wizard A file on many word processors and most desktop publishers that guides the user in designing documents. (See p. 118.)

word order The arrangement of the words in a sentence, which plays a large part in determining the grammatical relation among words in English.

writing process The activities involved in producing a finished piece of writing. The overlapping stages of the process—developing or planning, drafting, and revising—vary among writers and even for the same writer in different writing situations. (See Chapters 1–3.)

writing situation The unique combination of writer, subject, audience, purpose, and other elements that defines an assignment or occasion and helps direct the writer's choices. (See pp. 4–6.)

zeugma A figure of speech in which one word governs two or more other parts of a sentence: *The robber took my wallet and then the next train.*